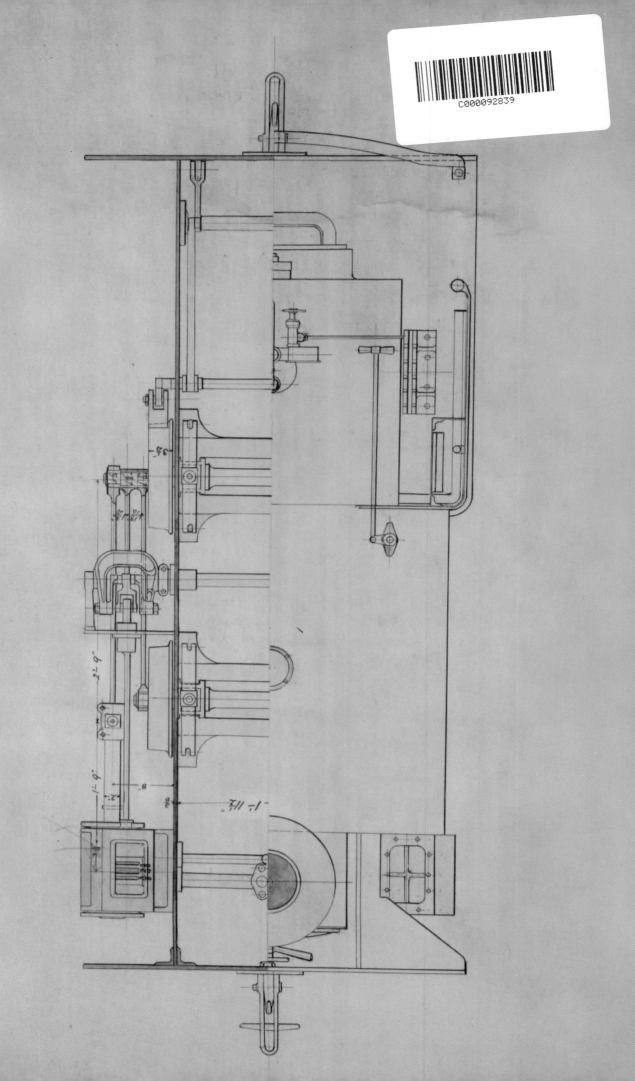

BAGNALLS
OF STAFFORD

Typical example of a locomotive designed and built at Castle Engine Works; Manufacturer's number 1971 of April 1913, one of the first batch of a fleet eventually totalling 30 of these Indian Railways 2ft 6in gauge W class 0-6-2 tender engines. Indian Western Railway No 569, it is seen here on the turntable at Nadiad, headquarters of a narrow-gauge system north of Baroda, on 15 January 1977.

BAGNALLS
OF STAFFORD

Builders of Locomotives for the World's Railways
A History of the Firm & Its Folk

BY

ALLAN C. BAKER & T. D. ALLEN CIVIL

THE PHYLLIS RAMPTON NARROW GAUGE RAILWAY TRUST

First published in Great Britain
The Phyllis Rampton Narrow Gauge Railway Trust
(registered Charity No 292240)
12 The Martins
High Halden Kent TN26 3LD
MMV111

ISBN 978-0-9544546-2-3
A catalogue entry for this book is available
from the British Library

Reproduced on the end-papers are two early general arrangement drawings, the originals of which
are on linen and as can be seen beautifully coloured.

Front of book:
Drawing number 5065 dated 14 July 1899 of manufacturer's number 1443 of 1895, a 4½in cylinder locomotive being a typical
example of the smallest of the standard narrow-gauge circular firebox designs - the valve gear is Modified Baguley. Notice the
drawing was made some time after the locomotive was built; part of a set of drawings coloured in this way covering typical
locomotives of the period commissioned for promotional purposes.

Back of book:
Drawing number 4061 dated 4 October 1895, of manufacturer's number 1475 of 1895, a typical 7in cylinder member of the
standard narrow-gauge circular firebox locomotives - in this case the valve gear is the original Baguley patent. Notice that
this locomotive, and the one illustrated on the front end papers, have castings acting as both the axle-box horn-guides and
the main-frame stretchers. This practice, dating from about 1895, was employed on the standard narrow-gauge designs,
although after the 1903 introduction of Bagnall-Price valve gear, which prevented it from being used on the driving axle due
to the eccentrics, it was gradually superseded by more conventional plate frame stays.

Designed and produced by

L G Typesetting & Design Ashford Kent
Typeset in 11/13pt Goudy Old Style
on 130gm² Matt Lumisilk
Printed and bound in Wibalin by
The Amadeus Press
Cleckheaton West Yorkshire England

DEDICATION

The young craftsmen at Warden House School, where Richard Gordon Bagnall first practised his woodworking skills. He is second from the right with the saw.

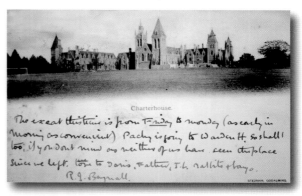

Postcard from Charterhouse School sent by Richard Gordon Bagnall to his mother and dated 11 May 1902.

Richard Gordon Bagnall 1885-1916; younger son of William Gordon and Jessie Bagnall, 2nd Lieutenant Royal Garrison Artillery. A picture taken in about 1902.

He was killed in action 1 July 1916 while serving with the 114th Heavy Battery, 2nd Heavy Artillery Group at Bouzincourt on the Somme.

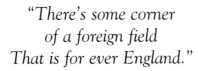

*"There's some corner
of a foreign field
That is for ever England."*

Rupert Brook

A recent photograph of part of the military cemetery at Bouzincourt. RG Bagnall's grave is 5th from the right with Bombardier Mortimer, who fell along side him, 4th from the right.

Richard Gordon Bagnall in Malay as a rubber plantation manager; picture dates from about 1913.

ARMORIAL BEARINGS OF
THE BAGNALL FAMILY

This is the coat of arms of the Bagnall of Broseley branch of the family, as it appears in John Sleigh's *A History of the Ancient Parish of Leek* - see Bibliography. This is the branch of the family that William Gordon Bagnall descended from. As will be observed it comprises four sections. They represent:

Top Right: The coat of arms of the Bagnall family of Bagnall, near Leek in Staffordshire. Lion rampant *azur* (blue).

Bottom Left: The coat of arms of the Bagenhall (later Bagnall) family of Newcastle-under-Lyme and Hanley. Lion rampant *azur* (blue) two bars *or* (gold).

Bottom Right: The coat of arms of the Bagenholte of Staffordshire branch of the family. Sable (dark background), an inescutcheon (a small escutcheon within a larger one) *argent* (silver) charged with a leopard's face *gules* (red colour marked on engraved figures) within an *orle* (border within a shield) of eight martlets (swallows without feet) of the second.

The branch of the family to which William Gordon Bagnall was a member also had a crest with an antelope *sejant* (sitting down, fore-limbs erect), *argent* (silver), ducally gorged, *or* (gold).

Mottos: *Dat Deus Incrementum* which is Latin for God Gives Increase.
        Seur et Loyal which means Trustworthy also Loyal

CONTENTS

Aerial of the Castle Engine Works in 1948, before the post-war improvements and extensions. Compare with the plan on page 452.

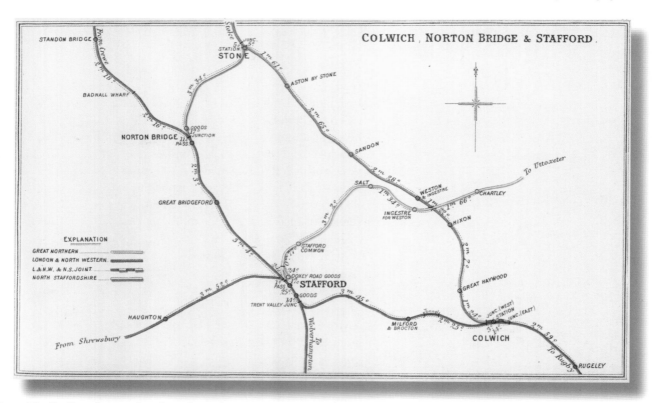

Map of Stafford's railways taken from the Railway Clearing House Book of Junciton Diagrams 1902

FOREWORD

BY NICHOLAS GORDON BAGNALL

Every time I went through Stafford station, which I did quite often on my way to points north in my early days as a journalist, I would look up and see my grandfather's name. It was in enormous white cut-out letters on a factory roof, supported by a network of rods behind them. And my heart would swell. Now WGB is long gone and the firm he founded has gone too; but those letters were yet another reminder of the times when ours was a major manufacturing country whose goods were bought throughout the globe, rather than the nation of entrepreneurs that is all it sometimes seems to be now. Hindsight is of course easy and nostalgia is pointless, but I still like to remind myself that the products of my grandfather's business went to so many places. I think particularly (to give but one example) of that amazing feat of engineering at the steep approaches to Spezia Harbour on Italy's gulf of Genoa. Many were the ingenious varieties of locomotive and stock designed to work in strange climates or with amazingly restricted track and loading gauges. They are all described in this book, whose authors have been all over the world in search of what remains, whether in museums or even, though rarely, still at work, of that wide industrial empire.

The man who founded this, one of a number of firms similarly engaged, died long before I was born, and I myself am an octogenarian now. But his traces were still to be found - even if only in the furniture his widow still then had, the clocks, or the fine chests that his ancestors had got from Dieulacresse Abbey - in the small house in Shropshire where I often stayed and where she lived on for several decades. My grandmother spoke surprisingly seldom of him, but I know then, and it's consistently confirmed in this book, that he was an exceptionally popular employer, which could certainly not be said of some other bosses of the time. Evidence of this popularity crops up many times here. Particularly touching was the splendidly expensive and finely inscribed gold watch that my uncle Richard Gordon (killed in the First World War) was given by the firm's workers, something that could

surely have happened only in a firm whose employees admired their bosses.

I often admired my grandfather's engineering skill, remembering, for example the Bagnall valve gear that was presumably invented by him, or so I imagined. Again Messrs Baker and Civil put me right on such matters, explaining that his brilliance lay more in the finances of the business and in his genius for public relations. Bagnall catalogues in his day were all designed by him and were very splendid. He seemed to have few enemies, except for one or two on the Staffordshire County Council of which, as you will read, he was a prominent member on the Conservative side. But having myself looked at some of the surviving newspaper reports of council meetings, it seems to me that the animosity was political rather than personal. The family still has the tributes to him paid for having been largely responsible for improving the sanitation (previously a little primitive sometimes) of the area.

His popularity is exemplified in the charming story of his wedding. Early in the morning of the ceremony some local enthusiasts fired a salvo in the bride's honour– and went on firing through the day. (And he was still popular.)

How I wish I had known him. The photograph of him I have on my study wall does not I feel sure do complete justice to him, being very solemn if not forbidding with the frown as well as the big moustache fashionable at the time. Even the picture I've seen of a relaxed WGB in sporting gear, a 12-bore on his arm, carries an austere expression. Not only my father Harold, as well as my late elder brother John, inherited his gift and were very good shots.

I have often wondered, incidentally, why so successful a businessman should have left his widow with apparently so little to spend, though I have the impression from the authors of this book that he was an over-generous man, dying in debt. It was at my grandmother's house on the hill above Church Stretton that I was able to foster my own pleasure in railways, since we looked down on the main line south from Shrewsbury and the line was close enough to identify through glasses all those big taper-boilered Collets and Churchwards, wonderful creations. I learn from the book that Bagnall actually built a number of 0-6-0 tanks for the Great Western Railway, to the GWR design. Its own productions were of all sizes, but its specialisation was of course in small tank engines, which went, as I say, all over the world, as well as to many industrial sites here at home. I have myself seen one or two of them still at work many years after their first coming out of the factory.

Messrs Baker and Civil, both professional engineers with a great deal of experience behind them working for the railways, have been able to describe the specification of every one of these machines, and the identity of the people who designed and made them (each of them named), as well their later vulnerability to takeover bids, all chronicled here; and I have learnt from it more about my own family than I knew myself. The book is a marvellous monument to its authors' persistence, and it's not just family pride that makes me recommend it, for it's very much worth reading by anyone in the least bit interested in such matters.

A word about copy-editing. There are roughly three sorts of publisher's editor – the American, who thinks himself or herself more important that the author; the British, who at least recognises that the work is the author's and not the publisher's; and the copy-editor who queries apparent inaccuracies or solecisms and looks where necessary after spelling and grammar. That's me.

Lewes, Sussex. May 2007.

PREFACE

This book is the culmination of almost 50 years of researching and otherwise delving into the history of a comparatively small British private company that specialised in the manufacture of railway locomotives, rolling stock and other ancillary equipment. However, the Company was much more than just a builder of locomotives and other equipment as in the majority of cases the staff also undertook all the design and development work. As well as the locomotives and rolling stock the Company made a speciality of designing, building and manufacturing just about all the equipment necessary to build and operate a narrow-gauge light railway. Light-railways for agricultural, mining, plantation and other similar types of use were becoming very popular at the time the Company started business and if this was not enough, general engineering work was also undertaken including designing and building stationary steam engines, boilers and a host of other equipment.

WG Bagnall Limited of the Castle Engine Works at Stafford can be fairly said to have stood alone in the annals of the British private locomotive building industry for a company of its size, in the diversity of its products, the size and impact of its export business and the professionalism and innovation of its people. The company never employed more than around 600 people yet locomotives and rolling stock built at the Castle Engine Works found their way to numerous countries and in each and every continent.

Over a good number of years several of its people had a significant influence within the British private locomotive building industry, way beyond what might have been expected of such a comparatively small company. Small it might have been materially, but large in the position its people established within the industry it operated. In its post Second World War literature the Company coined the phrase Builders of Locomotives for the World's Railways - and while this might have been somewhat of an exaggeration, it was by no means a completely unjust claim.

The above should at the very least give some indication as to why the authors of this book have spent a life time in their research and quest for accuracy and completeness in the story presented here. This is not their first book on the subject but it will almost certainly be the last. It is not, nor is it intended to be, a second edition of an earlier book with the same title published as long ago as 1973. As the authors pointed out in their opening remarks of that book, they were anxious at the time, after some 10 years of research, to place on record at least some of the results of their work. That said, it has to be added that despite a number of deficiencies the earlier book has stood the test of time and still commands a high price on the second-hand market. Conscious of its deficiency in illustrative content, both in the number of illustrations and their equally important reproductive quality, the authors followed their initial offering with two of what were in effect pictorial sequels. The first of these was published in 1990 and covered some of the narrow-gauge locomotives built by the Company while the second, which appeared in 2001, encompassed some of the locomotives built to suit standard and broad-gauges; both are now out of print. By the medium of these two books which were termed Pictorial Albums, the authors were able to present a vastly better and more comprehensive pictorial coverage of the Company and its products. They also hope, to have reached a much wider readership, and if the three books between them have achieved no other object, they will almost certainly have helped foster a greater interest and understanding in this quite incredible company, its products and equally importantly, its folk.

As well as these three books nearly 50 articles have been written by the authors over the last 40 years or so, on various aspects of the Company's products and its people - in fact the first one appeared as long ago as 1966. By and large, and perhaps understandably, these articles have appeared in a relatively small number of specialist society magazines and journals and will not therefore have been readily available to the more general reader. While some, but by no means all, of what has already appeared in print under the authors names is perforce repeated in whole or part in the pages of this book, the intrepid reader in search of more detail will find a complete listing of the articles, and where to find them, in the acknowledgements & bibliography.

Readers of this book might justifiably ask: why the authors particular interest in WG Bagnall Limited? Since they are lifelong railway enthusiasts and professional railway engineers, with a love for, and fascination in, anything with steel wheels running on steel rails, need any more be said? Indeed, Allen Civil's engineering apprenticeship in locomotive engineering was served at the Castle Engine Works; what better parentage therefore, in the case of one of its authors, could this book have? Allen was with the firm until it was acquired by the English Electric Company Limited in 1961; he was thus a part of it for the last 10 years or so of its independent existence. In my case, a fascination of those small locomotives, seen on train and bus journeys around my native Stoke-on-Trent as they fussed around in steelworks, collieries and the like, with names and usually no numbers and not to be found in the famous Ian Allan ABC train-spotters books - that was but the start. On my train-spotting trips to Birmingham and Wolverhampton to see the engines of other regions (ones that always seemed to be clean and with lots of shiny brass) the train would pass the Castle Engine Works at Stafford and the occasional glimpse of strange engines would be savoured. It was often possible to see new or recently repaired engines as the train passed by and eager eyes would be well positioned, with the benefit of past experience, to be sure of getting the best view.

In my late father's collection was a Bagnall catalogue and a series of the Company's publicity photographs of locomotives it had built; I used to pore over these endlessly on winters evenings. They had been given to Dad by a former employee of Bagnalls and a fellow member of the local Model Engineering Society. Following this my father, who was himself a keen and extremely accomplished live-steam model engineer, acquired a partly built live-steam working model of a Bagnall narrow-gauge locomotive. This came via the widow of a deceased friend in Stafford - ironically also named Bagnall - but no direct relation of the Company's founder. The construction of this delightful little engine had been started before the war by a Bagnall employee; it

was accompanied by a large collection of drawings, photographs and other material relating to the company. My interest was roused to a new pitch! The model had been commenced as a hobby some 30 years earlier and, as Dad and I were to discover later, parts of it had actually been made at the works. Dad was able to trace the fellow who had started to build the engine, still alive and kicking, albeit well into his 70s. I recall so well, although almost 50 years ago, calling on Horace Lorton quite un-announced one Sunday afternoon at his bungalow in Sawpit Lane, Brocton. We could not have been made more welcome, and among the literally hundreds of people who have helped the authors in their quest for information, Horace Lorton is singled out here as without him this book might never have been written. On that Sunday afternoon, followed by a series of subsequent visits over the next year or so when we were always made so welcome by Horace and his wife Edith, a veritable mine of information and literature came to light. From his shed, from his garage, from his loft and from other sundry places, each time we visited more and more information came to light! And even after he and his wife had emigrated to New Zealand to join his daughter and family, the odd package arrived by post. Horace had worked at the Castle Engine Works for 15 years or so from 1921 onwards. Being rather a compulsive collector, as he worked in the Cost Office this gave him plenty of opportunity to acquire publicity literature and other items of historical interest. Dad and I were so pleased that we were able to show Horace and his wife the little engine he had started to build all those years ago, completed by Dad and in steam, before they left these shores. Thereafter, it goes without saying that my interest knew no bounds and a letter to the local Stafford newspaper requesting information about the Company brought a reply from Allen Civil. Allen also had ideas on compiling a history of the company he had trained with and he, too, had started to collect material; the rest as they say, is history.

Unfortunately, although perhaps understandably, after the Company was acquired by English Electric in 1961 a decision was made to cease locomotive and other railway work at Stafford. Following this decision a significant culling of the Company's records and other historical material took place prior to the transfer of locomotive work to the Darlington works of Robert Stephenson & Hawthorns Limited. Such, however, was the decline in the private locomotive building industry in this country that only a couple of years later the Darlington Works were closed and the residual locomotive business concentrated at the former Vulcan Foundry in Newton-le-Willows; both these companies were subsidiaries of English Electric. Yet more records and literature was lost in this second move. Nevertheless, by the kind offices of Andy Forret, for many years in charge of the industrial locomotive spare part drawing office at Vulcan, and Mike Scott in charge of publicity at Trafford Park, we were able to have unrestricted access to what records did remain. We are therefore grateful to the management of English Electric, and its successor companies GEC Traction Limited and GEC Alsthom Limited, for permission to visit the Vulcan Foundry and Trafford Park on numerous occasions from around 1965.

Despite the fact that so much material was lost, the farsightedness of a number of individuals meant that much historical material relating to the firm has nevertheless survived, and it has been the authors self-imposed task over the last almost 50 years to locate as much of this material as has proved possible. Days, indeed weeks, have been spent in all number of depositories, some rewarding and others less so, some offering obvious potential and others not, but all in the quest for finality. Along with the Company's former records information has been unearthed in numerous other places, some of them seemingly most unlikely to bear fruit, but very often did. Several former employees have also been of enormous help and from all levels - indeed, from the one-time managing director down! Added to these sources are countless railway and locomotive enthusiasts all over the world, along with other companies and railways that bought or used the products of the Castle Engine Works.

It is the authors most sincere hope that all those individuals and organisations that have helped, particularly private individuals, are mentioned in the acknowledgements. However, it is felt that a few are deserved of a special mention, singled out here but in no particular order. As for the others, we emphasis that this does not in any way diminish our indebtedness to each and everybody who has helped, no matter how small or seemingly insignificant their individual contribution may have been.

We are very fortunate that the late Ralph Russell, an extremely diligent enthusiast of the British private locomotive building industry with a reputation for the most meticulous attention to detail, took a great interest

in the firm. Through the good offices of the late Vic Betteley, a senior manager with the company, Ralph was able to explore the records and make extensive extracts and notes before much of it went to the proverbial bonfire. Whilst Vic managed to save quite a lot of material himself, he would leave Ralph alone among the archives on Saturday afternoons, with instructions to drop the latch when he left! The late WA Smyth, the managing director in the 1950s, took a great interest in the heritage of the company he presided over and he too managed to salvage some records which would otherwise almost certainly have been destroyed. All these three gentlemen were of enormous assistance. Other former employees of the Company who deserve special mention here are the late Harry Davies, an employee over many years and latterly general manager, Harold Wood and Bill Brookes, both chief draughtsman at different periods, along with Ivor Farr, a senior draughtsman and designer. We have been invited into their homes, given unreserved access to their collections and conducted endless correspondence, so that no stones were left unturned. Unfortunately Vic Betteley, who took such a great interest in our efforts, and who would have loved to see this book in print at least as much as anybody else, passed away some years ago. Vic had an enormous affection for the company where he had his engineering training, where he gave so much of his life, and for which it had no greater advocate. Through the kindness of his wife Doris and son Colin, we have continued to have access to his collection.

While not in any way diminishing our indebtedness to the individuals mentioned above, without doubt the most treasured memories of the authors are with the Bagnall family themselves. After the publication of *Bagnalls of Stafford* in 1973, we were contacted by Jessica Gordon Alsop, William Gordon Bagnall's daughter, who, despite her father having died when she was quite young, had a host of memories of him and other stories to tell. Although we knew at the time that Gordon Bagnall had two sons, both of whom had already passed on, we had no idea he had a daughter too. As a result of meeting Jessica we were able to compile a much more detailed picture of the early history of the Company and the man behind it all. Over the past few years, having re-established contact with the Bagnalls, we have had enormous help, wise council, encouragement and most importantly, the friendship of the descendents of William Gordon Bagnall, particularly that of Jill Hutchinson Smith. Jill was actually christened Ursula Mary after one of her grandmother's sisters but has long been known as Jill; she is Jessica Gordon Bagnall's daughter, and granddaughter of WG Bagnall and his wife Jessie. Jill's cousin Nicholas Bagnall, who is one of the three sons of Harold Gordon Bagnall (the eldest of the WG Bagnall's children) and therefore a grandson of WG Bagnall, has aided and abetted his cousin. Nicholas is an accomplished journalist with a distinguished career in newspapers and his name on several books. Not only has he proofread the entire manuscript, making numerous useful suggestions and often correcting matters of grammar, but has also penned the Foreword. This Bagnall family input has, we feel, added enormously to any value this book might have.

Words are not enough to express the gratitude the authors feel to the hospitable Bagnall family. We have been invited into their homes and allowed free and completely unrestricted and unfettered access to a whole plethora of family memorabilia. This has not only been by Jill and Nicholas, but other members of the family too, and very special thanks are due to Jill's late husband David, Nicholas's wife Ann and daughter Catharine, along with sisters-in-law Shelia and Philippa Bagnall. Both Jill and Nicholas have particularly cast their critical eyes on what we have written of family matters and, as mentioned above, the whole of this book has been read and expertly commented on by Nicholas. Jill has an absolutely amazing memory for family history, and not just the Bagnalls but the numerous other families entwined in the Bagnall story too. Having spent much time with her mother and grandmother, she absorbed all she was told and it has been an amazing experience for the authors to explore with her so much family lore. On many occasions the authors have been able to feed the incredible Jill with some incomplete tit-bit recalled by other family members or unearthed by the authors somewhere along the line, subsequently leaving her to ruminate for a while. Some time later, it may have been minutes, hours or even on occasions days, the answer would invariably come forth, or at the very least a lead would emerge to take us on another fruitful line of research. With Jill and her late husband David we have spent many happy hours, for the bulk of the family archive lives with that branch of the family. Jill is a fellow of the Royal Agricultural Society of England (FR Ag S) and was not only its first woman fellow, but also at one time chairman of the fellows; Jill also has a Nuffield Scholarship. Jill's grandfather Gordon Bagnall was an accomplished gardener with an interest in agriculture, and at various times also a member of the Royal Agricultural Society of England. This part of his make-up was inherited by his daughter Jessica, and by her daughter Jill. As a result of these and numerous other family efforts on our behalf, this book has we feel been truly enriched by Bagnall family lore. The Bagnall family's approval has given the authors enormous satisfaction.

Because of the great confidence bestowed on them by the Bagnall family, it came upon the authors that this book should with great respect be dedicated to one of them - the late Richard Gordon Bagnall. Like many Bagnalls before and after him, Richard Gordon took up arms and in his case made the supreme sacrifice. The authors have learnt a lot about this man, who in the prime of life left a secure employment on the other side of the world to come home and fight for King and Country. He was an incredible young man, loved by family and close friends and respected by almost everybody else who came into contact with him. Having learnt so much about him over the last few years, and having visited his grave on the Somme where he fell on the first day of that great battle in July 1916, like several of the family members we too, feel as if we could have known him. Alas, none of the surviving members of his family ever did.

Many parts of the world have been visited in the quest to locate Bagnall locomotives, in many cases at the time when they were still working in commercial service. India in particular, where almost a third of the Company's total locomotive production went and where until the early 1980s more than a hundred of them were still at work. The authors correspondents have also been spread world wide.

The objectives in writing this book have been fourfold. First, to publish as comprehensive a single-volume history of the Company and its people as possible within reasonable size constraints, bearing in mind the primary source documents available; as a sub-objective, as accurate a company history as possible without neglecting the more restricted and in-depth interests of the locomotive and railway enthusiast. Next, to compile the most comprehensive published history to date of a British private locomotive builder. Then to explore the position the Company occupied in the context of the industry in which it operated - where and how it fitted into that industry, with particular emphasis on the influence its people had. Put another way, the Company's total contribution to railway engineering, and in particular locomotive engineering, in its widest context. Last but by no means least, to explore how one man came to achieve what he did, who he was, why he did what he did, who his family were, what they did and what influence they had. After so many years research the authors sometimes feel as if they had known William Gordon Bagnall, as well as other long deceased members of his family. The interest taken in this book by surviving members of the Bagnall family has without doubt led to a far better understanding of the early activities of the Company, and at the expense of repeating what has already been said, one of the most enjoyable and certainly most rewarding aspects of the research that has gone into this book has been the involvement with the descendents of William Gordon Bagnall. The authors can but hope that the family feel their efforts have been worth while.

Whilst of course it is left for its readers to judge how successful or otherwise this book is in meeting the objectives outlined above, it is hoped they will recognise both the width and depth of its declared scope. The vast majority of those who open its pages will almost certainly be railway or at least locomotive enthusiasts; the much wider range of company and family history will nevertheless, it is hoped, be given equal consideration. There are several ways an author might consider on how to lay out a history of a company like the one covered in this book - how to marshal the facts and opinions, how to weave all the strands together, how to illustrate the salient points etc. However, it seems to us that there are two fundamentally different approaches: the story can either be told in strict, or as strictly as possible, chronological order, or it can be compartmentalised so that particular issues are grouped together. In this book, for example, locomotives could have been separated from rolling stock, people issues could have been grouped together; legal and financial aspects could similarly have been separated out into one chapter. The authors have had to decide which method they consider best, because if this was not done at an early stage they can easily have made themselves a lot of unnecessary work. In the case of this book a decision was taken to write as continuous a chronological narrative as possible, and whilst on occasions during the last five years or so this might have appeared not to have been the best idea, now the task is complete it is felt on balance that the method adopted has been the correct one. Having said that, with the best intensions it has not always been possible to strictly adhere to this objective in each and every case. For example, a large proportion of the Bagnall and other related family history issues are concentrated in the first chapter, as it was felt spreading them through the first few chapters would have made it extremely difficult to follow the rather complicated and interrelated aspects of this part of the story. Moreover, this does give the opportunity for the railway or locomotive enthusiast, who might be less interested in these aspects, to skip, or at least speed-read, this chapter. Inevitably in the light of the approach taken there is duplication in other areas of the book, but perhaps this is not altogether a bad thing, as in many cases it helps to make chapters stand on their own, saving the reader frequently having to refer to earlier ones. We have also felt it essential to complement the book with what is, we hope readers will agree, a comprehensive index.

It goes without saying that if any reader feels the authors have failed in any or all of their self-imposed objectives, the responsibly rests with them, and with them alone. If any such failings are detected it will be understood that they are not through the lack of trying or enthusiasm. Maybe the authors have left a stone unturned somewhere, or somebody can add to the story; if this is the case, then the authors can but apologise. If any reader can add significantly to the facts as presented here perhaps they would be good enough to write to the authors via the publisher. It is almost inevitable, that somewhere there lurk facts and figures that ought to have been located - oh that time might have allowed!

The actual writing of this book has occupied the last six years or so, the collection of the material 50 odd years, as related above. The selection of what to include and what to exclude has not been easy, and if the result is felt to be unbalanced in any particular area, this is due to the lack of material rather than any deliberate intention; but the authors have tried hard to ensure as adequate and equal coverage as possible with the material available. The most difficult decisions have been around the selection of the illustrative material, photographs, drawings and other illustrations. An attempt has been made to choose as representative a selection of photographs of the locomotives as possible, bearing in mind those that have appeared in print before, at the same time ensuring that no significant design feature is ignored. Likewise a good balance has been attempted between the 'official' works views along with others of the locomotives after delivery.

Similar objectives have been applied in illustrating the firm's other products, the workshops, the people, publicity material etc. In the case of drawings, then once again, considering the size of the book, pains have been taken to ensure that the salient design features are adequately covered along with a selection of other drawings to give a reasonable general coverage of the Company's products. From literally thousands of photographs and drawings available to the authors this has been no easy task, but it is hoped that the readers will agree that a reasonable balance has been achieved.

Two more statements are necessary before closing these remarks allowing readers to move on to the book itself. First of all we thank most heartily all the numerous people who have over the years helped the authors. Only a few have been mentioned here, but as briefly outlined earlier, it is most sincerely hoped that everybody else who has at some stage come to the authors assistance is named in the acknowledgement section towards the end of the book. If perchance anybody has been missed this not intentional and our most sincere apologies are offered. The correspondence files connected with this research are several feet, nay yards, thick, and it is the intension of the authors to one day, deposit the source material where it can be made available for public inspection and research. Secondly, what is written here is the work of the authors and theirs alone, and they take full responsibility for it. Any errors of fact fall to the authors account, as does the assembly of the information and any opinions that form part of the narrative. An attempt has been made to provide as much information on the products as possible in the various appendices at the end of the book, but anybody who has ever been involved in compiling lists of this nature will be well aware of the pitfalls and difficulty in getting each and every fact and figure correct.

Nevertheless, it is hoped that a large measure of success has been achieved in this particular area - one of the most difficult to achieve.

Consideration has been given to the principle of providing detailed source references. These could have been either in the form of foot or chapter end notes, and this would have either enlarged the book or maybe resulted in some other areas having to be abridged: but these were not considerations in a decision not to follow this path. Our reasoning has been the fact that the firm's remaining records are almost exclusively in private hands and not generally available for public inspection; similarly of course, the Bagnall and other family records are held privately. So it would have been difficult, if not impossible, for readers wanting to access much of the source material to be able to do so. However, wherever possible brief details of the primary source material that is available are outlined in the acknowledgements and bibliography, which as a result are rather more extensive than might otherwise be the case.

Last but by no means least, the authors offer their most sincere and heartfelt thanks to their own families for their forbearance over all the years that this project has been under way. In particular Angela and Pearl, two wonderful ladies who the authors feel sure, will not only be happy to be grouped together in this way, but as glad as the authors themselves to see this book finally in print.

Allan C Baker.
Highfield House,
High Halden,
Kent.

January 2007.

INTRODUCTION

This is a history of Bagnalls of Stafford; the firm and its folk, with apologies to the late Edwin Kitson Clark, author of one of the pioneering histories of a British private locomotive builder, *Kitsons of Leeds*, published by the Locomotive Publishing Company in 1938. As it was one of Clark's objectives, so it has been one of the present authors, to chronicle not just the firm and its products, but most importantly its people; and it has to be added, not just the principals and managers, but a much wider scope. Far too many authors of railway-related books neglect in your authors opinion, the importance, indeed the supreme importance of the contribution made by the people. If it were not for the people there would be no need for industry of any sort, and with no industry it follows there would be no need for railways, and consequently locomotives and rolling stock, which were the principal products of the firm chronicled in these pages. So we hope this book will be judged in that light; a history of the firm and its folk.

The subject is a comparatively small provincially-based engineering company, whose place in history will largely be judged by its activities in designing and building railway locomotives. However, this was much more than just a manufacturer of locomotives, with railway rolling stock, track-work components and many other railway and other related products to its credit. WG Bagnall Limited had its roots in the Staffordshire county town of Stafford, originally formed in 1875 but with a lineage going back a few years earlier. In 1875 William Gordon Bagnall became the principal of the Company which established itself at the Castle Engine Works, to the north of the town, and the firm made its first locomotive in that year. Thereafter expansion was relatively rapid and a speciality soon evolved in the design and manufacture of small narrow-gauge steam locomotives and associated rolling stock, with an emphasis on supplying most of the mechanical equipment necessary to construct and operate light, and in particular, narrow-gauge railways. In those early years of the firm's existence the advantages of light and narrow-gauge railways was becoming increasingly apparent all over the world. Such railways, sometimes referred to as tramways, could be built and operated comparatively cheaply in comparison with their main-line contemporaries, at a period when the advantages of mechanical assistance in the movement of materials of just about any sort, shape or description, was realising enormous economies. It was this significant shift in technology that provided much of the impetus for the firm's development.

William Gordon Bagnall was a incredible individual by any standards and the firm's early locomotives, almost certainly designed by him, were distinctive and in many respects unusual by conventional standards. However, as time progressed he enlisted the help of others, bringing with them both financial and engineering knowledge and experience. For example Thomas Walter, a member of the family that were for many years proprietors of *The Times* newspaper, and Ernest Baguley an already accomplished engineering draughtsman with experience in the design of locomotives and other machinery; others soon followed. The firm is perhaps best remembered in locomotive circles for its small narrow-gauge locomotives with circular-firebox boilers and various unusual valve gears, two of which were patented, one by Baguley and another by Bagnall and his one time works manager Samuel Price. But in fact the range of locomotives built was enormous, and from just before the First World War a market was established on the Indian sub-continent for locomotives for both the 2ft 6in and metre-gauge railways that were rapidly expanding in that country.

Bagnall had a very wide range of interests, and came from a family with associations in the Black Country iron industry, all of which are explored in these pages. The lineage of his wife and the careers of his children are also given extensive coverage, as they are both interesting, and help the reader appreciate the man, and the company he formed, developed and led until his untimely death at a comparatively early age in 1907.

The various chapters of this book therefore, not only take the reader from the early beginnings of the Company along with its predecessor, but also explore at some length the Bagnall family, its antecedents, and other genealogical connections. The story of the Company is followed with much illustrative content, through its expansion in terms of its plant, people and products, and the multifarious issues confronting it during two world wars along with the difficult trading conditions in the years between. Successive changes in the ownership are explored, until its final demise in 1962. The whole range of its products is given coverage, including imaginative efforts to diversify between the two world wars when orders for steam locomotives were increasingly difficult to come by. For example an agreement with a German firm to build under a form of licence in this country diesel locomotives, and with its own resources a small petrol-paraffin engine was designed and built along with such diverse items as concrete mixers and other general engineering products. Not neglected are the war-time activities when much of the workload was in the production of munitions related items and other military equipment.

The main text is accompanied by a series of comprehensive appendices listing details of all the locomotives built by the Company, along with those that came to the works for repairs or overhaul. The principal dimensions of all the locomotives are outlined, giving sufficient detail for readers to form a view on the technical characteristics. There is also a list of spare boilers supplied over the years to help readers have a better understanding of how significant a workload this particular activity was. Details are given of all the Bagnall built locomotives that are known to have survived into preservation, and there is a brief summery of the numbers of locomotives ordered and built year by year. The appendices do not confine themselves to locomotives, for there are details of the principal officers involved in the Company, as well as family trees of the various families that are in some way or other entwined in the story. Finally, brief financial information is listed although these issues are well covered in the main text too.

Although never a big company - the maximum number of people employed was around 600 - WG Bagnall Limited established a formidable reputation in the industry in which it operated and many members of its senior staff became prominent in railway and more particularly locomotive engineering. Roughly two thirds of its output

in locomotives and rolling stock was for export, and about half of that for India, Burma or Ceylon. After the last war its management coined the phrase 'Builders of Locomotives for the World's Railways', and whilst perhaps a small exaggeration, it was by no means an idle claim. In those post-war years leading up to its final demise, diesel-electric locomotives were built in conjunction with another company, along with the design and development of a range of diesel-mechanical and diesel-hydraulic locomotives conducted completely independently. Among its contemporaries in the medium sized British private locomotive builders WG Bagnall Limited had no equal, in the diversity of its products, the range of countries it exported locomotives and rolling stock to, and the influence its people had in the industry in which it operated. This then is their story.

A short note on nomenclature and other related issues might not go amiss. An attempt has been made in the pages that follow to ensure readers can differentiate where confusion might otherwise exist, between the individual construction numbers allocated to locomotives by the firm, and those allocated by customers. Where there might be confusion, the Bagnall numbers are prefixed by the words 'manufacturer's number', whilst in the case of customers, 'No.,' or 'Nos.,' are used as a prefix. All dimensions are given in Imperial measures as this was the convention during the entire existence of the Company, and of course, conversion tables are readily available. Likewise financial information is quoted in pre-decimal configuration, although usually with the nearest decimal equivalent in parenthesis alongside. No attempt has been made to illustrate the effects of inflation, as once again multiplying tables are readily available to enable readers to equate earlier financial information with the equivalent cost today. Rather, the aim in this book has been more in line with giving readers a means of comparing the effects of inflation over the years the firm was in business, as well as providing a comparison between locomotives of different sizes and specifications.

The spelling of place names can often be the cause of confusion. In this book we have tried to adhere to the Anglican form, however there are many cases, particularly in India, where the spelling has changed over the years. There are others too, where the names have altered significantly, in both their spelling and pronunciation. As a general rule we have used the form prevalent at the particular period under discussion.

Chapter One

The Bagnall Family;
The Firm; The Antecedents

Our story starts in three separate locations, at Wednesbury in the Black Country, at Cliff Hall near Tamworth and at the Staffordshire county town of Stafford. At Wednesbury, nearby West Bromwich and other locations in the vicinity, John Bagnall & Sons Limited, carried on business as iron founders and colliery owners and several members of this particular Bagnall family were involved in these operations. At Cliff Hall, three-and-a-half miles south of Tamworth on the present A 423 road and adjacent to the hamlet of Cliff, on 19 January 1852, as son, William Gordon, was born to Richard and Julia Bagnall (nee Gordon). Lastly at Stafford, this particular member of the Bagnall family was to make the town famous for 'The Building of Locomotives for the World's Railways' - as the company he later formed proudly boasted. It will be seen as the story unfolds that this was by no means but a boast and locomotives built at what became the Castle Engine Works, were indeed supplied to public railways and other railway operators all over the world.

The branch of the Bagnall family concerning us in this book and in earlier times variously known as Bagenhall and Bagenold, goes back many generations. The first records available are as far back as 1135 and the family appears to have derived its name from a grant of land at Bagnall, near Endon in North Staffordshire. The branch of the family we are concerned with however, seem to have settled at Broseley in Shropshire around 1672 and John Bagnall, who was born in 1640 at Leek in the Staffordshire Moorlands and about four miles south-east of Endon, married Margaret Roper at Broseley on 1 May 1672. John died before 1716 and his wife in that year; they had two children, both born in Broseley, a son called John who was born in 1673 and a daughter Sarah, born in 1698 - although she was baptized in Leek on 21 February 1698. John married Margery and they had eight children, four boys and four girls; he died in 1742 and his wife in 1728. Their second son, also John, who was born in 1704 married Elizabeth Powell of Broseley on 7 November 1725 and they had five children, three boys and two girls. This particular John died in 1764 and his wife in 1752; their second son, another John, who was born in 1730 married Margaret, daughter of Edward and Mary Dixon who were also from Broseley, where she was born in 1730. The marriage took place on 2 December 1753. Despite Broseley being but one mile south of Coalbrookdale where the birth of the industrial revolution can fairly be said to have taken place, John, together with his wife and young family of four sons moved to West Bromwich, seemingly to establish himself in the trade of Coal & Iron Master in and around that part of the Black Country. He was it appears anxious to take advantage of the burgeoning business in the coal and iron trade as the industrialisation of that part of the country got under way.

John died on 6 March 1800 and his wife on 9 February 1815, but their sons William, born 1754; John, born 1759; Edward, born 1761 and Daniel, born 1765 continued the business their father had started and more will be heard of them and the business of John Bagnall & Sons later in this Chapter.

Richard & Julia Bagnall, William Gordon Bagnall's father and mother. Both parents were born in West Bromwich, on the 18 November 1809 and the 14 December 1824 respectively, and Richard was the eighth son and youngest child of John Bagnall, whilst his wife was the daughter of the Rev. William & Louisa Gordon of Christ Church. Married on 11 February 1845, the ceremony was performed at Christ Church by the Rev. Henry Bagnall, one of Richard's brothers. The couple had no less than 13 children between 1845 and 1867, and Gordon Bagnall was the fourth child and third son. Although Richard inherited much of the family fortune he was a reluctant participant in the trade of coal and iron master; he died on 6 September 1877, and his wife passed away on 15 February 1885, in both cases at the family home at Severn Bank in Worcestershire.

However, the second son John, married first Phoebe, who died 27 October 1791 and secondly Mary Royall, daughter of Henry and Mary Royall of Wednesbury on 13 May 1792 (she was born in 1764). They had eight children, all boys, of whom Richard, the youngest, was

the father of William Gordon Bagnall. John died on 23 November 1829 and his wife on the 22 January 1826. Their youngest son Richard was born on 18 November 1809 and he married Julia, who was born on 14 December 1824 and the daughter of William and Louisa Gordon of Christ Church, West Bromwich. The wedding took place on 11 February 1845 at Christ Church.

Richard and Julia Bagnall had a large family and Gordon Bagnall, as family and friends always knew him, was the third son and fourth child of no less than 13 children, having six brothers and six sisters all born between 23 November 1845 and 13 August 1867. William Gordon was baptized on 18 May 1852 at Kingsbury Parish Church, which is about one mile south of Cliff, as indeed were some of his brothers and sisters. There exists in the family collection a very fine silver christening set consisting of a plate, knife, fork and spoon, the plate being inscribed with the initials WGB and JB - this is James Bagnall one of his uncles. The neat specially made wooden box containing the set marks the presentation with the date 1852. The family had lived at Coopers Hill, a large house in Beeches Road, Dartmouth Park (formerly part of the much larger Sandwell Park), West Bromwich, where the oldest two children were born; Richard Samuel in 1845 and James Jervis in 1849. Coopers Hill had earlier belonged to the Jesson family, Richard Jesson being resident there by 1766. The house stood (it has long since been demolished) on the edge of the park which had been given to the public by the Earl of Dartmouth; this family had considerable estates in this part of Staffordshire and were prominent in local affairs. The house may have been built by the Earl and it later served as a Vicarage for the incumbent of Christ Church, being thus used until a new Vicarage was built on Bratt Street within the church grounds. Christ Church was situated in the High Street, West Bromwich and was consecrated on 17 January 1829; unfortunately it was destroyed by fire in October 1979, only the lych gate remaining. At the time of the 1881 Census Coopers Hill appears to have been in use as a Vicarage, as the Rev. Robert Hodgson the Vicar of Christ Church and his family were in residence. The Jessons by the way, were one of the earliest families to be involved in the Black Country iron trade and appear to have been the first to puddle wrought iron using

William Gordon Bagnall - the earliest known portrait dating from around 1890 when he would have been 38 years old. Born at Cliff Hall near Tamworth on 19 January 1852, the fourth child and third son of Richard and Julia Bagnall.

coke. As far back as 1773, a Jesson in partnership with a fellow called Wright, were granted a patent for such a process. John Bagnall (1794-1840), the eldest son of John Bagnall (1759-1829) and the bother of WG Bagnall's father, married a Jesson by the name of Ann, but she died at or shortly after childbirth in September 1827; she was only 29 years old and the daughter, also Ann, passed away two years later. By 1850 this branch of the Bagnall family had moved to Cliff Hall and as well as William Gordon four brothers and three sisters were also born there; Julia in 1850; John in 1853;

All that remained of Cliff Hall, near Kingsbury in Warwickshire on a dull December day in 2003, was this and another nearby building, former out-buildings of the Hall. Perhaps this one was originally part of the stable block. The Hall, which stood to the right of this building, was demolished following a fire some thirty years earlier; it was at the Hall that WG Bagnall was born.

Marian in 1855; Louisa in 1857; Robert Henry in 1858; Reginald in 1861 and George in 1862.

By 1864 there had been another move of home, this time to Charlemont Hall (in earlier times usually spelt Charleymount which was also the name of the adjacent hamlet), also in West Bromwich, about a mile and a half north of Coopers Hill, in the suburb of Bird End. However, Charlemont Hall had been in the Bagnall family since 1854 when it was purchased by John Nock Bagnall - who we shall meet again later in the story. In earlier times this large house had also been owned and lived in by the Jessons who sold it to Samuel Dawes of Handsworth in 1825; John Nock Bagnall purchased it from the Dawes trustees, along with three adjacent fields, in 1854. The last three children, all daughters, were born at Charlemont: Jessie in 1864; Gertrude Mary in 1866 and Norah in 1867. Richard Bagnall seems to have been quite nomadic if the number of houses he and his family occupied is anything to go by, as the 1871 Census has the family living at Bescot Hall. In any event the Bagnalls had sold Charlemont Hall in 1871 to John Hunt Thursfield, he was Mayor of Wednesbury in 1890 and 1901, and the Hall was eventually demolished in 1948. The original manor house at Bescot, situated roughly half way between Wednesbury and Walsall, was very old - it was there by at least 1311 - but this building was later demolished and a new house built in the eighteenth century a little to the north-east. This second house, Bescot Hall, was itself demolished in about 1937. The site is now part of Pleck Park between the park entrance in Bescot Way and the M6 motorway.

Although Gordon Bagnall's father Richard, was a somewhat reluctant participant in the family business that carried the Bagnall name, it nevertheless should come as no surprise that Gordon Bagnall undertook his practical engineering training with John Bagnall & Sons Limited. Gordon Bagnall, along with some of his brothers and sisters, spent several years living as a family at Severn Bank. This was a sizable country seat at Severn Stoke in the parish of All Saints, two miles north of Upton-upon-Severn in Worcestershire and on the east bank of the river. The family seem to have moved there in the early to mid 1870s, and they were certainly there by 1877 when Richard died. The 1881 Census for the occupancy of Severn Bank, albeit after Richard has passed on, shows no less than seven

Severn Bank, the family seat sitting on the east bank of the River Severn half a mile south of Severn Stoke in Worcestershire, and around two miles north of Upton-on-Severn. This large property was acquired or perhaps only leased by Richard and Julia Bagnall in the early 1870s, and the younger members of the family were brought up there. WG Bagnall would have spent time here with his family, especially before he got married in 1883.

domestic servants of one description or another along with one Governess. Gordon Bagnall was also there at the time of this Census, so it would seem that he was at least a frequent visitor until he got married in 1883; in fact he may only have stayed in Stafford during the week. His profession is given as an engineer employing 68 men. The Stafford Almanac for 1880 however, gives an address of 1 Station Road in the town, whilst the 1883 edition has Eastgate House as his residence. When interviewed in later years Gordon Bagnall always stated that his early education was undertaken 'privately'; the 1861 Census when the family lived at Cliff Hall, describes him as a scholar.

There follows a measure of uncertainty and contradiction as to where Gordon Bagnall had his theoretical engineering training. His daughter Jessica, when interviewed in 1976 said quite categorically that her father had attended Coopers Hill College which she said was in North London. However, Coopers Hill Engineering College was at Egham, just south of the River Thames in Surrey, where it had been established

in 1872. This college had been established specifically to train young men, principally in civil engineering, for service in India with the Public Works Departments (PWD) of the various states. At the time India was suffering an acute shortage of trained engineers to help undertake a multifarious and extensive programme of public works improvements, projects like road and bridge building, irrigation and of course railway construction. Jessica Bagnall went on to relate that it was at the college that her father had first met Percy Rooper (pronounced Roper), and whilst Rooper later spent much of his career involved with the railways of India, the friendship continued - indeed the Rooper family became great family friends of the Bagnalls. A quantity of records relating to the college survive in the India Office collection housed in The British Library, including a hand written foolscap book said to contain (and appearing to) an alphabetical list of all those who attended the college from its opening in August 1872, until closure in 1911. There is an entry in this list for a PL Rooper, who entered the college in September 1879 and left to take up an appointment to the PWD in India in 1882. This could well be the Percy Rooper, but if so, his period at the collage would be far too late for him to have met Gordon Bagnall there, as by 1875 Bagnall was in business on his own at Stafford. Moreover, there is in fact no record of Gordon Bagnall ever having attended the college. So we are left wondering; remember that at one period the family lived at Coopers Hill House in West Bromwich, so was Jessica confused, but being aware that the family friend Percy Rooper had been a student at the college assumed her father had been there too? There is however, a further twist to this part of the story. Some years later Gordon Bagnall was joined in a successful Patent application - of which more will be said later - by AH Heath who gave a Coopers Hill, Surrey address. Arthur Henry Heath was a Professor at Coopers Hill College where he taught applied mathematics, he was there from 1875 to 1901, and one could be forgiven for assuming that Bagnall met Heath as a tutor there. However, the Heath family of which Arthur Henry was a member were related to the Bagnalls through marriage, and this connection will be explored later in the story. It is of course possible that Arthur Heath had been involved in Gordon Bagnalls 'private education' referred to earlier, but this would have been before the family relationship that followed his marriage.

The Rooper family friendship would appear to have been instrumental in Rooper's father, WO Rooper, who owned a developing emery wheel and grindstone manufacturing business at Greenwich, transferring part of his operations to Stafford in 1893. By this date Rooper was already a partner in a small electrical business - Rooper & Harris Limited - situated in Eastgate Street at Stafford, although he established his grinding wheel workshop on about half an acre of land forming part of the Castle Engine Works site, which he sub-leased from Bagnall. In 1905 Rooper's firm was acquired by a rival concern, Moser, West & Bateman Limited, which also transferred its operations to Stafford and in 1914 this Company combined with a Sheffield company in the same trade to form The Universal Grinding Wheel Company Limited. A new factory was established as the firm expanded operations; this was just north of the Castle Engine Works and on the opposite side of the Stafford to Wellington railway line. However, due to the increased requirement during

the First World War for grinding wheels and the other abrasive products the firm manufactured, it was not until 1920 that the area within the Castle Engine Works site was finally vacated. The new works at Burley Fields was expanded later with further land being occupied for works extensions at nearby Doxey, so that by the late 1950s it occupied no less than 44 acres. Following a number of subsequent amalgamations within the grinding wheel business that need not detain us here, the firm since 1997 has been part of the French Saint-Gobain business and trades as Gobain Abrasives Limited.

The Rooper family under discussion here is the same one that over many years were involved in a number of Liverpool-based shipping lines. Percy Lens Rooper of The Elms at Gresford in Denbighshire, married Alice Nancy (Daisy) Royden on 27 June 1889; Daisy, as she was known, was a member of another well known Liverpool family with interests in the shipping industry - Thomas Roydon & Sons. Daisy's brother Thomas Royden, later Sir Thomas Royden 2nd Bart (1871-1950; succeeded his father the 1st Bart in 1917) and who later became Lord Roydon C.H., of Frankby Hall near Hoylake on the Wirral in Cheshire, was for many years a director of the LMS Railway and the Midland Bank. Roydon was also chairman of the Cunard Steam Ship Company Limited and a director of a number of other companies connected with both shipping and power generation. The Roydon shipping line was an old one dating from the 1830s, and at one period built its own vessels at Liverpool; latterly at Queen's Dock. Like the Roopers the Roydons too, had over many years, connections with several other Liverpool based shipping lines. Percy and Daisy Rooper had three sons two of whom, Ralph and Trevor were killed in action during the First World War. The third son Jack, did not serve as he suffered from asthma. The families ill fortunes however, continued after Jack married Iris, as two of their four children (three boys and a girl) were killed in action during the Second World War. The brothers Anthony and Ralph Rooper gave their lives for their country; Ralph was commissioned in the Royal Navy (Fleet Air Arm) and killed off the coast of Holland; he is buried on Dutch soil and near where he fell. The third son David, and the daughter Shirley, survived and had children.

After working at his Grandfather's Company along

with whatever other engineering training he may have had, Gordon Bagnall spent two and a half years working at a bank and it would have been during this part of his training that he doubtless acquired the financial acumen that stood him in such good stead when he commenced business on his own. The 1871 Census return for Bescot Hall lists WG Bagnall in residence there along with all his brothers and sisters except John and Marian - surprisingly their mother Julia is not listed either. As well as the family there was a Governess, two nurses and three domestic servants. William Gordon Bagnall's occupation is listed as a 'Clerk in a Bank'. Unfortunately we have no knowledge of which bank he worked, but in all probability it would have been Lloyds, or one of its associates. Lloyd's were John Bagnall & Son's bankers and a bank originally formed by Quakers to support the then burgeoning industrial activity in the Black Country. There is however, no evidence that any members of the branch of the Bagnall family concerning us here, were ever involved in the Quakers sect. James Jervis Bagnall, one of Gordon's elder brothers, who is also listed in 1881 as living at Severn Bank, has his occupation shown as an articled clerk in a solicitor's office. James would perhaps, have been employed by the Birmingham based part family firm of solicitors, Rowland & Bagnall, and he may have been involved when this partnership assisted Gordon Bagnall in forming his own business at Stafford.

Attention must now turn to the county town of Stafford, standing on the River Sow with a history going back to the eighth century and with significant castle remains overlooking the town from a prominent position to the west. This castle, which dates originally from around 1350, was built by Ralph de Stafford, although there was a major reconstruction in about 1817. Stafford is somewhat of an enigma, sitting as it does almost in the centre of Staffordshire and acting with nearby Cannock Chase as a sort of divide between the northern and southern parts; the county is still, somewhat surprisingly perhaps, at least 50% agricultural. There is a point of view that the county of Stafford should actually be two, as there is hardly anything to be had in common between its north and south and from almost any point of view. The southern part of the county embraces much of Wolverhampton and forms a significant part of the colloquially known Black Country. North Staffordshire on the other hand,

clustered around the pottery towns and villages that later formed the City of Stoke-on-Trent, along with its neighbour the loyal and ancient Borough of Newcastle-under-Lyme, grew largely out of the pottery industry and form an enclave almost all on their own. If one was to divide the county into two, one might ask in which half Stafford should be; ask the average resident of the town and they would in all probability opt for the north.

As well as being a thriving market town Stafford was famous for its boot and shoe making industry, a trade in the town going back to as early as 1476, with small engineering workshops growing out of the need to serve the requirements of this industry. By the late 1700s William Horton (1750-1832), who became the first manufacturer of shoes at Stafford on a large scale, was employing both direct labour and outworkers, the latter numbering over 1,000 by 1813. Thomas Bostock and his son Edwin later came to dominate the boot and shoe industry in the town, where they started making boots in a factory at Goalgate in 1820. By 1834 the Bostocks employed some 200 men, moving to new premises at Foregate some years later. In 1919 the Bostock Company amalgamated with another large shoe manufacturer in the town, JJ Heys, to form Lotus Limited, a Company that continued to dominate the town's boot and shoe industry and now part of the Fii Group. Shoes are no longer manufactured in Stafford, production having ceased by the end of the 20th century and today part of the remains of the main Lotus factory is but a service depot with the remainder of the site a housing estate. But the boot and shoe manufacturing industry must not be forgotten as it was families like the Bostocks that were partly instrumental in the town's 18th, 19th and early 20th century development. At the time of the Battle of Hastings the population of Stafford numbered about 900 souls, climbing to 1500 in the 13th century; it did not top 2000 until the early 1800s. The coming of the industrial revolution brought significant growth to the town with the population rising to 7,000 in 1831 and over 10,000 ten years later. In 1881 it was almost 20,000, and the 1951 Census gives a figure of 40,275.

Stafford was early on the main-line railway map when the Grand Junction Railway (GJR) main-line from Birmingham, running north to Newton near Warrington, opened on 4 July 1843. At Birmingham it connected with the slightly earlier London &

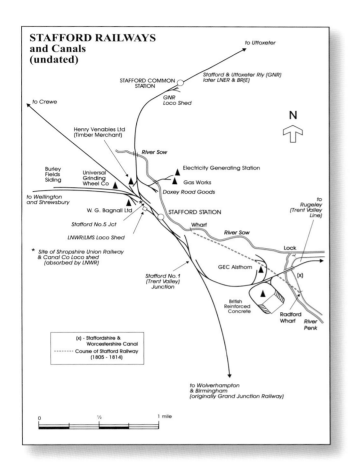

Simplified map showing the main line railways at Stafford at their fullest extent, together with the Staffordshire & Worcestershire Canal and the River Sow, with the entrance lock from the canal to the river. The course of the Stafford Railway is also shown running from Radford Wharf to the town - it followed the course of the main road - Lichfield Road. Additionally the map illustrates the location of the Castle Engine Works and other establishments mentioned in the text.

Birmingham Railway and on 16 July 1846, these two railways together with the Manchester & Birmingham Railway (which only ran from Manchester to Crewe) amalgamated to form the London & North Western Railway (LNWR). Then on 1 December 1847, the LNWR opened a more direct line south from Stafford to Rugby - the Trent Valley line - thus shortening the journey times for trains not needing to go via Wolverhampton and Birmingham. At its southern end this line rejoined the original route at Rugby. The LNWR was joined at Stafford in May 1848 by the North Staffordshire Railway (NSR); its trains arriving in town by means of running powers over the LNWR from

Norton Bridge, almost five miles north of Stafford and where the new line from Stoke-upon-Trent made a junction. It was not long before these two railways were joined by a third, the Shropshire Union Railways & Canal Company whose line to Wellington via Newport opened on 1 June 1849. But this line was leased to the LNWR even before it opened although its owning company remained independent until the grouping of the railways in 1923. Last of all the independent Stafford & Uttoxeter Railway opened its line from Uttoxeter on 23 December 1867. In 1879 the Stafford & Uttoxeter Railway, in effect gave up its independent struggle and reached an agreement with the Great Northern Railway (GNR) to operate its line. The GNR had been busying itself in moving its influence westwards - although in the event it got no further than Stafford - and in 1881 it absorbed the smaller company. As a result of this railway building Stafford became a hub of railway operations with an industry in its own right growing up in support. Soon there were goods marshalling yards, warehouses, locomotive sheds and a whole range of all the other activities that were becoming so familiar in supporting the nineteenth century expanding railways. This activity by the railway companies was an enormous boost to the town, assisting both its existing industries as well as encouraging the development of new ones. For many years Stafford was the frontier point between the Southern and Northern Divisions of the LNWR and when separate Locomotive Departments existed for each Division, prior to 1859, engines were changed at Stafford on many of the through trains. Because of this need there were two separate locomotive sheds at Stafford, albeit side by side, one for the Northern Division locomotives and another for the Southern Division. At one point it was seriously considered by the directors of the LNWR that Stafford, rather than Crewe, 25 miles to the north, should have been the site of the Company's principal locomotive workshops.

It is perhaps worth mentioning that a railway had existed at Stafford earlier than the coming of the Grand Junction, for in November 1805 The Stafford Railway, as it came to be known, opened a flanged railway between Radford Wharf on the Staffordshire & Worcestershire Canal, south-east of the town, and the town itself. This line was one-and-a-half miles long and its principal traffic for the town was coal and lime carried in open wagons hauled by horses. Its route paralleled the road between the two termini and it used the same Radford road bridge to cross the Sow. The Staffordshire & Worcestershire Canal had opened its entire 46-mile route between the River Severn at Stourport and a junction with the Trent & Mersey Canal east of Stafford at Great Haywood, in 1772. The Stafford Railway appears to have fallen out of use in 1814 after a comparatively short life, because the River Sow had been canalised between the Staffordshire & Worcestershire Canal and a wharf adjacent to the Royal Brine Baths (demolished in 1976) in the centre of the town. However, this navigable part of the Sow along with the necessary lock between the river and canal just north of Radford, does not seem to have become operational until 19 February 1816.

The embryo of the first sizable engineering undertaking in the town came in 1870 when William Henry Dorman started business to support the boot and shoe industry. The Company carrying his name was originally situated in Stone Road, Foregate, and grew into a large engineering manufacturing business, later specialising in internal combustion engines. There was a gradual movement of the manufacturing activities of WH Dorman & Company Limited, as the firm became known, in the years up to 1925 to larger premises in Tixall Road. As designers and manufacturers of diesel engines the Dorman name became well known all over the world. After a number of owners in more recent times the Dorman Company is today part of the American-owned Caterpillar Group; it will nevertheless, enter the story again, but not for over 80 years!

Our attention, however, must turn to a small millwrights business in Crabbery Street at Stafford, owned and operated by a partnership of Bernard Massey and John Hill. This business seems to date from 1870 or thereabouts and an 1872 reference in a local trade directory refers to Bernard Massey as an engineer and millwright of Foregate Street, so he must have taken John Hill into partnership and moved to Crabbery Street sometime after that. These two gentlemen described themselves as Mechanical & Electrical Engineers and it would be interesting to know just what electrical work, if any, they performed at this early date. Bernard Massey was born in 1838, a native of Newport in Shropshire and lived with his wife Ellen, who came

from Sutton Coalfield, and their son Joseph William (born 1871) at 3 Greyfriars in Stafford. Unfortunately we know nothing about the facilities at either Foregate Street or Crabbery Street and in any event the partnership cannot have been at the latter location very long, for in March 1873 a lease was entered into for a tract of land at Castle Town. This was north of the station on the west side of the railway and between what became known as 'Bagnall's Bridge' - which takes Castle Street over the railway - and the junction of the Shropshire Union Railways & Canal Company's line to Wellington. At the time development of this part of Stafford was quite new; it had been established to serve the burgeoning needs of the railway workers. Originally known as Newtown, it was soon renamed Castle Town, being overlooked as it is by the castle remains.

Mention was made earlier that for a number of years after the coming of the railways Stafford served as the frontier point between the Southern and Northern Divisions of the GJR and later LNWR; most trains therefore, not only changed engines at Stafford but the crews too. As a result of this the railway became a sizable employer of labour in Stafford and large numbers of houses were built for its servants - as they were called in those times - many of which are still standing today. Once the move to Castle Town had taken place the workshops must have been reasonably well equipped as Massey & Hill, describing themselves as 'Engineers etc., of Stafford', exhibited at the Royal Agricultural Society of England (RASE) Show at Bedford in July 1874. There were three exhibits consisting of a three horsepower patent vertical water tube boiler and attached horizontal engine, a similar but seven horsepower version and in this case fitted with an expansion valve under the control of a governor; lastly a series of what are described as 'patent water tubes'. These tubes were the subject of patent No 3313 of 13 October 1873, 'sealed' on 9 April the following year and titled: Certain Improvements to Steam Boilers. The patent was in the joint names of Bernard Massey and John Hill, trading as Massey & Hill, Engineers of Stafford. The invention consists of an arrangement whereby water tubes could be accommodated in otherwise fire-tube boilers to improve the circulation of water; it is not unlike the principle of a thermic siphon. The accompanying drawings of a vertical boiler illustrate the principle of the tubes in a circle around

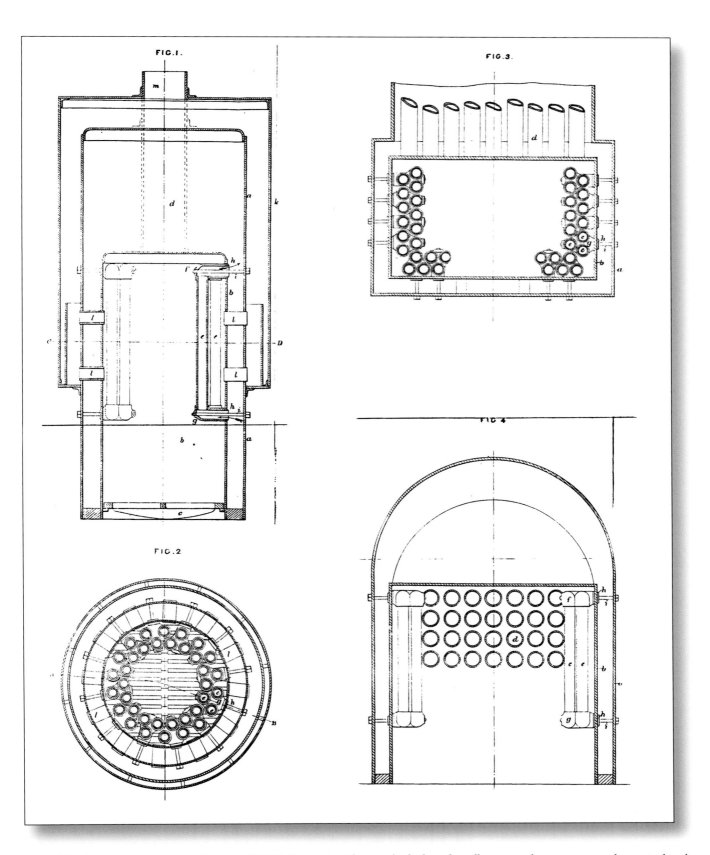

One of the drawings accompanying Massey & Hill's Patent Specification for boiler tubes, illustrating the arrangement for vertical and horizontal boilers as described in the text.

the inner firebox on the fire side extending from just above where the top of the fire would be to the roof of the firebox; they are connected to the water spaces at top and bottom. In nests of three the drawing shows 12 clusters of three tubes each which together completely encircle the firebox. In the locomotive type boiler illustrated the tubes are again shown vertically but in this case along each side of the inner firebox, whilst in a Lancashire or Cornish boiler, an example of which is not illustrated here, they are shown angled at about 45% from the top to bottom of the firebox. Presumably these patent tubes were fitted to the boilers exhibited at Bedford and accompanying the boilers was a separate example of the tubes. How successful or otherwise these tubes were appears to have gone unrecorded, but in any application they must have been subjected to considerable direct heat from the fire and potential mechanical damage from the fire irons. This was the first and only time Massey & Hill exhibited at one of the RASE shows, although (as will be seen in the next Chapter) on taking over the partnership Bagnall used the shows extensively to exhibit his products.

An entry in the *Staffordshire Advertiser* dated 19 June 1875 reads: 'Notice is hereby given that the partnership hitherto subsisting between us the undersigned Bernard Massey and John Hill at Stafford as mechanical and electrical engineers, iron and brass founders under the style or firm of Massey & Hill, was on 30th day of March 1875 dissolved by mutual consent. All debts owing from or due to the late firm will be discharged or received by the said John Hill who for the future will carry on the business on his own account. Dated this 12th day of June 1875 Bernard Massey: John Hill'.

There is no obvious evidence to suggest exactly why Bagnall moved to Stafford, or indeed why he wanted to go into business on his own, as despite the family firm being in financial difficulties at the time he would undoubtedly have been offered a job there. However, we are aware of his entrepreneurial sprit from his later activities and from those who knew him. It may be he saw or heard of the notice mentioned earlier that appeared in the *Staffordshire Advertiser*, because he joined forces with John Hill and in the same paper for 22 January 1876, we find Hill & Bagnall of the Castle Iron Works advertising themselves as: 'Millwrights, iron and brass founders, makers of engines, sawing machines, mortar mills, hydraulic rams for supplying

gentlemen's houses etc., with water. Wheels for contractors earth wagons, castings of all kinds, portable engines and thrashing boxes. Repairs of all descriptions promptly attended to. Priced catalogue on application, all issues 1876 up to this one'. The hand of Gordon Bagnall can be clearly detected in this advert, especially in the reference to catalogues, because the design and compilation of these over the succeeding years became very much a personal activity for him, lavish and extremely comprehensive publications they were too. However, quite what 'all issues 1876 up to this one' meant, when it was only January, appears to have gone unrecorded.

Be that as it may, a little over a month later the *Staffordshire Advertiser* has the following notice in its issue dated 26 February 1876: 'Notice is hereby given that the partnership hither fore existing between John Hill and William Gordon Bagnall both of Stafford, engineers and iron founders trading as Hill & Bagnall, is dissolved from the date hereof. All accounts owing to or by the late firm must be paid and forwarded to the said WG Bagnall, by whom the business is being continued. 25 February 1876. Rowland & Bagnall, 25 Colmore Row, Birmingham, Solicitors to the said WG Bagnall'. This is the same firm of solicitors mentioned earlier.

From this point on the 'company' traded as WG Bagnall & Company and it appears that whilst Bagnall himself effectively retained almost total control, he had a somewhat less involved partner by the name of Thomas Walter. Thomas Walter was a member of the Walter family of Bear Wood in Berkshire, several members of which, were connected with the well established *The Times* newspaper. Indeed Thomas was one of the great grandsons of John Walter (1739-1812) who was the paper's founder; its first issue appeared on 1 January 1785. John's second son - also John (1776-1847) - became the proprietor of the paper on the death of his father in 1812, and his eldest son, also John (1818-1894) married Emily Francis Court in April 1848 and they had seven children. There were six boys and one girl and the second son - Arthur Frazer (1846-1910) - took over from his father as proprietor of *The Times*. Thomas was the fifth son of this marriage but after the death of Emily in 1858, in 1861 John married Flora Macnabb and there were four more sons and another daughter. Unfortunately we do not know very much about Thomas Walter's early career, but he later described himself as an engineer from Stafford with addresses variously of the North Western Hotel Victoria Road in 1891, and 46 Greengate in 1892. However, whilst there is no evidence that he ever trained in engineering, he did become the principal contributor of capital in the partnership.

Thomas Walter was born on 20 July 1854 in London and baptised at St Catherine's Bearwood in Berkshire on 28 August that year. From September 1865 to the summer of 1870 he was educated at Eton School in Edmond Warr's House; Eton had been his father's school and at least some of his brothers were educated there too. Whatever his physical involvement with the activities of the Castle Engine Works may have been, it appears to have been relatively short lived as by the early 1890s he was living in the Waikato (sometimes spelt Waikata) district of New Zealand, with an address of Lake House, Hamilton. There he met and on 12 December 1894 married, Ellen Mary Gore, daughter of Richard Benjamin Gore of the Colonial Museum in Wellington. There was one child, a daughter, Catherine Gore who was born in New Zealand on 8 April 1896. It is not known what Walter did in New Zealand but by

Thomas Walter's grave in the church yard at St Peter's at Witherley in Warwickshire, photographed on 29 March 2005 with the spring daffodils.

1906 the family were living in this country at Stoke, a suburb of Devonport near Plymouth. Evidently by this time Thomas Walter had decided to become a Church of England Cleric as a result of which he studied for Holy Orders. The relevant notices having been read on 1 December at St Michael's Church in Stoke, Walter was ordained by the Lord Bishop of Exeter, A Robertson DD, on 19 December 1907. Some short time earlier he had been offered and had accepted subject to a successful ordination, the position of Assistant Curate (Deacon) to the Rev. Walter M Smith-Dorrien, Vicar of The Collegiate Church of The Holy Cross at Crediton in the Exeter part of the Devon Diocese.

Walter remained at Crediton until 1910 when he became Priest of the Anglican Church in Orotava on the island of Tenerife - one of the Canary Islands. By 1919 he was at Christ Church in Naples and in 1921 was Chaplin at Holy Trinity in Rome in the Diocese of Gibraltar, after which he appears to have returned to this country. Walter and his family then settled in the small village of Witherley in Warwickshire, a little south of Atherstone and immediately to the east of Telford's famous London to Holyhead road - the present A5. This would have been around the turn of the year 1922 as he had been appointed rector-elect of St Peter's church in the Parish of Witherley. At this time the rector of St Peter's was Charles George Gordon-Yaudin, the incumbent since 1909, was on the verge of retirement, he had been seriously ill for some time; Walter was therefore in temporary charge of the Parish. As events unfolded Walter never formally took over the Parish from Gordon-Yaudin, as within a very short period both Gordon-Yaudin and Thomas Walter passed away. Walter died on 25 April 1923 at The Rectory at Witherley, just three weeks after the incumbent rector, and his remains are buried in the churchyard of St Peter's. The cause of death was given as a perforation of duodenal ulcer and plastic peritonitis.

One of Thomas's elder brothers by the way, Major Henry Walter (1850-1931), who was the fourth son of John and Emily Walter, also took Holy Orders later in life and from 1896 until his death was Rector of St Paul's at Wokingham in Berkshire. This is very near the family 'seat' at Bear Wood. Henry Walter was present at the time of his brother's death and helped to conduct the funeral service. According to the local press the late Rev. T Walter 'had gained the respect and esteem of the whole parish, and much sympathy is felt for Mrs and Miss Walter in their sudden bereavement'. We are left wondering perhaps how and why Walter came to settle in Witherley with the intension of taking up a position apparently somewhat removed in status from his immediately proceeding ones. The Walter family never seem to have been short of finance; perhaps he just wanted a few more years job satisfaction in a quieter role. And why Witherley? Was this a church decision or was it a place he knew from his earlier days in nearby Stafford? Be that as it may, after the death of Thomas his wife and daughter returned to New Zealand residing at Salamanca Road in the capital of Wellington; his wife died there on 8 July 1926. Walter left a gross estate of £8,403 in this country and there was a separate will relating to his New Zealand estate. It is worth noting that until his death in 1921, one of Walter's executors was a friend from schoolboy days at Eton, Gilbert Henry Claughton (1856-1921). Walter's wife left £3,810 on her estate in this country and once again there was a second will concerning her New Zealand estate; her executers in this country were two of her husband's brothers.

Gilbert Claughton was created a Baronet on 4 July 1912 and his mother, Julia Susannah Humble, was the sister of the 10th Lord Ward whose eldest son and her brother was the 1st Earl of Dudley; his father, the Rev. TH Claughton, was the 1st Bishop of St Albans. For many years from 1891 Gilbert Claughton was the chief mineral agent of the Earl's mining estates and his many other industrial interests in and around South Staffordshire. He was also involved in a number of other industrial undertakings; for example, in the years leading up to the First World War he had been appointed a director of the South Staffordshire Waterworks Company, the Mond Gas Company as well as being chairman of Round Oak Works Limited at Brierley Hill. Residing for most of the time at The Priory in Dudley, Claughton was a director of several other industrial companies many of which were based in the Black Country. In 1905 he was elected to the board of the London & North Western Railway and was its chairman from 1911. Having been given full negotiating powers by the Railway Companies Association, Claughton was largely responsible for the improvements in labour relations on the railways of this country in the years leading up to the First World War, and it was for

this that he received his Baronetcy. He also gave his name to what became perhaps the most famous class of LNWR locomotive. Engine number 2222, the first member of a fleet of express passenger locomotives introduced in 1913, was named SIR GILBERT CLAUGHTON and the class were subsequently and universally known as 'The Claughtons'. Among his civic duties Claughton was a Justice of the Peace for Staffordshire and Worcestershire, an Alderman of Staffordshire County Council at the same time as Gordon Bagnall and for many years chairman of its finance committee. A very well-known and respected personality in and around Dudley - its Mayor 1890-1895 - and surrounding area he would of course have been well-known to the West Bromwich branch of the Bagnall family. There is a distinct possibility that it was an introduction by Claughton that brought William Gordon Bagnall and Thomas Walter together in a business partnership. Walter would have been looking for investment opportunities and Bagnall wanted cash to develop his business.

Gilbert Claughton was also well known and respected in the City, which included the proprietors of *The Times* newspaper. This paper, along with John Bagnall & Sons Limited and Gordon Bagnall banked with Lloyds. Whilst Claughton was a director of Barclays Bank, he would have had considerable sympathy with engineers having served an engineering apprenticeship with the Gorton based locomotive builders Beyer Peacock & Company Limited, afterwards studying engineering at King's College in London. After a long illness following the enormous pressures of his war-time work-load which necessitated retirement from most of his business affairs including the chairmanship of the LNWR, Gilbert Claughton passed away on 27 July 1921. The funeral service took place at the Parish Church in Dudley on 1 July and his remains were interned in the church yard there; as he was unmarried the Baronetcy became extinct. A great railwayman and far-sighted employer, it is said he liked nothing more than going around his numerous industrial and railway interests meeting the people; one can imagine he would have got on very well with the Bagnalls, also well known for their benevolence with those who worked for them.

The site chosen for the new works at Castle Town in Stafford was leased from the landowner, Lord Stafford

(The Right Honourable Henry Valentine Stafford Jerningham), and there were two leases. The original one was for a little over one acre and dated 25 March 1873 whilst the second one covered a further four acres plus 28 perches (one perch = five and a half square yards) and although dated 10 November 1884, both leases were to run for 99 years from 25 March 1873. This increase in the land occupied helps illustrate the expansion of the Company and in terms of people employed from the 30 men and boys on the pay-role at the time of the original Bagnall-Walter partnership. Further extensions to the land leased from Lord Stafford followed such that by June 1904, the site consisted of over seven acres.

Mention has already been made of the catalogues illustrating and describing what the Company produced and these became very much a part of the advertising strategy. These publications started as they were to continue as lavish affairs, the design and production of which Bagnall took so much on to himself. Almost all issues had dark red covers and many were hardbound and beautifully finished with embossed lettering and

Front cover of Catalogue No 1 dated August 1876. Red as a colour for the covers of the firm's catalogues was to remain almost, but not quite, the standard for the entire series which terminated with No 19, issued just before the First World War (probably in 1912; unusually this and No 18 are the only ones undated). The drawing of the medal is the one awarded to Gordon Bagnall for his 'Stafford Empress' engine and boiler combined at the Staffordshire Agricultural Society's Meeting in 1876. The crest is that of Stafford town.

illustrations on the covers. They were sequentially numbered starting from issue Number 1 in August 1876 and continuing until just before the First World War with Numbers 18 and 19. There were also several editions published in foreign languages, Spanish and Portuguese for example - much later and after the First World War, there was even one in Russian! The first issue - Number 1 - describes itself as: 'Illustrated Catalogue of Steam engines, Builders, Contractors, Colliery Proprietors & Farmers Plant, Constructed by WG Bagnall, Castle Engine Works, Stafford'. It also mentions the Company having been awarded the Staffordshire Agricultural Society Medal. Inside Bagnall claimed to be a 'Millwright, Iron & Brass Founder and the maker of the Challenge and Empress Engines, and Stafford Pump'. Numerous other claims are made and the 37-page catalogue has several engravings of all sorts of machinery. The horizontal steam engines came in two configurations, one for horsepowers up to 12 and the other from 12 to 50, supplied with feed pumps, along with condensers and air pumps if required; Cornish boilers were also available. The 'Stafford Empress' engine and boiler combined had the horizontal engine mounted on the side of and half-way up a vertical boiler and is the design claimed to have received the medal at the Staffordshire Agricultural Society's meeting. The 'Challenge' engine and boiler combined was somewhat bigger, with the horizontal engine alongside the boiler, the two sitting on a common bedplate; this type of engine could also be supplied separate from a boiler. The catalogue goes on to illustrate by engravings steam and hand cranes, steam hoists, band saws, saw benches, mortar mills and the 'Stafford Steam Pump', which came in several sizes and employed the principle of the Scotch crank. There is much more too: ship's engines, brick making machinery, grinding mills, a portable steam engine in the style of a traction engine and of particular interest, two railway locomotives. The catalogue concludes with a comprehensive price list along with many other claims. Exactly what was built from this compendium has alas largely gone unrecorded, but we do know that stationary steam engines and boilers did emerge from the Castle Engine Works and over a good few years. The 'Challenge' engine and boiler combined seems to have been particularly popular.

The next catalogue of which a survivor is known is

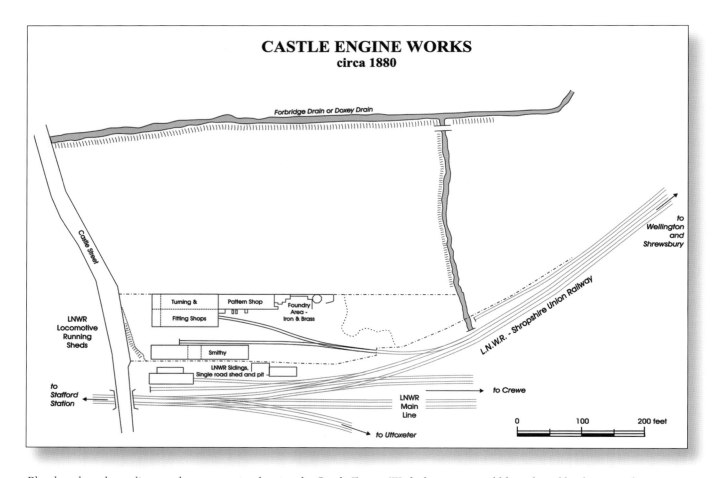

CASTLE ENGINE WORKS
circa 1880

Forbridge Drain or Doxey Drain

Castle Street

to
Wellington
and
Shrewsbury

LNWR
Locomotive
Running
Sheds

Turning &
Fitting Shops

Pattern Shop

Foundry
Area -
Iron & Brass

Smithy

LNWR Sidings,
Single road shed and pit

L.N.W.R. - Shropshire Union Railway

to
Stafford
Station

to Crewe

LNWR
Main
Line

0   100   200 feet

to Uttoxeter

Plan based on the earliest one known to exist showing the Castle Engine Works layout; it would have been like this around 1880. As well as the workshops it shows the original plot of land leased from Lord Stafford, and the main line railways as they existed at the time. The small main-line locomotive shed that can be seen alongside the works was actually demolished some time in 1879, when the junction arrangements were altered to cater for the quadrupling of the lines between Stafford and Crewe. The four track section was completed and opened for freight traffic March 1876, followed by passenger traffic in November. For some reason it took a few more years before the junction here (1881), later controlled from Stafford No 5 signal box, was altered to suit. The small locomotive shed may originally have been intended for the Shropshire Union Railway & Canal Company's engines, before it was agreed that the LNWR should work this line from opening; nevertheless, according to the LNWR records it seems to have been used for locomotives until early 1879.

numbered 2B and dated 1 July 1878, or at least that is the date when the price list within it became effective. As well as all the items in the earlier version, this issue expands the Company's potential somewhat. For example there is an improved thrashing machine, hydraulic ram, grinding mill, loam and mortar mill, various rail and land mounted cranes both steam and hand powered, saw benches, jacks and there are engravings of three locomotives. In the case of two of these engravings they depict locomotives that had been built, unlike the two in the previous catalogue which had not - the third one is an artist's impression of what

appears to be a Black Hawthorn locomotive, of which more details below. The two locomotives that were built are manufacturer's numbers 94 and 120 respectively, ADA and WOOTON. However, perhaps the most significant item is the claim that both iron and brass castings could be supplied from which it can perhaps be deduced that the works was equipped with both an iron and brass foundry. Prices are quoted for everything described although it would appear almost certain that if for example, a thrashing box was ordered, it would have been sub-contracted and Bagnall may have established contacts with other specialist firms for

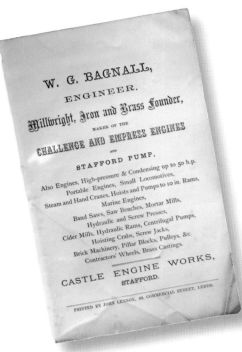

Title page from the first catalogue issued in August 1876; the following three illustrations are also from this catalogue.

The 'Stafford Empress' Engine & Boiler combined as illustrated in the 1876 catalogue. Notice the neat arrangement with the crankshaft straddling the boiler. These combined units could be supplied in a range from 2 to 6 horse power and at prices from £60 to £130. As mentioned in the accompanying description, one of these engines and boilers received a medal at the Staffordshire Agricultural Society's Meeting, the one illustrated by a drawing on the cover of the catalogue.

Another example from the 1876 catalogue this engraving illustrates 'The Stafford Steam Pump', which as can be seen employed the principle of the 'Scotch' crank. The one illustrated is of the double-ram type although single-ram ones could also be supplied. The sizes of the double-ram type water pistons varied from 2in to a 10in diameter and they could deliver between 700 to 18,000 gallons per hour depending on the size; the prices varied from £28 for the smaller to £176 for the larger.

Unlike the 'Stafford Empress', the 'Challenge' engine and boiler combined has its engine mounted on the bedplate which doubled-up as a water tank. These engines and boilers could be supplied in a size range from 1 to 12 horsepower, and a price range of £40 to £194.

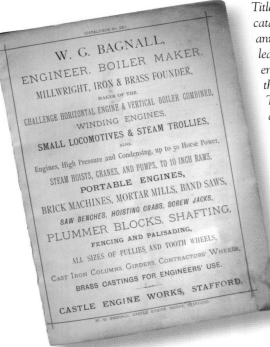

Title page from the second edition of the firm's catalogue, although in this case from an issue annotated as number 2B, dated 1 July 1878 - at least this is the date of the price list towards the end. Note the expanded list of products from the earlier version and the reference to Steam Trollies, although nothing that seems to fit this description ever seems to have been built.

Another page from catalogue 2B illustrating a 'Challenge' engine and boiler combined and in this example complete with a winding drum. These units could be supplied from 3 to 12 horsepower and in a price range from £105 to £325, and of course, unlike the other versions illustrated this particular type has a valve gear capable of reversing the engine. Notice that this engraving includes a manufacturer's plate on the boiler with the number 111, perhaps indicating that in this case the engraver, whoever he was - John Swain is the name on this and many other pages - had done his work alongside an actual example.

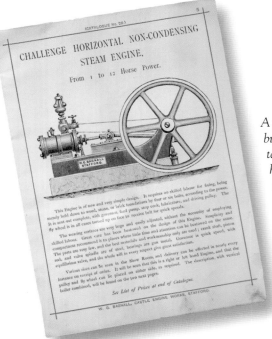

A page from catalogue 2B illustrating a 'Challenge' engine but in this case not associated with a boiler. The description tells us that these engines could be supplied from 1 to 12 horsepower and further in the catalogue we learn that the cylinder dimensions varied from 3x4in to 12x16in and the prices ranged from £15 to £88; the flywheel diameters varied from 1ft 6in to 5ft 6in. This is a 'true' artist's impression as there does not appear to be any method of driving the valve!

some of the items. To give an example of prices for locomotives, a 4x6in cylinder narrow-gauge 'tank locomotive engine' with 1ft 3in diameter wheels and weighing in working order two tons and 15 cwt was priced at £250 - and an extra £10 for a copper firebox and brass tubes. At the other end of the scale a locomotive with 12x18in cylinders and 3ft 6in diameter wheels weighing 15 tons in working order cost £1,050 - with an extra £60 for a copper firebox and brass tubes. All sizes of locomotives listed were four wheels coupled; however the point is made in the introduction to the locomotive section that the prices quoted were approximate and subject to customers individual requirements; for example track gauge and the particular type of work the engines were to be engaged on etc.

Neither of the two locomotive engravings illustrated in the earliest catalogue were of types of locomotive that had been or were built. One of them depicts what is without doubt an exact copy of a standard-gauge Black, Hawthorn (a company based in Gateshead-on-Tyne and established in 1865) four-coupled saddle tank of that manufacturer's standard design. The second one is an artist's impression, and not a particularly good one, of a four-coupled vertical-boiler machine with a twin-cylinder vertical-engine. No locomotives had been built at Stafford by this date - August 1876 - and it is interesting to speculate what motivated the use of what is clearly a Black, Hawthorn locomotive for illustration purposes. However, Bagnall must have had the designing and building of locomotives in mind by his Company and very soon after he did just that; but we can only speculate on what made him turn his hand to this particular branch of the engineering.

Engraving from the first catalogue issued in August 1876 and clearly showing a type of locomotive that was a standard product of the Gateshead builder Black, Hawthorn & Company. One is left wondering how and why Bagnall came to use this illustration for his own purposes and what the management at Black, Hawthorn might have thought! Whilst history is littered with examples of one company encroaching on another's designs for publicity purposes, there cannot be many as fragrant as this. The catalogue tells us that prices were only available on application, but in catalogue 2B of July 1878, where the illustration was used again, we are told locomotives of this type could be supplied in the cylinder range from 12 to 20in diameter, with prices varying from £620 to £1,050; there was a surcharge for a copper firebox and brass tubes in the range from £30 to £60.

This is the other engraving in the 1876 catalogue showing a locomotive. However, in this case it is very obviously an artist's impression; moreover, this particular engraving does not appear in any later versions of the catalogue. Catalogue 2B of 1878 does nevertheless, mention vertical boiler locomotives along with the steam trollies listed on the title page. Cylinder sizes for the vertical boiler locomotives ranged from 3in to 9in diameter and the prices from £175 to £420. However, if a geared version was chosen the price increased to a range from £187 10/ (£187.50) to £445.

On 3 April 1878 agreement was reached between WG Bagnall and the LNWR for a siding connection between the works site and the main-line. The actual connection was with the Shropshire Union Railways & Canal Company's line from Stafford to Wellington, which as already mentioned was operated from opening by the LNWR, although it remained independent until the provisions of the Railways Act 1921, grouped the main-line railway companies into four larger undertakings. The agreement called for the LNWR to pay the £135 involved, with Bagnall agreeing to maintain some six yards and a few feet of the railway company's track on the land leased from Lord Stafford. There was an annual payment to cover the cost of maintaining the connection and what the LNWR termed a 'signal service'. A plan from the Borough Surveyor's Office at Stafford dated December 1877, today deposited in the William Salt Library at Stafford, shows a single building on the Castle Engine Works site some 200 feet long and 25 feet wide and this would have been the original workshop.

Little has survived in the way of records of the early products of the Company and those that are known to be extant are clearly copies of original documents written up many years later. There appears to have been but a single numerical list of orders with locomotive production mixed up with whatever else the Company built or repaired. The registers that have survived only list locomotives and there are therefore many gaps in the numbering sequence. In a few cases the engravings of products other than locomotives, and used in the catalogues have manufacturers plates complete with a number and this helps to identify them. Cases to point include a combined Challenge horizontal engine and vertical boiler with the number 79 on its plate which appears in catalogue No 2B, and therefore dating from around 1878. There is also a Challenge winding engine of similar configuration but with a winding drum added and this one carries the number 111. In August 1894 the Company supplied spares for 'a portable engine (made by us) number 506' to the order of WCT Mynors, who was the agent for the Earl of Shrewsbury, the owner of the nearby (Staffordshire) Ingestre Estate. We also have the evidence of various medals presented to Bagnall for his exhibits at shows and currently in the collection of the surviving members of the family. A particular one was awarded by

the Cheshire Agricultural Society at Chester in 1876; this one in respect to a Wright Engine Pump, although none of the early catalogues describe any of the numerous varieties of steam pump by this nomenclature. Another medal presented by the same Society, but this time at its Knutsford Show in 1878, refers to a 'Combined Challenge Horizontal Engine & Vertical Boiler'. Yet a third, this time presented by the Staffordshire Agricultural Society in September 1879, refers to a collection of engines, steam pumps and a boiler.

The two sides of the engraved bronze medal awarded to Gordon Bagnall by the Cheshire Agricultural Society for the exhibition of the Wright Engine Pump at Chester in 1876

An advert by Bagnall in the *Staffordshire Advertiser* of 10 June 1876 lists the following items of equipment for sale: 'New 30in endless band saw with $^3/_4$ hp engine and boiler combined; second hand $1^1/_2$ hp engine £10; $2^1/_2$ hp engine and boiler £25; 8 hp Patent vertical tubular boiler £30; 6 hp same as previous one £40; 6 hp semi-portable boiler £25; Range of three sets of mill gearing in one line £30; Hornsby 1 hp mower £10'. An interesting selection and notice no price is quoted for what would appear to be the only new item, the 30in band saw. Presumably the mower was a lawnmower made by Richard Hornsby of Lincoln. This advert tells us that at this period Bagnall was dealing in a lot of second-hand equipment, doubtless in some cases after overhaul or repairs of some description. *The Western Mail* in its edition dated 20 December 1876 has an advert for a well established Newport (Monmouthshire) based machinery dealer of the period, CD Phillips of the Emlyn Foundry. Among the numerous items of

Another medal, in this case presented to WG Bagnall by the Staffordshire Agricultural Society in September 1879, for a collection of engines, steam pump & boiler. Presumably, in view of the ring, in this case it was intended to be worn by the recipient!

machinery in the advert is a '2hp vertical engine and boiler combined, by Bagnall - new and in stock'. We shall meet Phillips again later in our story as Bagnall seems to have established a relationship with his company by quite an early date, and as well as Phillips advertising on his behalf, Bagnall also placed his own adverts in the *Monthly Machinery Register* that was issued by Phillips. This Register had a wide circulation as Phillips not only advertised equipment he had acquired himself and had on hand, but also machinery and other equipment on behalf of others. The registers contain trade adverts too, like the Bagnall one mentioned above.

Evidence of the early products also exists in contemporary reporting in journals like *Engineering*. In the issue dated 4 July 1879 *Engineering* reported on the Royal Agricultural Society of England Show at Kilburn and mention is made of the WG Bagnall stand. On this stand was to be found: 'Bagnall's special form of engine, the Challenge', and no fewer than nine examples were exhibited ranging from one to 12 horsepower. There were also six combined horizontal engines and vertical boilers ranging from one to six horsepower and differing from the Challenge type; the journal went on to describe them as being: 'of the double-bearing type, with bent crankshafts and continuous under-bedplate. They have marine piston rod guides, with considerable surface and each is fitted with a horizontal spring

governor placed on top of the cylinder and acting on an equilibrium stop valve above the steam chests. By means of hand wheels the governor can be readily adjusted to different speeds'. An illustration of this governor accompanies the notes and is reproduced overleaf. There are a number of other similar references around this period, as well as adverts in the local press. For example in the *Staffordshire Advertiser* dated 10 September 1881, Bagnall advertised, inter alia, a range of stationary engines both new and second-hand as well as stone breakers and chaff cutters - locomotives and railways are mentioned too! He also exhibited stationary engines at a number of other shows, for example the Herefordshire Agricultural Society Kington Meeting in June 1878, the Royal Agricultural Society of England Show at Bristol in July the same year and the Cheshire Agricultural Society Show at Knutsford in August 1878; here as mentioned earlier he was awarded a medal. There were others shows too, of which more in Chapter Two.

A few Bagnall-built stationary engines have been recorded in more detail, for example the *Hereford Times* of 29 June 1878, in reporting the Bagnall exhibits at the Herefordshire Agricultural Show records a three horsepower vertical engine and boiler by Bagnall recently installed at PJW Mackenzie & Company of the Hereford Mineral Water Manufactory - it goes on to say that this was the chief improvement in a recent re-modelling of those works. Another, a three horsepower Challenge engine and boiler combined was with a Mr. Taylor of Elsdon near Kington in Herefordshire, and also considered a great success. In 1879 The Stafford Skating Rink Company Limited experimented with lighting its rink by electricity and according to a contemporary newspaper report, a six horsepower Challenge horizontal engine and vertical boiler was loaned by Mr WG Bagnall to provide the power. The owner of the generator and lighting equipment, a Mr Patterson from London who used a Siemens generator, opined that the governor used by Mr Bagnall - doubtless of the type mentioned earlier - was: 'all that could be desired, the regularity of the speed of the engine being the great desideratum'! We also have catalogue claims of engines and boilers being supplied to Holland, Java and The Café Monico in London; in all these cases for electricity generation.

The journal *Model Engineer & Practical Electrician* in

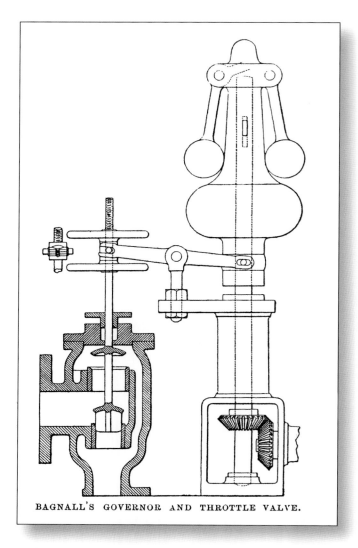

BAGNALL'S GOVERNOR AND THROTTLE VALVE.

A drawing taken from the journal Engineering, issue dated 4 July 1879, illustrating the throttle valve and governor fitted to a 'Challenge' engine exhibited at the Kilburn Royal Agricultural Society Show in 1879.

its issue dated 21 May 1936 contains a letter from a gentleman by the name of Anthony Atthill who hailed from Norwich. In this letter he describes and illustrates a Bagnall engine and boiler he had acquired, which he thought had been used for driving a bottle washing plant at a brewery. The unit consisted of a vertical boiler three feet high and a separate horizontal engine with a single cylinder - dimensions 3x4in. Several of the engines that drove machinery around the Castle Engine Works in its early days and described in a 1905 Inventory of Plant, had been built by the firm themselves. The timber yard of Henry Venables, which

was situated on the opposite side of the LNWR main line to the Castle Engine Works, had until comparatively recent times a Bagnall built Lancashire boiler with a manufacturer's plate with the number 599 and a date of 1884. It is good to record that while the whole timber yard is now no more, a housing estate having grown up in its place, the back-head of this boiler has survived and is preserved in the museum of the Foxfield Railway at Blythe Bridge, a short distance south of Stoke-on-Trent.

Manufacturers number 295 of 1880 was allocated to a vertical boiler exported to New Zealand and such information as is available comes from sources in that country, rather than this. The New Zealand Government pressure vessel records outline the main dimensions of this boiler as three-foot diameter, 5ft8in high with two cross tubes and a working pressure of 60psi. Apparently its first owner and perhaps Bagnalls customer was one James Girr, but by 1892 the boiler was in the ownership of A McIntosh of Seacliffe, Otago, remaining in his ownership until 1918. From that date the owner is recorded as GS Meredith at Waimate, Canterbury. The boiler pressure was reduced to 50psi in 1926 and the boiler seems to have passed out of use the following year, but survived until at least 1931. Rated at three horsepower it is recorded as being for use with a 6in cylinder engine, but if such an engine was part of the Bagnall order it has gone unrecorded in so far as the New Zealand records are concerned. However, it would seem more than likely that a small engine would have been supplied along with this boiler.

One more illustration of the diversity of work that Gordon Bagnall was prepared to tackle, comes from some interesting reporting and correspondence in *The Stafford Chronicle* in June 1878. The Town Council were engaged in new road building and had invited tenders for iron girders to construct a bridge, to be known as Broad Eye Bridge, to take Doxey Road over the River Sow to the north-west of the town. Bagnall tendered for this work and in fact submitted the lowest tender, at £193 7/ 6d (£193 37p), almost £56 less than the one accepted. At a Council meeting on 4 June a question was submitted asking why the lowest tender had not been accepted. The answer given was that in his tender, Bagnall had made clear that he was not able to test the girders to the required strength, but the committee appointed to scrutinise the tenders, on the

This illustration shows the back-head of a 'Lancashire' boiler built at the Castle Engine Works, manufacturer's number 599 of 1884. At the time the photograph was taken in December 1977, the boiler was still in use, albeit working at a low pressure for space heating and fired on waste timber and shavings. Located at the timber yard of Henry Venables Limited, it was but a few yards from where it was built as the yard was on the opposite side of the main-line railway. The back-head of this boiler, the part seen, but not the complete boiler, has been saved and is located in the museum of the Foxfield Light Railway at Blythe Bridge, just south of Stoke-on-Trent.

advice of JB McCallum the Borough Surveyor, considered testing necessary. Gordon Bagnall was quick to respond with a long two column letter in the following week's copy of the paper. He defended his contention that testing was not necessary in view of the design of the girders and the material he proposed using, and he also commented on the short time he had been allowed to submit his tender, together with the considerable inconvenience he had been subjected to by the Council officials in establishing exactly what was wanted. The correspondence dragged on with claim and counter claim which need not detain us here. However, the salient points we can take from this issue are in the first instance, that the Company was capable of undertaking structural engineering, in fact Gordon Bagnall mentioned in his letter that at the time he was manufacturing similar girders to those required for Broad Eye bridge, for the Aston Aquarium - whatever

that was. Secondly, as he personally worked on a Saturday afternoon to make the necessary calculations so that his tender could be submitted on time, we can conclude that he was heavily involved in day-to-day design issues and had the necessary training and experience to do so. Incidentally, he was asked to tender at 1100 on Saturday morning 4 May, and the tender had to be submitted by 1100 on the Monday following - the other companies asked to tender had apparently, been allowed a significantly longer period.

As mentioned earlier we know not at this distance of time why Bagnall went in to the locomotive and railway engineering business, but he very soon made a speciality of small and light narrow-gauge locomotives and other railway rolling stock and equipment, including complete portable, or semi-portable, railways. However, among his early products are two standard-gauge locomotives, one of them being the very first locomotive to appear in the surviving records. These two were manufacturer's numbers 16 and 120 and named BUCKINGHAM and WOTTON respectively. Over the years much controversy has surrounded these two locomotives, not least whether in fact the works had the plant and equipment at the time to construct complete standard-gauge locomotives. The late Samuel Thomas Price, whom we shall meet later and who was for many years works manager, told the late Ralph Russell when interviewed by him in May 1952 (he died aged 94 in December 1954), that these two were definitely not built at Stafford, but just 'finished off' there. Price opined that Henry Hughes of Loughborough, who he claimed was a friend of Bagnall actually built them. However, Price did not arrive at the Castle Engine Works until some years later, in around 1882 at the earliest, so his statements could only have been based on here-say rather than anything he had personally witnessed. Nevertheless, he told Ralph he had joined Bagnall at Stafford in June 1877, but as he was not born until December 1861, he would have been but 15 years old at that time. This issue will be explored in more depth later in the narrative. The second of these early locomotives was of a particularly unusual design, albeit having features in common with the first narrow-gauge engine the Company built which predated it by a few months. This could lead one to conclude that this second standard-gauge locomotive was in fact built at Stafford, and as it was not a big locomotive either, the cylinders were only 8in diameter, extensive facilities may not have been necessary except perhaps for construction of the boiler. In any event it would appear reasonably conclusive that the design of the engine was that of Bagnall and his team, and on balance of the available evidence it is the considered opinion of the authors that these two locomotives were built at Stafford, despite the difference in the design characteristics between them. It may be the case that some of the larger components might have been sub-contracted, in particular the boilers, and in such cases Hughes could have been involved - hence the statement by Price.

Henry Hughes was somewhat of a colourful character within the railway manufacturing industry. Born in 1833 he was employed in about 1855 by a Loughborough firm of engineers, Capper & Moon; this Company was established at what was called the Falcon

Engine Works about two years earlier. Moon appears to have left the business at quite an early date and in about 1857, when Capper moved on to pastures new, Hughes acquired the business with some financial assistance from an aunt. In 1864 a move was made to larger premises as the business expanded, still in Loughborough and alongside the Midland Railway main-line from London to Derby and Nottingham - it retained the name of the older premises. Locomotive construction had started around 1861 and Hughes later - from about 1876 - made something of a speciality in designing and building street tramway locomotives. The Hughes's Locomotive & Tramway Engine Works Limited was formed in 1877, but soon got into financial difficulties for which Hughes was blamed by his fellow directors, and he was removed as a director in December 1880. A financial reconstruction took place in 1882 under the name of The Falcon Engineering & Car Works Limited, but Hughes did not take his dismissal lightly. In a subsequent legal case it was claimed that he had continued to represent himself as having a connection with Falcon and even attempted to intercept correspondence and execute by other means orders intended for Falcon! It was during this period that Bagnall built a locomotive to an order from Hughes - manufacturer's number 377 of July 1881 - which Hughes re-sold for use on the Pacific island of Sidney (in the east of the Phoenix group). This would seem to confirm a friendship between the two men. Hughes then went into business as a patent agent and eventually emigrated to New Zealand, where he also traded as a patent agent. He died in New Zealand at Wellington in April 1896.

It is worth a mention at this juncture that a few years later in 1889 the Falcon Company became part of what had been the American Brush Electric Light Construction Company Limited, the two Companies in effect amalgamating to become the Brush Electrical Engineering Company Limited. This had the mutual advantage of electric traction equipment from one company combining with the tram building capabilities of the other, in tackling the burgeoning electric street tramway market that was rapidly replacing steam. It is also worthy of a mention that Brush was a company that Bagnall became closely associated with some 58 years later!

We must now return to the story of WG Bagnall

himself who, very soon after arriving in the town became quite a prominent figure. In November 1882 he successfully campaigned as a Conservative for the then new West Ward of Stafford Town Council, polling 805 votes to beat his nearest rival by 317 votes. In 1889, when it was formed, he became one of the original members of Staffordshire County Council as a representative of Stafford Borough, and in 1892 was made an Alderman of Stafford Borough Council. In 1893 he was asked to become Mayor, but declined in view of his other heavy commitments, not least the public work he was already engaged in. With his involvement on the County Council he would of course have come into contact with fellow council member Gilbert Claughton, providing a possible link as to how Thomas Walter came to be involved in helping to finance the Bagnall business. Gordon Bagnall was instrumental in 1889 in the formation of the Stafford Town Sanitary Committee and was its chairman for over 14 years; additionally for a long time he was chairman of the Staffordshire Country Council Sanitary Committee. Among his multifarious activities in connection with sanitation Bagnall was instrumental in the works surrounding the purification of the River Tame, part of the enormous improvements in sanitation and drainage in the areas the river passed through. He was in fact quite passionate about sewage and a whole range of public health issues surrounding poor sanitary facilities. His efforts in this direction extended to housing for the working classes, both permanent and lodging, and he campaigned endlessly for improvements in sanitary arrangements and for legislation to be introduced to enforce local authorities to improve conditions. It is perhaps worth quoting the concluding sentence of one of the many papers he presented on the subject. 'In short, to make people happy, contented, strong, resolute, industrious, sober and clear headed from that which generally follows practical sanitary legislation by HEALTH'. Worth noting too, is the result of a recent (January 2007) report which concludes that the establishment of close control of sanitary arrangements has been the most significant single development in improving the nation's health in the 19 and 20th centuries.

When the Staffordshire County Council Education Committee was first formed Bagnall was one of its members and for many years he was a member of the governing body of Stafford Grammar School. He was also, as would be expected in view of his business, involved with the management of the Stafford Technical College.

A notable shot both with a revolver and a rifle, Bagnall was for several years a prominent member in the Second Volunteer Battalion (Prince of Wales) F&G Companies, North Staffordshire Regiment (formed in January 1860). Having been instrumental in forming the Stafford Volunteers he joined-up on 1 July 1881 and was gazetted Lieutenant on 11 July, promoted Captain on 18 July 1885 and Major on 22 July 1893; he appears

Unfortunately this is a rather indistinct photograph, but it is the only one known to exist showing Gordon Bagnall as a volunteer in the Second Volunteer Battalion (Prince of Wales) Regiment. Bagnall is in the centre of the view sitting down, and as he seems to have pips on his epaulettes, it would have been taken when he was a Captain and before promotion to the rank of Major - this dates the view at some time between 1885 and 1893. So obviously in command, the picture shows Bagnall with his fellow officers and NCOs and one wonders if that is Thomas Walter, lying down in the foreground? None of the others have been identified.

to have retired from active participation around 1895. Whilst the headquarters of the Battalion was located in Burton-on-Trent, there was base and armoury at the Guildhall in Stafford. Noted for his expertise with both a rifle and a revolver Bagnall won the revolver prize open to all officers in both 1893 and 1894. He also shot

This illustration shows the National Rifle Association woven badge with the date 1886, which would have been worn by Gordon Bagnall on his army uniform.

The Whitehead Challenge Cup was awarded to Army Volunteers (today we would call them Territorials) at the annual pistol shooting competition at Bisley in Surrey, site of the well known Army shooting ranges and training ground. Gordon Bagnall won the trophy in 1894 and 1895; this is the clasp awarded to him in 1894, along with a bar for the following year.

A shooting party along with their dogs, about to set-off onto the moors at Stanhope in County Durham. On the extreme right is Gordon Bagnall and the lady is his wife Jessie. Unfortunately it is not known who the other gentlemen are but they may well include Sir Richard Powell Cooper and Richard Myddelton, two of his close friends and shooting partners.

Sheriff of the county in 1901, had a second seat at Stanhope Castle in County Durham. Among the favourite haunts of these three and their other companions were, not surprisingly, the wild and barren moors on Stanhope Common in County Durham. There the party would hire a train on the Stanhope & Tyne Railway to gain access, a trip that included being rope hauled on its various inclines! This would be at weekends when the line would not be overly utilised for commercial purposes, although on occasions the special wagons for the party's use were attached to service trains. As fellow members of Staffordshire County Council and with Cooper a Deputy Lieutenant of the County, these relationships may have originally brought Bagnall and Cooper into contact with each other; a common interest in shooting would do the rest. His two hand-crafted 12 bore shot guns - numbered one and two - and made by the well known London gun-maker Charles Boswell of 126 The Strand, survive in the family collection and still find occasional use with his grand daughter and great, great grandsons.

Incidentally Thomas Walter was also a member of the same Volunteer Regiment as Bagnall - today we

in the international rifle matches over many years, including those at Bisley where he won The Whitehead Challenge Cup for volunteers in both 1894 and 1895, as well as at Wimbledon. A member of the National Rifle Association his name usually appeared in the prize lists of any other competitions he entered. Among his shooting friends in civilian life were Richard Myddelton (-1913) of Chirk Castle in Denbighshire, and Sir Richard Powell Cooper (1847-1913; later 1st Bart-1905) of Shenstone Court near Lichfield in Staffordshire. Cooper, who from 1892 was also a member of Staffordshire County Council and High

Gordon Bagnall and his wife Jessie on the moors of Stanhope Common. The shotgun under his arm, one of two magnificent weapons made by the famous London gun-maker Charles Boswell of The Strand, survives in the family collection and along with its partner is still used.

The shooting part disembarking from low sided open North Eastern Railway wagons somewhere on Stanhope Moor. Notice that two of the wagons are loaded, so presumable the vehicles used by the party were on this occasion at least, part of a regular working - clearly Sir Richard Powell Cooper was influential in these parts! Notice too, the fellow with the pack horse on the left, doubtless waiting to accompany the party with their lunch!

would call them Territorials. Walter joined in 1885 and was gazetted Lieutenant on 11 July that year, doubtless encouraged to join-up by Bagnall. However, he does not seem to have progressed at all and the last entry relating to him in *The Army List* - still shown as a Lieutenant - is dated July 1893. This does however,

perhaps indicate that he was still closely involved with the firm's business until about the same time and just prior to departing for New Zealand.

Between 1888 and 1895 Gordon Bagnall was Captain of the Stafford Volunteer Fire Brigade, in fact he was instrumental in its formation back in June 1876 and among his many other public duties he acted for no less than 18 years up to 1905 as Honorary Auditor of the Staffordshire General Infirmary. For a number of years he was president of Stafford Rangers Football Club, a club he had played for in his younger days and being quite a sport, he was a keen cricketer and a member of Cannock Chase Golf Club. At one period too, he was involved with Wednesbury Town Football Club and in this case the family have a medal presented to him to prove it! As a devote Christian he preformed the duties of churchwarden at St Mary's, Castle Church in Stafford where the family worshiped. For a long time too, Gordon Bagnall was president of the Stafford Conservative Association and a practising Freemason, being a member of the No 662 Dartmouth Lodge within the Provincial Grand Lodge of Staffordshire at West Bromwich. As if this was not enough to keep him occupied Bagnall was an extremely enthusiastic gardener, a pigeon fancier and very much a family man. He was extremely proud of the garden at his last residence at Castle Hill House, Deans Hill in Stafford.

On 28 March 1883 William Gordon Bagnall married Jessie Gibson, at the Parish Church of St Paul's, Lichfield Road, Forebridge in Stafford. Jessie, but 18 years old at the time - born 13 April 1864 - was the daughter of the late John Gibson; she lived in Stafford with her step-father Dr. Samuel Cookson and her mother Jane Grace Cookson (nee Gibson and before that her maiden name of Day). Jessie had two brothers and two sisters and along with four stepbrothers and three stepsisters this rather large family resided at 9 Lichfield Road in Stafford. The Gibsons, however, hailed from Mains of Park, a large house about half a mile south-west of Glenluce in Wigtownshire, and almost on the banks of the Water of Luce as it runs into Luce Bay. Jessie's father, John Gibson (8/3/1820-25/3/1866) was a barrister by profession, educated for the Scottish Bar and a 'Writer to the Signet' (the Scottish equivalent of a QC), later becoming a land agent or factor for Lord Londonderry. Apparently John Gibson had written an article for an agricultural journal,

Jessie Bagnall, nee Gibson, a picture taken around the time of her marriage to Gordon Bagnall, which took place on 28 March 1883. Jessie had an 18in waist at the time of her marriage and she was still able to get into her wedding dress after the birth of the first child; this apparently gave her enormous pleasure. The dress survives in the family collection and has been worn by her granddaughter, Jill Hutchinson Smith, in more recent times.

The two Jessies'. On the right Jessie Bagnall (nee Gibson), and on the left her sister-in-Law Jessie Bagnall - 11th child of Richard & Julia Bagnall. She married Reginald Brooks-King in 1893; the two girls were the same age.

John Gibson, father of Jessie, Gordon Bagnall's wife. John, a Scotsman, was born in 1820, a Barrister by profession, if he practiced law at all it was not for very long as he became a Land Agent for Lord Londonderry. John Gibson died comparatively young at the age of 46 in 1866 - nevertheless he had eight children from his two wives; his first wife died at a very young age.

as he had an interest in agriculture, and this brought him to the attention of Lord Londonderry, via his father James Gibson who was himself acquainted with the peer. As a result John Gibson went on to manage the peer's estates in Ireland, Wales and Dorset, later moving home to Dorset in view of his wife Agnes's health - they married in 1849 - and on medical advice. Here he acted as factor for the Milton Abbey estate of Charles Joachim, Baron Hambro and the Blandford estates of Viscount Portman. At one time too he also looked after some of the Hambro interests in Sunderland, and his two children that survived were born there.

Gibson's first wife was Agnes Brown, she was from Maybole in Ayrshire, and after she died he married secondly Jane Grace Day. Jane lived with her parents in Tipping Street at Stafford, although it is not known how the two of them became acquainted. Jane was born in Newcastle-under-Lyme on 16 December 1835, daughter of Henry and Elwyna Day (nee Heath); the family lived in King Street at that time and she had a

brother Henry, who was two years older. Jane spent at least a part of her education at her aunt's boarding school (Mrs Day's Boarding School) at West Beech in Lytham; she was there in 1851. John Gibson and Jane Grace Day were married at the Parish Church of St Mary's in Stafford on 9 March 1858; John's address is

Jane Grace Day, Jessie Bagnall's mother. Jane was born in 1836 and married John Gibson as his second wife on 9 March 1858. After John Gibson's death she married Dr. Samuel Cookson at Stafford on 6 September 1870. Jane had 12 children, two boys and three girls from her first marriage and four boys and three girls from her second. Jessie Bagnall was the youngest child from her first marriage.

given on the marriage certificate as Milton Abbey in Dorset; Jane was 23 years old at the time. There were three children from John Gibson's first marriage, James born in 1850 and Jane Hutchenson born the following year, together with a younger sister Jessie who died very young. Of the five children from the second marriage there were three boys and two girls, Charles John, Agnes, Henry Day, Ursula Mary and lastly Jessie, who was to take WG Bagnall's hand in marriage. John Gibson died at the comparatively early age of 46 following a riding accident, and he spent the last few months of his life in a bath-chair; he is buried in Hilton Parish churchyard, Milton Abbas in Dorset.

Jane Day's father Henry, a physician, was born in 1806 in Surrey and had part of his training at the University of St Andrews; early in his career he practiced in London and lived in Arlington Street which was, and is, off Piccadilly. Jane recalled many years later that when she was about four years old and on a visit to see her father in London, she rode on a Colonel's horse down St James Street, along Pall Mall and onwards to Charing Cross as he led his regiment to war. She recalled the regiment was heading for the Crimea, but as the action in the Crimea was in the period 1853 to 1856, she may have been mistaken, as her ride must have taken place about 1840. Elwyna Day, her mother, was a Heath, born in Newcastle on Christmas Day in 1800, the only daughter of Joshua Child Heath and Sarah Mayer; one of her brothers (she had three, Thomas, Edward and Josiah) Edward, had a

son, Arthur Henry, the Coopers Hill Professor mentioned earlier.

On John Gibson's death his widow, Jane Grace, was left rather impoverished; it appears John had lent a considerable sum of money to Baron Hambro's son, a debt he was unable to discharge and his father would not help either. As a result Jane and her own children, went to live with her parents in Stafford, whilst the children from John Gibson's first marriage went to live with their mother's relations; this was despite the eldest son James, being named in his father's will as an executor, and Jane as his guardian. Nevertheless, Jane Grace Gibson and her children were back in North Staffordshire by December 1866 when her late husband's will was proved.

At Stafford she made the acquaintance of Dr. Samuel Cookson, who had recently lost his young wife and was childless; he was a general medical practitioner in the town. Cookson was born in 1837 at Great Easton, a suburb of Leicester, son of the Rev. F Cookson one time Vicar of Wilby in Norfolk; he trained as a surgeon at Great Ormond Street Hospital in London and was there in 1861. Family legend has it that Samuel Cookson proposed to Jane Grace Gibson three times before she accepted his hand in marriage; she did not feel it fair to saddle him with a family of five children. However, he prevailed and Jane Grace Gibson married Samuel Cookson at St Paul's Church in the Parish of Forebridge at Stafford on 6 September 1870; Cookson was 33 years old at the time and Jane was 36. The service was taken by Jane's brother, Henry J Day, who was the Rector of St Paul's at the time and they went on to have seven children, all born in Stafford.

Samuel Cookson appears to have been reasonably well-off financially, as not only did he bring up the combined family of 12 children, but he also employed no fewer than four domestic servants at 9 Lichfield Road. Later he became a financial supporter of William Gordon Bagnall in his business. There were seven children from this marriage: Fredrick Nesfield (later Dr) born in 1872, Samuel born in 1874, Ethel Maud born in 1875, Ida Mildred born in 1877, Dorothy Hilda born in 1878, Charles Edward born in 1879 and Geoffrey Edmund born in 1881. The youngest son served a premium apprenticeship with WG Bagnall Limited and later went to Canada where, apparently, the valve setting skills he had leant at the Castle Engine Works

Family picture of Dr. Samuel Cookson and his wife Jane Grace (nee Gibson and Day) along with some of their children.
On the back row from left to right are: Fredrick Nesfield Cookson; Jessie Gibson (later Jessie Bagnall); Ida Mildred Cookson; Agnus Gibson; Samuel Cookson (junior); Ursula Mary Gibson; Dorothy Hilda Cookson.
Front row: Ethel Maud Cookson; Dr. Samuel Cookson; Charles John Gibson; Jane Grace Cookson; Henry Day (Hal) Gibson

stood him in good stead with traction engines owned by farmers where he found employment. Jessie's eldest natural brother Charles John Gibson, 24 years old at the time of his sister's wedding, was also a Doctor of Medicine and a Surgeon at Edinburgh University. Charles subsequently retired from medicine on his 40th birthday and took a farm at Swalcliffe near Banbury in Oxfordshire, where among other pursuits he successfully bred thoroughbred racehorses. One of those he bread was sold to the German Kaiser - this would be Kaiser Wilhelm 11, Queen Victoria's grandson - and a painting of the horse named ROJESTVENSKY (by Pevigord out of Rosa Bonhure), and personally signed by the Kaiser, survives in the family collection to this day. In 1907 this horse came second in the German Derby and was the winner of the Union Prize of 5,000 sovereigns in Berlin that same year - the horse was popularly known as 'The Kaiser's Charger'.

According to the local press reports the wedding of William Gordon Bagnall and Jessie Gibson was quite a grandiose affair with a large crowd assembling in Lichfield Road - 'for the greater part of the morning and presenting a lively appearance'. When the church doors were opened the building was rapidly filled to

overcrowding and large numbers had to content themselves with standing places in the open air'. This perhaps illustrates how popular in Stafford the couple were. The service took place at 11.30 am and the bride was given away by her stepfather Dr. Samuel Cookson, whilst the best man was Dr. George Reid. Dr. Reid, a native of Aberdeen, was the Staffordshire County Medical Officer at the time and of about the same age as Gordon Bagnall; he was a good friend and fellow campaigner for improved sanitary arrangements, hence the friendship. A crimson carpet had been laid all the way from the alter to the church yard gates and the bride arrived with her stepfather in a carriage drawn by two grey mares. Part of the service was conducted by the Rev. Charles J Johnstone of Marden Vicarage, Devizes in Wiltshire, who was the husband of Louisa, one of Gordon Bagnall's sisters. However, the actual marriage ceremony was conducted by the Rev. Edward Heath, curate-in-charge of St Mary's Magdalene at Brighton, a cousin of Jessie's mother Jane and another member of the Heath family already mentioned - he was the father of Arthur H Heath later of Coopers Hill.

The wedding 'breakfast' was held at the North Western Hotel in Stafford where another large crowd had gathered to greet the couple and the band of 5th

Staffordshire Rifle Volunteers (Bagnall's battalion of his Regiment) played at intervals during the meal. However, apparently during the whole course of the morning and until the couple departed for London by train at 3.30 pm, 'employees of Mr Bagnall made loud accentuation by repeated firing of cannon, an occupation which they had been engaged on from an early hour'! One presumes they had 'borrowed' the cannon from his Regimental colleagues! After a few days in London the honeymoon was spent on the continent. There were numerous presents many of which were engraved to mark the happy event and most of which survive in the family collection to this day. They include a rather fine silver salver from the employees of the Castle Engine Works inscribed: 'Presented to William Gordon Bagnall Esq. on the occasion of his marriage by the employees at the Castle Engine Works Stafford March 28 1883'. Even by this quite early date, Gordon Bagnall was clearly a popular and well respected employer - he continued to be so.

The probable sequence of events in Jessie Gibson meeting Gordon Bagnall would have been via the medical profession. Her grandfather Henry Day would have been known to Samuel Cookson, as they were both, or had been in Henry's case, general practitioners in the town and this would almost certainly be how her mother, Jane Grace Gibson (nee Day) met Cookson. Both Henry Day and Samuel Cookson would be known to George Reid, a friend of Gordon Bagnall and the

This is the inscription on the silver salver presented to Gordon Bagnall on the occasion of his marriage on 28 March 1883, by the employees of the Castle Engine Works.

medical officer for Staffordshire who, as well as his professional connections, also lived in the town. We can therefore be pretty sure it would have been Reid, who introduced Jessie to Gordon, and this is almost certainly why Bagnall choose Reid as his best-man rather then one of his brothers. Family members today, testify to the very close friendship between Gordon Bagnall and George Reid that was often spoken of in earlier times, and Reid was among those who administered to Bagnall in his final fatal illness.

Gordon and Jessie Bagnall established themselves at 11, Newport Road in Stafford and by 1891 they employed three domestic servants, later moving to Castle Hill House, Deans Hill, which was off the Newport Road in Stafford. This was a large property with a big garden where Bagnall was able to indulge in his horticultural hobby, and the development of what became a very impressive garden modelled on the Alpine style was soon put in hand. As if Gordon Bagnall did not have enough interests external to his business to occupy his leisure hours, along with his wife he became heavily involved in amateur dramatics and according to family legend, the pair loved nothing better than getting dressed up in various period costumes to enhance their roles. Indeed, there are a number of photographs in the family albums of the couple so attired. In this actively they were joined by WO Rooper, sometimes acting himself and sometimes managing the stage, Dr. Reid his best man, with Thomas Salt often providing the plants and flowers to decorate the stage. The performances were usually at the Lyceum Theatre in Stafford and in favour of various charities. On occasions the performances were reported nationally, for example a performance of *The Cricket on the Hearth*, on Monday 3 May 1886 was reported in the trade journal *The Stage*, issue dated 14 May 1886. In the article the rendition of blind Betha by Jessie Bagnall was considered both exquisite and presented with rare skill. Bagnall played Caleb Plummer and according to the correspondent 'showed a power of self-suppression quite remarkable for an amateur'. Dorothy Cookson, nine years old at the time and a step-sister of Jessie, played the fairy; apparently she looked pretty and played her lines with simplicity and clearness! In the case of this performance the proceeds were in aid of the Midland Counties Home for the Incurables.

Castle Hill House at Deans Hill off the Newport Road in Stafford. Gordon Bagnall and his wife moved here in early 1890. The people from left to right are: Richard Gordon Bagnall, the youngest son, Jessie Bagnall, Jessica Bagnall the daughter, and another lady who may be a relation or the governess. For a number of years the family employed a young Swiss lady Mathilde Rahl, to look after the children and this could be her. This is a large and quite grandiose house, extended before the family move in, with a sizable garden where Gordon Bagnall was able to put his 'green-fingers' to good effect.

The Bagnall family at Castle Hill House in about 1897. Jessie Bagnall is holding the arm of her daughter Jessica, who was born in 1892. The eldest son, Harold Gordon, who was born in 1884 is standing on the left, whilst his younger brother Richard Gordon, born in 1885, is sitting on the right. Gordon Bagnall stands erect and the picture is completed by the family's pet dog Banjo. Despite Gordon Bagnall being a well known, likable and friendly character, not unknown on occasions as somewhat of a prankster, unfortunately we have no pictures of him smiling!

The couple had three children, all of whom took Gordon - the name by which WG was always known to family and close friends - as their second Christian name. Harold Gordon was born on 3 January 1884; Richard Gordon on 25 May 1885; and lastly Jessica Gordon, the only girl, on 2 March 1892 (the boys were born at Newport Road and the daughter at Deans Hill). Of the two boys only Richard Gordon became involved in his father's firm; to family and friends, like his father, he was always known as Gordon, or occasionally and especially to the girls as 'Gordie'! Both the boys were educated at Warden House, a small preparatory school at Deal in Kent, followed by public school at Charterhouse, which is near Godalming in Surrey.

Harold Gordon - known to the family as 'Halla' - was at Charterhouse from the autumn of 1897 until the summer of 1901, where among other sporting activities, played for the football First X1. According to family legend Harold had, from an early age always wanted to be an engineer, like his father, but a Royal one at that. Hence on completion of his education he joined the Army with the intention of being commissioned into the Royal Engineers; however, in the event he was actually commissioned into the Royal Garrison Artillery

(RGA) as a 2nd Lieutenant on 15 July 1903. Once again family legend has it that at Woolwich where he undertook his initial training, Harold did not pass the examinations for the Engineers so instead went into the Artillery - whatever the case it seems to have done him no harm as he went on to have a long and extremely distinguished military career. Harold Bagnall became a full Lieutenant in July 1906 and in October 1914, whilst posted in Hong Kong and shortly after the outbreak of the First World War, was promoted to the rank of Captain. Harold, who served his country throughout the war, was posted to France on 17 July 1915, embarking at Southampton on that day. With a detachment of his regiment he disembarked at

Harold Gordon Bagnall DSO, as a Captain in the Royal Garrison Artillery - the left hand ribbon represents his decoration of the DSO. Harold was re-called to active service in the early part of the Second World War, but he eventually took Holy Orders and became the Vicar of St Jude's at Tilstone Fearnall near Tarporley in Cheshire.

Harold Gordon Bagnall, the eldest son, in his formal dress as a Subaltern in the Royal Garrison Artillery. Harold - Halla as he was affectionately known to family and close friends - went into the Army straight from school and retired with the rank of Colonel in 1939. He was however (on the outbreak of the Second World War) recalled for a couple of years.

Boulogne the following day and initially served with the 23rd Brigade RGA, which later became the 23rd Heavy Artillery Group - he was serving with this battery during the first month of the Battle of the Somme. Later, from 29 July 1916, he was with the 1st Siege Battery at Flanders. On 24 March 1917, with the acting rank of Major, Harold Bagnall took command of the 1st Siege Battery before returning home on leave shortly after. For his service in France Harold Gordon Bagnall was Mentioned in Despatches on 30 April 1916 for 'gallant and distinguished conduct in the field' on the recommendation of General Sir Douglas Haig, GCB. KCJE. KCVO. ADC; the relevant entry appeared in the Supplement to *The London Gazette* - issue dated 15 June

1916. At the time Haig was the Commander in Chief of the British Army in France and Belgium.

After his promotion to the rank of Major in October 1917 Harold Bagnall served with the Egyptian Expeditionary Force (EEF) in Egypt and Palestine; he departed from Southampton on 6 October 1917 and arrived at Alexandria on 21 October. Initially attached to the General Base Depot, on 16 December 1917 he took command of the 21st Corps, Heavy Artillery and did not return home until January 1919. For his service with the EEF Harold Gordon Bagnall was, on 23 October 1918, again Mentioned in Despatches and on this occasion on the recommendation of General Sir EHH Allenby, GCMG. KCB., the Commander in Chief of the EEF. Notice of this recommendation did not appear in the Supplement to *The London Gazette* until its issue dated 22 January 1919. During the war years Harold Gordon Bagnall became an extremely experienced and a very distinguished 'Gunner'. For meritorious service throughout the years of conflict he was elected to membership of The Companion of the Distinguished Service Order (DSO) in the King's New Years Honours List for 1919. The decoration was presented to him by King George V at Buckingham Palace. Along with, of course, many of his contempories, during the war Harold Gordon Bagnall experienced some terrible experiences which, according to his family he could never be persuaded to talk about. In the family papers there exists an extract from a hand written note of an unknown source, but a few words from it are worth quoting. It dates from November 1917, just after Harold Gordon's transfer to Palestine and appears to have been written by a fellow officer who renewed his acquaintance with him there - and who shortly after returned home. It reads: 'They (the Heavy Artillery Battery) have a new Major, Bagnall by name, whom I met just before I came home from France last year. He is a good sort. He looks as if he had quite enough of France, looks much older and full of sort of nervous jerks and way of speaking that he hadn't had before, or I never noticed them before'. A few words that perhaps, say a lot.

After his wartime service Harold Gordon Bagnall was posted in November 1919 to Hong Kong again, on this occasion with the No 1 Mountain Battery, becoming Adjutant of his Regiment there in June 1920. In September 1922 on return to this country he was posted to the Institute of Gunnery at Woolwich where he remained until August the following year; subsequently he went to Larkhill in Wiltshire (another gunnery establishment) until December 1923. Harold then served with J Coast Battery at Plymouth until taking up the post of Instructor in Gunnery at Larkhill in June 1924. In June 1927 he took command of 19th Light Battery RGA., and in March 1932 went to India where his first posting was at Lahore, then the capital city of the Punjab (now part of Pakistan) and near the North West Frontier. His appointment was as Battery Commander 28th Field Brigade Royal Artillery, as the RGA had by then become - the RGA and the Royal Field Artillery combined in 1924 to form the Royal Regiment of Artillery. The RGA had been responsible for fixed siege and mountain batteries.

Promoted Lieutenant Colonel in July 1932 and Colonel in March 1936, Harold Gordon Bagnall

became Commandant of the School of Artillery at Kakul in June 1936 with the acting rank of Brigadier, where he was also involved in conducting operations against the dissident hillmen of Waziristan. At the same time he also took up the posting of Commander Royal Artillery 1st (India) Division. These were to have been his last service appointments as he retired (officially) from the Army on 24 August 1939. Not only was Harold Bagnall one of the most experienced 'Gunners' in the Army at the time of his retirement, but like his father he was a also a notable shot with both a rifle and a shotgun - he was in fact in the words of his son Nicholas, a great all-rounder with for example, a golf handicap of two.

On retirement from the Army Harold Gordon Bagnall studied theology at Wycliffe Hall Theological

Harold Gordon Bagnall passed away on 29 October 1944 after a long illness. He lies along with his wife of 25 years, Dorothea, in the churchyard at St Jude's at Tilstone Fearnall where he had been the Rector since 1942. He was well known for his sermons which never lasted more than 14 minutes!

College in Oxford and then took Holy Orders, being ordained in May 1940 before becoming Curate to the Reverend Turner at Wem in Shropshire. However, after but a couple of months in June 1939, shortly before the outbreak of the Second World War, Harold Bagnall was recalled to the service of his country and with the rank of Lieutenant Colonel took charge of the School of Gunnery, 41st Survey Training Regiment at Preston Barracks Brighton. Later, from September 1941, he was in command of the School of Artillery at Larkhill -

where he himself had done much of his training. Harold Bagnall was recalled in view of his considerable expertise as one of the Army's foremost Gunnery Officers and once these Schools and training establishments had been put on a proper wartime footing in November 1941, he was released to take up his appointment again at Wem. In 1942 he became Vicar of St Jude's, Tilstone Fearnall near Tarporley in Cheshire, a delightful small church with a large and diverse congregation spread of several square miles of this lovely part of Cheshire. Most unfortunately after such long and distinguished service for his country, Harold Gordon Bagnall did not live long to enjoy his new calling. He passed away at the Vicarage at Tilstone Fearnall on 29th October 1944 after a period in hospital in Chester suffering from cancer of the liver. He lies along with his wife in the small but rather enchanting churchyard at St Jude's.

Harold Gordon Bagnall had married Dorothea Livett, daughter of Canon Grevile Mairis Livett and Clara Livett (nee Creed) at Wateringbury in Kent on 18 October 1919 - the service being conducted by the bride's father. Grevile Livett had been Canon at Rochester Cathedral where he was also Canon Precentor and therefore, in charge of the Cathedral music. Later in life and, according to the family to 'maintain a living', he became Vicar of Wateringbury in Kent where he was colloquially known as an 'Honorary Canon', although of course, all those who reach such exhaled positions in the church have this title. Among his other achievements Grevile Livett was a Fellow of the Society of Antiquaries and he helped compose the 1928 Prayer Book. Dorothea Livett's mother died in 1896; Clara Creed had been a very successful illustrator of children's books under the name T Pym. Grevile Livett married secondly Florence Leney, by whom he had four daughters, the eldest, Barbara, being a witness to the marriage certificate of Harold and Dorothea. There were three sons from this marriage, John was born in 1920 and twins Nicholas and Richard in 1924; in family tradition all three were given Gordon as their second Christian name. Dorothea Livett came to know Harold Gordon Bagnall through his sister, Jessica Gordon Bagnall, who we have yet to meet in any detail. On the death of her husband Dorothea Bagnall had to move out of The Rectory at rather short notice and she became Housekeeper at Port Regis Preparatory School,

the preparatory school at one time attached to Bryanston School near Blandford Forum in Dorset, but during the last war evacuated to Gorhambury near St Albans, the home of the Earl & Countess of Verulum. Her sons Richard and Nicholas had received part of their education at this school when it was at Blandford Forum. Later she went to live in Oxford and became a Landlady taking in students; she even took to riding a motor scooter at 65 and was quite pleased when she passed her driving test weeks before one of her students aged 20, who started lessons on the same day! Dorothea Bagnall was a formidable lady who drove her scooter through the centre of Oxford with enormous nerve and dash and she was particularly loved by her three daughters-in-law. She passed away in 1978 and, as mentioned earlier, is buried with her husband at St Jude's, Tilstone Fearnall.

Harold's eldest son, Brigadier John Gordon Bagnall OBE. MC (1920-1997), followed his father into the Army and also became a distinguished gunnery officer. He was gazetted a 2nd Lieutenant in the Royal Regiment of Artillery 16 December 1939 and won his

Richard Gordon Bagnall, like his father always known to family and friends as Gordon (and sometimes Gordie), was without doubt the light of his mother's life - and a very handsome young man to boot. His good looks show up well in this picture taken when he would have been about 10 years old.

Military Cross while serving with the F Battery 12th (HAC) Royal Horse Artillery in Italy during 1944 on the recommendation of his commanding officer, Lt Colonel John Barstow. His Division, the Sixth Armoured, supporting the 17/21 Lancers were attacking the Gustav Line north of Naples, which was strongly fortified by the Germans during the Allied advance in May 1944. On 16th May Captain Bagnall's tank was immobilised but although close to the enemy lines and under heavy mortar and shell fire for over five hours of remaining daylight, John Bagnall continued directing the guns until retiring after darkness. The next day having got his tank back to base and repaired, he returned to the scene of action and destroyed another anti-tank gun. John Bagnall was made an OBE in the 1965 Queen's birthday honours. He had married Sheila Hartley on 21 August 1946 and they had three daughters, Jane in 1952, Sally in 1953 and Joanna in 1958. Like his father and grandfather before him John Bagnall was a distinguished rifleman and competed in many competitions, some whilst still a schoolboy.

Although the Bagnall name will become extinct in this branch of the family, as mentioned earlier Harold and Dorothea had two other sons, twins Richard Gordon (1924-1986) and Nicholas Gordon (1924-), and Nicholas has one son, Timothy Grevile born 1955, and one daughter Catharine, born 1957 by his wife Ann (nee Haly). The late Richard Gordon married Philippa Williams on 16 September 1950 and they had two sons, Paul Gordon born in 1953, and Charles Gordon born 1960, along with a daughter Penelope Georgina, born 1955, so the Bagnall name lives on in these branches of the family. Like his father and elder brother Richard Gordon was also a gunner in the Royal Artillery, as was his wife's father Ronald Williams. However, Nicholas's son Timothy, like his grandfather is an engineer, a chartered engineer and Member of the Institution of Mechanical Engineers.

Following Warden House School the younger son Richard Gordon Bagnall, like his brother went to Charterhouse; he was there between the summer of 1900 and the autumn 1902 (so they were there together for a short period) and on leaving school joined his father in his railway engineering business. In May 1906, on the occasion of his 21st birthday, the Company held a small ceremony at the Castle Engine Works presided over by John Gifford, a director and cousin of his mother, Jessie Bagnall, when George Fletcher, the secretary, made a presentation. On behalf of all the employees Richard Gordon was presented with a suitably inscribed gold pocket watch made by the local firm of J Mottram. The very neatly engraved inscription reads: 'Presented to Mr RG Bagnall on the Occasion of his 21st Birthday by the employees of Castle Engine Works Stafford May 25th 1906'. This lovely timepiece still exists in the family collection, sees occasional use and keeps perfect time. Unfortunately his father was unable to be present due to his ill health but in thanking each and every man individually, Richard Gordon mentioned the constant enquiries he received about his father and the whole company sent their very best wishes that he might be restored to good health by the end of the year. Richard Gordon Bagnall was extremely well liked by just about everybody he came into contact with, a tall and very handsome young man with his mother's blue eyes; he was particularly popular with the fairer sex and was always keen to help others. Like his father and mother he was a keen golfer, enjoyed a game of tennis, was a member of the choir at St Mary's Castle Church and loved to walk and cycle on Cannock Chase. He was in fact an excellent all-round sportsman having won a number of awards whilst at school. The

Like his elder brother Richard Gordon went to Warden House preparatory school at Deal in Kent; he is in the centre of the front row. His brother incidentally, was on the roll-call of the first five pupils when this school first opened.

Richard Gordon Bagnall as a young man with his first powered transport; later he bought a car which he still owned at the time of his death. Photograph taken at the Milford house where the family moved shortly after his father's death and not long before he went to work in Malaya. The E prefix to the registration was the letter for Staffordshire.

family have a nice cup presented to him in 1900, when he was at Warden House School for winning a quarter mile race. Alas his father's health did not improve and as we shall see in more detail later in the story he passed away in 1907.

In May 1911, the family having disposed of their remaining shares in WG Bagnall Limited, Richard Gordon Bagnall decided on a complete change of career. On the recommendation of Arthur Henry Bagnall, who was involved with rubber plantations in the Straits Settlements (Malaya), he went to that country to take up a position in the rubber industry. Arthur Bagnall of Field Burcote, Towcester in Northamptonshire, was the second son - there were five sons and two daughters - of Charles Bagnall, a cousin of

WG Bagnall; Charles will appear again later in the story. Eventually Richard Gordon became divisional superintendent of the Merlimau Rubber Plantation in Malacca: a British company the Merlimau Rubber Estates Limited was registered in London on 18 September 1909 - Arthur Bagnall was a director. The British agents for the rubber plantation were the London based RG Shaw & Company, a company who acted as agents and secretaries for a number of Indian and colonial based organisations and who incidentally, were customers of WG Bagnall Limited. There does not, however, appear to have been any specific connection in this case. Jack Rooper, youngest son of Percy and Daisy, was with Richard Gordon Bagnall at Merlimau for a period and photographs exist of the two of them there together.

Answering the call to serve his country Richard Gordon Bagnall returned home of his own volition in the spring of 1915 and immediately volunteered for military service. He was commissioned on 29 June as a 2nd Lieutenant and at his own request, was posted on 5 July to his brother's Regiment - The Royal Garrison Artillery. Among the referees for his commission was

Richard Gordon Bagnall, pipe in hand, at the Merlimau Rubber Plantation in Malay in about 1913.

Richard Gordon Bagnall again, second from the right in his uniform as a 2nd Lieutenant and resting on some tennis courts during his training; a photograph probably taken at either Chatham or Woolwich in the autumn of 1915. Unfortunately none of his companions have been identified but the fellow on the left would appear to be in the Navy and not Army. This photograph and a couple of others taken on the same occasion are in all probability the very last ones ever taken of Richard Gordon Bagnall - 'Baggy' to his mess mates - before he departed for France; there would not be any others.

one of his former masters from Warden House School at Deal, Hugh W Mullins MA., by this time the head master there. After officer training at Woolwich and Chatham Richard Gordon Bagnall joined the Special Reserve Division of his regiment which was already on active service on the Western Front in France; he joined his new colleagues in December 1915. With his detachment, the 114th Heavy Battery of the 2nd Heavy Artillery Group, he was involved in the terrible Battle of the Somme. For the first three weeks of June 1916 his detachment was involved in placing the batteries and digging them in at Bouzincourt, about two miles north-west of Albert, before the great offensive started on the 24th of that month. There followed several days of heavy artillery fire prior to the commencement of the infantry advance scheduled for 1 June - the first day of the infamous Battle of the Somme, long to go down in the history books as one of the bloodiest human carnages of all time.

The rest of the story is perhaps, best told in the words of his group commending officer, Lt. Colonel RH Massie

RGA, writing to Richard Gordon's sister Jessica, on 25 July. He writes: 'The 114th Battery was chiefly engaged during the period 24th to 30th in firing on the enemy's wire at some special points which the field artillery could not reach. In order to do this successfully it was necessary for someone to direct the fire from a place quite close up, whence it could be clearly seen [the fall of shot]. Captain Apletre and I found a suitable place in a trench about 400 yards from the German trenches and it was fortified as well as we could with a steel plate for a roof, covered with sandbags. It seemed fairly safe and your brother practically lived in it, or anyhow was there part of each day acting as observation officer for his battery all the time and did most valuable work in correcting fire. Unfortunately a trench mortar battery was (after we had built the observation point) put just behind it and the 'Huns' located it. It was evidently a shell intended for the trench mortar which burst just in front of the peep hole. A number of shrapnel bullets came through - one only struck your brother and punctuated his brain so he probably knew nothing about it. So you see Gordon was doing his duty nobly to the very last. Captain Apletre tells me that he spoke to him on the telephone only a few minutes before the end and he was sending down reports of our fire and the progress of the assault quite undisturbed'.

His death took place at approximately 11 am on the morning of the 1 July, the day of the great advance when over 19,000 men lost their lives. With him at the time and also killed was Acting Bombardier J Mortimer whilst his other companion, Gunner P Jackson was seriously wounded; they were both acting as observers and telephonists. As a Subaltern being selected as an observation officer and especially on the day of a battle like that on 1 July was, according to Lt. Colonel Massie, illustrative of the high regard Richard Gordon Bagnall was held by his commanding officer, Captain RC Apletre. To continue in Massie's own words - 'in these days of hole-and-corner shooting where our guns are tucked away out of sight and the people near them cannot see anything but are fairly safe, to be selected for such a post is a high honour'. Such an assignment was well known as being one of the most dangerous of all on the front line and few who undertook it survived for any great length of time. At the time of his death his brother was Adjutant of the 23rd Group RGA., and not far away, so a message was passed to him on the very day Richard Gordon was killed; Harold was therefore able to write to his sister the following day. Although Lt.

Colonel Massie recommended Richard Gordon Bagnall for a 'Mention on Dispatches', in the event nothing came of the recommendation; his promotion to Lieutenant was also about to take place. Later Major J Inder RGA, in command RGA Section 3rd Echelon British Expeditionary Force, was able to send his mother the telescope and compass that were with him when he perished, along with a letter he had written on the morning of the day he died and addressed to her that was found in his pocket, as well as all his other possessions. The family still have them all. Richard Gordon Bagnall was buried at 11 am on Sunday 2 July 1916, the day after he was killed, and he lies in the English Military Cemetery at Bouzincourt, very near to where he fell. The inscription of his grave stone reads: 'Second Lieutenant R.G.Bagnall Royal Garrison Artillery 1st July 1916 Age 31', and the Regimental crest with the words: 'UBIQUE QUO FAS ET GLORIA DUCUNT' (Whenever Right and Glory Lead). Nearby lie six members of the same Regiment killed on the same day including Bombardier J Mortimer, a married man from Oldbury; in fact Bagnall and Mortimer are in adjacent graves.

'There's some corner of a foreign field That is for ever England'.

Richard Gordon Bagnall's name appears on the Stafford Town War Memorial which was unveiled on 28 October 1922 (despite the fact he was not a resident there at the time of his death - he was nevertheless a son of the county town) and in St Mary's Castle Church there are two memorials to him. His name also apppears in the Memorial Chapel at Charterhouse School, consecrated on the 18th June 1927, along with 685 other 'old boys' of the school who fell during the war. A brass plaque in St. Mary's bears the inscription: 'In Loving Memory of Richard Gordon Bagnall, younger son of William Gordon and Jessie Bagnall born May 22 1885 Killed in Action France July 1 1916 While Serving in The Royal, Garrison Artillery'. Mounted above it is a wooden cross-inscribed with the words: 'In Memory of 2nd Lieut Richard Gordon Bagnall 114. H.B. R.G.A Killed in Action July 1 1916 RIP' - the initials meaning Heavy Brigade Royal Garrison Artillery. These two memorials are placed above where Richard Gordon used to sit in the choir, so placed at the suggestion of the

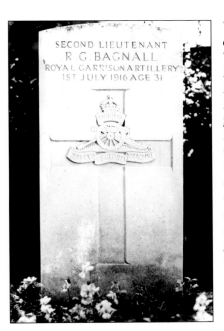

'There's some corner of a foreign field That is for ever England'. Richard Gordon Bagnall's last resting place in the Bouzincourt Communal Cemetery Extension. This cemetery is located north-west of Albert and near where he fell on 1 July 1916. The first day of The Battle of the Somme.

The memorial plaque in St Mary's Castle Church Stafford. At the suggestion of the Vicar at the time, the Rev. Melville Scott, it is mounted beneath the replica wooden cross on a wall near to where Richard Gordon Bagnall's normal place was when a member of the church choir. The bottom of the replica wooden cross made at the Castle Engine Works can be seen above; the original had been brought back from France

Gordon's first burial place in France. The cross had been sawn off at ground level, presumably when the permanent grave stone replaced it, and it had been brought to St Mary's where it had remained ever since. It is not known at this distance in time how the cross came to be in Stafford, but it may well have been brought over from France by his brother as the family would undoubtedly have wanted it to be near where his father was buried. The cross was infested with woodworm and the Vicar was at a loss as to what to do with it; later examination by 'experts' pronounced it to be beyond redemption. Smyth arranged for it to be measured and photographed and then reverently destroyed in the presence of himself, the Vicar and a number of older Bagnall employees. An exact oak replica was then made, very fittingly by the joiners at the Castle Engine Works and placed in the church where it remains to this day; on its rear and out of sight

then Vicar, the Rev. Melville Scott, who had been a fellow chorister. After some correspondence between his mother, her solicitor and the War Office and in view of the fact that his father was already dead, Jessie Bagnall was eventually awarded a war pension (£100 per annum); she was also paid her son's salary at a rate of 8/ 6d per day (42½ p) until 31 December 1916. It is worth mentioning that Richard Gordon's sister Jessica, maintained contact with his Battery and was able to send collections of books for his former colleagues to read during their long hours of inactivity. She also conducted correspondence with several of them and managed to trace via his mother Gunner P Jackson, a Gloucestershire lad who was in a military hospital in Edinburgh; later with her mother she was able to meet him. Jackson spoke very highly of Richard Gordon as they had obviously been together for some time: 'I feel it more than as if he was my own brother, he was such a gentleman and a good Officer'. This probably speaks more than quoting any of the many other accolades from fellow officers, coming as it does from 'The Ranks'.

There is a nice story surrounding the cross in St Mary's Church as it is not the original. One day around the mid 1950s the then Vicar of St Mary's called on WA Smyth, at the time managing director of WG Bagnall Limited (we shall here much more of him later in our story), carrying the wooden cross from Richard

The original wooden cross from Richard Gordon Bagnall's grave that was later brought to Stafford and mounted in St Mary's Castle Church. The cross there today, is an exact replica of this one.

is a small brass plate explaining the need for the replacement. Unfortunately, neither Smyth nor the Vicar was able at the time to locate any of the Bagnall family to witness these events. Many years later in 1975 when contact was made with William Gordon Bagnall's daughter Jessica, alive, well and living in Shropshire, it was possible to put Smyth in touch with her and he was able to relay the story of her brother's cross at first hand. As can be imagined this gave his sister much comfort; it also gave a lot of pleasure to WA Smyth as well as the authors of this book.

The loss of Richard Gordon, a very handsome young man as can be seen from the photographs, was a tremendous loss to his family and his sister said that her mother never got over it, despite living until her 83rd year in 1947. Surviving members of the family who knew Jessie Bagnall testify to the reverence and frequency with which Richard Gordon was recalled and the constant reminders of him around her house, all of which survive in the family collection. She is remembered by her grandson Nicholas 'as a handsome old lady with hooded lids and a patrician nose, bright blue eyes and wavy hair that was still gold. She spent most of her days in the bay window of her small house in Church Stretton and in memory of her son always wore blue, which she explained as a sort of half-mourning'. Nicholas goes on to recall that he was

Jessica Gordon Bagnall, daughter of Gordon and Jessie Bagnall and affectionately known to family and close friends as Doris - although in later years the family knew her as 'Jeeka'. She would have been about 12 years old when this portrait was taken; a very beautiful young lady and perhaps for understandable reasons, her father's favourite.

allowed to smoke a pipe in the drawing room, because Richard Gordon had smoked one, but never a cigarette! As will be seen from the photographs Jessie Bagnall had been a very beautiful lady in her younger days. Richard Gordon was an accomplished carpenter and put his skills to good use in the wood-working department of his father's business. There exist in the family collections to this day examples of his handiwork, including a chest of drawers and a sideboard. He also made a number of his father's gun chests and as can be imagined his father was extremely proud of them. A particular one is a really magnificent piece of the cabinet maker's art with beautifully carved panels and, according to family legend, made from several items of furniture that came into the family's possession having previously been at Dieulacresse Abbey (sometimes spelt Dieularces). This Cistercian Abbey dates from 1214 (on this site - it was earlier at Poulton in Cheshire) and was situated in the hamlet that took the same name about one mile north of Leek in Staffordshire - there are some remains to this day. Following the abolition of the monasteries by Henry V111, at the dissolution of the Dieulacresse Abbey in 1539, it was given by King Edward V1 to Sir Ralph Bagenall, together with all its lands in Leek, Frith, Tittisworth (now spelt Tittesworth and the site of a large reservoir of quite recent construction) and Thorncliffe, along with a number of other properties. Bagenall's descendent Sir Henry Bagnold and his wife Elianor, sold the estates in 1597 to Thomas Rudyerd of Rudyerd (now spelt Rudyard); this is also the site of a reservoir - albeit known as a lake - and of much older construction than Tittesworth. However, it seems that some of the furniture from the Abbey was retained in the family and handed down the generations.

Jessica Gordon Bagnall was but 15 years old when her father died, but she inherited his 'green fingers'. Educated at Stafford High School and subsequently at the Horticultural College at Swanley in Kent (an establishment later combined with the very well known Agricultural College at Wye, also in Kent), on leaving college in 1912 she took up a teaching post at Cambridge Girls High School where she was also the head gardener. The following year she moved to Bedales School at Steep, near Petersfield in Hampshire, a progressive co-educational school where she was also head gardener. Around this time Jessica spent a period in Paris and helped design the gardens of the British Embassy there. However, she was still living at Steep with her mother when her brother Richard Gordon returned to this country prior to joining the Army; the two of them were there when the dreaded telegram arrived telling them of Richard Gordon's death in action. Soon after this mother and daughter moved to London where they rented 69 Overstrand Mansions at Battersea Park. Jessica had joined the Board of Agriculture and took up a position as one of its inspectors covering Kent, Surrey, Sussex and parts of Hampshire, and one of her duties was to organise the wartime land girls. This was a Government initiative to get younger women to work in farming replacing men who had joined the forces. In this phase of her life Jessica met Dorothea Livett and through this friendship she introduced Dorothea to her elder brother Harold, when he was on leave from his regiment and as noted earlier this resulted in their subsequent marriage. For around one year after the end of the war Jessica worked for the War Graves Commission in France, helping with the laying out of the permanent memorials and one is left wondering if during this time, she might have come across her brother's grave and it was her in fact that brought over the original wooden cross. If she did, it was never mentioned to any surviving members of the family.

On her return from France Jessica rented a farm at Birtsmorton, which is some four miles or so east of Tewkesbury and on 11 July 1922, at the Parish Church there married Maurice Lingard Alsop. Moll, as he was always known to family and friends, was a childhood friend from Stafford and by the time of the marriage a cotton buyer based in Liverpool, although he had served throughout the War as a volunteer with the Cheshire Regiment and was Mentioned in Despatches. Moll hailed from Acton Trussell and Bednall, three miles south of Stafford, where his father was the Vicar - Rev. Arthur Richard Alsop. Moll was the youngest of six children and his father, who performed the marriage ceremony of the couple at Birtsmorton, along with his father before him, were the Vicars of the Parish of Bednall for over 70 years. Soon after the marriage in November 1922, Jessica and Moll went to America and lived in Memphis Tennessee for around a year, whilst Moll was engaged in buying cotton for his employers - Andrews Gabbatt, cotton merchants from Liverpool.

On their return to this country they rented a farm at Huxley, three miles west of Tarporley in Cheshire which enabled Moll to travel to and from Liverpool for his work. Subsequently, in September 1928, they moved to Hinton Bank Farm, just north of Whitchurch in Shropshire, and in about 1933 Moll gave up his daily journey to Liverpool to concentrate on the farm. At Hinton Bank Moll bred pedigree pigs with great success and incidentally, Daisy Rooper, wife of Percy Rooper whom we met earlier and who was a life long friend of the Bagnall family, lent Jessica and Moll some money to help them buy the Farm. A few years later the Alsops acquired the nearby Hinton Manor, which in effect became subsumed by the Farm and the family became famous cheese makers, discovering the wonderful Blue Cheshire formula which previously had only happened by accident, and nobody knew why! Most unfortunately, since it stopped being made at Hinton Bank, the recipe has been lost.

Major Maurice Alsop although never a regular, served throughout both world wars as a volunteer in the Cheshire Regiment and gave distinguished service in a number of theatres. In 1945 he was awarded the Territorial Decoration. It was at Hinton Manor in 1975 that the authors first met Jessica along with her husband and other members of the Bagnall and Alsop

The Little House at Trevor Hill in Church Stretton where Jessie Bagnall lived from around 1922 until her death in 1947. This had originally belonged to the golf course, and the rear garden backed onto the Golf Club House and the first tee. As a keen golfer Jessie did not have far to go for a round.

families, and in more recent times the daughter Ursula Mary (known as Jill) and her husband the late Group Captain David Hutchinson Smith AFC. Jessica Gordon Bagnall died at Hinton Manor on 6 April 1980 and her husband on 24 August two years later. Jessica, or Doris as her close family affectionately called her, although in later years at least, the family always knew her as 'Jeeka', was extremely fond of her father. She recalled that it was her father who first 'christened' her Doris, although she knew not why and she remembered him so clearly and with enormous love, pride and respect; she outlived him by no less than 73 years. Her mother Jessie Bagnall went to live in Church Stretton at 'Little House' on Trevor Hill. Although this relatively small house survives to this day it has been renamed Bank House and the road leading to it is now called Stanyeld Road, which leads off Trevor Hill. It is quite hilly thereabouts, Trevor Hill climbing from Cardingmill Valley Road which lies at the same level as most of the rest of the pleasant Shropshire town of Church Stretton. A love of a game of golf took Jessie Bagnall to Church Stretton as there were a number of excellent golf courses nearby although it seems she only played on the one in Church Stretton itself.

From the forgoing readers will have gathered that in its wider context the Bagnall family was a large and influential one, as indeed to a somewhat lesser extent were the Cooksons, the Gibsons and the Wards. Mention has been made of the lavish catalogues Bagnall produced to promote his products and these are indeed models of their kind, even of a period in time when it was quite a common practice for manufacturers to go to endless lengths and expense in producing publicity literature. There is however, an interesting family story about them, which goes someway to illustrate the esteem with which Bagnall himself and moreover his family, held them. It also helps to emphasis how important they were to his business activities. On 23 June 1885, at their home at Severn Bank, three of Gordon Bagnall's younger sisters, Gertrude Mary, Jessie and Norah, respectively 18, 19 and 21 years old at that time, sat down and composed a poem. Doubtless they were musing on a sunny afternoon after lunch! This poem, which in view of its interest is reproduced as Appendix XIII, is titled *The Portable Catalogue* and is written in the fair hand of one of the sisters. The verses mention the catalogues and the success they brought

Bagnall and his business activities along with the names of some of the locomotives that were illustrated in them. There is also a specific reference to a substantial order for locomotives and other equipment for the Sudan received a few months before the poem was composed, part of which was later diverted for use in this country. Moreover, in the reference to a 'great and famous victory' in the concluding verse, perhaps more than any other illustrates just how much the family saw the success of the Company being partly at least a result of the catalogues. The original hand written copy of the poem survives in the family archives.

Before continuing the story much further it is worth exploring Gordon Bagnall's forebears, briefly mentioned earlier and in particular the company that later became John Bagnall & Sons Limited. The John Bagnall we are largely concerned with here (1759-1829) was the father of Richard Bagnall who was in turn William Gordon's father. We saw earlier how John Bagnall (1730-1800) and his young family had moved from Broseley to West Bromwich in the mid to late 1700s and how John had wanted to enter the iron trade. However, it appears he might first of all have been a ground bailiff at Tipton, but towards the end of the 18th century purchased coal mines at Toll End, Coppice and Lea Bank at Wednesbury. After John's death in 1800 his second son, also John (1759-1829), along with his younger brother Edward (1761-1805), formed a company trading as John & Edward Bagnall and in 1803 appear to have entered the iron trade by purchasing an existing furnace at Leabrook that had been built by Michael Toney. After Edward's death in December 1805, over a period of time John took into partnership five of his eight sons. Thereafter the Company traded as John Bagnall & Sons. Surviving evidence suggests that the sons John (1794-1840), William (1797-1863) and James (1804-1872) took the most interest in the Company affairs. William and James, along with their brother Thomas (1799-1863), were elected as associate members of the Institution of Civil Engineers; this was in 1841 and only a few years after it was formed. Additionally William was a member of the Institution of Mechanical Engineers, to which he was elected in 1848. They remained members until they died.

John Bagnall & Sons became a very well known and respected company in the Black Country iron trade erecting the very first blast furnace in West Bromwich at

Another of the Bagnalls - this is James - he was born 31 December 1804 in West Bromwich and married Catherine, daughter of Joseph and Anne Hateley. She died very young on 16 June 1837 and there were no children. James, who became a JP for Staffordshire and Deputy Lieutenant of the county, died 12 January 1872 - at that time his estate was valued at £250,000, an enormous sum of money in those days. James was very fond of his nephew William Gordon, and presented him with the exceptionally nice engraved christening set mentioned in the text. James was the last survivor of the sons of John Bagnall to take an active interest in the family firm. James, perhaps more than his brothers, was the motivator in the firm taking an enormous moral and spiritual interest in the welfare of its workers and their families. He continued this support until he died and rather than retiring to the countryside, he remained living in the area at Meyrick House, Hill Top in West Bromwich. His funeral cortège was followed by literally thousands of local people and after a service at All Saints Church, he was laid to rest at St James Church in West Bromwich

Gold's Hill in 1820. The Company was also able to establish itself over the following few years with an impressive portfolio of coal mines, iron works, brickworks and other ancillary operations in and around West Bromwich, Wednesbury, Darlaston, Bilston and Willenhall. This was achieved by a combination of acquiring the undertakings of existing companies and partnerships as well as establishing completely new operations. The quality of the Company's products achieved a reputation that was second to none with the various brands of iron being much sought after. As a result the name of Bagnall became synonymous with excellent quality iron at a time when there was a lot of inferior production on the market. But these were the golden years of the Black Country coal and iron trade and it was not to last. As the elder brothers died, John in 1840 (2 February), William in 1863 (12 August) and James in 1872 (12 January) for example, more and more of the day-to-day management fell on Richard, William Gordon's father.

This responsibility falling on Richard's shoulders was it seems one he was far from happy with. The prosperous years of the iron and coal trade in this part of Staffordshire had made the family a rich one. For example when William died in 1863 his estate was valued at a little under £140,000, and when James passed on nine years later, his estate was valued at only a fraction under £250,000 - these were enormous sums of money in those times. Therefore, Richard was anxious to rid himself of the responsibility and live the life of a country gentleman. To this end on 21 March 1873 a limited liability company was formed - John Bagnall & Sons Limited - to manage the operations and relieve Richard Bagnall of the day to day managerial issues. The original capital of the new company was £300,000 divided into 30,000 shares of £10 each, the articles making provision to borrow a further £200,000 by the issue of mortgage debenture bonds. Initially shares to the value of £140,000 were issued to the vendors who were: Richard Samuel Bagnall, William Sutton Nayler and Joseph Nayler - collectively the trustees and executors of the late James Bagnall, James being the last brother who had been involved in the company to die, with of course, the sole exception of Richard. The Richard Samuel Bagnall referred to here however, was not WG Bagnall's father but his elder brother and the eldest son of Richard Bagnall - he was born on 23 November 1845.

In promoting this new company it would appear that quite large sums of money were paid to various individuals. This included a sum of no less than £85,000 to a Mr Carlton and there were undertakings underwritten by Richard Bagnall to pay the brothers

Memorandum of Association

OF

JOHN BAGNALL AND SONS, LIMITED.

1. The name of the Company is "JOHN BAGNALL AND SONS, LIMITED."

2. The Registered Office of the Company will be situate in England.

3. The objects for which the Company is established are:—

　　1. The carrying into effect the agreement following, or any modification thereof which may be agreed upon by the parties thereto and the Company, that is to say:—

　　　An agreement dated the 6th day of March, 1873, made between Richard Samuel Bagnall, William Sutton Nayler, and Joseph Nayler, trustees and executors of the will of James Bagnall, late of Gold's Hill, Staffordshire, Coal and Ironmaster, deceased, of the one part, and George Bytheway, of Walsall, Staffordshire, Accountant, as a Trustee for and on behalf of the (then intended) Company, of the other part, for the purchase of the Goodwill of the business carried on under the firm of "John Bagnall and Sons," and of the several Iron Works and Collieries referred to in the said agreement, and which are carried on and worked in connexion with the said business, and of the plant, stock and other properties connected with the said collieries and works respectively.

[13472]　　　　　　　　　　1

Title page of the Memorandum of Association of John Bagnall & Sons Limited, registered as a Limited Liability Company on 21 March 1873. Notice that the Naylor brothers are prominent, as discussed in the text of this Chapter

Joseph and William Sutton Nayler, the managing directors, £6,000 each plus an annuity of £500 for seven years. This was all exposed in May 1875 when a Mr Dick - a shareholder of the new company - being unhappy with the payment attempted to get his name struck off the list of shareholders with an action in the Court of Exchequer. It transpired in the court proceedings that although Joseph Nayler (his brother William Sutton had died by this time) claimed that the money paid to him and his brother was for services rendered prior to the formation of the new company and had no reference to it, the Brothers had in fact been connected with the Bagnall Company for many years. They had powers over the disposition of the property of the old Company under the terms of James Bagnall's will and they had declined to permit completion of the new company documents until the payments outlined

above had been agreed. They were described as 'trustees and managers' of the old company prior to it becoming one with limited liability. The will of James Bagnall which is dated 5 July 1870, confirms the Naylor brothers claims and along with Richard Bagnall, they were join-executors of his estate. Clearly, the brothers had been well thought of by the Bagnalls, having had much to do with their success. This issue dragged on for several years and was not helped by a general down-turn in the iron trade at the time which seriously affected the company profits - a loss of over £10,000 in 1874 for example. Notwithstanding his dislike of a business life, as events turned out Richard Bagnall had managed to get-out just in time!

By a special resolution dated 11 July 1878, which itself followed an EGM on 18 June 1878, the capital of the Company was reduced by no less than £108,000 to £192,000. This was accomplished by the cancellation of 14,000 shares that had never been issued and a reduction in the value of those that had been issued; it was claimed that the full value of the issued share

An contempory advert for John Bagnall & Sons after the Company became one of Limited Liability in 1873. Notice that the Managing Director was Joseph Naylor.

JOHN BAGNALL & SONS,

LIMITED.

GOLD'S HILL

IRON WORKS,

WEST BROMWICH.

MANAGING DIRECTOR,

JOSEPH NAYLOR, Esq.

BRAND　👑 I.B.　'BAGNALL.'

William Gordon Bagnall, a portrait taken about the time he was involved in the restructuring of his grandfather's old company - John Bagnall & Sons Limited. He would have been around 35 when this picture was taken.

capital was no longer represented by the Company's available assets. On formation of the limited company iron bars were trading at £16 per ton and large profits were being made, but as the trade slumped the Company found itself unable to pay the interest on the £140,000 debenture issue, let alone any dividends to the shareholders. The Company prospects did improve for a few years later on, but it was not for long and at a special general meeting held on 16 June 1882, a motion was passed for the voluntarily winding up of the Company. Unfortunately this motion was not in time to prevent a petition by Lloyds Banking Company Limited - the Company's principal bankers - dated 16 June 1882 and brought before a Chancery Court on 25 July 1882, to the effect that the winding up procedures had to be undertaken under the supervision of the Chancery Division. The liquidators appointed by the Court were Edward Gem who was one of the principal shareholders and a Director, along with William Gordon Bagnall who it seems, became involved in an effort to save

something of the family name. As the *London Iron Trade Exchange* put it - 'remove the stigma of liquidation from the title of John Bagnall & Sons' - and we saw earlier the reputation for quality products attached to the Bagnall name. Worth noting at this juncture is the fact that WG Bagnall's father Richard, had passed away at the family home at Severn Bank, on 6 September 1877; he did not live long therefore, to enjoy the fruits of his family's financial success. Richard Bagnall left an estate equal to £35,000 and his wife Julia, his eldest son Richard Samuel Bagnall and William Gordon Bagnall were the executors of his will.

Following the Court Order and a lot of time and effort, Bagnall and Gem, together with the manager of the Company Michael James Whitehouse, managed to effect a financial reconstruction of the Company. But in so doing a number of the collieries and other undertakings owned by the Company were either sold or closed down. Following a meeting of the shareholders and debenture holders - many of whom were Bagnall family members - on 26 February 1885, a scheme of reconstruction was placed before the Court of Chancery. On 20 March that year the Court agreed to 'stay' the winding up procedure for three months so as to give the liquidators time to put a permanent reconstruction scheme in place and get agreement of all interested parties. A further Court hearing on 15 May 1886 confirmed the proposed reconstruction arrangements and agreement was reached to hand over the remaining assets to a new board of directors consisting of WG Bagnall, E Gem, AE Wenham and GF Griffin.

From the Court proceedings it appears that the £20,000 capital required to form the re-construction assumed the writing off of all the existing capital. There was a mortgage held by WG Bagnall from which it can be deduced that he had been financially helping out the 'old' company; the sum was £21,000 and under the agreement was reduced to £10,000. There was another mortgage for £23,000 held by Lloyds Bank - the company's banker - and in this case agreement was reached to reduce it to £10,000. Included in the arrangements was the sale of the Imperial and Leabrook iron works estimated to be worth £20,000, thus realising the amount of capital required to get the Company on its feet again. However, opinion was voiced that in what would in effect be a 'forced' sale, such a sum was

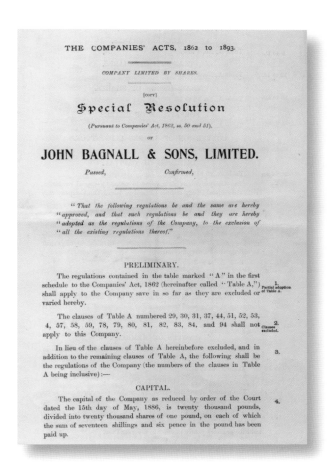

THE COMPANIES' ACTS, 1862 to 1893.

COMPANY LIMITED BY SHARES.

[copy]

Special Resolution

(Pursuant to Companies' Act, 1862, ss. 50 and 51),

or

JOHN BAGNALL & SONS, LIMITED.

Passed,   Confirmed,

"That the following regulations be and the same are hereby
"approved, and that such regulations be and they are hereby
"adopted as the regulations of the Company, to the exclusion of
"all the existing regulations thereof."

PRELIMINARY.

The regulations contained in the table marked "A" in the first
schedule to the Companies' Act, 1862 (hereinafter called "Table A,")
shall apply to the Company save in so far as they are excluded or
varied hereby.

The clauses of Table A numbered 29, 30, 31, 37, 44, 51, 52, 53,
4, 57, 58, 59, 78, 79, 80, 81, 82, 83, 84, and 94 shall not
apply to this Company.

In lieu of the clauses of Table A hereinbefore excluded, and in
addition to the remaining clauses of Table A, the following shall be
the regulations of the Company (the numbers of the clauses in Table
A being inclusive):—

CAPITAL.

The capital of the Company as reduced by order of the Court
dated the 15th day of May, 1886, is twenty thousand pounds,
divided into twenty thousand shares of one pound, on each of which
the sum of seventeen shillings and six pence in the pound has been
paid up.

*The title page of the Special Resolution of John Bagnall & Sons
Limited, confirming the Court Order to write-down the capital to
£20,000.*

unlikely to be paid. During the period of liquidation a sum of £11,737 had been accumulated in sales and after paying interest on the mortgages, a net profit of £7,111 had accrued. The re-construction went ahead in May 1885 and as events turned out the Leabrook Ironworks was not sold and it continued to trade under the Bagnall name for many years. Gordon Bagnall, who put a tremendous amount of effort and money into saving the Company and the family name, remained a director after the financial reconstruction and became its chairman. He was still on the board although no longer chairman at the time of his death in 1907. The Company continued to trade in the iron and steel business and members of the Bagnall family remained as shareholders until October 1918, when the majority of private shareholders were 'bought-out'. Moreover, the Company carried on trading under the Bagnall name until April 1991 when it was renamed Triplex Lloyd

Automotive Products Limited, having for some years previously diversified into the automotive line of business under Triplex Lloyd ownership. It was finally dissolved on 22 December 2000. The Leabrook Ironworks at Wednesbury was the last connection of the Bagnall name with the Staffordshire iron and steel trade when it closed in May 1984 - the Bagnall family had originally acquired it in 1864 some 120 years earlier.

As might be expected the Bagnall family, which as we have seen was a very large one, became significant benefactors in the area in which they resided and conducted business. The family financed the building of the Gold's Hill School in 1854-5 at a cost of £5,500, ostensibly for the children of their workers, along with numerous houses in and around the area. The school could accommodate over 500 pupils of all ages and was of advanced design for the period being centrally heated with gas lighting. The church of St Paul, in the Parish of St James in Bagnall Street Gold's Hill, still standing as a place of worship today, dates from 1881. However, its origins go back to 1853 as a mission centre built by the Company and within the precincts of the Gold's Hill Ironworks itself, where the Company appointed the Reverend Francis Hutton, Curate of St James in Wednesbury, as Chaplin. An entry in Hutton's handwriting in the Gold's Hill baptism register records the first communion service held there on 4 September 1853. Much of the structure of this building was transferred to the new church of St Paul which was opened for divine worship on the 4 July 1882, the first sermon being delivered by the Dean of Lichfield. The Reverend George Hummings (1876-1884) was the first Curate, but it was not until 6 September 1887 that the Bishop of Lichfield consecrated the building and the Reverend Ralph Blanch Ronson (1848-1911) was appointed the first Vicar, having been Curate since 1884. The stained glass windows situated immediately behind the alter were originally part of the mission centre at Gold's Hill; they had been paid for as a tribute to the Bagnall family by the staff of the ironworks when the original building was constructed. As well as bearing the Bagnall family crest the window has the inscription 'Messrs John Bagnall & Sons 1854'. Until the new church was available divine service on Sundays was held in a room of the Gold's Hill School, one of the larger rooms being used which could accommodate around 700 worshippers.

The Church of St Paul in the Parish of St James in Bagnall Street at Gold's Hill, seen here on 9 June 2004. Dating from 1881 it was partly paid for by the Bagnall family as sections of it date from 1853, and were transferred from the Gold's Hill Ironworks where they had been part of a mission centre.

The New Parochial Hall & Sunday School Room of St Paul's Church, and adjacent to the church itself in Bagnall Street at Gold's Hill, another photograph taken on 9 June 2004. Unfortunately the Hall is no longer used for its original purpose, but the commemorative stone laid by Gordon Bagnall can be seen under the end window.

The commemorative stone laid by Gordon Bagnall on 6 June 1898, as surviving in the end wall of the Hall; as can be seen it was laid in the presence of the then Vicar of St Paul's, the Rev. RB Robson. Ralph Blanch Robson was the first Vicar of the Parish and he continued to serve until his death in 1911.

The Company were also supportive of the locality and its workers in a whole range of other activities and some of the family lived in a large house nearby - they were considered good employers and benefactors. Even

after reconstruction of the Company such support continued and we find WG Bagnall himself laying the foundation stone of the New Parochial Hall & Sunday School Room of St Paul's Gold's Hill, on 6 June 1898. The inscribed silver trowel he used for this purpose and presented to him survives in the family collection and the stone he unveiled survives too, mounted on the end wall of the hall facing the road. The hall itself is adjacent to the St Paul's Church but unfortunately is no longer used for its original purpose. The church however, remains much as originally constructed from the materials removed from the ironworks; however, bricks were used in lieu of the cinder blocks of the original and there has been a later enlargement to encompass a new organ. Today this small place of worship is exceptionally well kept despite diminishing congregations. The resident minister (2005) is the Reverend Dagogo Hart and the churchwarden John Smith, who with his family display that tender loving care so much a part of the numerous small churches throughout this country. Gold's Green is but a shadow of the place it once was; the school was demolished in 1950 and many of the narrow streets of terraced houses built by the Bagnall family to house their workers have long since disappeared - as has the large house where the family themselves once lived.

Independently of John Bagnall & Sons other members of the family entered the coal and iron trade in the Black Country. Another of John Bagnall's (1759-1829) sons, in this case not involved in the family

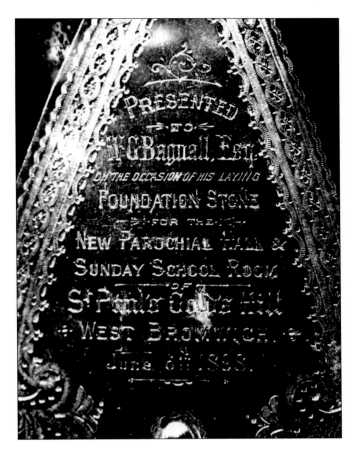

The silver trowel presented to Gordon Bagnall when he laid the foundation stone of the New Parochial Hall & Sunday School Room of St Paul's at Gold's Hill, on Monday 6 June 1898. This beautifully inscribed trowel remains in the family collection, the stone however, could hardly be described as part of the foundations, situated as it is, halfway up a wall.

business, was Thomas; he was born in 1799 and eventually became High Sheriff of Staffordshire in 1863. By his first wife Mary Keen, born in 1803 and the only child of John and Mary Nock - they married on 1 June 1825 - there were four children, all boys. Three of the sons, John Nock the eldest born in 1823, Charles born in 1827 and Thomas born in 1829, went into business trading as J Bagnall & Company in the 1850s. There was a fourth son too, William, who was born on Christmas Eve in 1831; unfortunately his mother passed away six days later and he did not live long either - he died in October 1843. The surviving brothers operated collieries at Bloxwich and Leamore in Walsall and were helped in this by another old established Black Country coal and iron master, William Ward. This connection with William Ward was doubtless aided and abetted by

John Nock - who was mentioned earlier when he purchased Coopers Hill House - as on 3 October 1848 he married Ward's eldest daughter, Mary Ann. Family legend has it that John Nock Bagnall was the great philanthropist of the family, encouraging and developing enlightened practices for the welfare of the staff at all the operations where the various branches of the family were involved. This was a philosophy that Gordon Bagnall adopted in the family tradition, and continued in the industrial relations, as we would term them in more modern times, at the Castle Engine Works.

In November 1860 Charles Bagnall, who it would seem was somewhat of an adventurer and indeed world traveller, also married, in this case Harriet Curtis Chapman, a daughter of John Chapman of Whitby in Yorkshire. With his new bride Charles went to live at Sneaton Castle near Ruswarp and soon realised the potential of the Cleveland iron trade, so that his brother Thomas soon joined him. Among other enterprises thereabouts which included ironstone mines, the brothers built and operated the Grosmont Ironworks commencing operations in April 1863. Like the Black Country iron trade the industrial depression in the latter part of the 19th century also effected the operations in North Yorkshire; finding it impossible to compete on price with the growing iron making operations on nearby Teesside, the Grosmont ironworks of C&T Bagnall, as the partnership had become known, closed down in August 1891. Charles, who once stood unsuccessfully for Parliament to represent Walsall, was subsequently elected Conservative Member of Parliament for Whitby, serving in this capacity from July 1865 to November 1868. In the hope that the southern seaside climate might help his failing health, Charles Bagnall and his wife went to live in Brighton where he died on 25 February 1884. It was one of Charles's children, Arthur Henry, who encouraged Richard Gordon Bagnall to seek pastures new in Malaya. Charles and Harriet had seven children, five boys and two girls; Harriet died on 14 January 1900.

Brother Thomas however, initially remained in the Whitby area but later moved to Milton Ernest Hall at Bedford and in 1879 became High Sheriff of Bedfordshire, although he remained involved with the operations in Yorkshire. Thomas lived until January 1912 and family legend had it that before Grosmont closed down in 1891, he had told all the staff in plenty of time to allow as many of them as possible to get alternative employment, keeping the works going as best he could until the majority had done so. John Nock Bagnall moved on to a completely different sphere of activity and was later (1879) elected a Deputy Lieutenant of the county of Staffordshire. He also reached the rank of Lieutenant Colonel in the 4th Battalion Staffordshire Volunteers. John Nock Bagnall later lived at The Moss, Shenstone, some two miles south of Lichfield where he died on 18 October 1884. Together with his wife Mary Ann, he had nine children, three boys, one of whom died in infancy and six girls.

Thomas Bagnall married a second time on 31 July 1839, to Caroline, daughter of Lancelot and Harriet Haslope; they had six children, two boys and four girls. As will be seen the Bagnall family was a large one!

On 21 July 1887 the partnership of WG Bagnall and Thomas Walter, trading as WG Bagnall & Company had grown to the extent that it was felt appropriate to form a joint stock company limited by shares under the provisions of the Companies Acts of 1862 and 1883. Thus came into being WG Bagnall Limited - company number 24807 and one with limited liability. The capital consisted of £30,000 divided into 2,500 ordinary shares and 500 deferred shares (hence a joint stock company) all valued at £10, of which 1,700 ordinary shares and all the deferred shares were fully paid up. The purchase price of £22,000 was paid by issuing WG Bagnall 663 ordinary and 320 deferred shares and Thomas Walter 1,037 ordinary and 180 deferred shares; from this it will be observed that Walter had been and remained, the principal shareholder.

The articles stipulated that the board was to consist of no more than five members with Gordon Bagnall as chairman and Thomas Walter vice-chairman, the two of them being joint managing directors; Bagnall's initial salary was £400 and Walter's £150. The actual transfer of the assets took place on 1 April 1887. The other shareholders were: Samuel Cookson - as mentioned earlier a local doctor of medicine, a Surgeon and step-father in law of Gordon Bagnall - he held 75 ordinary shares; Edward Salt - Vicar of All Saints Parish Church at Standon in Staffordshire - he had 50 ordinary shares; Richard Samuel Bagnall - the eldest brother of Gordon Bagnall - he also held 50 ordinary shares; Jessie Bagnall - this was not Gordon Bagnall's wife but one of his

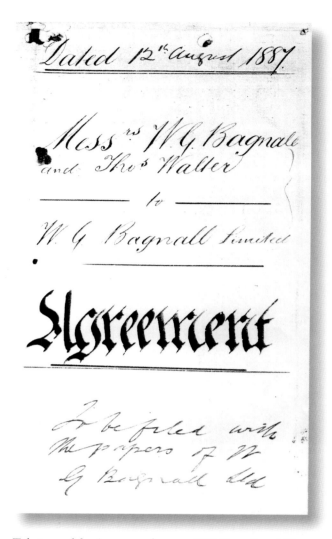

Title page of the Agreement between WG Bagnall and Thomas Walter dated 12 August 1887, to form a limited liability company - WG Bagnall Limited. This was to remain the Company's 'official' title for the remainder of its trading life.

sisters - with 50 ordinary shares; Anne Keay - 10 ordinary shares. As well as Bagnall and Walter the directors were Edward Salt and Samuel Cookson and the company secretary Robert O Bate.

Anne Keay, who remained a shareholder for a good number of years was a member of the Black Country Keay family, several members of which were also engaged in the iron and steel trade. Her brothers Ernest Charles and James A Keay had works at both West Bromwich - the Cyclops Works - and Darlaston - the James Bridge Works - as well as offices in Birmingham itself. The Company was formed in 1875 and in March 1893 became EC & J Keay Limited; the principal

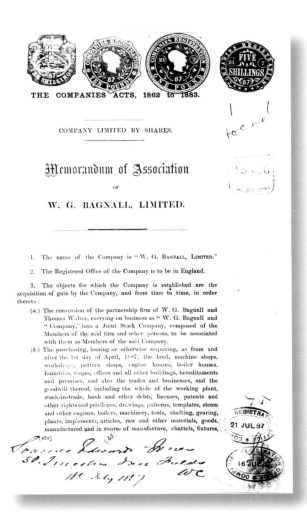

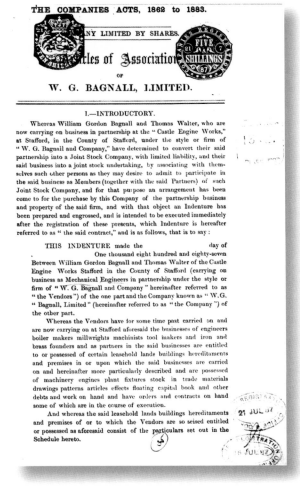

Copy of the original title page of the Memorandum of Association of WG Bagnall Limited, confirming the agreement between WG Bagnall and Thomas Walter dated 1 August 1887. Soames, Edwards & Jones of Lincolns Inn Fields in London, whose name can be seen hand written on the bottom, acted for the partners in forming the limited company. They were the Walter family solicitors.

First page of the Articles of Association of WG Bagnall Limited, registered on 21 July 1887 - on the register as company number 24807.

activities of the two works were structural iron and steelwork but the firm also traded as boilermakers and general iron and steel merchants. Additionally, the company were contractors for the erection of bridges and other structures that largely consisted of structural metal work and later partly specialised in railway signalling equipment. The Keays were known to the Bagnalls both personally and as customers. Anne Keay remained unmarried, living in West Bromwich where she died in the early part of 1924 at the age 72; she was at the time of her death a significant shareholder in the

family firm. One wonders if she might have been a school friend of Bagnall and maybe an earlier lady companion as they were the same age.

A great supporter of Bagnall in both his business and local government activities was Sir Thomas Salt Bart (1830-1904: created 1st Baronet August 1899) of Standon Hall in nearby Eccleshall. Thomas Salt was a prominent conservative representing Stafford in Parliament for many years between 1859 and 1892 (1859-1865; 1869-1880; 1881-1885; 1886-92). He was the chairman of the North Staffordshire Railway from

1883 until his death in 1904, and from 1886 to 1898 chairman of Lloyds Bank. Among his other banking interests he was a partner in the private banking firm of Stevenson, Salt & Company (Stafford Old Bank) at Stafford. For a long time Thomas Salt was a Captain in the Stafford Militia and doubtless was responsible for encouraging Bagnall in this area of his interests. A letter exists written by Thomas Salt from his London residence of 85, St George's Square SW, dated 23 April 1884 and addressed to 'My Dear Bagnall' giving his advice on how Gordon Bagnall might go about forming a limited company. It discusses, inter alia, the amount a capital that might be required, how the shares should be apportioned, the number of directors to be appointed and the form of business they should conduct. Clearly the two men were on intimate terms and we can be pretty sure that the Reverend Edward Salt, one of the initial shareholders of the Company would be a relation of Sir Thomas, although it has not been possible to trace a connection. At the time the Company was formed, Edward Salt was 39 years old, born in Standon, the incumbent Vicar there since at least 1881. One of his sons, Arthur Henry, born in 1879, served a premium apprenticeship with WG Bagnall Limited and later became a civil engineer.

It is possible that the friendship with Thomas Salt, which may initially have been fostered by family connections, was what brought Bagnall to Stafford in the first place. It may also have a bearing of how Bagnall came to know and be associated with Thomas Walter as a business partner. Notice that for a number of years Salt was chairman of Lloyds Bank, which as already outlined was the banker of John Bagnall & Sons and later WG Bagnall & Company, as well as *The Times* newspaper. For lengthy periods while Salt was the Member of Parliament for Stafford, William Gordon Bagnall was the chairman of the Stafford Conservative Association and there are numerous examples in the local newspapers where the two of them were jointly engaged in a whole plethora of the sort of public-spirited activities our Victorians forbearers got up to in those times.

To cite but one example, according to the *Staffordshire Advertiser* dated 19 April 1884, Bagnall as president of the Stafford Conservative Association presided over a presentation of a Testimonial to Salt's son - Thomas Anderdon Salt (1863-1940, he succeeded his father as 2nd Bart) - on the attainment of his majority. Thomas Salt had married Emma Helen Mary Anderdon in July 1861. This rather grand event took place at the then newly erected Assembly Rooms of the Association at Eastgate Street in Stafford. Thomas Anderdon Salt went on to have a distinguished career in the Army with the 11th Hussars. He served on the west coast of Africa 1887-1888, in India (Punjab Frontier) 1897-1898, and during the Boar War in South Africa in 1902; he was twice Mentioned in Despatches and decorated several times. Retiring as a Major in 1904 he was recalled and served during the First World War retiring once again with the rank of Lt. Colonel in 1919. A Deputy Lieutenant and JP for Staffordshire, Thomas Anderdon Salt was appointed High Sheriff for the county in 1909. It is interesting to note that Thomas Salt's youngest son (he had seven sons and four daughters) Harold Francis, who was born in 1879, had part of his education at Coopers Hill College. He was there from September 1897 to January 1900; presumably he was contemplating a career as an engineer with the PWD in India. However, he left the college to join his brother as an Army officer and was commissioned into the Royal Horse Artillery. He too served with distinction throughout the First World War and was Mentioned in Despatches no less than three times; he was also awarded the DSO in 1919. Retiring with the rank of Major-General in 1939, he was later recalled and served with the Ministries of Aircraft Production and Works throughout the Second World War.

Chapter Two

Early Locomotives & Other Products: The Giffords Arrive

Mention has already been made of the unusual design of the early locomotives, both standard and narrow-gauge and this will be explored in more detail in this Chapter. Also outlined in the last Chapter was the sparseness of the known surviving records of early production; clearly most, it not all, having been compiled at a later date from whatever original source material existed. It is therefore, opportune at this juncture to say a little about such records as exist. There are a series of small registers listing the locomotives built and this is the term by which they will be referred to here, each one 4½x16in when opened out. A single-line entry across both pages applies to each locomotive, or in some cases a series of locomotives, with columns headed respectively: When Ordered (date of order): Engine Number (i.e. manufacturers number): Built For (customer): Cylinders (bore and stroke): Number and Diameter of Wheels: Steam Pressure: Water Capacity: General Description (i.e., type of tank, or if fitted a tender and in some cases type of boiler): Gauge: Wheelbase: Name or Number. The words in brackets are the authors. These books only list locomotives, hence there are many missing numbers until consecutive numbering of locomotives started at E No 1410 of 1892. It is also assumed, as outlined earlier, that prior to this date all products were numbered in the same list; after number 1410 a series of general order numbers were introduced and used for everything other than locomotives.

Once separated from the locomotives the numbering of these general orders started at one each January, but in August 1916 3,000 was added to the then total for that year of 699, making the next order number 3700 - this was to avoid any confusion with the numbering sequence used for the locomotives. From that date onwards the numbers were allowed to run to 9999 which was reached in 1921, when a new series starting at 2500 commenced and this series was also allowed to run to 9999. Thereafter, each time 9999 was reached a new series started at 2500, but this start point was later advanced to 3500 as the locomotive order number sequence got close; once again to avoid any confusion between locomotive order numbers and general order numbers. In addition, after the introduction of 'general' order numbers, the locomotive progressive numbers were prefixed with a capital E, which presumably indicated Engine, as a colloquial term for a locomotive. As a result of these initiatives in the numbering of orders, for products built under general order numbers an approximate date as well as a number is essential in tracing specific orders. The series of registers listing the

				Cylinders					Gauge	Wheel base			
Nov 1881	210	Bowman Bros	4½×7½						1-8"	2-9"	Darwin
Nov	212	Manlove Alliott & Co	4½×7½						2-2"	3-0"	Julita
Nov	214	Manlove Alliott & Co	4"×6"						1-11⅝	2-9"	Cancas
Dec	216	Laughland Mackay & Co	5"×7½"						3-6"	3-0"	Mentoni
Dec 1882	218	Bates Stokes & Coy	4½×7½"						2-6"	3-3"	Sydney
March	228	J Glasbrook	6½×8"						2-4"	3-3"	Stanley
March	230	J A Ruddell	5"×7½"						2-0"	3-0"	Prince of Battenberg
April	236	Bolling & Low	5½×9"						2-6"	3-6"	Piedmont & Bay
May	240	Denniston Cross Hy	8"×12"						2-6"	9-0"	El Congreso
June	250	G B Hins & Coy	7"×10½"						3-0"	5-0"	Rialto

An exact copy of two pages from one of the registers describing the early locomotives. Notice the sparse amount of detail and the numbering sequence. The missing numbers are assumed to have been allocated to other than locomotive orders, because when this and other registers were compiled only the locomotive details were transcribed. Presumably too, information to complete the empty columns was absent from the source material used.

early locomotives - they can hardly be called order books - are three in number and indications are that one set each was kept in the managing director's and chief draughtsman's office's. The individual volumes do differ, particularly where entries have been altered to reflect later owners etc., and up to about manufacturer's number 1410, they have all clearly been compiled from some other source, or sources, at a later date. One of the books does not commence until number 1418 of 1893, whilst there is a fourth volume that was not started until as late as 1958, and quite obviously therefore, has but a few entries before locomotive production ceased. There are many gaps in specific locomotive details, especially in the early years and prior to consecutive numbering of the locomotives starting at number 1410. Presumably therefore, such details were not available in whatever source material whoever compiled these registers used. However, there are a number of cases where additional and even less complete entries have been made, usually consisting of an order date, order number, cylinder size and nothing else and it is assumed that these may have been stock orders that for whatever reason were not proceeded with. Additionally, in the early years and prior to about 1892, locomotives with carrying wheels are often described as for example: 'six wheels four coupled', thus leaving the reader to guess if the locomotive in question had an 0-4-2 or a 2-4-0 wheel arrangement! From about the end of the First World War the three sets of

books reduce to two, the third one being full, until the fourth one mentioned above was commenced in 1958! More extensive records exist for later years, for example a series of much larger books with much additional detail and starting at works number 2409 of 1929.

As well as the books mentioned above there are two larger, foolscap-size books, again obviously compiled at a later date. Whilst duplicating much of the information that appears in the smaller books, these two contain a significant element of additional detail, and quite importantly some financial data. The financial details illustrate the actual net works costs of manufacture, minus any packing, delivery or commission charges, followed by the total cost ex-works which includes any 'extras' agreed with the customer, delivery charges for example, and then the final selling price. Profit and loss on individual locomotives can therefore, be gleaned from these sources. One of the books contains additional details on boilers, listing the material used in both firebox and tubes, doubtless because this would have had a major effect on the costs - copper verses steel fireboxes for example. As well as the financial information this book has a further column headed Date Finished, which research would seem to indicate is actually the date the locomotives were despatched from the works. A particular feature of this book is its title on the first page - *Locomotives Completed to December 31 1892* - as in fact, it continues to list locomotives built until the final entry for E No

1884 of 1908. It also contains a summary by cylinder size of the quantity of locomotives built each year, up to and including 1892. However, the nature of the handwriting and the level of detail against the earlier entries in these two books, would lead one to suspect that, like the registers, they were copied from some other source - at least the entries prior to 1892. After this date they appear to have been compiled concurrently. On the inside of the front cover of one of them in Gordon Bagnall's own handwriting appears the following statement: 'As this book is large enough to last a hundred years (although entries finish in 1908, there is plenty of room left) it should be of the best quality. I notice that the best books are ordered for short use and the worst for long which makes no sort of common sense'. Clearly an admonishment for somebody; the book is indeed somewhat battered!

Despite the scarcity of information in the registers and books mentioned above it is indeed fortunate that the late Ralph Russell, an extremely diligent locomotive historian specialising in the British private locomotive building industry, made it his business to study the history of WG Bagnall Limited. Detailed mention is made of his efforts in the Acknowledgements, suffice it to say here that in numerous visits to the works and with the permission and good-will of the then management, Ralph was able to examine a whole plethora of other material that subsequently disappeared. From his researches Ralph made extensive notes which later came into the authors possession and these have been of enormous help in compiling this book. Nevertheless, even Ralph was unable to unearth anything very much pertaining to locomotives built before about 1892, other than what appears in the registers and the other books outlined above - except that is, for a few orders for spare parts. It can only be assumed therefore, that whoever copied the information into the records that have survived, as well as those seen by Ralph that do not appear to have survived, used sources that themselves omitted much of the detailed information on the early locomotives.

Virtually no drawings of the early locomotives have survived, except for the odd one drawn at a later date when it had been found necessary to fulfil a spare part order. Quite what form the original early records took is therefore somewhat of a mystery, along with of course, what may have happened to them. Nevertheless it is fortunate for historians that WG Bagnall himself, being such an excellent salesman went to great lengths to make people aware of his business. Great efforts were made to publicise the products, in particular the locomotives and not only in the lavish catalogues already mentioned, but also in the contemporary press. For example the journals *Engineering* and *The Engineer*, *Implement & Machinery Review*, *The Colliery Guardian* and *Iron*, all contain extremely useful articles for our purposes that were often accompanied by engravings and drawings of the locomotives. Gordon Bagnall appears to have realised almost from the day he started in business, the vast potential for publicity in having exhibition stands at for example, the Royal Agricultural Society of England Shows - as had Massey & Hill before him when they exhibited at Bedford in 1874. Bagnall exhibited machinery, including locomotives at the Royal shows held at Birmingham in 1876, Liverpool in 1877, Bristol in 1878, Kilburn in 1879, Derby in 1881, Reading in 1882, Shrewsbury in 1884 and Windsor in 1889. Exhibiting at these shows had the added advantage for historians as the shows themselves were always reported in the trade journals of the time, often with detained descriptions of the exhibits together with illustrations. And of course there are the show catalogues, copies of which survive in the library of the Royal Society.

It is also worth noting that Bagnall did not confine himself to exhibiting his products at events in this country. From early December 1883 until 10 March 1884 a large exhibition of machinery was held at Calcutta in India. Bagnall sent a complete narrow-gauge railway for exhibition at Calcutta and the organisers allocated a prime location so he was able to lay a two-foot gauge railway around a lake, which was itself the centre piece of the exhibition ground. As well as a locomotive, passenger and goods vehicles were exhibited and the railway consisted of the maker's portable rails, sleepers and other fittings. The equipment served a useful purpose too, in transporting visitors around a part of the exhibition site. Although there is no evidence to prove one way or the other if Bagnall himself went to India during the period this show was running, certainly somebody from the firm must have attended and he may well gone himself, at least for part of the time. The engine exhibited was eventually supplied to Messrs Walsh Lovett &

Company Limited, a company trading as merchants and commission agents and based in Ludgate Hill, Birmingham. This Company is known to have traded as agents in India, although nothing survives in the records to indicate where, or for what the locomotive was subsequently used. John Fowler & Company of Leeds, as well as the French manufacturer of light railway equipment Decauville Aine, also exhibited locomotives and other light railway material at the exhibition which attracted no less than 630,000 visitors during the three months it was staged.

Gordon Bagnall was one of the very few manufacturers to exhibit locomotives and light railway material at the Royal Agricultural Society of England shows (RASE); moreover, he was the first manufacturer to actually exhibit a locomotive - he had one on his stand at Liverpool in 1877. The company that is perhaps, considered the original protagonist of light railways as we know them today, certainly one using all-metal components (Decauville's Patent Iron Carrier, as the contempory advertisements have it), was the French firm of Decauville Aine of Petit Bourg, Seine et Oise; the name Decauville becoming synonymous with portable and semi-portable narrow-gauge light railways the world over. This Company dates from 1853 and whilst originally manufacturing sugar refining machinery, under the management of Paul Decauville, the son of the founder Amand Decauville, developed a system of narrow-gauge light railways in the autumn and winter of 1875-6. This initiative was the result of a very wet autumn in 1875 when it proved almost impossible to harvest the French sugar beet crop by conventional horse and cart, and the Decauvilles themselves had a large sugar beet estate of their own. Temporary railway lines were therefore quickly designed by Paul Decauville, and they were laid in a number of locations. Such was the success of these light railways that the Company started to develop a business in manufacturing light railway equipment.

Decauville first exhibited at the RASE shows at Liverpool in 1877, as in that year he had entered into an agreement with John Fowler & Company of Leeds, to manufacture light railway equipment and rolling stock under licence in this country, and his equipment appeared on the Fowler stand. This was also the case with the equipment exhibited on the Fowler stand at Bristol in 1878 and Kilburn the following year. The

Leeds Company is perhaps better known for its road steam engines, and in particular its steam ploughing equipment, the development of which it was a pioneer. The Company was already known to Paul Decauville, having supplied him with steam ploughing tackle, and in fact, from 1867, Decauville had been licensed by Fowler to build ploughing implements at its works in France; this did not however, include the ploughing engines themselves. Later Fowler developed its own light railway track and equipment, outside the Decauville licence agreement, and in the case of locomotives these were always to its own designs.

It was not long before Paul Decauville turned his attention to small light weight steam locomotives, but the first locomotives were built for him by the Paris firm of L Corpet in 1878, whilst the Belgium builder Couillet built some too; it was some years later before the Decauville company itself built any steam locomotives. However, in actual fact the first Bagnall locomotive designed for use on a light railway pre-dated the initial Decauville developments in locomotive power. Paul Decauville also exhibited his light railway equipment on his own stands at some of the RASE shows, first appearing at Reading in 1882 (as did Fowler) with no less than 35 exhibits. The exhibits consisted of light railway track, fixtures and fittings, several different types of wagons and various other light railway equipment, but no locomotives. There were further Decauville displays at York in 1883 and Shrewsbury in 1884, but at none of the shows was a locomotive on exhibition; in fact Decauville never did exhibit a steam locomotive on any of his stands. The agents for the Decauville Company in this country were Messrs R. von Glehn & Sons of 7 Idol Lane, Great Tower Street, London EC.

John Fowler & Company, with its significant agricultural machinery business, was a prolific exhibitor at each years show and a light railway exhibit of one sort or another - but rarely a locomotive - usually accompanied the other exhibits. In fact Fowler locomotives were only on exhibition at Kilburn in 1879 and Preston in 1885. At Kilburn Fowler also displayed a narrow-gauge light railway of two-foot gauge which was laid right through the centre of the show ground and on this line a locomotive and a selection of passenger vehicles were kept running the whole time the show was open. This was fortunate because this event was marred by absolutely awful weather such the whole show ground degenerated into a veritable quagmire with the railway providing an excellent method for the visitors to get about! The other manufacturers to have exhibited light railway equipment at the RASE shows were J&F Howard of the Britannia Iron Works in Bedford, and William A Stone of Prague - then a part of Austria. Howards were another firm like Fowlers, specialising in steam powered agricultural machinery, but also manufactured light and narrow-gauge railway equipment. J&F Howard first exhibited light railway equipment, including wagons, at the Preston show in 1885, but thereafter became quite a consistent exhibiter. In later years the firm also designed and built small petrol and diesel locomotives. William A Stone had nine exhibits at Windsor in 1889, the only show he attended, consisting of 'field railways' and wagons manufactured by R Dolberg of Rostock for which he acted as agent. Worth a brief mention at this point is a series of three narrow-gauge Bagnall locomotives that were supplied to an order from Stone in 1889. It is interesting to speculate if this order was negotiated with Gordon Bagnall at the show; in any event we can be pretty sure, the astute character he was, that he would have taken the opportunities presented at the shows to have a good look at his competitors products!

Gordon Bagnall was one of the few railway engineers of the day to place so strong an emphasis on the potential benefits that the use of light railways in agriculture could bring. Shortly after he started business as a railway engineer he seems to have realised the potential commercial advantage in supplying not just locomotives and rolling stock for light railways, but in effect complete light railway systems. In fact everything from the locomotives to the humble water column and for all sorts of traffic, be it general goods, minerals, plantation type operations and even passenger carrying. In particular he emphasised the advantages of lightweight portable track materials that could be moved about easily and quickly to suit farm and plantation developments, as well as contractors construction sites. Bagnall advertised his firm's products and ability far and wide and in all sorts of journals and the contemporary press; he used both specialist technical journals and others covering a wide range of interests. Adverts appeared in the journals already mentioned as well as for example: *Machinery Market, Contract Journal, Industries, The Timber Trades Journal, The Mechanical World & Steam Users Journal, London Iron Trade Exchange* and the much more unlikely, *The Country Gentlemen's Estate Book* and *Bells Weekly Messenger,* to name but a few. He let few opportunities pass to advocate the cause of light railways and his name often appeared in the correspondence columns of journals like those mentioned above, whenever such issues were being debated. Frequently he managed to get articles, as

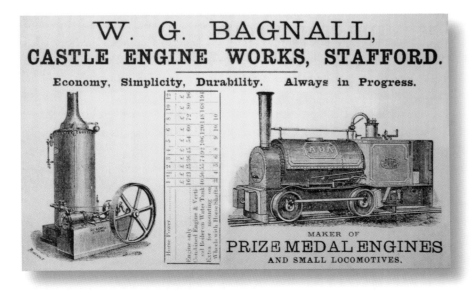

ADA was only the second locomotive in the registers, number 94, despatched in September 1877, but not before being exhibited at the Royal Agricultural Society of England Show at Liverpool in May that year. Ordered in April, construction must have been quite quick, and presumably for stock with the intention of meeting the show date; it later worked at Maesarddafen Colliery near Llanelly in South Wales. The illustration is part of a Bagnall advert that appeared in Phillips Register of New & Second-Hand Machinery mentioned in the text. The vertical boiler and horizontal engine combined are part of the Bagnall Challenge range, to which the table of sizes and costs refer. This advert appeared in the edition of the Register dated 1 June 1878.

opposed to advertisements, about his products in a whole range of publications and this was not only in this country as there are examples in: *The Australia & New Zealand Gazette; The Federal Australian; Moniteur Industriel & L'Ingenieur* (French) and *Annalen Fur Gewerbe Und Bauwesen* (Dutch). Not to be forgotten and another profitable source was *The British Mail*, a paper that circulated widely throughout the English speaking countries as well as just about everywhere where British enterprise existed. *The Federal Australian* by the way, in an 1879 article mentions a company called Aird & McCrae, described as colonial agents acting for Bagnall, although there is no surviving evidence that this company brought any business to Stafford. Gordon Bagnall was also willing to present papers to learned and other societies on the subject of light railways; in these he advocated his views very strongly. For example he presented a paper with the title: *Locomotion Past & Present*, to the Stafford Institute Field Club at its meeting on May 30 1881. On another occasion in the summer of 1895, he presented a paper titled: *Light Railways in Agricultural Districts*, to the Staffordshire Chamber of Agriculture - and there were others.

The Royal Agricultural Society of England mentioned earlier was established in 1838 (as The English Agricultural Society - its Royal charter was granted in March 1840) and from the following year held an annual show at varying locations around the country. With the development of machinery and in particular the steam engine, these shows gradually gained a reputation for being just about the principal show case for machinery developments of all kinds; the machines exhibited by a whole range of manufacturers were by no means exclusively for agricultural use. Obviously the burgeoning steam road traction and portable engine building industry were prolific exhibiters, but Bagnall very soon formed the view that they would be useful events to advertise his products too. To this end he joined the Society and as we have already seen attended his first show at Birmingham in 1876. There were seven Bagnall exhibits at this show consisting of an Empress horizontal engine and boiler of three horsepower (for sale at £80); a Challenge engine and boiler of similar configuration but of only two horsepower (available at £53); a 4½in double ram and a 2in single ram Stafford vertical steam pump and boiler

combined (these cost £50 and £15 respectively): a Stubb's Patent brick making machine (cost £150); a 10 horsepower engine (cost £80) and a cast iron tank which was said not to be for sale! At the next show he attended which was at Liverpool in early May 1877, he exhibited for the first time a locomotive and his stand at this event had seven exhibits. They consisted of four sizes of the Challenge combined engine and boiler embracing one, two, three and four-horsepower examples, along with a separate six-horsepower Challenge engine. There was also a 2in ram Stafford steam pump and of particular interest, a small 22in gauge locomotive. This locomotive was only the second one to appear in the registers, manufacturer's number 94 ADA, of which more anon. Attendance at this show by the way, which ran for eight days, totalled 138,354.

The following year at Bristol Bagnall was more conservative and only exhibited three models of Challenge engines, one each of three and four-horsepower and in both cases combined with vertical boilers, as well as another of eight-horsepower but in this case without a boiler. Once again however, he exhibited a small narrow-gauge locomotive, in this case manufacturer's number 138 which carried the name DEE. Attendance was down on the numbers that attended at Liverpool the previous year, with a recorded figure of 122,042 - but on this occasion the show only ran for six days. However, at Kilburn in June the following year Bagnall was at his most ambitious, with no less then 19 exhibits making the Bagnall stand the largest display of vertical and horizontal steam engines at the show. There were six Challenge engines and boilers combined, nine Challenge engines on their own - the largest of 12 horsepower - two vertical boilers, one with cross tubes, and two locomotives. The locomotives were number 210 which was named BRICK, along with the one from the previous year - number 138 named DEE. This show, despite extremely bad weather during the whole seven day period it was staged, nevertheless had an almost record attendance of 187,323, which was almost certainly the result of its location in London.

At the Derby show in July 1881 the stand contained two Challenge engines, one with a boiler and one without, along with an eight-horsepower compound engine with a horizontal boiler, a selection of components of a portable railway and once again a

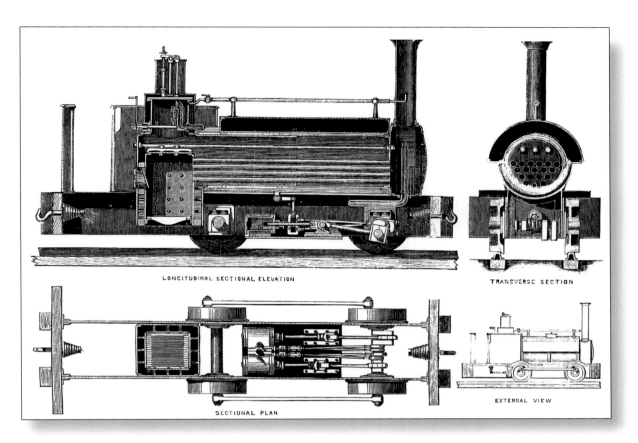

LONGITUDINAL SECTIONAL ELEVATION

TRANSVERSE SECTION

SECTIONAL PLAN

EXTERNAL VIEW

Engraving of ADA as it appeared in The Engineer, issue dated 3 January 1879. This illustrates well the 'reverse' arrangement of cylinders and motion driving the leading axle and mounted on a sub-frame which could, according to the accompanying description: 'be easily disconnected and taken away for repairs and replaced without any chance of error'. The short article also describes the engine as being one 'divested of all details not absolutely necessary and designed especially for use on light railways, tramways and contractors work'. There followed an extremely comprehensive list of dimensions suggesting that detailed working drawings must have existed; no such however, for this or any other of the other early locomotives appear to have survived.

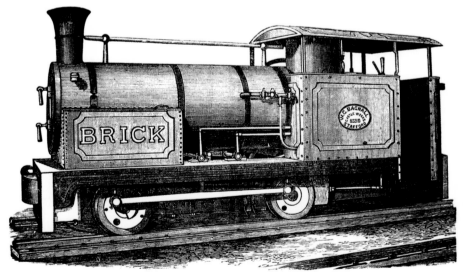

BAGNALL'S SMALL LOCOMOTIVE.

Another of the 'reverse' cylinder locomotives was BRICK, number 210 despatched in March 1879 to the Beckenham & Penge Brickworks in Kent for use on a 1ft 8in gauge railway system there. Notice how these locomotives have a long coupled wheelbase with the leading axle right at the front. Like ADA, BRICK was also exhibited at a RASE show, in this case at Kilburn in June 1879. As the engine had already been set to work by this date it was, according to contemporary press reports, loaned by the owners of the brick works so that Bagnall could exhibit it. Unlike ADA this engine has an inverted saddle tank, the tank in this case passing underneath the smokebox and doubling up as its saddle.

locomotive. In this case the locomotive was manufacturer's number 358 and the only locomotive exhibited by any manufacturer at the show; moreover, it was 'in motion but stationary'! From this we can perhaps infer that the engine was in steam and had been jacked up with its wheels clear of the ground! When the same locomotive was exhibited at the Staffordshire Agricultural Society Show held at Stafford in September, it was running on a small circle of portable track and with two small carriages gave rides to many of the visitors who attended the show. At the Reading Royal Show in July 1882, Bagnall again limited himself to four exhibits, in this case consisting of a Challenge engine and boiler, a 12 horsepower horizontal boiler, several small narrow-gauge wagons and a portable railway along with, once again, a small locomotive. The exact identity of the particular locomotive on this occasion does not appear to have been recorded, but is more than likely to have been one of either number 418 or 434. Both these two were new at the time of the show, and otherwise on-hand.

There was then a gap in Bagnall's attendance at the Royal shows until Shrewsbury in July 1884 where, according to the show catalogue, there were four exhibits. In the catalogue these are listed as a three-horsepower Challenge engine and boiler combined, along with four and five-horsepower Challenge engines, but in these cases without boilers. The catalogue also

lists a locomotive as being on the Bagnall stand, but according to contemporary press reports there were in fact two locomotives, along with examples of narrow-gauge sugar cane and tipping wagons. The locomotives were manufacturer's numbers 434 named MENDIP - which may have been at Reading the pervious year - and 512 named SOUDAN. The last Royal Show that Bagnall attended was the Windsor Show in June 1889, where the stand had no less than nine exhibits but only one of these was a stationary engine - a four-horsepower Universal example. The other exhibits were all railway related, perhaps indicative of the changing fortunes of the Bagnall business. They consisted of three different types of tipping wagon, one being an end tipper, a turntable, sections of portable railway, cast chilled wheels and two locomotives. One of the locomotives was specially named WINDSOR for the show, manufacturer's number 1092, and the other possibly number 1122.

If contemporary press reports at the time of these various shows are to be believed, then they provide evidence that a significant number of orders were obtained by Bagnall for his products. In particular mention is made of orders from farmers and others for stationary engines and pumps, rather than for locomotives and railway equipment. Perhaps this was why, as the firm concentrated more and more on the locomotive and railway side of the business, at the

WINDSOR was so named for exhibition at the RASE show at Windsor Park in June 1889. Number 1092 it is one of the later four-coupled inverted saddle tank engines that became popular with contractors. Ordered in March 1889 and fitted with 8x12in cylinders, it only seems to have carried its name for the purpose of the exhibition and may have been originally laid-down to stock. It was eventually despatched in November the same year to fulfil an order by Kerr, Stuart & Company, which at this period had no manufacturing facilities of its own, but the end customer and destination are unknown.
There are a number of conflicting entries in the registers for this locomotive, but whilst it appears to have been built to suit a track gauge of three-foot, when despatched it had been altered to suit the metre-gauge. Likewise, whilst India appears in one register as a destination, the engine is known to have actually worked in Malaya, although it may of course, have been moved from one country to the other.

MESSRS. BAGNALL'S LOCOMOTIVE.

This is number 1092 again, at work in Malaya. The photograph was taken in September 1904, when the locomotive was being used by Hill & Rathbone, the contractors engaged in construction of the extension southwards of the Sungei Ujong Railway in Negoi Sembilan, to link with the Johore State Railway at Gemas. Unlike earlier lines in Malaya, the Sungei Ujong Railway was a private concession, since the State of Ujong could not afford to build it as a public sector investment. The line ran from Seremban to Port Dickson and opened on 28 July 1891. The State of Sungei Ujong became a part of the State of Negri (now spelt Negeri) Sembilan in 1895; however, the Sungei Ujong Railway retained its independence until it was taken over by the Federated Malaya States Railway in 1908. The State Railway line from Kaula Lumper southwards to Johore Bahru (for the Johore Straits and Singapore Island) was opened in 1909; from that date the Port Dickson line became a branch. The photograph shows a construction train, perhaps taking the men to site, or are they just posing for the photographer, at Remban (now spelt Rembau) Station which is just south of Seremban and where what later became the branch line to Port Dickson left the main line. The engine's ultimate fate has gone unrecorded. (Collection John Benson)

expense of stationary engines and other machinery likely to find favour in agriculture, Bagnall stopped attending the Royal shows.

There is a particularly interesting aspect of Bagnall exhibiting at the Royal shows well worth exploring before we move on and this is perhaps, an opportune juncture to do so. It concerns a disagreement Gordon Bagnall had with the Officials of the RASE. In Victorian times this Society appears to have been wonderfully authoritarian and of the 114 shows held between 1839 and 1962, no less than 68 of them lost money, leaving one speculating how the Society came to last so long! The 1879 Kilburn event seems to have been a complete fiasco due to the weather and from the point of view of the Society, as it lost £15,000, a large sum of money in those days. One of the accepted practices of the Officials appears to have been to treat exhibitors almost like children with an ever-changing set of rules and fines for those who transgressed! At

Kilburn an enterprising group of exhibitors 'borrowed' a quantity of railway sleepers from a nearby London & North Western Railway stockpile to help make a roadway to the site, which was otherwise disappearing into the quagmire mentioned earlier, as the show was held during a very wet period. Attempts were then made by the Officials to identify the delinquents - whilst one might have expected them to be rewarded! At Reading in 1882 with the weather forecast again projecting a wet period, the Officials attempted to guard against a repetition (the Great Western Railway presumably being the target on this occasion) by insisting that all exhibits were on site at least a week before the show started. Bagnall of course, being one of the delinquents (undiscovered it has to be added!) at Kilburn, did not bother himself with this, in his view yet another 'new' rule, and together with his exhibits he only turned up five days before the event. As a result he was, somewhat predictably, turned away. As if this was not bad enough he subsequently found out that other exhibiters - friends of the Officials - had been allowed on site despite not appearing until two days before the start. So, after some long and acrimonious discussions and arguments he was eventually allowed on site - one wonders where he 'camped' in the meantime!

These events left a nasty taste in Bagnall's mouth and thereafter, irrespective of any other motives, he often vetoed the shows. He also wrote a number of letters for the correspondence columns of the contemporary press on what were in his view, the ill-gotten ways of the

Society, for example in *The Engineer*, issue dated 7 July 1882, his letter inferring he was not allowed onto the show at Reading whilst in fact he was. These actions cannot have endeared him to those in charge, but he seems to have later patched up his differences, at least sufficiently to exhibit at Shrewsbury in 1884, and more importantly at the Windsor Show in 1889. Bagnall would have been particularly enthusiastic to have a stand at Windsor in view of its extra publicity value; not only was it the 50th anniversary of the Society, but no less than Queen Victoria herself had agreed to be president - hence the location. But it was his last! In

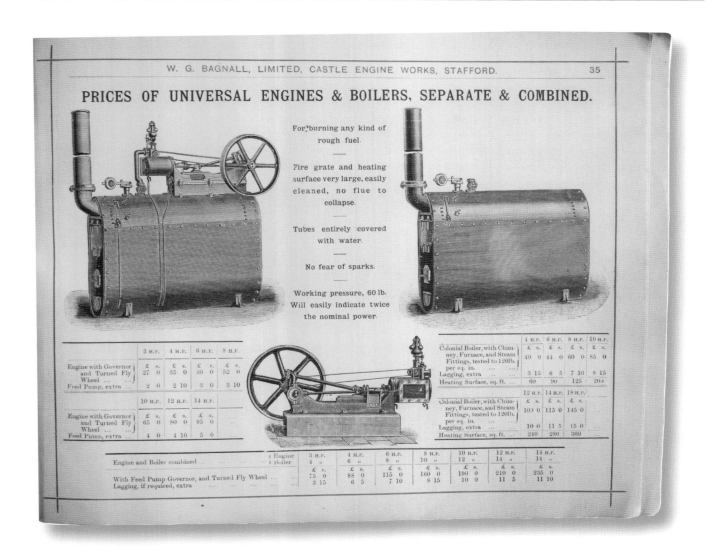

This is a page from catalogue 10 of May 1888, illustrating the Universal engines and boilers, one of which Bagnall exhibited on his stand at Windsor in 1889.

fact he had resigned his membership of the Society after the Shrewsbury show but he did join again for a short period to cover the 1889 event!

Two distinct and almost unique features characterised many of the early locomotives. One was what Bagnall called an under-tank, but we shall use the more familiar term inverted saddle tank, the other the arrangement of cylinders and motion mounted between the wheel sets and driving the leading axle - this will be referred to as the 'reverse cylinder arrangement'. However before doing so the first locomotive to appear in the registers needs to be described and as it took the number 16, the inference is that the firm had completed 15 orders of one sort or another earlier. Described as four-wheels coupled, standard-gauge, cylinders variously as 7½ or 7⅝in diameter - depending on which register is consulted - with a stroke of 11in, the wheelbase was 4ft 6in and a copper firebox and brass tubes were fitted. Ordered in May 1876 and finished December the same year the eventual selling price is quoted as £600. Two of the registers quote in the customer column just 'South Wales', presumably indicating a destination, but one register has Chaplin & Horne as the customer. All however, quote the engine's name as BUCKINGHAM. It would seem from available evidence that Bagnall built this locomotive without a positive order, doubtless as a speculative venture. This assumes that it was in fact actually built at Stafford in the light of the statement by ST Price quoted in the previous Chapter. As will be observed from the dimensions quoted BUCKINGHAM was by no means a large locomotive, indeed the boiler would not have been much bigger than those used for the bigger versions of the Challenge stationary engine range. It would seem quite plausible that if the Challenge engine boilers were actually made at the Castle Engine Works, which is nevertheless by no means certain, then the boiler for this first locomotive may well have been built there too.

About the time the engine was completed the Duke of Buckingham was looking for additional motive power for his Wotton Tramway in Buckinghamshire. At this period motive power on the tramway consisted of two Aveling & Porter traction engine type locomotives and the available evidence suggests they were proving to be relatively unsuccessful. Whilst this design of locomotive, which was in effect a traction engine,

mounted on rail wheels with a roller chain drive, may have had some merit for shunting purposes and where light axle-loads were essential, it was not so successful for longer journeys. In any event it would seem to have been the requirement for a very light axle load that prompted the use of this type of locomotive on the Wotton Tramway, as the light weight track weighed but 30lb per yard. The Wotton Tramway would appear to have been the only railway to use this form of traction engine type locomotives for 'line', as opposed to shunting work. The Tramway ran some three and three quarter miles from Quainton Road on the Aylesbury & Buckingham Railway to Wotton; it was built to serve the Duke's estates and was formally opened by him on 1 April 1871. In April 1872 it was extended for a further two and three quarter miles to Brill and there was a one and three quarter mile branch to Moate Farm. The original motive power was by horse with the first Aveling & Porter locomotive arriving in January 1872; its sister arrived in June.

At the time the first Bagnall locomotive was built the Duke of Buckingham was the Lord Lieutenant of Staffordshire, along with of course, many other commitments. In this capacity he would almost certainly have been known to the Bagnall family, if by no other means through his political activities, and it is not beyond the bounds of possibility that the two families were more than just acquainted. The Duke as a member of the House of Lords, and Sir Thomas Salt as the local Member of Parliament, would also be known to each other and we have seen how Thomas Salt knew the Bagnalls. Somewhere in this tangle of acquaintances and relationships is the most probable way the Duke became aware, of a small light-weight locomotive Bagnall had available that might just be ideal for his tramway. We also know from his later writings that Bagnall himself visited the tramway. In any event, this little locomotive was working on the Wotton Tramway by 1 January 1877 - hence its name recorded in the registers as BUCKINGHAM. Moreover, it seems to have been a success, or in any event more so than the Aveling & Porter engines and the manager of the tramway was impressed. He recorded that the locomotives was capable of hauling 60 tons from Quainton Road to Wotton and 30 tons on the return journey, easily managing 30 tons on the steep gradient of 1 in 50 between Wotton and Brill. The engine is known to have been employed on the tramway until March 1878 when it was replaced by a second Bagnall locomotive; in this case one purchased specifically, as it appears BUCKINGHAM had only been on hire. The cost of hiring BUCKINGHAM up until August 1877 amounted to £600, but once a second locomotive had been ordered from Bagnall the continued use of BUCKINGHAM was free of charge, at least until the new engine was delivered. This figure of £600 would appear to be why this same figure appears in one of the order books mentioned earlier, ostensibly as a selling price. At the time BUCKINGHAM was on hire the Duke's agents were Messes Chaplin & Horne and the obvious assumption is, that this is the reason for the entry of their name as the customer in one of the registers. We can perhaps deduce from these events that Bagnall almost certainly agreed to loan BUCKINGHAM for trials on the tramway, and that its success over the Aveling & Porter engines led to an order for a new locomotive. After the new engine was delivered BUCKINGHAM was returned to Stafford.

Such evidence as is available suggests that on return to Stafford BUCKINGHAM was overhauled, or at least repaired, before being advertised for sale. In *The Engineer*, issue dated 9 August 1878 we read: 'For sale or hire, locomotive BEE, 7½in cylinders, standard-gauge, boiler Lowmoor iron, copper firebox and brass tubes, short wheelbase, saddle tank, 120 lbs pressure, only done 14 months work, £400'. There is little doubt that this is a reference to BUCKINGHAM, but why it was renamed BEE is a mystery. A photograph exists taken at the Castle Engine Works of what might just be this locomotive with the painted name TARGET on the saddle tank. Presumably, if the photograph does depict BUCKINGHAM, it must have returned to the works once again and for some sort of attention, perhaps after another period of hire as it appears to be in a pretty rough condition. Nothing further has ever been uncovered on the ultimate fate of this locomotive, and the photograph may be of an entirely different one. The reference to South Wales in one of the registers might suggest that at some stage in the engine's career it was either sold or hired to a customer in that part of the Wales. For a standard-gauge locomotive BUCKINGHAM had a surprisingly short wheelbase recorded in the registers, shorter in fact than the track gauge. If the illustration of TARGET is one and the same as BUCKINGHAM, then number 16 was a conventional four-wheeled saddle tank with outside cylinders and inside frames. However, the engine in the photograph appears to have a circular firebox and a wheelbase somewhat longer than 4ft 6in; this suggests it may not on balance be BUCKINGHAM at all, but an engine of some other builder at Stafford for repairs of other attention. Bagnall is known to have advertised his willingness to repair other builders locomotives, as well as taking them in part-exchange for new ones. On occasions he even advertised locomotives for sale on behalf of what he called 'his friends', in cases where he had himself supplied a new one.

The next locomotive listed in the registers and the following three narrow-gauge ones were all four-coupled with no carrying axles and fitted with the reverse cylinder arrangement briefly mentioned above. Cylinders were inside the frames driving the leading axle and the advantages claimed by Bagnall for this arrangement were: 'it will be seen that all the working parts are between the side plates and are fixed by a pair of angle irons. This makes a rigid connection of the whole frame and as the plate in which the parts are fixed is only fastened by turned bolts and not riveted, the whole of the working parts are easily disconnected and taken away for repairs and replaced without chance of error'. By way of further explanation, the whole assemblage of the cylinders and valve chests were mounted on a plate, which equalled the width between the frame plates and was fixed to them using the fitted bolts referred to along with angle irons. Of course, with this arrangement, to accommodate the cylinders, slide bars and motion between the axles, the coupled wheelbase had of necessity to be much longer than with a more conventional configuration.

In the case of the first of the four locomotives - manufacturer's number 94 named ADA - the wheelbase was 4ft 3in, and as the track gauge of this locomotive was only 1ft 10in, the point about a long wheelbase will become apparent. ADA had a conventional saddle tank; cylinder dimensions were 4x6in, the wheel diameter was 1ft 6in and it was 'finished' in September 1877. This was the locomotive exhibited by Bagnall at the RASE show at Liverpool in July, before being sold to W Rees. An article describing ADA in *The Engineer* - issue dated 3 January 1879 - tells us it had been working for about eighteen months on a narrow-gauge colliery and ironworks tramway in South Wales. The location of this 'colliery and ironworks' is almost certainly the Maesarddafen Colliery near Llanelly in South Wales, a colliery known to have had a 1ft 10in gauge railway and owned during the period in question by a Mr Rees. This is the same gauge as ADA, and a testimonial recorded in one of the early company catalogues substantiates the view that the engine worked at Maesarddafen: 'I have been very pleased with the quality of the materials in the locomotive we have had from you and should like to do business with you again. After six years work. Llanelly 30 October 1885'. Maesarddafen Colliery closed in about 1887 and in the *Western Mail* for 1 August 1891, we find that CD Phillips, the Newport machinery dealer had for sale: 'EMLYN 53, 4½in cylinder locomotive by Bagnall, 4 wheels coupled and 22in gauge, very good condition £120'. This almost certainly refers to ADA, and is the last record of the locomotive it has been possible to trace. Emlyn was the name of Phillips works, and he often used it together with a number, to identify the engines and other products he had for sale.

The following three narrow-gauge locomotives as well as having the same arrangement of cylinders also had the inverted saddle tank. In this design the water tank passed under, rather than over the boiler, and in some cases it also helped to form the smokebox support saddle. Where this was the case there were apertures through the tank for the steam and exhaust pipes and the locomotives thus fitted gave the appearance of having more conventional wing, or as sometimes described, front tanks. For this arrangement Bagnall claimed: 'A special feature of the design is the position of the tank, which is placed under the smokebox end of the boiler, thus effecting good distribution of weight, the leading wheels carrying rather more than half the total load when the engine is full and rather less than half when the tank is empty. As compared with a saddle tank it has the advantage of allowing the boiler to be raised, without getting to a high centre of gravity, thus giving more room for getting at the motion etc., and enabling a deeper firebox to be used'. This arrangement of tank continued to be used over a long period of time on many of the four-coupled narrow-gauge locomotives; in some cases the tank was set back from the front of the locomotive and placed under the boiler rather than the smokebox, and in other examples it encompassed both the smokebox and part of the boiler barrel. However, on some of the larger locomotives, notably those built for standard-gauge, whilst photographs give the impression that inverted saddle tanks are employed, the tanks are in fact wing, or front tanks. As such the tanks do not continue underneath the smokebox or boiler, are completely separate, but connected together by a simple balance pipe.

The first of the three narrow-gauge locomotives with the reverse cylinders was manufacturer's number 128, despatched in December 1877 and built to suit a track gauge of 1ft 10½in; the cylinder dimensions were 5x7½in and the wheelbase five-foot. Named SISSY the customer is listed as Henry Lodge, and this would appear to be the Henry Lodge who owned Hill Main Colliery near Royston in South Yorkshire, where a 1ft 10½in gauge 'tramway' is known to have commenced operations in the period 1874-5. But nothing is known about the operations there or the little engine's ultimate fate

The second engine was manufacturer's number 138, despatched in March 1878, a three-foot gauge locomotive, like the earlier one with 5x7½in cylinders, but in this case a slightly shorter wheelbase of 4ft 9in; the weight in working order was four tons and the total boiler heating surface 90 sq ft. The name quoted in the registers is ERNEST, and the customer the River Dee Company, which fits with the name DEE that the engine is recorded as having carried when Bagnall exhibited it at the RASE show at Bristol in July 1878. There is an engraving illustrating this locomotive with the name DEE - reproduced here and from the journal *Iron*, issue dated 10 August that year - as a part of its report on the Bristol show. This is the same locomotive Bagnall exhibited at the following year's RASE show at Kilburn, which ties in nicely with an advert in *The Colliery Guardian*, issue dated 17 January 1879: 'For Sale, 3ft 0in gauge locomotive, ordered by a firm but not required owing to unforeseen circumstances, will be sold at a reduced price WG Bagnall'. *The Engineer*, which was published on the same date as *The Colliery Guardian*, has the following advert: 'For Sale new 3ft 0in gauge locomotive (cancelled order) WG Bagnall'. The inference is that the River Dee Company originally ordered the locomotive in November 1877, and may even have taken delivery, but in any event it remained on Bagnalls hands and he took the opportunity of exhibiting it at the two shows. Apparently the River Dee Company (this is the North Wales River Dee) started work in 1869, building a two-mile embankment to reclaim land in the river's estuary near Chester, but in 1877 part of the embankment was breached and despite desperate attempts to reseal it, the work was abandoned the following year. It may be that this little locomotive was ordered for work in connection with the resealing works and that when the job was abandoned it was returned to Stafford, later being sold with the name ERNEST. But there are no other clues in the surviving records as to what might have happened to it, or of any customers other than The River Dee Company.

Last of the trio was manufacturer's number 210, despatched in March 1879, a 1ft 8in gauge locomotive with 4x6in cylinders and a four-foot wheelbase; weight in working order was two tons and 16 cwt and the total boiler heating surface 52 sq ft. Built to a reduced loading gauge this small engine was but 4ft 10½in from rail level to chimney top and according to *Engineering* - issue dated 4 July 1879 - was designed to work in a tunnel with a minimum height of 5ft 1in. The journal goes on to say that the driver had perforce, to permanently occupy a sitting position. This locomotive, named appropriately BRICK, was

despatched new to the Beckenham & Penge Brickworks in Kent, which *The Implement & Machinery Review* tells us belonged to Messrs J Rhodes & Son of 17 Southwark Street, London. This firm loaned the engine so that Bagnall could exhibit it at the Kilburn show in 1879, where it could be seen alongside DEE. Quite why the owners were prepared to be without their new locomotive when Bagnall had the similar DEE to exhibit anyway, has gone unrecorded. The brickworks opened in 1878 and were situated at the junction of Kent House Lane and Kent House Road; originally it had been owned by a partnership of John G Rhodes and Frederick Cooper, but seems to have closed about ten years later; however it re-opened in 1895. According to a 'correspondent' writing in *The Railway Gazette* - issue dated September 1957 - BRICK later worked in Ireland at the Ravenhill Patent Brick & Tile Company in Belfast, but this has not been substantiated. An advert in the June 1898 issue of *The British Clayworker*, would appear to refer to this locomotive being for sale: '20in gauge locomotive, can be seen at the Brickworks, Kent House Road, Beckenham - very cheap having no use for same'. This is the last record we have.

To give an idea of the value of locomotives at this period it is worth exploring what these three locomotive cost to build, along with the price they were sold for.

For this engraving of number 138 DEE, we have to thank the journal Iron, issue dated 10 August 1878 reporting on the exhibits at the RASE Bristol show in July that year. The article accompanying the illustration tells us that the total heating surface of the boiler was 90 sq ft, the working pressure was 120 psi, and the weight in working order four tons. It goes on to say: 'The design and proportions of the engine are pleasing to the eye and the workmanship under our examination was very good indeed'. Notice the steam pipe for the blower, running along the top of the boiler, which doubled up as a handrail.

SISSY is recorded as having cost £246 1/ 6d (£246 7½p) to build, being sold for £360. ERNEST cost £279 19/- (£279 95p) to build and was sold for £345, whilst BRICK cost £236 9/ 7d (£236 48p) to build and was sold for £189 1/- (£189 5p). In this last case showing a loss of almost £50. The bigger standard-gauge engine WOTTON described in the next paragraph cost £524 3/ 1d (£524 15p) to build, with a selling price of £640. It was quite brave of Bagnall to enter the market for small narrow-gauge locomotives at the time he did as there were a number of firms already well established in the business. Mention has already been made of the activities of John Fowler & Company of Leeds and the French firm of Decauville, albeit the latter firm initially sub-contracted the building of locomotives; but this in itself indicates that other builders were active in the market too. There were also several other British manufacturers already in the field, including another Leeds based firm The Hunslet Engine Company, as well as for example, Sharp Stewart & Company then based in Manchester, the Avonside Engine Company in Bristol, Black, Hawthorn at Gateshead and Hawthorn, Leslie in Newcastle, to name but some of them. The success of the Castle Engine Works products however, seems to have stemmed from their comparatively low cost. Bagnall achieved significant success in pairing down the steam locomotive to its bare essentials and by these means, he was able to undercut his competitors, and very often by substantial margins.

These early reverse cylinder'locomotives have been dealt with in some detail in view of their unusual design, but we must now turn our attention to the third locomotive in the registers and the second one for the standard-gauge. We saw earlier how the Duke of Buckingham and his manager, having been impressed with the locomotive BUCKINGHAM he had on loan from Bagnall, ordered a new one. The order for manufacturer's number 120 was placed by the Wotton Tramway Company and the locomotive which was named WOTTON, was despatched in December 1877. This locomotive was an 0-4-0 with the reverse cylinders and an inverted saddle tank, although in this case the tank went under the boiler barrel immediately to the rear of the smokebox and not the smokebox itself. Cylinders were 8x12in, wheel diameter 2ft 6in, wheelbase 6ft 3in, weight in working order nine tons and 10 cwt and the total boiler heating surface

FOUR WHEEL COUPLED TANK LOCOMOTIVE ENGINE.

This Engine, which has lately been specially designed for Locomotive work, includes many advantages and improvements. To avoid any rocking, and to ensure steady running, the weight has been brought down between the frames, and as low as possible.

The tank rests on the frames and forms a support for the boiler. The cylinders are bolted rigidly to an angle plate, which acts as a stay between the frames ; so all the working parts can be seen from the foot plate when running, and also lubricated.

It will be seen by this design, that little or no overhanging is necessary, as in the ordinary class of outside cylinder Tank Engines.

A powerful screw brake is made to lock all the four wheels at the same time.

The engine is very simple, and has as few working parts as possible ; the detailed design can be seen on application to the works, when a tracing can be forwarded to all intending purchasers.

As in the case of smaller engines, certain particulars are required before a price can be given ; either copper or Lowmoor fire boxes, brass, steel, or iron tubes are supplied. Fire boxes are enlarged for abroad, where refuse wood, or other such fuel can only be obtained.

The fittings and mountings are complete, including draw bar and hook, fitted with spring at back, spring buffers, laminated springs for axles, &c.

See List of Prices at end of Catalogue.

W. G. BAGNALL, CASTLE ENGINE WORKS, STAFFORD.

Page from catalogue 2B, dated July 1878 illustrating number 120 WOTTON. Notice in the case of this locomotive the inverted saddle tank does not support the smokebox, but sits entirely under the boiler.

194 sq ft. This was indeed an unusual locomotive for the standard-gauge and again we must consider Samuel Price's statement mentioned earlier to the effect that this locomotive was not built at Stafford, or at least not in its entirety. It would appear however, that in view of its unusual features it was designed by Bagnall and his team and at the very least would have been assembled there. Mention was made earlier that perhaps some of the larger items, the boiler for example, might have been sub-contracted but it should be noted that as was the case with BUCKINGHAM, this was by no means a very big locomotive.

In the journal *The Engineer*, describing and illustrating ADA - issue of 3 January 1879 - there is a statement that: 'Engines similar to these (i.e. reverse cylinders) but of the 4ft 8½in gauge are made by Mr

Bagnall and two of them work the Wotton & Aylesbury line of the Duke of Buckingham'. However, as we have seen not only were the two locomotive unlikely to have been in use on the tramway at the same time, but BUCKINGHAM cannot have been of the reverse cylinder type in view of its short wheelbase. As might be expected having being specially designed for the purpose, WOTTON was a great success on the tramway and its mileage figures tell their own story. For example in 1878 the little engine is recorded as having achieved a total mileage of no less than 12,238, against a combined total of only 2,138 for the two Aveling & Porter locomotives. Positive details of its eventual fate nevertheless, have gone unrecorded, but it is known to have been in use on the tramway until 1894 at least. As a locomotive of relatively light construction and after almost 20 years work it is fair to assume it would have been in need of some pretty extensive attention. Nevertheless it seems probable that WOTTON is a locomotive occasionally advertised for sale by the machinery dealer Charles D Phillips (Machinery) Limited, by this date with operations in both Newport (Monmouthshire) and Gloucester. The Phillips company is known to have had an involvement with the tramway, as at least one locomotive was hired to it in the summer of 1893. Therefore it is quite likely that when the tramway acquired a locomotive to replace WOTTON in 1894, Phillips took the Bagnall in some

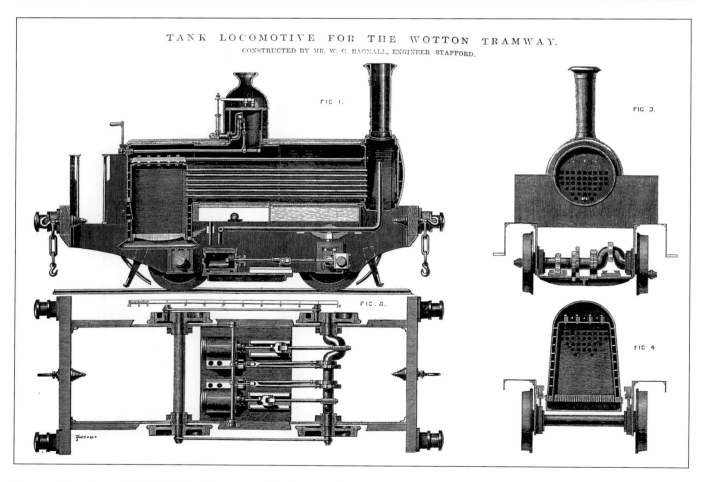

Engraved drawings of WOTTON as they appeared in the journal Engineering, issue of 3 January 1879. These drawings show well not only the reverse cylinder arrangement and the inverted saddle tank, but also what a simple machine this was. As with the feature on ADA that appeared in the sister journal The Engineer, an extremely comprehensive list of dimensions accompanied these drawings. We learn such fine details as for example that the travel of the valve was 2in; the width of the steam ports was ⁵/₈in and the throw of the eccentrics 2¹/₂in, along with much other intricate detail. Notice that the crank-axle if a forging; it is most unlikely that the Castle Engine Works at the time this engine was built would have had facilities to undertake such a forging

This is the only known photograph as opposed to an engraving, of WOTTON. The engine is seen with its mixed train about to leave Quainton Road station on the Wotton Tramway; this was the junction with the Aylesbury & Buckingham Railway, later part of the Great Central & Metropolitan Joint Line. The picture would seem to have been taken late in the engine's life on the Tramway, notice the split in the wooden buffer beam and lack of dome casing; the chimney also appears to have been modified. Notice too, that the engine is still without any protection for the crew. The crank-axle and eccentrics can just be discerned underneath the buffer beam.

a steel firebox and iron tubes, whilst they were copper and brass when new and perhaps this indicates that at some time heavy boiler repairs had been undertaken. This might have taken place when Phillips acquired the engine as part of a plan to make it saleable; whatever the case it does not appear to have been successful and we are left to assume that the locomotive was subsequently scrapped.

The next locomotive in the registers is manufacturer's number 265, and the engine's name is recorded as KENT. This little engine was a three-foot gauge 0-4-0 inverted saddle tank but in this case with a conventional cylinder layout allowing for a much shorter wheelbase; nevertheless the cylinders were still inside the frames on this and the next dozen or so locomotives. In the case of number 265 the cylinder dimensions were 6x9in and the wheelbase 3ft 6in; all the small four-wheeled locomotives however, which included the following 20 or so, were fitted with inverted saddle tanks. The movements of KENT are particularly interesting as the engine was originally ordered by a Kentish contractor named HB James; it was despatched to him in October 1879. At the time James was engaged on work for the South Eastern Railway at Hythe in Kent where the railway company

sort of deal, perhaps for example, in part payment of the hire charges. Phillips may also have been instrumental in providing the Tramway's replacement locomotive, as this was a second-hand one. An engine described as EMLYN No 86 (Emlyn as we saw earlier was the name of one of the Company sites) and fitting the description of WOTTON, recorded as built by Bagnall, appears consistently in the Phillips *Register* of plant for sale from 1902 to 1908. Phillips also included the same engine in its adverts in contemporary journals during the early years of the last century, and EMLYN No 86 last appears for sale in its January 1908 *Machinery Register*. On this occasion the engine was stated to be: 'in good condition, painted lined and varnished and in use'. If this statement is taken literally, perhaps Phillips had been using it as a yard shunting engine at Newport, indeed an earlier September 1902 *Register* entry states: 'in use in own yard'. In a last ditch attempt to sell the engine perhaps some paint and varnish had been applied! The engine is also quoted as being fitted with

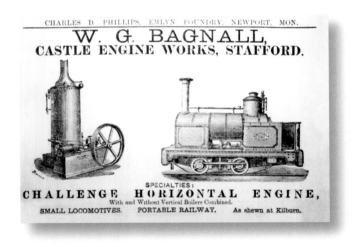

Another of the adverts that appeared in Phillips Machinery Registers, allows locomotive number 265 to be illustrated, once more accompanied by a Challenge combined engine and boiler. This is the locomotive named KENT, and the first of the small narrow-gauge locomotives with a conventional arrangement of cylinders, albeit still inside the frames. With an inverted saddle tank and large dome mounted on the firebox, the next dozen or so locomotives, externally at least, would have been very similar to this one.

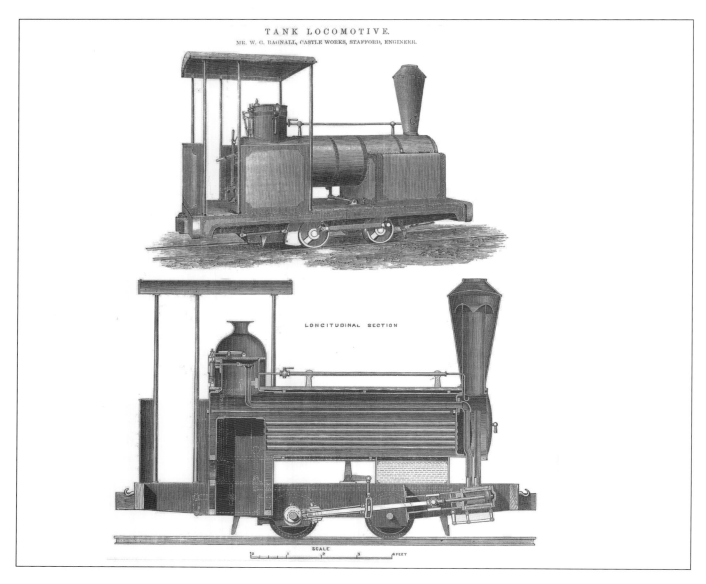

TANK LOCOMOTIVE.
MR. W. G. BAGNALL, CASTLE WORKS, STAFFORD, ENGINEER.

LONGITUDINAL SECTION

SCALE

Once again we are indebted to The Engineer for illustrations of what is almost certainly number 284 MERCEDITA, a 2ft 2in gauge locomotive new in January 1889 for Manlove Alliott & Company of Nottingham. The notes accompanying the illustrations mention that this design of locomotive could be supplied in three sizes. The number one size had 3½x6in diameter cylinders and 12in diameter wheels, and one of this size and 2ft 6in gauge was 'working on an overhead railway at Winsford'. This would be number 272 of December 1879, despatched to Stubbs Brothers who had a salt works at Winsford; according to the registers the cylinder stroke was 5¼in and the track gauge 2ft 7in. The notes go on to say that when tested on a rough portable railway the engine took five tons net up a 1 in 90 gradient despite only weighing two tons itself. The number two size had 6x9in cylinders, 1ft 8in diameter wheels and one of 3ft 0in gauge is described as working on an incline of 1 in 15 and taking loads of 3½ to 4 tons, the empty weight of the engine being four tons - this could be a reference to number 265. The number three size which is the one illustrated, had 4½x7½in cylinders, 1ft 3in diameter wheels, a wheelbase of 2ft 9in and working pressure 140 psi; the track gauge was 2ft 2in and this engine was one of several sent to sugar plantations and fitted with spark arresters. In the case of engines for use on sugar plantations the ashpans were made to contain water, a cock being provided to enable refills as necessary, and prevent any ashes that escaped from setting fire to the sugar cane. The engine illustrated was designed to take loads of five tons up inclines of 1in 25, running on 16lb per yard rail and around curves of 20ft radius, the engine itself weighing three tons in working order. Apparently, the proprietor of the sugar plantation where it was working had written to say: 'the engine can easily take up to 12 tons gross load on gradients from 3 to 4%, extending 400 yards, and we find no difficulty in keeping up steam. This would seem to confirm that in fact MERCEDITA was destined for a sugar plantation, although the next locomotive, number 285 of February 1880, which was of a similar size and despatched to Cuba, would almost certainly have also been for use on a sugar estate.

were building a large hotel on the sea front - The Imperial - it is still there today, albeit no longer railway owned. The works included a new road along the sea front towards Sandgate, complete with an embankment and sea wall as some land had to be reclaimed from the sea. To assist with the works James built a tramway in late 1879 and the little engine appropriately named KENT, was for use in connection with these works. On completion of the work James returned the engine to Stafford and after a period on hire to the Marland Brick & Clay Works in Devon during 1883, where it was named TUDOR, it was sold to another contractor by the name of Henry Fotherby & Sons. Fotherby used the engine on his contract to build the Cant Clough Reservoir near Burnley in Lancashire, where it was so employed along with two other Bagnall locomotives (manufacturer's numbers 840 and 902 of 1887) in January 1888. There is unfortunately no record of its ultimate fate on completion of this job, but it was probably scrapped.

The first order for a locomotive to be exported was in January 1880, and from a company mentioned in the last Chapter - Manlove Alliott & Company, Nottingham based manufacturers of stationary engines and other plant, in particular equipment for sugar estates and factories. The locomotive was allocated manufacturer's number 284, an inside cylinder 0-4-0 with an inverted saddle tank for 2ft 2in gauge. The cylinders dimensions were 4½x7½in and this quite small machine was despatched to the West Indies island of Porto Rico in January 1880 at cost of £250; it was named MERCEDITA. Correspondence with the Company in 1967, when it was still in business in Nottingham, could only suggest that any locomotives supplied would have been for re-sale to cane sugar plantations, possibly as part of a package of material to completely equip a new sugar factory. There is every possibility that at the same time this locomotive was delivered, Bagnall might also have supplied track work and wagons and that the sugar mill and plantation it was all destined for was named Mercedita. A testimonial in catalogue number 10 of May 1888, almost certainly concerns this locomotive. It quotes from a letter sent from Porto Rico and dated 8 January 1880; it reads - 'The engine can easily take up to 12 tons gross load on gradients from 3 to 4 percent, extending 400 yards and we find no difficulty in keeping steam up

with dried cane as fuel'. Added to this statement by who ever compiled the catalogue, is a note that the locomotive in question had 4½x7½in cylinders, and this pretty positively identifies the reference to MERCEDITA. The January date of the testimonial is interesting as the registers quote the locomotive as being finished in that month, so either the catalogue has the wrong date or the locomotive was actually delivered a short while earlier - or perhaps a very quick sea passage! In more recent times a sugar plantation and factory in what is now known as Puerto Rico, was owned by Central Mercedita Inc., and located at a place on the island called Mercedita - this would seem to be where the engine worked.

During the following few years there was an ever increasing series of orders for the type of small narrow-gauge locomotive like MERCEDITA, which the Company seems to have been successful in promoting - the majority of them being for export markets. Manufacturer's number 358 of February 1882 would appear to have been the first locomotive of a significantly different design, it had outside as opposed to inside cylinders and, as mentioned earlier, was exhibited at the RASE show at Derby in July 1881. This was still a design for a very small locomotive and this particular one had cylinders 4½x7½in, wheels 1ft 3in diameter and a weight in working order of just three tons and five cwt. Ordered in February 1881 it would seem that this locomotive was actually built for stock, possibly with exhibition at the show in mind, but if in fact this was the case, it seems strange that the unusual track gauge of 2ft 4in was chosen. In any event the locomotive was eventually sold to Figee Brothers of the Haarlem Engine Works in Amsterdam, a company acting as agents for Bagnall in Holland and the Dutch colonies. The firm of Gebr Figee, trading in this country as Figee Brothers, occasionally advertised around the period in question in the British technical press; they claimed to be engineers and in particular builders of cranes. Named TUNIS this little engine was despatched in February 1882 and was initially used by an Amsterdam based contractor by the name of C Langeveld, but later with a variety of other Dutch firms engaged on contract work. In August 1896 spares were ordered by Luis Smulders & Company, a company of Dutch engineers, at the time, undertaking some repairs to the engine. According to Dutch pressure vessel

LIGHT RAILWAY
BRENDON HILL MINES.   N° 8.

Although this is quite a familiar photograph, it is one of very few showing these early inside cylinder inverted saddle tank locomotives actually at work. The engine is seen here with a train of side-tip mineral wagons on the two-foot gauge railway of the Somerset Mineral Syndicate; this line served the Brendon Hill Mines in the Brendon hills south of Watchet. The operation dates from the period 1907 to 1910 so the picture would have been taken some time between these dates. The locomotive is almost certainly number 300, a two-foot gauge engine with 5x7½in cylinders new in June 1880 to WB Beauchamp and named TERRIER; it was sent to the Windsor Hill Quarries near Shepton Mallet. These quarries seem to have closed by 1889 and exactly what happened to the engine then is not known. There is a suggestion that the Syndicate, on acquiring the locomotive had it overhauled at the Castle Engine Works, but if this was the case there is no surviving record. However, in September 1907 and May 1908, the Syndicate did order spares from Bagnall for a two-foot gauge locomotive, but the surviving records give no manufacturer's number from which it could be positively identified - just quoting: 'has been used for tunnel work in a quarry'. In the illustration the locomotive has a chimney and cab of much later design than 1880, so it may well have been back to Stafford; nevertheless it is strange that a manufacturer's number was not quoted for the spares orders. After the quarries closed the engine was, apparently, sold for scrap fetching the princely sum of £20 on 28 June 1910. Very few of these early small locomotives were supplied for use in this country and this helps the conclusion that this one is almost certainty number 300.

records the boiler of the locomotive ceased to be insured in 1916, after which it is assumed the locomotive was scrapped.

There is however more to the history of this small locomotive because it was involved in some interesting activities before it was sold to Figee Brothers. Presumably as a result of its exhibition at the RASE Derby show, it was loaned to the Glyn Valley Tramway at Chirk in North Wales. The owners of this horse-worked tramway which, coincidently had a track gauge of 2ft 4in, were at the time of the show considering converting the tramway to use locomotives; clearly they must have felt a trial with a suitable locomotive would

be appropriate prior to making any decisions. The first trial on the tramway took place on 23 July 1881, and on 25th of the same month there was a further trip but in this case complete with passengers; presumably using one of the horse drawn tramcars. The locomotive was back at Stafford by September and whilst it appears the trials were successful, the tramway did not change over to locomotive haulage until some years later. The Glyn Valley Tramway commenced locomotive haulage in 1888, but this was not until some relatively extensive engineering work had been undertaken to improve the permanent way and its formation. This was to enable locomotives with much heavier axle-loads than little

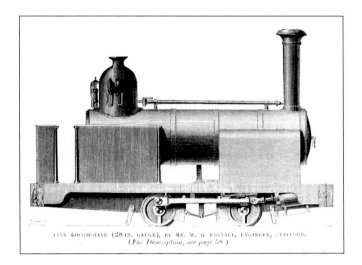

Vlissingen, Blikken Tunis

TANK LOCOMOTIVE (28 IN. GAUGE), BY MR. W. G. BAGNALL, ENGINEER, STAFFORD.
(For Description, see page 58.)

At the RASE show at Derby in July 1881 Bagnall exhibited this locomotive, an illustration taken from Engineering, issue dated 15 July 1881. This is number 358 and in all probability the first narrow-gauge locomotive built by the firm with outside cylinders. Note however, that it retains much of the rest of the early design characteristics, including the inverted saddle tank, dome on the firebox and brakes between the wheels.

This is number 358 again, seen here engaged on sewage construction work in the streets of Vlissingen (now Flushing) in Holland. By the time this photograph was taken the engine had acquired a very un-Bagnall cab and chimney, as well as a small auxiliary tender - but it still has its name TUNIS, apparently painted on the water tank. (Collection S de Lange; courtesy Hans de Herder)

TUNIS to be employed - they eventually came from the Gorton, Manchester based builder Beyer Peacock & Company Limited.

In yet another twist to the story of this locomotive, some reports in the contemporary press discussing the Derby show, where it was the only locomotive of any builder on display, quote it as carrying the name THE TIMES, rather than TUNIS. For example in *The Engineer* of 15 July 1881, it is quoted as TUNIS, while the *Contract Journal* of 27 July has it as THE TIMES. Press reports of the Glyn Valley Tramway trials also quote the engine's name as THE TIMES. On exhibition it may of course have had a different name on each side, and if it did in fact carry the name THE TIMES, this would almost certainly be that of the newspaper of that name and in view of the Walter family connection with *The Times*. Whatever the case and as briefly outlined in Chapter One, after the engine returned from the Glyn Valley Tramway it was exhibited as part of the Bagnall stand at the Staffordshire Agricultural Society Show at Stafford in mid September 1881. On this occasion a small circle of track was laid, the engine was in steam coupled to some passenger carrying vehicles the Company had built, and rides were given to the show visitors. Following this and a period

back at the works when it was advertised for sale, it was despatched to fulfil the Figee Brothers order in February 1882. Despite its unusual track gauge this locomotive would appear to have been built speculatively, unless that is it was always intended as a possibility for the Glyn Valley Tramway, and Bagnall took the opportunity to exhibit it at Derby first.

Design and development of larger locomotives soon followed and the first with six wheels appeared in 1882. Manufacturer's number 440 was an 0-6-0 with 8x12in cylinders and a nine-foot wheelbase; the cost in this case was £643 10/- (£643 50p) which returned profit of £86. A copper firebox and brass tubes were fitted and the track gauge was 2ft 6in; although the records are silent, it is assumed that this locomotive would have had side tanks. The customer was Denniston Cross & Company and despatch was in August 1882; named EL CONGRESO, unfortunately no destination is quoted in any of the surviving records, neither did this customer order any further locomotives. Perhaps surprisingly, considering it was the first locomotive built with six coupled wheels no illustration appears to have survived. The next two locomotives were the first ones built by the Company fitted with carrying wheels, manufacturer's numbers 450 and 451, new in

Numbers 450 and 451 were the first locomotives built with carrying wheels, but as can be seen from this engraving taken from The Implement & Light Machinery Review, issue dated 2 February 1884; they retained many of the design characteristics of the small four-wheel engines. These two were despatched in September 1882, they were ordered by the Bagnall London agents G Bailey Toms & Company. The registers give 450 the name RIATA and 451 CUBA from which it is assumed they were destined for use on a sugar plantation in Cuba. Most of the water supply would appear to be in the side tanks, but there may have been another tank under the bunker. The notes accompanying the illustration describe the locomotive as having a water tank under the smokebox!

BAGNALL'S LOCOMOTIVE FOR PORTABLE RAILWAYS.

September 1882, ordered by GB Toms & Company. Whilst these two were ostensibly 2-4-0 side tanks, they may in fact have had the water tanks at the rear and where a fuel bunker might otherwise be expected to be. Therefore, what appears to be a side tank in the engraving purporting to show 451, might in fact be a bunker. Cylinders were 7x10½in, the fixed wheelbase was five-foot and the track gauge three-foot; they cost £537 each. The two engines were named respectively RIATO (this may however be RIATA, as it is spelt thus in one of the registers) and CUBA, suggesting that the second one at least was destined for that country. Around the time these engines were built the London based G Bailey Toms & Company acted as agents for Bagnall and although it does not seem to have been involved in many orders for locomotives, it may have been involved in orders for other equipment. G Bailey Toms also acted as London based agents for the iron trade and for several years had on occasion acted for John Bagnall & Sons Limited; it would almost certainly have been through this connection that WG Bagnall became involved. Between 1879 and 1888 at least, G Bailey Toms had the same London address as WG Bagnall, 7A Laurence Pountney Hill, London EC and during this period at least acted as export agents for John Bagnall & Sons Limited. All three companies appear to have used the same London office to conduct business. Nevertheless, a *Colliery Guardian* advert of 11 July 1879, quotes C Williams & Company of 90 Cannon Street as WG Bagnall & Company's agents in London. The name CUBA, suggesting that the engines were destined for that country and if so, doubtless would be for use on a sugar plantation.

Two more similar 2-4-0 side tanks followed in October 1883 and February the following year, numbers 511 and 512, smaller this time with 5x7½in cylinders and costing ex-works £408 5/- (£408 25p) for the first, and £364 7/9d (£364 38p) for the second. One of these two, according to the journal *Engineering* dated 18 April 1884, was the engine exhibited at the Calcutta Exhibition that year as part of the complete portable railway mentioned earlier. The line was two-foot gauge and laid around a lake, it consisted of 16lbs per yard rail in 10ft lengths secured to channel sleepers by means of clips, which fitted up close to the web of the rail. There were eight wagons of various descriptions, bogie and otherwise, suitable for carrying sugar cane and other colonial produce as well as three passenger coaches, these were made of pitch pine and could accommodate 12 persons each. The engine weighed 4½ tons and could traverse curves of 35ft radius, the boiler had a total heating surface of 90 sq ft and a working pressure was 150 psi. Designed to burn wood fuel, interestingly, the water tank is described as being behind the footplate, hence the comment above regarding the earlier locomotives of this wheel arrangement. An engraving of the locomotive and a very primitive passenger-carrying vehicle accompanies the article, the engine bears the name SIRDAR and the number 512; although all but one of the surviving registers credit this name to the locomotive numbered 511. Presumably one of these two locomotives with the name SIRDAR, along with the other equipment, was shipped to India for the exhibition and as noted earlier, Walsh Lovett & Company are recorded as the customer of the engine with this name. Whatever happened to the engine after

ENGINEERING. [APRIL 18, 1884.

LOCOMOTIVE AND CAR FOR PORTABLE RAILWAY.
CONSTRUCTED BY MR. W. G. BAGNALL, ENGINEER, STAFFORD.
(For Description, see Page 335.)

Once again we have to thank one of the technical journals, in this case Engineering of 18 April 1884, for an illustration of the Bagnall exhibits at the Calcutta Exhibition that year. Although this illustration shows an engine named SIRDAR with the manufacturer's number 512, all the registers credit this number to the sister engine SOUDAN. However, there is no doubt it would be an engine named SIRDAR that would go to Calcutta. The other illustration shows one of the small passenger coaches that not only accompanied the engine to India for exhibition, but were also used on the demonstration railway. Once again this little engine displays all the previous design characteristics, including the pull-out regulator and small disc wheels, but notice that the dome has been moved to a position central on the barrel, rather than on the firebox as in some of the earlier engines.

An early six-coupled engine was this one, number 566, specially designed with a very long wheelbase of no less then nine-foot. New in December 1883 and ordered by the North Devon Clay Company, it was a quite a large three-foot gauge engine with 7½x10in cylinders. The reason for the long wheelbase was to give a wide spread of axle-loading, a feature essential as the line the engine was to work on in North Devon, had a number of very slender trestle viaducts. The Torrington & Marland Railway was six and a quarter miles long and ran from Torrington to quarries at Marland; opened in 1881 it was designed and engineered by John Barraclough Fell, a well known civil engineer who is perhaps best remembered for his involvement in mountain railways. Fell had earlier been the engineer for the line across the Mont Cenis pass in Switzerland, and nearer home the Snaefell Mountain Railway on the Isle of Man, a line that additionally used his patent centre-rail system. At Snaefell this system is only used for braking purposes but the principle can also be used for traction, as in the case of the former Rimutaka incline on the north island of New Zealand. Actually the Fell patent covered the method of engaging the centre rail, rather than the rail itself. The rear cab extension of the locomotives is a later addition and whilst the engine was named MARLAND in the registers, this is not evident from any of the known photographs. This particular one was taken about 1913 and the engine lasted until 1925. One of the manufacturer's plates from this locomotive is on display in the Railway Museum at York - the oldest known surviving plate from a Bagnall locomotive.

the Calcutta show, along with the rest of the equipment, remains a mystery. But whatever it did, or wherever it went, it cannot have done the Company's reputation any harm as over the succeeding 80 years or so no less than a third of the Company's locomotive production went to India.

The sister engine, whichever one it was, is recorded as carrying the name SOUDAN and as mentioned in Chapter One was exhibited at the Shrewsbury Show of the RASE of England in 1884. In this case the eventual customer is shown as Stothert & Pitt, who were engineers based in Bath and well known for the manufacture of cranes and structural iron and steel work. Once again nothing further is known about this locomotive but the name would suggest an export order, but not in this case for India. As both these locomotives were ordered in January 1883, it can safely be assumed they were built to stock, one subsequently

going to India towards the end of that year, and the other one sold to Stothert & Pitt in February 1886 - the lower price for the second one perhaps indicating that Bagnall was anxious to get rid of it as the profit was a mere 5/3d (26p)! Also exhibited at the Shrewsbury show in 1884 was another locomotive - MENDIP - this was number 434, ordered in March 1882 which a press description confirms as a two-foot gauge 0-4-0 inverted saddle tank. The locomotive in question was originally ordered in March 1882 by the Glasgow based export agent John H Riddle, but in the event was not delivered and would therefore have been on Bagnalls hands and available for the exhibition. Subsequently named BATTERS, it was despatched from Stafford in September 1885 to the order of CJ Batters, and sent to Point of Ayr Colliery near Talacre in North Wales. The cylinders were 5x7½in, the wheelbase was three-foot and the selling price £292 10/- (£292 50p), which returned a profit of a little over £6; again perhaps an indication of Bagnall wanting to be rid of an engine that had been left on his hands for some time.

The small 2-4-0 side tank design, or perhaps rear tank, although some engines may even have had a combination of the two, became quite popular for export markets. They were used on portable, semi-portable and other light railways in connection with plantations and similar operations and several were built over the next few years. All of them would have exhibited the typical Bagnall design features of the period which included small disc wheels, single slidebars, boiler feed by one injector and an axle-driven pump between the frames, pull-out type regulators in the dome, dome mounted Salter balance safety valves and open cabs. Another common feature of the early engines, albeit not on all these 2-4-0s, was a handrail running along the top of the boiler which also acted as a steam pipe for the blower; good design economy but quite what the crews thought if they had to use it when the blower was in use has gone unrecorded! As well as India, in the period being covered in this Chapter examples of these 2-4-0 tank engines went to Cuba; Mexico; Tasmania; Brazil and Hungary. In most of these cases, if not all, the locomotives would have been

Another engine for Henry Rogers was number 1212 of January 1890, C DE DE FIGUEIREDO, a development of the smaller version of the 2-4-0 side tank design. This one had 6x9in cylinders and although destined for Pernambuco, nothing else is known and no spares orders are recorded in surviving records. The engine had a plate with Rogers name and not Bagnalls; this was often the case with agents and always so with Rogers, so they, and not Bagnall, might receive any repeat enquiries or spares orders.

accompanied by track work, wagons and other light railway material. An interesting aspect worth mentioning regarding the 2-4-0 side tank design was the class and telegraphic code name used for a somewhat larger version (8-9in cylinder diameters) introduced a few years later. The name was JESSIE, which was the Christian name of Gordon Bagnall's wife. One of these locomotives, manufacturer's number 1412 of 1893, was photographed with this name and used extensively in catalogues and other publicity material. The particular locomotive was ordered by the Wolverhampton based export agents Henry Rogers Sons & Company Limited, a company that over the years become good customers of Bagnall. JESSIE had 9x14in cylinders, a track gauge of 2ft 5½in and with the actual name UNIAO, it was despatched for use on a sugar estate of that name in Pernambuco Province of Brazil. The eight and nine inch cylinder versions of the 2-4-0 design were quite large locomotives with outside frames and a fixed wheelbase of around five feet; as the coupled wheel springing was equalised, large and distinctive equalising beams were used. The first engine of this type was manufacturer's number 1399 of November 1891, also ordered by Henry Rogers with the name FRATERINDADE; it too, would have been destined for a sugar plantation in Pernambuco.

This is number 1412 UNIAO, an example of the lager and later designs of 2-4-0 side tank, in this case with 9x14in cylinders and outside frames. This one was new to Henry Rogers Sons & Company; the Wolverhampton based agents for the Pernumbaco Province in Brazil. JESSIE, was the class name for this type of locomotive for publicity purposes and Jessie was the Christian name of Gordon Bagnall's wife, also one of his sisters. UNIAO was a 2ft 5½in gauge engine which went to a sugar plantation of that name in Pernambuco.

An illustration of another order for Henry Rogers, in this case a horizontal circular firebox boiler and single cylinder engine. Fitted with a 'Pickering' governor, presumably it was intended to drive some sort of machinery via a belt from the flywheel. The small bogies it is standing on are not part of the order, but would be used for internal movements about the works. Unfortunately nothing more is known about this order, it would date from around 1900 and like the locomotives ordered by Rogers would have almost certainly have been destined for somewhere in the Pernambuco province of Brazil.

The Rogers Company was an old established one which not only acted as export agents and merchants specialising in the sugar, jute and cotton industries, but also designed factory and plantation installations and superintended their erection. In more modern terminology what we would refer to as a turn-key contractor. For many years members of the Twentyman family were principals of the company and as well as being family friends of the Bagnalls, the two families were in fact related, as will be covered in some detail in Chapter Five. When correspondence with the Henry Rogers Company was entered into by the authors back in 1965, not only was the Company still engaged in

exporting sugar making machinery to South America, but a member of the Twentyman family - JA Twentyman - was still in charge.

Between 1884 and 1950 Bagnall supplied 16 locomotives to Rogers's orders, all destined for Brazil, most of which would have been for use at sugar plantations in Pernambuco Province - now Recife. There is evidence too, in some records the Rogers Company had retained, that as well as locomotives Bagnall supplied light railway material including track work and wagons, along with small stationary steam engines and boilers. It is extremely fortunate in connection with the early Bagnall locomotives that one of those originally supplied to a Rogers order has survived. As the oldest Bagnall locomotive known to be extant we can learn a little more of the design characteristics than the surviving records tell us, bearing in mind that no drawings are known to exist. The locomotive is manufacturer's number 1058, but carries plates with Rogers name and its reference number 736, along with a date of December 1888. All the locomotives supplied to Rogers had plates with its name and reference number on them rather than Bagnalls. This was common practice with agents who often stipulated that their name and not the manufacturers should appear on the locomotives, thus ensuring that any future enquiries and spares orders would be directed their way rather than the builders. Whilst this ploy usually worked, there are examples where it did not, customers finding out exactly who built the locomotives and subsequently dealing direct.

According to surviving Bagnall records number 1058 was supplied in January 1889 at a cost of £330, it had cylinders 4½ x 7½ in, a wheelbase quoted as 2ft 8in and 2ft 11in, and a track gauge of 1ft 11¹¹/₁₆in. Although the actual wheel arrangement is not quoted, the two wheelbase dimensions give the clue to the engine being either a 2-4-0 or an 0-4-2; in fact it is the former. The records show the engine as having the name CASTRO when new, and as there is a place of this name in Alagoas, the state south of Recife (Pernambuco) and on the Sao Francisco River close to the railway connecting the two states, it is presumed this is where it may have originally been delivered. This little engine is beautifully preserved in the Curitiba Railway Museum in Brazil, it carries the running number 38 painted on both sides of the dome as well as on the front of the

Three views of the small 2-4-0 locomotive number 1058 of January 1889 - although the plate gives December the previous year and Rogers, and not Bagnalls number - supplied to Henry Rogers and now in the Curitiba Railway Museum in Brazil. Pictures taken in 1988. This is a remarkable survivor and the earliest Bagnall locomotive known to be extant. (Uwe Bergmann)

smokebox - the significance of this number is however, not known. Unfortunately no details are available of where it originally came from or at what date, but when photographed in 1988 it appeared to have been recently restored. There was however, a small plate stating that the restoration was undertaken at Ponta Grossa Works (known to be a locomotive repair workshop) which is located west of Curitiba in the inner country of Parana.

A close examination of the engine reveals just about as simple a steam locomotive as imaginable. The small disc driving wheels are of about one foot diameter and the leading ones something like nine inches, steeply inclined cylinders drive the leading coupled axle via slender connecting rods which are outside the coupling rods and the slide bars are single with box type crossheads. The leading wheels are fixed to the frames and there is no evidence of a swivelling truck; Stephenson's link motion inside the frames drives slide valves on top of the cylinders via rocking shafts. The only apparent place for the water supply is in what might otherwise be considered the side bunkers and there is no evidence of any boiler feeding arrangements. Except that is, for some obviously dummy pipes leading from below the foot plating to the side of the boiler barrel - presumably for appearance purposes. They may however, be an axle driven pump between the frames which cannot be seen from the photographs. The boiler gives the appearance that it might in fact be a simple replica and whatever form the firebox takes is unclear - the smokebox door is of the lift-up type. The general conclusion reached is that this locomotive might have been found in a very derelict condition, doubtless with much of its upper works rusted away and that replica replacement parts have been made in accordance with somebody's ideas. Nevertheless, the work appears to have been well executed and the locomotive enables us to learn something more than the surviving records tell us about these early Bagnall locomotives. It would seem however, that such knowledge is confined to the works below footplate level, although as built the engine would clearly have had a 'proper' leading truck with sideways movement about a pivot of some sort. The Rogers plates, being brass, have of course survived.

In examining this locomotive we are able to see just how simple many of these early small Bagnall locomotives must have been and therefore, why it was possible to market them as such comparatively low prices. This fact, combined with Gordon Bagnall's imaginative approach and flair for publicity, along with the excellent catalogues he produced and the small overheads his operations at the time would attract, are perhaps the key reason why the Company was able to flourish. This was no small achievement in a supply base that was already verging on being over-subscribed. When one compares these simple machines with the contemporary products of builders like Hunslet and Manning Wardle, to cite but two, it becomes clearer how Bagnall was able to undercut the more established builders on price. And there is plenty of evidence to illustrate the longevity and durability of the engines with many customers coming back time and time again. Another factor must surely be the ability of the Company to supply track work, rolling stock and other light railway equipment as a part of complete light railway package. This ability would have been extremely attractive to agents and export merchants in this country acting on behalf of customers thousands of miles away, perhaps themselves just embarking on the initial mechanisation of transport arrangements in connection with plantations and other developing industries.

In March 1883 an order was received for what turned out to be the largest engines built to date and only the second order for locomotives to incorporate six-coupled wheels. Manufacturer's numbers 523 and 524 had cylinders 11½x16in, a wheelbase of 10ft 0in and a track gauge of 3ft 6in. Delivered in a commendably short

time of three months the selling price was £826 17- 6d (£826 87p) each, which gave a profit of £192 11/ 10d (£192 59p). The customer is quoted in the registers as Schulle & Schemman, but neither names nor running numbers are recorded for them. However, spares orders for both locomotives in October 1894, May 1902 and again in August 1906, but in the last case for number 524 only, came from the Lautaro Nitrate Company, a company known to have operated nitrate mines in and around Taltal in Chile. A number of later locomotives were supplied for use in the nitrate industry in Chile, including others for use by the Lautaro Nitrate Company, so presumably Schulle & Schemman were acting as agents in this case. It is also possible of course, that they were an earlier owner of the operations in Taltal. Unfortunately, and once again somewhat surprisingly, no illustration appears to have survived to show us what these locomotives looked like; nevertheless it is considered they would have been similar to maker's number 614, which was the first large six-coupled engine of which an illustration is available.

With the notable exception of the two early standard gauge locomotives used on the Wotton Tramway, in November 1883 the first order was received for locomotives to operate on a public passenger carrying railway, in this case one situated in Italy. Fortunately substantially more technical details are available for these locomotives than the sparse information in the registers, as their despatch was reported at some length in the local Stafford newspapers. The two locomotives, manufacturer's numbers 592 and 593, were six-coupled 0-6-0 side tanks with 12x18in cylinders, 2ft 9in diameter wheels and a wheelbase of 6ft 6in; weight in working order was 20 tons and the working pressure 150psi. Ordered by Lavista they were both despatched in April 1884 and named FOSSANO and MENDOVI respectively.

The locomotives were for use on the Fossano-Mondovi-Cavadella-Rochetta Railway, situated between Turin and Genoa in the province of Cuneo. This 950m/m gauge railway (the gauge quoted in the registers is 3ft 1³/₈in) opened in 1884, was 24 kilometres long and these two Bagnall locomotives were its first motive power. The Stafford press claimed they were the first 'English locomotives to run on Italian Railways', which it has to be added they were not! The engines were designed to haul 300 tons on the level and 40 tons

IDDESLEIGH, number 614 of August 1885; this is the earliest known surviving photograph taken at the works. Even so, an engraving of this engine rather than the photograph was often used in catalogues and other publicity material. The engine is an example of the larger six coupled design, in this case standard-gauge and with 12in diameter cylinders. However, engines of this basic design were built for gauges from three-foot upwards and with cylinders up to 14in diameter. This would have been one of the largest engines built at the works by the date. Notice the very large wooden brake blocks.

on a gradient of 1 in 40; the selling price was £1,014 each, against an individual building cost of £961 14/ 8d (£961 74p). Unfortunately no information appears to have survived on how successful or otherwise they were and the next locomotive the railway obtained came from a Swiss builder. Between 1904 and 1913 the railway obtained four new locomotives, also from continental builders and ostensibly to replace the 'older stock', so it is pretty safe to assume that the Bagnall locomotives would have been scrapped or otherwise disposed of in this period. The railway closed in about 1940. Once again no image of any description has survived to show us what these two locomotives actually looked like, but we can be sure that they too, would have been similar externally to manufacturer's number 614, albeit in this case with a much shorter wheelbase.

Several more six-coupled locomotives were built over the next few years, some of which were also for use on public passenger carrying railways. The first one was manufacturer's number 614, a photograph of which exists, in fact the earliest known photograph of a new

locomotive taken at the works. This was a standard gauge locomotive with cylinders 12x18in, a wheel diameter of three-foot and the wheelbase 10ft 6in; the weight in working order equalled 20 tons. Named IDDESLEIGH it was ordered by Dorman Brown & Company, a firm of merchants with offices at Gracechurch Street in London. The locomotive was despatched in August 1885 and as it was sold for £800, there was a loss of £110 recorded against the order. The first record we have of this engine's use was by the contractor Fredrik Arvidsson Posse & Carl Sprinchorn, a company engaged in building the Malmo-Kontinenten Railway in Sweden between 1897 and 1898. It may be that Dorman Brown ordered the engine on behalf of this, or another Swedish customer, and its original destination was in fact Sweden; nevertheless we do not know this for certain. In any event the locomotive later passed to the ownership of the well established Swedish engineers and locomotive builders Nydqvist & Holm at Trollhattan, where it was used for many years as a works shunter. In 1908 after an extensive overhaul at Trollhattan, which included a new boiler and some other external modifications, the locomotive went to work on a Swedish private railway - the Laxa-Rofors Railway. This railway dates from around 1908 so the engine was one of its first, in fact it became No 2 in the railway's listing and also carried the name K BOHNSTEDT. It remained on this railway and would appear to have given good service until broken up for scrap in 1928. If this engine was intended for a Swedish customer when it was ordered, the choice of the name IDDESLEIGH is perhaps strange. Could it be significant that Stafford Henry Northcliffe was created 1st Earl Iddesleigh in 1885, the year the engine was built? Iddesleigh is a village in North Devon where the Earl was the Member of Parliament at the time the engine was built and his Earldom created. Despite a photograph having been taken, for many years Bagnall used instead an engraving of this locomotive for publicity purposes. In later years a much more modern six-coupled side tank locomotive was used for publicity purposes, but this one too, was referred to as 'Type IDDESLEIGH'.

In 1886 and 1887 the company supplied four slightly larger locomotives to the same general design as IDDESLEIGH, but in this case with larger 13in and 14in diameter cylinders. The four engines were the first motive power for three-foot gauge West Clare Railway situated on the south-west coast of Ireland; they were also the first locomotives of this wheel arrangement supplied to an Irish narrow-gauge railway. The initial section of this railway opened between Ennis and Miltown Malbay on 2 July 1887, and these four locomotives formed the entire motive power for the first five years of the line's existence. The first two had 13x20in cylinders, manufacturer's numbers 730 and 738 and West Clare Railway numbers 1 & 2; they were despatched in January and June 1887 respectively. The second pair has slightly larger 14x20in cylinders, manufacturer's numbers 792 and 793 and they became West Clare Railway numbers 3 & 4; despatch from Stafford in this case for both engines was in January the following year. The West Clare Railway route was extended southwards by the South Clare Railway from Miltown Malbay to Kilrush and Kilkee; opened for passenger traffic on 23 December 1892. This give the combined railways which were always operated as if they were in fact one, a final length of no less than 53 miles. The West Clare Railway as the complete system

was always known, soon acquired a somewhat dubious reputation for its reliability and timekeeping. It is perhaps worth mentioning however, that it was not one of these Bagnall locomotives, underpowered as they were for the job required of them, that caused the well known Irish poet Percy French, to write his famous Ballard: *Are You Right There Michael Are You Right*. French missed a concert engagement at Kilkee on 10 August 1896 due to the engine of the train he was travelling on breaking down at Miltown Malbay; he later won a legal case against the railway for the recovery of his lost earnings! In fact it was one of the later and much larger engines supplied by the Glasgow builder Dubs that failed, but ironically it was one of the Bagnall locomotives that came to the rescue - West Clare No 4 which by this date had acquired the name BESBOROUGH. Its sister by the way, No 3 was also later named, in this case CLIFDEN. Spare boilers and fireboxes were supplied for these engines in the early 1900s and they lasted to the period between 1900 and 1915.

These four Bagnall locomotives had a combined selling price of £5,300, although they were actually ordered and priced separately. The first pair cost £1,250 each and the second £1,400, the construction costs recorded against them totalled £3,922 7/ 6d (£3,922 32.5p) which gave a total profit of almost £1,478. However, presumably as an incentive to get the contract from the otherwise impecunious West Clare Railway Company, Bagnall agreed to take in lieu of the entire sale price shares in the railway company. In this deal Bagnall acquired a total of 530 £10 shares in the 4% stock of the Railway and these shares at that price, appear on the asset side of the first WG Bagnall Limited balance sheet when the limited liability company was formed in 1887. With the benefit of hindsight this was always likely to be a dubious financial deal and despite the occasional small dividend payments - a little over £369 up to and including May 1891 - a loss of £214 1/ 9d (£214 8p) was recorded against the sale of 499 shares disposed of between September 1890 and December 1891. The remaining 31 shares were subsequently written off, so perhaps even considering the apparent perpetual perilous financial affairs of the West & South Clare Railways prior to them becoming part of The Great Southern Railway in 1925, the Company did not come off as badly as might be expected. The total loss

St PHILIP, number 1308 of 1890, one of two large side tanks new to the 3ft 6in gauge Barbados Railway but later used in New Guiana. Notice the similarity with the standard gauge IDDESLEIGH, but with a bigger and more commodious cab. Notice too, the later style of manufacturer's identification plate.

amounted to a little over £524, minus the meagre dividends that had been paid over the years. In any event, it did not prevent the sale of another engine to the Railway in 1908; however, on this occasion it was cash before delivery!

In 1890 two more locomotives of this same basic type were supplied, in this case for the Barbados Railway, manufacturer's numbers 1308 and 1310. This pair also had 14x20in cylinders and a weight in working order of 25 tons. The Barbados Railway was a 3ft 6in gauge line the first section of which opened in October 1881. It ran from Bridgetown on one side of the island to St Andrew's on the other, a distance of 24 miles and was finally completed in the summer of 1883. Apparently the original locomotives, two comparatively small 2-4-0 tender engines with 12x18in cylinders and built by the Avonside Engine Company of Bristol, were found to be underpowered. The railway had a long and steep climb from the coast at Bridgetown to the plains and a couple of Vulcan Foundry 2-6-2 tank engines with 12½ x17in cylinders, do not appear to have fared much better than the Avonsides. This seems to have prompted the railway company into considering locomotives with all the weight available for adhesion, particularly for use on the goods trains, hence the order for the two Bagnalls. Not surprisingly however, the new locomotives with an 8¼ ton axle-load were found to be very heavy on the track, which it would appear was not particularly well maintained anyway, with the result that it was soon

found that the idea behind buying heavy six-coupled locomotives with no carrying axles was not a very good one after all! As a result the two Bagnalls were sold to the Demerara Railway in New Guiana and we know they had arrived there by at least February 1898, as spares were ordered at that time for delivery to New Guiana. The Barbados Railway Company by the way, was in receivership by 1897 and closed soon after. Worth a brief mention is the fact that the well established light railway advocate and engineer ER Calthrop, was later commissioned to re-engineer the Barbados line and it re-opened as a 2ft 6in gauge railway in 1899. The two Bagnall locomotives meanwhile, which originally carried the names St PHILIP and St ANDREW respectively and were numbers 6 & 7 in the Barbados fleet, were last heard of in New Guiana when spares were ordered for them in February 1901. For some years a photograph of St PHILIP was used in the Bagnall catalogues and in other publicity material, but described as Type IDDESLEIGH.

The north country based public works contractor Enoch Tempest was another good customer of the firm. Tempest ordered his first locomotive in 1887, the first of 17 supplied up to 1904. All the locomotives supplied to Tempest were built to suit a track gauge of three-foot, a popular gauge for the type of work Tempest was largely engaged on. With the country's growing population and the ongoing development of large centres of population, together with general improvements in

An obviously posed line-up of Tempest's engines at Clough Bottom. From left to right: HAROLD, number 912 of 1887, this one was also later sold back to Bagnall and accompanied ANNIE to South Wales; ADA, number 1420 of 1893 which was new here; ANNIE number 1076, MINNIE number 699, and bringing up the rear is a locomotive built by the Hunslet Engine Company of Leeds, named LITTLE EGRET; it was manufacturer's number 175 of 1877. Out of the total number of locomotives that over the years are known to have been owned by Tempest - a total of 21 - only three were not products of the Castle Engine Works.

MINNIE was the oldest Bagnall locomotive owned by the public works contractor Enoch Tempest. Number 699 it dates from May 1887, but there is some uncertainly whether it was acquired direct from the maker's or second-hand from another contractor. Some of the registers show the customer as J Evans and the name MARTHA, others as Enoch Tempest and the name MINNIE. In the registers where Evans is shown his name has been crossed out and Tempest substituted along with the new name. It is possible that the engine came back to Stafford and was re-sold to Tempest, or that Evans cancelled his order before delivery and Bagnall sold the engine directly to Tempest, or that Tempest acquired it second-hand from Evans. In any event Tempest used in on a number of his jobs and it is seen here on the construction of Clough Bottom Reservoir at Waterfoot in Lancashire, a job for Bury Corporation undertaken in the years 1891 to 1896. This illustration shows to good advantage an example of the early four-wheel inverted tank design, in this case for three-foot gauge and with 6½x10in cylinders.

This is one of the larger four-wheel inverted tank engines, number 902 of 1887, new to the contractor H Fotherby & Son and named VICTORIA (1887 was the year of Queen Victoria's Golden Jubilee); it had 9x13½in cylinders. Initially used by Fotherby on his contact to build Cant Clough Reservoir for Burnley Corporation, it is seen here much later in life when owned by another contractor, H Arnold & Son, and engaged on reservoir construction works at Embsay for Skipton Urban District Council. The photograph was taken some time in the period 1908 to 1910 when apparently, it was named TODMORDEN, although this is not apparent from the photograph. Notice the cab roof extension and that despite some 20 odd year's hard work on construction sites, the remarkably good external condition of the engine. Perhaps the fellows along side are those that drove and tended its needs; if so they appear to have done a good job.

Another picture taken on Tempest's Clough Bottom job, this time illustrating a later and larger locomotive than MINNIE, but of the same basic design; this one had 7x10½in cylinders. ANNIE was number 1076 of 1889, new to Tempest at Clough Bottom. On completion of the works ANNIE was sold back to Bagnall and after repairs re-sold to Crawshay Brothers (Cyfathfa) Limited for use in South Wales.

sanitary arrangements, there was a burgeoning need for clean water supplies. This resulted in a spate of reservoir construction and other ancillary works in the latter part of the 19th and early years of the 20th century. Tempest made a speciality of this type of work which was, of course, as outlined in Chapter One, a subject very dear to the heart of Gordon Bagnall and there is evidence to suggest that Tempest and Bagnall become more than just business acquaintances. There is little doubt that the best known of Tempest's works is the chain of three large reservoirs at Walshaw Dean which he built for Halifax Corporation. These reservoirs lie in a moorland valley of the Yorkshire Pennines a little above Hebden Bridge, and were constructed between 1900 and 1915. As events turned out this job was Tempest's last, as following problems with the construction works and in particular retaining the impounded water, he was declared bankrupt in 1908. The shock of this seriously affected his health and he died the following year. Following his death the works were partly completed by his executors and eventually finished by another contractor. In fairness it would appear from the available evidence that not all the blame should have been attributed to Tempest, in view of the extremely difficult terrain where the reservoirs were situated.

Although from a later period this advert from the Machinery & Implement Review shows the locomotive DORIS, number 1485 of 1897 which was new to Enoch Tempest. Gordon Bagnall's daughter Jessica, claimed that this locomotive had been named after her, as this was the 'nick-name' her father gave her, and the one by which she was known to family and close friends.

CAMPECHANA *was the first locomotive built with a 2-4-2 wheel arrangement and although not a very good illustration, is worthy of inclusion on that count. Number 680 of 1885, this engine was new to the FC Merida a Campeche Railway in Mexico. Notice the lift-up type of smokebox door, cow catchers front and rear and the outside valves driven by rocking levers from the inside motion. Later and bigger developments of this design were quite popular with a range of customers.*

No fewer than 12 Bagnall locomotives were used by Tempest at Walshaw Dean, nine of them supplied new. Of the three that had been used on earlier construction works, one was a small 5in cylinder four-coupled saddle tank, manufacturer's number 1485 of 1897 which was named DORIS. This was an engine Tempest had already used on several contracts and Gordon Bagnall's daughter claimed it was named after her, as despite her name being Jessica, her father for whatever reason we know not, gave her the nickname Doris, and this stuck with family and close friends. An engraving of this little engine with its name often appeared in publicity material and this is perhaps, indicative of a friendship that had built up between Gordon Bagnall and Enoch Tempest. Later in the story we will explore other professional relationships between these two men. The early locomotives supplied to Tempest were all four wheel coupled of the inverted saddle tank design, a type that became popular with contractors generally. Over the years several others of similar type were supplied to other companies engaged in public works and other construction type activities. For example the contractors Henry Fotherby, C Braddock and J&M Hawley had engines of this type, as did Oldham Corporation which undertook reservoir construction itself with direct labour. Subsequent engines supplied to Tempest, including those supplied new to Walshaw Dean, were of a later design and fitted with conventional saddle tanks; one of them, manufacturer's number 1669 of 1901, was a much bigger six-coupled machine. Although jumping ahead of our story

somewhat it is worth mentioning that this six-wheel engine which was named TENACITY, was ordered specifically for work on the main-line part of the construction railway at Walshaw Dean. This was the section between the plant depot near Hebden Bridge and the actual reservoir sites. TENACITY was fitted with a special seat in the cab, this was for Enoch Tempest to sit on when the engine was sent to collect him from the Hebden Bridge on his site visits!

Another public railway Bagnall supplied locomotives to, the three-foot gauge FC Merida a Campeche Railway, a Mexican line in the State of Yucatan; this was a line eventually running some 112 miles from Campeche City on the Gulf of Mexico to Merida. The construction had started in January 1892, but was not completed until six years later on 2 June 1898. Bagnall supplied two locomotives, a 2-4-0 side tank named LERMA, manufacturer's number 646 of November 1884, together with a much larger 2-4-2 side tank named CAMPECHANA, manufacturer's number 680 of March the following year. The first engine cost £472 10/- (£472 50p) and the second £902 1/ 11d (£902 10p). LERMA was quite a small engines with 6x9in cylinders and may have been intended for construction work and later yard shunting. However its much larger sister had 10x17in cylinders and would doubtless have been intended for work on the main-line. Both these engines had valves on top of the cylinders actuated by rocking shafts from the inside Stephenson's link motion which although a relatively unusual arrangement for Bagnall at this period, was often used on narrow-gauge locomotives with leading trucks. CAMPECHANA was the first locomotive the Company built with this wheel arrangement and it became the prototype for a number of later locomotives with similar external design characteristics. In the case of both these locomotives the customer quoted in the registers is no more than Ybarrondo. Whether this was an agent, or somebody connected with the railway has gone unrecorded, but it is worth a mention that the Gateshead builder Black, Hawthorn & Company, also supplied two locomotives to this same customer, one of which - Black, Hawthorn number 585 of 1880, was a three-foot gauge 2-4-0 side tank for the Merida & Progreso Railway - this was a line adjacent to the FC Merida a Campeche. The Bagnall locomotives appear to have disappeared from the railway by 1902, and in 1900 the line had been absorbed into the much larger Compania de les Tranvias Railway, later on it became part of the Unidos de Yucatan system. In some of the catalogues and advertising material an engraving of a locomotive very similar to the photograph of CAMPECHANA is used, but with the name PROGRESO on its side tank. There is a port of this name, part of the Yucatan peninsula in the Gulf of Mexico, and this is presumed to be the logic behind it.

In November 1887 the Company despatched what was in effect the first standard-gauge industrial shunting locomotive built for the home market. Manufacturer's number 660 was an 0-4-0 listed in one of the registers as a 'saddle tank with cab'. Cylinder dimensions were 10x15in and the wheelbase 5ft 3in, a copper firebox and

brass tubes were fitted. With the name BIGNALL HILL the engine was for use at the colliery company of that name located near Red Street at Newcastle-under-Lyme in Staffordshire. The colliery became quite good customers with two more Bagnall locomotives, one of them delivered in 1901 in a part-exchange deal with BIGNALL HILL. Number 660 was subsequently overhauled and re-sold to the Blackbrook Colliery near St Helens in Lancashire, where it became SAMSON. It came back to Stafford again in December 1902, this time for repairs and was last heard of when spares were supplied to Blackbrook Colliery in December 1903. The next few standard-gauge four-coupled industrial shunting locomotives were all fitted with front water tanks which, as already mentioned, gave an external appearance similar to engines fitted with inverted saddle tanks. As the inverted saddle and front tanks were popular design characteristics of Bagnall locomotives in this period, largely in view of the claim that they gave a better overall weight distribution for a four-coupled engine, it is interesting to speculate why this locomotive, the first for the standard gauge industrial market, had a saddle tank.

Actually there were only three standard-gauge four-wheel industrial locomotives built with the front tanks before the more conventional arrangement of saddle tank was re-introduced - we will explore this design change in the next Chapter. The first of the engines with front tanks was manufacturer's number 954 of February 1889; this one had 10x15in cylinders and was sold to M&W Grazebrook & Company, iron masters at

Although displaying an incorrect name for publicity purposes, this engraving from an early catalogue illustrates the first standard-gauge shunting locomotive built and fitted with front water tanks; notice the external similarity with the inverted saddle tank design which often leads to confusion. Number 954 of 1889 had 10x15in cylinders and was new to M&W Grazebrook & Company of Netherton in the Black Country. In 1895 it was traded in part-exchange for a new locomotive and in February that year after overhaul, was sold to Murgatroyds Syndicate Limited for use at its Middlewich factory in Cheshire. However, by 1899 this locomotive was at the Brunner Mond & Company Limited works at nearby Northwich, where Bagnall supplied a replacement boiler in 1899. The engine appears to have disappeared in 1931, presumably for scrap.

LOCOMOTIVES FOR ORDINARY GAUGE.

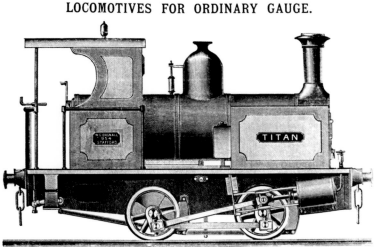

A bigger version of the standard gauge front tank design was ALEXANDER, number 1402 of 1892, seen here at the works and ready for delivery. It went to the Birchenwood Colliery Company at Kidsgrove, which was immediately north of Stoke-on-Trent and where it operated for all its life. Notice the elaborate way the engine has been cleaned and the large manufacturer's plate on the cab side, this was the standard pattern for the period; these plates gave both the month and year of completion.

Netherton in the Black Country. The next one was manufacturer's number 1392 of October 1891, the second locomotive supplied to the Bignall Hill Colliery. The last of the trio was manufacturer's number 1402 of March 1892, which was ordered by a Manchester company of iron and steel merchants, John Needham & Sons. Both these last two engines were slightly larger with 12x18in cylinders, but were otherwise almost identical to the earlier one. John Needham was connected with the Birchenwood Colliery Company at Kidsgrove in North Staffordshire and this is where the engine was sent. Named ALEXANDER after one of Birchenwood Company's original partners, Alexander P Dickinson, when the locomotive was sent back to Stafford in June 1922 for overhaul, it was found to be in such bad condition that agreement was reached to supply a new locomotive instead. The replacement was one of the much later standard 14in cylinder 0-4-0 saddle tank design - manufacturer's number 2107 - however, a bit of the old engine lived on as the brass nameplates were transferred from one to the other. At the time of writing one of these nameplates adorns the walls in the public bar at Caverswall Road Station on the Foxfield Light Railway near Blythe Bridge, a short distance south of Stoke-on-Trent.

In February 1885 the Company obtained one of his largest single orders to date. The technical journal *The Engineer*, in its issue dated 6 March 1885, had the following to report: 'A considerable contract from the Government for portable railway plant and small locomotives for the Soudan. This railway, it is understood, will be used as a feeder for the wider gauge permanent railway to be laid down by Messrs Lucas & Aird, conveying the materials for its construction and running alongside of it. As the order has to be completed in a limited time, it is intended to at once enlarge Mr Bagnall's works'. The order was, as the report in *The Engineer* states, in connection with the much larger scheme to build a railway in the Sudan from Saukin on the Red Sea coast inland to Berber on the Nile. Berber is south of Khartoun and was chosen to enable onward transport of troops and supplies by the river; the whole scheme followed General Charles Gordon's death at the siege at Khartoum in January 1885. This is not the place to go into details of the whole debacle surrounding the siege and the General's death, which was an enormous embarrassment to the Liberal Government of the day under Gladstone's second ministry. Suffice it to say, as a direct result the Government fell on 9 June. However, following the General's death, the Liberal's decided that this had to be avenged for which an improved line of communication had to be established. As events turned out the railway scheme was aborted but not until it was reckoned to have cost the British taxpayer in excess of one million pounds - a lot of money in those days. This was not however, before an inquisitive Member of Parliament, presumably from the opposition benches, commented in the 'House': 'was it not true that the head of a Stafford firm which had received the contract for the locomotives was the president of the Stafford Conservative Association'. Gordon Bagnall was the chairman of the Stafford Conservatives at the time, but whether this had anything to do with his Company getting the order has gone unrecorded! *The Engineer*, in its Editorial dated 13 March 1885, opined that there were far more important issues in connection with this railway than the 'puerile interrogations put to the Government concerning the status of Mr Bagnall and his politics, intended to ascertain if he was a fit and proper person to be entrusted with the construction of five 18in gauge locomotives'!

As events turned out none of the locomotives ordered from Bagnall went to the Sudan, but it would appear that at least some of the other light railway equipment ordered at the same time did. There used to be a 'story' told around the Castle Engine Works that the locomotives, or some of them, did in fact depart these shores but that the ship on which they were loaded was turned back whilst en-route. This is unlikely, as the whole scheme was abandoned in late April or early May and the locomotives were not ready for despatch until June. Of the 2,500 tons of 18in gauge rail, along with 600 steel sleepers that had been shipped and landed in Saukin, some would undoubtedly have come from the Castle Engine Works.

In the introduction to the November 1895 catalogue (Catalogue Number 13 - and repeated in several subsequent editions), Gordon Bagnall stated that in his opinion had the Saukin to Berber Railway been built to two-foot or 2ft 6in gauge, rather than the attempt to build it to standard-gauge, it might well have been completed and subsequently have been very successful. He felt it could have been completed in six months, subject of course to no interference from the enemy - the distance was no less than 240 miles! As it happened it was in fact interference from the enemy that was one of the reasons why the attempt to build the line was abandoned! Bagnall went on to suggest that if the railway had been completed as a narrow-gauge line, enormous benefit would have accrued in connection with British activities in that part of the world! As events unfolded it was not until September 1898, after several more railway schemes and the battle of Omdurman, that the Dervishes were finally conquered and General Gordon's death avenged when Kitchener finally entered the ruined fortifications at Khartoum. It is worth mentioning that Bagnall was not alone in his ideas on the use of a narrow, rather than standard-gauge for the Saukin to Berber Railway.

Engraving used in Catalogue Number 10 of May 1888, showing one of the five 18in gauge front tank locomotives intended for the Sudan. SERAPIS was number 711 and notice again the similar external appearance of the front tank engines to those with inverted saddle tanks. An inverted saddle tank would not have been very practicable on an 18in gauge locomotive of this comparatively large size, with the necessity of keeping the boiler, and hence the centre of gravity, as low as possible in view of the narrow track gauge. With its sisters this engine found years of useful employment at the Royal Arsenal at Woolwich, despite this not being the original intension of the design.

The five 18in gauge Bagnall locomotives were eventually sent, along with all the other material that had not already been shipped to the Soudan, to the Royal Arsenal at Woolwich. There was already an internal 18in gauge railway system at Woolwich and the locomotives were utilised on the system there. John Fowler & Company of Leeds, and the Vulcan Foundry of Newton-le-Willows, also built locomotives for the abortive Saukin scheme, and they too, eventually found their way to various Government establishments with 18in gauge railway systems which included the Royal Arsenal. The Bagnall locomotives were interesting little machines with an 0-4-2 wheel arrangement and front side tanks; as outlined earlier this design of tank can easily be confused in the engraving for an inverted saddle tank. The frames were outside due to the narrow track gauge and the cylinder dimensions $7\frac{1}{2}$x12in; the valves were on top of the cylinders and driven by rocking shafts from the inside Stephenson's link motion. These engines were quite big for such a narrow track gauge and had an all-up weight in working order of 10½ tons. The manufacturer's numbers were 710 through to 714 and the engines had bestowed on them a series of rather apt names, derived as they were from Egyptian mythology. Respectively they were christened: OSIRIS; SERAPIS; ANUBIS; ISIS and APIS - although some registers reverse the locomotive manufacturer's numbers of the engines carrying the names OSIRIS and SERAPIS.

Useful employment seems to have been found for these five locomotives at the Woolwich Arsenal as there were numerous orders for spares parts over the succeeding years; indeed one of them, number 710,

came back to Stafford for a rebuild in July 1894. They all appear to have remained in use at Woolwich until at least shortly after the First World War, apart from number 711 that is, which is recorded as being scrapped in 1912. Despite attempts by the Darlington based dealer JF Wake to sell the others, which were purchased as surplus in the post First World War reduction in munitions activities, they all appear to have eventually been scrapped at Darlington. Worthy of note in connection with these locomotives is a paper read by Leslie S Robertson, to the Institution of Mechanical Engineers at its summer meeting in 1898. The paper is titled *Narrow-Gauge Railways, Two Feet & Under*, and in it the author states that the Bagnall locomotives in use at Woolwich Arsenal (this has to be those in question)

Panoramic view of the railway at Spezia in Italy. This view looks down on the harbour works and the town of Spezia from high up on Monte Cappuccini. Three trains can be seen on the circuitous railway designed and equipped by Gordon Bagnall, climbing from the harbour works towards the quarry. The three locomotives are numbers 760 and 761 of April 1886, and 872 of May 1887. Unfortunately, we have no knowledge of what became of the railway and its locomotives and rolling stock after the harbour works and defence wall were complete, but the whole operation may have survived for a time in connection with maintenance works. This is a combination of two seperate photographs, hence the reason it does not quite match in the middle.

This view shows parts of the wall of defence and other fortifications at Spezia under construction and once again with all three locomotives in view. Notice the different types of wagons, some side-tip and others low sided - they were all supplied by Bagnall.

were rather apt to leave the rails; he goes on to claim that: 'the bogie arrangement not being entirely satisfactory for the work'. Gordon Bagnall obviously got to know about this, despite not being in attendance at the meeting, and replied to the comment in correspondence. In his letter, which is printed in the Institution's proceedings, he points out that he had proposed an alternative arrangement to that used on the locomotives, but the 'authorities' would not agree to its use. Unfortunately, as no drawings are known to exist, it is impossible to comment on the design of bogie used. However, this comment indicates that somebody within a Government source, had quite a bit to do with the design of the locomotives.

Mention has already been made on several occasions how Gordon Bagnall's missed almost no opportunity to make his name and products known, and his response to the paper discussed in the last paragraph is but one example. The firm continued to advertise extensively and Bagnall personally travelled to many countries in the furtherance of the business. To give an example of the range of products outlined in a catalogue of the period here under discussion, it is worth a look at catalogue No 10. This one is dated May 1888 and like its predecessors is a lavish affair, in this case with a landscape format measuring 8x10in and containing 42

pages. Along with locomotives there are detailed lists, in many cases illustrated with engravings, of a whole range of railway equipment including track work incorporating a patent sleeper - of which more later - turntables of which the firm made a speciality and a very comprehensive range of goods and passenger rolling stock for light railways. The catalogue also contains lists of a not dissimilar range of stationary steam engines and boilers to those listed in earlier versions, including for example the still apparently popular range of Challenge combined engines and boilers. There is even a rather complicated looking sulphate of ammonia plant, although whether such was ever supplied has not been recorded! Perhaps one of the most interesting aspects of this catalogue is a series of pages containing a number of Unsolicited Testimonials for Locomotives, which have clearly been extracted from correspondence received from satisfied customers. These encompass locomotives sent to a wide range of countries and are accompanied by a few extracts from technical journals reporting on the firms products. In all the cases it is possible, often by a process of elimination, to identify which locomotives are being referred to.

A particular contract that brought the Company a lot of publicity as well as enhancing its reputation

The Spezia locomotive seen here is named DINA, number 760, although this name is not recorded in the registers. The engine is somewhere on the Spezia construction railway and possibly in the town of Spezia itself; in any event it is surrounded by some quite impressive and indeed magnificent buildings. Rarely can a Bagnall locomotive have been seen in such a regal location! The three engines supplied for use by the contractor Conti at Spezia, were all of this four-wheel inverted saddle tank design with 10x15in cylinders and in view of the sharp radius curves on parts of the line, the wheelbase was only 3ft 6in. This and the previous two photographs, along with a number of others taken at around the same time but not showing any locomotives, are from a Bagnall family album which supports the legend that Gordon Bagnall, on one occasion at least, was accompanied by his wife on his business trips to this part of Italy.

significantly, was the complete light railway including locomotives and rolling stock supplied for use at Spezia Harbour in north-west Italy. This equipment was required in connection with a wall-of-defence and other fortifications, and along with extensive coverage in the catalogues, the scheme was described and illustrated at some length in the technical engineering press at the time. In the case of this contract not only did the company supply the equipment, but it was also made clear that Gordon Bagnall himself had designed much of the installation. Engravings showing some of the works at Spezia and with the railway prominent appeared in the catalogues for several years, and in the journal *Industries* for example, issue dated 20 August 1886, there is a detailed description and it is extracts from this journal that appear in the catalogues.

The Spezia harbour contract was undertaken in the years 1885 and 1886 and as outlined in the proceeding paragraph, was a very significant one for Gordon Bagnall, consisting as it did of a large quantity of track work, wagons, three locomotives and a host of other ancillary equipment. Success in being awarded this contract would appear to have been instrumental in further orders for locomotives and light railway equipment required for other works in and around

Spezia, in some cases ancillary to the main harbour construction. The principal contract consisted of a 2ft 7½in (800 m/m) gauge railway some two miles long climbing up the side of Monte Cappuccini at Spezia in North-West Italy; the gradient was at an average of 1 in 12 and curves as sharp as 33ft radius. As might be imagined from these gradients and curves a somewhat circuitous route was necessary to gain sufficient height. The purpose of the railway was to gain access to newly developed stone quarries and transport the material to Spezia, where it was needed in connection with the construction of a harbour and a new naval anchorage. Known as the 'Mura di Cinta' (perimeter wall), the scheme consisted of an extensive protected harbour for part of the Italian battle fleet, along with a wall of defence and other fortifications. Although the gradients were largely in favour of loaded trains this was not exclusively so. The locomotives supplied were of the standard 0-4-0 design with inverted saddle tanks and 10x15in cylinders; they were capable of hauling up to six loaded wagons of 2½ tons each on the 1 in 12 gradients. Three locomotives were supplied, manufacturer's numbers 760 and 761 in April 1886, followed by number 872 in May the following year; the first two cost £700 each and the third one £680.

Gordon Bagnall claimed in the catalogues and technical press that many folk, including 'several engineers', had stated that small locomotive like the ones supplied to Spezia would not be able to haul paying loads up such steep gradients and around such sharp curves, but he had been confident they could and he had been proved correct. *The Engineer* of 22 October 1886 used rather stronger language and quoted Gordon Bagnall as saying that the idea was 'ridiculed by engineers'! Bagnall also claimed that savings of up to 60% over the original estimates had regularly been achieved in the operation of the railway at Spezia. The contractor for the Spezia works is quoted is the registers as Centi, but in actual fact it was Impresa (contractor) Conti e Ing Fabbiani, apparently a quite well established Italian civil engineering contracting firm at the time. The railway to serve the quarry, known as the Cappuccini-Botteghe Spezia Railway, was fully operational on 14 March 1888, but the locomotives and some of the other equipment supplied, had first of all been used on its construction.

Another Italian contractor by the name of Ing Pegazzono, had an associated operation with a narrow-gauge railway line about two and a half miles long from Spezia to Biassa. With gradients of 1 in 18 and curves of 20ft radius, this line was also used to bring stone from a quarry having become fully operational on 18 August 1887. A similar locomotive to the ones supplied to Conti was despatched for use this line, manufacturer's number 870 of May 1887, but strangely the track gauge was different and is quoted in the registers as 2ft 4½in - Italian sources have it as 0.71m. Gordon Bagnall appears to have made several visits to this part of Italy, and on at least one occasion he may have been accompanied by his wife. His personal interest seems to have resulted in a further contract, in this case consisting of at least two locomotives, some track work and wagons. The customer was another contractor, A Piatti & C of Pontremoli, at the time engaged in building the main line railway from La Spezia to Fidenza (later extended to Parma), which included a 4½ long mile long summit tunnel at Borgallo. This tunnel is between Borgotaro (now known as Borgo Val di Tar) and Pontremoli. The two locomotives were manufacturer's numbers 812 of October 1886 and 905 of June the following year, both 0-4-0 inverted saddle tanks similar to the Spezia ones but slightly smaller. The first engine had 8x12in

cylinders and the second 9x13½in, and they were used on a line three and three quarter miles long and 2ft 7½in (800 m/m) gauge connecting a brick and tile works at Casa Corvi with Guinadi. This railway was on the southern, Spezia side of the tunnel and had curves as sharp as 33ft radius and gradients, like Spezia, of 1 in 12. The contractor had a third locomotive delivered some years later, in December 1889 in fact, similar to its predecessors but with slightly larger 10x15in cylinders. However, in this case the track gauge is quoted in the registers as 2ft 7⁹/₁₆in, but as this is so close to 2ft 7½in, it is considered a fair assumption that it would have been used somewhere on the same railway construction works as the others.

Yet another Bagnall locomotive appears to have been used in this same area of Italy, based on the fact it was named SPEZIA. Manufacturer's number 778 was a 1ft 11½in gauge 0-4-0 inverted saddle tank supplied to Fedozzi; despatched in June 1886 it had 6½x10in cylinders and cost £440. So far it has not been possible to locate where this particular engine may have worked, but it could have been used on a short, approximately half mile long line from Cave di Rebocco to Cantiere dell' Impresa. This line was near Spezia and operated by a company called Impresa Mazzorini e Boccalari - it opened on 8 November 1887. On all these Italian contracts, as well as locomotives, rolling stock and track work, Bagnall may also have supplied other light railway equipment including for example, turntables, water tanks and small cranes.

The 1888 catalogue contains a list of no fewer than 30 countries where the Company had supplied locomotives and while it has not been possible to identify exactly which locomotives went to a few of these, it is perhaps worth listing them to illustrate the range of the Company's markets. The list reads: England; Ireland; Scotland; Wales; Norway; Sweden; Holland; Germany; France; Russia; Spain; Italy; Egypt; Siberia; South Africa; Zanzibar; Cuba; Porto Rico; Sandwich Islands; Java; Mauritius; United States; Brazil; Peru; Chili (sic); Argentine Republic; India; Mexico; Australia; New Zealand. Of these it has not been possible to identify which locomotive(s) went to: Norway; Russia; Siberia; Peru and Argentina. However, to the list should be added Hungary and Ceylon where it is known locomotives had been despatched. The locomotives supplied to the Italian Fossano-Mendovi

Railway are reputed to have been partly responsible for Bagnall getting the Spezia Harbour contract, along with the other contracts in Italy mentioned in the proceeding few paragraphs.

Another notable order of the period came from North America, in fact the only Bagnall locomotive ever sent new to that country and a special one for use underground in a Pennsylvania coal mine, the Hartley and Marshall Coal Company of Banksville. Manufacturer's number 590 of April 1884 was ordered by Hartley & Marshall, a two-foot gauge 0-6-0 with 5x12in cylinders (notice the long stroke) and an overall height of 5ft 3in. The working pressure was no less that 250psi, making this perhaps the highest pressure used in a locomotive boiler built in this country up to that time. Appropriately named EXPERIMENT, a copper firebox and brass tubes were fitted and the little engine cost £375. In a letter that appeared in *The Engineer,* issue dated 2 October 1884, Gordon Bagnall quoted from a letter received from the owners of this engine: 'Pittsbugh 1 August 1884. We are pleased to say that the engine is doing daily service and is doing much better than we ever expected. The engine is one mile underground and never comes to daylight. We are not doing full work at present, but when trade revives we expect to move 1,000 tons of coal one mile daily. At present we are moving each trip 30 wagons, each wagon containing 3,300 pounds of coal, weight of wagon empty being 1,225 pounds, making a gross load of 67 tons and we can add 10 wagons to above load if need be'. On the face of it this would be some achievement and one is left wondering about the health of those employed where the engine was working! Perhaps the high boiler pressure was intended to facilitate the engine operating for lengthy periods without firing? The Hartley and Marshall Coal Company was later taken over by the Pittsburgh Coal Company and the mine closed about 1908. However we have no record of the later history of this locomotive.

Another interesting engine was manufacturer's number 934, more so as we have some local lore about its operation. It was ordered by Hawley & Bridgewood a company of coal masters working the Mossfield & Bentilee Collieries at Longton in nearby Stoke-on-Trent. The engine was an 0-4-0 inverted saddle tank, the cylinders were 7x10in and the track gauge was 1ft 11in; it was despatched from the works in November 1887 and cost £425 16/- (£425 80p). An interesting aspect of the design was the very low overhaul height and the footplate at the rear was almost at track level; obviously the engine had to negotiate some very restricted clearances and perhaps for this reason, it was appropriately named MIDGE. The colliery company had a tramway about one mile long from the pit itself to a landsale wharf in Longton, and as the line had to pass over some high ground, there were 1 in 20 gradients on both sides. Commenting to a representative of the *Staffordshire Evening Sentinel* on 26 March 1954, a subscriber from Cheadle made the following statement, faithfully reproduced in the local Pottery dialect. 'When ar sowe in th' Sentinel a photo uv er ingine uz was cowd ISABEL, uz wuz er midget, me mind went back fir a number er years un ar remember ut th' owd Sall pits (Mossfield Colliery nar) uz thee was a little

This locomotive, MIDGE, is aptly named and as can be seen it was specially designed to clear a very low loading gauge. Number 934 of 1887, it was photographed on the 1ft11in gauge railway that connected the Mossfield & Bentilee Collieries at Longton in Stoke-on-Trent, with a landsale wharf and main-line railway connection in Longton itself. Notice the sandbox in front of the inverted saddle tank with its operating rod from the cab. This little engine finished its life at the Barrasford Quarry of the Northumberland Whinstone Company Limited, and was last heard of by the maker's when spares were sent there in April 1916; nevertheless it seems to have lasted until 1926.

This illustration is almost certainly of number 1198 of 1889, one of three of these small 6x9in cylinder 2-4-0 side tanks sent to Austria-Hungary to fulfil an order by William A Stone of Prague. This particular example, No 1 in the fleet of a Czech contractor called Lanna, is said to have been photographed in 1928 at the Vitkovice Steelworks. Czech records have the manufacturer's number as 1189, but this is almost certainly a mistake for 1198. The engine's final demise is not known, but its two sisters worked on the Hungarian Railways.

ingine theer uz eust fer pull tubs ur coal ut th' top uth' runs. It wanna ar dunna think uz big us th' one in th' Sentinel, un it wus coawd The Midge, un wus peented graen un gowld. It wuz a reel gem. Ar wunda what becum er that? Con ony er thee readers uz live on th' Hill, ur ony wheer else, tell me what becum on it?' What a lovely story, and as the engine left the colliery at around the turn of the century, the storyteller must have been in his late 60s or early 70s when he recalled his memories. What actually happened was the replacement of locomotive haulage by a stationary engine and endless ropes, as a result of which MIDGE went north in about 1901 to work at a quarry in Northumberland. The new owners wasted little time in altering the cab the give the driver more room, as well as extending the chimney to lift the smoke and exhaust higher. Before we leave this 'reel gem', it is worth noting that when William Rigby & Company took over operation of the collieries from Hawley & Bridgewood, MIDGE had been sent back to Stafford for rebuilding; this was in March 1894.

A couple more orders are worthy of mention before we leave the description of specific locomotives in this Chapter as they also illustrate the diversity of countries and markets the Company was penetrating. In 1889

and 1890, three of the small 2-4-0 side tanks were supplied, in this case with 6x9in cylinders and costing £394 7/ 6d (£394 37¹/₂p) each. They were ordered by WA Stone of Prague in what was then Austria, a company acting as agents. Readers will recall we met Stone earlier in this Chapter at the RASE show at Windsor in 1889 and this order may have stemmed from that occasion. The first two locomotives, manufacturer's numbers 1188 and 1190 were delivered in November 1889 for a track gauge of 2ft 6¹/₃₂in (762.8mm), whilst the third, manufacturer's number 1198 was despatched in November the following year - in this case the track gauge was 2ft 3⁵/₈in. All three locomotives however, were ordered together in July 1889 and whilst the first two were named MEZOHEGYES and PEREG respectively, the third one does not appear to have carried a name. The two names are those of towns in Hungary and these two at least, were for the Magyar Kiralyi Menesbirtok (Hungarian Royal Stud Estate) at Mezohegyes, in part of what was then the Austria-Hungarian empire. Gordon Bagnall's daughter Jessica once recalled to the authors a number of the countries she recalled her father having visited in the furtherance of his business, and Hungary was one of them. Doubtless therefore, his visit to that country would have been in connection with these three locomotives and in all probability, other light railway material would have been supplied at the same time.

The later history of these engines is somewhat obscure, but one of them, reordered as number 1189 (which it is considered must be a mistake for 1198), worked for a well established Czech contractor named Lanna, and was used on a 700mm (as near as makes no difference to 2ft 3⁵/₈in) gauge railway employed in building the Labe river port of Usti nad Labem. This would be around 1901 and the engine is recorded as Lanna's fleet number 1. Apparently this locomotive was still serviceable with Lanna as late as 1909, when it disappears from available records for some years but in 1928, on the occasion of the centenary celebrations of the Vitkovice Factory (Ostrava), it was exhibited, still carrying the Lanna number plate 1. This is the last record we have. The Vitovice Factory had a 790mm gauge railway system but there is no evidence that the Bagnall was re-gauged and worked there. The other two (by process of elimination works numbers 1188 and

1190), appear to have become Hungarian Railways (MAV Gazdasagi Vasutak) GV34 and GV33 respectively, and after nationalisation of the railway systems in that country they were still in service at the beginning of the 1950s and employed on an agricultural railway at Mezohegyes. This was a railway that had formerly belonged to the Hungarian monarch and had an unusual track gauge of 762.8 mm, this metric dimension equates exactly to the otherwise rather strange gauge quoted in imperial measurements in the Bagnall records of 2ft 6¹/₃₂in. Amazing that two of these early engines should have survived so long, but the records available are unfortunately silent on their final demise. It is of interest to note that these three locomotives are among the very few British built steam locomotives (only one other is positively known) to have been exported to what became Czechoslovakia.

Another interesting series of four small locomotives are recorded in the registers for a customer named Diekmann. The first three, manufacturer's numbers 770 of April 1886, 874 of March 1887 and 968 of March 1888, were all four-wheel inverted saddle tanks with 4¹/₂x7¹/₂in cylinders, whilst the fourth one was a 2-4-0 side tank with 6x9in cylinders - number 1258 of March 1890. The first three were 2ft 6in gauge and the last one 2ft 5¹/₄in, which might suggest it went to a different location. Diekmann Brothers & Company had offices in London, whilst an associate company, Diekmann Barckhausen & Company had offices at both Bassein and Rangoon in Burmah. The business was one of rice millers and merchants as well as exporters and dealers and as might be imagined, the Diekmanns and Brackhausens were of German origin. When these two companies amalgamated to become Diekmann Brothers & Company Limited in October 1902, among the assets was freehold and lease hold land at Poozoodoung (sometimes spelt Pazundang) and Malagon near Rangoon, as well as at Bassein. Bassein is in the south-west corner of Burmah and on the banks of the River Bassein, which in turn runs into the Mouths of the Irrawaddy. It appears reasonably safe to assume therefore, that these locomotives were used at rice plantations, or other similar plantation type operations in and around Rangoon and Bassein.

Over the years to encompass the increased production and the larger locomotives being built, the Castle Engine Works was gradually extended and we saw earlier that a further three acres or so of land was leased from Lord Stafford in November 1884. The journal *The Implement & Machinery Review*, issue dated

Whilst this is quite a well know photograph it deserves reproduction here as it shows not only one of the small Bagnall inverted saddle tanks designs, but also a contractors railway typical of the conditions many of the small locomotives had to contend with. This particular locomotive is number 970 of 1888, originally built for use on a forestry railway in Mid-Wales, but seen here about 1897 when engaged on building the Lynton & Barnstable 1ft 11¹/₂ in gauge railway in North-Devon. Originally built as a 0-4-0, notice the engine has been converted to an 0-4-2 wheel arrangement with a larger cab and bunker. The spark arrester chimney bears testimony to the engine's earlier forestry duties. Cylinders were 5x7¹/₂in and driving wheel diameter but 1ft 3¹/₂in; this little engine finished its days at the Portland Stone Quarries in Dorset and as far as can be ascertained, was scrapped in 1932.

2 November 1883, reported that over 100 men were employed and that in the previous four years equipment to a value of £50,000 had been produced. As early as October 1883, 60 sugar cane and bogie wagons had been shipped as a single order to Cuba and in the half year ending 30 June 1883, £15,000 of equipment alone had been exported. Noted earlier was *The Engineer* of 6 March 1885, reporting that the company had been awarded the Soudan contract and this article also mentioned that the works was being extended to accommodate the work, and although the Soudan scheme was abandoned, most of not all the equipment ordered was in fact built and delivered. Separate shops were built for the different manufacturing processes, with the main erecting shop developing alongside the main railway line; it was eventually flanked by the fitting shops to the east - main line side - and the machine shops to the west. There were separate shops for boiler work, pattern making, an iron foundry and one specifically for the construction of carriages, wagons and track-work components. By 1890 around

300 men and boys were employed. Mention has also been made of Samuel Thomas Price who became in effect works manager. Price was born on 1 December 1861 at St Georges, Oakengates in Shropshire, the son of Thomas and Caroline Susanna (nee Astbury) Price, his father being described as an iron founder. Samuel served his apprenticeship, initially with the local Lilleshall Company at Oakengates (which is presumably, where his father was employed), and later with the Midland Railway Company at Derby. Subsequently the family seem to have moved to Stafford and young Samuel was employed as an engineer at nearby Milford Pumping Station, a post he appears to have occupied for approximately two years; he then joined Bagnall at the Castle Engine Works. The Price family was a large one and it would appear to have been Samuel's father who moved his branch of the family from Shropshire to Stafford, and Samuel married a local girl Alice Mary, from nearby Aston. At one period (1901) three houses in the Stafford suburb of Doxey, 108, 109 and 110 Doxey, were occupied by no

GRANTHAM *was number 1000 of 1888, and unusually for the period fitted with a conventional saddle tank. This engine was new as ROBINSON, to Manchester Corporation for use on the 2ft 6in gauge system around the sewage estate railway at Carrington, which is near Partington in Cheshire - that is where this photographs was taken on 21 June 1934. Bagnall supplied a new boiler in 1929 and the engine lasted until 1939, but it had been moved to the Chat Moss estate in 1938 when Carrington closed down. The engine was originally named after Alderman Robinson, but when he ceased to serve on the Cleansing Committee it was renamed. The original boiler had the dome on the firebox, so when this boiler was fitted the saddle tank had to be modified (or a new one supplied). Notice the small home-made tender, but whether the engine originally had a back to the cab is not known. (Late Derek Stoyel)*

less than 21 members of the Price family! One of Samuel's sons, Sam, is described in 1901 as an engine fitter, his elder brother George (born St Georges 1858) a brass caster, and George's son Frank, a pattern maker; like Samuel these three may also have been employed at the Castle Engine Works.

Discussed earlier was the claim by Price, when interviewed by the late Ralph Russell, that he joined Bagnall in or about 1877, and his seemingly authoritative remark regarding the building of the first two standard-gauge locomotives. However, in view of his age and the earlier employment referred to here, this would have been impossible and the absolute earliest he could have moved to the Castle Engine Works would be 1882. We also have the evidence of a newspaper report of Gordon Bagnall's wedding, where reference is made of a Mr McRae, said to be the manager of the works, in attendance at the ceremony together with his wife; he made a presentation of a black marble timepiece. As this was in 1883, it would seem pretty conclusive that Price could not have taken up the position of works manager until some time after that date. However, when he did, he seems to have taken charge of general works management and production leaving Gordon Bagnall to concentrate on designing and marketing issues. In 1881 the workforce totalled some 68 men and boys, expanding to some 300 10 years later and this gives some idea of the developing business. Mention has been made of Thomas Walter's principal interest in the Company being a financial one and he was by far the largest shareholder in the partnership. When the partnership was dissolved and a Joint Stock Company limited by shares was formed in July 1887, Walter was not only the largest single shareholder, but his total holding was greater than the sum of all the other shareholders including Gordon Bagnall.

In the year ending 31 March 1887 the Company had a turnover of £28,499, rising in the year ending 30 September 1890 to £39,040; in 1887 the total wage and salary bill amounted to £6,043, in 1888 it was £8,613, and by 1889 had risen to £10,343. The 1887 figures represent the first specific financial statistics that are available and were compiled as a part of the arrangement to convert the partnership into a limited company, hence their survival. A breakdown of the assets of the Company at that time gives the following valuations (rounded to nearest £); land and buildings

This picture shows one of the oldest locomotives to be photographed at the works. MARGARET was number 1052 of 1889, a small 1ft 11in gauge, 4x6in cylinder four-wheel inverted tank design for Hall & Boardman, Swadlincote & Cadley Hill Collieries in Derbyshire. However, the engine in not new in this view but rather returned to the works for overhaul, or perhaps for re-sale. It later belonged to George G Blackwell & Sons & Company Limited at Grindleford in Derbyshire where it was named SPAR QUEEN - it was there by May 1906. Whilst there is no surviving record of it ever having come back to Stafford, as can be seen from the photograph it is clearly not new, but nonetheless in good external condition. The illustration shows well the design of rectangular manufacturer's plate in use at the time the engine was built, and although this has the date January 1889, the records show the engine was actually delivered in the following month. This was one of the smallest engines built, with hardly any room for the identification plate!

£2,862; machinery £4,125; loose plant £2,115; office furniture £173; patterns and drawings £1,866; stores £3,677; finished stock £1,000; foundry material £290; work in progress £3,420. Between the date when the limited company was formed and September 1895, although jumping ahead of the story somewhat, a total of £2,051 was spent on building improvements and additional buildings which included extensions to the foundry and erecting shop. A lot of emphasis in this and the proceeding Chapter has been placed on the advertising activities and catalogues the firm produced. To give an indication of the finances involved in this sort of activity, in the period 1887 to 1890, £1,752 was spent on advertising - a sizable sum in those times - and there was a separate account for the cost of producing the catalogues and making the engraved plates of the illustrations. As well as the share capital the newly formed Company was also partly financed by a series of bank loans. For example, the Worcester Bank £6,602, Manchester & Liverpool Bank £453 and Lloyds Bank £991, and there was also a loan from Bailey Toms & Company - the London based agents mentioned earlier - to the tune of £750.

We must now introduce into the story the Gifford family, as the brothers John Gifford Gifford and James Caldwell Gifford, eventually joined Gordon Bagnall in his business and of the two, John became by far the more active. The Giffords hailed from Glenluce in Wigtownshire and only a few miles from the home of the Gibsons, not surprisingly therefore, the two families were acquainted and one of John Gibson's sisters married William Gifford. John Gibson and his sister Jane Ralston Gibson, were two of the seven children of James and Jannet Gibson (nee Cauldwell - note the different spelling from the second Christian name of James and other family members). The Cauldwells had in part descended from the Scottish Ralstons, a family with a lineage going back to the 12th century, and Jane was born on 13 April 1822 at Glenluce. On 19 March 1851 she married William Gifford, also born in Glenluce and a few years older - he was born in 1819. The Giffords were quite a large family and William had eight brothers and four sisters, all born in and around Glenluce. Together with his wife William moved south

Two for the price of one in this picture taken on the Scropton Tramway of JC Staton & Company, near Tutbury in Staffordshire. The two three-foot gauge locomotives are number 1232 of September 1891 leading, and number 1050 of January 1889 behind. The larger engine has 8x12in cylinders and the smaller one 6x9in; notice the different design characteristics between the two locomotives, for example chimney, smokebox door and dome, all typical of their respective periods. The Scropton Tramway was almost two miles long and ran from the North Staffordshire Railway line at Scropton Crossing just north of Tutbury, to alabaster mines at Fauld. It opened in 1889 and the earlier Bagnall locomotive was the first motive power. Both these locomotives later passed to new owners, the smaller one to Joseph Boam Limited for use at Middleton Towers in Norfolk; it had disappeared from Scropton by 1894, while the larger one went in January 1903 to Manchester Corporation for use at the Davyhulme Sewage Works.

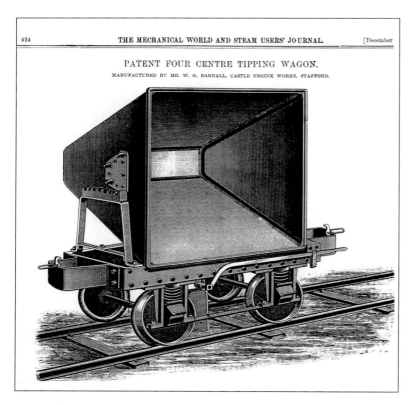

424   THE MECHANICAL WORLD AND STEAM USERS' JOURNAL.   [December

PATENT FOUR CENTRE TIPPING WAGON.

MANUFACTURED BY MR. W. G. BAGNALL, CASTLE ENGINE WORKS, STAFFORD.

An good example of technical publicity literature for rolling stock as opposed to locomotives is this engraving of what is described as a Patent Four Centre Tipping Wagon. This illustration accompanied a short description in the December 1884 issue of The Mechanical World & Steam Users' Journal, once again highlighting the ability of Gordon Bagnall to get his products into all sorts of trade journals. Despite the mention of a patent, there is in fact no patent in Bagnall's name for such a wagon, and when this and similar illustrations were used in the catalogues and other publicity material, no such claim was made. The 'four-centre' refers to the four spigots on the end of the wagon body about which it could be tilted, and provided a very stable arrangement to allow unloading. There are however, a number of alternative arrangements to the same end and it really was a matter of personal opinion which was the best; most manufacturers had its own preferred method. In 1895 one of these wagons for 2ft 6in gauge and with a capacity of 20 cub ft, or one ton, could be purchased for £9 5/- (£9 25p), and there was a discount to be negotiated for bulk orders!

to Tranmere on the Wirral, and by the time of the 1851 census they were in lodgings there at 153 Clifton Park - William gave his occupation as master mariner. Several of his brothers and sisters also migrated south, and they all settled in and around Liverpool where, over the years the brothers variously gave their occupations as master mariners, ship owners and eastern merchants. For many years William Gifford and his family lived at 79 Upper Parliament Street in Bootle, whilst several of his brothers, some of whom remained bachelors resided at 4 South Street in Toxteth.

William and Jane Gifford had five children, the two boys mentioned earlier, James and John, and three girls two of whom, Margaret Caldwell who was born in 1857, and Helen Mary who was born in 1861, remained unmarried. Jessie Caldwell was the youngest of the sisters, she was born in 1854 and on 18 December 1877 married Norman McLeod. He was a year younger and came from Edinburgh, the service was at St Andrews (Scottish) Church in Liverpool, conducted by the groom's father the Rev. Donald McLeod DD, and under the Church of Scotland rites; Donald McLeod was Chaplin to Queen Victoria. This marriage was not an altogether happy one, eventually Jessie and her young

children, the couple had two sons and a daughter, went to live with her brothers James and John. This was after the brothers had moved to Stafford, as will soon be related. The daughter, Norma Agnes Maxwell McLeod, who was born in 1880, later married Charles Maitland, and we shall return to this family later in the story.

All William Gifford's brothers appear to have lived in the Toxteth or Bootle areas of Liverpool after they moved south, and they were all involved in shipping or as agents of one description or the other. Indications are that for a short period at least, William Gifford took up farming and moved further south to Stafford, as on 2 April 1856 when his first child James was born, the address was given as 28 Earl Street in Stafford. William's occupation on the birth certificate is a farmer, although when the younger son John was born on 11 March 1860, the family had moved back to Liverpool with an address of Merton Road in Bootle. William's profession was then listed as a ship owner; he died at Bootle on 17 September 1868 and in his will he is once again described as a master mariner. The various Gifford family members appear to have accumulated considerable wealth in their activities as master mariners, ship owners and eastern agents, and as several of William's brothers remained un-married, and some of those that did had no issue, much of the cumulative inheritance passed down the male line. When William's brother Alexander Gifford passed away on 3 March 1888, he left a seventh of his estate, which in total was valued at almost £61,000, in trust to his Brother William's wife Jane Ralston Gifford. The will was drawn-up in such a way that on her death (she died 6 February 1897), the majority of the money would pass to her son, James Caldwell Gifford. This and other bequests that eventually passed to the brothers from their uncles made James and John wealthy men.

John Gifford served an engineering apprenticeship with the Birkenhead shipbuilders Cammell Laird & Company Limited, whilst his elder brother was involved with the family shipping business and was for several years its agent in Argentina, based in Buenos Ayres. However, by 1901 when he was only 45, he had to all intents and purposes retired from active business. We have no particular knowledge as to why the Gifford brothers moved to Stafford; they were of course cousins of Gordon Bagnall's wife Jessie, and James had been born there. We do know that the Bagnall Company needed capital for expansion at the time and it appears that the Rev. Edward Salt wanted to release his investment. We also know that Gordon Bagnall was heavily involved in the restructuring of his uncle's old business, during the course of which he had to write down his own investment from £21,000 to £10,000. This was a personal loss of £11,000, a large sum of money in those days which he could ill afford to loose. Whatever the specific circumstances John commenced work with Gordon Bagnall in 1886 as a draughtsman, initially lodging with the Fowke family at 18 Market Square. The Fowkes were chemists in the town and some years later in 1904, one of the sons, George, formed a partnership with Paul Weiss and acquired the principal photographic studio in the town from Harold Tilley. Situated in Victoria Street, this partnership and its successors eventually became the official photographers to WG Bagnall Limited, and continued to act in this capacity almost until the final demise of the firm. However, whether John Gifford's connection with George Fowke had anything to do with this has gone unrecorded, but it may have done. By 1901 John had been joined in Stafford by his brother James and his sister Margaret Caldwell, neither of whom ever married,

and they all lived in the Burton Manor district of Stafford, which adjoins the Wolverhampton Road south of the town.

John became a shareholder in WG Bagnall Limited on 1 November 1889. On that date he bought the 50 ordinary shares held by the Rev. Edward Salt, paying the face valve of £500, and at the same time purchased 100 new shares, also at the face valve of £1,000. This issue of new shares increased the paid-up share capital of the Company by £1,000, to a total of £25,500. Later, on 24 January 1890, John bought a further 45 ordinary shares, this time from Gordon Bagnall and again at par. John Gifford was originally listed in the firm's books as a draughtsman, and he was certainly involved in the drawing office as his initials appear in the drawing registers and on numerous drawing in the period from 1892, which is when the surviving records begin. The last entries in the registers with his initials, and therefore the last drawings he was personally involved with, date from as late as July 1905, so he would have still been engaged in design issues at that date. Nonetheless, by July 1901 John Gifford had been appointed a director of the Company. The Giffords later moved, about 1911, to a large house at Weeping Cross, south of the town, called Crossfields, and like his brother and sister John never married. In 1893 John was instrumental in the formation of the Cannock Chase Golf Club, which later became the Brocton Hall Golf Club, and golf seems to have been the only excursion into public life of both brothers. After the death of Gordon Bagnall in 1907, as will be discussed in some detail later, John Gifford became managing director of the Company but James never appears to have been very much involved in the day-to-day management issues.

The patent railway sleepers manufactured by the firm have already been briefly mentioned, in fact Bagnall was not slow in using the protection of the Patent Acts and there are several in the period 1887 to 1889, both in his name and in association with others. There are no less than three patents in connection with steel railway sleepers, the principal one having a provisional date of 26 January 1888 - patent number 1202 it was confirmed 10 August the same year. Jointly named in this patent with Gordon Bagnall was Arthur Henry Heath, whom we met earlier and who gave his address as Coopers Hill, Englefield Green in Surrey, and his occupation as a civil engineer. Heath was however as outlined in the last Chapter, employed as a Professor at Coopers Hill College. The principle of the sleeper covered by this patent is described thus: 'Pressed out of steel rectangular plate by hydraulic pressure and has great resistance to buckling at mid length owing to the convex or thrown up corrugations. The sleeper becomes wider under the rail seat so that it has great strength where required at mid length and greater bearing surface under the rail seat where width is necessary. The centre channel, which is practically a concave corrugation, is extended to the ends of the sleeper, gradually deepening for draining purposes and for strengthening the sleeper under the rail seats'. Among the advantages claimed was the strength given by the corrugations and that the material used could be thinner and lighter and hence ideal for light railways.

Two further patents were subsequently granted for steel sleepers; both improving on the original idea and in each of these cases the patent was granted solely in Gordon Bagnall's name. The first, number 3037 with a provisional date of 20 February 1889, was confirmed on 23 March the same year while the second, number 4255 with a provisional date of 11 March 1889, was confirmed on 13 April 1889. The principle of patent number 3037 was a sleeper specifically intended for very

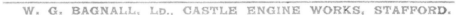

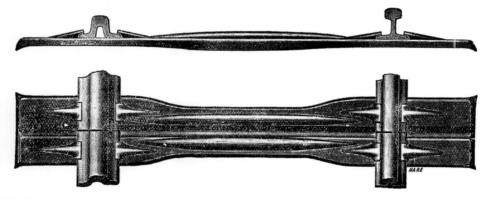

W. G. BAGNALL, LD., CASTLE ENGINE WORKS, STAFFORD.

Rivetless-joint
Sleeper

For Collieries,
Ironworks, &c.

BAGNALL'S PATENT RIVETLESS SLEEPER: a perfect Sleeper for Colliery and General Use, made to suit any Section of Rail.

It will be seen from the illustration above that the sleeper is of very strong make ; the convex corrugations in the centre prevent it from buckling, and the concave corrugation throughout the sleeper adds great strength, especially under the rail seat, where the sleeper is punched out for the chairs. The rail easily slips into position and out again when desired and the chairs are not liable to break or get out of shape, being greatly strengthened by corrugations. The width under rail seat is 5 inches. The sleepers are made of steel and are all dipped into anti-corrosive composition before being sent away, they have been designed especially for colliery use and are suitable for any class of rail. The usual gauges about collieries are from 18in. to 26in. Price to suit these gauges, for lots of 50 and under 1/5 each, 250 and under 1/4 each, 500 and under 1/3 each, over 500 1/2 each, delivered to any part of the United Kingdom. All sizes from the smallest up to main line are made, and special prices will be given for sleepers suitable for 3 rails or any other class that may be required. These sleepers are lighter, more portable, more easily fixed and stored away, and will last much longer than wood sleepers ; they are cheaper and in every way superior to the rivetted metal sleepers in ordinary use ; there are no sharp edges to wear ropes in cases where they pass over the sleepers, and horses are not liable to trip up, as on flat sleepers. With order, section of rail in use should be sent.

The following is an extract from *The Colliery Guardian:*

" A NEW SLEEPER FOR MINING PURPOSES.—A new sleeper, the form of which is worthy of note, has been specially designed for colliery use. It will be seen from the appended illustrations that by the central convex corrugation the sleeper is made strong in the centre to prevent any possibility of buckling. The central concave corrugation lying between the convex corrugations is extended to the ends of the sleeper, gradually deepening ; it thus serves for carrying off water, for strengthening the part under rail seat, and where the jaws are punched out of the solid. It will be observed that the sleeper is a rivetless one. The jaws or chairs thrown up have strengthening corrugations at the back, and the sleeper, slightly weakened at this part, is made amply strong by the above-named concave corrugations. The sides are turned down, as are also the ends, to retain the ballast and to prevent lateral movement, especially on curved lines. The jaws can be thrown up to suit either the ordinary bridge section of rail as shown on the left or the T rail as shown on the right-hand side of sleeper. It is the general custom in colliery work to lay the rails in short lengths, simply using the sleepers for the joints ; on this account, as will be noticed, the sleeper is made extra wide, and, coupled with this advantage, the general form and design give great strength."

The Engineer says—

" The sleeper is one which, by its lightness, strength, and simplicity, must strongly recommend itself."

A page from Catalogue No 13 dated November 1895, illustrating the Patent Rivetless Sleeper. Actually the sleeper illustrated combines the first and last of the three Bagnall patents embracing steel sleepers for light railway use. The first patent - jointly with Arthur Henry Heath - covered the principle of the corrugations to give added strength, whilst the third covered the arrangement seen here of retaining the rail on the sleeper, the chairs in effect being integral with the sleeper itself. The second patent - not illustrated here - usually had the chairs riveted to the sleeper rather than pressed out of the parent metal.

light railways or tramways as it embodied a more complicated series of corrugations than the earlier one. Designed to give even greater relief of the vertical load on the rail seats, the seats were inclined inwards which in turn relieved the load on the chairs. The corrugations were also designed with greater emphasis than on the earlier design, of preventing any water accumulating on the sleeper. The third and last patent embodied the concept of the rail chairs being integral with the sleeper itself, the chairs being pressed out of the parent metal. Additionally, if the width of the sleeper was doubled, it could also provide a method of joining rails together rather than by the use of conventional fishplates. In these cases the sleeper had four integral chairs, two on each side, one each to support the respective ends of the rails to be joined. In this design where the rail fastening (chairs) were pressed out of the sleeper there were additional corrugations to compensate for the otherwise reduction of strength in the area of the pressings.

It has to be said that there are significant similarities in the principles embodied in these three patents, somewhat surprising therefore, that Gordon Bagnall was able to convince the Patent Office through his agents that each one was sufficiently different to warrant a further patent being granted. Nevertheless, aided by these patents Gordon Bagnall was able to develop a sizable business in manufacturing light railway track-work and he established the Company as a significant player in the market. There was plenty of competition too, both from manufacturers in this country like John Fowler and J&F Howard already mentioned, and from continental builders like Decauville for example. The Rostock based R Dolberg, mentioned earlier in this Chapter in connection with the RASE shows, had three British patents granted in 1888, all involving light railway equipment including rail joints, points and crossings.

In the catalogues and other advertising material great emphasis was made of the advantages of the various arrangements of sleeper. A short article appeared in *The Engineer*, issue dated 14 April 1889, and there is a much more extensive, illustrated feature in *The Implement & Machinery Review* of 1 June 1889. This article is accompanied by several illustrations and has detailed descriptions of the three types of steel sleeper along with a simple arrangement of fishplate. This

fishplate is described as 'Bagnall's automatic fishplate', an arrangement only requiring the plates to be physically attached to one of the rails to be joined, this rail then being slid onto its partner. By this simple method, and it has to be added there were other similar examples by other manufacturers, pre-assembled sections of track for portable or semi-portable railways could be easily and quickly laid. In the period 1889 to 1902, Gordon Bagnall drew Royalty payments for his patent sleepers sold by the Company to a total of £1,323. However, there is no evidence of any other payments as a result of other manufacturers adopting the designs.

Another patent applied for about the same time as the sleepers was one jointly by Gordon Bagnall and a member of the Stafford boot and shoe making Bostock family. The application was dated 26 May 1887 and is described as: 'Scoring Paste, Straw Card and Boards, for boxes, cases etc'. The exact details of what this application was intended for is somewhat of a mystery as a patent was never granted, but one presumes it was in connection with boxes in which boots and shoes were packed. One is also left wondering if Bagnall had ideas about manufacturing such boxes; whatever the case it does illustrate Gordon Bagnall's involvement with other manufacturers in the town.

An example of the all steel light railway track laid out in the works yard, a photograph used for publicity purposes and in this case it illustrates a turn-out. Notice the arrangement of fishplates, the female part being attached to the rail ends, the male part would be on the connecting rail and the two would come together to form a joint, the male part slotting inside the female.

Another example of the lightweight semi-portable track work, in this case a more complicated double turn-out, again laid out in the works yard and another picture used for publicity purposes. Notice in this and the previous illustration the sleepers are not of the corrugated pattern, and that they employ yet another arrangement for retaining the rail.

On the locomotive side of the business the company continued to build a variety of narrow-gauge locomotives for both the home and export markets, many of them of individual designs and with hardly any two exactly the same. This Chapter has covered individually and in some detail, a significant number of the early locomotives, those built in the first almost twenty years or so of the firm's existence. The point has been made that comparatively little is known about most of them from official documents, but as will have been seen much has been gleaned from a wide range of other sources. Many of the early locomotives are felt to be of considerable technical and historical interest, hence the attention they have been given in this Chapter. But the types of locomotive being built and their design characteristics was soon to change, as indeed was the whole way the Company conduced its engineering and other affairs, when Ernest Edwin Baguley joined in 1892. We do not know at this distance in time what attracted Baguley to join Bagnall, but we can be pretty sure that Gordon Bagnall would have been on the look-out for additional design and organisational talent as the business expanded. Prior to Baguley's arrival and his subsequent organisational

initiatives, very few locomotives had been exactly the same; little thought seems to have been given to production techniques or the standardisation of components. Nonetheless, the firm had done extremely well as a rather late entrant to the well established market of building locomotives, and we have seen how Bagnall was able to keep the cost of his locomotives very competitive.

But Gordon Bagnall was nothing if not a realist, and he appreciated that the way the Company had been undertaking production and generally conducting its business could not continue, especially with the more advanced developments in production engineering that were all around him. The existing practices in the building of locomotives at the Castle Engine Works, and indeed the design of the locomotives themselves, were clearly becoming less and less economic and if the Company was to keep pace with its competitors it had to change.

The firm had done very well in capturing a significant slice of the light railway market, as the advantages of light railways became more and more apparent, but times were changing. Despite the fact that the catalogues and other advertising material claimed that

Two more examples of the small narrow-gauge wagons which were a significant part of the works production during the period covered by this Chapter. The one on the left is a bolster wagon and the one on the right a colliery mine-tub.

the locomotives were built 'to gauge and template', this does not always seem to have been the case. Older employees told stories in later years of the difficulty in supplying spare parts for the early locomotives; even to the extent of men having to visit locations where the engines were working so that measurements could be taken and sketches made! For engines located in other countries this was not so easy and even more significant problems arose! Sketches had frequently to be requested of exactly what part was required! But it is time to move on and study the activities of the Company after Ernest Edwin Baguley arrived on the scene, along with the Giffords making cash available for expansion.

Another product of the Castle Engine Works iron foundry was these cast bollards, the particular ones illustrated here were situated on the footpath at the entrance to Victoria Park in Stafford itself, surrounding part of the gardens in front of the railway station. The pictures were taken in 1969, but unfortunately the bollards have now disappeared. They were know in the Works as 'Bean' bollards.

Title page from catalogue No 10 of May 1888; the locomotive is manufacturer's number 902, according to the records new in May 1887, although the plate on the cab-side has the month of April. Built for the public-works contractor Henry Fotherby & Sons, and first used on the contract to build Cant Clough reservoir for Burnley Corporation. One of the three-foot gauge 0-4-0 inverted saddle tank designs that were popular with contractors at this period. See page 82.

Another of the four-wheel inverted saddle tank locomotives used on public-works construction is the one shown here, manufacturer's number 891 of May 1887 named DENSHAW. One of two, the other was 892 PIETHORN, new to Oldham Corporation for use on the construction of Castleshaw reservoirs near Delph in Lancashire which, unusually, were undertaken by the Corporation with direct labour. This photograph of a rather splendid gathering was taken in the summer of 1887 to mark the ceremony of cutting the first sod of the reservoir. It would appear that at least some of the party had arrived on site in the rather make-shift vehicle attached to the locomotive. Notice the White-Ensign flying, normally only seen on a man-of-war.

Chapter Three

THE ERA OF ERNEST BAGULEY

Brief mention was made in the last Chapter of the lack of knowledge, at this distance in time, as to why Ernest Edwin Baguley joined Gordon Bagnall at Stafford; we can nevertheless be sure, that Bagnall would have been on the look-out for experienced assistance. Whilst Gordon Bagnall had been rather busy, and perhaps a little side-tracked, sorting out his grandfather's old business, he was conscious that a step-change was necessary in the areas of locomotive design and drawing office organisation if the Company was to remain competitive. In later years there was a family connection between the Bagnall and Baguley families, albeit a somewhat tenuous one and in any event dating from some time after Baguley arrived at Stafford. His wife Eileen was the sister-in-law of Maurice Lingard Alsop who we met in Chapter One; Alsop married Bagnall's daughter Jessica Gordon Bagnall.

At the expense of a little repetition it is worth exploring some of the background to the success Bagnall had achieved prior to Ernest Baguley arriving on the scene, not least because Baguley assumed complete control over design issues. Statements made by Samuel Price to the effect that Gordon Bagnall was a friend of Henry Hughes, and that Hughes may have had been involved in the manufacture of some of the

larger parts of the early Bagnall locomotives, have already been outlined. Also discussed was the supply of a locomotive to an order from Hughes at a time when he had been deposed from what had been his own company - this was manufacturer's number 377, supplied in July 1881.

There is evidence that Gordon Bagnall was an acquaintance, and may even have been a personal friend, of Sir Arthur Percival Heywood (3rd Bart 1849-1916 - succeeded his father Sir Thomas Percival in 1897) and that the two of them may well have first met at the Royal Agricultural Society of England Show (RASE) at Derby in the summer of 1881. Alternatively they could have met on a visit to Sir Arthur's private 15in gauge railway at nearby Duffield Bank, as this was open to the public during the period of the show. Heywood was a great protagonist of narrow-gauge railways; in particular 15in gauge which he reckoned was the narrowest gauge practicable for commercial use. With his own private capital and as something of a hobby, he built the 15in gauge railway at Duffield Bank and manufactured locomotives and rolling stock so as to provide practical demonstrations of his ideas. On occasions he made the railway at Duffield Bank available so that interested parties could study the principles of his ideas. For example, shortly after the

1881 RASE Derby Show representatives of the Royal Engineers made a visit and showed considerable interest. The Army gave consideration at the time to the concept that the 15in gauge might be ideal for lightly constructed temporary field railways; in the event the slightly wider 18in gauge found favour. However, Heywood did achieve one commercial success in designing, building and supplying the equipment for a light narrow-gauge railway to serve the estate of the Duke of Westminster. This was at Eaton Hall near Chester, and the works were completed in May 1896. Sir Arthur Heywood died in April 1916, shortly after which two of the Duffield Bank locomotives went to work for the Ministry of Munitions at Gretna, but later found their way to the Ravenglass & Exdale Railway in Cumberland. This former three-foot gauge railway was converted to 15in gauge in 1915 and the two locomotives gave many years service; one of them - MURIEL - still exists, albeit in a much rebuilt and externally altered condition as RIVER IRT.

To help advance his ideas at the time of the RASE Derby Show, Heywood wrote and published a small book, or pamphlet as he called it, *Minimum Gauge Railways*; enlarged and expanded editions appeared in 1894 and 1898. The 1894 edition was issued to coincide with a special three day opening to the general public of the Duffield Bank Railway. The 1898 edition coincided with the completion of the railway at Eaton Hall, and includes considerable detail of that railway and its equipment. A first edition of this book, currently in private hands, personally autographed by the author and with Gordon Bagnall's signature, might just indicate that Sir Arthur gave Bagnall a copy, either at the RASE Derby Show or at Duffield Bank. The two of them may have met at earlier Royal Shows. In 1844 Sir Arthur's father, Sir Thomas Percival Heywood (1823-1897), was elected a life governor of the RASE, and of course at various periods Bagnall was a member.

One of the principles of Sir Arthur's locomotive designs was a boiler with a circular firebox; it is tempting to speculate that the later adoption of this type of boiler and firebox on small narrow-gauge locomotives built by Bagnall, stemmed from Heywood's designs. The Bagnall version, which was not introduced until Ernest Baguley took over design responsibility, differed from Heywood's as the firebox outer wrapper diameter was considerable larger than the barrel, the two being almost concentric with each other. This feature allowed the diameter of the firebox to be considerably enlarged, with a greater heating surface than would otherwise be the case. In the Heywood version the firebox outer wrapper and barrel were the same diameter - in fact it was one continuous barrel. Nevertheless, the logic for the adoption of a circular arrangement was the same in both cases; with no conventional firebox and grate protruding below the barrel, the boiler could be located on the engine frames in such a way as to equalise, or very near equalise, its weight over the individual axles. Heywood claimed his ideas in this direction stemmed from the boilers designed by the London & North Western Railway (LNWR) locomotive engineer John Ramsbottom. Ramsbottom built some small shunting engines at Crewe with circular firebox boilers, ostensibly for the same reason of weight distribution.

Gordon Bagnall was also acquainted with John William Hartley (1845-1942); a principal of the Stoke-upon-Trent based engineering company, Hartley Arnoux & Fanning of the California Works. A native of Wentworth in Yorkshire, on leaving King Edward grammar school in Sheffield, Hartley had his engineering training between 1862 and 1867 as a pupil of TW Dodds of the Holmes Engine Works in Rotherham. There followed short periods as a draughtsman with the Yorkshire Engine Company at Sheffield, and as a foreman of the template making department with Sharp Stewart & Company at Manchester, both companies being engaged in designing and building locomotives. In 1870 Hartley followed his mentor Thomas Weatherborn Dodds to Stoke, Dodds having been appointed engineer of the North Staffordshire Railway (NSR), a post which in those days included responsibility for all aspects of engineering, civil and mechanical. Hartley's appointment was, in effect, not just chief draughtsman of the locomotive and rolling stock department as in his own words he 'took control of the locomotive building department at this time in a very backward state. I can claim that I brought this department up to contract shop form in a very short time'. Indeed he did, as it was during his tenure that Stoke Works started to build significant numbers of locomotives, as opposed to the NSR buying them from contractors. The reference to 'contract shop form', is a comparison of the commercial processes and procedures of companies building locomotives as a core business against competition, as opposed to a railway building and repairing locomotives for its own use. At the time when Dodds and Hartley descended on the NSR, Robert N Angus was the locomotive superintendent, or locomotive foreman as the post was then designated. Hartley however, reported directly to Dodds, as of course did Angus. In 1874 John Hartley left the NSR and went into business at Stoke in partnership with Leon & Ferdinand Arnoux, trading as general engineers. The Arnouxs, a French family, were connected with the local pottery and china industry, which of course, Stoke-on-Trent is famous the world over. In October 1886 the partners were joined by Walter Harley Fanning and the partnership, which originally traded as Hartley & Arnoux Brothers, became Hartley, Arnoux & Fanning. Worthy of a brief mention at this juncture is that Dodds too, left the NSR in 1874, in his case under somewhat of a cloud following the use of his patent Dodds Wedge Motion on a number of the company's locomotives. This form of valve gear did not prove to be the success anticipated and there followed a series of breakdowns when locomotives would neither more forwards or backwards, culminating in an incident involving a fatality.

John Hartley seems to have been both the engineering and commercial brains behind the new company and he was responsible for laying out the new workshops which became known as the California Works. The site was literally next door and just south of the NSR Stoke Works, its east side directly alongside the main railway line from Stoke to Colwich and Stafford. On its west side and at a slightly lower level runs the Trent & Mersey Canal, which in turn follows the River Trent. The range and diversity of engineering products designed and built at the California Works is bewildering to say the least. They included such diversity as complete gas holders, wrought iron and later steel bridges, colliery head-gears, stationary steam engines and boilers, along with small locomotives and light railway rolling stock. Most of the railway equipment which was not confined to locomotives and rolling stock but included track components and complete light railway systems, was sub-contracted from the Glasgow and London based Kerr, Stuart & Company. This company was already a well established

supplier of light railway equipment with an extensive world wide customer base, but at the time with no manufacturing facilities of its own. In 1890 Hartley took up a five year contract to manage the Kilmarnock based Britannia Engineering Works in Scotland, of Dick Kerr & Company. This was another firm who undertook sub-contract railway work for Kerr, Stuart. On completion of his contract Hartley returned to Stoke-on-Trent having been offered the management of the California Works, which by this time was in the ownership of Kerr, Stuart & Company Limited. Kerr, Stuart had in effect, acquired the works of one of its principal sub-contractors.

John Hartley remained with Kerr, Stuart until 1902, when he went into another partnership, this time under the title Hartley, Causton & Richmond, with workshops in nearby Fenton. Later, in 1916 he opened completely new workshops at Etruria, north of Stoke-upon-Trent, where he traded with his sons as Hartley Sons & Company Limited, the firm later becoming Hartley's (Stoke-on-Trent) Limited. At Etruria the new company soon began to specialise in designing and building sanitary and sewage equipment. This was largely the result of John Hartley's 1904 invention of a rope driven wind balanced rectangular sewage distributor. This form of sewage plant enabled the company to obtain a contract for no less then nine acres of sewage distributors for Stoke-on-Trent. Railway related work was also undertaken at Etruria, in particular track and rolling stock components, axle-boxes for example, and on occasion the repair of local industrial locomotives. However, Hartley's new venture did not build any locomotives or rolling stock at Etruria.

John William Hartley was an incredible man, an ingenious and commercially minded engineer with numerous patents to his name - no less than 80 in fact - although some were in joint names; he also had many other achievements to his credit. The patents covered a very wide range of engineering including locomotives and rolling stock, railway civil engineering, stationary steam engines, boilers, and of course sewage disposal equipment. He was still actively involved with his sons in the business at Etruria, almost to the end of his long life - he was 96 years old when he passed away. Amazingly, it was not until 1931 when he was 86 years old, that one of his old pupils, WS Edwards the general manager of WG Bagnall Limited, persuaded him to

An example of one of the locomotives built to an old design but after Baguley has assumed design responsibility. The type of locomotive illustrated here, a four-wheel coupled inverted saddle tank, had proved to be very popular with public works contractors, and this was yet another example. Number 1434 of 1894 was new to Preston Corporation for use on the construction of Alston No 2 reservoir near Longridge, which the Corporation was constructing with direct labour. As delivered the engine was named ALSTON, the STAFFORD name plate - which was actually a wooden pattern - was for publicity purposes only. Built to suit the traditional three-foot gauge of reservoir construction works it had 8x12in cylinders and two-foot diameter wheels. After completion of the works at Alston in 1901, the engine went on to have an eventful life in the contracting industry. In 1907 for example, it was with Sir John Jackson at Kinlochleven in Scotland and it finished its days with P& W Anderson on a job at Torrington in North Devon, after which it seems to have been scrapped some time in 1925 or 1926.

apply for membership of the Institution of Mechanical Engineers (I Mech E). John Hartley's application was of course accepted, and the 'brief resume' of his career ran to no less than 11 closely typed foolscap pages! Needless to say it makes a fascinating read - truly he was as the *Staffordshire Evening Sentinel* commented on the occasion of his 86th birthday, the 'Grand Old Man of Local Engineering Industries'. John William Hartley died on 11 March 1942 and among the mourners at his funeral was WS Edwards, who attended not only in his own right as an old friend and pupil, but also to represent WG Bagnall Limited.

Hartley's achievements have been dealt with at some length as a background to the relatively close relationship that existed over many years between the two companies of WG Bagnall Limited and Kerr, Stuart & Company Limited. Situated as they were but 16 miles apart by rail, there was significant movement of

people between the two companies and this will occupy a lot of our attention later in the story. In earlier times Bagnall had supplied a locomotive to Hartley, apparently for resale, manufacturer's number 918 of 1887 and later still, one was supplied directly to Kerr, Stuart, in this case number 1092 of 1889. This was one of those exhibited as the RASE Jubilee Show at Windsor in June 1889, appropriately named WINDSOR for that occasion. Despite the show catalogue and press reports stating that this locomotive was three-foot gauge, it was actually a metre-gauge four-wheel inverted saddle tank with 8x12in cylinders that later worked in Malaya. Before we leave the story of Kerr, Stuart in the period covered by this Chapter, mention needs to be made of one other person who has a particularly significant part to play in the Bagnall story. Francis Henry Barham Harris had trained under John William Hartley at Stoke and took up the position of chief draughtsman of Kerr, Stuart in 1901. WS Edwards briefly mentioned above and one of the most influential people in the history of WG Bagnall Limited was also trained at Kerr, Stuart; initially under JW Hartley and later FHB Harris. The professional relationship of Gordon Bagnall with John Hartley has already been mentioned, and Bagnall would have known Harris too, and it was via these connections that Bagnall became aware of a promising young engineer at the California Works by the name of William Sydney Edwards.

We must now return to Ernest Baguley who arrived at the Castle Engine Works some time late in 1891, when he was 29 years old. The first drawing he appears to have signed in his capacity as chief draughtsman has the number 3000 and the date 1 January 1892; a motion arrangement for locomotive manufacturer's number

1408. Ernest Baguley was born at 86, Gloucester Road, Newcastle-on-Tyne on 14 January 1864, to George Joseph and Margaret Mary (nee Carr) Baguley. His father's occupation as quoted on the birth certificate is a glass painter journeyman. From 1873 Baguley's education was at Dr Bruce's Academy in Newcastle-on-Tyne, and between 1882 and 1886 he served an engineering apprenticeship with Messrs Hawthorn, Leslie & Company Limited. His training was initially at the Hawthorn Leslie shipyards on the Tyne, but later at the Forth Bank Works in Newcastle itself, where the company designed and built locomotives. On completion of his apprenticeship and following only a couple of years in the drawing office, this obviously promising young man was appointed assistant chief draughtsman at the Forth Bank Works. He moved directly from Hawthorn, Leslie to Stafford in 1891.

Mention is made in the text of the lack of surviving drawings of the early pre-Baguley design locomotives, but this is an exception. Number 1408 was a small 6in cylinder 0-4-0 inverted saddle tank new in 1892 for Hall & Boardman at Swadlincote where they had a colliery. It was named JACK.

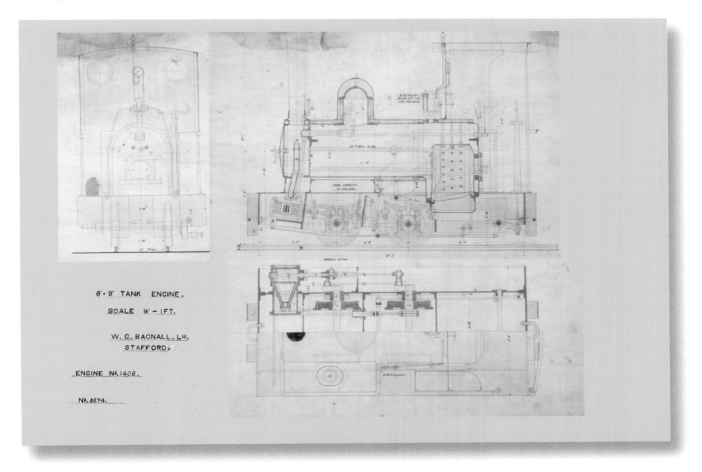

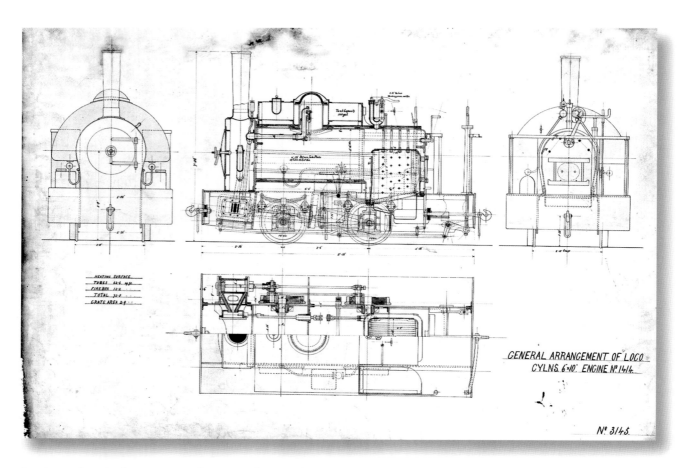

HEATING SURFACE.
TUBES 12·4 4 ft
FIREBOX 15·2
TOTAL 31·2
GRATE AREA 2·9

GENERAL ARRANGEMENT OF LOCO
CYLNS. 6·10. ENGINE Nº 1414.

Nº 3145.

Another early general arrangement drawing is this one of number 1414, new in 1892 for the Bowling Iron Company at Bradford. Whilst this locomotive had a conventional saddle tank, the design was nevertheless pre the Baguley design principles being introduced at the time.

When Baguley made a successful application for membership of the I Mech E in April 1899, he described himself as a 'Manager of the Engine Works of WG Bagnall Limited at Stafford'. Supporting his application was EW Mackenzie Hughes - 'late of HM Imperial Service' - who wrote: 'Messrs WG Bagnall Limited are narrow- gauge locomotive builders, I know their works well. I have found their work of a high class'. Edward William Mackenzie Hughes was quite an interesting character and worth a brief study as later in his career he was an inspecting engineer for the Egyptian Government. This was the situation that brought him to Stafford and is almost certainly how he came to know Baguley; indeed he may well have been instrumental in encouraging Baguley to apply for membership of the I Mech E. Born in about 1850, Mackenzie Hughes served an engineering apprenticeship as a pupil of Joseph Armstrong on the Great Western Railway at

Swindon. By 1870 he was, according to his own application for membership of the I Mech E., head draughtsman of the Madras Railway where he later officiated as assistant locomotive superintendent.

In April 1871 he was appointed assistant engineer with the Public Works Department in India, when he was placed in charge of the railway and canal workshops of the Scinde Canal at Rupal. In June 1876 he took up the appointment of executive engineer and locomotive duperintendent of the Scinde State Railway. At the time of his application for I Mech E membership in September 1881, Mackenzie Hughes was locomotive duperintendent of the Indus Valley State Railway in the Punjab. Among Baguley's other supporters in his application for membership was Percy Wheeler, at the time general manager of the Oldbury Railway, Carriage & Wagon Company. For much of his time at Stafford Baguley lived at 'Lyndhurst' in Rowley Park, which lies between the Newport and Wolverhampton Roads as they leave the town to the south-west.

Ernest Baguley, like John Hartley, was a remarkable engineer with an extremely inventive and fertile mind. As he was very ambitious too; he found plenty to occupy his enthusiasm during a comparatively short tenure at the Castle Engine Works and in doing so he left a very significant legacy that lasted until the end of the Company's independent existence. Little in the way the Company was managed did not come under Baguley's scrutiny and benefited from his obvious organisational skills. In particular the processes and procedures involving the design of locomotives and other products were totally influenced by Baguley's ideas. Moreover, in the running of the Company generally his influence spread with Gordon Bagnall clearly giving him a pretty free hand; his role went far beyond what might be considered the job of a chief draughtsman. Studying the surviving records today one inevitably draws the conclusion that almost from the day Baguley arrived on the scene, he must have set himself the task of completely reorganising the drawing office. Doubtless after the well organised procedures he was familiar with at Hawthorn, Leslie, he would have been appalled by the apparent lack of similar systems at the Castle Engine Works. Having established very quickly that systems on the lines of those he had been brought up with were equally relevant to the type of undertaking that was emerging at Stafford, rather than the more ad-hoc general engineering and millwrights business that the Company had been conducting; he went about his business with tremendous enthusiasm. Briefly mentioned earlier was Gordon Bagnall's understanding that some pretty drastic action was essential if the Company was going to be successful in a market that was getting more and more competitive. Clearly with a stronger aptitude to salesmanship than perhaps engineering, Gordon Bagnall would have been happy to let Ernest Baguley get on with what so obviously needed to be done. Significantly the processes and procedures, methods of record keeping and other systems that Baguley put in place at Stafford from 1891 bear a remarkable resemblance to the surviving records of Hawthorn, Leslie.

A specific early decision that has already been briefly outlined, was the separation in the order books of locomotives from any other work the Company undertook, a separate series of order numbers being introduced to cover none locomotive production. Thus, from locomotive number 1410 ordered in February 1892, the series of order numbers that had been used by the Company up until then was henceforth, reserved exclusively for locomotives. The numbering of locomotives then became more or less consecutive with any blank numbers usually indicating a cancelled order, or an order not proceeded with for one reason or another. At the expense of some repetition, the registers referred to earlier that list the early locomotives all appear to have been started in 1892, or shortly after. In these registers the entries covering locomotives built prior to 1892 have clearly been entered en-bloc, in or about 1892; numerous entries are in the same handwriting for example. The existing drawings, except for a few odd earlier ones, start in 1892, as do the two sets of drawing registers. One set of drawing registers lists all the drawings applicable to individual locomotive orders, whilst the other set lists the drawings by consecutive drawing number, along with the date entered in the resister and the initials of the draughtsman. As the existing drawing numbers, with a very few exceptions, start at 3,000, it is presumed the earlier numbers were reserved for earlier drawings to be assimilated in to the same system: but if any were, little record appears to have survived. It is worth mentioning that on the odd occasion after Baguley took over the design initiative that a locomotive was built to an earlier design, a series of new drawings were usually made. There were not many such cases, but occasionally an existing customer would request a locomotive to the same design as one it already had; there were also of course, numerous orders for spares to be supplied to suit earlier locomotives and these often necessitated new drawings being made. There are in existence a few odd drawings numbered in the 1,900 and 2,000 ranges, and these appear to be replacements for older ones. Baguley also introduced a separate list prefixed W, for wagons, turntables and other rolling stock, in fact anything not directly connected with locomotives. For reasons not apparent at this distance of time, this list starts at 33 and the first drawing is dated 28 March 1895. Once again a few older drawings appear, apparently re-numbered into this series.

To the lay-man, Baguley's singular most significant contribution to the Company was the introduction of a whole range of new design principles, which in turn brought a series of completely different external features to the locomotives built at Stafford. Some of these external design features stemmed from his experience with Hawthorn, Leslie, for example the standard-gauge 0-4-0 saddle tank design for industrial use introduced and built in small numbers, bore a remarkable resemblance to those built at the Forth Bank Works. Gone were the front tanks that so characterised the early Bagnall standard-gauge industrial shunting locomotives, and henceforth the likeness to the Hawthorn, Leslie product remained until the end of steam locomotive production. But perhaps the design that Baguley will be best remembered for, along with the Company itself, is the comparatively small, narrow-gauge saddle tank locomotives with a circular firebox boiler and patent valve gear. The use of circular firebox boilers has already been touched on in connection with Sir Arthur Heywood; its advantages were three fold. In the first instance circular surfaces require little in the way of stays, as a direct result boilers with circular fireboxes are much cheaper to construct than a conventional locomotive type boiler. Additionally, steel lends itself as a material for the construction of a circular firebox, far more readily than in a 'locomotive' type boiler, where the much more expensive copper was the preferred material. This gave a further reduction in

cost without a proportional reduction in durability or whole life. In the second instance by the simple removal of a row of rivets around the circumference of the boiler back plate, along with the tubes, the whole firebox could be quite easily removed. Last but by no means least is the point already mentioned in connection with the Heywood locomotives. In designing a locomotive with a circular firebox boiler, there is no necessity to allow space between the frames for the lower protrusion of the firebox and ash-pan of a conventional locomotive type boiler. The complete boiler can therefore, be mounted on top of the locomotive frames and its weight evenly distributed, with the obvious beneficial effect on axle-loading. In the light of these characteristics locomotives with circular fireboxes were significantly less expensive to build than their contemporaries, and the boilers were cheaper to maintain too.

It is worth reminding ourselves at this juncture, that the point about equalising the axle-loads by a better distribution of weight on the frames was one of the principles around the design of the inverted saddle and front tanks. It is interesting to speculate on the discussions that might have taken place between Gordon Bagnall and Ernest Baguley on the issue of weight distribution, and this may have been a factor in the agreement to phase out the inverted saddle and

TRIUMPHO, number 1416 of 1893; this was the Baguley designed prototype of what became the classic Bagnall narrow-gauge locomotive with a circular firebox. This one differed from the production versions as it had bar-frames and Walschaerts valve gear. Notice the screw reversing gear which was not persevered with either. The large oval manufacturer's plate with both month and year of construction was typical of this period, whilst the nameplate is in fact a wooden pattern and only in position for publicity purposes.

This is number 1416 again, a posed publicity picture taken in the works yard on the type of portable track and with a train of side-tip wagons the firm manufactured. Notice it has neither name nor manufacturer's plate in this view; an engraving taken from this photograph was used in the contemporary catalogues. The train looks as if it has been propelled to this spot for the photographer, as there does not appear to be any track behind the last wagon.

front tanks designs and introduce the circular firebox. In the catalogues this new design philosophy was explained thus: 'The engine is divested of all unnecessary fittings, the object being to construct a simple engine, the initial cost of which would be very low and the item of repairs reduced to a minimum. There is every facility for repairing, the firebox can be renewed in a day and the workmanship is equal to the best practice, the material being similar to that specified by the Admiralty and War Office. All the motion is outside the frames and can be readily attended to'. There was however a disadvantage with the circular firebox boiler, albeit not one mentioned in the publicity! This was the length of time required to raise steam, around half as long again compared with a conventional locomotive type boiler, but this does not appear to have deterred too many customers. There are numerous examples of customers coming back time and time again, doubtless encouraged by the other qualities of the design, and not least its very competitive price. The circular firebox boiler was always known at Stafford as the Bullhead type, presumably from its appearance

when on the shop floor, with the firebox end of a much larger diameter than the barrel, rather than when fitted to a locomotive.

It was not long after his arrival on the scene that Baguley designed, and the workshop built, a locomotive on these new principles. Manufacturer's number 1416 was laid down to a stock order in July 1892, a two-foot gauge four-wheel saddle tank with a cylinder size that became a standard for the rest of the history of the Company - the bore had a 6in diameter and the stroke was 9in. Driving wheel diameter was 1ft 6in, whilst the wheelbase was three-foot; the boiler had a total heating surface of almost 74 sq ft and the working pressure was 140 psi. With 100 gallons of water and five cub ft of fuel, this little engine turned the scales at 5½ tons. As a prototype it differed in several respects from the production versions that soon followed, for example it had bar frames, Walschaerts valve gear and screw reverse, none of which were perpetuated. The design characteristics of the valve gear complete with screw reverse remind one of small engines used in marine installations, and this might have been the result of

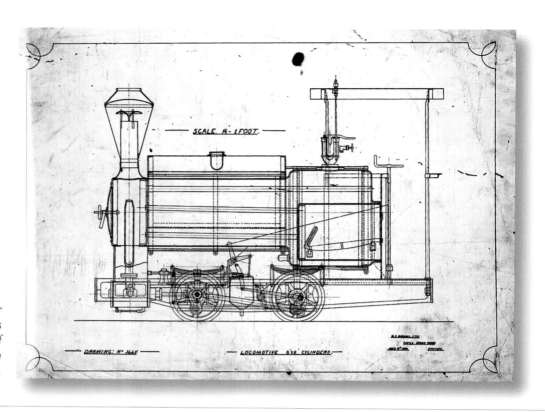

SCALE. ¼- 1 FOOT.

DRAWING: Nᵒ 144Y

LOCOMOTIVE 6"x9" CYLINDERS.

Side elevation of number 1416 - this drawing was used in some editions of the contemporary catalogues.

Baguley having undertaken some of his training in the shipyards of Hawthorn, Leslie. The use of Walschaerts valve gear at Stafford was not quite unique, as it had been used on one earlier occasion outlined in the next paragraph.

In 1891 Walschaerts valve gear was specified to be fitted on manufacturer's number 1260, a 2ft 6in gauge 0-4-2 side tank named CHESHIRE, which was built to Government order. There is a view that this locomotive was originally intended for use by the War Department at Crewe, where the 2nd Cheshire Engineer (Railway) Volunteers had a depot - hence its name. It was not a locomotive of a Bagnall design, but one of two similar machines ordered by the Government on behalf of the War Department, each one from a different builder and for trial purposes. The main frames of the locomotives were in two sections bolted together so that the front half, complete with driving wheels cylinders and motion, could be separated from the rest. The logic of the design was that the two halves could be interchanged between locomotives of a similar type, so that if, for example, one locomotive required boiler attention and another repairs to wheels and motion, one serviceable locomotive could be made out of two. It was claimed of the design that separation took 20

minutes and reconnection 40 minutes. But whether any interchange actually took place during the life of the two locomotives, as no others were built, apart from the initial trials that is, appears to have gone unrecorded. The design was that of Colonel McGuire-Batt, the inspector of iron structures for the Army between 1888 and 1895. The other locomotive of similar type was supplied by the comparatively small Whitehaven based Lowca Engine Company, manufacturer's number 220 of 1893, and this one was appropriately named CUMBERLAND. But note it was two years younger than the Bagnall, suggesting that perhaps somebody, somewhere, was not quite as enthusiastic of the principle as Colonel Mc Guire-Batt! Nevertheless, trials were conducted using these two locomotives which appear to have successfully demonstrated the principles, although for whatever reason we know not, the idea was not proceeded with and no further engines of the type were built.

Some years before this Bagnall was delivered, locomotives of similar outward appearance had been supplied to the War Department by the Yorkshire Engine Company of Sheffield. These engines however, were not, despite some reports indicating they were, capable of being separated in the fashion of those

These two views show CHESHIRE, number 1260 of 1891 (although the manufacturer's plates have the year 1890), and were in all probability taken on the Chattenden & Upnor Railway in Kent. As described in the text the design was one of Colonel McGuire-Batt, the British Army's Inspector of Iron Structures, whereby the boiler and rear end could be separated from the front, the principle being well illustrated here. The front portion, in the process of either being removed or fitted, would appear to be from the Lowca built engine CUMBERLAND, as it has a different design of motion bracket to the Bagnall. Whether the two engines ever ran in service with each others parts, has however, gone unrecorded.

supplied by Bagnall and Lowca. Other interesting features of the design included a Belpaire firebox boiler, outside frames and a rather ingenious arrangement of suspension. The weight of the locomotive was taken at three points, a system of rollers and a large transverse inverted leaf spring embracing the entire width between the frame plates transferred a proportion of the weight to the trailing truck. This included the firebox end of the boiler as the firebox was fixed to the frame plates, instead of resting on the main frames as in conventional practice. The remainder of the weight of the boiler, which sat in a cradle, was taken by two more inverted leaf springs situated under the coupled axle-boxes on which the cradle rested via the spring buckles. This arrangement transferred the remainder of the weight to the coupled wheels and at the same time allowed for the expansion of the boiler and firebox. This rather complicated arrangement, the Colonel claimed, helped reduce the time taken in uncoupling and re-coupling the two halves, and he also claimed that: 'it gave for a very steady and even running locomotive', although whether or not it actually did, history does not appear to have recorded. In any event, it would seem from a study of the design, that if one of the coupled wheel springs broke, the consequences would have been quite serious. The cylinders were 10x15in, the driving wheel diameter was 2ft 9in and total weight in working order 21 tons 18 cwt. It was claimed that the engines could haul 250 tons on level track and 80 tons on an incline of 1 in 50.

At this distance in time it is unclear what, if anything, the WD would have wanted with the locomotive at Crewe and there is no confirmation it ever went there. Nevertheless, in January 1887, under the leadership of the well known LNWR chief mechanical engineer Francis William Webb (although he was given that all embracing title later), a number of his managers and men were pioneers in the new art of mechanical warfare using railways. Webb and his men formed a Railway Engineers Volunteer Corps at Crewe, and within a year 24 officers and 610 railwaymen had enlisted embracing almost the complete and wide ranging grades and skills of the LNWR employees. The Corps later became known as the 2nd Cheshire Engineer (Railway) Volunteers and no fewer than 285 of its officers and men were on active service during the Boer War (1899-1902). In 1908 the Corps became part of the then

recently constituted Territorial Army. It is possible of course that CHESHIRE was initially sent to Crewe, to assist in training the men there; remember the Lowca engine was not delivered until over a year later, so trials in exchanging the parts between the two would have to have waited anyway. That such trials did take place is confirmed by photographs showing the operations in progress. If the engine did go to Crewe when new it cannot have been there long, and one is left wondering what Webb and his team might have thought of its design. In any event, CHESHIRE is known to have later joined CUMBERLAND and to have worked on the Admiralty operated Chattenden & Upnor Railway in Kent, which is almost certainly where trials to interchange the parts took place. Moreover, CHESHIRE is said to have lasted at Chattenden until as late as 1932, although CUMBERLAND seems to have disappeared much earlier, by 1904 in fact.

Having departed from strict chronology to discuss the first use by the Company of Walschaerts valve gear, we must now return to the Baguley prototype. This small locomotive was initially named TRIUMPHO, but only for publicity purposes, as the nameplate used for the photographs was a wooden pattern. Photographs of the engine running on a short test track in the works yard and hauling a string of side-tip wagons, show no identification at all. In these pictures the engine also sports a balloon stack spark-arresting chimney, and an engraving made from this picture and used in the catalogues was obviously directed at potential export markets. Engravings of this locomotive, again without a name, also appeared with a description of its design characteristics in several articles in the technical press. However, in the catalogues it was often described as Type Triumpho, but again without displaying the name on the locomotive itself.

We do not know exactly what prompted Baguley to introduce the circular firebox boiler. We have explored its advantages along with its earlier use by Sir Arthur Heywood, which both Baguley and Bagnall would be familiar with. It may have resulted from Baguley's experience with Hawthorn, Leslie, a company of shipbuilders as well as locomotive engineers and this type of boiler was common in marine engineering. Whatever the reason circular firebox boilers continued to be used on a wide range of narrow-gauge locomotives, large and small, and until steam

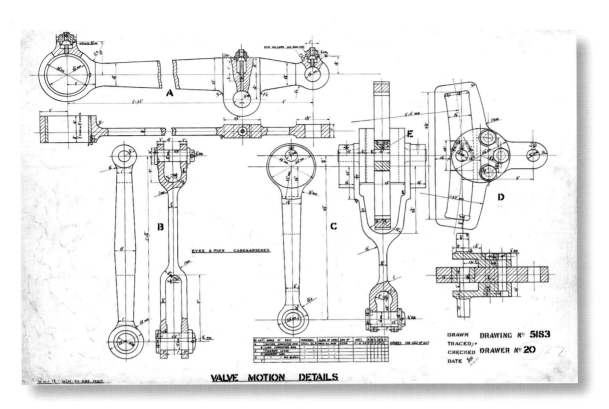

These two drawings illustrate Baguley valve gear, the one below shows the general layout as fitted to number 1704; this was a 7x12in cylinder three-foot gauge 0-4-0 saddle tank of the standard Margaret design. The second drawing shows the valve motion details and was actually drawn in connection with a spare part order for number 1617; nevertheless, it illustrates well the various component parts and between the two it should be possible to follow the description in the text on how this valve gear worked.

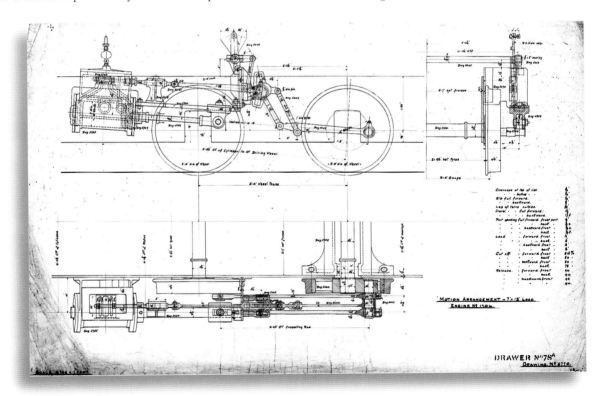

locomotive production ceased. But the use of bar frames and Walschaerts valve gear were only a feature of this particular locomotive, as neither were perpetuated on the production versions. The little engine was eventually sold, but not for almost a year, when it was despatched in December 1893 to fulfil an order from W Barrington. Although we have no conclusive evidence, it might have been for use on a scheme reclaiming land on the banks of the River Fergus in the southwest of Ireland. It is known that a William Barrington was the engineer for this scheme and that two locomotives worked there. This one was painted with the designation FRS No 2 before it left the works, which might just stand for Fergus Reclamation Syndicate No 2. Whatever did take place, nothing more is known about this rather special locomotive; this is a pity, as it played such a significant part in the development of the type of locomotive that became such a hallmark of the Castle Engine Works products.

Conventional plate frames were used on subsequent locomotives and why Baguley experimented with the bar frames is a mystery, but he may have wanted to see if they could be produced at less cost. Gordon Bagnall would have been anxious to maintain the ability of the firm to offer small locomotives at as lower price as possible, so we can be sure Baguley's remit would have been very clear in this respect. There is however evidence as to why he moved away from the use of Walschearts valve gear; indeed, it might only have been

employed on number 1416 because his own ideas were not sufficiently advanced at the time. Baguley wanted to retain the advantages of a radial valve gear with two components of valve motion, one for the main valve travel and one for the lap and lead, but he appears to have wanted to obviate the return arm of Walschaerts gear. This component is so vulnerable to the sort of trackside obstructions etc., typical of the likely conditions these small engines were designed to operate in. He may also have wanted to avoid paying any royalties; Walschaerts valve gear was originally patented in Belgium as far back as November 1844 in the name of M. Fischer, engineer of the Belgian State Railways, although Egide Walschaert was named as the inventor in the papers. In any event, against the ideals Baguley had set himself he designed a new valve gear which was eventually patented. Known as Baguley Valve Gear the patent number was 11,469 which was provisionally accepted on 12 June 1893, and finally embossed on 17 March the following year.

Baguley valve gear is a radial motion as opposed to a link motion. However, it is one of the few radial gears to use a curved link to give the primary component of motion to the valve, the secondary component to affect the lap and lead, being superimposed by means of a radial lever; in the description below referred to as the combining lever. The gear is an ingenious arrangement embodying the most important design feature of any radial valve gear and the one that made Walschaerts

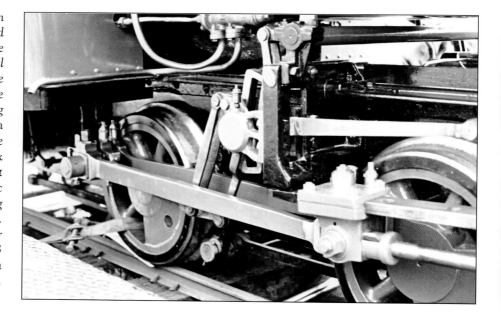

This is Baguley valve gear; notice in particular the motion connecting rod between the big-end and side-rod on the trailing crank pin, the near vertical vibrating and combining levers, the latter towards the front of the locomotive, and the link. The vibrating lever rocks the link about it's fulcrum in the conventional manner, whilst the combining lever moves the link backwards and forwards on an almost horizontal plane and via an eccentric bush located in the circular casting which also houses the link fulcrum. The locomotive is ISABEL, number 1491 of 1897, a picture taken on 13 October 1990 shortly after restoration of the engine to working order.

valve gear so popular with locomotive engineers. This is the constant lap and lead motion of the valve irrespective of the valve travel and percentage cut-off. The design of the Baguley gear also eliminates the need for the return arm of Walschaerts gear which was one of the designer's objectives. In the case of Baguley gear the two separate components of motion are both derived from the main crank and like Walschaerts gear, it employs a conventional link which is rocked in the conventional manner. In this case however, the drive is directly from the main crank via a motion connecting rod and not a return arm - this provides the primary component of valve travel via a vibrating lever connecting the motion connecting rod to the link. The secondary and in-phase component to provide the lap and lead motion is derived from a combining lever which also derives its motion from the main crank via the same motion connecting rod. This combining lever however, moves the link backwards and forwards about an eccentric pivot point as opposed to the rocking motion of the link provided by the primary component.

As with any valve gear using a curved link, the valve rod is moved up and down the concave - towards the valve - link to give forwards and backwards movement of the locomotive, rather than the link itself moving as in, for example, Stephenson's link motion. Similarly, the intermediate valve rod is made the same length as the radius of the link. It follows therefore, that in mid-gear, with the valve rod in the mid position in the link, no movement is inparted on the valve via the primary component of valve motion; the lap and lead movement however, via the combining lever, remains constant. In view of its ingenuity and use on a large number of Bagnall locomotives it is perhaps worthwhile listing in full the advantages Baguley himself claimed:

1. Few working parts and reduction in first cost.
2. All gearing well up from the ground.
3. There are no overhanging parts, all rods being in a perfectly straight line from the crank pin to the slide valve.
4. The steam chest and motion are much nearer the frames.
5. The motion being derived from the intermediate space on the crank pin dispenses with the return crank, which is an expense to make and difficult to repair when damaged.
6. There are very few working parts and the die is practically stationary in the link when working.
7. The whole motion also affords easy facilities for efficient lubrication.
8. The leads, port opening, and cut-off are all equal.
9. The motion is obviously capable of modification so as to be suitable for an inside cylinder locomotive.

Despite the reference to the possibility of the valve gear being used on an inside cylinder locomotive, there are no known examples of this ever being the case. Although not specifically mentioned (see point 4 above) by Baguley in the list above, in some applications another advantage of the gear was the ability to make the cylinder assembly protrude less on the loading gauge. With Walschaerts gear as the return arm has of necessity to be outside the crank and therefore the connecting rod, the valve chest has to be offset to the outside of the cylinder bore; in some circumstances this increases the overall width of the locomotive. It is of course possible to counteract this by an offset somewhere in the line of motion, but this is not good practice, increases the loads on the valve gear and can lead to a number of other problems; designer's dislike it. With the Baguley arrangement as all the valve gear is situated between the coupling and connecting rods, the valve chest is offset in the opposite direction, that is towards the middle of the locomotive, rather than the reverse. Whilst this might not be a great advantage on small locomotives with small diameter cylinders as the overall locomotive width is not affected, on larger locomotives with bigger diameter cylinders it can facilitate the overall locomotive width being less than would be the case with Walschaerts gear. Despite its advantages, it is a fact that so far as is known, Baguley gear was never used on locomotives other than those he was responsible for designing at Stafford, and later when he was in involved in business at Burton-on-Trent. A weakness of the gear was the slender dimensions of the vibrating and combining levers, the former taking the bulk of the load of driving the valve, and space constraints limiting much in the way of larger parts. A modification that was made after some experience was the position of the attachment of the vibrating lever to the motion connecting rod; this point was moved in a vertical plane below the centre

The first locomotive fitted with Baguley valve gear was, perhaps ironically, one to an otherwise pre-Baguley design. Here it is, number 1424 of December 1893, in February 1952 at the Northern Outfall Works at Beckton of London County Council. The gear itself cannot be seen on this particular photograph as it is obscured by the cross-head driven pump. (Frank Jones Collection - Industrial Locomotive Society)

line of the rod. This in turn allowed the attachment of the vibrating lever to be at the same horizontal centre line as the link, which had the effect of improving the equality of valve events between forwards and backwards movement of the locomotive.

Baguley valve gear was described and illustrated in some detail in *Engineering* - issue dated 15 June 1894 - together with details of the first locomotive it was fitted to. Perhaps ironically this was actually an engine built to an otherwise earlier Bagnall design. Manufacturer's number 1424 was a 0-4-0 inverted saddle tank with 7x12in cylinders supplied in December 1893 for the 3ft

6in gauge railway of London County Council serving its Northern Outfall Sewage Works at Beckton. Nevertheless it was not long before the Baguley valve gear was used on the design of locomotive derived from number 1416, and this one became the true forerunner of the standard narrow-gauge types that were to become so popular. The locomotive in question was manufacturer's number 1429, which was despatched in October 1894, for use on the 1ft 8in gauge railway at Essington Farm Colliery near Wolverhampton. As the engine was named MARGARET, this became the class name and was used for publicity purposes for this basic

MARGARET, *number 1429 of 1894, was the first of the small narrow-gauge locomotive embodying all the Baguley design features, and a development from number 1416. The engine is seen here on two small trollies for movement around the works and for testing. The Baguley valve gear is quite noticeable in this view and an engraving of this locomotive was used in the catalogues and Margaret became the class name for this type of locomotive with 6x9in cylinders and 1ft 6in diameter wheels and for several years. Sometimes the larger 7in cylinder engines were also given this class name.*

The slightly longer 0-4-2 version of the Baguley inspired narrow-gauge locomotive was known as the type Pekoe-Tip, and here is PEKOE-TIP itself, number 1438 of 1894, although this was numerically the last of three locomotives of this type consecutively numbered and built at the same time. The other two, numbers 1436 and 1437 were the first of many supplied to the Assam Railways & Trading Company, for use at coal mines and associated operations in Upper Assam. PEKOE-TIP was for the Jokai (Assam) Tea Company, and last heard of when spares were ordered in October 1930.

design of locomotive over the next few years. MARGARET cost £290 to build and was sold for £315, which illustrates how cheaply these small engines could be built for and how small the profit margin was. Like its earlier sister, an engraving was produced and used in the catalogues and adverts as well as accompanying articles in the contempory press. About the same time that MARGARET appeared a slightly bigger version was introduced with an 0-4-2 wheel arrangement to improve the riding characteristics and allow an increased fuel capacity. The first three, which had slightly smaller 5½in diameter cylinders, manufacturer's numbers 1436 to 1438 were for export and went to India. The last of the three, despatched in September 1894 for the Jokai (Assam) Tea Company was named PEKOE TIP. Like MARGARET, this became the class name for the type of locomotive with an 0-4-2 wheel arrangement and an engraving frequently appeared in the catalogues and other publicity material.

A lot of thought was put into the design of these small locomotives, they were divested of almost any finery and were well able to compete on cost terms with anything the contemporary locomotive building trade could produce - both in this country and abroad. Nevertheless they were well built and as the catalogues claimed 'of the best materials', a point well supported by

the longevity many of them achieved. Easy to drive and maintain examples found their way all over the world and repeat orders from satisfied customers were numerous. Particular emphasis was placed in maintaining a balance between the general sturdy-ness of the design, yet at the same time in reducing the amount of material involved, providing a locomotive that would stand rough treatment, be long lasting, affordable as well as being both cheap and easy to maintain. That these often conflicting characteristics were achieved and stood the test of time, with but few alterations and modifications over the years, is evidenced as examples were still being built almost until the end of the Company's independent existence. Moreover, until only a comparatively few years ago, examples were still in everyday commercial service. Among the early modifications to the design was the position of the regulator. The first few had smokebox mounted regulator valves, but it was soon found that engines so fitted were prone to prime quite seriously on anything other than level track. The design was soon changed with the regulator valve mounted in a steam collecting dome on the firebox.

Whilst much else needed to be done to improve the design characteristics of the other locomotives the firm built, it was not possible for Baguley to change them all

An example of the larger 7x12in cylinder 0-4-2 design with 1ft 9½in diameter wheels is illustrated here, albeit in this case the cylinder diameter was 7½in. Notice the larger boiler and firebox and the rack for additional supplies of fuel - doubtless in this case bagasse (sugar cane waste) as the engine was for use on a sugar cane plantation. LIMOERINHO (although the name has faded on the photograph) was number 1483 of 1896, new to agents James Milne & Company - that would be its plate on the bunker and not Bagnalls - for Usina Mameluco, a sugar factory and plantation in Pernambuco Province, Brazil. Four Bagnall locomotives went to this estate, the last one in 1909. Notice how the water valve for the injector is actually inside the tank, also the large head-lamp and the position of the whistle.

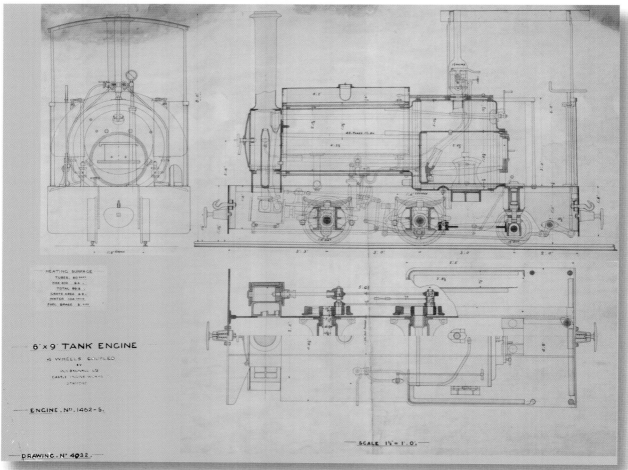

General Arrangement drawing of a locomotive of type Pekoe-Tip illustrating a typical use of Baguley valve gear as well as a popular design of locomotive of the period. The drawing shows one of numbers 1462 to 1465, four locomotives for the contractor Lewis Jones & Company despatched to India in October 1895. The track gauge was 1ft 8in and along with 20 miles of 16lb per yard rail with patent sleepers that was supplied at the same time, the engines were used on construction of the Badarpur to Lumding section of the Assam Bengal Railway, a line almost 119 miles long completed in December 1903. Part of the agreement for the construction was for all the equipment to be purchased by the railway company on completion of the works, but what happened to these small locomotives has gone unrecorded. Notice the combined castings for frame stretchers and axle-box horn guides.

The last locomotive built to a completely pre-Baguley design was number 1596 of 1900, which rejoiced in the name SALISBURY. Unfortunately it does not appear to have posed for its official photograph, but it was a repeat order of FITZ, number 1435 of 1894 which is seen here. Both the engines were ordered by the Butterley Company, for use on the 3ft 9in gauge system at the Hilt's Limestone Quarry at Crich in Derbyshire. Cylinders were 8x12in and the wheel diameter two-foot; obviously Butterley wanted a second engine exactly like the one it already had. Inverted saddle tanks were fitted; however, when a new boiler was supplied for 1596 in 1927, at the same time the engine was modified to have front side tanks rather than the inverted saddle type, and new tanks were designed and supplied the following year. There is however, no record of FITZ having the same attention, but clearly in a requirement for a new tank, the opportunity was taken to eliminate the original design; perhaps problems had been apparent. Both locomotives were scrapped in 1939.

at once. Indeed some of the design features used hitherto had some merit and during the first few years of his tenure in the drawing office locomotives of what might be termed the old and new design schools were built. Some locomotives even embodied features of both, evidence the Beckton Sewage Works locomotive mentioned earlier. This locomotive whilst being fitted with the new Baguley valve gear was otherwise built to existing design principles; but of course, Baguley would have been anxious to try it out his new gear as soon as possible. There are other examples of this sort of thing, but generally the older designs were gradually phased out with the last engine to a completely pre-Baguley design appearing in 1900. This was manufacturer's number 1596, a repeat order for the Butterley Company Limited for use at Hilt's limestone quarry near Crich in Derbyshire.

Despite Baguley's increasing role in the management of the Company Samuel Price remained active in the production department and mention has been made of the Gifford brothers becoming involved. John Gifford became a shareholder in January 1890 and by the following year only John Gifford, Gordon Bagnall and Thomas Walter were drawing a salary as opposed to a wage - although Walter had long ceased to take any active role. In 1892 John Gifford became a director and remained one until his death in 1932, nevertheless he was still employed in the drawing office as he was signing drawings as late as July 1905, albeit only occasionally. On 4 October 1892 an agreement was entered into between the Company and Thomas Walter where Walter agreed to accept an annual 4% dividend on his preference shares in lieu of his existing rights. This is indicative of his lessening activities in the affairs of the Company although he remained a major shareholder for some time to come and continued to draw a salary. In the two years ending 30 September 1892, the average turnover of the Company was

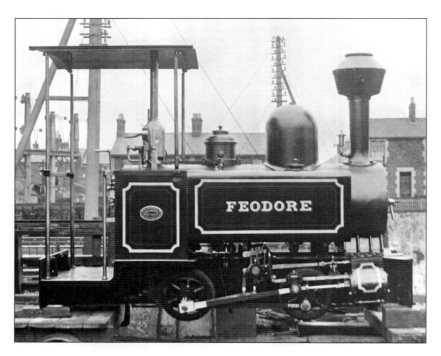

A variation on the small narrow-gauge locomotives was FEODORE which, whilst displaying many of the Baguley features introduced with MARGARET, had a locomotive type firebox and dome in the conventional position. Notice too the spark arresting chimney, boiler mounted sandbox and reduced height at the rear end. Number 1529 of 1898, this small locomotive had 4½x6½in cylinders and 1ft 3¼in diameter wheels. The customer was H Ahrens & Company and despatch to Japan, originally for use by the Japanese Imperial Navy, however by 1935 it was in use on the Sagami Railway and involved in breakwater maintenance works. Sagami in now included in Kanagawa ken, which includes the south peninsular on the west side of the Bay of Tokyo. The gauge of the locomotive was two-foot, but it is mounted on trolleys to allow for testing; in the background is the LNWR main line and some of the houses in Castle View.

£35,210 and the profit increased from a meagre £6 in 1892 to £601 the following year. With the exception of an occasional dip below the line the Company thereafter became relatively profitable on a year-by-year basis with the average annual profit steadily increasing until the end of the First World War.

Over the next few years locomotive building gradually became the principal activity of the Company absorbing increasing levels of the production activity and space. Rolling stock and other railway material continued to be made but at a decreasing percentage of total output. The Implement & Machinery Review in its issue dated 1 November 1896 reported on recent extensions to the works including a new iron foundry, wagon and boiler shops along with hydraulic machinery and new tools. The journal went on to add that despite these improvement the works was barely able to cope with the demand for portable railways and that the output had been doubled in the present year. Brief reference has already been made of the turntables built by the Company and their design and manufacture become quite a speciality remaining in production almost until the end of the firm's existence. Made in a range of sizes the smallest were but 2ft 6in diameter and the largest anything up to 20ft diameter with a capacity of 65 tons. The smaller ones were usually made of two cast components, either iron or steel to suit customers'

requirements, one part for the outer ring and the other the table itself. The larger ones were made from a variety of cast and fabricated components often with wood decking. As well as railway rolling stock in the strictest sense, specialist wagons were made for a whole range of other activities, some with flanged wheels others not. For example there were blast furnace charging tubs and special vehicles designed for use in pottery kilns. With the pottery industry at nearby Stoke-on-Trent, various designs of vehicle for use around the potteries were quite a popular line. By 1895 the Company claimed to have supplied over 1,000 narrow gauge side-tip wagons all over the world. Stationary engines also remained in the product line and in 1895 it was stated that steam driven electric generating power plants had been supplied to Holland and Java, as well as an installation at the prestigious Café Monico in Piccadilly, London.

The firm continued to make great play in its catalogues and other publicity material of its ability to provide complete light railway systems and in 1895 did just that. The Company supplied almost all the equipment for the three-foot gauge line that was two and a half miles long, and built to connect Rye in East Sussex with the local pleasure spot at Camber Sands. This was the Rye & Camber Tramway which opened in July 1896 and as well as the rolling stock and track,

The Rye & Camber Tramway was a two and a half mile three-foot gauge line connecting Rye in East Sussex with Camber Sands, a popular local beach; the line also served golf links about three quarters the way along. Opened in July 1895 the original equipment came from the Castle Engine Works. This is the line's first locomotive, a small 2-4-0 side tank CAMBER, number 1461, a popular design from earlier times. Notice the engine is already loaded onto an LNWR flat wagon for delivery. The side-tip wagon to the right was part of a publicity display visible from passing trains. CAMBER was later joined by a slightly larger sister VICTORIA, number 1511 of 1897. CAMBER had a new boiler in 1921 and lasted until 1947, although little used latterly and in any event the tramway closed on outbreak of the Second World War.

Bagnall supplied a small 5½x9in cylinder 2-4-0 side tank which embodied a number of the older design characteristics. Manufacturer's number 1461 it was despatched in November 1895 and appropriately named CAMBER. A second locomotive followed in June 1897, number 1511, a little bit bigger with 6x10in cylinders and named VICTORIA - to commemorate the Queen's Golden Jubilee that year.

Baguley's influence can clearly be identified in the only 'miniature', as opposed to narrow-gauge locomotive the Company built. Manufacturer's number 1425 was an 18in gauge engine largely based on the famous Great Northern Railway (GNR) 4-2-2 express passenger tender engines popularly known as The Stirling Singles. The name is derived from their designer, Patrick Stirling, the well known locomotive engineer of the GNR. The engine however exhibited a number of features not found on the prototype; presumably to better adapt it for its intended purpose as

a working locomotive rather than a model. For example the carrying wheels were smaller than scale to assist the engine in traversing the sharp and not to scale curves usually found on miniature railways. The engine also had a domed boiler which housed the regulator, and whilst GNR engines did not, ironically several years later some of them were fitted with boilers having domes! The miniature engine was built for a railway being constructed on the Easthampstead Park Estate near Crowthorne in Berkshire which belonged to the 7th Marques of Downshire, and it was delivered there in September 1893. Decked out in fully lined GNR green livery with the number 778, as well as the engine two vehicles were supplied, an open passenger coach with toast-rack type seating for six and a small brake van; track and other material were also supplied. The small, neat, and well built locomotive was one of the first miniature locomotives, as opposed to a model, built anywhere, so the opportunity was taken to make use of

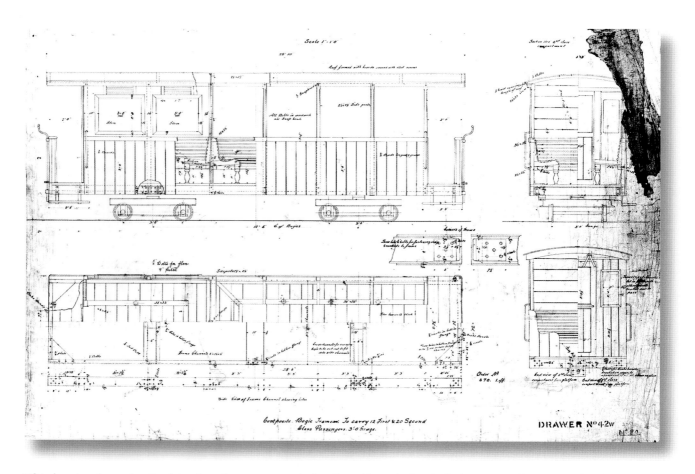

This drawing shows details of the three-foot gauge coach that Bagnall supplied with the locomotive CAMBER, for the opening of the Rye & Camber Tramway.

its publicity value. There were pictures and articles in a number of journals and magazines, and not just technical ones, *The Strand Magazine* for example.

The Easthampstead Park estate of Lord Downshire, is but a couple of miles from the Bearwood estate of the Walter family and one assumes the families were acquainted with each other; especially with *The Times* newspaper connection. It is thus tempting to speculate that the order for this locomotives came about through this connection. The Marques wanting a miniature railway around his estate, and the Walters knowing of the involvement of Thomas in WG Bagnall Limited. The Marques also had estates in Ireland, at Hillsborough Castle near Belfast as well as Murlough House at Dundrum in Country Down, and there have been suggestions that at one time the miniature railway may have been used at Hillsborough. *The Belfast Independent* in one of its issues in October 1896, refers to a one and half mile miniature railway laid down by a London firm in the grounds at Hillsborough and operated by a engine weighing three tons, capable of running at 40 mph and costing £1,000. The actual order for the locomotive and other equipment was placed with Bagnall by the London based firm of Faulkner, Bedford & Company, with premises in Shaftsbury Avenue and known to have been agents for the supply of miniature and model railway equipment. The locomotive actually cost £362, but together with the rolling stock and other equipment the total cost may have been in the region of £1,000.

Before this little engine and its accompanying vehicles left the works the opportunity was taken to operate the complete train on a specially laid length of track in the works grounds. On a Saturday afternoon a large number of guests were invited including the Mayor and the Corporation of Stafford, of which of course Bagnall was a member, along with other nobility. A photograph of the event which was widely publicised

A good time was had by all! Photograph taken on the occasion of the open day at the Castle Engine Works when the 18in gauge miniature locomotive based on a Great Northern Railway Stirling Single, was put through it paces. As well as many of Gordon Bagnall's friends, relations and fellow Councillors, the local and technical press were also invited along. The vehicles are those supplied with the locomotive and as well as this train further trials were undertaken with a train of side-tip wagons; and there were conducted tours around the workshops for those interested. The engine is being driven by Samuel Price and Gordon Bagnall is standing alongside the brake van on the right, with Ernest Baguley to the left. The left hand tall gentleman with a beard and homburg behind the coach is Samuel Cookson, Jessie Bagnall's step-father, whilst she is sixth from the extreme right peeping over the shoulder of the lady in white. Richard Gordon Bagnall, the youngest son, is third from the right and the hand on his shoulder is that of Samuel Bagnall, Gordon's elder brother. The elder son, Harold Gordon Bagnall is in the brake van. In the contempory catalogues and press reports the engine is described as: 'useful for light passenger work on narrow-gauge lines or for purposes of inspection'.

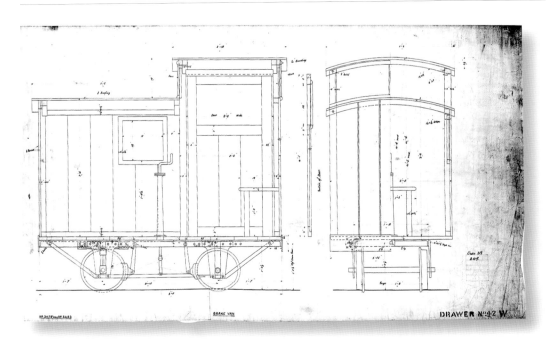

Drawing of the 18in gauge brake van supplied to Lord Downshire, at the same time as the miniature Stirling Single locomotive.

This is the engine built by the Regent Street Polytechnic from parts supplied by Bagnall and later completed by EFS Notter. In the period 1964 to 1973 this locomotive was completely rebuilt with a new boiler when in the ownership of the late RG (Bob) Pratt, having been rescued from years of semi-dereliction in Cambridge. It was sold on completion of the work to Bevan Braithwaite of Fulbourn in Cambridgeshire and is seen here in his front garden on 4 September 1976. The mechanical lubricator would not have been original.

shows Samuel Price at the regulator and Gordon Bagnall and Ernest Baguley standing by the brake van. Jessie Bagnall and the two sons are there too, and although most of them cannot be positively identified, so are other family members; it would certainly appear that a good time was had by all. Indeed the contemporary press, several of whom were present, tell us that the engine was kept busy all afternoon going backwards and forwards on the line which was about a quarter of a mile long, and with several curves that the engine took 'very nicely'. This intriguing locomotive had a long and interesting history and survives as part of a private collection at Preston, near Canterbury in Kent where occasionally it is available for inspection, although in a rather dilapidated condition with several parts missing and minus its tender.

In 1897 the Company supplied a set of drawings, castings, forgings and a complete boiler to the Regent Street Polytechnic in London, to enable students there to build a similar engine. Among their number at the time was Henry Greenly, who later became a very well established designer of miniature steam locomotives; he was for example responsible for the 15in gauge engines built in 1925 and 1926 for the Romney, Hythe & Dymchurch Railway in Kent. The students appear to have largely completed the locomotive before it passed to the ownership of EFS Notter, at the time GNR locomotive superintendent at Kings Cross, who over a period of several years completed it in about 1911. Due to the similarity of these two engines over the years

there has been much confusion as to which was which, as they both moved around the country with successive owners. The Polytechnic engine is the one that worked on the Fairbourne Railway in North Wales and later, from about 1936, was used on a miniature railway at Jaywick Sands in Essex. This one also survives as part of the Country Life Museum collection at Sandy Bay, near Exmouth in Devon.

Mention has already been made of the standard gauge 0-4-0 industrial saddle tank design Baguley introduced to replace the earlier versions with front side tanks. The first one to the new specification was manufacturer's number 1411 of November 1893; with 12x18in cylinders it was for use at the Tipton Green Blast Furnaces of Roberts & Company in the Black Country - the sale price was £740. The next one was sold in part exchange for one of the earlier front tank designs, the new engine was manufacturer's number 1432, despatched to M&W Grazebrook Limited of Netherton in February 1895 at a cost of £755. The engine it replaced has already been mentioned in the last Chapter, number 954 of 1889.

In the year 1895 two separate orders covered no less than 13 metre-gauge 0-4-0 locomotives for the Admiralty; the engines were for use on construction works in connection with harbour extensions at Gibraltar; together they represented the largest number of locomotives for one customer. The works at Gibraltar were in connection with the Naval Works Acts of 1895, 1896 and 1897, which interalia, provided

The is No 4 in the fleet of 13 four-coupled inverted saddle tank engines supplied to the Admiralty for use at Gibraltar Dockyard. Number 1450 of May 1895, notice that the Admiralty specification called for Ramsbottom safety valves on the firebox and a Salter balance on the dome along with a spark arresting chimney. The wagons behind the engine are again those on display to passengers on passing trains - as pointed out in the text on several occasions, Gordon Bagnall missed no opportunity to advertise his products!.

WASSELL, number 1502 of 1897, is an example of the larger four-wheel locomotives for industrial works shunting. This one had 10x15in cylinders and 2ft 6in diameter wheels and was built to suit the unusual track gauge of 3ft 2½in, for Shelagh Garratt & Sons, of the Corngreaves Brickworks and New British Collieries at Cradley Heath in the Black Country. The design of saddle tank was popular at the time but quite why is not clear. This engine came back to Stafford for a new boiler and other repairs in March 1905, and spares were still being supplied until August 1913 at least. Once again the display of wagons can be seen behind the engine, which is on trolleys due to its unusual gauge, and that is Castle View again in the distance.

for a significant enlargement of the size and protection of the naval docks at Gibraltar, following a decision to station the Mediterranean Fleet there. Hitherto its ships had been spread around the Mediterranean, although the majority of them spent most of their time based on Malta; torpedo attack of ships at anchor and in port was a particular concern at the time. The locomotives were built in two batches, manufacturer's numbers 1447 to 1451 of 1895, followed by numbers 1467 to 1474 of 1895 and 1896; their fleet numbers ran consecutively from 1 to 13. These locomotives are an excellent example of the transition period in old and new design schools outlined earlier. Quite small locomotives with 8x12in cylinders, whilst they had inverted saddle tanks they also embodied a number of features introduced by Baguley. Originally the work at Gibraltar was undertaken by the Admiralty with direct labour, but in December 1898 the entire responsibility was handed over to the contractors Topham, Jones & Railton. The enlargements and extensions were extensive, they included extending the existing breakwaters, building new breakwaters, constructing a large mole and five coaling jetties, extending the ship yard and the addition of three large graving docks. One of these docks was big enough to accommodate the largest battleships and there were also several smaller slipways and numerous other ancillary works. The work was not completed until December 1905.

After the locomotives passed to the ownership of Topham, Jones & Railton, several of them went on to have long and varied careers in the contracting industry, and whilst some of them remained in Gibraltar and eventually reverted to Admiralty ownership, others migrated with the contractors for use on harbour construction works at Singapore; one of these later became Royal Siam Railways No 1. Others later returned to this country and one found its way during the First World War to a gunpowder factory at Faversham in Kent; this was despite its unusual gauge for a railway in this country. As well as the locomotives rolling stock and track work was also supplied to Gibraltar and Gordon Bagnall himself spent some time there in connection with the contract. There were no less than seven miles of metre-gauge railway in and around the docks, the track consisting of 78lb per yard rail and hardwood sleepers; not on this occasion any of the varieties of patent steel sleepers.

Yet another variation of the narrow-gauge locomotives of Baguley design was this one, number 1572 of 1899, one of two supplied to the Crown Agents for the Colonies for use by the Perak Public Works Department, Perak at the time being a protected British State on the Malayan Peninsular. Modification from the standard Pekoe-Tip design is the flat topped saddle tank to accommodate the wood fuel rack. The discerning will be able to pick out the connection of the motion vibrating lever on the motion connecting rod seen protruding below the main connecting rod, which illustrates the modification to the gear to better align the top connection of this lever to the horizontal centre line of the link pivot. The dome on the firebox indicates that the position of the regulator has been repositioned from the smokebox, which was another later development of the design as outlined in the text. There was a follow on order for Perak, a third identical locomotive being supplied in 1900, number 1593.

One of Baguley's other achievements was the design and introduction of a series of standard components, that could be used in as wide a range of the locomotives the firm built as possible. This was all part of the policy of reducing the production time, and therefore the cost, of building locomotives. For example a driving wheel was designed that was easy to cast as it did not have conventional spokes, the patterns were easier to make too. This reduced the workload of the pattern makers, moulders and the foundry with a consequent reduction in costs in all three departments. A range of boiler fittings was designed that could be used on just about every type and size of locomotive. Another example was the smokebox saddles on the small circular firebox narrow-gauge locomotives. A small ranges of sizes were introduced and where there was a variation that the range could not directly cater for, the next smallest size would be used and packing pieces made and inserted between the saddle casting and the frame plates to make up the difference. By these and other initiatives, production costs were kept to a minimum.

Obviously specialist designs were still built if considered appropriate, for example two locomotives for the 3ft 6in gauge Jersey Railways & Tramways, where the specification called for an improvement on the Manning, Wardle locomotives already on the line.

Another example of the small 2-4-0 side tanks was CONCORD, number 1421 of 1893, new for the three-foot gauge system at the South Metropolitan Gas Company's Old Kent Road Works in London. A new firebox was supplied for this delightful and diminutive locomotive in 1934; the cylinders were only 5½x9in and it lasted until the system closed in 1953; what a pity it was scrapped two years later. A sister engine named UNITY, was supplied in 1898, number 1534; less likely engines for shunting in a gas works it would be hard to find!

Both designs were 2-4-0 side tanks and the first of the Bagnall engines, which had 13x20in cylinders, was manufacturer's number 1418 named CORBIERE. It was delivered in June 1893 and the second one, number 1466 with the name St BRELADES, followed in January 1896. The 1895 catalogue contains an extract from a letter sent by the manager of the Jersey Railway: 'The engine gives every satisfaction and burns less fuel for the amount of work done than Nos. 1 and 2 (these were the Manning Wardle locomotives). It also takes the sharp curves much steadier than either of the other engines'; so they seem to have fulfilled the requirement

to be an improvement on the Manning, Wardle pair.

There is an interesting story about these two Jersey locomotives, albeit much later in their lives. Some time in the early 1930s, Percy Critchley, a young draughtsman with the Company, happened to mention that accompanied by his girlfriend he was going on holiday to Jersey. When the managing director, WS Edwards, got wind of this he suggested to Percy that he might call on the manager of the Jersey Railway, enquire of the engines and pass on his regards etc - there had apparently, been no spares orders for almost 10 years! Well Percy did as he was bidden, but he got a brusque

St BRELADES, number 1466 of 1896 was the second of the two engines supplied to the 3ft 6in gauge Jersey Railways & Tramways. The two engines were of a special design, specifically intended to be similar to the lines earlier engines supplied by the Leeds builder Manning, Wardle & Company, but at the same time an improvement on them. These were quite large engines with 13x20in cylinders and an all-up weight of 23 tons. A new boiler was supplied in 1908 and the two engines lasted until the railway closed following a disastrous fire which destroyed most of the passenger rolling stock in 1936, after which they were scrapped. No 4 is seen here just outside the terminus station at St Hellier, in about 1930.

Another variety of 2-4-0 side tank was RIO DO OURA, number 1565 of 1899 and in this case fitted with a circular firebox boiler and Baguley valve gear, where once again the lower connection of the motion vibrating lever to the motion connecting rod can be seen protruding below the main connecting rod. This was quite a small engine with 8x12in cylinders; it was supplied via a Portuguese agent John M Sumner of Lisbon, for use on a sugar estate, the Conde De Valle Flor, on the island of St Tome, which was a Portuguese Colony at the time. In the catalogues this type of engine was often referred to as type Fortuna, which was the name of a much earlier 2-4-0 side tank of similar size, but in that case in pre-Baguley design days. This is an interesting example of an older design of locomotive being re-designed to embody the principles of the new Chief Draughtsman.

reception and the manager made it clear that if Bagnalls were only going to get in touch with him via junior members of staff whilst on holiday, they might as well not bother! When this reception was reported back to Edwards, Percy got nothing more than a shrug of the shoulders and concluded from the body language that there was some 'history' that Edwards was saying nothing about. He felt quite distinctly that he had been 'set up'!

There is another interesting and rather complicated story of the period we are discussing; it involves a small locomotive manufacturer's number 1444, and a court case. This engine was a very small version of the standard circular firebox saddle tank locomotives, in this case with cylinders 4½x7½in, a wheel diameter of 1ft 1¾in and a wheelbase of 2ft 6in; the track gauge was 1ft 8in. The engine was ordered in June 1897 by the Carthago Exploration Syndicate Limited for use in Tunis; it was despatched from Stafford on 21 July that year with the name EXPLORER. Delivery was to Carthage, an area northeast of Tunis in French Tunisia

and the engine cost £250. Very soon after delivery this locomotive was in trouble; apparently it was 'on the rails' at Carthage on 10 August but not steamed until the 16th. Albert Owen, a fitter from Stafford had accompanied the locomotive and he: 'fitted up the railway and tried the engine', as the Company also supplied 3,000 metres of railway line and some wagons. Soon after the trials the locomotive was put in charge of a man called Paul Schaeffer, who was to be its regular driver, but in his charge it promptly 'broke down'. In fact it frequently 'broke down', and on one occasion at least, either the combining lever or vertical link (later described in court as a fulcrum lever) of the Baguley valve gear on one side of the engine broke. As Owen seemed unable to fathom out exactly what was causing the problem, Frank Keeley, another fitter and the one who had actually built the engine and supervised it's testing prior to despatch, went out to Tunisia. He seems to have quickly assimilated the situation; the railway was laid over land that consisted of very fine sand impregnated with salt and the prevailing weather was

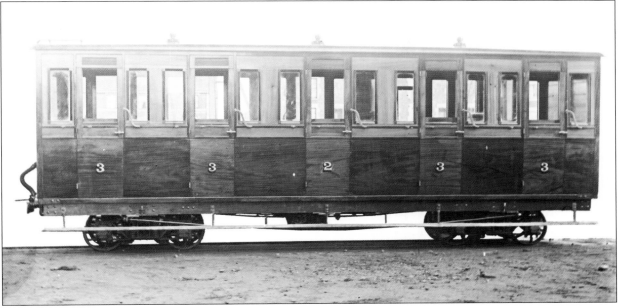

No 3 SODUPE was a type Jessie design of 2-4-0 side tank with a locomotive type boiler and largely pre-Baguley design characteristics; however it does have Baguley valve gear hidden behind those dust skirts. It was one of two locomotives supplied in 1900, numbers 1615 and 1616; the other one was No 1 ARC ENIEGA. The track gauge was 1ft 11⅝in and the cylinder size the standard for the type, 8x12in; the customer was Rosing Brothers & Company with delivery to Spain. Unfortunately nothing is positively known about where these two locomotives worked, but their names are of two places in Spain; Sodupe is about 11 miles south-west of Bilbao and Arcenieca (spelt as one word and with a 'c' and not a 'g') eight miles or so further in the same direction. One presumes therefore, that they may have operated a railway between these two places and that an engine numbered 2 already existed. As well as the two engines six bogie passenger coaches were supplied, one of which can be seen in the above illustration; notice both engine and coach are vacuum brake fitted. Spares were later supplied for the locomotives to the order of Materials De Construccion y Pavimentacion of Zaragoza, which is of course, some way from Bilbao. Strange in view of the railway enthusiast interest in Spain, that nothing seems to be known about these two locomotives or any railway they may have worked on.

TIMBO REAL No 1, number 1507 of 1897, was a 6x9in cylinder 1ft 11 ⁵/₈in gauge locomotive ordered by Hurst, Nelson & Company, acting a agents for Usina Timbo Real, a sugar plantation and factory in the Santa Valley of Brazil. This photograph is taken at Hurst, Nelson's Motherwell factory, presumably as the engine was part of a larger order from Hurst, Nelson; this Company designed and built railway rolling stock. The engine was despatched from Stafford with Hurst, Nelson plates and not Bagnall ones and although the specification called for the engine to be a wood-burner, there does not appear to be any special provision for carrying the fuel - the chimney is described in the registers as an 'American funnel'. The illustration shows the Baguley valve gear to good advantage. (Hurst, Nelson Collection; Motherwell Public Library)

windy. It was sand getting in the bearings that was causing various seizures that eventually resulted in the complete failure of the locomotive. Resulting from this series of failures, and despite spare parts having been despatched, the locomotive was returned to Stafford. A ledger entry of 5 January 1898 for £32 13/ 8d (£32 68p), covered the freight charges for bringing the engine back from Carthage.

We know all about these problems from two sources. The Carthago Syndicate Limited were taken to court by WG Bagnall Limited, claiming a sum of £615 17/ 4d (£615 87p), and the case was heard at Stafford Assizes by Mr Justice Mathew on Tuesday and Wednesday 26 and 27th July 1898. Secondly, there exists a hand-written notebook dated June 30 1898, which contains notes of the court proceedings along with sketches of the valve gear. Against many of the notes and on the opposite side of the page are comments in Bagnall's own handwriting; as might be expected these are very much in favour of his side of the arguments! The Bagnall claim was based on the expenses incurred as well as the total costs for the engine and other equipment, because it was claimed nothing had so far been paid. In court

Mr AF Bosanquet QC and the Hon. A Lyttleton MP (of Messrs Hand & Company of Stafford) both representing WG Bagnall Limited, went to great lengths in describing the business of the Company and its reputation as a designer and builder of light railway equipment and locomotives. When Gordon Bagnall was in person called to give evidence he claimed that the Company had built over 60 engines of the same type as the one in question, all running successfully and that in addressing the specification for the railway in Tunisia, whilst he was aware it was to transport salt, no mention had been made of the adverse conditions of the terrain where it was to be used. He went on to say the engine was designed to haul 20 tons up a gradient on 1 in 100 and that it had been successfully tested before despatch. Both Owen and Keeley also gave evidence of their activities in Tunis and Keeley gave details of the tests he undertook with the engine before it was delivered. There was evidence too, of the mishandling of the engine by Schaeffer, in particular placing it in reverse whilst it was running despite having been trained by Owen not to do so. Samuel Price was also called and described himself as a mechanical engineer and

DREFUS-RAU, number 1661 of 1902, was another locomotive ordered by Henry Rogers Sons & Company Limited, and intended for use on a sugar plantation in the Pernambuco Province of Brazil. This is another engine of the Pekoe-Tip type with 6x9in cylinders but in this case with a partly enclosed cab. It was one of eight locomotives laid down to a stock order on 24 October 1901, some of which were actually completed as 0-4-0s, whilst others were longer and with a trailing axle like this one. The last of the eight, number 1668, was not positively ordered until April 1903. This is a good example of the Company building for stock locomotives of popular designs, completing them as customers came along. Construction would only be proceeded with far enough for differences in track gauge etc., to be agreed once a firm order was placed.

foreman at the works - not works manager note, as on many occasions he claimed he was. Price testified that on the engine's return to Stafford it only took three hours to make the necessary repairs, using the same parts that had been sent to Tunis, after which he was requested by Mr Bagnall to 'see if he could smash it' (the engine). Accordingly, he raised steam and attached the engine to two empty and two loaded main line wagons (one wonders how?) and had a man stand on the break of one of them, 'and in spite of this severe test no part of the gearing gave way and there was no sign of any weakness'.

EW Mackenzie Hughes, who we met earlier in this Chapter as a supporter of Ernest Baguley, was then called as an expert independent witness; he described

himself as a consulting and inspecting engineer and for some years an assistant locomotive superintendent of the State Railways of India. Mackenzie Hughes described his experiences with engines for the Egyptian Government, from which we can deduce that he was the inspecting engineer for the locomotives Bagnall had recently built for that country - hence being known to Ernest Baguley. He gave a very complementary account of the workmanship at the Castle Engine Works and described his examination of the little EXPLORER on its return from Tunis. His opinion was that the first breakdown appeared to have been caused by seizure of the valve spindle rod and that repairs subsequent to the breakdowns had been 'very crude'. He went on to point out that as almost all the breakdowns were to the left

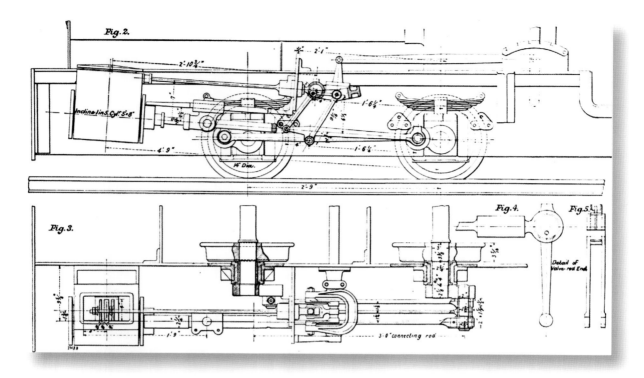

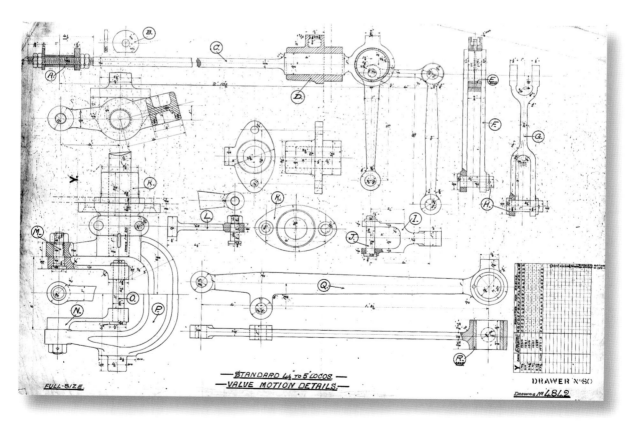

Two drawings to illustrate the Modified Baguley Valve Gear. The first is an general arrangement of the gear as fitted to number 1439 of 1894, whilst the second shows details of the individual parts which should give a good understanding of the design characteristics if studied in combination with the description in the text. This second drawing is for the small 4½ and 5in cylinder locomotives numbers: 1560, 1581, 1610, 1651 and 1687.

hand side of the engine, and that this was doubtless due to the prevailing wind coming from that direction. The Judge eventually concluded that the conditions under which the engine was intended to work had not been specified adequately by the Syndicate, no member of whom attended the hearing, but it was represented by Messes AT Lawrence QC and L Smith of Messrs Faithful & Owen of London. The Syndicate's case rested on the engine being warranted as reasonably fit for the purpose for which it was sold in any part of the world, but the Judge did not agree. WG Bagnall Limited was awarded the full amount claimed along with an additional and unspecified sum to cover the 'plaintiff's' cost of attending to give evidence on commission in Tunis. However, whatever this latter issue consisted of appears to have gone unrecorded. It would seem from the evidence that the Syndicate was eventually satisfied by an engine which was both bigger and stronger and with its parts protected from the sand - but it was not a Bagnall. No record seems to exist regarding the fate of the Bagnall track and wagons which presumably remained in Tunis. However, the little EXPORER was resold to fulfil an order of November 8 1897, but not until it had been rebuilt to suit a track gauge of 2ft 9in. With the name MABEL it went to the Gas, Light & Coke Company for use at its Bromley-by-Bow gas works in London, and was despatched there on 31 January 1898. As this was before the Court case, it would have been an interesting exercise if Mr Justice Mathew had asked to see the engine during his proceedings later that year!

Ernest Baguley designed a second valve gear whilst at Stafford, usually referred to as Modified Baguley valve gear. No patent was granted for this gear and as far as can be traced one was never applied for. This was another radial gear and whilst similar to the earlier gear in that both components of valve motion - the valve travel itself and the in-phase lap and lead motion - are derived from the main crank, there is no expansion link. In the case of this gear the link is replaced by twin sets of two each short radius rods working inside a horseshoe shaped yoke. As in the earlier gear both sets of radius rods are connected via a vibrating lever and motion connecting rod to the main crank; this gives the primary component of valve motion, whilst at their opposite ends one set of radius rods is connected to the yoke, and the other set to a combining lever, which also derives its motion from the main crank via the motion connecting rod. The combining lever provides the secondary component of valve motion - that is the lap and lead. Movement of the yoke up and down and thus the radius rods, the secondary set of which are also connected to an eccentric similar to the link pivot in the earlier gear, provides for forwards and backwards movement of the locomotive, as the pivot is a part of and at the end of, the valve rod.

It has been suggested that the principles of this gear are similar to Brown's valve gear, in particular the form of 'correcting' motion, and this is the reason why it was never patented. Charles Brown (1827-1905), although an Englishman, in 1871 founded the Swiss Locomotive & Machine Works at Winterthur; he patented his gear in 1878. The principal advantage of the Modified Baguley gear over the original one appears to be have been obviating the need for the link, which was a time consuming and therefore expensive component to make. Slotted links in valve gears are also subject to considerable wear; the die block working within a link is directly in the load-path and takes the full load of driving the valve; this is especially so on locomotives with unbalanced slide valves where the level of friction between the valve and the valve chest face, is very high. An additional disadvantage is that any wear between the link and the die directly translates itself into lost valve motion. Against these disadvantages of a link, the modified gear had its disadvantages too, in particular the high vertical load imparted on the valve rod, hence its support by a large bush in a substantial casting forming the motion bracket. The modified gear bears a similar relationship to the original Baguley valve gear as Walschaerts valve gear does to Baker valve gear - that is replacement of the link by a series of radius rods.

The reason for the development of this modified arrangement seems to have been two fold. In the first place, the weakness of the necessarily slender vibrating and combining levers of the original gear; these were the components that were the downfall of the engine Bagnall sent to Tunisia and the subject of the legal case referred to earlier. Secondly, on locomotives with very small wheels it was difficult to make the vibrating and combining levers long enough to get an equal swing of the link, and therefore, equal valve events in both directions of travel. This was why in the case of the

IRIS, number 1439 of 1894, was the first locomotive fitted with the Modified Baguley valve gear, which is clearly seen in this view - note in particular the heavy motion bracket and support for the valve rod necessary in view of the high vertical loads. Despite being the prototype for this gear, this little engine is otherwise to a pre-Baguley design complete with inverted saddle tank and a conventional locomotive type boiler. Cylinders were 5x8in, the wheel diameter was 1ft 2in and the track gauge was two-foot; outside frames were used despite the very low centre of gravity, and the engine was designed to give clearance in the coke retorts. Despatch was to the Nine Elms gas works of the Gas Light & Coke Company and the locomotive is seen here posed for publicity purposes with a train of side-tip wagons, standing on sections of the firm's portable track and patent sleepers.

ANT, number 1651 of 1902, is an example of the small 5in cylinder locomotives with a circular firebox boiler which were the normal recipients of Modified Baguley valve gear; these were the smallest versions of the 'standard' narrow-gauge designs and often referred to as type Doris. This one was originally laid down to a stock order in February 1901, and appears to have been completed to suit 1ft 6in gauge track and sent on loan to Willans & Robinson at Queensferry later that year. It was subsequently sold to Blackbrook Colliery Company and despatched in August the following year, and this may be the colliery of that name between Taffs Well and Caerphilly in Glamorgan. If so, this is presumably where this delightful photograph was taken but there were other collieries of this name, including one near St Helens in Lancashire. Notice the splendid attire of the gentleman on the footplate! (Collection Colonel Stephens Museum)

original gear, after experience with the first few engines that were fitted, the vibrating lever was lengthened by moving its point of attachment to the motion connecting rod, in a vertical plane below the centre line of that rod, thus enabling it to be longer between its centres of attachment.

Ironically, as with the original Baguley valve gear, the first use of the modified arrangement was on a locomotive largely built to the principles of the 'old' design school. This engine was manufacturer's number 1439, a two-foot gauge 0-4-0 inverted saddle tank with 5x8in cylinders, 1ft 2in diameter driving wheels and a 2ft 9in wheelbase. With the name IRIS, this little locomotive was sent to the Nine Elms Gas Works of the Gas, Light & Coke Company in London on 21 November 1894; it was illustrated and described in *Engineering*, issue dated 7 June 1895, where particular reference was made to the valve gear. A repeat order for an identical locomotive was placed in the following year and number 1460, named AJAX, was delivered in November 1895.

Use of the modified gear was not extensive on

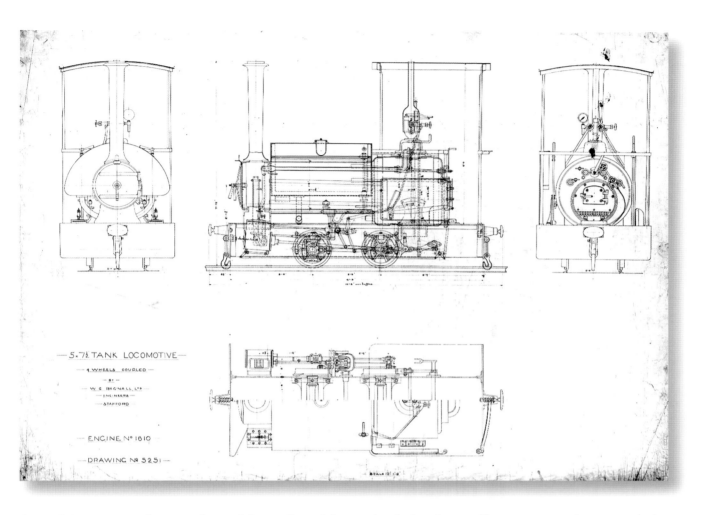

—5·7½ TANK LOCOMOTIVE—

4 WHEELS COUPLED

— BY —

W C BAGNALL LTD

— ENGINEERS —

— STAFFORD —

— ENGINE Nº 1610 —

— DRAWING Nº 5251 —

General Arrangement drawing of one of the smallest of the circular firebox design of locomotives, in this case with 5x7½in cylinders but generally of the type Margaret. Engines of this small size were fitted with the modified arrangement of Baguley valve gear and this one was number 1610, new in 1900. Built to suit two-foot gauge it was ordered by the Crown Agents for the Colonies for use in Nigeria, resounding in the rather grandiose name SIR RALPH, it was smartly turned out in sultan red picked out in lemon chrome - a train of side-tip wagons was supplied at the same time. Amazingly this little engine came back to Stafford for overhaul in July 1910, returning to Nigeria again afterwards

locomotives built at Stafford and only 14 were fitted between 1894 and 1902; they were all quite small ones with cylinder diameters between in the range 4½ to 5in. However, after Baguley left the Castle Engine Works he eventually became managing director of Baguley Cars Limited, a Company that later became Baguley (Engineers) Limited, with works at Burton-on-Trent. In the period 1920 to 1928 these companies manufactured a small number of narrow-gauge steam locomotives designed by Ernest Baguley, and of the 23 known to have been built, they all had one or other of the Baguley gears and no less than 18 of them were fitted with the modified gear. Observe that the designer of the two

gears appeared to prefer the modified arrangement, and this may well be significant in terms of the ease of establishing equal valve events in both directions of travel. Only one standard-gauge locomotive was constructed by the firm and this one had the original gear. Not surprisingly, all the narrow-gauge locomotives built by Baguley at Burton-on-Trent, had similarities with the Stafford product.

Ernest Baguley was only party to one other patent whilst at the Castle Engine Works, although he was involved with several others after he left Stafford. Jointly with Gordon Bagnall, Patent No 576 was accepted on 11 November 1896; it was titled

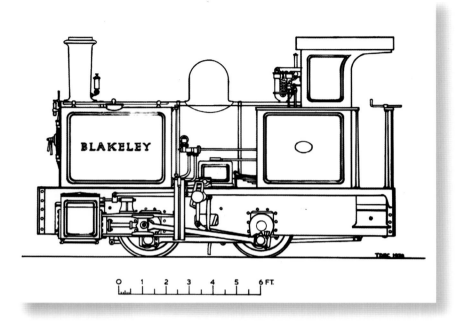

Unfortunately a photograph does not seem to exist of number 1504 of 1897; the only engine built thought to have embraced the Bagnall and Baguley patent gauge convertible axles. However, here is an artists impression by one of the authors and based on the available drawings. As this engine had rather large diameter wheels, 2ft 7½in in fact, presumably to make it more viable if used on standard-gauge railways, the expansion link of the Baguley valve gear had to he mounted higher that normal so as to clear the connecting rod. For this reason the intermediate valve rod was connected to the valve rod itself as shown here, which resulted in longer vibrating and combining levers, and the upwards angle of the motion connecting rod where it connected to the latter. These modifications to the normal layout were necessary to ensure an equal swing of the link in both directions - itself a key requirement of the gear.

'Locomotive to run on Various Gauges'. The patent covered the principle of a locomotive with outside frames and cylinders, the wheels of which could be adjusted to several different track gauges. This was achieved by sliding the wheels along the axles and then locating them by a rather clever system of keys and wedges. So far as we are aware the arrangement may only have been used on one locomotive, manufacturer's number 1504, supplied in May 1897 to Huddersfield Corporation, for use in connection with the construction of Deerhill & Butterley Reservoirs. These reservoirs are situated east of Marsden, and the Corporation was undertaking the work with direct labour. The locomotive was in fact built to an old Bagnall design, surprising perhaps in view of Baguley's involvement; it was an 0-4-0 inverted saddle tank with 10x15in cylinders, 2ft 7½in diameter wheels and the wheelbase was 4ft 9in. Baguley valve gear was fitted and it was thus, one of very few of the older designs to have one or other of the Baguley gears, but clearly in this case there would be no room for the eccentrics on the axles necessary for Stephenson's link motion.

As supplied the track gauge of the engine was set at three-foot, but may have been capable of being adjusted to run on any gauge up to and including 4ft 8½in. As this adjustable track gauge facility could have been part of the specification when the engine was ordered, perhaps the Corporation had in mind conversion to standard-gauge would enhance its resale value when the contract was complete. Be that as it may, with the name BLAKELEY, which was the name of one of the dams being constructed, the engine later worked with a number of other contractors, some of whom are known to have used standard-gauge railways. However, there is no evidence that it was ever used on anything other than three-foot gauge railways, and on the last contract it is known to have been used, with Sir John Jackson Limited at Loch Leven in Scotland, the railway was three-foot gauge. The sales literature on conclusion of this job which was dated August 1921, nevertheless quotes for BLAKELEY: 'extended axles for standard-gauge'. So it may well have been used on the standard-gauge at some time in its career; in any event it seems to have retained a facility to change the gauge to the end of its life. Perhaps surprisingly, no mention of this arrangement ever seems to have been made in the firm's

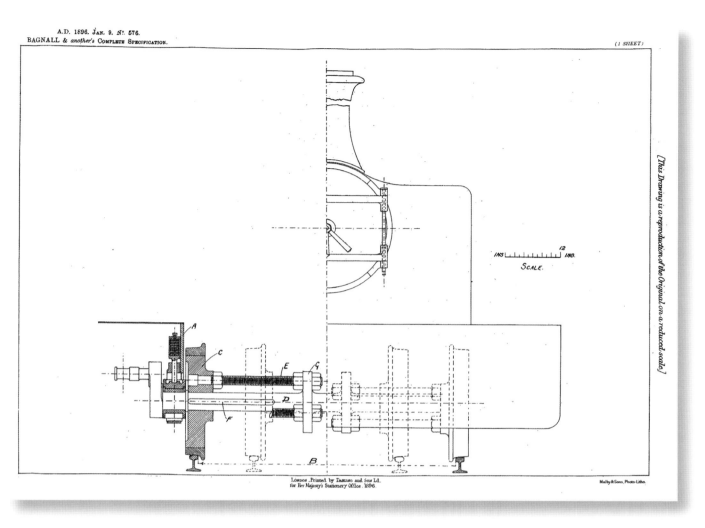

A.D. 1896. JAN. 9. N°. 576.
BAGNALL & another's COMPLETE SPECIFICATION.

(1 SHEET)

[This Drawing is a reproduction of the Original on a reduced scale.]

SCALE.

London. Printed by Darling and Son Ld.
for Her Majesty's Stationery Office. 1896.

Malby&Sons, Photo-Litho.

This is the drawing that accompanied the patent application for the method of changing the gauge of a locomotive as may have been fitted to number 1504. Notice how the wheels could slide along the axle under the control of the long key and key-way on the axle F, studs E, and locking arrangement G. Obviously this arrangement left no room between the frames for any valve gear; hence the only locomotive fitted had Baguley valve gear outside. This was one of very few examples of locomotives built to older designs having either of the Baguley gears.

publicity material. BLAKELEY had the largest cylinders, 10in, ever used on a Bagnall locomotive fitted with Baguley valve gear.

Another particularly interesting locomotive was supplied in March 1897, manufacturer's number 1501, designed and built to run on a circular railway, presumably of a type then popular with showman. Surprisingly no photographs seem to exist of this engine, but a few drawings do and from these we can glean that outwardly at least, it had the appearance of a conventional six-wheeled side tank. Named JENNIE, it had inside frames and outside cylinders, a tall chimney and no cab as such; the overall height to the top of the

tall, slender and neat copper capped chimney was a little over seven foot. The boiler was of the standard circular firebox type with a large dome mounted on the firebox complete with Ramsbottom safety valves and clad with a brass cover. This was unusual, but a specific request on the order confirming perhaps, its intended use in a fairground. The track gauge was three-foot but thereafter the similarity with a conventional locomotive ceased, as the right hand wheels were 1ft 0¼in diameter and the left hand 1ft 3¼in diameter, the three wheel sets being arranged radially so as to equate to a radius of 18ft 9in, which was the radius of the circular track the engine was designed to run on - measured from the centre of the three-foot gauge track this gave a circle of 37ft 6in diameter. The right hand wheelbase of the engine was 3ft 2in and the left hand 3ft 6³/₈in; the 5x9in cylinders drove the intermediate axle via normal connecting rods, but the drive to the leading and trailing wheel-sets was by a series of gears. These were mounted on the centre of the axles with intermediate gears on lay shafts between the axles, necessary of course, to ensure all the wheels rotated in the same direction. Inside Stephenson's link motion drove valves mounted on top of the cylinders via rocking shafts with two sets of twin eccentrics, one set each side of the centrally mounted gear trains. The engine was designed to operate in a clockwise direction with the smokebox leading. If it was in fact intended for the quite light loads expected to be hauled on a circular fairground railway, one wonders why it was necessary to drive all three axles. Most of the contemporary fairground locomotives appear to have had only a single set of driven wheels, or in the case of those built by John Fowler of Leeds, two sets, presumably at the expense of horrendous tyre wear! However, unlike the engines built by for example Savage Brothers of Kings Lynn, the frames of the Bagnall were parallel, with the horn guides and axle boxes set both axially and radially to suit the track radius. It is also strange for the design to embody inside valve gear with the restrictions already imposed by the gear wheels, and one is left wondering why the Baguley gear outside the frames was not specified; and why did it need to be reversible?

Fairground tunnel railways, as they have been termed, were popular about the time JENNIE was built. The concept of a tunnel under the English Channel was in vogue, and the public imagination had been roused. Several showmen, along with their traditional suppliers of machinery and equipment were not slow to rise to the challenge. Savage Brothers, well known in the trade as designers and builders of fairground equipment, were in the forefront - they seem to have built at least six, and possible seven small locomotives, along with other equipment for circular railways. Mention has been made of John Fowler of Leeds, which, along with its neighbour Thomas Green & Sons, also built locomotives to run on circular fairground railways; there was at least one other builder involved and there may have been more. It was quite logical therefore, for Bagnall to become involved, but JENNIE was a much

more sophisticated locomotive than any of its contempories, and we can perhaps see the hand of Baguley as the brains behind it.

The building of this locomotive was recalled in a letter to WA Smyth - managing director at the time - in response to his request in the letter columns of a number of journals in the mid 1950s, for information on the company's early locomotives. A gentleman by the name of WG Bostock of Tunbridge Wells responded in 1951: 'In 1896, I was either articled or apprenticed to Mr Bagnall. There was an engine built for a fair to run on a round track, the three sets of wheels were set at an angle to each other, the centre pair being square to the frames and driven by outside cylinders'. We know Bostock was with the Company at that period as he appears in the company books with an apprentice premium being paid (presumably by his parents) in the years 1896 through to 1899. Most unfortunately, nothing else is known about the later history of this locomotive, or indeed where it was delivered, other than the brief details of the customer recorded as Walker Hill & Company. A company of this name with a Church Gate, Nottingham address appears to have acted as machinery dealers and occasionally advertised locomotives for sale in the trade journals in this period. For example *Colliery Guardian* in the period 1894 to 1903, *Machinery Market* in its issue of 1 December 1899, and *The Engineer* in the period 1899 to 1904. The original order from Walker Hill, dated 19 May 1896 and was for a 'four coupled' locomotive, albeit also designed to run around a circular track and 1492 was allocated in this case. However, this order was cancelled and substituted by the specification for the engine outlined above on 1 September 1896. This suggests perhaps, some lengthy discussions regarding exactly what the customer wanted.

At the time JENNIE was built it was the usual practice to have an official photograph taken of any locomotive that was of a special design, for the obvious publicity value. There were a few exceptions over the years, nevertheless it is rather strange that one does not seem to exist for this engine, or at least one has not so far come to light. Gordon Bagnall was not slow in this respect and one would have expected a new design like this to have been yet another addition to his catalogues. There is the possibility that it may have been seen as an aspect of railway engineering he did not want his

The Groudle Glen Railway is north of Douglas in the Isle of Man, a delightful short two-foot gauge line but three quarters of a mile long running from the glen itself onto the headland overlooking the Irish Sea. There used to be an enclosure near the terminus where sea lions and polar bears were kept, hence the name of this, the line's first locomotive. SEA LION is number 1484 of 1896 and seen here on 3 September 2000, at the terminus of the line and near to where its namesakes used to be kept. After lying derelict for several years and at a number of locations this little engine, the cylinders are only 4½in diameter, has been beautifully restored and continues to do the job it was built for. It is painted in the Bagnall standard livery of the period it was built and although hardly discernable in this view, it is fitted with Modified Baguley valve gear. This diminutive locomotive, one of the smallest the Company built, returned to Stafford for overhaul in 1907 and has visited the mainland again in more recent times.

Company to be to closely associated with. There is evidence that in accepting the contract to build the first of the very small locomotives for the Groudle Glen Railway in the Isle of Man, he took some persuading. The story goes that the owners of the Groudle Estate in seeking a builder for a small locomotive for their planned miniature railway, were having difficulty in finding a builder interested in designing and constructing one. As eventually built, the diminutive SEA LION, manufacturer's number 1484 of May 1896, had cylinders of but 4½x7½in. It was a tiny locomotive by any standards as anybody who has seen it can testify; the overall height is 6ft 6in, length 10ft 9in and width

4ft 2in. Gordon Bagnall in agreeing to build this locomotive appears to have played down any publicity for what might have been considered a 'toy railway'. Nevertheless, this is in itself surprising, especially in the light of the publicity solicited when the miniature Great Northern Railway Stirling Single was completed only a few years earlier, an engine that did appear in the catalogues; even on the cover of some of them!

There is an interesting sequel to the possibility of JENNIE being built for use at a fairground. In *The Engineer*, issue dated 8 July 1898, the following advert appears: 'For Sale, New Patent Circular Oscillating Railway, mounted on road wagons with specially constructed locomotive and cars, suitable for pleasure resort or fairs £500. WG Bagnall Limited, Stafford'. What one wonders was this, does it refer to JENNIE and was the locomotive part of a bigger package that had been left on the maker's hands? Whatever 'Patent' might have been involved it was not one in Bagnall's name as a diligent search of the Patent Office records has revealed nothing, in fact nothing relevant has been traced in the name of any patentee. Moreover, in the 6 July 1900 issue of *The Engineer* we find: 'For Sale tank locomotive, 8½in cylinders, 30in gauge, Walker Hill & Company, Nottingham' - this is the dealer referred to earlier. Could this be JENNIE too, although the cylinder size and gauge are wrong, could 30in be a mistake for three-foot perhaps? However, if the locomotive referred to in this advert was of such an unusual design one would have expected the fact to have been mentioned! Without considerable modifications JENNIE as built, would not have been of any use on anything but a circular railway!

Among other interesting locomotives constructed in the period being covered in this Chapter and in which Baguley undoubtedly had a significant input, were two built in 1897-1898 for the Government. Captain Johnstone is quoted as the buyer in some of the registers, and both locomotives were delivered to the Admiralty for use on the 2ft 6in gauge Chattenden & Upnor Railway in Kent. Although they were both six-wheel coupled with no carrying wheels and outside

cylinders, there the similarity ended and anecdotal evidence in later years suggested they were designed with a view to both evaluation of different design features, along with staff training. Just how much input the Admiralty, or perhaps the Army, might have had in the specifications has however been lost in the mists of time. Manufacturer's number 1513, which was named STAFFORD, was an outside framed side tank with 10x15in cylinders, a wheel diameter of 2ft 6½in and a 7ft 6in wheelbase; it had Baguley valve gear and a circular firebox boiler. However, the firebox itself was not the normal Bagnall design, but according to the records one built to conform to the Purves patent, with a corrugated steel inner firebox.

A year or so later when the subject of corrugated circular fireboxes on locomotives was raised as an issue in the journal *Engineering*, in this case as applied to an American 'Vanderbilt' locomotive, Gordon Bagnall wasted no time in writing to the editor. In his letter, which was dated 25 September 1899 and appeared in the issue of 29 September, Bagnall pointed out that his Company had built a boiler with a firebox of this (corrugated) type in 1897, which was fitted to a locomotive supplied to HM Government. He went on to say: 'English engineers are often too modest to get the credit they deserve for novel designs'; the inference being that circular corrugated fireboxes were a Bagnall design. This was despite such records as we have indicating it was to a Purves patent; a drawing of the

STAFFORD, number 1513 of 1897, a special design for the Government and used on the 2ft 6in gauge Admiralty Chattenden & Upnor Railway in Kent. Notice the Baguley valve gear and duplex water feed pump mounted on the top of the side tank. Unusually the manufacturer's plate is mounted on the smokebox and the engine has a neat copper caped chimney - it also has a circular firebox boiler, in this case a corrugated firebox design.

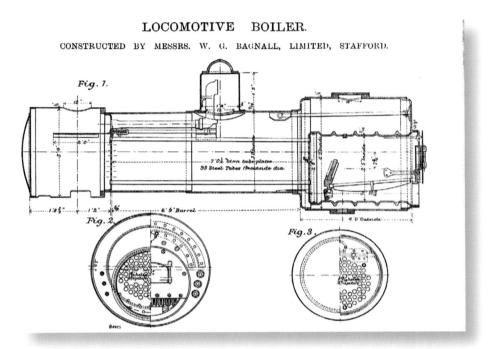

LOCOMOTIVE BOILER.

CONSTRUCTED BY MESSRS. W. G. BAGNALL, LIMITED, STAFFORD.

A drawing illustrating the circular firebox boiler as fitted to number 1513 with the corrugated inner firebox. Another unusual feature of this boiler was the use of a centrally mounted dome on the barrel; as a general rule the dome on this design of boiler was placed on the firebox.

Bagnall boiler, reproduced here, accompanied the letter. The article to which Bagnall was referring appeared in the 15 September 1899 issue of *Engineering* and concerned a New York Central Railway 4-6-0 freight locomotive. The engine had been built in the railway's own workshops at West Albany, and Cornelius Vanderbilt had designed the boiler with its corrugated circular firebox and tapered barrel; it was stated however, to be an experimental trial of this type of firebox. It was of course a much bigger boiler than the Bagnall one, with a total heating surface of 2,356 sq ft and a grate area of 35 sq ft. The corresponding figures for STAFFORD were 324 sq ft and 6 sq ft respectively!

This Bagnall locomotive was later renamed EARDLEY WILMOT and was remembered many years later by staff on the railway as: 'a remarkable locomotive with experimental valve gear which made it extremely economical with fuel, but valve setting was a nightmare'. Delivered in January 1898, along with the other engine ordered at the same time and still to be described, it is reputed to have worked in South Africa during the Boer War, but this is not substantiated. It was sold for scrap in April 1941, but lay out of use in a local scrap yard and was not broken up until 1946 - surprising in view of the war-time scrap drives. There is an interesting story regarding the change of this

engine's name. The story goes that in about 1912 an early form of diesel locomotive arrived on the Chattenden & Upnor Railway; it had been ordered from a company called McEwan Pratt which went bankrupt before it was completed. The completed parts were acquired by the Admiralty and shipped to Chatham Dockyard where the locomotive was completed, or ostensibly so, by the dockyard matey's. When it arrived on the railway it took enormous effort to get the engine to run, and even then somewhat erratically, such that the staff very soon became absolutely fed up with it, and after four years efforts completely so. However, luck was to hand, as in 1915 authority was obtained to scrap STAFFORD. The ingenious folk responsible for getting the diesel to work, decided this was an opportunity too good to miss and those readers who have followed the story thus far, can perhaps guess what they did. Yes, they swapped around the nameplates and the McEwan Pratt cum Chatham machine quietly, but effectively, disappeared; nobody shed any tears and nobody in authority appears to have been any the wiser. It has to be added however, that whilst this is a nice story, and may well be what happened, it does rely on hear-say and having been passed down over the years, may not be 100% accurate. The second engine, manufacturer's number 1514 had

BAGNALL was the second of the two engines supplied to the Admiralty for use on the Chattenden & Upnor Railway in Kent; and completely different from the first one. Number 1514 of 1898, a very heavily built engine with a conventional locomotive firebox boiler and a drum-head smokebox; notice the splendid finish complete with copper caped chimney, polished and burnished motion and fittings. The small plinth on the smokebox for mounting the head lamp is worthy of a closer look too. The background makes an interesting study with Henry Venables timber yard to the left, and the LNWR junction signals behind the engine. This photograph illustrates why the Company soon decided to erect a large wooden board near this spot, to act as a backcloth for the official photographer, and thus save him work later in painting out the background on the glass plate negatives so that the photograph could be used in catalogues.

inside frames and a saddle tank, cylinders were 11x16½in, wheel diameter was 2ft 6½in and the wheelbase 8ft 6in. The valve gear was Stephenson's link motion inside the frames and the springing was equalised between the axles. This was achieved via inverted leaf springs between the axles and coil springs in the end positions. The boiler was of the Haycock pattern with a raised firebox outer wrapper, the firebox being of steel rather copper, which was the usual material for this type of boiler. The boiler of this locomotive was mounted high on the frames with its centre line 5ft 4in above rail level, making the total height of the locomotive 9ft 6¼in. This was necessary because of the relatively short wheelbase and the firebox sat above the trailing coupled axle, rather than

between the intermediate and trailing axles, as would be more normal practice. This feature must have made emptying the ashpan quite a difficult operation. With the name BAGNALL this locomotive was delivered in March 1898 and despite both it and STAFFORD, sporting neat copper capped chimneys, this one was quite an ungainly looking machine compared with its counterpart. Like STAFFORD this engine is also reputed to have worked in South Africa during the Boer War, but this seems highly unlikely. It was recalled at Chattenden many years later as: 'an experimental locomotive for training Royal Engineers, it had a very high saddle tank, was very costly to run and quite unsuitable for narrow-gauge track'. Perhaps this is the reason it did not last very long, such records as we have suggesting it had been sold for scrap by June 1932. The cost of these two locomotives was £1,046 for STAFFORD and £1,006 8/ 9d (£1,006 43p) for BAGNALL, a profit of around £213 being recorded on the first and a loss of £104 on the second.

In view of the interesting and unique design features of the locomotives built by the Company in its early days, it is worth examining a few more that were built to the older designs in the period covered by this Chapter. Back in 1891 a diminutive small and neat inside cylinder four-wheeled inverted saddle tank locomotive had been designed to suit a very restricted loading gauge. It was designed to fit into coke oven retorts at the Bridgefoot Gas Works at Vauxhall in London of the South Metropolitan Gas Company. Manufacturer's number 1354, it was despatched in September that year with the appropriate name for a gas works engine of COKE, which for some reason was later changed to MEDEA. However, Coke was used as the 'type' name in the publicity material whilst the catalogues quote from a paper read by Charles C Carpenter CBE. Carpenter was the Gas Company's Engineer, and he read his paper before members of the Institution of Civil Engineers at the Second Metropolitan Conference of the Institution, which was held in London between 7 and 9 June 1899. The quote refers to the two-foot gauge railway at Vauxhall which was handing 60,000 tons of coke and breeze a year, and that use of a railway and locomotive had reduced the handling costs from 1/-

(5p) per ton to 3d (approximately 1p), effecting an annual saving of £2,250 per annum. Bagnall also supplied the track materials for the railway at the gas works as well as the rolling stock. The little engine called COKE had cylinders 5½x7½in, a wheel diameter of 1ft 3in; the overall height was 5ft 3in and the width of 4ft 6in. There were two repeat orders for similar locomotives for Vauxhall, number 1415 of October 1892 which was named JASON, followed by number 1536 of December 1898 named ORION.

Although Bagnall tendered for a new locomotive required by the gas company in 1929 (see page 342), updating the design as appropriate, the order went to the Bristol builder Peckett & Sons Limited; this was at a time of serious depression in the trade with some firms even taking orders at a loss, to keep their works employed. Prior to ordering a new locomotive the inverted saddle tanks on the earlier locomotives, or at least the later ones, had been replaced with more conventional front tanks, that is separate tanks each side of the smokebox. The Bagnall tender offered a locomotive with this feature. Peckett designed and built an almost exact copy of the earlier locomotives, but with the modified tank arrangement, the locomotive being externally similar to the Bagnalls. The inverted saddle tanks cannot have been easy to maintain, especially the part under the smokebox, even more so on such small locomotives, and in any event they would be susceptible to the corrosive effect of the

This is ORION, number 1536 of 1898, at the Vauxhall gas works in 4 April 1948. Notice that by this date this diminutive engine, the cylinders were only 5½ x7½in, has been rebuilt with separate front side tanks rather than the inverted saddle tank with which it was originally built. This and its sisters were delightful small engines and what a pity one was not saved. (Late RT Russell, Frank Jones Collection - Industrial Locomotive Society)

smokebox gases. These factors are almost certainly why Baguley phased them out of new construction. The Bagnall ORION, and the Peckett lasted until as late as May 1951; what a shame one of them was not saved.

Another interesting example of the occasional practice of building to the 'old' design principles

A photograph taken in 1941 on the Ashibetsu Forestal Railway in Japan, illustrating no 17, Bagnall number 1500 of 1896, and much modified from when it originally left Stafford. Nevertheless, it was still going strong 47 years after it was built. (Collection Y Oguma)

encompassed two locomotives sent to Japan in December 1896; they were only the second order of locomotives for that country. Manufacturer's numbers 1499 and 1500 were 0-4-0 inverted saddle tanks on 2ft 6in gauge with 7x12in cylinders, a wheel diameter of two-foot and an extremely short wheelbase of 3ft 3in. Ordered by a company of British agents who frequently represented Japanese interests, J Morrison & Company Limited, the order seems to have come Bagnall's way via a fellow by the name of GA Goodwin. At one period Goodwin appears to have been under contract to Bagnall as an entry in one of the ledgers refers to expenses paid to him; it reads: 'Goodwin's expenses to Japan'. Two payments were made, one on 30 September 1896 for £120 9/ 7d (£120 48p), followed by what was referred to as a 'second-half', on 31 December 1897 for £243 19 6d (£243 97½p). These were large sums of money at that time and we do not know exactly what Goodwin did for such remuneration, but one of the registers quotes the locomotives mentioned above as: 'sent to Mr Goodwin, Japan'.

When Lord Charles Beresford CB MP, the well-known Admiral 'Charlie B', famous for his almost life long feuding with Admiral Jackie Fisher of Dreadnought battleship fame, gave a paper to the

This drawing illustrates the inverted saddle tank, in this particular case as applied to numbers 1499 and 1500, supplied to Japan and among the last locomotives fitted with this type of water tank.

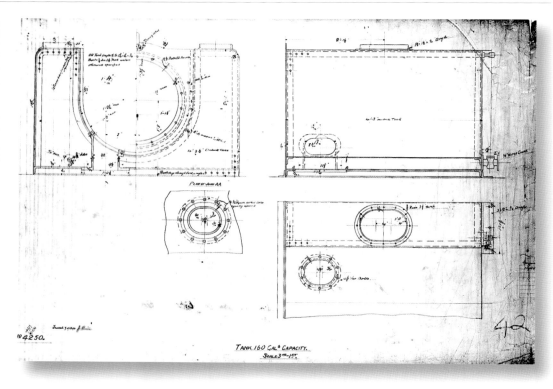

Institution of Mechanical Engineers in London on 24 November 1899, Goodwin contributed to the discussion. Beresford's paper covered his experiences following a period of time he had spent in Japan, China and other far eastern countries and was titled: *Openings for Mechanical Engineers in China*. Goodwin, in his contribution to the discussion following the meeting, mentioned that he had 'lately travelled in Japan and China for about two years'. Perhaps this was at Bagnalls expense, but whatever the case, there were no orders for Bagnall equipment for use in China until many years later! Over the next few years however, the firm did undertake a number of contracts for Japan and a further 16 locomotive were exported there. Just how much influence Goodwin might have had on these orders, if any, is nevertheless a matter on conjecture.

The two locomotives mentioned in the proceeding paragraph were named AUGUSTA and BEATRICE respectively; they were for use on a private colliery railway at Matsuura Colliery near Nagasaki, which is in the north-western corner of Kyushu Island. The colliery railway was later absorbed into the Sasebo Railway, and the locomotives became numbers 11 and 12 on that line. AUGUSTA seems to have been scrapped in 1941, but in the same year BEATRICE passed to the Ashibetsu Forestal Railway in central Hokkaido, where it became as No 17. Some time after this it seems to

have acquired a small four-wheel auxiliary tender. When the Sasebo Railway was taken over by the Japanese National Railways, both these locomotives had been converted to 3ft 6in gauge, which was the national gauge. It is interesting to speculate why they were built to an old design, but as they had a comparatively short wheelbase this may be the clue. In designing a four-wheel locomotive with a very short wheelbase, achieving a good balance of weight over both axles is extremely difficult, and we saw earlier that one of the advantages of the inverted saddle tank was that it allowed the designer to distribute the weight more evenly over two axles. Presumably the short wheelbase was part of the specification in view of the curves on the railway at Matsuura Colliery, but the engines would have been poor riders however well the weight was distributed. Whatever the reason, these two locomotives were among the last ones built with inverted saddle tanks.

In August 1897 Bagnall received an order for 10 locomotives for the Egyptian Delta Light Railways. In 1896 a concession had been granted by the Egyptian Government to a British company, John Birch & Company, to build a series of 2ft 5½in (750 mm) gauge railways on the Egyptian Delta. The lines were to follow what were referred to as agricultural roads. These roads which had only recently been built in the

Egyptian Delta Light Railways No 30, Bagnall 1602 of 1900 showing the lines of one of these locomotives as originally built. Notice the crosshead driven water feed pump, large headlamp, and neat chimney numerals. The engine is decked out in a special coat of light paint, easily removable, to highlight the detail for publicity purposes.

provinces of Behera and Gharbieh, were designed to help open up the area to agriculture, hence their name. They radiated from a central point at Damanhur, which is about 50 miles south-east of Alexandria and sometimes spelt Damanhour, and it was the success of these roads that led the government to the view that a series of light railways would serve the purpose even better. With Damanhur serving very successfully as a centre of the road operations, it was planned to have the centre of railway operations and workshops there too. In 1897 the railway became known as Societe Egytienne des Chemins de fer Agricoles (CFA), and the first 16 miles of line connecting Damanhur with Behera opened in April 1898. The original scheme which was underwritten by the Egyptian Government covered 120 miles of railway, but by the early part of the 20th century the total mileage was some 270 miles. The original motive power for all these lines came from

Stafford and the Company designed a neat outside cylinder 4-4-0 side tank that for obvious reasons eventually became known as the 'Delta' class. Cylinders were 9½x14in, driving wheels 2ft 6in diameter, total wheelbase 13ft 6in and the weight in working order 14½ tons. These first 10 locomotives, manufacturer's numbers 1519 to 1528 were delivered between January and May 1898; the running numbers 1 to 10, consisted of neat brass numerals on the chimneys - a la Beyer Peacock - as well as being painted on the rear of the bunkers! The initials CFA were painted on the side tanks and the locomotives were finished in an attractive yellow livery with elaborate lining, described in the registers as: 'picked out in chocolate with buffer beams in vermilion'.

Repeat orders followed as construction of the lines progressed. Ten more were ordered in April 1898, numbers 1540 to 1549 - CFA numbers 11 to 20; they

This is number 1602 again, but this time completed and ready for delivery. The later batches of these engines, numbers 1598 to 1607, EDLR numbers 26 to 35, differed from earlier ones in having the dust casing seen here. This followed problems with sand ingress to the motion parts in Egypt, which was perhaps not surprising, as for much of the distance the lines ran through very sandy areas! By the time this picture was taken the engine had been finish painted - the livery is described in the registers as: 'yellow, picked out in chocolate, buffers vermilion'. Dust casings were later supplied for the earlier engines and these were fitted in Egypt.

This is the first of the 35 locomotives of this basic type, supplied to the Indian States Railways between 1901 and 1905. Number 1620 of June 1901 is seen here on completion with the splendid array of LNWR signals as a backcloth. The ones to the left and immediately behind the engine are for the main line from Crewe, and those to the right for the Great Northern Railway line to Uttoxeter. The chimney and building to the left are part of the Henry Venables timber yard.

differed from the earlier batch in having Baguley valve gear outside the frames, whilst the earlier ones had Stephenson's link motion inside the frames. All the engines had the valves on top of the outside cylinders and the use of Stephenson's gear necessitated a somewhat ungainly arrangement of rocking levers and this, together with the difficulty of access to the inside motion made the arrangement unpopular with the railway. This was the reason for the substitution of Baguley valve gear on the later builds, and one is left wondering why it was not specified in the first place. This second batch of engines were delivered between December 1898 and April 1899, followed by another five between October and December 1899, numbers 1576 to 1580 - CFA numbers 21 to 25. In an effort to prevent the ingress of sand onto the moving parts which was proving to be a problem, the later engines were fitted with protection shields and casing over the driving wheels and motion. Finally, another 10 were delivered between April and November 1900, numbers 1598 to 1607 - CFA numbers 26 to 35. Together the orders for these locomotives comprised the largest order

for a single type of locomotive built at the Castle Engine Works by this date. The first batch cost £843 14/- (£843 70p) each and by the time the last ones were ordered the cost per engine had risen to £1,000 each - which included the dust skirts.

Thomas Betteley (1883-1968), father of Vic Betteley who was production manager at the Castle Engine Works in later years, was among the fellows who cut out from solid brass the chimney numerals for these locomotives, it was one of his very first tasks when he commenced his apprenticeship. After completing his apprenticeship Thomas Betteley continued to work for the Company, but he also spent time with nearby Kerr, Stuart & Company at Stoke-on-Trent, as well as at the English Electric works in Stafford.

The Delta system of railways was later extended following the injection of some German finance, but in 1900 the London based Egyptian Delta Light Railways was formed specifically to finance the works of the CF Agricoles, and a widespread system developed. Although some of the Bagnall engines did not

This is one of the later batches of the 2-4-2 saddle tank engines for India, in this case notice that the water tank capacity has been increased - 400 instead of 300 gallons - and a small four wheel tender added. The earlier engines had been found deficient in these respects as some of them were used on the 2ft 6in gauge Kushalgarh Kohat Thal Railway, a 91½ mile line built between 1901 and 1903 and part of the military railways on the North-West Frontier. Lord Kitchener, who became Commander in Chief of the Indian Army in 1902, was instrumental in the decision to build this railway as he was very keen to improve the communications towards the frontier with Afganistan. The later engines with bigger tanks and tenders replaced the earlier ones which were then placed in the military reserve. The narrow-gauge line originally connected with the North Western Railway main line - the main line railway operating the narrow-gauge line - via an aerial ropeway across the Indus, but in November 1907 a bridge was opened and the following year the 29½ mile section as far as Kohat was converted to broad-gauge. The corrugated iron building behind is the Sheet and Iron Stores and notice the engine is standing on temporary laid portable track which is laid across the standard-gauge connection to the Boiler House and Foundry. This line was used for the delivery of raw materials by rail, coal and foundry sand for example. The engine is from the penultimate batch built, numbers 1706 to 1715 of 1902.

This is one of the earlier batch of the Indian locomotives, numbers 1620 to 1629, although unfortunately the number has not been recorded. It is seen here being used for the construction work as Imperial Delhi Railway No 10, in September 1927. The additional plating around the cab doubtless dates from its use during the war in Mesopotamia (later Persia), where a number of these locomotives hitherto held in a military reserve in India, were drafted for the period of hostilities. (Kelland Collection - Bournemouth Railway Club No 50149)

At the time of the 1902 and 1911 Durbar celebrations in Delhi, specially commissioned 2ft 6in gauge railways were constructed to handle the crowds. On both occasions the motive power was supplied by these Bagnall 2-4-2 engines 'borrowed' from the military reserve. This picture was taken at Tis Hazari station in Delhi during the 1911 celebrations; it has one of the later engines with the 400 gallon full length saddle tanks on a well loaded train - no less that 23 of the engines are reputed to have been used during the 1911 event. (Collection JK Williams)

have terribly long lives, disappearing during the First World War - 15 of them had gone by March 1918 - the remainder soldiered-on for much longer although they were used on quite light duties. The conditions the locomotives had to operate under were difficult, with the particular problem of sand getting into the working parts mentioned earlier. As the lines were largely on the level the locomotives did not have to work very hard and the steepest gradient was 1 in 100 whilst the sharpest curve on the main-lines was two chains radius. After a few years locomotives from other builders supplemented the Bagnalls, but as it happened the very first ones to be withdrawn, CFA numbers 1 to 6 in 1916, were replaced by much larger 2-6-2 side tanks also built by Bagnall. The replacement engines, manufacturer's numbers 2022 to 2025, 2027 and 2032 however, belong to a later part of the story. Most of the other 4-4-0s lasted until the railway changed over almost completely to the Sentinel design of geared locomotive with vertical boiler and chain drive. Introduction of the Sentinel locomotives commenced in 1925, with the change completed over a comparatively short space of time, no less than 49 of these locomotives were delivered in the period 1924 to 1928. The Egyptian Government took over operation of the Delta Light Railways in 1945 and they had all closed by 1952.

Another significant order during the period under review and one which led to substantial follow on orders, came from the Indian State Railways on behalf of the military authorities. Over the years India became the biggest single market for Bagnall locomotives outside Great Britain, around one third of the total locomotive production being exported there. In the case of these engines, a series of 2ft 6in gauge 2-4-2 saddle tanks with 8x12in cylinders and 2ft 3in coupled wheels, between June 1901 and March 1905 a total of 36 were supplied. There were five separate batches, the later ones having bigger water tanks and small four-wheel auxiliary tenders. Some of them were intended for the Kohat Thal Railway in what is now Pakistan, whilst others were for a strategic military reserve of railway equipment located at Rawalpindi, and kept in connection with the protection of the North West Frontier. Many of these locomotives had extremely varied and complicated careers; for example some of them were used on the temporary railways laid as a part of the Great Durbar celebrations in Delhi in connection with the Coronations of 1902 and 1911. Others found their way during the First World War to Mesopotamia (present day Iraq) and Persia, where they were used on military operations in those countries. After the war several passed into industrial use at a number of sites in India and two are preserved; one of the earlier engines

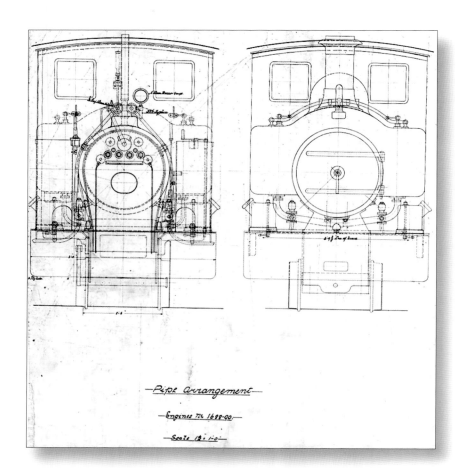

Pipe Arrangement

Engines 7½ 1688-00

Scale 1½: 1-0

The three drawings on this and the next page, are of the Indian States Military Railway locomotives. The first two are Pipe Arrangements of numbers 1688 to 1700, with the larger full-length saddle tanks holding 400 gallons of water and small four-wheel auxiliary tenders. The third shows the detail of the rather ingenious leading and trailing radial trucks - a novel arrangement giving plenty of side-play and applied to all the locomotives.

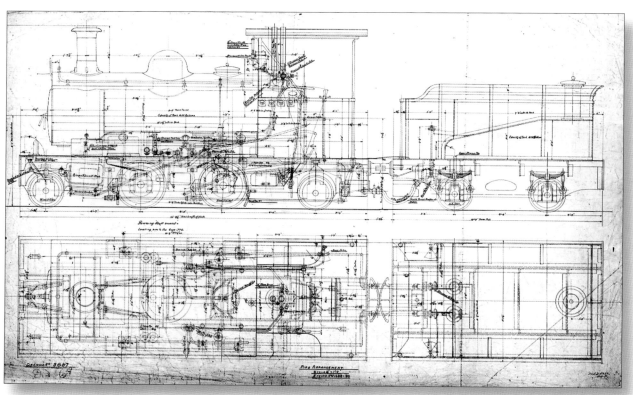

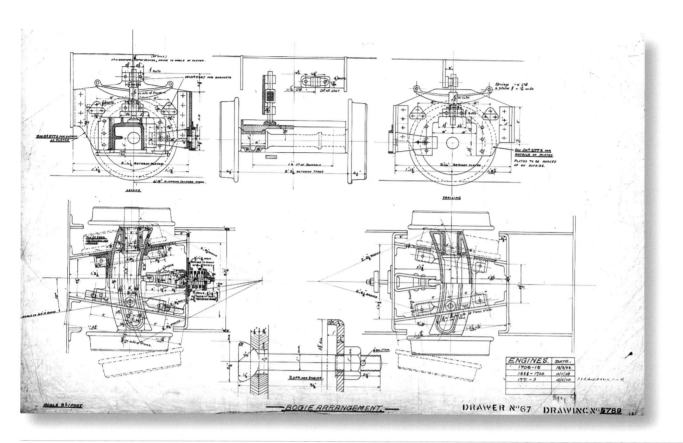

with a short saddle tank is at the railway museum in Mysore, whilst one of the later ones with a full length tank can be found at the Railway Museum in Delhi. The manufacturer's numbers and successive batches were: 1620 to 1629 of June 1901; 1688 to 1700 of August-November 1902; 1706 to 1715 of March-June 1903; 1771 to 1773 of March 1905. The total cost for all the 36 was £34,120.

It was during the period covered by this Chapter that the Company built its first non-steam locomotive, albeit only the mechanical, as opposed to propulsive parts. Two sets of mechanical parts were built for the small four-wheel electric locomotives used on the pioneer London tube railway - the City & South London Railway (C&SLR) - which opened on 18 December 1890. Bagnall only acted as a sub-contractor in both cases and both sets of parts were supplied in 1897, one to the order of the Electric Construction Company Limited of Wolverhampton, and the other for Crompton & Company of Chelmsford. In both cases these companies supplied the electrical equipment which included the traction motor and control gear. The parts built at Stafford included the frames, wheels,

drive mechanisms, brake gear and bodywork, but it is by no means certain where final erection took place. The Electric Construction locomotive became C&SLR No 19 and as it was the only locomotive supplied to the C&SLR by this Company it could well have been erected and despatched from Stafford. A picture of it featured in Bagnall catalogues for many years. The other set of parts were for C&SLR No 18 and are more likely to have been despatched to Chelmsford for final erection there, as this was only one of 31 locomotives of the same basic type ordered from Crompton. At the time these locomotives were ordered the C&SLR was experimenting with different manufacturers electrical equipment following problems with the original locomotives; hence these two different locomotives. In the event Crompton were the successful builder and went on to supply a further 30 locomotives, although Bagnall were no longer involved. It is interesting to note at this juncture that Arthur Hewitt Gilling, who joined the Company as general manager in 1908, had been a draughtsman at the Electrical Construction Company in Wolverhampton at the time No 19 was built. It might have been at this time that the young

This is the first non-steam locomotive built at the Castle Engine Works, City & South London Railway No 19, built in conjunction with the Electrical Construction Company of Wolverhampton in 1897. This picture, which may have been taken at Stafford as final erection was most probably undertaken there, was often used in the catalogues, although quite what sort of customer might have wanted a similar locomotive is a mystery!

Gilling first came to the notice of John Gifford, who was the managing director at Stafford at the time Gilling was appointed.

The Castle Engine Works continued to expand during Baguley's tenure with the annual production of locomotives, rolling stock and other railway-related material increasing year on year. In the 1 October 1895 issue of the journal *Machinery Market*, an extensive article appeared on the Company which included a summery of a personal interview with Gordon Bagnall. The article discusses in some detail light railways and in particular their good points, obviously influenced by Bagnall himself and emphasising the achievements of the Company in furthering their use. There are descriptions of the wide range of locomotives built, together with passenger and goods rolling stock, permanent way materials etc. There are also descriptions of some of the complete light railways the firm had supplied and a brief description of the

workshops. It is perhaps both opportune and interesting to quote directly from a section of the article relating the works:

"The works are well laid out for their purpose. Extensions have evidently been made rapidly at various times to meet the increasing demand on the company's resources as they have arisen, and there are excellent facilities both for doing the work thoroughly and with despatch. In the locomotive building department for example, the capacity is equal to turning out one locomotive a week. On the occasion of our visit we saw 20 locomotives in progress, nine being near completion. It will be of interest to note that four of the latter were for abroad, whilst among the home orders, one was for Sir A Hickman, another for a slate quarry in Wales, a third for a London gasworks, another for contractors use, a further one for the Admiralty - there were seven more in hand on Admiralty account - and so on. At the present time the shops are working night and day on orders, and the

HERCULES was an interesting design of 4-4-0 for use on a sugar plantation in Brazil, an unusual wheel arrangement for plantation use at this period. Number 1441 of 1894, metre-gauge with 8½x14in cylinders, the engine was noted at Usina Paranague in the state of Bahia in Brazil as late as 1976. However, despite the fact that the maker's had supplied a new boiler in 1920, by 1976 it had one of obvious continental design, and a saddle tank had replaced the side tanks.

Gold Coast Government Railway No 2 was a 3ft 6in gauge 0-6-0 saddle tank number 1595 of 1900. This engine had 9x14in cylinders and a long 9ft 10in wheelbase with Baguley valve gear, a cross head driven pump and a cab specially designed for hot climates. The livery is quoted as: 'sultan red, lined lemon chrome, vermilion buffers with No 2 painted in white on them'. It must have looked very smart.

addition of another machine shop has been determined upon - the tools for it having been ordered. The powerful hydraulic press for stamping out the sleepers deserves special mention. Power for this is supplied by an accumulator working at 1,500 lb per square inch, the pumps in connection with it being self acting. The various sizes and form of sleepers are pressed from dies which can be altered to fit any gauge. A large stock of sleepers is always kept on hand. There were some 8,000 to 10,000 of them ready for delivery at the time of our visit. In conclusion we may say that all the work of the establishment is turned out under Mr WG Bagnall's active supervision, and the handsome and valuable catalogue of the firm is his own personal production.

He is ably assisted by Mr Baguley the chief of the designing department, and Mr Price of the Works department."

The article goes on to mention that the drawing office was a light and well arranged room and there was accommodation for 12 draughtsman. Of particular interest in view of the earlier mention of supplying locomotives to the Far East, is a comment that a Mr George Abraham Goodwin, had recently been engaged to represent the firm in Japan. He was said to be an ex-president of the Society of Engineers.

A slightly earlier report of a visit to the works outlined in the 1 October 1893 issue of The Implement

& *Machinery Review*, mentions that the patent sleepers could be pressed out at a rate of three a minute. Mention was also made that the machine for making the clips (chairs) could produce them as a complete item at a rate of 50 per minute.

By the turn of the century Ernest Baguley was beginning to take a close personal interest in road vehicles and more particularly the internal combustion engine. In 1901 he designed a four-cylinder single acting piston valve steam engine, presumably with steam car propulsion in mind and this, together with a desire to develop the use of the internal combustion engine seems to have led to differences of opinion on the way the Castle Engine Works should develop its products. There may have been some heated discussions between Baguley and Gordon Bagnall regarding the respective ways each wanted to progress; be that as it may, Baguley was soon to leave Stafford and seek pastures new. Sometime in 1901 he appears to have interested three well established Burton-on-Trent businessmen in his steam car engine. They were Baron Burton, William Worthington and Robert Radcliff, all well known Burton surnames with interests in the local brewing industry for which Burton is famous. Resulting from his discussions agreements were entered into for a new company to be formed and the Ryknield Engine Company Limited was registered on 25 February 1902 to exploit the engine. Baguley left the Castle Engine Works towards the end of 1901, or perhaps early in the following year and took up his appointment with the

Ryknield Engine Company in January; he was appointed manager on 1 July 1902. In the event, developments in the internal combustion engine field overtook those of steam and the original plans to build steam cars at Burton were abandoned in favour of a series of vehicles with petrol engines.

Before leaving the subject of Ernest Baguley in his new venture at Burton-on-Trent, a relatively brief resume of his subsequent career is appropriate. This is relevant on two counts, in the first he went on to have an interesting and varied career in railway engineering and in the second, he later designed small narrow-gauge steam locomotives which, not surprisingly, had a similarity to those he had been responsible for at Stafford. Brief mention of this has been made earlier The Ryknield Engine Company was very soon in financial difficulties and in liquidation during October 1905. However, a financial reconstruction took place and the Ryknield Motor Company Limited grew out of the ashes of the old Company with Baguley once again the manager. With this new company he designed and developed a commercial road vehicle chassis. Evidence suggests that in conjunction with his financial supporters in this new venture, it was established that the motor car business was already too competitive for a small firm like this one to penetrate. The commercial chassis was used for bus and a lorry body, a notable application was passenger vehicles for the London General Omnibus Company. Nevertheless, it was not long before Baguley moved on again and in 1907 he was

This is an example of the smaller standard-gauge four wheel shunting engines of the period. Number 1612 was one of four supplied to the South Metropolitan Gas Company for use at East Greenwich Gas Works in London. Cylinders were 10x15in and the wheel diameter 2ft 10ins. This particular locomotive came back to Stafford for overhaul in December 1942 but was back at East Greenwich the following month. As fleet No 9 it is seen here on 20 August 1949.

NIDD is an example of the sort of three-foot gauge contractors locomotive that replaced the earlier inverted saddle tank designs so popular with public works contractors. Number 1658 of 1902 had cylinders of 8x12in and the wheel diameter 2ft 0½in. The customer in this case was the contractor Holme & King of Liverpool, and the engine was for use in connection with the Bradford Corporation waterworks in the Nidd Valley near Patley Bridge.

Loaded on an LNWR wagon and ready for despatch, this is number 1614 of 1900 which was new to George Farren of the Welsh Granite Company for use at Trevor Quarry near Penmaenmawr; a new boiler was supplied in 1921. This is a typical 7x12in cylinder Margaret type design of the period with a circular firebox boiler and Baguley valve gear but with the addition of a partly enclosed cab. The building behind is part of the sheet and iron stores.

New Zealand is the location of this picture of number 1718 of 1903 and a slight variation on the standard design with a straight sided saddle tank and timber rack for the fuel above. It also displays a few later modifications including the buffer beams, chimney and cab. New in 1903 for the New Plymouth Sash & Door Factory & Timber Company of Tariki on the north island, it was shipped from the Royal Albert Dock in London to Wellington. The specification stated that the engine was to 'haul logs in the Bush'! This picture was taken some time in the 1920s after several owners and when the engine was working for PG Smith at Raetihi, but still in the timber trade. This was one of the last locomotives built with Baguley valve gear. (Collection RJ Meyer)

In 1903 the Company supplied two 3ft 6in gauge locomotives for the British Central Africa Company Limited. They were 12x18in cylinder four-wheel coupled saddle tanks named THISTLE No 1 and SHAMROCK No 2, numbers 1705 and 1719 respectively, the first motive power on what later became the Shire Highlands Railway (the main line followed the River Shire) and later still the Nyasaland (now Malawi) Railway. They have both been preserved and this view shows number 1719 at the National Museum of Malawi in Blantyre. Although doubtless originally intended to assist with construction works, both locomotives remained in use for shunting purposes as late as 1970, and despite long years of use are in remarkably as-built condition.

appointed manager of a quite new motor division of the Birmingham Small Arms Company Limited (BSA); a division formed to develop the expanding motor vehicle business of BSA. In September 1911 Baguley was instrumental in the formation of yet another new company and on this occasion one bearing his own name - Baguley Cars Limited. Registered on 3 September 1911 the new company acquired the Shobnall Road works of the Ryknield Motor Company Limited; like its predecessor this Company had also passed into liquidation. Baguley was appointed managing director so he once again took charge at Burton-on-Trent. In 1913 Baguley Cars Limited acquired an established builder of small internal combustion engined locomotives, McEwan, Pratt & Company Limited, at a time when, as noted earlier, it was in financial difficulties. Following this development Ernest Baguley once again in his career became involved in designing and developing locomotives and other self propelled railway vehicles, albeit the majority were powered by internal combustion engines and not steam.

Whilst at Stafford Ernest Baguley, like Gordon Bagnall, joined the Army volunteers and enlisted in the same Regiment. He was gazetted Lieutenant 17 July 1895, Captain 19 February 1896 and Major 20 September 1907. As the second in command of the 6th Battalion (Prince of Wales Volunteers) North Staffordshire Regiment Baguley served in France during

the early months of the First World War. However, he returned to England in 1915, ostensibly to help Baguley Cars Limited to increase production to meet war-time targets. In April 1915 the McEwan Pratt company was re-constituted under the same name, but as a private company and a subsidiary of Baguley Cars Limited, and from a London office handled the sales of Baguley locomotives which went under the McEwan Pratt name. The Baguley Company undertook relatively large and significant contracts to assist the war effort and for a variety of government departments. Moreover, and of particular interest to the Bagnall story, in the period 1919 to 1920 Baguley designed and developed a range of narrow-gauge steam locomotives. As well as supplying these locomotives directly to customers, an arrangement was entered into with the Yorkshire Engine Company Limited of Sheffield. The agreement involved Baguley building small narrow-gauge steam locomotives for the Yorkshire Engine Company, whilst conversely the Sheffield based Company would build any standard-gauge steam locomotives for which Baguley (Engineers) Limited received orders. Not surprisingly and as alluded to earlier the narrow-gauge steam locomotives that were built bore a remarkable resemblance to the Castle Engine Works products; moreover, they all had one or other of the Baguley-designed valve gears. Despite the Yorkshire Engine Company agreement the Baguley

Company did build a solitary standard-gauge steam locomotive. This engine was completed in 1920 and utilised the frames of an earlier and uncompleted petrol locomotive with hydraulic transmission. Rather fittingly considering its birthplace it was sold to one of the Burton brewers, Thomas Salt & Company Limited. This locomotive was the only standard-gauge one fitted with Baguley's Patent valve gear; that is if one excludes Bagnall number 1504 mentioned earlier, which although built for a three-foot gauge railway had a patent arrangement of adjustable axles to enable it to run on standard-gauge track.

Some of the Baguley built narrow-gauge locomotives had Bullhead type circular firebox boilers, whilst others had a conventional locomotive type boiler; it would appear that at least some of the boilers were not built at Burton and whilst it is not known who did build them, they were not built at the Castle Engine Works. In all 30 steam locomotives are listed in the Baguley records, including an experimental chain driven vertical boiler machine, but no customers are recorded for a significant number of them. The considered opinion is that not all of the 30 listed were actually built and the figure of 23 mentioned earlier, is a more plausible number. This opinion is confirmed in the records as a number of the entries for the locomotives are noted as 'built for stock',

with no specific customer information suggesting that whilst orders may have been placed with the workshops, no work was actually undertaken. Or perhaps any parts actually made, were utilised on later locomotive orders that were completed. Most of the steam locomotives that were built were exported and it is nice to be able to record that one of them survives in this country. Manufacturer's number 2007 of 1919 was originally exported to India for the Calcutta Waterworks, a very small locomotive the cylinders of which are but 4in in diameter. It was discovered and purchased in 1963 by the late Mike Satow who was at the time working with ICI in India. In a pretty deplorable condition after years lying out of use, it was restored by the apprentices at the Rishra workshops of ICI in India and named RISHA in recognition. Subsequently, in 1971 Mike was instrumental in repatriating this delightful little locomotive and it is currently kept on the Leighton Buzzard Light Railway where it is maintained in working order. Fitted with the modified arrangement of Baguley valve gear it is well worth going to see on this account alone.

The Baguley Company went through a number of subsequent financial reconstructions, but all we need record here is that Ernest Baguley himself remained active in the industry almost until his death. He died at

An example of rolling stock built in the period covered by this Chapter is this metre-gauge refrigerator van built for the War Department for use at Gibraltar dockyard, in connection with the North Gorge Cold Stores. These vehicles would have been used to assist in victualling Royal Navy ships and were, presumably, partly filled with ice prior to being loaded.

his home, 58 The Ridgeway, Kenton in Middlesex on 13 October 1948 at the age of 84. His death certificate describes him as a mechanical and general engineer retired. His professional career had embraced almost 70 years. Unfortunately we do not know what if any relationship existed between Baguley and Gordon Bagnall after the two parted company at Stafford in 1901. Nevertheless it is worth mentioning that Bagnall wasted little time in introducing a new valve gear for the small locomotives to replace the Baguley gears and thereby avoid royalty payments. This is perhaps indicative that relationships were not as cordial as they might have been, but in any event it is perhaps strange that Gordon Bagnall allowed Baguley to patent a valve gear, almost certainly designed and developed in Bagnall Company time, without at least having a royalty-free right to use it on the locomotives built at Stafford. Much later, after Gordon Bagnall's death, the Baguley Company did order some equipment from the Castle Engine Works. For example Bagnall general order number 1373 of December 1915 covered 'drawbars for Baguley Cars Limited'. These were for Baguley number 566 of the following year, a standard gauge petrol locomotive of 60 horsepower. This locomotive was built for the use by the London & Thames Haven Oil Wharves Limited at its Reedham works in Essex. But there would appear to have been little else, and Baguley did not attend the funeral of Gordon Bagnall in 1907.

Before leaving the period covered by this Chapter and to give some idea of the scale of the non-locomotive production of the Castle Engine Works, a brief look at some of the diverse entries of the relevant drawing register will not go amiss. As well as conventional narrow-gauge rolling stock like side-tip, end-tip, sugar cane and platform wagons etc., we find entries for: tipping buckets; composite bogie tram to seat 32 persons; coal tubs; brick trucks; road gang pumping trolley; mining wagons; six-wheeled trolley to carry electric plant; sausage trucks; inspection car; torpedo trolleys; printing machine frame; accumulator frames; timber truck; workmen's car; furnace barrows; 23ft long bogie carriage; brick drying trolleys; steel mineral wagons; slag bogie; clay trams; velocipede; platelayers trolley, portable electric pump trolley; inspection car; platform truck for motor. And there are many others, along with numerous entries for track-work, patent sleepers, indeed complete track layouts, turntables and traversers - on some occasion's turntables and traversers combined. When complete track layouts were supplied these would be laid out in the works yard prior to delivery to ensure the whole arrangement fitted together, and photographs exit of such layouts. In the *Machinery Market* article referred to earlier Bagnall claimed to have built over 1,000 narrow-gauge side-tip wagons for a single customer. Although these wagons were of very simple construction, this was nevertheless a significant achievement and it is a pity that no record remains of exactly who the customer was.

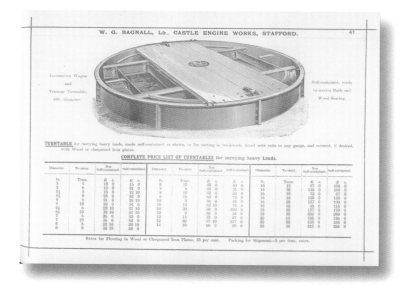

Page from catalogue No 12 of January 1894, showing part of the range of turntables supplied. Turntables were a regular element of production for almost the entire life of the Company.

Chapter Four

THE LAST YEARS OF WILLIAM GORDON BAGNALL

Further evidence that Ernest Baguley left the Castle Engine Works in somewhat of a hurry comes from the fact that it was almost a year before a new chief draughtsman was appointed. It is not clear who took on the role for the interim, but John Gifford may have assumed more responsibility in the area of design and we have already seen how he was becoming increasingly involved in the financial affairs of the company. By 1898 only Gifford and Baguley along with Bagnall himself were drawing a salary as opposed to a wage; note that at this time Price was on the wages, rather than the salaried staff. In April 1902 James Graeme Hepburn Warren arrived at Stafford to take on the role of chief draughtsman; he came from the Stoke-on-Trent based Kerr, Stuart & Company Limited, where he had been a leading draughtsman. Warren was not at the Castle Engine Works long as he returned to Kerr, Stuart in March the following year, but when he arrived at Stafford he brought with him as a leading draughtsman William Sydney Edwards. This young man was destined to take over as chief when Warren returned to the California Works and the two moves would appear to have been part of a well-planned answer to the immediate problem of finding a chief draughtsman, as well as a more permanent solution. Mention has been made of the friendship that existed

between Gordon Bagnall and John Hartley and in the period now under review Hartley was back in charge at the California Works. Doubtless too, Bagnall would have been acquainted with FHB Harris, the recently installed chief draughtsman at Kerr, Stuart. Reading between the lines it seems highly probable that Warren was in fact 'lent' to Gordon Bagnall, bringing the bright and ambitious Edwards with him both to gain some additional experience and to see if he 'fitted in' at Stafford. The end game was for Sydney Edwards to become chief draughtsman and for Warren to return from whence he came. Sydney Edwards was one of Harris's brightest young men and it cannot have been an easy decision to let him go, especially to a company that were, after all said and done, competitors - nevertheless this certainly appears to be what happened.

JGH Warren was born at Bridport in Dorset in August 1875 and served an engineering apprenticeship between August 1892 and August 1898, with the Glasgow based locomotive engineers Neilson Reid & Company - from 1903 a constituent part of the North British Locomotive Company Limited. On completion of his training he took up a position as a draughtsman with Neilson Reid, before moving south in February 1900 having been offered a leading draughtsman's

James Graeme Hepburn Warren, 1876-1935, Chief Draughtsman at Stafford 1902-1903. A picture taken later in life when he was Chief Draughtsman with Robert Stephenson & Company at Darlington.

position with Kerr, Stuart. On return to Kerr, Stuart from Stafford in March 1903, Warren became assistant chief draughtsman under Harris and in April 1904, at the age of but 29 years, was appointed chief draughtsman of Robert Stephenson & Company Limited at its then new Darlington works. It is perhaps worth mentioning that when Warren applied in 1906 to become a member of the Institution of Mechanical Engineers, among those who supported him was John H Adams the locomotive engineer of the North Staffordshire Railway. Doubtless he would have become acquainted with Adams during his time at Stoke-on-Trent, whilst another supporter was Henry Fowler the locomotive engineer of the Midland Railway. Unfortunately, James Warren suffered from ill health later in life, as a consequence of which he was forced to give up full time employment in 1923, when he retired from his position with Robert Stephenson & Company

Limited. Nevertheless he retained a strong interest in the industry in which he had spent all his working life and is perhaps best remembered today, for his monumental history of that very famous firm of locomotive engineers where he spent the last almost 20 years of his career. *A Century of Locomotive Building* was published by Andrew Reid of Newcastle in 1923; it had the full support of the Company and remains the standard work on its history to this day. It has to be added however, the book largely concentrates on the history of the Company prior to 1900, along with the very early locomotives it built. Indeed, fully seven eights of the book covers the period prior to the turn of the century. Warren was also largely responsible for the initiative to restore the former Liverpool & Manchester Railway locomotive LION to working order, and he was involved in the arrangements for the Liverpool & Manchester Railway centenary celebrations held at Wavertree in Liverpool in 1930. LION of course making an appearance there. James Warren retired to live in Bath, where he passed away in March 1935 at the relatively early age of 59.

William Sydney Edwards was a native of the Potteries, born in Hanley on 10 May 1882 the son of William and Emma Frances Edwards, the family lived in Gilman Street which was off Old Hall Street. His father was for many years the organist at St Mary's Wellington Church in Hanley; indeed he was a fellow of the Royal College of Organists but is quoted on young Sydney's birth certificate as a Bookseller. The family had a stationers business at 8 Pall Mall in Hanley and there were two other children, a daughter Frances, named after her mother and six years younger than Sydney, along with another son, also William who was born in 1897. William Edwards died relatively young, not long after the youngest son was born and by 1901 his widow, who continued to run the business, had moved the family to live over the shop in Pall Mall. Sydney was educated at Hanley High School before being apprenticed to Messrs Kerr, Stuart & Company Limited in 1898. One of his contempories at Kerr, Stuart, although a couple of years younger, was TF (Tommy) Coleman of Endon in Staffordshire; in fact they may have been at school together. Coleman later joined the North Staffordshire Railway and eventually rose to the position of chief draughtsman under the chief mechanical engineer of the LMS; he was largely responsible for the outline design work for several of the locomotives credited to Sir WA Stanier. The two men remained friends, despite Coleman having little time for the learned institutions that Edwards actively supported.

Having attained excellent grades at Hanley High School Edwards had further private tuition under FR Holt, who was an assistant manager at Kerr, Stuart and a part time lecturer for Staffordshire County Council. There is little doubt that this would have influenced Edwards in his choice of career, but he also had some additional private tuition under the well known Glasgow based Professor Andrew Jamieson. Jamieson is the author of several authoritative text books on mechanical engineering, some of which were standard works of reference in their day. At the California Works his training continued under both John Hartley and FHB Harris and for the last two years of his apprenticeship he was engaged in the drawing office. It will be appreciated from the forgoing that it cannot have been an easy decision for Hartley and Harris to allow their protégé to move on, especially so quickly after his training and of course, the full facts surrounding the move are lost in the mists of time. The result however turned out to be an excellent one for Gordon Bagnall as Edwards went on to become not only a key figure in the history of the Company, but one of the best known and indeed most respected names in the British private locomotive building industry. There is much more to be said about Sydney Edwards as the story unfolds, but this would be jumping the gun somewhat and we need to go back a little to his and Warren's arrival at the Castle Engine Works in 1902. But before doing so it is perhaps worth mentioning that when Edwards applied for membership of the Institution of Mechanical Engineers in 1912, among his supporters was James Warren. Ernest Baguley was another, which is interesting as the two of them were not at the Castle Engine Works at the same time, but clearly had become known to each other.

In July 1901 John Gifford became a director of the Company, indeed at that time only Bagnall and Gifford were directors, with Thomas Walter being far less involved in the day-to-day affairs of the Company; nevertheless he remained a substantial shareholder until some years later. From about 1898 Walter's address is quoted in the Company ledgers as the Walter family seat of Bearwood, Wokingham in Berkshire and his bank account was handled by Messrs Soames, Edwards & Jones of Norfolk Street, London WC. Latterly payments in his favour were paid to his father's account - John Walter - which would have been after he had elected to pursue ecclesiastical interests. At this period in the Company's history the secretary was George F Fletcher, who had been with Bagnall for a number of years and is often referred to as the chief clerk - there were never any 'fancy' job titles at the Castle Engine Works! In the year 1901 the Company made a profit after tax of £3,295 plus a few shillings; this was on a turnover of £61,034 making the profit in percentage terms 5.4%. The figure increased the following year to £4,601 on a turnover of £65,201 which equated to 7%.

For the next few years the firm continued to expand becoming more profitable in the process resulting in better returns on the capital employed. Using the rather crude measure of how many locomotives were ordered each year, the average in the early 1890s was 13 and this increased to an average of 35 by the turn of the century. However, the staple product continued to be small narrow-gauge contractors and plantation type locomotives, but in increasing numbers and with many repeat orders. Often track work, rolling stock and other light railway material was supplied along with the locomotives; in fact in some cases complete light railway systems. The Company missed no opportunity to peddle its wares, whether through general advertising in the trade journals, a continuing series of lavish catalogues and an increasing ability to get a mention in the specialist technical press.

Among the more significant orders for locomotives in the period covered by this Chapter were six two-foot gauge 4-6-0 tender engines designed and built on American design principles. They had bar frames, outside cylinders cast integral with the smokebox saddle, Walschaerts valve gear and a very American external appearance. These engines were for use on the Avontuur line of the Cape Government Railways where they were designated class B. Although designed and built under the general direction of the consulting engineers Sir Douglas Fox & Partners, all the design work was undertaken at Stafford and this was the first occasion bar-frames had been used since the little TRIUMPHO of 1893. The manufacturer's numbers were 1741 to 1746, cylinders 11¾x16in, driving wheel diameter 2ft 9in, overall length of engine and tender 44ft 5in and a weight in working order of 39 tons and five cwt. They were all delivered in mid 1904 and the cost £1,800 each against a building cost quoted as £2,008, so a loss was made on this contract. Nevertheless the engines all gave excellent service and remained in use for many years, a repeat order for one more locomotive being received in 1913 - manufacturer's number 1967. Most of them remained in use until the late 1920s - some lasted a little longer - being replaced by bigger engines as traffic levels increased. Two of them were used in 1929 to help build an experimental articulated locomotive on the Fairlie principle, two sets of frames, wheels and motion etc., were placed under a common frame on which was mounted a South African Railway boiler designed for a 3ft 6in gauge locomotive. However, this ensemble does not appear to have achieved much success and the

remains lay out of use at Avontuur for many years. However, it may have had something to do with the later adoption of articulated locomotives on the narrow gauge Cape lines; in the event it was the Garratt principle of articulation that was adopted and not the Fairlie. One of the locomotives (1741) went on to serve the Eastern Province Cement Company at its Chelsea Factory and for many years after being sold by the Government Railway; Bagnall supplied a new boiler for it in March 1932. Another (1743) was sold in 1919 to the Portuguese Caminho de Ferro de Lourenco Marques, which is the main-line railway in Mozambique.

For locomotives both designed and built in this country these Cape Government ones were unusual to say the least, but the Railway already had some American Baldwin built 2-6-0s and this undoubtedly influenced the specification Sir Douglas Fox & Partners had to work to. In 1908 two tank engine versions of the

This is the first of the six 4-6-0 locomotives built in 1904 to American design principles for the Cape Government two-foot gauge lines in Natal; it is seen here as No 1, on-test in the works yard. Numbers 1741 to 1746, the first three were originally intended for the line from Aliwal North to Gairtney which in the event was not proceeded with; all six were therefore used on the line from Port Elizabeth to Avontuur.

THE LAST YEARS OF WILLIAM GORDON BAGNALL

This photograph shows one of the two 4-6-2 tank engines, numbers 1866 and 1867 of 1908, based on the earlier tender engines and specifically designed for working a suburban line of the two-foot gauge Cape Government Railways from Port Elizabeth to the outer suburb of Walmer. The total distance from Port Elizabeth to Walmer was six and a quarter miles and the line opened on 15 December 1906. Until these tank engines arrived the earlier tender engines worked the branch. Unfortunately, bus competition became an issue in the 1920s and the line closed from 16 November 1928, after which these two engines were scrapped. Notice that whilst the engines were of a basic American design, a distinctive Britannic influence has prevailed over some of the external features. The fellow standing by the engine, probably to give a size prospective for catalogue purposes, would in all probability have been the fitter in charge of the engine's erection.

design were built specifically for the Walmer branch line of the Cape Government Railway. These two, manufacturer's numbers 1866 and 1877 were handsome machines with the same main dimensions as the tender engines and a weight in working order of 29 tons; they cost £1,890 each. Unfortunately when the Walmer branch closed in late 1928 no further use could be found for them with their restricted water capacity and high axle-load. Hence, after use on the track dismantling trains used on the branch line both were scrapped.

Another significant order was for two standard-gauge 0-6-0 saddle tanks completed in June 1905, to the order of Matheson & Company, the contractors building the Shanghai-Nanking Railway in China. These two may have been the first Bagnall locomotives for use in China, may have been because the 1888 catalogue already discussed might lead one to believe that a locomotive or locomotives had been supplied to China earlier. But if this was the case it is not clear

exactly which one, or ones were involved. The Matheson engines, manufacturer's numbers 1774 and 1775 had 15x20in cylinders, 3ft 7in diameter coupled wheels and a weight in working order of 32½ tons - they cost £1,395 each. Both later passed to the ownership of the Shanghai-Nanking Railway and as SNR numbers 4 & 5 were still on the operating stock list of the railway in the late 1920s. The design of these locomotives which were the first comparatively large standard-gauge six-coupled saddle tanks built at Stafford, became a standard for this type of locomotive. A number of similar locomotives but adapted for use by industrial customers in this country, continued to be built until the design was up-dated many years later.

As a counter-part to the 15in cylinder standard-gauge industrial shunting engine, the 14in cylinder four-wheel coupled version was re-designed and brought up to date about this time. The first one to the new design was number 1739, laid down to a stock order in July 1903, but was not delivered until almost four years later

This is one of the two 15in cylinder standard gauge six-coupled saddle tanks of a new design and initially used by the contractors for the construction of the Shanghai-Nanking Railway in China; they were despatched in July 1905, numbers 1775 and 1776. This design became a standard one for the home market and remained so, with but minor modifications, for almost another thirty years.

This is an example of the 12in cylinder four-coupled industrial shunting engine, number 1681 of 1903. New to Birmingham Corporation Gas Department for use at Swan Village Gas Works it lasted there until December 1950, when it was broken-up for scrap. This was a neat and quite popular design for gas works shunting.

in April 1907. The most significant external difference from the earlier design was the saddle tank, which was extended forward to encompass the smokebox and better distribute the weight. But there were numerous other less conspicuous refinements too. This particular locomotive was sold for £944 to the Exhall Colliery & Brickworks in Warwickshire and it had a long life. In fact it lasted until as late as 1969, latterly working at the Storefield Ironstone Mines in Northamptonshire. With but relatively minor alterations over the years this design of 14in cylinder four-coupled saddle tank shunting engine, a type so popular with industrial concerns, remained in production until the end of steam locomotive work at Stafford. Despite the various changes in the design details engines of this type bear a remarkable resemblance to those built by Hawthorn Leslie to similar overall dimensions. Although Ernest Baguley had moved on from Stafford by the time

number 1739 was designed and built, this similarity is another manifestation of his influence on the locomotive designs of the Company. The other principal dimensions were: wheel diameter of 3ft 6½in, wheelbase 5ft 6in, water capacity 660 gallons, total boiler heating surface 560 sq ft, grate area of nine sq ft, working pressure 160 psi.

With the passage of the years a loyal customer base was increasingly developed and a number of familiar names keep appearing in the order books. For example the first order from the Tongaat Sugar Company of Natal in South Africa was in 1906, on this occasion a two-foot gauge 2-4-0 side tank with 9x14in cylinders was supplied, number 1800. Two years later a slightly longer 4-4-0 version was designed, otherwise with the same basic dimensions. With modifications and improvements, the most significant being a change from inside to outside frames and a shorter coupled wheelbase, 13 more locomotives of this basic type were supplied to this customer - the last in 1946. Moreover, even after the last new locomotive was supplied rarely did the works not have an order on hand for some spare part or other for this customer. The first broad-gauge locomotives built at Stafford also date from this period - in 1906 the Madras Port Trust ordered a locomotive for use on the 5ft 6in gauge dock railways in Madras. For this customer a standard 14x20in cylinder four-wheel coupled saddle tank was adapted and delivered in October 1907. The manufacturer's number was 1811 and a further six of the same design were supplied over the next few years, the last one in 1921.

The Spanish based agent Adolfo T Simpson of Bilbao was another good customer, he ordered 10 narrow-gauge locomotives between 1906 and 1924. The locomotives were all comparatively small narrow-gauge

saddle tanks of the standard pattern with circular firebox boilers, and they all seem to have been used in connection with various mining operations. The Company had a significant measure of success over the years in the Spanish market with more than 30 locomotives exported there over the years. As well as locomotives Adolpho Simpson also ordered rolling stock, track work and other light railway material, as did other Iberian based customers. Mention was made earlier that at least one edition of the catalogues were produced in both the Spanish and Portuguese language, and provision was made in the first few pages for agents to add their own details. Often agents would request that their name and not Bagnalls should appear on the manufacturer's plates, so that any repeat orders, or orders for spare parts would come via them and not direct to Bagnall. Other countries that appear in the

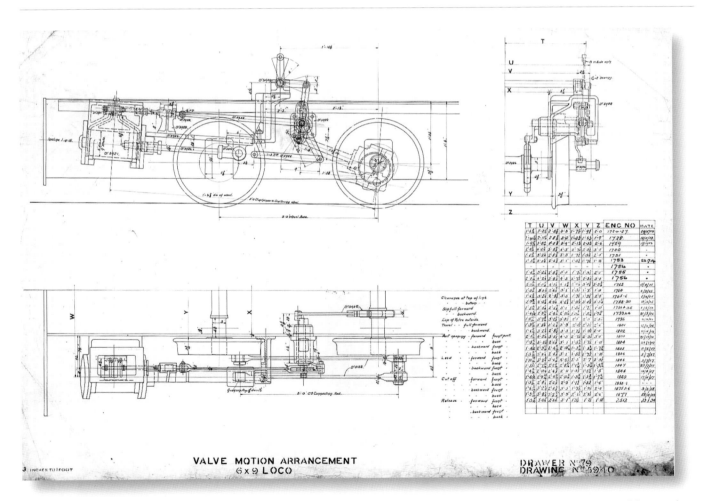

General Arrangement of Bagnall-Price valve gear as fitted to the standard 6x9in cylinder 'Mercedes' class locomotives and first used on numbers 1724 to 1727.

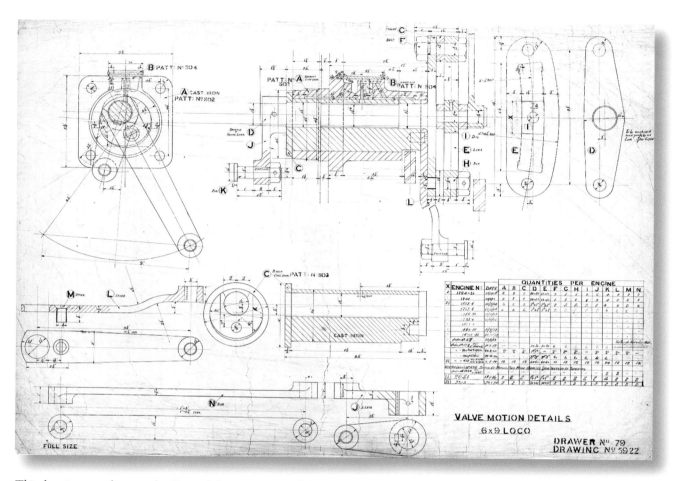

This drawing complements the General Arrangement and illustrates the detail of the various component parts of the Bagnall-Price valve gear. With the aid of these two drawings, the photographs and the description in the text, it should help the reader understand exactly how this gear worked.

Photograph showing the various component parts of Bagnall-Price valve gear, a photograph taken for use in the catalogues to help when ordering spare parts. Notice how some parts have been suspended with string, and how the negative, which would have been a glass plate, has been masked for use in a catalogue. This picture illustrates clearly the eccentric and drive to the shaft on which is mounted the link, and which passes through the oscillating shaft. This is a part of the gear that is otherwise hidden between the locomotive frames.

registers for the first time in the period covered by this Chapter include: Australia, Argentina, Borneo, Chile, Gold Coast, Siam and Portuguese West Africa.

In discussing the departure of Ernest Baguley in the last Chapter mention was made of a valve gear designed for use on the small standard narrow-gauge locomotives to replace the gears he had designed. This was the Bagnall-Price valve gear jointly patented by WG Bagnall and ST Price, indicating that perhaps Price had more to do with design issues than is at first apparent. The patent number is 11832 and the complete specification was dated 23 May 1903; it was accepted on 16 July the same year. This gear, like the Baguley gears, is a radial valve gear with two components of motion; the primary component to provide the valve travel and the secondary component, an in-phase movement with the crank, to provide the lap and lead characteristics of the valve. As with the earlier gears this one also uses the principle of an oscillating shaft, and like the original Baguley gear but not the Modified arrangement, on the oscillating shaft is an eccentrically mounted conventional slotted link. This link is rocked backwards and forwards about a imaginary fixed pivot point by a shaft that runs inside the oscillating shaft, and this movement of the link via a sliding die block and radius rod provides the primary component of valve travel. The shaft on which the link is mounted and hence the link itself, is rocked by an eccentric and rod usually mounted on the driving axle between the frames. However, unlike the Baguley gears where both components of valve travel are derived from the main crank, in Bagnall-Price the oscillating shaft is much bigger, moves in a comparatively large bearing which itself passes through a hole in the main frames of the locomotive, and is oscillated by a rod and fulcrum lever connecting it to the main connecting rod adjacent to the little end. This movement provides the secondary in-phase lap and lead motion by moving the link backwards and forwards about its imaginary pivot, as opposed to the rocking movement derived from the eccentric. As this secondary movement is derived from the connecting rod and therefore, has the same travel as the piston, it will be realised why the lap and lead travel of the valve is constant.

At the expense of labouring the point as it is quite complicated, it is significant to grasp that this secondary movement of the link, derived from the main connecting rod, is the one that actually oscillates the large shaft and is completely different to the primary component which maintains a fixed pivot point. Reversing is by movement of the die up and down the link, the die being connected to the radius rod. The reversing lifting link from the weigh-bar shaft is usually connected directly to the die itself, thus achieving minimum slip of the die whatever its position in the link. However, due to space considerations some locomotives were designed with the reversing gear lifting link connected to the radius rod rather than the die; in some cases the connection was in front of the link and in others behind, the radius rod being extended to allow for the latter. Any extension behind the link does not alter the relationship of the length of the effective part of the radius rod to the link itself, this part of the rod always being the same length as the radius of the link.

It is also possible with this gear to provide the primary component of valve travel via a return arm on the main crank, rather than an eccentric on one of the axles, and such an arrangement was on occasion used. Examples are where well tanks were used as they preclude the use of any motion between the frames, or if a conventional firebox was so close to the driving axle as to leave no room for eccentrics. This was sometimes the case on long wheelbase four-wheel locomotives, the firebox being so positioned to assist in a better weight distribution and axle-loading. The gear could also be adapted for use on inside cylinder locomotives and on one occasion it was - manufacturer's number 1941 of 1911. It would seem that while Baguley in his patent concentrated on both eliminating the use of a return arm and utilising one connecting rod from the main crank to provide both components of valve travel, he did not specifically mention in his patent application the principle of combining the two components of valve travel in an eccentric bearing - which both his gears did. This loop-hole, if that is in fact what it is, was exploited by Bagnall and Price in their patent and it is perhaps surprising that this simple application of geometry could still be patented as late as 1903. Be that as it may, Bagnall-Price valve gear was used over the years on numerous Bagnall locomotives as well as a few built by other manufacturers. Moreover, unlike the Baguley gears, its use was not confined to small narrow-gauge locomotives; in fact it found favour over almost the

MERCEDES, number 1730 of 1903, was the first engine with Bagnall-Price valve gear that appears to have posed for an official photograph. It is also one of the engines covered by the accompanying drawings. As a result of this picture, which was extensively used in the catalogues, 'Mercedes' became the type name for this class of locomotive, effectively replacing 'Margaret', the earlier version with Baguley valve gear. This particular engine was new to Greaves, Bull & Lakin at Harbury Cement Works in Warwickshire. It came back to Stafford for repairs in February 1911, but had a comparatively short life and was scrapped in 1922.

whole range of locomotives designed and built by the firm, including many standard-gauge designs and right until the end of steam locomotive production at Stafford.

Like all mechanical devices of course, this valve gear has its disadvantages. Because the housing for the oscillating bearing has perforce to be located between the coupled axles, there is little room for the eccentric rod and therefore this rod, of necessity, has to be quite short. Additionally, as the housing needs to be roughly in line with the valve chest, it has to be situated towards the top of the frames and this results in a steeply inclined eccentric rod. The cumulative effect of these

two issues, a short and steeply inclined eccentric rod, is that movement of the axle up and down the horn guides under control of the springs as the locomotive goes about its normal occasions, is acutely transferred to the oscillating shaft. To a greater or lesser extent, this unwanted movement of the shaft is then transferred to the link, the die block, the valve rod and lastly the valve itself, with detrimental effects on the valve events. Most steam engine valve gears suffer from the angularity of their component parts to one extent or another, and in Bagnall-Price valve gear it is more pronounced than in some, but it is no worse than many. Another area concerns the lap and lead motion derived from the connecting rod via the eccentric bush, geometrically producing an angular component to the link. This in turn produces a different horizontal component to the top of the link compared with the bottom, resulting in a lack of symmetry of the valve events for forwards and backwards gear. Nevertheless, and notwithstanding these issues, Bagnall-Price valve gear was far more robust and capable of withstanding rough treatment than either of the Baguley gears.

The first application of Bagnall-Price valve gear was on two small 1ft 11⅝in gauge standard four-wheel circular firebox saddle tank locomotives with 5x7½in cylinders. Manufacturer's numbers 1722 and 1723, it

was originally planned to fit the Modified Baguley gear to these locomotives and the drawings were suitably annotated, but a change was decided upon at a late stage and the new gear substituted. Ordered by the agents L Mitchell & Company, who specialised in equipment for Mauritius, they were despatched to that country in May 1903 for use on sugar plantations. They were in fact among several locomotives built around this time to orders from Mitchell, acting for sugar plantations in Mauritius. It is surprising being the first locomotives with Bagnall-Price valve gear, but they do not appear to have been the subject of an official photograph; no more were any of the next six

Another early recipient of Bagnall-Price valve gear was this one, number 1735 of 1904, in this case one of the larger versions of the standard circular firebox narrow-gauge locomotives. Nominally the cylinder dimensions were 7x12in, but in this particular case the cylinder diameter was 7½in. This engine was built to suit 2ft 5½in gauge and ordered by agents James Milne & Sons Limited for despatch to Pernambuco; it was sent to Harrington Dock in Liverpool on 29 December for shipment. Along with numbers 1475 and 1483 which had already been delivered, and 1909 delivered later, BS MATAPIRUMA No3 was for use at the Usina Maueluco sugar plantation and factory. Notice the rack on the saddle tank for the bagasse, the waste sugar cane used as a fuel; obviously intended to work at night, the enormous headlamp almost outshines the locomotive!

SANTA CLARA, number 1774 of 1905, was an updated version of the Rio Do Oura 2-4-0 side tank design popular with plantation railways and the like. In fact like RIO Do OURA, this one was for the same customer and doubtless for the same sugar plantation on the Portuguese island of San Tome.
In fact the order is annotated: 'as RIO Do OURA except valve gear', and also as 'Fortuna type'. Cylinders were 8x12in and the engine was dismantled for shipment and sent to Liverpool Docks on 21 February 1905.

In 1904 the Company received a further order for locomotives to be used on the Admiralty Dock Railways at Gibraltar. Like the earlier engines they were metre-gauge but in this case side tanks with 9x14in cylinders, circular firebox boilers and Bagnall-Price valve gear. The numbers were 1750 to 1752 and here is the last of the three posing for its official photograph. Painted black with lining they were originally numbered 1 to 3, but later became 4 to 6; a spare boiler was supplied in 1907. The engines were dismantled for shipment and sent to Canada Dock in Liverpool on 18 May, and Richard Gordon Bagnall, the younger son of WG Bagnall, went to Gibraltar in connection with this contract. Some rolling stock was supplied at the same time too. The engines lasted until the period 1953 to1954.

consecutively numbered locomotives which were also fitted with the new valve gear. In the event it was manufacturer's number 1730, new in July 1903, that was officially photographed and as this locomotive was named MERCEDES, this became the catalogue type name for the small standard narrow-gauge 6in and 7in cylinder circular firebox locomotives. It replaced the type name Margaret which had been used hitherto, the type Margaret of course featuring Baguley valve gear. MERCEDES was new to Greaves, Bull & Lakin Limited, for use at its cement works at Harbury in Warwickshire.

In 1905, and possibly in view of Gordon Bagnall's serious and debilitating illness at the time, Messrs Wheatley Kirk, Price & Company were contracted to undertake a valuation of the plant and equipment, work-in-progress etc, of the Company. The valuation was on the basis of the Company being a 'current going concern' and the report is dated 31 October that year. The total figure including the complete stocks of stores of material including the work in progress amounted to £38,783. Included in this figure were the stocks and stores valued at £10,205, together with work-in-progress valued at £4,351. The work-in-progress consisted of no fewer than 19 locomotives, one boiler repair, several locomotive spares orders, 12 wagons of one sort or another, nine turntables, a number of items of permanent way equipment including a single order for no fewer than 1,000 steel sleepers, along with miscellaneous other items of railway equipment. The valuation of the work-in-progress was broken down into wages, material and establishment charges, or what we would today perhaps call overheads. The document is an extremely comprehensive inventory with the stock and stores occupying no less than 144 pages; with approximately 28 entries per page this equates to some 4,000 stock lines. Included in the stock as opposed to work-in-progress, were a number of completed products, presumably built specifically for stock and to ensure quick delivery. Among these items were for example, two 18in gauge sugar cane wagons, one two-foot gauge tip wagon, 15 18in gauge side-tip wagons, 39 two-foot gauge side-tip wagons, several turntables together with a substantial quantity of permanent way material and a whole host of spare parts for locomotives and wagons. These spare parts - most of which were relatively common items - would have been to fulfil

customers orders quickly, or to speed up production of new locomotives and wagons once orders were placed. The Company made great play in its publicity material of the possibility of early delivery for its 'standard' products.

At the time of the inventory the land on lease consisted of eight acres and 13 perches (one perch = 30¼ sq yds, therefore 13 perches = 393.25 sq yds), all under lease from Lord Stafford. This total area included some additional land over and above that mentioned in earlier Chapters, but also leased from Lord Stafford, the lease running for 68 years from 25 March 1904. A total of half an acre of the site was sub-let to Messrs Rooper & Harris Limited, predecessors of the Universal Grinding Wheel Company Limited as briefly mentioned earlier. The entire land package was valued at £2,120, presumably based on the length of the lease and any conditions attached. The principal buildings on the site are best listed along with their main dimensions and significant fixed equipment:

Smiths, boiler & tank shop: 97ft long and 95ft 9in wide, three bays, centre bay 22ft high at eaves, side bays 12ft 6in high at eaves. Principal equipment consisted of three steam hammers, five, 10 and 15 cwt capacity, hydraulic riveter, two six-foot arm radial arm drills, punching and shearing machines, bending rolls, several jib cranes and a six-ton hand worked overhead travelling crane.

Boilersmiths shop: 24ft 6in long and 16ft 6in wide, nine-foot high at eaves. Contained several hearths, a furnace and a three-cwt steam hammer.

No 1 Boiler shed: 48ft long and 11ft wide, housing a Lancashire boiler 30ft long and seven-foot diameter made by the Bowling Iron Company in 1892.

No 2 Boiler shed: 70ft 6in long and 14ft wide, housing a Lancashire boiler 26ft long and eight-foot diameter; maker and date made not recorded.

Pattern store: 72ft long and 25ft wide, nine-foot high at eaves.

Pattern shop & fettling shop: 72ft long and 12ft wide, 6ft 6in high at eaves. Equipment included two wood turning centre lathes and a band saw.

Iron foundry: 73ft long and 30ft wide, 22ft high at eaves. Equipment included two cupolas and a five-ton hand worked overhead travelling crane.

Brass foundry: 24ft long and 14ft wide, 7ft 6in high at eaves. Equipment consisted of a melting furnace.

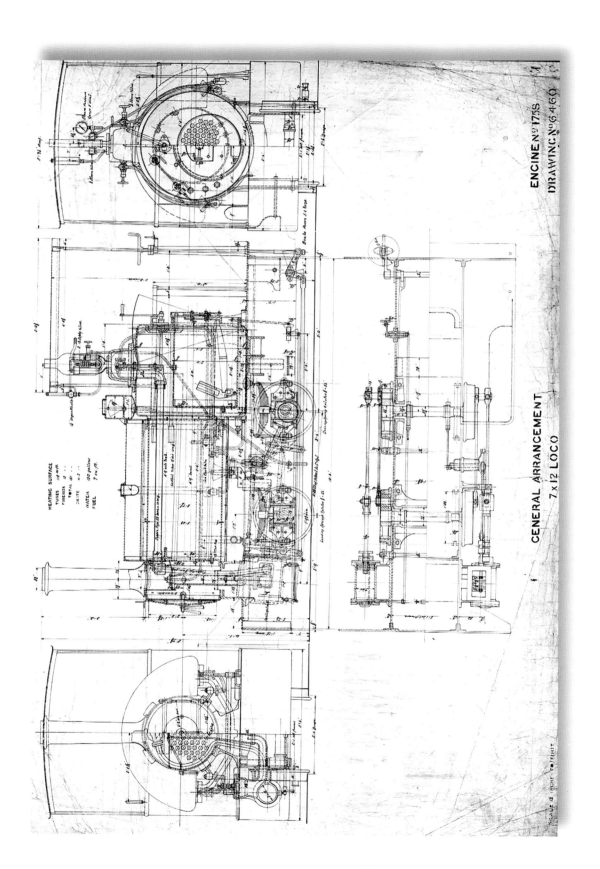

General Arrangement Drawing of a 7in cylinder four-wheel saddle tank with circular firebox and Bagnall-Price valve gear. This drawing is of manufacturer's number 1758, new in April 1905 for Mitrovich Brothers of Liverpool, agents with offices in Chile at both Iquique and Antofagasta. Like most of the engines ordered by this Company it was 2ft 6in gauge and intended for use at nitrate mines in Chile, in this case the Santiago Nitrate Company.

Wagon shop: 121ft long and 130ft wide, three bays each 12ft 6in high at eaves. Equipment included a plate furnace for making the steel permanent way sleepers, a vertical hydraulic press, a strip furnace, hydraulic presses, hydraulic riveter, various bending rolls, shears and punching machines, further plate furnaces, power operated drilling machines, a wheel press, power saws, several drilling machines and centre lathes along with two hydraulic accumulators to provide the hydraulic power.

Pattern maker's shop: 62ft 6in long and 21ft 6in wide, 9ft 6in high at eaves. Equipment included wood turning centre lathes and power saws.

Machine shops: there were several buildings housing the extensive range of machine tools; one described as an Engine House (a brick building - most of the others were corrugated iron), was 75ft long and 25ft wide, 13ft high at eaves. This one contained the edge planer and one of the stationary steam engines used to power the machinery and was adjacent to a second shop, 77ft 9in long and 25ft wide, 13ft high to the eaves. Another shop at the west end was 76ft long and 25ft wide, 20ft high at eaves and there were two more shops, the first was 53ft long and 25ft wide, 20ft high at eaves and the second one was 94ft long and 25ft wide, 13ft high at eaves. All these shops were clustered round the main erecting shop, at each side of it and at its south end. The extensive collection of machine tools including 32 centre lathes of various sizes along with planeing, slotting, milling, screwing, shaping and drilling machines.

Wagon erecting shop: 61ft 6in long and 43ft wide, 9ft 6in high at eaves. Equipment included slotting, shaping and planning machines, grinding machines, a hydraulic wheel press and several jib cranes.

Erecting shop: 220ft long and 28ft wide, 22ft 6in high at eaves with four brick lined erection pits each 62ft long. There was a second shop of sorts, on the north side, 160ft long and 20ft wide, 13ft high at eaves and open on its south side. The only equipment in the Erecting Shops were several jib cranes and two overhead travelling cranes, both hand worked and of seven and 10 tons capacity respectively. The inventory mentions that both these two cranes were made by the Company itself.

Old smiths shop and stores: 162ft long and 18ft wide, 13ft high at eaves. Equipment included several hearths and furnaces, a three-cwt steam hammer, a two-cwt gas hammer, a jib crane and a steam driven horizontal Ingersoll-Sergeant air compressor and reservoir. The compressor was quite a big one; the steam cylinder was 12in diameter, the air cylinder 14in diameter and the stroke a common 12¼in.

A somewhat heterogeneous collection of other buildings completed the picture, mostly of corrugated iron construction, for example: coke shed; rivet stores; pump house & cabin; tarring shed (for wooden sleepers); weighing machine house; bar iron dhed; paint store and of course the offices. Occupants of only two private offices were specifically mentioned, those of Mr Bagnall and Mr Price and the only other private office was for the chief draughtsman; unlike Messrs Bagnall and Price this obvious lesser mortal was not mentioned by name!

All the power was supplied by on site machinery, steam coming from the boilers mentioned above. Two of the engines, both built by the Company itself drove the machine shop, the larger one which dated from 1892, was a 14 horsepower horizontal engine with a single cylinder 12x24in; this one drove the main line shafting. The second engine, for which no date of manufacture is quoted, was much smaller - only four horsepower - but once again a horizontal engine in this case with a cylinder 6x10in. These two engines were No 1 & 2 in the works plant list. The wagon shop had a seven horsepower horizontal engine with a cylinder 8x10in, as well an eight horsepower engine of similar configuration but with a cylinder 9x12in; both these two were also built by the Company but with no dates recorded - engines 3 & 4 in the plant list. In the boiler shop there was another engine built at the Castle Engine Works - engine No 5 in the plant list - once again with no recorded build date; this one was rated at seven horsepower - another horizontal engine in this case with a cylinder 8x12in. Water pressure was supplied by a double cylinder and double plunger vertical pump, with pump cylinders 5x5in and made by Cameron & Company Limited; the hydraulic pressure was supplied by this and other pumps driven from the line shafting. Electricity supply came from a 26 horsepower vertical steam engine with twin cylinders 16x16in; this engine ran at 150 rpm to drive a 40 kW generator running at 860 rpm and designed to deliver 180 amps at 220 volts DC. It was

Although taken a few years later than the period covered by this Chapter, this is a view inside the Erecting Shop looking towards its extreme southern end. In view of the adjoining description of the works this is nevertheless, an opportune juncture to include it. The locomotive on the right is number 1890 of 1911, a 6in cylinder 'Mercedes' type with a square saddle tank and wood fuel rack. Named PAMPINO when delivered, the customer was A Trugeda & Company and the track gauge 2ft 6in. As will be observed it is almost ready for delivery but first of all it will be moved outside the shop for steam testing and any minor adjustments. This was one of three engines of this type and size originally laid down to stock in September 1908, but in this case not ordered by a customer until June 1911, and not despatched until September. Unfortunately we do not know the final destination but the engine's name is Spanish for an inhabitant of the Chilean pampas, for what that is worth! The engine behind is at an earlier stage of construction and of a similar type but with larger 7in cylinders and a conventional shaped saddle tank. Notice the rather crude condition of the shop, the hand operated overhead travelling crane, the gas lighting and the Blacksmiths hearth at the side of the rear locomotive. The Machine Shop is behind the wall to the right.

built by Marshall Sons & Company Limited of Gainsborough, their No 39775 of 1903, whilst the generator was made by The British Thomson-Houston Company Limited, their number 54719 and made in America - the engine was plant no 6.

It will be seen from this description that the site was somewhat littered with a mixed bag of buildings, those of corrugated iron construction doubtless having been built somewhat piecemeal by the staff themselves. The whole works layout had developed rather haphazardly as the Company had expanded. Main-line rail connection came from the Shropshire Union Railways & Canal Company line towards Wellington and in the works yard itself there was 490 yards of permanent

This is one of the works stationary engines used for driving the machinery - notice the pulley behind the fly-wheel and the drive belt to the line shafting. As this is quite a large engine it is assumed to be the larger of the two that drove the Machine Shop; notice too, it is none reversing and under the control of a Pickering governor. We do not know who the two fellows are or why the picture was taken, but it would be especially nice to know who the dapper chap on the left is and what he was doing there - notice he is not looking at the camera! If this is one of the Machine Shop engines, and there would seem to be no alternative, then it is one of those built in the works although it was not running at the time the picture was taken - the other fellow has his hand on the valve rod.

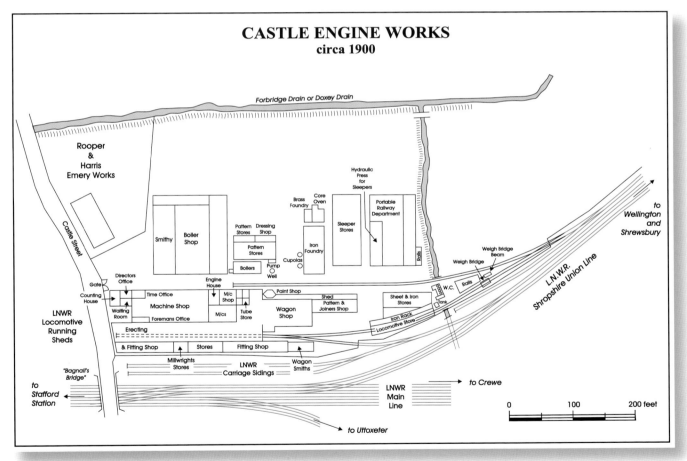

Plan of the Castle Engine Works as it was about 1900. Notice how it has expanded from the earliest days and this basic layout was did not alter very much over the next few years, although there was expansion westwards towards the Forbridge Drain. Notice too, the area used by Rooper & Harris - incidentally, despite being spelt Rooper, it was pronounced Roper.

The largest locomotives built to date were two standard-gauge 2-4-2 side tanks for the Egyptian Delta Railway. This is the second of the pair, numbers 1812 and 1813. These engines had a fixed pair of carrying wheels at the front and a radial axle at the rear.

standard-gauge track. There was also 154 yards of what is described as portable standard-gauge track and no less than 725 yards of 18in gauge. The narrow-gauge system was used by small bogie wagons (one late survivor had the Bagnall works order number 599 on a plate) to move material around the site and it included seven single turnouts (points) and two double ones, together with two turntables all of which had been built in the works. For use on the railways there were 17 standard-gauge four-wheeled trolleys - as they were referred to - along with 13 18in gauge bogies; there were also three 30in and two, two-foot gauge bogies and these would appear to be the ones used on the multi-gauged test track. Locomotive built for track gauges that were not encompassed by the various gauges on the test track, would be mounted on either the 30in or two-foot gauge bogies for movement around the erecting shop and the rest of the site as necessary. Although not specifically listed, part of the standard-gauge track had a number of other rails laid within it to give a variety of gauges for testing locomotives of different track gauges. The main erecting shop ran parallel to the LNWR main-line and was flanked by the machine and fitting shops on either side, with a further machining area at its southern end which abutted Castle Street. The wagon shop was to the north of this complex of erecting, fitting and machine shops, whilst the rest of the shops were

completely separate and to the west. But the site was much larger than the area occupied by the buildings and together with that sub-let, provided room for considerable expansion.

Despite the relative hotchpotch nature of the workshops - and there is plenty of evidence to suggest they were not unlike some of the Company's contemporaries - some amazing feats of engineering were undertaken. At the time the inventory was compiled production was almost exclusively railway equipment as the manufacture of stationary engines and boilers had all but ceased. It is notable though that a lot of the plant and machinery was driven by engines built by the firm, but strangely not the Lancashire boilers, although this type of boiler had been built at Stafford in the past. We saw earlier how Henry Venables & Company, another old-established Stafford firm, timber merchants with a works on the opposite side of the LNWR main line to the Castle Engine Works, had a Lancashire boiler built by Bagnall. Henry Venables was not just a customer, but a supplier of timber too.

In May 1906 the Company received an order for its biggest locomotives to date, two inside-cylinder standard-gauge 2-4-2 side tanks for the Egyptian Delta Light Railway. They were for use on the Helwan line, which ran from Helwan to Cairo and from 1915 part of the Egyptian State Railways. The inside cylinders were

15½x24in and the coupled wheel diameter 4ft 6in; the length over buffers was 34ft 5¾in and the overall height 12ft 6in. Stephenson's link motion was fitted together with Richardson's balanced slide valves and the engines had Belpaire firebox boilers and a weight in working order equal to 45¾ tons. The coupled wheel axle-load however was only 11.95 tons against a maximum allowed in the specification of 12 tons, and whilst the leading carrying wheels were fixed, the trailing pair had a radial axle-box arrangement which allowed 2½in of deflection in each direction - five inches in total. The two engines, manufacturer's numbers 1812 and 1813 were despatched on 28 May and 15 June 1907 respectively, in both instances dismantled and packed in crates for shipment via Salford Docks. The running numbers were 12 and 13 and the engines appear to have

lasted until some time after the last war. It is perhaps worth mentioning at this juncture that the Castle Engine Works never had a facility to forge crank axles for inside-cylinder locomotives, except perhaps the very small ones on the early locomotives. These components were sub-contracted, although in many cases they would have been machined at Stafford. Some of the very early small inside-cylinder locomotives may have had built-up crank axles rather than forged ones, in which case they would undoubtedly have been made at Stafford.

The two Egyptian locomotives, whilst they were designed at Stafford, the work was under the general supervision and inspection of the consulting engineers Messrs Rendel & Robertson, and this was the Company's first involvement with this particular firm of

Among the largest locomotives ever built by any manufacturer for 18in gauge railways were four 0-4-2 well tanks built in 1906 for the South African De Beers Consolidated Mines located at Kimberley in the Cape. Numbers 1814 to 1817 they appear to have remained in use until at least shortly after the last war and two of them have been preserved. This is number 1814 OLIVE, preserved at the Kimberley Mine Museum and photographed on 4 April 1974. Notice the Bagnall-Price valve gear has the eccentric bush oscillated by an outside eccentric rod and return-crank on the main crank pin. This was necessary as the well tank, itself necessary to keep the centre of gravity low due to the narrow track gauge, left no room between the frames for a conventional eccentric drive on one of the axles. There was a small additional water tank under the bunker and the balance pipe between the two tanks can just be discerned in front of the rear buffer beam. Unlike continental practice where the engine frames on well-tank locomotives usually form the tank sides, in this case a completely independent tank is located between the frames. (Uwe Bergeman)

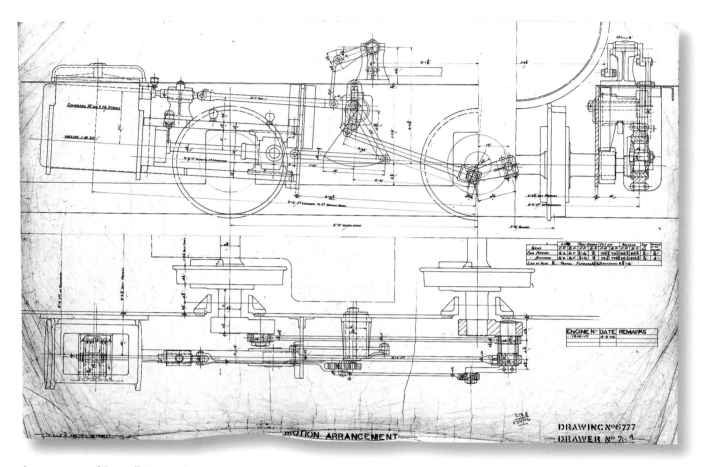

Arrangement of Bagnall-Price valve gear as applied to the De Beers locomotives numbers 1814 to 1817, illustrating the arrangement with the link bush oscillated by a return arm and eccentric rod outside the frames. Notice too, the outline of the well tank between the frames.

consulting engineers. Rendel & Robertson was a partnership between Sir Alexander Rendel and Frederick Robertson, predecessors of the consulting engineers Rendel, Palmer & Tritton (RP&T). Both Rendel and Robertson had spent much of their earlier life in India, largely but not exclusively, involved in railway civil engineering and RP&T later became the consulting engineers to the Indian Government on all railway related matters. RP&T was instrumental in the design and development of various standard locomotive designs that were introduced for use on the railways in India, and locomotives of the same designs also found their way to Burma. The Egyptian order was a significant one for the firm, and whilst we do not know for certain how or why it came to Stafford, it was the prelude to an extremely successful relationship between the RP&T and WG Bagnall Limited; in particular its

later principals Sir Seymour Biscoe Tritton and his son Julian S Tritton. It may of course have been nothing more than the tender price, which was it appears an extremely competitive £2,211 10/- (£2,211 50p) per locomotive, whilst the works costs are recorded as £3,000 3/ 9d (£3,000 19p). This was a substantial loss and it may have been nothing more than ensuring the order came to Stafford so as to prove that the Company was in fact capable of building such comparatively large locomotives.

Another very interesting order of the period covered by this Chapter consisted of four locomotives that were among the largest ever built for use on the 18in gauge. Ordered in May 1906 by De Beers Consolidated Mines Limited, they were for use on the railway system around the diamond mines at Kimberley in South Africa. The wheel arrangement was 0-4-2 and the cylinders no less

Another engine with the Bagnall-Price valve gear using an outside return-arm and eccentric rod was this one, number 1798 of 1906. In this case however, the reason was quite different, involving the close proximity of the trailing wheel-set to the firebox, which left no room for an eccentric on the axle. When circular firebox boilers were used this constraint did not apply, and this was one of the factors in their favour. This rather neat side tank locomotive had 10x15in cylinders and a 4ft 9in wheelbase; it was ordered by the Crown Agents for the Colonies and sent to Ceylon for use by the Government Irrigation Department. There was a repeat order in 1907, number 1859, and both locomotives were last heard of in November 1914 when spares were ordered for them.

than 12in diameter with a stroke of 15in; to keep the centre of gravity as low as possible for such a large locomotive on so narrow a gauge, well tanks were situated between the frames. The diameter of the boiler was 3ft 3¼in, the total heating surface equalled 500 sq ft and the grate area was seven sq ft. Manufacturer's numbers were 1814 to 1817 and the four locomotives were despatched via Morpeth Docks in Liverpool during November and December 1906. Two of them survive to this day preserved at Kimberley. The trailing truck on these locomotives had radial axle-boxes of the type that later became familiarly known as 'Cortazzi' (after its Italian inventor); this was the same

arrangement later used by Nigel Gresley, chief mechanical engineer of the LNER, for many of the locomotives he is credited with designing. As the locomotives were fitted with Bagnall-Price valve gear and in view of the well tanks the drive for the oscillating shaft was via a conventional return-arm on the main crank, rather than an eccentric. As mentioned earlier this arrangement had been allowed for in the patent application.

Despite the different types of locomotive just described the staple diet for the Company in the period being covered in this Chapter remained comparatively small narrow-gauge contractor's and plantation type

THE DOLL, number 1787 of 1905, is an example of a slightly larger version of the standard narrow-gauge design, in this case with 8x12in cylinders. This one worked at the Briton Ferry Works Ltd, an iron and steel works near Neath in South Wales and the picture was taken on 2 April 1956. By this time the works was owned by Guest, Keen & Baldwins Limited, hence the GKB initials on the cab side, and the engine lasted until 1959. (Industrial Railway Society - Bernard Mettam Collection)

locomotives. But the customer base was an ever widening one and locomotives were being sent all over the world. There were numerous individual designs too, but they all had a family likeness leaving the discerning in nodoubt where they were designed and built. Despite a general slackening off in orders for anything other than locomotives the firm continued to turn its hand to all sorts of general engineering as profitable opportunities presented themselves and an interesting non-locomotive order came from the War Office just after the turn of the century. In the aftermath of the South African Boer War it became necessary at short notice to house the large number of troops on their return to this country. In the first instance many of the returning men were accommodated in somewhat temporary accommodation consisting of large wooden huts at

Longmoor Camp. This was in the Woolmer Forest and near Liphook in Hampshire, and the camp was later the site of the extensive Longmoor Military Railway. Due to the damp and un-healthy conditions in the forest at Longmoor, in 1903 a decision was made to establish more permanent arrangements at nearby Borden. As the distance between these two sites was only some four and a half miles, to save expense it was decided to move the wooden huts from Longmoor to Borden, rather that building new ones. Nevertheless, this was no small operation even by today's standards, as the huts measured 72ft x 21ft and weighed between 30 and 40 tons each.

To help perform this logistic the 53rd Railway Company were summoned from Chattenden Barracks in Kent and the men and equipment arrived during May 1903. The Company then proceeded to lay 18in gauge

Four illustrations of typical narrow-gauge wagons built during the period covered by this Chapter, although similar types had been built for many years previously, and continued to be so for many more years. The two types of side-tip wagon show both inside and outside frames, this would largely depend on the track gauge specified, also cast-iron and fabricated supports for the body. Neither wagon has any springs, although wagons of this type could be supplied with sprung axles, along with hand brakes if required. The sugar cane wagon is sprung, but otherwise of very simple construction, whilst the small mine tub is also un-sprung and has wooden frames cased in steel.

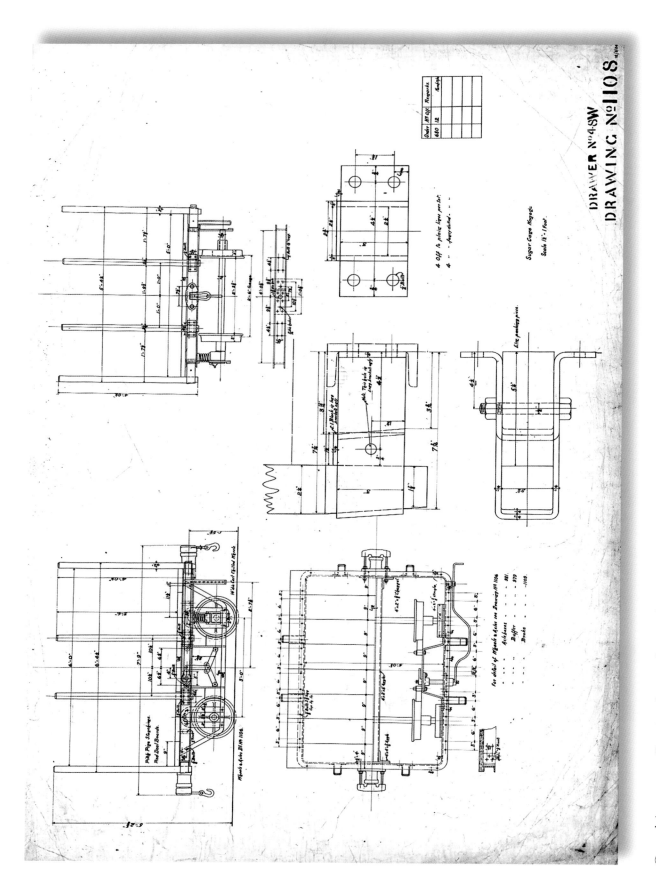

General Arrangement Drawing of a typical type and size of rolling stock built during the period covered by this Chapter. This is a 2ft 6in gauge sugar cane wagon, 12 of which were supplied to general order number 680 of March 1905.

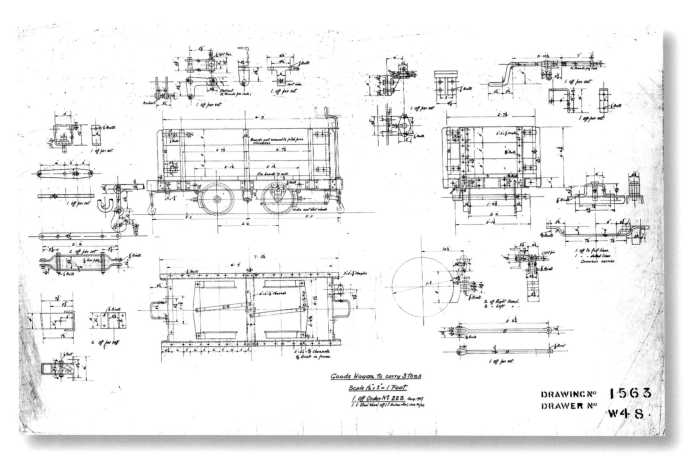

General Arrangement Drawing of a four-wheel three ton goods wagon for two-foot gauge. In the case of this drawing, although showing a pretty typical type of wagon, only one was supplied to general order number 233 of August 1907.

railway lines across the woodlands between the two sites, having first cleared the way. In fact two parallel lines were laid 22ft apart as it was intended to move the huts in one piece. A set of 14 small 18in gauge bogies which were arranged in seven pairs were used under each hut. The gauge of railway was dictated by use of a similar gauge at Chattenden and the availability of some of the equipment needed; however, the pairs of trolleys were made at the Castle Engine Works and it may be that some of the railway track was purchased new too. The huts were first of all jacked up and the bogies placed underneath with seven trolleys - as they were termed - on each side of the hut, each trolley being connected by a series of rods to its opposite number under the other side of the hut. Each line of seven trolleys then sat on one of the parallel lines of railway. Hauling power was a steam-powered winch and vertical boiler, both mounted on a platform running on four identical trolleys (but different to those used under the

huts) that were also supplied by Bagnall. It is possible that the boilers and winches came from Stafford too, but if so no record seems to have survived. There were two of these machines which it appears, were colloquially known to the men as 'contraptions'! The method of movement was for the winch trolley to be attached to the hut being moved and for the rope to be plied out some 400 yards or so and attached to a convenient tree. The winch would then be used to wind in the rope and thus, move the whole lot forward. This sequence of events was then repeated, time and time again, until the destination was reached. Altogether 68 huts were moved by this method at an average of four huts per week. The trolleys were interesting as they were suitable for both road and rail use, road wheels of 1ft 10in diameter, as opposed to the 10in diameter of the rail wheels, also being supplied. There was a facility to fit the road wheels as the axles extended beyond the rail wheels and in view of their

Picture taken in 1902 and showing if not all, certainly, most of the staff of the Castle Engine Works. This was the occasion of a presentation to Gordon Bagnall and his wife of an Illuminated Address. Bagnall is on the left sitting in a chair among the grass, and apart from those sitting on the fences, is the only person not standing. To his immediate right with the prominent beard and holding his

larger diameter, once they were fitted the rail wheels were lifted well clear of the track. They were sometimes used for the final positioning of the huts, an operation usually assisted by teams of horses and a steam ploughing engine, which of course also had a winding drum. After this interesting operation one is left wondering what happened to the trolleys; doubtless they languished for many years in a War Department store somewhere, just in case any more huts ever needed moving!

Extensive details of the careers of Gordon Bagnall's sons have already been documented in Chapter One, suffice it say here that once he was old enough Richard Gordon, Bagnall's youngest son became involved in the affairs of the Company but his elder brother Harold Gordon did not, joining the Army straight from school.

lapels is Sam Price, and that is probably George Fletcher, the Chief Clerk, with the boater and also holding a lapel to his left. The other chap with the boater some distance to his right is Richard Gordon Bagnall, and on his right with the cloth cap, waistcoat and tie, is WS Edwards - then a very young man. Studying this photograph one is left wondering what they are all looking at!

Richard Gordon trained as an engineer with the firm and later accompanied his father on many of his 'salesman' trips, both in this country and abroad - his sister particularly recalled a trip to Gibraltar in connection with the locomotives, rolling stock and other equipment supplied for the naval base there. By the turn of the century the works employed some 300 hands, many of whom had been with the Company for a long time, some of them going back to Massey and Hill days. Gordon Bagnall seems to have been a benevolent and considerate employer, popular with his people and always game for a joke. Nevertheless surviving portraits of him do no give such an impression; they all show a much more serious stature leaving one with the impression he would have been more akin to the arch-typical Victorian factory owner of the history books. Obviously he had a good business brain, but all the evidence suggests a kindly and considerate nature. In 1902 or 1903 the staff presented Gordon Bagnall and his wife Jessie with an illuminated address and photograph as a mark of their esteem. At the time of the presentation the entire work force assembled in the works yard for a photograph, and Gordon Bagnall the only one sitting down! An interesting aspect of the only known copy of a photograph taken on this occasion is that almost all the 300 odd souls are not looking at the camera; most of them are looking in another direction, so there may have been other views taken at the same time. Richard Gordon appears in the picture with his father, along with Samuel Price, the other Foreman and 'white collar

staff' as well as everybody else. Mrs Bagnall however, is conspicuous by her absence; indeed there are no females in the picture at all. One aspect of Gordon Bagnall's business strategy was the recruitment of what were referred to as premium apprentices, boys taken on and trained in locomotive engineering with their parents paying a premium for the privilege. This was in contrast to the more normal trade apprentices, but quite a popular practice within engineering companies at the time, and particularly within railway engineering with almost all the main-line railway companies adopting it. Obviously the training was often at a different level than the trade apprentices received, and for example, included periods in the drawing office. At various times and for various periods between 1887 and

Two portraits of Gordon Bagnall later in life, the second one probably taken after the debilitating illness that eventually killed him, was beginning to take its toll.

1906, no less than 30 boys were employed at Castle Engine Works under these sort of arrangements, including the sons of a number of Bagnall's friends; the brothers G and H Bostock for example, of the Stafford boot and shoemaking family. This practice ceased after Bagnall's death, but we know not why, and the training of apprentices other than trade apprentices, was not resumed until after the First World War, and then under completely different arrangements and conditions.

In 1906 significant changes took place in the shareholding of the Company, the most important being the transfer of almost all the shares held by Thomas Walter. Readers will recall that Walter's day to day involvement in the affairs of the Company had never been great, and from around 1892 on an even lesser scale than hitherto. Walter sold 1,037 ordinary and 180 deferred shares which were valued at par - £10 each - to the Gifford Brothers at a total cost of £12,170; the majority went to John Gifford but 50 ordinary shares went to his brother James. At the time of the transfer Walter's address is quoted as: c/o Messrs Soames, Edwards & Jones of Lennox House, Norfolk Street, London. This was a partnership that had acted as the Company's solicitors for a number of years, having been involved in the formation of the limited company back in 1887. However, on this occasion Thomas Walter's business affairs appear to have been conducted by his father John, as he would have been out of the country at the time as described in Chapter One. The transfer of shares took place on 22 December 1906 and left Walter with a small holding of 50 ordinary shares; there was however, a loan to the Company of £3,000 still outstanding and paying interest at 4% - this was not discharged until March 1923. Incidentally, in the initial formation of the Company back in 1887, the deferred shares represented the goodwill of the business as opposed to the capital employed, and the issue of 500 deferred shares therefore, valued the goodwill at £5,000. As the deferred shares were only allocated to Bagnall (320) and Walter (180), this gave them respectively £3,200 and £1,800 of the value of the goodwill. It still stood at this figure in 1938 when it was written off in the profit & loss sccount for that year, and removed from the balance sheet thereafter.

Earlier in 1906, on 25 January, other share transfers had taken place. Gordon Bagnall acquired the 75 ordinary shares held by Samuel Cookson as well as 50 ordinary shares held by his brother Richard Samuel Bagnall, along with 50 ordinary shares held by Mrs King - formerly Jessie Bagnall and later Mrs Brooks-King - and 15 ordinary shares held by Mrs Spurway - formerly Gertrude Mary Bagnall. Jessie and Gertrude Mary were sisters of Gordon Bagnall. As was the case with Walter's holding all these shares were valued at £10 each and were bought at par. At the same time, 25 January 1906, one ordinary share was transferred from WG Bagnall to his eldest son Harold Gordon, along with another to his wife Jessie. Thereafter the shareholding of the Company consisted of: WG Bagnall 806 ordinary shares and 320 deferred; Thomas Walter 50 ordinary shares: James Gifford 51 ordinary shares: Anne Keay 10 ordinary shares: Harold Gordon Bagnall one ordinary share: Jessie Bagnall one ordinary share: John Gifford 1131 ordinary and 180 deferred shares. As a result of these changes in the shareholding of the Company John Gifford became not only the largest shareholder, but he also held a majority and in effect, had control of the Company.

At the time of these share transfers Gordon Bagnall was suffering from serious ill health of a most debilitating kind and from 1903 he had been compelled to give up much of his activities in the public service, including his membership of the County Council. Such documentary evidence as is available leads one to the belief that his time on both Stafford Town Council and later Staffordshire County Council had not always been harmonious. He was very outspoken on a whole range of issues and by no means the most popular member among his contempories! Nevertheless, the plethora of letters of praise for the good work he had done and commiserations on his illness when he retired from public life were both sincere and numerous; many of them survive in the family archive. A quote from but a few of them gives a general flavour and will have to suffice for our purposes. Sir Thomas Salt, whom we met earlier in the story, wrote on 2 August 1903: 'My Dear Bagnall, I am very very sorry that you are leaving the County Council. It will not be the same place to me when you have gone'. Later, 8 September 1905, The Earl of Lichfield wrote from the Staffordshire General Infirmary as its president, quoting a general committee minute: 'The committee desires to place on record its appreciation of the efficient and painstaking services of Mr WG Bagnall as honorary auditor for the past

When the Stafford Town sewage works was ceremonially opened on 15 September 1897, a scheme Gordon Bagnall had campaigned long and hard for, he was asked to perform the ceremony. On this occasion he was presented with a lovely inscribed key contained in a well made small case, and this photograph shows the inscription. It reads: 'Presented to WG Bagnall Esq., First Chairman of the Sewage Committee of Stafford Corporation at the opening of the Sewage Works on September 15th 1897'.

eighteen years, and regrets exceedingly the loss of his valuable services through ill health'. There was a not dissimilar minute dated 1 August 1903 from the County Council Sanitary Committee, of which he had been chairman since its inception in 1889.

Hopefully by this point in the story readers will have formed the view that William Gordon Bagnall was indeed an incredible character. As well as running his own company, we have seen how keen a politician, businessman and accomplished sportsman he was, representing for many years the Conservatives on Stafford Town Council and later Staffordshire County Council. As well as being chairman of the local Conservative Party, he also chaired at various times several committees of both the town and county

councils. A prominent and practising Freemason, Gordon Bagnall was also an accomplished marksman with both a revolver and a rifle and for 18 years until 1905, as recalled above by the Earl of Lichfield, was the honorary auditor of the Staffordshire General Infirmary. By all accounts in his early days he was also something of a character and his daughter, who thought the absolute world of him and whose recollections of her father were so clear when your authors interviewed her in 1976, told many a story. For example on one occasion during the run-up to some local elections, along with several others of similar political leanings, he ventured out late one night and helped paint some prominent structures in the town blue! He would appear to have always been 'game' for a bit of fun, which as mentioned earlier is not perhaps apparent from the sternness displayed in surviving photographs. Along with his wife Jessie he was active in the town in amateur dramatics; both of them appearing on occasions in shows held at the Lyceum Theatre. Whilst this was usually in aid of the local Conservative Association, it was not always so, as on occasions other local and worthy charities were subscribed to.

Another of Gordon Bagnall's very active interests outside his business and political pursuits was gardening, and we saw earlier how he developed a large garden on the Alpine style at Castle Hill House. He also made himself somewhat of an expert in root pruning of fruit trees and there are letters from his pen on the subject in both *Gardening Illustrated* in November 1901, as well as *The Staffordshire Advertiser* in January 1903. Apparently these notes were so popular that in September 1904 he had them reprinted in the form of a handout. For a number of years in the 1890s, at least from 1893 to 1899, the Company rented Glyn Farm near Stafford and Gordon Bagnall seems to have taken an active interest in the management of this undertaking.

In view of Gordon Bagnall's particular involvement with Stafford's public health, it is worth having a closer look at some of his achievements in this area. A Special Sewage Committee was put in place in October 1891 and the following month Bagnall was elected its chairman. The committee was formed for the purpose of establishing a new sewage system covering a large part of the town and a Mr E Pritchard of 1 Victoria Street, London SW, was appointed consulting engineer to the Council for the development of a scheme. Soon after the formation of the committee Bagnall, along with his fellow members were busy visiting various towns in the country to study the relative merits of different systems of sewage disposal; for example filtration plants. There were visits to Acton, Hendon, Ealing, Wednesbury and Wolverhampton to name but a few and Bagnall participated in many of them. There appears to have been some sort of disagreement with Pritchard following the visits as to what form the system should take and at a meeting of the committee on 24 February 1893, JE Willcox of 118 Colmore Row, Birmingham was appointed in his stead. His fee by the way was £10 10/- (£10 50p) per day, excluding travelling expenses, which was a tidy sum in those times. Tenders were subsequently invited for the agreed works which included several miles of sewers that were divided into three sections. A filtration plant was planned at Lammescote, south of the town, and there were various other ancillary installations, whilst as part of the overall scheme it was also planned to erect a waste destructor complete with boiler.

No fewer than 25 tenders were received for the sewage scheme ranging from £19,705 as the lowest to £33,336 6/ 1d (£33,336 30p) as the highest and a small sub-committee consisting of Wilcox, who had been appointed borough surveyor, and Gordon Bagnall was elected to review them. The destructor and boiler contract was awarded to the Nottingham firm of Manlove Alliott & Company at a figure of £2,060; remember that some years earlier whilst acting as agents this Company had purchased from Bagnall small narrow-gauge locomotives and light railway equipment for overseas customers, so it was one known to Gordon Bagnall. The Town Council had also done business with the company in 1880 and 1881, when it traded as Alliott, Fryer & Company; waste treatment equipment had been supplied on that occasion. The contract for the principal works was awarded to another Bagnall customer of long standing, Enoch Tempest; his tender price was £21,320 15/- (£21,320 75p), but he was persuaded to make a reduction of 1½% and eventually undertook to complete the work for £21,000. Tempest attended a meeting of the committee held on 11 September 1894 when the contract was signed. Later, in January 1896 it was agreed to pay Tempest an additional sum of £1,201 11/ 11d (£1,201 60p), to cover

the costs of a sewage reception tank not part of the original scheme; nevertheless this was only after competitive tendering. Indications are that the total works were completed in or about January 1896.

It is interesting to speculate what influence Bagnall might have had in this contract being awarded to Enoch Tempest. Tempest had been a good customer of Bagnall and the two of them would almost certainly have struck up a friendship of sorts. Bagnall may well have been instrumental in getting Tempest on the tender list in the first place, nevertheless he was at the time one of the foremost public works contractors in the north of the country. It is tempting to speculate that Tempest may have used light railways, and even locomotives on this job at Stafford, but if so no records appear to have survived. If railways and locomotives had been used the equipment would almost certainly have been built by Bagnall, and one would expect a mention in the local press, if only by Gordon Bagnall's critics once again accusing him of profiting from his public work! In any event, in September 1895 Gordon Bagnall tendered his resignation as chairman of the Special Sewage Committee; it was said in view of business conflicts and this may have had a bearing on Tempest having been awarded the contract. The committee, in accepting his resignation at its next meeting desired: 'to place on record great regret that he was disqualified from taking further part and the high appreciation of the services done at great sacrifice to him personally'.

On 19 July 1907, in the morning and at his home Castle Hill House, Deans Hill in Stafford, William Gordon Bagnall passed away at the comparatively early age of 55 years. His youngest son Richard Gordon was at his side and the death certificate records: 'Pachymeningitis Paralysis', indicating a very unpleasant last few years of his life. In fact he had been bed-ridden for almost two years and latterly at least, was unable to speak. His almost life-long friend Dr. George Reid, the county medical officer, was among those who tended his needs and signed the death certificate. Between 1903 and 1905, on medical advice, Gordon and Jessie Bagnall took a number of what would have been expensive holidays abroad, and the family archive contains a number of postcards sent to Richard Gordon and Jessica. For example they were aboard a Bibby Line ship at Marseille on 20 May 1903, the Norddeutscher Lloyd liner SS STUTTGART on 22 July 1903, the White Star liner SS CYMRIE at Queenstown on 8 November 1903, and a Royal Mail Steam Packet Company liner at New York on 4 December 1904. On 24 March 1905 they were on the P&O liner SS MACEDONIA at Plymouth returning from a trip as the postcard was written as the ship crossed the Bay of Biscay. The author of his obituary in *The Locomotive Magazine* had among other things this to say: 'His comparatively early death has now finally removed a noteworthy figure, not only from the engineering profession, but from other spheres of activity'. How very true these words were.

As would be expected his funeral, held at St Mary's Castle Church on Monday 22 July, was well attended with six of his oldest employees acting a pallbearers; Messrs S Barns; G Price; J Whittaker; E Hawkins; S Hubball and F Kemsley were those chosen. Led by his sons and his eldest brother Richard Samuel, were members of the large Bagnall family including his other brothers, his father-in-law and brothers-in-law, and other family members although his wife and daughter did not attend. The authors were told by his daughter that as her mother was so distressed and felt unable to attend, she stayed at home to comfort her. Stafford Town Council was represented by the Mayor, Alderman A Andrews and the town clerk R Battle, along with a number of other aldermen. Captain The Hon GA Anson represented the local Volunteer Force of The North Staffordshire Regiment of which Bagnall had been such a keen supporter in his earlier days. Stafford Fire Brigade was represented by the Captain F Bailer, Superintendent LP Dodd and many of its members all in full dress uniform as an acknowledgement of Gordon Bagnall having once been their Captain. There were many others present, including many prominent local businessmen, and of course, a large group of his employees. The Gifford brothers led those members of the staff who attended, although Samuel Price was unable to attend due to ill health, he was represented by AE Owen, the Cashier.

William Gordon Bagnall was laid to rest in the churchyard of St Mary's and a rather fine stone cross was later erected. Forty years later his wife Jessie, who passed away at Church Stretton on 21 November 1947 at the age of 83, joined him. Her daughter Jessica Gordon Alsop was present at her death and the death certificate records her as the widow of 'William Gordon Bagnall - Locomotive Engineer'. Jessie Bagnall was, like

The Star of the National Skating Association. This is the one presented in 1895 to Gordon Bagnall's wife Jessie.

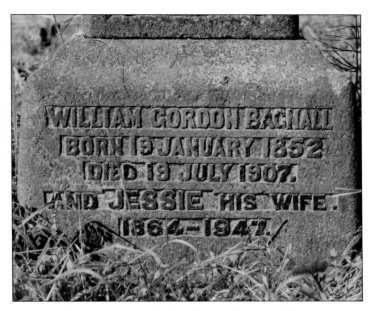

WILLIAM GORDON BAGNALL
BORN 19 JANUARY 1852
DIED 19 JULY 1907.
AND JESSIE HIS WIFE.
1864 - 1947.

William Gordon and Jessie Bagnall are buried together, in the church yard of St Mary's, Castle Church in Stafford, and despite the 40 years separating their deaths. This is their tome stone.

her husband, a keen gardener and an accomplished golfer. In her younger days she had also been an acclaimed ice skater and the Star of the National Skating Association was among her accomplishments, but an accident whilst skating in about the year 1925 which resulted in a broken hip, put an end to this activity. Unfortunately an operation to re-set the hip was not completely successful and she spent a lot of time in Oswestry Orthopaedic Hospital; this left her with a rather bad limp as a result of which in later years she rarely went out. Gordon Bagnall always referred to his wife as Jess and she called him Will; despite the rest of the family and friends using his second Christian name Gordon. As his mother's maiden name all three children were christened Gordon as their second Christian name and many family members have similarly been given Gordon as one of their Christian names. At the time of her death Jessie Bagnall held shares in the Merlimau Rubber Estates in Malay; these had belonged to her youngest son Richard Gordon and although worthless at the time, they were passed to one of her grandchildren, her daughter Jessica's son Giles Richard Gordon Alsop. Some years later they attracted a small value when the otherwise almost defunct company was able to sell some land! Family legend has it that Jessie had an 18in waist when she got married and was able to get into her wedding dress again after

the birth of her first child, which apparently gave her enormous pleasure! Among the mourners at the funeral which was held at St Mary's in Stafford, was Elizabeth Edwards, widow of WS Edwards who was for a long time managing director of the Company - Elizabeth would have known Jessie as 'the bosses wife' when Gordon Bagnall was still alive. It was a nice touch too, for the Company to be represented and Harry Davies, the general manager was there to represent WG Bagnall Limited.

As a result of Gordon Bagnall's illness John Gifford, Sydney Edwards, Samuel Price and Richard Gordon Bagnall all became more involved in the day-to-day management of the business. Without doubt too, John Gifford would have had an eye on the longer term strategy, although this does not seem to have had the attention devoted to it than was the case when Gordon Bagnall was around. The speculation earlier in this Chapter on the motives regarding the 1905 inventory of plant and equipment along with the significant transfer of shares the following year, is poignant. Both these events were clearly connected with Gordon Bagnall's declining health and one can speculate John Gifford would have wanted a professional opinion of the value of the business prior to increasing his shareholding. This would have been especially so in view of the level of his increased investment.

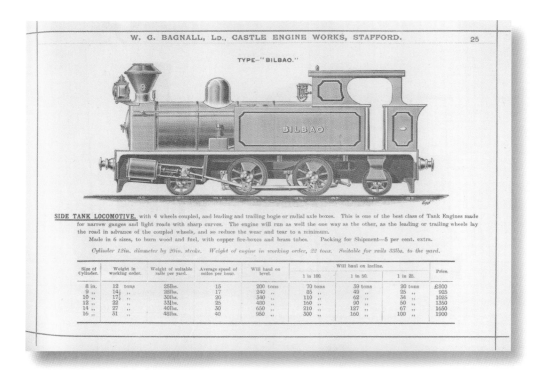

W. G. BAGNALL, Ld., CASTLE ENGINE WORKS, STAFFORD.   25

TYPE—"BILBAO."

BILBAO

SIDE TANK LOCOMOTIVE, with 4 wheels coupled, and leading and trailing bogie or radial axle boxes. This is one of the best class of Tank Engines made for narrow gauges and light roads with sharp curves. The engine will run as well the one way as the other, as the leading or trailing wheels lay the road in advance of the coupled wheels, and so reduce the wear and tear to a minimum.

Made in 6 sizes, to burn wood and fuel, with copper fire-boxes and brass tubes.   Packing for Shipment—5 per cent. extra.

Cylinder 12in. diameter by 20in. stroke.   Weight of engine in working order, 22 tons.   Suitable for rails 33lbs. to the yard.

Size of Cylinder.	Weight in working order.	Weight of suitable rails per yard.	Average speed of miles per hour.	Will haul on level.	Will haul on incline.			Price.
					1 in 100.	1 in 50.	1 in 28.	
8 in.	12 tons	25lbs.	15	200 tons	70 tons	39 tons	20 tons	£800
9 ,,	14½ ,,	28lbs.	17	240 ,,	85 ,,	49 ,,	25 ,,	925
10 ,,	17½ ,,	30lbs.	20	340 ,,	110 ,,	62 ,,	34 ,,	1025
12 ,,	22 ,,	33lbs.	25	480 ,,	160 ,,	90 ,,	50 ,,	1350
14 ,,	27 ,,	40lbs.	30	650 ,,	210 ,,	127 ,,	67 ,,	1650
16 ,,	31 ,,	48lbs.	40	950 ,,	300 ,,	160 ,,	100 ,,	1900

Although this is a page from a catalogue of an earlier period than the one covered by this Chapter, No 12 of January 1894, illustrating the design of 2-4-2 side tank, this was a design that remained popular - see page 224 for example.   Although no locomotive was actually named BILBAO, the engraving is a likeness of manufacturer's number 1427, new in February 1894, metre-gauge with 12in diameter cylinders for Sim & Coventry Limited.   Shipped to Spain it was for use at iron-ore mines at Astillero near Santander, in the northern part of the country, hence for the purpose of the catalogue, its name.   In fact the engine built was named ASTILLERO, and the Company commissioned a second engraving showing the opposite side which was also used in catalogues.   The engine was still in use at the mines at late as the mid 1960s.

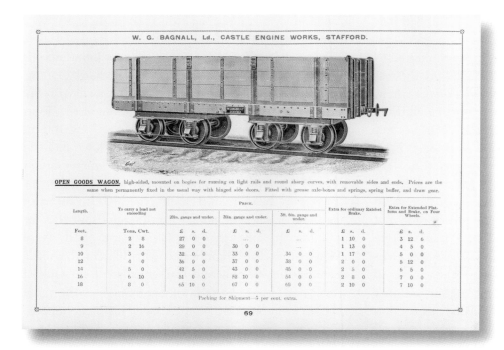

W. G. BAGNALL, Ld., CASTLE ENGINE WORKS, STAFFORD.

OPEN GOODS WAGON, high-sided, mounted on bogies for running on light rails and round sharp curves, with removable sides and ends. Prices are the same when permanently fixed in the usual way with hinged side doors. Fitted with grease axle-boxes and springs, spring buffer, and draw gear.

Length.	To carry a load not exceeding	PRICE.			Extra for ordinary Ratchet Brake.	Extra for Extended Platform and Brake, on Four Wheels.
		20in. gauge and under.	30in. gauge and under.	3ft. 6in. gauge and under.		
Feet.	Tons. Cwt.	£ s. d.	£ s. d.	£ s. d.	£ s. d.	£ s. d.
8	2 8	27 0 0	....	....	1 10 0	3 12 6
9	2 16	29 0 0	30 0 0	....	1 13 0	4 5 0
10	3 0	32 0 0	33 0 0	34 0 0	1 17 0	5 0 0
12	4 0	36 0 0	37 0 0	38 0 0	2 0 0	5 12 0
14	5 0	42 5 0	43 0 0	45 0 0	2 5 0	6 5 0
16	6 10	51 0 0	52 10 0	54 0 0	2 8 0	7 0 0
18	8 0	65 10 0	67 0 0	65 0 0	2 10 0	7 10 0

Packing for Shipment—5 per cent. extra.

69

Page from catalogue No 16 of October 1905, probably the last one Gordon Bagnall would have personally been involved with, illustrating yet another type of wagon the Company was prepared to build.

Chapter Five

JOHN GIFFORD IN CONTROL: TOWARDS THE FIRST WORLD WAR

After the death of Gordon Bagnall business carried on more or less as usual with John Gifford assuming the mantle of the only director, but he was soon joined by Richard Gordon Bagnall after which Gifford became the managing director of the Company. At this time all the issued shares in the Company, both ordinary and deferred and valued at £10 each, were fully paid. The shareholders consisted of the estate of William Gordon Bagnall, for which the executors were his wife Jessie and son Richard Gordon, holding 806 ordinary and 320 deferred shares. Also held by the family were one share each in the names of Jessie - the widow - and the elder son Harold Gordon. John Gifford held 1131 ordinary and 180 deferred shares, while his brother James held 51 ordinary shares. The other shareholders, both remaining from the original incorporation of the Company, were Thomas Walter and Miss Anne Keay, holding 50 and 10 ordinary shares respectively. On the 30 June 1908, the 50 ordinary shares still held by Thomas Walter were acquired by John Gifford, and two days earlier, in accordance with the terms of the will of William Gordon Bagnall, 50 ordinary shares held by him at the time of his death, were transferred by his executors to his youngest son Richard Gordon Bagnall; this was necessary to enable him to become a director,

as the articles of the Company stipulated 50 shares as a minimum shareholding to hold such office.

From the forgoing it will be observed that the Giffords were already majority shareholders in the Company. The will of William Gordon Bagnall was 'proved' in London on 2 November 1907, estate valued at £5,811, but there were complications. Despite the fact that the Company had been generating substantial profits, and dividends had been declared, only a small cash distribution had been made. Gordon Bagnall had however, been paid certain sums on account of his share of the profits and dividends, but apart from honouring the agreement with Thomas Walter dated 4 October 1892, and mentioned in Chapter Three, the remainder of the cash had been left in the Company's account. At a meeting of shareholders on 26 August 1908, it was established that from the profits generated a dividend of 6% on each fully paid up share of £10, both ordinary and deferred, was payable for the period 1 April 1887 to 31 December 1897, and thereafter 12% for the year 1898, 36% for the years 1899 and 1900, 12% for the year 1901, 6% for the years 1902 and 1903, 12% for the years 1904, 1905 and 1906, and 6% for the year 1907. In cash terms, with interest agreed at 4% less tax, this amounted to £30,642 2/ 6d (£30,642 12½p).

On 14 December 1908, an agreement was entered

into between WG Bagnall Limited and the shareholders; the executors of William Gordon Bagnall (his son Richard Gordon and his wife Jessie), Harold Gordon Bagnall, Jessie Bagnall, Richard Gordon Bagnall, John Gifford, James Gifford and Anne Keay. This agreement discharged the liabilities to the shareholders in terms of unpaid dividends as outlined above, and the cash released was divided in accordance with, and in proportion to, the individual shareholdings. The bulk of the cash released was due to the estate of William Gordon Bagnall, in accordance with his share holding at the time of his death; however, the calculated figure of £22,273 14/ 3d (£22,273 71p) was in fact exactly the same sum recorded in the books of the Company as having already been paid to him. There was therefore, no cash payment made to the estate. In the case of John Gifford, part of the monies owing to him by the terms of this agreement which in total amounted to £7,436 0/ 7d (£7,436 2½ p) including interest, was discharged in an allocation of newly created and previously unallocated shares. On 13 September 1908, 450 £10 ordinary shares were issued to him at par, but ranked for dividends only from the date of issue. This share issue took the issued and paid-up share capital of the Company to the total permitted by its articles of £30,000, and this was the first time this had been the case. John Gifford however, only took £2,000 of the residual in cash, as he agreed to leave part of that owing to him and amounting to £936 0/ 7d (£936 2½p), in the Company to assist its cash flow. Similarly, he also left the sum of £264 18/ 2d (£264 91p) in the Company, which was the interest on the total sum owing to him for the period 1 January to 13 September 1908. The combined figure of £1,200 18/ 9d (£1,200 92p) was in effect a loan, for a period of five years accruing interest at £5 per cent/per annum. The agreement by the way, was signed by all the parties involved except Harold Gordon Bagnall, for whom his mother and brother acted under powers of attorney, as he was out of the country on military service at the time. There was a similar agreement in respect of Anne Keay, and she received £262 6/- (£262 30p) in cash.

Because of the agreement reached on 4 October 1892 between the Company and Thomas Walter, whereby the latter agreed to a 4% preferential dividend in lieu of any other rights by virtue of his share ownership, the shares in the Company formerly belonging to Walter, and by this time owned by the Gifford Brothers, were excluded from the agreement outlined above. Also excluded, were the 50 shares transferred to Richard Gordon Bagnall, under the terms of his father's will.

At the conclusion of these negotiations the shareholding was:

Executors of William Gordon Bagnall 756 ordinary and 320 deferred;
John Gifford 1,631 ordinary and 180 deferred;
James Gifford 51 ordinary;
Richard Gordon Bagnall 50 ordinary;
James Keay 10 ordinary (these were transferred from Anne Keay on 30 June 1908);
Harold Gordon Bagnall one ordinary;
Jessie Bagnall one ordinary.

This gave a total of 2,500 ordinary shares of £10 and 500 deferred shares of similar value, all fully paid. Thus, the paid up share capital of the Company equalled the total of £30,000 allowed by its articles, and this was an increase of £4,500 since Bagnall's death, brought about by the 450 new shares issued to John Gifford. From the forgoing it will be seen that John Gifford increased his stake in the Company, and according to the late WG Bagnall's daughter Jessica Gordon Alsop, when interviewed by the authors in 1976, it had originally been suggested that the Giffords might sell the firm. Although it was not put on the market as such, several enquiries were apparently made, including what she described as a tempting one from the German company of Arthur Koppel, via its London office. Arthur Koppel was a well established German company specialising, like Bagnall, in light railway equipment, so acquisition of an established manufacturing base in this country, and a well-known name, would have been an attractive business proposition. There were long standing links and associations between this Company and the better known one of Orenstein & Koppel, and while these need not detain us here, suffice it to say that in 1908 an amalgamation of the two companies took place.

Jessica went on to say that she was instrumental in this sale not proceeding, having pleaded with John Gifford, 'not to sell Daddy's firm to the Germans'! In the light of the activities of the Gifford brothers, in particular John in acquiring shares over the previous year or so, it may seem a little improbable that they would want to sell anyway, but if the Koppel offer price was high enough perhaps they would. However, as a figure of £16,000 was mentioned, which against an issued and fully paid share capital at the time of Bagnall's death of £30,000, this would not seem to have been the case. But Jessica was recalling events of many years earlier and she could have been confused over the price. It may be of course, that the figure of £16,000 was only for the shares held by the Giffords, but even if this was the case, it would have valued them at considerable less than their face value. In any event, the Company was not sold and with John Gifford as managing director and Richard Gordon Bagnall as the only other director, business continued. At about the same time, at an extraordinary general meeting (EGM) of the Company held on 3 June 1908, a special resolution was passed to alter the articles of association. The principal reason for the new articles was to convert the Company from a public one to a private one, following the enabling legislation embodied in the Companies Act of 1907, an enabling Act that allowed for the distinction between a public and a private company. Thereafter, no invitation could be made for the public to subscribe for any share, or debenture in the Company, although in fact, no such invitation had ever been made. This resolution was confirmed at a subsequent EGM on 26 June 1908, and thereafter, the Company was a private company within the meaning of the various Companies Acts under which it was constituted. It was to remain so, until the end of its existence.

Reflecting on the earlier paragraphs it will be observed that Gordon Bagnall's estate appears to have valued his shares in the Company at considerably less than the face value. It may be that at probate, cognisance was taken of the cash he had already received from the Company, but even so he still held shares in the Company at a face value greater than his estate suggests and doubtless we shall never know the full story behind this. From the forgoing it will also be seen that the late WG Bagnall's beneficiaries, which according to his will divided his estate one half to his wife, and the other half split in to five parts, two parts to each to his sons and one part to his daughter, got no

John Gifford Gifford, a picture taken much later in his life, but the only portrait we have.

cash out of the Company at this stage. The bulk of the rest of his estate was bound up in shares of John Bagnall & Sons Limited, of which he was still a director at the time of his death, and his executors sold the 1,304 shares in that Company on 20 February 1908. This sale raised £912 16/- (£912 80p) of which £500 plus interest was owing by the late WG Bagnall to his friend and shooting partner Sir Richard Powell Cooper of Chirk Castle (see Chapter One); presumably therefore, at some stage Cooper had loaned Bagnall the cash. By an agreement dated 22 February 1908, Gordon Bagnall's three children forwent their rightful share of the residual in accordance with their late father's will, in favour of their mother. Moreover, Bagnall did not own the family home at Castle Hill House, it was in fact leased and laterly paid for by the Company. In the Company accounts from 1897 onwards there were regular monthly payments of between £16 and £20 in respect of the property. As a result and soon after the death, the family moved to much smaller accommodation, renting a house at nearby Brocton, around two miles south-east of the town.

The financial settlements following the death of Gordon Bagnall obviously ranked badly with his family, especially his wife Jessie, and there was, and remains in the family to this day, a feeling that the Giffords dealt the Bagnall family a poor hand. However, there is evidence that Gordon Bagnall had been living beyond his means. His hobbies and interests were expensive ones, especially his game shooting and the company he kept when involved in these activities would have had expensive tastes. The holidays he and his wife took latterly, albeit on the recommendation of his doctors and due to his health, would have been expensive too. There were not many people in those times who took passage by steam ship in first class accommodation to such far away places as they did. There is also a suggestion that he had a liking for the turf and lost significant sums of money. Geoffrey Cookson, the youngest of Jessie Bagnall's step-brothers who, it will be remembered, served an apprenticeship in the works, recalled in later years when interviewed that Gordon Bagnall's gambling habits, whilst well known around the works, were unknown to the family! John Gifford would of course, have been well aware of this, as well as the other issues connected with the cash payments and the house ownership. It may be he decided to turn a blind-eye to these activities, especially during the period when Gordon Bagnall was incapacitated, and in deference to his cousin Jessie. There does not appear to be any evidence that the business was not conducted in anything other than with the utmost integrity in the period that Bagnall himself was indisposed; there is no suggestion of a deliberate down-turn in an attempt to make a Gifford 'take-over' easier. It is a fact that there were rather less orders than had been the average for a few years prior to Bagnall's death, but this could have been the result of a number of reasons, not least the lack of his charismatic promotion of the Company and salesmanship.

Castle Hill House would have been expensive to run, with a number of servants and a governess for the children - a lady named Hocky. The family moving to much smaller premises at nearby Brocton, and so soon after Gordon Bagnall's death, is indicative of a serious shortage of cash. We saw earlier how Jessie Bagnall became largely dependent on her children, and the basis of being granted a war pension on the death of her youngest son, was that she was dependent on him. Jessie Bagnall lived to a ripe old age at Church Stretton where she became very well known and a keen golfer; like her husband and daughter she was an enthusiastic gardener too. We saw earlier how in her younger days she had been an accomplished ice skater, and in 1895 won the 'Star' of the National Skating Association; unfortunately after breaking a hip in 1925, which was not properly re-set, an end was put to this type of activity and she walked with a limp, and with the aid of a stick for the rest of her life. Although Richard Gordon Bagnall left £2,115 to his mother in his will, the bulk of its nominal value was in shares of the Merlimau Rubber Company Limited, the Teluk Anson Rubber Company and the Malakoff Rubber Company, which were all pretty worthless at the time and do not seem to have generated any cash in her lifetime. Jessie Bagnall died at Church Stretton on 29 November 1947, and as mentioned earlier, she lies with her husband who predeceased her by no less than 40 years, in the churchyard at St Mary's Castle Church in Stafford.

We do not know what relationship as fellow directors John Gifford and Richard Gordon Bagnall enjoyed, but they were difficult years and whilst a dividend of 5% was declared in the years 1908 to 1911, in fact trading losses had been made and in those years the average loss was £1,716. Whatever the circumstances, Richard Gordon Bagnall seems to have decided in late 1910, or perhaps early the following year, that his future probably lay elsewhere and we saw in Chapter One, how in 1911 he went to work in Malaya on the recommendation of his father's cousin, Arthur Henry Bagnall. This seems to have precipitated the family disposing of their remaining shares in the Company, which were sold to John Gifford, the transfer taking place on 4 May 1911; on the same day Richard Gordon Bagnall resigned as a director. With the sole exception of James Keay, who still held 10 shares, the entire share capital in the Company was now in the hands of the Giffords. We do not know at this distance in time, and there does not appear to be any way of knowing, what price Gifford paid for the remaining Bagnall family shares. In view of the trading losses the Company had been making he would have been in a good position to negotiate a price below par, and because of the change in the articles mentioned earlier, without John Gifford's permission, the family could only sell their shares to him. No more could they change the articles without his agreement! It may be it was this issue that left the family so bitter, rather than the earlier financial arrangements when Gordon Bagnall died which were much more straight-forward - again it is unlikely we shall never know the exact circumstances.

At an EGM of the Company held on 18 April 1911, it was again agreed to alter the articles of association, and this was confirmed at a second meeting held on 4 May 1911 when Richard Gordon Bagnall resigned.

Thereafter, the articles allowed the Company to have only one director provided it was John Gifford Gifford and not less than two otherwise. To all intents and purposes, the Company now belonged to John Gifford, and the involvement of the Bagnall family ceased; he was in fact the sole director until 1921.

Before leaving WG Bagnall himself, it is perhaps opportune to discuss in a little more detail the firm's catalogues. Mention has already been made of the publicity the firm generated, and this was in no small means due to the lavish catalogues issued from time to time, which were models of their kind. We saw earlier

This is the cover of the catalogue dated May 1888 and numbered 10; as far as is known it is the only edition that did not have a red cover. It would also appear unlikely that seven editions had been issued between No 2B of 1878, the highest numbered issue known to exist previous to this one, and 1888. One wonders if at some point the numerical sequence jumped to No 10, maybe in an effort to impress customers - a not unknown ruse of manufacturers!

that the first one was issued in August 1876; quite a lavish 37 page affair for what was then, but a very small company, but it introduced the familiar maroon cover that was to be the hallmark of almost all further issues over the next 40 years. The earlier catalogues prior to number 17 covered all the Company's products, but with the issue of numbers 18 and 19 of about 1911, locomotives were given separate coverage. Locomotives appeared in No 18, with all the other products which by this date mainly consisted of other railway equipment, appearing in number 19. There was also a combined edition of numbers 18 and 19 bound together. Over the years the catalogues varied in size, for example number one measured 6x9¼in in portrait format, whilst number 10 was 10x8in in landscape format, and in most cases the maroon cover remained, the later issues being hard bound with beautiful embossed covers. There were odd editions that took an A or B suffix, along with some small abridged 'pocket' versions that were not numbered at all, and others in foreign languages, in particular Spanish and Portuguese. These sometimes took the same number as their English equivalents in the numerical series, but often the issue

dates were different by a month or so. For example catalogue number 16 was dated June 1905 in its English version, but October the same year for the Spanish and Portuguese edition. Numbers 18 and 19 were the last of the traditional issues and post-war the Company satisfied itself with a beige covered soft back version of number 18. This one appears to have been made up of pages that had already been printed, and doubtless were already on hand. By cleverly substituting some new pages illustrating more recent locomotive for others showing some rather dubious artists impressions of locomotives that in a number of cases had not been built, the original pagination was retained. Thereafter, small pamphlets were the order of the day, except for one quite lavish affair produced much later in 1949.

Gordon Bagnall was extremely proud of his catalogues, and was largely responsible for their design and compilation, personally writing a Foreword in all cases. They are indicative of his commitment to his customers and his pride in the reputation of the firm and its products. Gordon Bagnall made it his business to make personal contact with almost all his customers and he conducted long and cordial correspondence

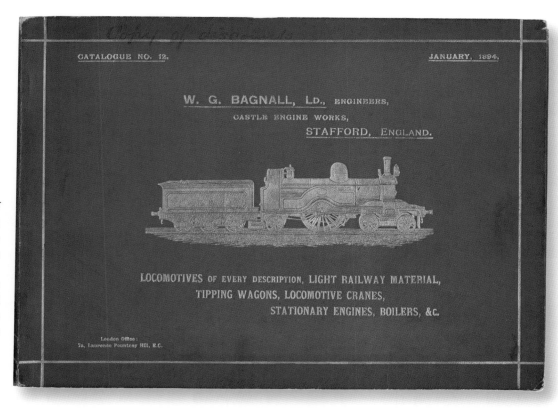

The cover of Catalogue No 12 dated January 1894, is in the familiar red. Notice it shows an embossed engraving of the 18in gauge Stirling Single, manufacturer's number 1425.

with them, some of which has survived. Similarly the various agents he had cultivated around the world, of which there was an impressive portfolio. Undoubtedly the time and expense Gordon Bagnall personally put into the production of the catalogues and other advertising material, and the relationships he built up with customers and agents, was to a considerable extent responsible for the Company being in the forefront of light railway engineering in this country at the time of his death. It is perhaps worth exploring briefly, the expense the Company went to in its publicity. In the years 1894 and 1895, £273 was invoiced by a local printer who was often involved, J & C Mort & Company of Stafford, for the production of catalogues - this Company also published *The Staffordshire Advertiser*. Between 1894 and 1905 no less than £1,460 was spent on having engraved printing blocks made of the products for use in the catalogues and other sales literature. Between 1900 and 1907 the average spend on advertising, excluding the catalogues and printing blocks, was £400.

Following the death of Gordon Bagnall and once the issues regarding the shareholding had been resolved, the business continued to expand, new customers placing orders along with many of the existing ones coming back time and time again. John Gifford took on the mantle of senior salesman and in 1910 Keith F

Pearson joined the Company as its representative based in London; we will cover this appointment in more detail in a later Chapter. An example of a long standing customer frequently placing orders was Henry Rogers Sons & Company Limited, the Wolverhampton based agents mentioned briefly in Chapter Two and largely acting for sugar estates in Brazil. Rogers was one of the very early customers of Bagnall and whilst this may have been initiated through a family connection with the Twentyman family, who were principals in the Rogers Company during much of its existence, it could certainly have been fostered by the family relationship in later years. Gordon Bagnall's father's eldest brother John (1794-1840), by his second marriage to Mary Anne Robbins, had a daughter Jane; born in 1836 she was both the second child and the second daughter. Jane Bagnall married Henry Ward of Rodbaston Hall near Penkridge at Monmouth in 1855, and one of their daughters, Evelyn Mabel Ward, married Llewlyn Howell Twentyman.

Alfred Charles Twentyman JP, for many years the chairman of the Rogers Company, was born in Clapham (then considered part of Surrey) in 1833, and in 1857 married Mary Anne, the daughter of Henry Rogers, and by her had two daughters; unfortunately his wife died at childbirth in 1860. He married secondly Mattie Louisa Howell of Welshpool and they had three sons, Llewlyn

This is one of the small engines supplied to the Wolverhampton agents, Henry Rogers Sons & Company; notice it has a Rogers plate on the cab-side with the Rogers number 2196. The Bagnall number was 1843, and the building date 1907. The track gauge was 1ft 11⁵/₈in and the cylinder size 4½x7½in; notice too, the 0-4-2 wheel arrangement and the wood fuel rank on the saddle tank. Like all Rogers engines it would have been destined for a sugar plantation in the Pernambuco Province of Brazil.

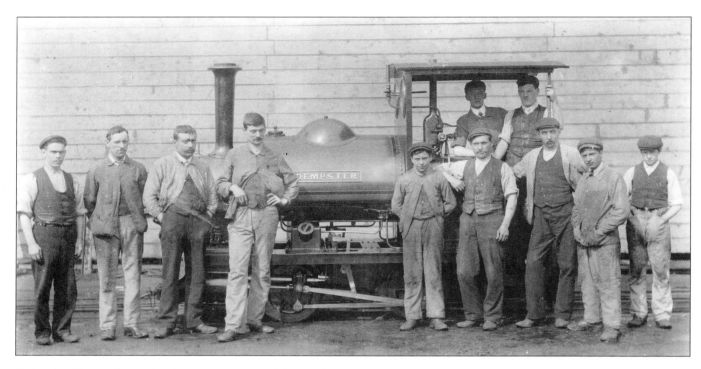

DEMPSTER, number 1858 of 1907, was a special design of 0-4-0 with 4½x10in cylinders - a more sturdy looking engine than the 'standard' type and in this case fitted with a conventional locomotive type boiler, but still employing Bagnall-Price valve gear. Built for the Glasgow agents Dempster Moore & Company and shipped to Yokohama in Japan, where at some stage it appears to have been owned by Sato & Company. Bagnall did occasionally have official photographs taken with a member of staff standing alongside, presumably to give an idea of size; however, it was unusual to include so many! Presumably this is the team who built the engine and the tall gentleman fourth from the left is Charles Pearson, with what may be his father, John Pearson, third from the right. If it is John he could have been the Foreman Blacksmith at the time. Unfortunately none of the other fellows are identified, but they seem to include at least three apprentices. (Collection Stuart Pitchford Pearson)

SUCCESS, number 1873 of 1907, was the second of the 14 two-foot gauge locomotives built for the South African sugar estate of the Tongaat Sugar Company in Natal. Apart from the first engine which had a 2-4-0 wheel arrangement, all the subsequent ones were 4-4-0s like this one, and they all had circular firebox boilers and Bagnall-Price valve gear. However, there were alterations to the design over the years, including a change to outside frames and a shorter coupled wheelbase.

Howell (1867-1932) who at noted above married Evelyn Mabel Ward, Harold Edward (1869-1946) and Alan Howell (1871-?); all of whom entered the service of the Henry Rogers Company. The couple also had two daughters. On the death of Alfred Charles Twentyman in 1908, the chairmanship of the Rogers company passed to his eldest son Llewlyn, and on his death in 1932 to his brother Harold. In 1946 on Harold's death, his son J Anthony Twentymen become chairman. The Twentyman family was also known to the Keay family, who we met earlier in connection with the original shareholding in WG Bagnall Limited, and when Harold Edward Twentyman applied for membership of the Institution of Mechanical Engineers in September 1905, his application was seconded by

Brazil, and there was a steady trickle of other light railway rolling stock and equipment supplied too. After a gap of some 30 years, two more locomotives were supplied as late as 1950.

Another Twentyman, Leonard, was the Godfather of Ursula Mary (Jill) Alsop, a grand-daughter of WG Bagnall by his daughter Jessica Gordon Bagnall and Maurice Lingard Alsop; we met Jill in Chapter One. She met her husband the late David Hutchinson Smith (later Group Captain RAF) via the Twentyman's as the Hutchinson Smiths were neighbours at Codsall. The Twentyman family lived at Castlecroft, just south of Tettenhall and some two miles west of Wolverhampton, as well as at Codsall, which is about two miles north of Tettenhall. The Wards seat was Rodbaston Hall, a

This illustration shows one of the neat and tidy six-wheel side tanks which were popular for a variety of customers. This one is number 1825 of 1906, new to Hurst Nelson & Company of Motherwell, presumably at the time supplying equipment to the British Columbia Sugar Refining Company of Tumansa in Fiji, because that is where it was eventually sent. However, it was first despatched from Stafford to Motherwell, albeit packed for shipment. This picture is a good illustration of how the use of a circular firebox allowed the weight of the boiler to be evenly distributed as there was no firebox to protrude below the frames. Several of the engines supplied to Mitrovich Brothers for use in Chile which are mentioned in the text were of this basic design, and like this one for 2ft 6in gauge.

James Keay, brother of Anne. Harold Twentyman had joined the firm of Henry Rogers in 1888 as a junior draughtsman, and prior to becoming its chairman on the death of his brother, was heavily involved with its engineering activities. Between 1884 and 1910, Rogers ordered 14 locomotives from the Castle Engine Works, all for use on sugar plantations in Pernambuco Province

couple of miles south of Penkridge and only about eight miles south of Stafford. Part of the Rodbaston estate embraced the reservoirs at Gailey - known as Calf Heath - and alongside the A5, a stretch formerly part of the Roman Watling Street. These reservoirs collect water from the high ground of Cannock Chase and were built to feed the summit section of the Staffordshire &

Worcestershire Canal. This waterway opened throughout it's 46 miles route from a junction with the Trent & Mersey at Great Heywood, which is just south of Stafford, and the River Severn at Stourport in May 1772. It later became a significant feeder of water to the Birmingham Canal network and the water rights from the reservoirs helped make the Ward family a rich one. Henry Ward DL JP (1828-1906), was High Sheriff of Staffordshire in 1872, and for many years until he died a director of the London & North Western Railway (LNWR). Worth a brief mention is the fact that after his death, the vacant seat on the LNWR board was taken by Gilbert Claughton, who we met in Chapter One. Henry Ward's son Herbert Henry Ward JP, who was born in 1857, and a brother of Evelyn Mabel, was a volunteer in the 3rd Battalion of the North Staffordshire Regiment, a major from 1891 and in this capacity would have been well known to Gordon Bagnall.

The Company did good business in the South American markets, and another good customer was the Liverpool based agents Mitrovich Brothers, with offices in Chile at both Antofagasta and Iquique, acting for various nitrate companies in that country. Between 1901 and 1924 31 locomotives were supplied via this Company, mostly of 2ft 6in gauge, but some of two-foot and metre-gauge, and varying in size from small four coupled saddle tanks with 5in cylinders, to much larger six wheel side tanks with 13in cylinders. Significant quantities of rolling stock and other light railway material was also supplied, as Mitrovich Brothers sometimes acted as consulting engineers to the nitrate companies, superintending the construction of processing plant and associated railways. It was through this connection that Arthur Hewitt Gilling, who from January 1900 until 1908 was an engineer and later the chief engineer with Mitrovich Brothers, came to join

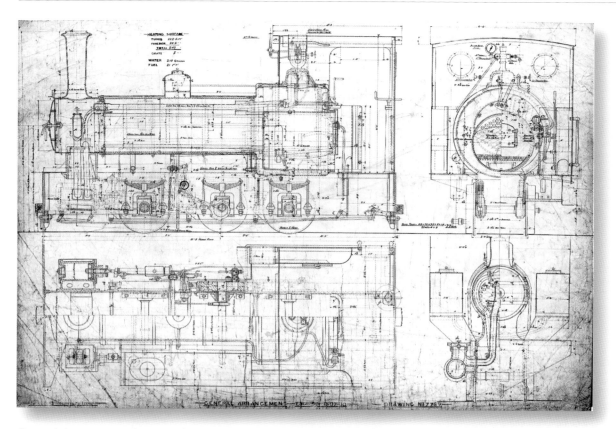

General Arrangement drawing of manufacturer's numbers 1807 to 1810 of 1906; very similar to the engine in the previous illustration. These particular engines were among the 2ft 6in gauge 0-6-0 side tanks built for Mitrovich Brothers, and shipped to Antofagasta in Chile. The drawing is worthy of study as it also illustrates a number of characteristics common to several of the narrow-gauge locomotives built in the period covered by this Chapter. Notice in particular the circular firebox boiler and Bagnall-Price valve gear; compare with the drawing of number 1797 DENNIS on page 211.

WG Bagnall Limited in 1908 as general manager. We met Gilling earlier, when he was a draughtsman with the Electrical Construction Company in Wolverhampton, in connection with the City of South London Railway locomotive jointly built with Bagnall.

The position of general manager at Stafford was a new one, considered necessary as the firm expanded its activities, and with John Gifford not wanting to take on quite the same role and workload that Gordon Bagnall had. By this time WS Edwards was firmly established and gaining a reputation in the drawing office, whilst Sam Price would have been fully occupied in works production and day-to-day management. John Gifford therefore, needed help at a senior level with the more general company administration and marketing. Gilling was born on 13 December 1873 in Liverpool, where he attended Crosby High School and later had his technical education at the Bootle & Liverpool School of Science. In 1890 he joined the Liverpool engineers David Rolls & Sons, where, after serving his apprenticeship he was employed as a draughtsman. In 1896 he left to join The Electrical Construction Company of Wolverhampton where as a draughtsman he may, as related earlier, have been involved with some of the design work for the City & South London Railway electric locomotive. On leaving Mitrovich Brothers Gilling moved briefly to Morris & Bastert Limited of Loughborough, where he had been appointed assistant general manager, but after only 12 months took up the position at Stafford. John Gifford would have been instrumental is securing this appointment, and may well have been impressed with Gilling following his involvement in the locomotives and other railway equipment the Company had supplied to Mitrovich Brothers. Arthur Gilling was elected an associate member of the Institution of Mechanical Engineers on 13 March 1900, and he became a full member on 18 March 1904. Having spent a lot of his previous career in Chile, superintending the erection of plant and railways in connection with nitrate mining and soda manufacturing plants, Gilling spoke fluent Spanish and Portuguese. This was a great asset to the Company at a time when the market in Spanish and Portuguese speaking countries was growing.

We must now move on and explore some of the locomotives and other products built in the period covered by this Chapter. Another good customer was the Spanish agent Adolfo T Simpson of Bilbao, who ordered 11 locomotives as well as rolling stock and other light railway material between 1906 and 1924; all for use by various mining companies in Northern Spain. The London based L Mitchell & Company acted for sugar estates on the Indian Ocean island of Mauritius, and was another good customer. Between 1902 and 1938, Mitchell ordered 10 locomotives for use in Mauritius and once again there were orders for rolling stock and other light railway material too. Orders for locomotives to be used on the Indian sub-continent increasingly became a feature in the period covered by this Chapter. The first order for one of the Indian main line railway companies was in 1906, two metre-gauge 0-4-0 saddle tanks, manufacturer's numbers 1830 and 1831, for the Bengal & North Western Railway. These two were chunky looking machines with 12¼x18in cylinders, based on an earlier design of the Glasgow based Neilson & Company, later Neilson Reid & Company Limited, and from 1903 a constituent of the North British Locomotive Company Limited. Despatched in August 1907 they were specifically designed for shunting vehicles on and off the river ferries that crossed the Ganges at various points in East Bengal. This was a job they seem to have performed well, as many years later, in 1936 in fact, a repeat order for two more was received, numbers 2461 and 2462 being supplied at that time and identical in almost every respect.

Futher locomotives built to a track gauge wider than 4ft 8½in also date from this time in the Company's history, as mentioned in the last Chapter, a series eventually consisting of six 14x20in cylinder 5ft 6in gauge 0-4-0 saddle tanks, based on the standard-gauge industrial shunting locomotive design for use in this country. These four were supplied between 1907 and 1921 for the Madras Port Trust in India, for shunting on the docks at Madras. Broad-gauge locomotives were never a significant element of works production, but there was a sprinkling of orders over the years for India and Ceylon.

Two more locomotives for the Indian main-line railways were ordered in 1909, manufacturer's numbers 1903-4, metre-gauge 4-4-0 side tanks with 11x18in cylinders and 3ft 6½in coupled wheels. This was an unusual design for the Indian railways, in this case for the Madras & Southern Mahratta Railway where they carried the running numbers 204 and 205; they cost £1,455 each. Despatched in November 1909, some years later they were converted to tender engines in an effort to reduce the axle-loading on the lightly laid lines where they were used. Several of the metre-gauge Indian railways became good customers for the Company over the succeeding years, including this one. Another interesting order in 1909 was for three small 0-4-0 side tank locomotives with 5x7½in cylinders and an unusual track gauge of 1ft 7¹¹/₁₆in, which in metric equates to 500mm. They were unusual in having outside fames due to the narrow track gauge and a conventional firebox boiler rather then the more common circular pattern, although Bagnall-Price valve gear was used. The customer was the Central Uruguay Eastern Extension Railway, a British owned company with a concession from the Uruguayan Government to build railways. Dismantled and shipped between April and June 1909, the manufacturer's numbers were 1896 to 1898, and a fourth one was ordered later, number 1913, despatched in December and unlike the earlier ones this one was shipped in one piece. These little engines which only cost £312 each are assumed to have been used on construction works in connection with both completing the Eastern Extension Railway as originally contemplated, along with a branch line that was projected some time later. The original Eastern Extension Railway dates from 1 September 1891, when 128 miles of line were opened, northeast from

Montevideo and running from Toledo to Nico Perez. There were however, delays in finishing the line onwards to the Brazilian frontier at Artigas, and further agreements were entered into with the Uruguayan Government dated 20 April 1906 and 8 January 1909. By these agreements it was intended to both complete the main-line and build a 64 mile branch from Nico Perez to Treinta-y-Tres and whilst the branch was completed and opened on 1 October 1911, the main-line only proceeded another 118 miles further northeast to Melo. This section opened on 1 August 1909, but the line never went any further and stopped some 36 miles short of its intended terminus at Artigas.

In October 1910 three 2ft 6in gauge 0-6-0 side tanks with 9x14in cylinders were ordered by Dodwell & Company Limited from a London address - manufacturer's numbers 1930 to 1932. They carried plates on the cab sides with the following inscription: 'LJ Healing & Co Ltd Contractors London, Yokohama, Kobe, Tokio'; shipping instructions were for despatch to Takao (note the differing spellings for Tokyo) and they were despatched in December for the first one and February the following year for the other two. Whilst it seems certain that these locomotives were shipped to Tokyo, research by knowledgeable Japanese enthusiasts has failed to reveal where they might have worked in that country. There is however, a suggestion that they may have worked in Formosa (Taiwan), perhaps being transhipped there from Japan. They were neat and quite handsome locomotives with very clean lines, and

The London agents John Birch & Company Limited, ordered several locomotives over the years. This one is a side-tank version of the 7x12in cylinder standard design with a circular firebox boiler and Bagnall-Price valve gear, but in this case with a more substantial cab and foot-framing. Number 1854 of 1909 it was sent to Alexander Dock in Liverpool on 7 January 1909, for shipment to Manilla. There is circumstantial evidence to suggest that this 2ft 6in gauge locomotive worked for the Meiji Sugar Refining Company on the island of Formosa (Taiwan), and John Birch is an agent known to have acted for far eastern customers.

One of the four specially designed 0-4-0 side tanks for use on the construction of the Central Uruguay Eastern Extension Railway. These locomotives had locomotive type boilers and in view of the narrow-gauge of 1ft 7^{11}/$_{16}$in (500 m/m), outside frames. The first three, numbers 1896 to 1898, were actually ordered in two separate orders, despite being consecutively numbered, the first order in February 1909 was for two locomotives, and the second order in April covered the third. The fourth locomotives was not ordered until October 1909, number 1913. The one shown here in number 1898. Notice the small plate above the expansion link of the valve gear; this reads - Bagnall-Price Patent Valve Gear. Also the initials C.U.E.E.R. and the date 1909, around the more normal design of manufacturer's plate.

this design of six coupled side tank with outside cylinders, a locomotive type boiler and Bagnall-Price valve gear, built to various track gauges and with cylinders of between 8 and 10in diameter, was quite a popular one at this period.

A slight variation on the 0-6-0 side tank was an 0-4-2 version, with outside frames and Bagnall-Price valve gear. Two two-foot gauge examples were built for the Leicestershire based quarry company, the Cliffe Hill Granite Company Limited, owners of quarries at Markfield. The first, manufacturer's number 1943 named MARY, was delivered in July 1911, and the second, number 2034 JACK, in 1915. Cylinders were 8x12in, driving wheel diameter 2ft 0½in, and the weight in working order 12 tons 5 cwt. The painting instructions simply stated: 'as Midland Railway locomotives'; so presumably they were in a shade of

maroon - fully lined-out they would and have looked the proverbial picture. MARY incidentally, came back to Stafford in mid 1942 for boiler repairs, returning to Cliffe Hill in September. Sydney Edwards frequently used to tell his people that this design was one the handsomest designs the Company built and one of the most useful for use on narrow-gauge lines where short distances had to be travelled, as opposed to pure shunting. He was of course, the chief draughtsman when the design work was undertaken. The Cliffe Hill Granite Company was a good customer of Bagnall, having eight locomotives over the years, as well as wagons and track work components. Indeed, one of the locomotives eventually came back to the Castle Engine Works for preservation, but that is jumping ahead of our story.

Complementing these side tank designs was a saddle

JC GRAY, number 1863 of 1907 is an example of the 'standard' circular firebox narrow-gauge locomotives, but in this case with a non-standard cylinder size of 6½x10in; nevertheless, it shows well the salient characteristics of the design. Despatched in November this engine was for use on the two-foot gauge system of the North Wales Quarries Limited at Bethesda. By 1920 the engine was with the contractor Henry Boot and working on a housing estate in West Bromwich, but it finished its life at the Friars Wash Sand & Gravel pits at St Albans. Notice the seemingly excessive supply of coal, in view of the small amount of running the engine would do prior to delivery! This was probably done so that the photograph could be used in catalogues, as indeed it was.

MARY, number 1943 of 1911, was the first of two of these 0-4-2 side tanks supplied to the Cliffe Hill Granite Company of Markfield in Leicestershire. Notice the cross-head driven water feed pump and lack of cab, although full cabs were later fitted to both locomotives at Cliffe Hill. The wooden board behind the locomotive was situated just outside the Erecting Shop, specifically for use as a backcloth for the official photographs. MARY lasted until the two-foot gauge system at Cliffe Hill was replaced by road transport in 1948, although along with most of the other locomotives it was not scrapped until 1957.

Manufacturer's number 1874 was one of three 3ft 6in gauge 0-4-0 saddle tanks with 10x15in cylinders and Bagnall-Price valve gear, ordered by the Crown Agents for the Colonies and sent to the Gold Coast. This one was supplied in 1908 and the others in 1906 and 1911, all for use at Accra Harbour; two of them later migrated to the Gold Coast Government Railways. Four similar locomotives, also ordered by the Crown Agents, were for use at Lagos Harbour in Nigeria, in their case between 1907 and 1911. Notice the double cab roof to promote a circulation of air, a popular feature on locomotives intended to work in hot climates.

PIONEER, number 1980 of 1913, was a type of locomotive popular with East-Midlands ironstone quarries. This was one of two supplied to the Eastwell quarries of the Eastwell Iron Ore Company Limited. Cylinders were 13x18in making this a powerful locomotive for a track gauge of three-foot. Notice the use of Bagnall-Price valve gear and that the engine is loaded on a LNWR well-wagon ready for delivery.

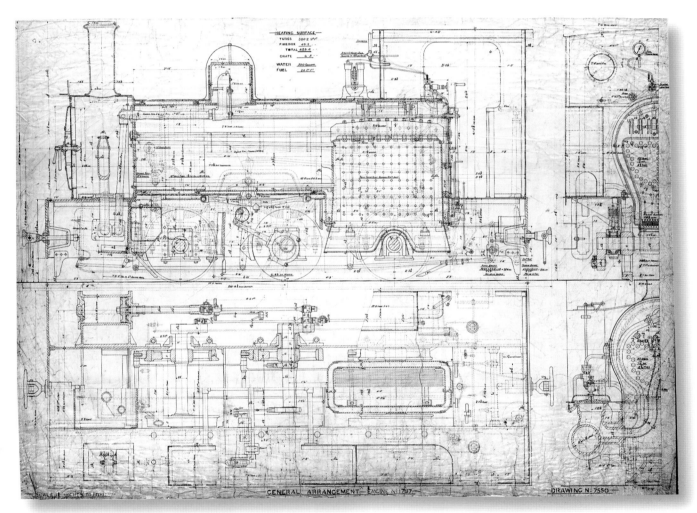

General Arrangement drawing of manufacturer's number 1797 of 1906. DENNIS was for the Snailbeach District Railway in Shropshire, a 2ft 4in gauge line serving lead and granite quarries in the foothills of the Stiperstones. This locomotives is quite typical of several other six-coupled side tank locomotives built around the period covered by this Chapter, in this case fitted with a locomotives type boiler and Bagnall-Price valve gear. Compare it with the circular firebox six-coupled side tank shown on the drawing on page 206.

This is one of the two metre-gauge four-wheel overhead wire electric locomotives supplied in 1910, in conjunction with another Stafford based company Siemens Brothers, for the Mysore Gold Mines in India. This picture shows a completed locomotive at the Castle Engine Works, confirming that the locomotives were fully assembled there, although they may have gone to the Siemens works for testing before delivery.

tank version which could also be supplied as either an 0-6-0 or and 0-4-2. Three of the six coupled version were delivered between September and December 1912, ordered by the Executors of P Phipps for use by the Hunsbury Iron Company at Hunsbury ironstone quarries in Northamptonshire. Manufacturer's numbers 1955 to 1957, the track gauge was an unusual 3ft 8in, the cylinders were 13x18in and the wheel diameter 2ft 9¼in, making them quite powerful machines - the tractive effort at 85% of the 150psi working pressure was 11,577lb. Bagnall-Price valve gear was fitted and they cost £890 each. Unfortunately this trio did not have very long working lives as the quarries at Hunsbury closed in 1921. Doubtless because of the unusual track gauge no further use was found for them which is nevertheless surprising, as they would appear to have been in reasonable condition and the cost of altering them to a different gauge would not have been excessive. In 1937, after lying out of use, one of them moved to the nearby Finedon Quarries - this was number 1956 - but it was never used there. This one lasted until 1947 when it was scrapped; its sisters had already succumbed to the war time scrap drive in

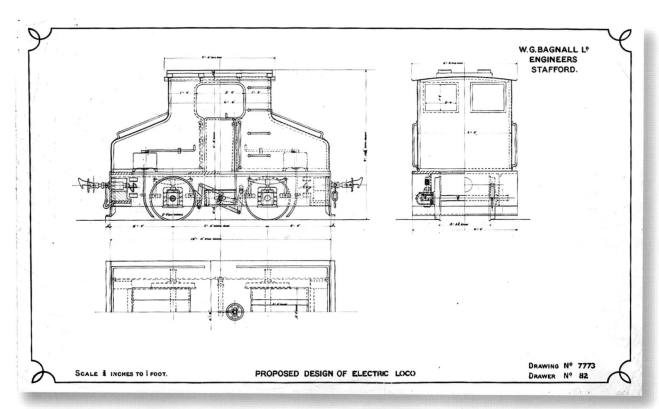

W.G.BAGNALL L⁰
ENGINEERS
STAFFORD.

SCALE ¾ INCHES TO 1 FOOT.   PROPOSED DESIGN OF ELECTRIC LOCO

DRAWING N⁰ 7773
DRAWER N⁰ 82

Outline drawing of the Mysore Gold Mines electric locomotives.

1940. There were a number of similar locomotives of this basic design and built around this period, including others for the east midlands ironstone quarries.

Between 1904 and 1910, as sub-contractors to established firms of electrical engineers, 10 sets of mechanical parts were constructed for electric locomotives, and these were the first non-steam locomotives built since the two for the City & South London Railway back in 1897. In conjunction with the Stafford based Siemens Brothers Dynamo Works Limited, in 1910 two neat and tidy steeple-cab metre-gauge four-wheel locomotives equipped for overhead power collection, were supplied for use at the Mysore Gold Mines in India. These two were completely erected at the Castle Engine Works, but may have then been moved to the nearby Siemens works for testing. In 1907 and 1908 three four-wheel locomotives, also with

overhead power collection, were built in conjunction with the Trafford Park, Manchester based British Westinghouse Electrical Manufacturing Company Limited, in this case standard-gauge and with an extremely rudimentary body - in fact almost no body at all! Final erection was at Stafford, but they were despatched to Trafford Park, presumably for testing, and prior to delivery to the Great Cobar Copper Mines in New South Wales, Australia. The remains of one of these locomotives survives to this day. Converted to a brake van it was used until the mid 1960s at the Hebburn Colliery in the South Maitland coalfield, and has since been returned to Cobar where it is located in the museum.

Also supplied in 1907, and again in conjunction with Westinghouse, were three substantial Bo-Bo metre-gauge locomotives, in this case for the Thameshaven

Picture taken in about 1912 at the Australian Great Cobar Copper Mines in New South Wales, illustrating one of the three standard-gauge four-wheel electric locomotives constructed in conjunction with British Westinghouse. As built the locomotives had no more protection for the crew than a roof supported by six pillars, but notice how the locals have improvised a somewhat better arrangement; the overhead line supplied current at 250 volts DC. Purchase of the locomotives along with electrification of the railway system at the mines, was part of an extensive expansion programmes by an English company which had acquired the undertaking in 1905. However, the operations seem to have been beset by all sorts of problems and despite a revival during the period of the First World War, the whole lot closed down in 1920. Two of the locomotives were acquired by the Hebburn Colliery in the South Maitland coalfield, with aspirations to electrify part of the railway system there. In the event this did not take place and as outlined in the text, the remains of one of them survives to this day. Converted to a brake van after many years use, it is now at the Cobar Regional Museum, housed in the former office building of Great Cobar Company. (Collection John Shoebridge)

Bann (Thamshavnbanen), a Norwegian private railway running 14½ miles inland from Thameshaven, which is near Trondheim, to Lokken. This was primarily an iron ore carrying railway, although a passenger service was also operated. Equipped with four 40 horsepower motors the overhead line power supply was 6.6 Kv 25 cycles, and this railway, of which these were the first locomotives, was one of the first single-phase alternating current electrified railways in the world. Hitherto, most electrified railways using alternating, as opposed to direct current, had a three-phase power supply. Once again final erection appears to have been at Stafford, but the locomotives almost certainly went to Trafford Park for testing, and perhaps the installation of some of the electrical equipment. One of these locomotives - No 2, they were numbered 1 to 3 - is preserved at Trondheim.

There was also an interesting small 0-4-0 with jackshaft and rod drive, the jackshaft being driven by a single motor situated between the axles. This one was built in 1907 for the 2ft 6in gauge lines of the Scottish Oakbank Oil Company at Winchburgh in Lothian, again in conjunction with British Westinghouse. Final erection of this neat little machine which was equipped for overhead wire current collection, in this case at 500 volts DC, was at the Trafford Park works of Westinghouse. At Winchburgh it became No 3 in the fleet; the earlier locomotives were American and built by Baldwin. The Westinghouse locomotive lasted until the end of the railway system at Winchburgh in February 1961, after which it was scrapped. There were others too, Ellis & Ward Limited of Hadfield being another of the main contractors involved. All these sets of mechanical parts were allocated numbers in the 'general', as opposed to the 'engine' order books; hence they do not appear in the works list as such.

In 1912 the first internal combustion locomotives were built by the Company, three appearing before the

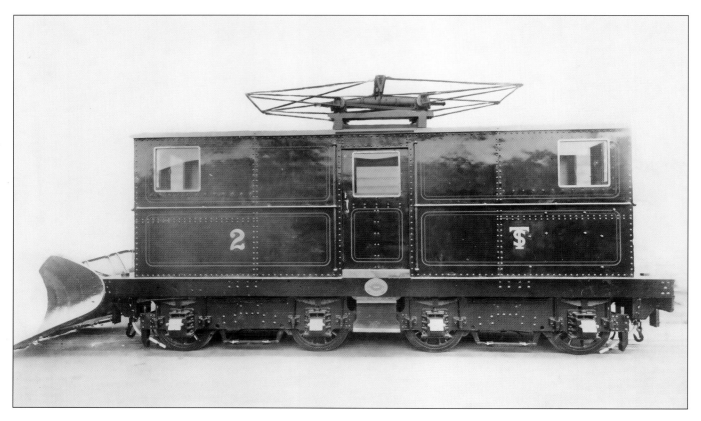

This is one of the three Bo-Bo overhead wire electric locomotives, the mechanical parts of which were built at Stafford for British Westinghouse, with eventual delivery to the metre-gauge Thameshaven Bann in Norway. Notice the snow plough and the combined Westinghouse and Bagnall manufacturer's plate situated under the cab door. This picture was taken at Stafford, and the locomotives went to Trafford Park for the electrical equipment to be fitted as well as testing prior to delivery.

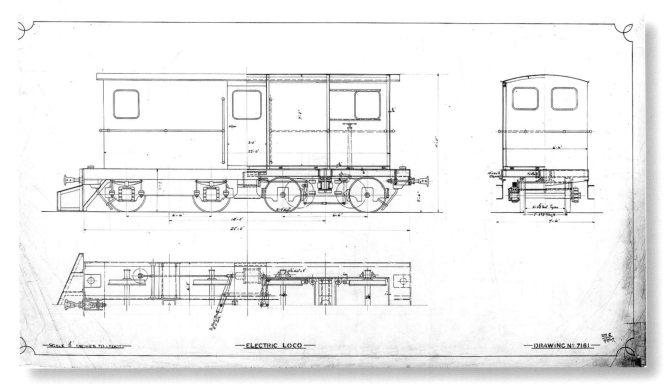

Outline diagram of the Norwegian Thameshaven Bann electric locomotives.

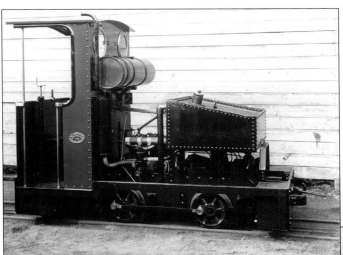

Two pictures of the first petrol locomotive built by the firm, two-foot gauge and designated P50 of 1912. One view shows the locomotive with the engine cowling removed to expose the engine, along with the large tank provided for the cooling water; there was no radiator as such. Notice the position of the transmission in front of the engine and under the tank, with the drive on the leading axle. The second illustration was taken to the rear of the workshops, and shows the locomotive on test with a string of Bagnall built side-tip wagons - this was land later occupied by workshop extensions. Notice the words painted on the wagons for publicity purposes. This locomotive went to Assam.

ESTELLA was P52 of 1912, a
slightly different design but of the
same power; the gauge was
1ft 11½in and via a Glasgow agent
it was sent to the Philippines.
Notice that unlike P50,
in this case the engine exhaust
via a conventional steam
locomotive chimney.

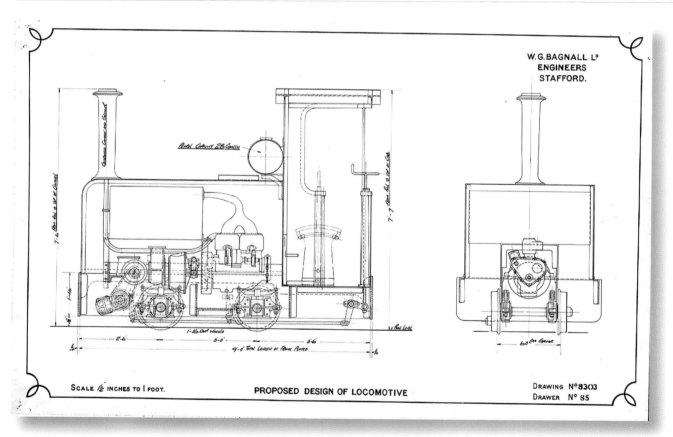

Outline drawing of P52; however, the locomotive as built differed slightly from this early proposal. Nevertheless it shows well the
arrangement of the engine, gearbox and chain drive together with the water cooling and fuel tanks.

outbreak of the war, two in 1912 and one the following year. They were all small four-wheel machines with petrol-paraffin engines and mechanical transmissions. For reasons now lost in the mists of time and like the mechanical parts for the electric locomotives, they were not given numbers in the 'engine' list, but in a new list with the prefix P - presumably for petrol - and starting at 50. Thus, the first one was numbered P50, a two-foot gauge 20 horsepower locomotive delivered in June 1912 for use at tea plantations in Assam - the customer was the Eastern Assam Company. This locomotive had a Coventry Simplex four-cylinder four-stroke engine and a two-speed gearbox giving road speeds of 3.1 and 8.2 mph, the drive from the gearbox was via roller chains to the leading axle and then conventional side-rods. Spares were supplied for this locomotive as late as 1930. The last of the trio, designated P52, was almost identical to P 50, but built to suit a 1ft 11½in track gauge; named ESTELLA, it was ordered by the Glasgow agents George Wilson & Company and despatched in August 1912 to a customer in the Philippine Islands. The second one was also for 1ft 11½in gauge, designated P51, but substantially bigger and fitted with a 40 horsepower Dorman four-cylinder four-stroke engine. Road speeds were 4 and 8 mph and in this case the drive was by a shaft from the two-speed gearbox to a worm drive reversing gearbox mounted on the trailing

axle, and thence side rods - there were no chains in the case of this locomotive. Unlike the earlier two, which had inside frames P51 had outside frames and fly cranks. Named MARIA, although supplied in June 1913 to a different Glasgow based agent than P52, it too, went to the Philippines, and the only subsequent knowledge we have is a spares order covering both P51 and P52; dated October 1914 this suggests that both locomotives worked at the same location. The second locomotive numerically was originally laid down to stock in March 1912, hence its despatch later than P52. As events turned out these were the only locomotives numbered in the P list, and when further petrol locomotives were built after the war, they were numbered in the main 'engine' list.

It is perhaps worth mentioning a few more unusual orders of the period we are covering in this Chapter, before moving on to discuss general company administration and people issues. For example, manufacturer's number 1917 of June 1910, a 2ft 6in gauge 0-4-0 side tank with 8½x12in cylinders and a boiler inclined forwards at 1 in 20, in the fashion of locomotives built for mountain rack-assisted railways. Named ZURIEL, it was specially designed for the Lunedale Whinstone Company, for use at its quarry at Middleton-in-Teesdale in North Yorkshire, where one presumes, it habitually had to work on an incline of

MARIA was P51, third of the petrol locomotives built before the First World War, and much larger than the other two. Notice the outside frames and cranks, also the traditional steam locomotive double cab roof for hot climates along with the acetylene head lamps and the method of blowing the whistle. When a cord was pulled from the cab, it lifted the whistle over the pipe and diverted part of the engine's exhaust! Like P52, this one was also 1ft 11½in gauge and was sent to the Philippines. Unfortunately, we do not know where either of them actually worked.

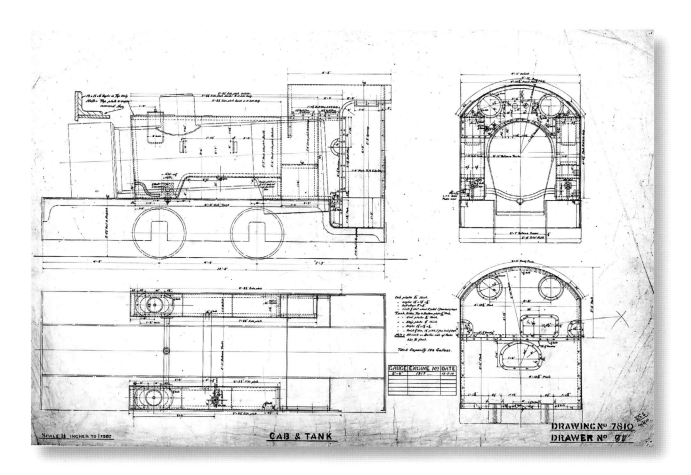

This is the Cab & Tank drawing for number 1917 of 1910, included to illustrate the boiler inclined at 1 in 20, as described in the text.

about 1 in 20. Manufacturer's number 1941 was another special design, in this case ordered by the United Alkali Company Limited, for use at mines at Huleva in Spain. This 2ft 6in gauge locomotive was built to clear a very restricted loading gauge, it was only 6ft 1¼in high and restricted in width to four feet, presumably for working in the confined trackside clearances of a mine. Resulting from these restrictions the 7½x12in cylinders were inside the frames, although the frames themselves were inside the wheels. However, the most remarkable aspect of the design was the use of a specially adapted version of the Bagnall-Price valve gear. Considerable redesign of the gear was necessary as space between the frames was somewhat cramped and as the only locomotive built to this design, it was the only time Bagnall-Price valve gear was used on an inside cylinder locomotive. The engine's name was TEJON, which translates in Spanish to the very apt Badger. Despatched in June 1915, a new boiler was

supplied in July 1927. Subsequently United Alkali ordered several other locomotives for use in connection with its mining operations in Spain, but they were of more conventional types. An interesting aspect of some of these locomotives is that they were supplied as a kit of parts to be assembled on location in Spain, with castings and forgings only rough machined.

Readers will recall that back in 1885 and 1886, among the early locomotives built by the Company were four 0-6-0 side tanks, the first locomotives for the West Clare Railway in Ireland. This railway came back to Bagnall in January 1908 following a competitive tender for another locomotive. However, before describing this order, it is opportune to explore the history of the shares in the West Clare Railway that the Company acquired in part payment for the earlier engines. Five hundred shares were received in part payment for the original engines, and assuming they were valued at their face value of £10, and as the total

W. G. BAGNALL, Ltd., Castle Engine Works, STAFFORD

TEJON - the name is Spanish for Badger - and quite apt in view of this engine's restricted dimensions. The only locomotive built to this special design it was for use in a mine in Southern Spain near Huelva, at Sotiel Coronada; it was also the only inside cylinder locomotive fitted with Bagnall-Price valve gear. Manufacturer's number 1941 of 1915. Perhaps surprising in view of its loading gauge, it had a conventional locomotive type boiler, and not the circular pattern.

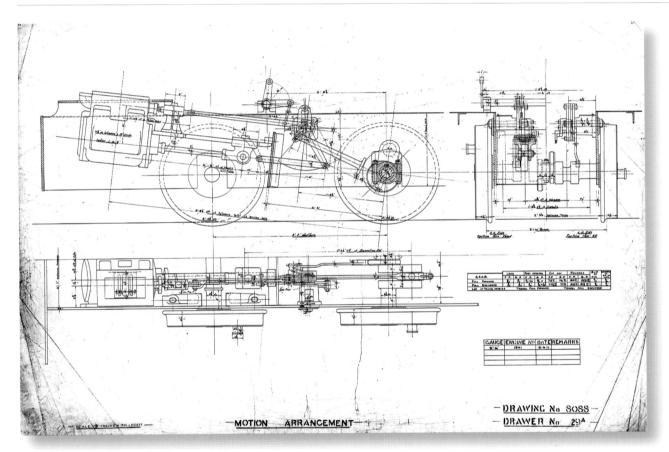

MOTION ARRANGEMENT

DRAWING No. 8058
DRAWER No. 29ᴬ

Motion Drawing of number 1941, showing the arrangement of Bagnall-Price valve gear fitted to this inside-cylinder locomotive.

cost of the locomotives amounted to £5,300, Bagnall only took £300 in cash for the transaction! Small dividends were paid in the period 1887 to 1891 - about £369 in total - and 400 shares were sold on 30 September 1890 at a loss of £179 5/- (£179 25p). On 11 December 1891 a further 99 were sold, and on this occasion a loss of £34 16/ 9d (£34 84p) was recorded. There does not seem to be any record of what happened to the odd share left, but doubtless the Company were glad to see the back of them! But such were the vagaries of the financial plights of the Irish narrow-gauge railways! In the case of this new locomotive, manufacturer's number 1881, a cash payment for the agreed sum of £1,863 7/- (£1,863 35p) was made! The design was broadly based on an earlier engine supplied by Kerr, Stuart & Company of Stoke-on-Trent, itself based on some earlier engines built for some of the other Irish narrow-gauge railways. Perhaps the most significant difference from the Kerr, Stuart engine was the use of Bagnall-Price valve gear. The design was a 4-6-0 side tank with 15x20in cylinders and 3ft 6in coupled wheels - a very handsome machine and the prototype of three further ones, but in those cases built

by the Hunslet Engine Company of Leeds; one in 1912 followed by two more in 1922. These two incidentally, were the last new steam locomotives supplied to any of the Irish narrow-gauge railways. The Bagnall was named KILKEE, and all the design work was undertaken at Stafford. Interestingly, the first of the three built by Hunslet, manufacturer's number 1098 of 1912, was identical to the Bagnall, even to the extent of having Bagnall-Price valve gear; one of the very few locomotives fitted with this gear and not built at Stafford. The two later ones had Walschaerts valve gear, but were otherwise almost identical apart from the size of the side tanks. The Bagnall lasted until diesels arrived on the West Clare Railway and it was scrapped in 1953.

The Powelltown Tramway was a three-foot gauge railway in the Australian bush of Victoria near Melbourne. It ran 14½ miles from Yarra Junction to Splitters Camp, and the principal traffic was as might be imagined, logs and finished timber. However, on the 10½ mile section between Yarra and Powelltown, a general goods and passenger service was also provided. For this line Bagnall designed another interesting

POWELLITE was number 1965 of 1913, new to the Powelltown Tramway in the bush near Melbourne in Australia. Whilst displaying many of the external design features becoming so much a hall-mark of a Bagnall locomotive, this one was nonetheless, a special design. Notice the unusual position for the nameplate on the tender.

locomotive, manufacturer's number 1965 of January 1913, an neat 0-6-0 tender engine with 11x16½in outside cylinders and 2ft 6in coupled wheels, the six wheel tender was necessary in view of the length of the line; it had a water capacity of 800 gallons and 150cub ft of space for fuel which was of course, wood. Unusually the engine's name of POWELLITE was mounted on the tender and not the engine. The customer was the Victorian Powell Wood Process Company Limited, a company formed in 1911 to exploit the Powellising process for preserving timber, which had been patented by an Englishman named Powell. Unfortunately this was not a success and in 1915 the assets passed to the Victorian Hardwood Company Pty Limited. The tramway closed in July 1944 and the engine was sold via a Melbourne agent to the British

Phosphate Commission and shipped to the Pacific island of Nauru, where the Commission operated a three-foot gauge railway. However, it appears that in 1948 the boiler was sent back to Australia, ostensibly for repairs, but never to return. After languishing around the remains of the engine went to Japan for scrap, but not until 1967.

Worth a mention at this juncture in view of its unique nature and the interest it generates, is a small standard-gauge locomotive dating from 1893, and the only locomotive built by Alfred Dodman & Company of King's Lynn - a company better known for its road steam, stationary and portable engines. The locomotive was one of the smallest standard-gauge ones ever built, and the customer a local King's Lynn gentleman of some means - William Burkitt was twice Mayor of the

This is an example of the smallest of the standard designs, number 1885 of 1909, albeit in this case with a locomotive type boiler and not one with a circular firebox. Notice how much higher the boiler is mounted with the firebox sitting on top of the frames, despite the engine being built to suit three-foot gauge. This little engine with 5x7½in cylinders was ordered by the Liverpool agents Jones, Burton & Company and sent to Cartagena in Colombia, and although not bearing a name when it left Stafford, it was later christened CURARACHA, which means Cockroach! It was used on railway construction and maintenance works, latterly at least, on the Ferrocarril Del Tolima, a comparatively small three-foot gauge line towards the centre of the country.

MURIEL was another special design, but embodying many standard components. It is in fact a six-wheel coupled version of the standard 7x12in cylinder circular firebox design with Bagnall-Price valve gear and a rack for wood fuel. Manufacturer's number 1900 it was new in 1912 for the Arakan Flotilla Company Limited, for use in constructing the 2ft 6in gauge Buthidaung to Maungdaw Tramway in Burma's Naff Valley - this was in the Arakan Province in the north-west of the country. The locomotive was actually ordered by Edward Calthrop & Partners, the consulting engineers for the railway. Notice that fine array of LNWR signals protecting the junction of the Wellington and Shrewsbury line and the Henry Venables timber yard and chimney behind.

town and an influential business man. Burkitt had a great interest in locomotives and railways, and seems to have been on very good terms with the officials of the Great Eastern and Midland & Great Northern Joint Railways - in fact the engine, although built by Dodman, was apparently designed by a Mr S Stone of the Great Eastern. Burkitt was given permission by these two railway companies to use the locomotive for his travels over their systems on business trips, presumably with a main-line crew or at least a driver! For this purpose there was seating accommodation where one might otherwise expect to find a bunker. Named GAZELLE, this extremely small locomotive had a 2-2-2 wheel arrangement and the cylinders were only 4x9in; the single driving wheels were 3ft 9in diameter and the water was in a well tank underneath the footplate. There was absolutely no protection from the weather for either Burkitt or the crew - he must have been a hardy fellow! At some point around 1910 - presumably after Burkitt's death - this diminutive locomotive was acquired by the Sheffield machinery dealers TW Ward, and subsequently sold in February 1911 to that well known advocate of light railways, Colonel HF Stephens, who appears to have taken a fancy to it for possible use as an engineer's inspection

unit. It may be he intended to use it on several of the light railways he was involved with, in the event however, it went to the Shropshire & Montgomeryshire Railway where it remained; it was still there when the line was requisitioned by the War Department at the commencement of hostilities in 1939. When the Colonel purchased the engine he was in the process of resurrecting the Shropshire & Montgomeryshire Railway after years of closure and dereliction, so the little engine would have been quite useful when he was inspecting progress of the works.

The reason for mentioning GAZELLE in this book is the suggestion that certain modifications that the Colonel instigated were undertaken by WG Bagnall Limited. The locomotive was converted to an 0-4-2 wheel arrangement, a cab was added for the crew, and a special compartment for the passengers. However, despite the legend that the work was undertake at Stafford, which appears to have initially stemmed from an article in The Locomotive Magazine - issue for 15 January 1927 - there is absolutely no evidence in the surviving Bagnall records that the work was undertaken at the Castle Engine Works. As explanation has already been given regarding the incompleteness of the firm's records in certain areas; however, in terms of locomotives that came to the works for attention during the period in question, they are considered to be complete. The explanation may lie in the fact that while on the face of it, to convert the locomotive from a 2-2-2 wheel arrangement to a 0-4-2 appears to be job of some magnitude, in fact, the way it was achieved was quite simple. To accommodate the new and smaller driving wheels the short rod between the bottom of the spring buckles and the top of the axle-boxes has been replaced with a longer one so as to locate the axle-boxes in their new positions at the bottom, rather than the top of the horns. The springs therefore, remain in their original positions and the fames plates have not be altered in any way - but the consequences of a displaced or even a broken spring, would have been quite serious. The cylinders were not moved either, and to allow for the different angles of the connecting rods and eccentrics, with the original crank axle being much lower, the piston and valve rods were shortened. Fortunately, there was sufficient clearance for this, but what effect it might have had on the valve events has gone unrecorded! Obviously new driving wheels were needed along with a set of coupling rods, and crank-pins were required on the leading wheels; some alterations to the brake-gear were necessary too, and *The*

Locomotive Magazine article tells us that the leading wheels were used as a pattern for the new driving wheels.

Having considered the available evidence and made a close inspection of the engine which still exists, it is the considered opinion that if Bagnall did undertake the rebuilding, the locomotive would have remained on the Railway and men would have been sent there to undertake the work, making sketches of what was needed and taking parts back to Stafford for modification as necessary - this would also fit in with the Colonel's well known and astute control of finance! If the engine had been sent to the Castle Engine Works it is inconceivable that proper drawings would not have been made, in which case there would be entries in the drawing office registers - with the work being undertaken on-site, sketches would doubtless have been sufficient - and the new parts were not complicated ones. There is evidence that Bagnall did do work for the Colonel's various railways on other occasions, and in some cases the locomotives are known to have come to Stafford for the attention - so this explanation is a plausible one. In fact in March 1916, a whistle was supplied for GAZELLE. The Company was not slow in promoting its activities, and this has already

New Zealand was a country that provided a sizable market for Bagnall locomotives for almost the entire time they were in production. The one shown here, number 1902 of 1911, was another engine ordered by the London based agents John Birch & Company; it is a John Birch plate on the cab side. The engine is a 7x12in cylinder 'standard' design with an 0-4-2 wheel arrangement built to suit the standard New Zealand track gauge of 3ft 6in; adapted to burn wood fuel with a rack on the saddle tank. Shipped to Wellington it originally worked for the New Powell Wood Process Company at its mill at Rangataua near Ohakune in the central North Island, and later went on to have a varied career with a number of other owners.

been discussed at some length, and whilst one might have expected a letter of response to the article in *The Locomotive Magazine*, it may be that in view of the rather crude form the job took, it was felt best to say nothing! GAZELLE is today part of the National Collection, and on loan to the Colonel Stephens Museum on the Kent & East Sussex Railway at Tenterden in Kent. For readers interested in the conversion work, and the conclusions reached above, it is well worth a study.

In October 1912 the Company secured its first substantial order for the main-line railways of the Indian sub-continent. This was a completely new design of locomotive, and the Company was entrusted with the complete detail design work against a general outline. Actually there were two separate orders placed but two days apart, by the consulting engineers Rendel & Robertson. This Company had been formed by Fredrick Ewart Robinson (1847-1912) and Sir Alexander Meadows Rendel (1829-1918) in 1898.

Both these gentlemen being distinguished civil engineers, who had spent much of their carriers in India, largely engaged in the construction of railways. As a result they became very well known and respected to both the India Office in London, and the Indian Government. On going into business in partnership as consulting engineers, they were able to secure contracts from the Indian Government, as well as some of the independent Indian railways, and not only acted as consulting engineers, but also in effect as procurement agents. Later, in November 1912, Seymour Biscoe Tritton (knighted in 1918) who had also spent much of his career in the sub-continent, joined the partnership, and on Robertson's death the firm became Rendel & Tritton. Later still, in April 1913, Fredrick Palmer, yet another civil engineer having spent much of his working life in India, joined the partnership and the Company became Rendel, Palmer & Tritton (RP&T).

Robertson had been a member of the original British Engineering Standards Committee, formed in 1903, and

SINHASINHA, number 1905 of 1909, was an updated example of one of the earliest designs, a 2-4-2 side tank and in this case for metre-gauge with 13x18in cylinders - a quite powerful locomotive. Ordered by the Liverpool agents Jones, Burton & Company, it was one of two, the other one was number 1954 of 1912, and that is the actual customer's name on the side tank - owner of the Usina Passagem, a sugar estate in Brazil. In 1981 this locomotive was located at a different sugar estate, the Usina Paranagua at Terra Nova, whilst its sister was still at the Usina Passagem, which is near Santo Amaro. The specification called for these locomotives to have a 'showy finish', and this certainly seems to be the case with the one illustrated.

ANNIE, number 1922 of 1911, another locomotive sent to New Zealand and one of the smallest of the 'standard' designs with a circular firebox and patent valve gear, but in this case with side tanks rather than the more popular saddle tank. ANNIE had 5x7½in cylinders and the track gauge was 2ft 6in. The customer was Gisborne Corporation and the engine was for use at the Corporation's Gentle Annie Tramway, a 13 mile line built to transport road making materials to the town. In 1916 the engine moved to the Motuhora Stone Quarries north of Gisborne and worked there until 1924. After many years lying out of use ANNIE was buried in the old quarry workings, but was rescued in 1976 and the remains are today preserved at the East Coast Museum of Technology at Makaraka, which is just outside Gisborne. A full-size replica of ANNIE has been built by Richard Booth; it currently lives on the Groudle Glen Railway in the Isle of Man, where it keeps excellent company with Bagnall number 1484 of 1896 - SEA LION.

chairman of its Locomotive Design Conference, in effect a sub-committee charged with establishing a standard range of locomotives for use in India. These locomotives were known as the British Engineering Standards Association designs (BESA) and were for both the broad and metre-gauge railways. Building on its Indian associations, RP&T became principal consultants to both the India Office and the Indian Government for all railway matters, and supervised the detail design of the BESA standard types of locomotives as they were developed. The detail design work of the different types was allocated to several of the British private locomotive builders, such that any manufacturer with the necessary facilities could then build locomotives to any of the designs. After the First

World War, when it was decided to update the designs in line with modern locomotive practice, and introduce a new range, RP&T were again involved in a similar capacity. The designs in this case were known as the Indian Railway Standard designs (IRS), and as well as the broad and metre-gauges, in this case they also encompassed 2ft 6in gauge locomotives. Once again the detail design work was entrusted under RP&T supervision to the various British builders, as was building of the prototypes.

Seymour Biscoe Tritton was born in 1860; he served his apprenticeship and had his technical training with the marine and railway locomotive engineers R&W Hawthorn & Company Limited at Newcastle-on-Tyne, subsequently spending much of his career in India.

Western Railway of India W Class 2ft 6in gauge 0-6-2 tender engine No 577, on the turntable at Bilimora on 11 January 1977, sporting the rather smart livery applied to Western Railway steam locomotives at the time. Bagnall number 1992 of 1913, new to the Gaekwar's Baroda State Railway as No 27, it was in excellent condition when photographed despite it's 64 years. The narrow-gauge line at Bilimora, which opened in sections between 1914 and 1929, runs east a little over 39 miles inland to Waghai. Bilimora itself is 132 miles from Bombay on the former Bombay Baroda & Central India Railway broad-gauge main line. Replaced by diesels in the late 1980s, this engine has survived, mounted on a plinth outside the Western Railway Rajkot Divisional Headquarters.

Unlike his colleagues he was a locomotive engineer rather than a civil engineer, but like Robertson was a member of the Engineering Standards Committee and the Locomotive Design Conference. Seymour Tritton had worked in the locomotive departments of the Bengal & North Western, Indian States and East Bengal Railways and therefore, had much experience of locomotive operating in India; he was thus, a great asset to RP&T in its locomotive activities - especially in its formative years. As a prominent member of both the Institutions of Mechanical and Locomotive Engineers, he was elected president of the Locomotive Engineers in the 1926-1927 session. Sydney Edwards was also very active professionally in both these Institutions, as a result of which he was able to cultivate an excellent working relationship with both Seymour Tritton and other RP&T senior people, and this undoubtedly helped in getting contracts from RP&T, for work to be undertaken at the Castle Engine Works. We shall explore this in more detail in a later Chapter.

The locomotives referred to in the Indian order mentioned in the last paragraph, were the prototypes of what became a well established 2ft 6in gauge Indian Railways class, the W class, a neat and tidy 0-6-2 tender engine popular with the railways in the western states. In the period up to 1948, 30 members of this class were constructed, all of them at Stafford and prior to the post-war introduction of the IRS 2-6-2 ZB class, the W class were the standard engine for many of the narrow-gauge lines in Western India. They were also used on the Jacobabad Kashmor Railway, which was west of the Indus in what is now Pakistan, and operated by the North Western Railway. Most of these engines survived until recent times, indeed a modified version appeared as late as 1948, also designed and built at Stafford, and examples of both classes were still running well into the late 1980s. Cylinders were 11x15in, driving wheel diameter three-foot, engine wheelbase 13ft 6in, total wheelbase engine and tender 27ft 1¾in, weight in working order engine and tender 29 tons 4 cwt and the tractive effort at 85% of the 160 psi boiler pressure 6,875lb. The initial four, manufacturer's numbers 1968 to 1971, were despatched in June and July 1913 for the Bombay Baroda & Central India Railway, whilst the second batch consisting of five locomotives numbers 1972 to 1976, were despatched in July and September the same year; in this case for the Baroda State Railway. The four delivered after the Second World War were classified W1, and differed from the earlier engines in having Walschaerts valve gear instead of Bagnall-Price, along with roller bearing axle-boxes on the carrying and tender wheels, and a few other modifications to bring them into line with more modern practice. It was nevertheless, a testimony to the original basic design that even after the introduction of more modern designs, the W class was still considered appropriate for some of the light axle-load sections of the Gaekwar's Baroda State Railway (GBSR), owned and worked by the Baroda State.

In August 1927 Bagnall despatched to the GBSR a new boiler for one of these W class locomotives, it was part of an order to convert one member of the class to superheat, and new piston-valve cylinders were supplied at the same time with a kit of parts to aid the conversion. In later years at least, manufacturer's number 2196, as Indian Railways 589 - old GBSR 36 - had a superheated boiler and piston valve cylinders, so it is presumed this is the locomotive that was converted in 1927. However, the boiler supplied in 1927 is especially interesting as it was fitted with a circular firebox, whilst the locomotives were all built with conventional, locomotive type boilers. Presumably the railway wanted to experiment with the circular firebox design as well as superheat; however, when one of the authors saw number 2196 at Bhavnager in January 1977, whilst it had a superheated boiler and piston-valve cylinders and was classified WS, the boiler was of a conventional type. Other spare boilers supplied for this class of locomotive over the years were all of the conventional type and not fitted with superheaters.

Another of the Western Railway of India W Class engines, No 584, which was one of the later examples, Bagnall number 2142 of 1921, new to the Bombay Baroda & Central India Railway. The train is leaving Mahunha on the 28 mile long line formally part of the BBCIR system, running due east from Nadiad to Kapadvanju. Nadiad in about 30 miles due-north of Baroda (now Vadodara) and this 2ft 6in gauge line opened throughout in 1913. The train is heading west for Nadiad and crossing over a dried-up river bed on 15 January 1977 - notice the additional water capacity in the tank on the wagon behind the engine.

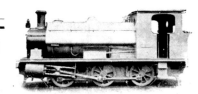

W. G. BAGNALL, L^{TD.} STAFFORD.

BUILDERS OF
STEAM, PETROL AND ELECTRIC
LOCOMOTIVES

WEIGHING FROM 3 TO 50 TONS, FOR ANY GAUGE, OF HIGHEST-CLASS WORKMANSHIP AND MATERIAL.

SPECIALITY :—

NARROW-GAUGE

STEEM

LOCOMOTIVES.

Also Makers of Tipping Trucks, Sugar-Cane, and other Special Wagons.

Telephone:—No. 15.   Codes :—" Engineering."   " A.B.C."   " Bedford McNeill's," and " Western Union."   Telegrams :—Bagnall, Stafford.

This rather nice advert appeared in the Locomotive Magazine, its January issue of 1913, as it accompanied a calendar for that year. The locomotives are, left to right, number 1881 KILKEE, three-foot gauge of 1908 for the West Clare Railway in Ireland; number 1875 of 1908, CHITI-DAND, two-foot gauge for the Punjab Coal Company; number 1866 of 1908 for the Cape Government Railway, and lastly number 1775 of 1905, standard-gauge for the Shanghai Nanking Railway in China. This is good representative cross-section of the types of locomotive the Company could build at the time.

Following on from the W Class came orders from two more Indian railways, in this case for an already established metre-gauge design - the old and well known F class, which could be found on almost all the Indian metre-gauge railways. Four were ordered in November 1913, two each for the Rohilkund & Kumaon and Bengal Dooars Railways, all being despatched in November and December 1914 - manufacturer's numbers were 2000 to 2003. The F class was an 0-6-0 outside frame tender engine with 14x20in cylinders, Halls cranks and 3ft 7in diameter coupled wheels. Subsequently Bagnall built a further 25 of these engines between 1915 and 1923, adding the Bengal & North Western and South Indian Railways to the list of railways supplied.

They also built some individual tenders, presumably either as spares, or for locomotives from other builders, and several batches of spare boilers. Examples of the F class were in use in India until quite recent times, in particular where they had been sold out of main-line service and into industrial use. These engines cost between £2,350 and £2,400 each delivered free on board at the docks.

It is perhaps worth explaining the principle of the Halls crank, named after its inventor. In this arrangement of fly-crank for outside frame locomotives, the crank itself is integral with the axle bearing journal, and is keyed onto the axle itself. The great advantage of this arrangement is a much larger axle bearing surface than would be the case with a more

Indian Railway F class metre-gauge six-coupled tender engine, a well established standard design for the metre-gauge railways of the sub-continent. The design dates from 1875, and Bagnall built the last ones as late as 1923. This is one of the first ones built at Stafford, in this case for the Bengal Doors Railway in 1914. Notice how the connecting rod is inside the side-rods, possible in view of the steep inclination of the cylinders, which allowed the designer to both reduce the size of the side-rod crank-pins on the intermediate wheelset, reduce the overall loading on the crankpins, and locate the cylinders closer together to reduce the piston loads imposed on the frame plates.

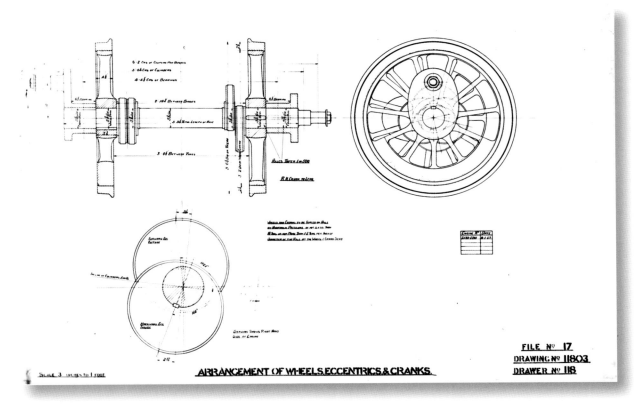

Bagnall drawing No 11803 of 1923, included here to illustrate the principle of Halls cranks as described in the text. Notice how the axle journal bearing is in integral with the outside crank, and how the axle itself is a shrink and key fit on to the crank. Whilst this drawing is of a driving wheelset, the leading and trailing ones were on the same principle, and although this particular drawing caters for a much later batch of F class engines (numbers 2199 to 2201 of 1923), once again the principle is the same. Observe how the drawing gives instructions on the pressures to be applied when pressing the wheels and cranks onto the axles, along with the setting of the cranks at 90°, and the eccentric setting allowing for the inclination of the cylinders at 1 in 8, and the angle of advance to give the valves lap and lead movement.

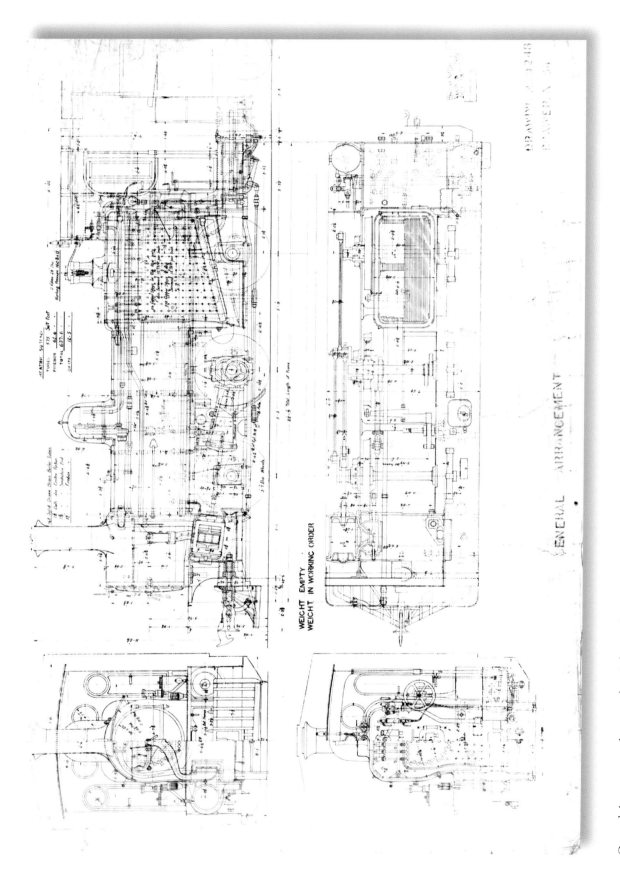

General Arrangement drawing of an Indian F class engine. Drawing number 9248 covers locomotive manufacturer's numbers 2000 to 2003 and 2011 to 2013 of 1914 and 1915. This drawing will repay close study, in particular the arrangement of the wheels, axles and crank pins, and how the arrangement of cranks allowed the cylinders to be closer together and for the connecting rod to be inside the side-rods, resulting in reduced loadings all-round.

This well proportioned 2ft 6in gauge 4-4-0 tender engine was one of two built for the Tezpore Balipara Railway, a 20 mile long line opened in 1894 and 1895, running inland from Tezpore-Ghat on the Brahmaputra River in Assam. Its primary function was to serve the local tea gardens. Manufacturer's number 1993 of 1914, a second one followed in 1920, number 2136, and in 1925 there was an enlarged 4-6-0 version - number 2255. The 4-4-0s were a development from the railway's earlier motive power which had been supplied by the Brush Company of Loughborough to an Alexander Penny design. The Tezpore Balipara Tramway closed some time after the last war when this engine, along with the 4-6-0, migrated to the Clutterbuck Ganj sleeper works of the North Eastern Railway at Izatnager, which is near Bareilly.

The Cutch State Railway was an isolated 2ft 6in gauge system on the island of Cutch, it dated from 1905 and eventually consisted of 72 route miles, the last section dating from as late as 1931. For this line Bagnall built six of these 4-6-0 tender engines, among the few engines of this wheel arrangement built for the narrow-gauge railways in India. The first two were delivered in 1913, followed by two more in 1929, and the last two as late as 1949. When the lines on the island were taken over by the Government in 1950, they were gradually converted to metre-gauge, and the Bagnall engines were moved to work on the 2ft 6in gauge lines of the Western Railway around Baroda. This is one of the last pair, number 2899 of 1949, as Western Railway P class No 606, shunting at Pratapnagar in the outskirts of Baroda. This was where the interchange took place between the broad and narrow-gauges, the narrow-gauge lines being part of an extensive system radiating from Dabhoi, itself a few miles south-east of Baroda (now Vadodara), and formerly part of the Gaekwar's Baroda State Railway. Photograph taken on the 12 January 1977.

This neat and tidy two-foot gauge six-coupled side tank with outside frames, Bagnall-Price valve gear and a duplex water pump mounted on the side tank, is number 1953 of 1912. New to T & W Morgan for the Hyderabad (Deccan) Company Limited, and sent to the Singareni Collieries which were about 108 miles east of Hyderabad in India. Notice the high pitch of the conventional boiler, as opposed to the circular firebox variety shown to good advantage in some of the other photographs. This engine has a double cab roof to promote the circulation of air.

conventional arrangement, where the fly-crank is only keyed onto the axle-end, leaving a smaller journal bearing. It was a popular design feature on most of the outside framed metre-gauge locomotives in India, and in the case of the F class, undoubtedly contributed to its popularity, as the propensity for hot axles would be reduced and the engines ability for hard work and ill-treatment increased. The use of these cranks facilitated another design feature to be adopted in the F class, once again to improve their performance and ability to withstand rough treatment, as together with a steep inclination of the cylinders, it allowed the connecting rod to be inside the coupling rod, yet still clear the slide-bars. The design could then encompass a larger bearing surface for the big-end, without unduly increasing the size of the coupling rod crank-pin bearing, and therefore, restricted the rotating weight that needed to be balanced. Having said that, the position of the cylinders would not have improved the ride characteristics of the locomotives, although they could be placed closer together with the connecting rod inside the coupling rods. Hall was an Englishman but

A photograph it illustrate a typical standard-gauge locomotive of the period under review, and one built for the home market. Number 1959 of 1912, a 12x18in cylinder 0-4-0 saddle tank, one of four locomotives supplied over the years to Coventry Corporation for use at Foleshill Gas Works. Picture taken about 1958; the engine was scrapped at the gas works in 1964.

he seems to have developed his crank whilst in the employ of the German builder, J&A Maffei of Munich. It become popular on a number of continental railways in the late 1800s, as well as with the Indian metre-gauge railways, but never seems to have been used on locomotives for use in this country.

Whilst we have described a number of the exceptional and more interesting designs in some detail, it is worth remembering that the staple diet in the period covered in this Chapter, and until the outbreak

valve gear, and in some cases not; cylinder sizes varied up to 11in diameter, and track gauges to 3ft 6in. There were also the occasional standard-gauge four-wheel saddle tank engines for the British industrial market, with cylinder diameters in the range 12 to 14in.

It is opportune to end this Chapter in bringing the reader up to date with a number of personal issues and more general business events. Arthur Gilling did not stay at Stafford long, and in 1912 was appointed chief mechanical engineer of the Rio Tinto Company, but he

A typical 6in cylinder circular firebox narrow-gauge locomotive, seen here in its everyday working surroundings. Number 1934 of 1913, at Judkins Tuttle Hill granite quarries near Nuneaton in Warwickshire on 13 July 1950. The home made cab and stovepipe chimney will be noticed. (Late Ralph Russell Collection - Industrial Locomotive Society)

of the First World War, was small narrow-gauge locomotives. These came in various shapes and sizes, still with strong bias to the design principles established by Ernest Baguley, but with the influence of Sydney Edwards becoming more and more apparent, especially noticeable in the external features. As well as the four-wheel saddle tank design, sometimes augmented with a trailing truck to allow for increased fuel and water capacity, a substantial proportion of the production were 0-6-0 and occasionally 0-4-2 side tanks, some times with the circular firebox boilers and Bagnall-Price

did return to locomotive engineering two years later when he became general manager and secretary of the Yorkshire Engine Company Limited of Sheffield. He remained with Yorkshire until 1928, and then acted for a short time as the London manager of Brown Bayley Steel Limited, the Sheffield steel maker. In 1930 he returned to railways again, taking up an appointment as chief mechanical engineer of the Dorada Railway in Columbia, but after three years returned home and after a couple of years acting as a private consultant, he was appointed in 1935 as general manager of RY Pickering

Two example of narrow-gauge wagons built in the period under review. The side-tip wagon is of all steel construction although the wheels would be made of chilled cast-iron; notice it is fitted with a brake. The other one is largely of wooden construction, has the ability to only tip in one direction, and would doubtless be for use in a mine of some sort. Notice the multi-gauge test track where the wagons are standing.

& Company Limited, the railway wagon builders of Wishaw. He joined the board of that Company in 1938, and remained a member until his retirement in January 1940; he died later the same year.

His place as general manager at the Castle Engine Works was taken by the chief draughtsman, William Sydney Edwards. This was a well earned promotion, although Edwards continued to keep a very close eye on design and draughtsmanship over the next few years, in fact, until a new appointment was made in December 1915, Edwards had the dual role of general manager and chief draughtsman. In view of his background, Edwards continued to keep a fairly close watch on all design and development issues until his death in office many years later, by which time he was the managing director.

In March 1911 Reginald John Gard had joined the firm as a draughtsman; Edwards soon identified this young man's flair and talent for design work and promoted him to a position of leading draughtsman. Reg Gard, a Welshman, was born in Cardiff on 3 May 1889 and was educated at St Mary's High School and Cardiff Technical Collage. In 1905 he joined the Taff Vale Railway at its Cardiff Works, a pupil of Tom Hurry Riches the locomotive superintendent. On completion of his training Gard became a draughtsman in the drawing office at Cardiff, but soon decided to try life at sea. Between November 1910 and until he came to Stafford in March 1911, he served in the Merchant Navy as a 4th Engineer. Reg Gard went on to have a brilliant career in locomotive engineering; he was elected an associate member of the Institution of Mechanical Engineers in November 1919, and among those supporting his application were WS Edwards, John Cameron and Thomas E Heywood. Cameron and Heywood were old colleagues from the Taff Vale Railway and by this time Cameron was the locomotive superintendent at Cardiff having succeeded Riches, while Heywood held a similar position on the Great North of Scotland Railway.

Almost on the commencement of hostilities, in September 1914, Reg Gard enlisted in the infant Royal Flying Corps, and whilst he clearly wanted to serve his King and Country, presumably his earlier experience in the Merchant Navy had put him off going to sea again. However, in December 1915 Reg Gard returned to Stafford as chief draughtsman, his release from military service almost certainly engineered by Edwards and

Gifford, doubtless as the Company started to take on significant War Office contracts. Sydney Edwards had an enormous respect for Reg Gard, and there were very few people employed by the Company over the years, he showed the same respect for.

Gard's appointment at Stafford allowed Edwards to concentrate on some pressing administration issues connected with running the business. There is evidence that Edwards and the works manager Sam Price, had never got on particularly well together. Edwards had come from an academic background and ruled by the slide-rule, whilst Price was from a shop-floor background and ruled more by the thumb. Edwards was a strict disciplinarian, whilst Price was not. In his position as general manager Edwards was becoming increasingly disillusioned with Price's management of the works production and there was an increasing number of disagreements. Whatever the exact circumstances we know not, but Samuel Thomas Price retired in 1915, ostensibly on ill health grounds and at the comparatively early age of 54. He continued to live in Stafford and had reached the ripe old age of 93, when he passed away on 5 December 1954. He lies in St Mary's Castle Church at Stafford, along with his wife Alice Mary (1864-1928). Sam Price had been with the Company for over 30 years, and was remembered as quite a character, being somewhat of a law unto himself, and one senses that relationships between him and Edwards, the latter as mentioned above a strict disciplinarian, had been gradually getting worse for some years. This relationship is almost certainly one of the reasons Edwards sought to get Reg Gard back into the fold.

Before we leave Sam Price, who had a large family of no less than 12 children, and was by all accounts both a devout churchman and 100% tea total, we should mention that he continued to take an interest in the activities of the firm. He also continued to collect his share of the Royalty payments for the use of the Bagnall-Price valve gear, although its general use on the small narrow-gauge circular-firebox saddle tank locomotives ceased about the time he retired, although it remained in use on more specialist designs until the end of steam locomotive production. Whatever the reason for his retirement, Sam Price made occasional visits to the Castle Engine Works until a few months before he died, and he could always be relied upon to

Samuel Thomas Price and his wife Alice Mary. Unfortunately we do not know the occasion of the photograph, but it would appear to have been taken in the rear yard of a house, perhaps theirs, and notice Price is holding what might be a certificate of some description. Could the table have formed part of a presentation when he retired one wonders, but if so why was the picture not taken at the works? Whatever the case, it is the only picture we have of Price other than in more general views.

comment on whatever he saw going on. Latterly at least, he was always accompanied on his walks around the shops by Sydney Edwards, doubtless these two extremely individual characters having put aside whatever the issues were they had earlier not seen eye-to-eye on. However, many of the older employees would jokingly comment that they hoped 'Old Price' was not making a comeback!

With Price gone Edwards persuaded William (Bill) R Parkinson, an old colleague from Kerr, Stuart, to come south to Stafford as works manager. Bill Parkinson was born at Hulme in Salford in 1859, a son of James and Mary Parkinson (nee Clarke). His father died when he was quite young and the family went to live with Mary's father Thomas Clarke, in the St. George district of Manchester. Thomas was a native of Kidsgrove in North Staffordshire and it appears that at some stage the family moved to the Potteries and Bill commenced his apprenticeship with Hartley, Arnoux & Fanning at the California Works. In lodgings in South Street

Fenton with a family called Sneyd, he became acquainted with the Dutton family who lived a few doors away, and in about 1883 he married George Dutton's daughter Sarah, and the couple went on to have two sons and three daughters. George Dutton was a widower employed as an engine-smith at the California Works where his youngest son George was a boilermaker; his eldest son Thomas was in the locomotive department of the North Staffordshire Railway and later became a driver. It was Bill Parkinson who Sydney Edwards spent much of his practical training with during his apprenticeship at Kerr, Stuart, and despite his age - he was 54 when he came to Stafford - he was obviously considered the right man for the job. Latterly he had been a senior foreman at the California Works.

Before bringing this Chapter to an end a few financial statistics will not go amiss. In the years 1912 to 1914 the Company continued to make a trading loss, the average figure for those three years was £838; however, a dividend of 5% continued to be declared. The average wages and salaries bill for the years 1907 to 1914 was £9,965, and the average turnover in the years 1907 to 1914 £51,662; this showed a steady increase from £45,448 in 1908 to £57,798 in 1914. However, a number of loans were taken out in this period to finance improvements to the plant and equipment as well as helping the cash-flow. With the outbreak of the First World War, this is a suitable point to bring this Chapter to an end, and move on to both a more difficult era, but also one where the influence of WS Edwards becomes an ever increasing issue in the Company's activities.

Two more illustrations of the standard circular-firebox narrow-gauge saddle tanks are appropriate as we come towards the end of this Chapter, as they were so typical of the products at this time. At the top is number 1875 of June 1908, a 6in cylinder engine for the Punjab Coal Company Chiti-Dand coal mines, at Abbottabad near Golpur in the Jhelum district of what is now Pakistan. Along with a sister engine supplied in 1911, number 1876 WADALA, although laid down for stock at the same time as this one, spares were still being supplied as late as 1949. The bottom photograph is another 6in cylinder engine, also laid down to a stock order in 1909, and in this case eventually sold for use in this country. Number 1877 of May 1911, it was for FB Thompstone & Son for use on a 2ft 6in gauge railway serving corn mills at Bosley near Macclesfield in Cheshire. Notice that both engines have cross-head driven boiler feed pumps and that MAGNET 11 is loaded on a standard-gauge railway wagon ready for delivery.

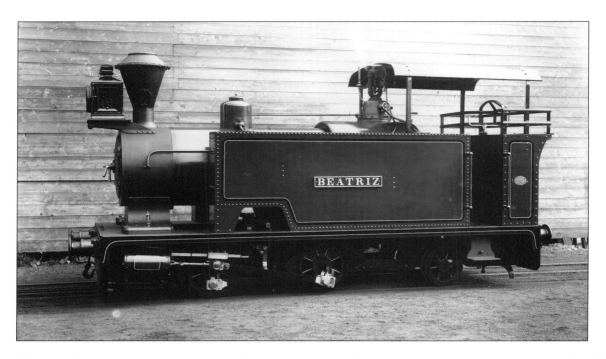

This is another of the engines supplied to the Wolverhampton agent Henry Rogers Sons & Company Limited. BEATRIZ, number 1925 of September 1910, a 2ft 5½ in gauge 0-4-2 side tank with 8in diameter cylinders a circular-firebox boiler and Bagnall-Price valve gear. For use at a sugar plantation in the Pernambuco Province of Brazil, Usina Santa Teresa de Goiana, it was still there, although no longer in use, as late as 1976, by then named CATU, although according to spares orders at one stage it carried the name BUJARY.

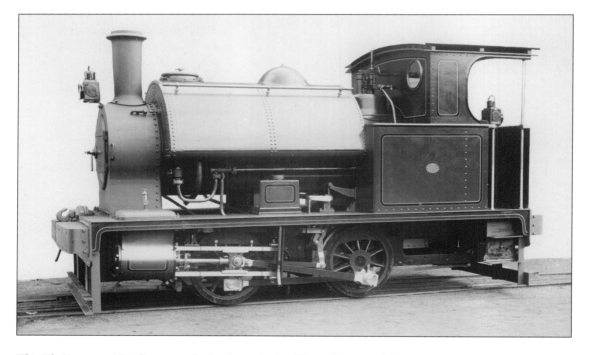

This 3ft 6in gauge 10in diameter cylinder four-wheel saddle tank is one of three supplied via the Crown Agents for use at Accra and Takoradi Harbours in the Gold Coast. Manufacturer's number 1950 of May 1912, together with one of the others it later passed to the ownership of Gold Coast Government Railway. Items to note are Bagnall-Price valve gear, double cab roof for a warm climate and the structure below the buffer-beams to assist in minimising damage following any derailments. Compare with the earlier engine supplied in 1908 illustrated on page 210.

Chapter Six

The First World War & The Ascendancy of WS Edwards

We have already seen how William Sydney Edwards after joining the firm in 1902, rose to become general manager in 1912. As briefly alluded to earlier, Edwards became a very prominent member of the British private locomotive building fraternity, and was very active in the professional institutions. He soon realised the benefits that could come from 'networking' in such circles, as we would refer to it now. He became an associate member of the Institution of Mechanical Engineers (I Mech E) in January 1913 with, as briefly mentioned earlier, Ernest Baguley and James Warren among his supporters. Another of his supporters was John Mitchell, at the time employed by Rendel & Robertson in its railway rolling stock department. Mitchell, who was born in Ceylon in 1874 of Scottish parents, was educated in Edinburgh and trained with the Caledonian Railway at St Rollex Works in Glasgow. On completion of his apprenticeship he had experience supervising the construction of locomotives built by contractors for the Caledonian Railway, and later joined Sir Alexander Rendel in 1899, and thereafter was involved in supervising the building of locomotives and railway rolling stock for Indian railways. We can be pretty sure Edwards met Rendel in connection with the orders for the W class engines mentioned in the previous Chapter.

Edwards became a full member of the I Mech E in September 1916, and in June the same year joined the infant Institution of Locomotive Engineers (I Loco E), which had been formed in 1911. Over the next few years he became particularly prominent in the I Loco E, serving on its Council from 1923 and elected a vice president in 1926; he continued to serve in both roles until the time of his death. Doubtless had he lived longer, a presidential term of office would have come his way. Although a regular attendee and contributor to the discussions following the presentation of papers at its meetings, he only presented one himself, at an ordinary meeting of the Institution held in London on 22 February 1923. The paper covered a topical subject at the time, and one in which he was both particularly interested and heavily involved in: *The Training of Apprentices*; it engendered a lively discussion.

Sydney Edwards was always extremely enthusiastic in the recruitment, further education and training of the firm's apprentices, ensuring encouragement in all aspects of their education, including facilitating spells in the drawing and cost offices. He encouraged their participation at the local technical college, provided facilities at the works for study after work, arranged for the Company to pay their fees provided they passed their examinations, and awarded prizes of technical

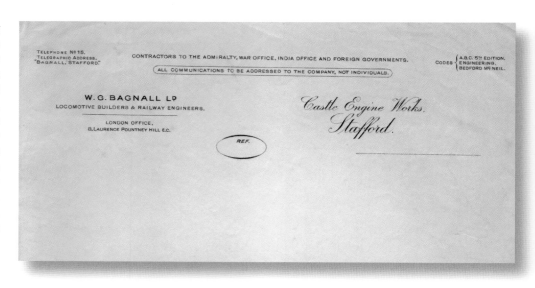

books. As well as this he encouraged other recreational facilities, and participation in the Company's sports club. In presenting the paper he mentioned that the Company employed 100 apprentices and among other things, there were no fewer than three football teams from among their number, with all three teams taking part in local fixtures. A proportion of the apprentices were always recruited from his native Stoke-on-Trent, a practice that continued until the end of the Company's existence. These healthy practices of recruiting and training apprentices so actively promoted by the general manager, with the shop foremen and others in authority also encouraged to show interest in the boys progress, helped in no small measure the Company to establish the position it achieved, in the private locomotive building industry in this country.

Each year the I Loco E arranged a summer visit of several days duration to railway installations and manufacturing industry. In the late 1920s and 1930s the Institution spread it wings wider, with on occasions, visits to European counties and Edwards almost always made it his business to attend. For example in 1928 the members went to Germany, and among the visits was one to the Henschel & Sohn Works at Cassel. Here members were given a copy of a book published by Henschel, *The Locomotive Engineers Pocket Book,* a very comprehensive volume and in this case an edition written in English. There exists a copy from this occasion with many of the participants signatures on the fly leaf, including that of Edwards, and in particular RP Wagner, the well established German locomotive

engineer and designer of many of the standard types of German steam locomotive. The pages of *The Locomotive Magazine* in its issues between the wars, find frequent mention of Edwards name at Institution meetings, luncheons and annual dinners, along with almost anything else involving the Institution that was reported. He never missed an opportunity to ensure the Bagnall name was as at the forefront of Institution activities. The I Loco E, and to a lesser extent the I Mech E, were particularly strong with members from the locomotive and rolling stock departments of the main-line railway companies, as well as with representatives of the manufacturers and consultants, enabling Edwards to make the acquaintance of, and in many cases become friends with, a whole range of the prominent engineers from these groups. With his enthusiastic involvement in these Institutions, and his other professional activities, Edwards was able to impart a significant influence in the industry, as well as enhancing the reputation of WG Bagnall Limited which without doubt helped the Company to win significant business. He let no opportunity go by, to advance the abilities of the firm and its achievements.

But we have jumped ahead of our story somewhat, and must return to the time of the start of hostilities against Germany in 1914. Two significant orders for locomotives were on hand at that time. The first was for a series of 2ft 6in gauge quite large 0-6-4 side tanks, ordered by the agents McLeod, Russell & Company Limited. This London firm had an Indian subsidiary, which had been granted a number of concessions from

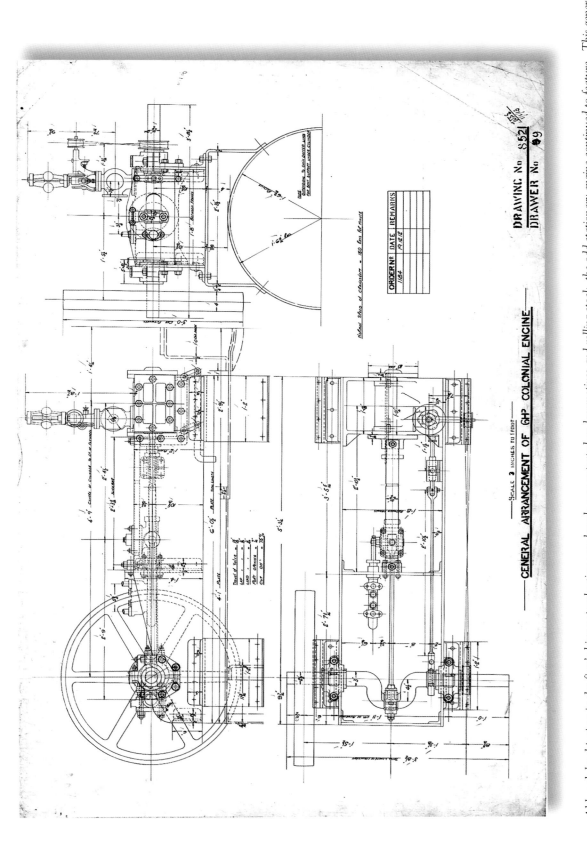

— GENERAL ARRANGEMENT OF 6HP COLONIAL ENGINE —

SCALE 3 INCHES TO 1 FOOT

DRAWING No. S.521
DRAWER No. 49

ORDER No	DATE	REMARKS
1184	1912	

Although by this time in the firm's history production was largely concentrated on locomotives and rolling stock, the odd stationary engine continued to feature. This general arrangement drawing illustrates one, a six horsepower example of what were referred to as Colonial engines, in this case designed to be mounted traction engine style, on top of a circular firebox boiler which was supplied at the same time. Points to note are that the engine in non-reversing, has a fixed cut-off, is controlled by a Pickering governor, and fitted with a crosshead driven boiler feed-pump. Notice too, the forged crankshaft which, due to its comparatively small size, may well have been forged in the works; larger ones for locomotives were sub-contracted. The cylinder size is 7½ x 9in. Unfortunately in surviving records the customer for this engine and its boiler have gone unrecorded, but it may well have been for an existing customer as by this date the Company was no longer promoting its ability to make stationary engines. The order number was 1184 of 1912; notice the initials of WS Edwards on the drawing; after scrutiny it was the practice of the Chief Draughtsman to initial each and every drawing produced.

The afternoon train from Katwa to Ahmadpur about to leave Katwa on 2 January 1977; this is one of the 2ft 6in gauge lines originally managed by McLeod, Russell & Company as discussed in the text. Katwa is on the west bank of the Hooghley River 90 miles north-west of Calcutta on the former East Indian Railway (EIR) BAK Loop Line from Bandel Junction to Aziganj. Ahmadpur is a little less than 32½ miles from Katwa on the EIR line from Calcutta to Jamalpur - the Sahibanj Loop - and the line from Katwa to Ahmadpur opened between May and September 1916; a second line to Burdwan opened a little earlier in December 1915. The locomotive is one of the 0-6-4 side tanks, manufacturer's number 2009 of 1915, BK4, and still on the same job it was built for 62 years earlier as proclaimed by the headboard. This reads: 'Ha Ha Ha You Retire At 58 Yrs I Am 62 Years Still Strong and Young I Remain Unmarried'. At the time 62 was the compulsory retirement age for Indian railwaymen! With several of its sister engines this one remained in use on the same railways it was built for until about 1994; today it is preserved as a static-exhibit at the Rambagh Palace Hotel in Jaipur - a long way from where it spent its working life.

the Indian Government to manage the construction, and later operate four projected narrow-gauge railways. Three of the four lines were not far from Calcutta, whilst the fourth was in the outer suburbs of that city, and they were all built to help the seemingly endless task of assisting the economic development of parts of that vast country. The lines were the Burdwan to Katwa and Ahmadpur to Katwa, 32½ and 32¼ miles long respectively, situated south of the Ganges in Bengal and some 60 miles north-north-west of Calcutta; the Bankura Damoodar River Railway, 60 miles long and also in Bengal, but south of the Hooghly River and about 100 miles as the crow flies from Calcutta; and lastly the Kalighat Falta Railway, 26¼ miles long in the southern suburbs of Calcutta. These lines opened between December 1915 and June 1917, and to operate them McLeods ordered from Bagnall 10 of the 0-6-4 side tanks between January and July 1914, along with three more in May 1915, with six somewhat smaller 0-6-2 side tanks following in August 1915. The 0-6-4s had 12x18in cylinders and 3ft 0½in diameter coupled wheels, and with outside frames, large fly

Another of the McLeod lines was the 60 mile long Bankura Damoodar River Railway, which ran from Bankura on the former Bengal Nagpur Railway line from Gomah to Khargpur, to Rainagar, south of the Damoodar River and west of Calcutta. Burdwan incidentally is about 12 miles north of Rainagar on the opposite side of the river. The line opened between December 1916 and June 1917, and as with the other lines Bagnall supplied these 0-6-4 side tanks for the opening. This one is manufacturer's number 2018 of 1916, from the second batch, and seen here in the evening sunshine at Bankura on 4 January 1977 - notice how it proudly proclaims its parentage and the letters on the smokebox are the code of its home shed at Bankura.

cranks and Bagnall-Price valve gear, they were bulky yet handsome machines. The smaller engines, which in the event were never built, would have had 10x15in cylinders and 2ft 6in coupled wheels, but were otherwise quite similar. In the event, and due to the outbreak of hostilities, only 10 of the 0-6-4 tank engines were built, manufacturer's numbers 2006 to 2009 and 2016 to 2021, and they were delivered from Stafford between December 1914 and as late as February 1917. Completion of the later engines was delayed due to a shortage of labour, along with other work considered more important and in connection with the war effort. The smaller 0-6-2 engines were cancelled by the Ministry of Munitions, after the firm

became a Controlled Establishment under the Munitions of War Acts, as described below.

The second significant order referred to above was for a dozen 2-6-2 side tank locomotives for the 2ft 5½in gauge Egyptian Delta Light Railways, in part to replace the earlier and much smaller 4-4-0 side tanks supplied by Bagnall in the period 1899 to 1900. On this occasion a much more substantial locomotive was designed with 12x16in outside cylinders and outside frames. Walschaerts valve gear was used with the drive on the trailing axle, resulting in a long and slender connecting rod; coupled wheel diameter was 3ft 0½in. In view of the part desert terrain where the engines had to operate, they had long high capacity side tanks extending beyond the smokebox and holding 500 gallons of water, resulting in a rather handsome locomotive, perhaps spoilt by side skirts over the motion in an attempt to keep out blowing sand. As with the earlier engines for the Egyptian Delta Light Railways, the specification called for brass numerals to be mounted on each side of the chimney, and the numbers were 1 to 12 - the manufacturer's numbers were 2022 to 2033. In the event, and like the McLeod, Russell orders as a result of the hostilities, construction of these locomotives was seriously delayed, and in fact three of them were diverted by Government direction to McLeod, Russell - in part to fill the gap left by the cancellation of the 0-6-2 tank engines mentioned earlier. These three, numbers 2028 to 2030, were

despatched to India in November 1916, and perhaps not surprisingly, became known on the McLeod Railways as the Delta class. Of the remainder, only six of them found their way to Egypt, four being released and despatched in April to July 1916, numbers 2022 to 2025, and the other two, numbers 2027 and 2032, not until late 1917 - they were numbered 1 to 6.

In the meantime number 2027, which was ready for delivery dismantled and packed for shipment, was unpacked in August 1917, re-erected and loaned for a short period for use on work in connection with the war effort at Ridham Dock in Kent, where a salvage depot had been established. Two of the others, numbers 2026 and 2031, were sent in July and November 1917 respectively, again on Government direction, ostensibly

This picture was taken at Katwa on 2 January 1977, and illustrates one of the 2-6-2 side tank engines originally ordered for use in Egypt, but diverted as a war time contingency to the McLeod lines in India. Manufacturer's number 2029 of 1916, it had originally been used on the Kalighat to Falta line in the outskirts of Calcutta; it would have arrived at Katwa in 1957 when the Kalighat line closed. The AK prefix to the number stands for Ahmadpur-Katwa; the locomotives on the former McLeod lines were never renumbered into Indian Railway stock when the lines were taken over by the State in March 1957. This particular locomotive has returned to this country after being acquired by the Phyllis Rampton Narrow Gauge Railway Trust, and is currently in store.

Despite not being designed for use on the Indian McLeod lines, the 2-6-2 tank engines intended for the Egyptian Delta Light Railways proved popular in their adopted country. So much so that engines of the same design were subsequently ordered by McLeod, Russell for use in India. The last ones in fact, and the last locomotives ordered for the lines, were not despatched until as late as 1953 - manufacturer's numbers 3053 to 3055. This photograph was taken on 4 January 1977 and shows the morning train from Rainagar departing from Chandra, which is 13 miles from Bankura; the locomotive is Bankura Damoodar Railway No 11 - Bagnall 3055. Notice that engines of this type were known in India as the Delta class! This was a mixed train with passengers not just on the roofs of some of the coaches, but also in one of the vans.

to the Indian Eastern Bengal Railway, but in actual fact appear to have been diverted to the Jacobabad Kashmore Railway. This was a line worked by the North Western Railway of India, west of the Indus in what is now Pakistan, and mentioned in the last Chapter in connection with engines of the W class. Last of all, number 2033, which rather strangely seems to have been left on the maker's hands and was even advertised for sale in the trade press towards the end of 1917 and early in 1918, was sent by order of the Secretary of State for India, in May 1918 to the Bengal Provincial Railway. Unfortunately it never got to this railway and was reported lost at sea; presumably its remains are lying on the sea bed somewhere. It is not a little surprising that this locomotives remained on hand so long, and one is left wondering why it did not go to

Egypt with the other six to help fulfil the original order. Clearly, in this case at least, not allowing the locomotive to go to Egypt had nothing to do with a need for it anywhere else, so there must have been another reason. Egypt was not a belligerent, so perhaps payment was the issue. In any event, some of the earlier 4-4-0 engines were still in use on the Delta Light Railways as late as 1927 - 17 of them in fact. For use in India and at Ridham Dock, these engines had to have their track-gauge altered to 2ft 6in. Before leaving these locomotives it is worth recording that despite not having been designed for the Indian McLeod railways, they were particularly popular with the staff on the Kalighat Falta line, and when additional locomotives were required in 1929, two of the same type were ordered - numbers 2411 and 2412. When further locomotives were required for all the lines as late as 1953, a slightly updated version of the Delta class was supplied.

New locomotive production during the First World War was severely limited, and against 31 locomotives ordered in 1913 and 25 in 1914, only five were ordered in 1916, 19 in 1917 and 13 in 1918. In fact the bulk of the orders consisted of the small two-foot and 2ft 6in gauge standard saddle tanks with the circular firebox, and the majority of these were ordered in 1917 and 1918, for work in connection with the war effort and its aftermath. However, the works was kept busy commensurate with the available labour force, reduced as men left to join the forces. During the war the Company became a Controlled Establishment under the terms of the various Munitions of War Acts. The first of these Acts was dated 1915 (5-6 Geo V Ch. liv; Royal Assent 2 July 1915), and to give a general flavour, has as its preamble: 'An Act to make provision for furthering the efficiency, manufacture, transport and

supply of munitions for the present war and for purpose incidental thereto'. This was the Act that established the Ministry of Munitions with David Lloyd George as its first incumbent minister - hitherto he had been chancellor and of course later became Prime Minister of the Coalition Government for the duration of the war. The post was later occupied by Winston Churchill. Together with subsequent Acts (5-6 Geo V Ch. xcviv: Royal Assent 27 January 1916, and 7-8 Geo V Ch. xlv: Royal Assent 21 August 1917), the Government had wide ranging powers regarding the allocation of work, the wages paid, movement of plant and machinery between factories, control of profits (in effect an excess profit tax) and a whole plethora of other issues connected with the efficiency of production. However, one of its most important clauses was in connection with the dilution of skilled labour. Perhaps understandably, despite the fact that many of their colleagues were fighting for their King and Country, with large numbers making the supreme sacrifice, most

Another picture taken at Katwa, this time during the early evening of 2 January 1977. On the left is BK4 again, waiting to leave with the afternoon train to Ahmadpur, whilst on the right is one of the 'Delta' class 2-6-2s, in this case BK14 - which stands for Burdwan-Katwa - Bagnall number 2030 of 1916.

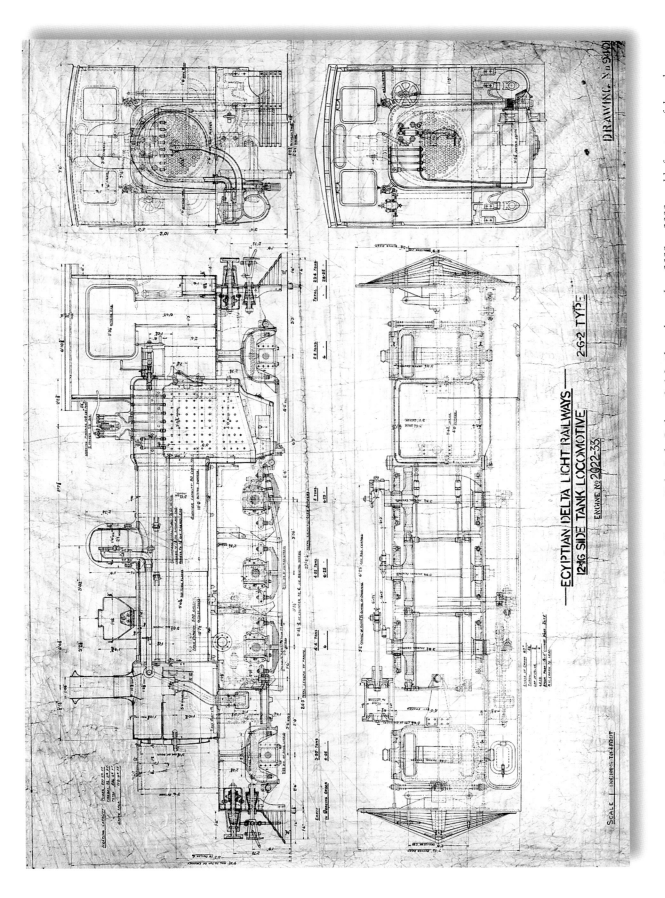

General Arrangement drawing No 9401, specially prepared for the Egyptian Delta Light Railway 2-6-2 side tanks numbers 2022 to 2033, and before part of the order was diverted to India.

of the Trade Unions had been completely against any dilution of skilled labour. In fact there had already been industrial action in the big armament firms culminating in Scotland at least, with withdrawal of labour in Glasgow.

The powers under the various Acts were not just in connection with the manufacturer of munitions, but the production and allocation of raw materials and just about everything else too. For example, at the discretion of the Minister, profits of individual firms were limited to the average of the two financial years prior to the outbreak of war, and there were restrictions and quotas on skilled men leaving to join the forces etc. In the case of WG Bagnall Limited, it seems to have been encompassed by the provisions of the Acts some time in 1916, and thereafter the Ministry of Munitions were largely in control of the allocation of work. Although the Company continued to supply spare parts for existing locomotives, and to work on a number of locomotives sent in to the works for repair, production was largely concentrated on work associated with munitions and other wartime requirements.

The Company was of course not alone in this respect, and most if not all its competitors, were also Controlled Establishments, suffering both loss of manpower to the forces, and being allocated work in connection with the manufacture of munitions. Most therefore, built far less locomotives on an annual basis that they might otherwise have done. Because of the significant amount of machining involved in the construction of a steam locomotive, all the manufacturers had sizable and well equipped machine shops, and machining capacity was in great demand, in particular for shell cases. Once serious military action started on the western front in France in 1915, the consumption of both heavy and light artillery exceeded the widest pre-war estimates; nobody had envisaged anything like the amount that would be used. It has to be added that this was in no small measure due to the destructive results of heavy artillery fire being far less than anticipated, not so much as a result of inaccurate fire, but perhaps more so in view of the vast length of the front being attacked, large quantities of defective shells and the difficulty in effectively cutting the enemy barbed wire defences, essential prior to any frontal assault by attacking infantry. It should be added that both sides seem to have suffered similar problems, both in knocking out

each others heavy artillery, and a sufficient supply of shells. The main line railway workshops were similarly employed during the war, as they too came under Munitions of War Acts, with the result that many locomotives that might otherwise have been scrapped, had to be kept running. The direct result of this was a significant number of locomotives ordered from American manufacturers, both for use in this country and on the western front in France and Belgium.

During the war the Company did get involved in a couple of issues in connection with the wages paid to certain groups of tradesmen. In 1916 an issue arose with The Boiler Makers & Iron & Steel Builders Society in connection with rates of pay for certain groups of trades. The groups and their rates were: holders-up 29/- (£1 45p); riveters, 36/- (£1 80p); angle-smiths 42/- (£2 10p); platers and markers-out 47/- (£2 35p) - all for a 50 hour week. The claim for an increase in the rates went to arbitration before Edward Forbes Lankester, one of Her Majesty's Counsel, and the hearing was held in Stafford on 11 August. The Society claimed parity with the rates paid to tradesmen in similar jobs in other parts of North Staffordshire, whose rates of pay were higher. The Company however, maintained that its standard week of 50 hours was less that the comparisons being made - although the works was in fact open for 62½ hours a week with overtime paid, the rates for which were not challenged. It was also pointed out that in the case of the Amalgamated Society of Engineers, the rates had been adjusted to take account of the number of hours worked. Nevertheless, the arbitrator gave in favour of the men, and a 2/- (10p) per week increase for all the grades was awarded. The Company for its part, whilst protesting, accepted on the basis it had agreed for the issue to go to arbitration in the first place. In sympathy with the Company this settlement does seem rather unfair, and to give one of the examples cited in its defence, that of the holders-up, who under the new rates would be paid 31/- (£1 55p) for a 50 hour week, which equated to 33/4d (£1 69p) for the 53 hour week worked by the firms with which the compassion was being made. In fact the same Boiler Makers Society had already agreed rates for a week of 53 hours, of 32/- (£1 60p).

The second issue did not arise until much later, in 1918 in fact, in this case involving the Ironfounders Society and once again going to arbitration, in this instance before Professor LT Hobhouse, who was appointed under the terms of the Munitions of War Acts. Once again the question was one of rates of pay connected with the firm working a 50 hour standard week, against other firms in Stafford - WH Dorman & Company Limited and Siemens Brothers Limited being cited - having a standard week of 52 hours. In this case, although the men claimed an increase of 3/- (15p) per week for moulders and coremakers, the award, which was dated 6 December 1918, whilst in their favour, was for an increase of only 1/- (5p) per week.

A number of improvements around the works to assist in increasing production were undertaken during the war. For example there was a northwards extension of the erecting shop, and in October 1917 a new bay for the boiler shop along with a quantity of new plant and machinery. Some of these improvements and additions were funded by a grant and loan from the Munitions Works Board, a body also established under the powers in the various Acts mentioned above, and a sum of £3,577 7/- (£3,577 35p) was involved. An overdraft arrangement was agreed with Barclays Bank dated 31 July 1916 to help fund the works, and this was secured by a debenture of £18,000; eventually redeemed in two instalments, £8,000 on 21 November 1921, followed by the remaining £10,000 on 31 December the following year. The improvements undertaken between the spring of 1916 and the early months of 1918, along with the new bay for the boiler shop mentioned above, included extensions to the smithy and machine shops, as well as other smaller shop extensions and work undertaken to improve the facilities in the wagon and fitting shops. The new plant and machinery installed all around the works, included steam hammers and hydraulic machinery along with a large vertical hydraulic accumulator and electric pump. Some of the work associated with the shop extensions was undertaken by the Company's own people - in particular parts for new and improved overhead travelling cranes with their tracks, and some smaller stationary jib cranes. Many of the foundations for the new and other additional machine tools were also undertaken by the staff, along with the actual installation work. Further improvements involved construction of a new power house, along with completely new power generation equipment, in this case consisting of enclosed vertical high speed steam

engines directly coupled to generators, and there was a new steam raising plant of increased capacity. This power generation equipment replaced most of the earlier and much older open-crank steam engines driving generators and line-shafting by ropes and belts, some of which had been built at the works many years earlier. Associated with the new generation equipment was a completely new electrical power distribution system. Alexander Smith & Sons undertook a valuation of the machinery and plant in 1916, and in a report dated 31 May, valued it at £12,845 5/ 2d (£12,845 26p).

One section of the works that was kept pretty busy during the war was the wagon shop. There was a plethora of orders right through the war years for wagons of all shapes and sizes, turntables and traversers along with track work. Unfortunately, no records appear to have survived with details of where the vast majority of this rolling stock and other railway equipment was destined, but some of it would almost certainly have been for military use and in any event, all the orders would have been scrutinised by the Ministry of Munitions officials. To give some idea of the war-time production not connected with locomotives or munitions, and taking as an example the year 1916, the list below illustrates some of the work undertaken:

Large quantity of ash skips for the main-line railway companies.
Four metre-gauge bogie sugar cane wagons.
Thirty 13½ cub ft end-tip wagons.
Two 4½ ton platform wagons.
Large quantity of skips for shell cases.

No less than 230 cast-iron and steel turntables of diameters from 3ft 6in to five foot, for an assortment of track gauges. Several large contracts for Edwin Bostock & Company Limited, the Stafford based boot and shoe maker. These orders covered castings and forgings of various shapes and sizes, and finished pulleys. It would appear Bostocks were expanding production, doubtless in connections with orders from military sources, and Bagnalls were supplying material and equipment for this end.

There were similar orders for castings and forgings and a whole host of other items for the Universal Grinding Wheel Company, in 1915, 1916 and the following year. This company was expanding into new and larger premises at the time, partly to meet the war-time demand for its products.

When interviewed for *The Railway Gazette* some years after the war, Sydney Edwards said that during the war the company supplied large quantities of light railway track, points and crossings and for a variety of military uses. There are indeed numerous entries in the drawing office registers, and some extant drawings for a multifarious selection of light railway track and components, and for several track gauges. It should also be remembered that there were at times acute man power shortages, both due to men enlisting in the armed forces and movement of labour between factories by the Ministry of Labour, under the control of the Ministry of Munitions. The labour shortages were partly addressed by the employment of females in some of the less skilled jobs, along with some trade dilution covered by the Ministry of Munitions Acts mentioned above. The employment of female labour of course, necessitated provision of additional toilet facilities. Towards the end of the war prisoners of war were drafted in to help too, but not used on munitions related work. They were billeted in parts of the recruiting and training camps mentioned below.

There is unfortunately, not a great amount of detail available concerning the munitions and weapons related work undertaken during the war, but in 1916 work did start on the manufacture of parts for 58 m/m aerial torpedoes, as well as machining shell cases and manufacturing parts for field guns and other smaller artillery. On nearby Cannock Chase, south of Stafford, large military training and transit camps were established, construction works starting in late 1914. The need for these camps was to accommodate the large numbers of men being recruited to join the army, vastly in excess of the peace time requirements and therefore, the existing facilities. The two camps were designated as Brocton and Rugeley, although they were respectively around two and six miles away from these places, and an extensive railway system was built to serve their needs, both by connecting the camps with the main-line railways, as well as forming a railway link between the two. The main-line between the two camps, over four miles long was laid early in the scheme of things to assist in the construction works of the camps themselves. WG Bagnall Limited was called on

to undertake a significant amount of work in connection with these camps, not only for the contractors undertaking the construction works, but also for the War Department (WD) once the camps became operational. Some of this work involved the repair and overhaul of the locomotives and rolling stock used on the railways, both by the contractors and the WD, but other jobs were in connection with various activities of a more general engineering nature. Often men were sent to the camps to undertake the work.

A wide range of other general engineering work was undertaken during the war years, some of it for the Ministry of Munitions and the War Department. A number of steam road traction engines and rollers belonging to the local authorities, as well as local farmers and private haulage contractors, came to the works for attention. This work was almost certainly because the original manufacturers were also busy on munitions type activities, and to save having to move the engines long distances.

On 31 January 1917, at Ministry of Munitions direction, the Company were appointed sub-contractors to Nasmyth Wilson & Company Limited, the Patricroft based locomotive manufacturers, to build 25 complete sets of mechanical parts for two-foot gauge four-wheel petrol-electric locomotives for the WD. Nasmyth Wilson itself was also a sub-contractor, in its case to the British Westinghouse Limited of Trafford Park Manchester, which had been awarded the contract to built 100 of these locomotives, sub-letting the mechanical parts to Nasmyth Wilson. Further sub-lettings by Nasmyth Wilson consisted of 25 to Bagnall, 25 to the Leeds Forge Company Limited, while it appears to have built the remaining 50 itself. A further 100 similar locomotives were built by Dick Kerr & Company Limited at its Preston Works, and in this case with its own electrical equipment.

The mechanical parts of the locomotives built at Stafford, along with the other 75, were sent to a workshop at Miles Platting, where the engines, generators, motors and other equipment were fitted. The completed locomotives were for use on the light railways supporting the allied army on the western front in France and Belgium. Internal combustion engined locomotives being preferred on the lines close to where the action was, as the smoke from steam locomotives could give away positions to the enemy - not considered

Three of the petrol-electric locomotives built for the War Department Light Railways, the mechanical parts of which were built at the Castle Engine Works in the first half of 1917, and under sub-contract to Nasmyth Wilson. View looking north in the Erecting Shop. The three seen in this illustration would appear to be complete and ready for despatch to Miles Platting, where the engines and electrical equipment would be fitted.

a very good idea. No numbers were allocated to these locomotives in the 'engine' list, and they were built under general order numbers 4397 to 4399 and despatch was complete by 10 July 1917, a commendable effort of almost five locomotives a month

In November 1917 the Company commenced supplying significant numbers of spare parts for the American built two-foot gauge Baldwin and ALCO (American Locomotive Company) 4-6-0 and 2-6-2 pannier tank locomotives which had been supplied earlier in the war. These locomotives had been built for the War Department Light Railways (WDLR) in the USA, as the British manufacturers, as mentioned above, were unable to meet the time scales, not least due to the level of munitions and other war work they were engaged in. Like the petrol-electric locomotives they were for use on the light field railways built to

service the western front supply lines, though in this case further away from enemy lines. This work for the WDLR as directed by the Ministry of Munitions, involved a significant amount of detail design work, as only a very few drawings appear to have been available, and Bagnall created no fewer than 120 new ones to support the work. Some time later, between June 1918 to September 1919, as many as 21 of the Baldwin-built locomotives and three of the ALCO built ones, came to Stafford for attention, usually delivered from a large war-time equipment store at Purfleet in Essex, where they were returned after attention. The repairs were of a very wide ranging nature, as might be imagined considering where the engines had been working, and in some cases there was not much left of them when they arrived; on occasions two or more locomotives had to be made into a lesser number. Cessation of hostilities in

November 1918 meant that not many of those that had been rebuilt or repaired saw any more active service, although the reason for continuing to repair them after the end of the war was a requirement in India, where 50 were sent. These 50 were for the strategic reserve on the north-west frontier, and in replacement of the earlier Bagnall locomotives that had been redistributed elsewhere during the war. A number of them later found use in industry, notably sugar factories and plantations. Of those that remained in this country, several were later sold by the Ministry of Munitions Disposal Board, and saw further use on light and industrial railways both in this country and the continent. In this country examples of those that had received attention at Stafford found their way to the Welsh Highland, Ashover and Snailbeach Light

Railways, as well as the British Standard Cement Company works at Rainham in Kent.

An interesting anecdote about these locomotives is worth recalling at this juncture. The late Albert Edwards, who started as an apprentice at the Castle Engine Works in February 1918, remembered the story. One day, not long after he started work, an LNWR main-line engine was shunting in the yard and for some reason or other a movement was misjudged, and the engine came bursting through the erecting shop doors. Several of the Baldwin locomotives were in various stages of repair, many on them elevated off the rails on stands, and they were all promptly knocked off! Doubtless the LNWR had a sizable claim to deal with! Albert thought the engine was a Claughton, but this was an express passenger locomotive so it seems

As outlined in the text the American Baldwin built two-foot gauge 4-6-0 pannier tank locomotives, supplied in large numbers (no fewer than 495 in fact, between October 1916 and April 1917) during the First World War, in later years sometimes found useful employment in other parts of the world. This photograph was taken on 6 February 1981 in India, at the Daurala Sugar mill near Meerut, which is north-east of Delhi. The locomotive is one of those overhauled at Stafford after Bagnall had been appointed by the Ministry of Munitions, on behalf of the War Department Light Railways (WDLR), to undertake repairs on them. This one is Baldwin number 44696 of 1917, formerly WDLR No 791; it arrived at Stafford on 21 November 1918 and after attention was despatched to the store at Purfleet on 7 February 1919. The repairs in this case cost a little over £189, which was a lot less than many of its contempories. Originally at the nearby Upper India Sugar Works at Khatauli, at some date it had migrated to Daurala as fleet No 4; out of use when this picture was taken the narrow-gauge system having ceased operations, its ultimate fate is not known. The small plate on the cab side reads: 'WG Bagnall Stafford England Rebuilt 1918'.

unlikely; unless that is, using such a large locomotive for a shunting move was part of the problem.

A few locomotive orders during the war period are worthy of mention, including four for Schneider & Company from a London address, ordered on behalf of the French Ministry of Munitions. Presumably these were intended to help the war effort, but despite being ordered in 1917, only two were delivered before hostilities ceased. Three of them were standard-gauge machines, one 0-6-0 saddle tank and two 0-4-0 saddle tanks, all with 14x20in cylinders and 3ft 6½in diameter wheels. All three were standard designs of the period for standard-gauge shunting locomotives; the six-wheeler was number 2057, despatched to France in January 1918, followed by the two four-wheelers, numbers 2064 and 2065, in April 1919. The fourth locomotive was a narrow-gauge one - 700 m/m gauge - and in this case one of the standard 7x12in cylinder circular-firebox 0-4-0 saddle tanks was supplied - number 2063 despatched in July 1918. All these locomotives were sent to the Schneider Factory at Le Creusot, and number 2064 has survived in preservation in France.

Towards the end of the war, and right through until around the middle of 1919, the principal locomotive production consisted of a large number of the standard circular firebox narrow-gauge locomotives. There were examples of both two-foot gauge with 6x9in cylinders and three-foot gauge with 7x12in cylinders, ordered by the Ministry of Munitions for use on various Government sponsored operations. No fewer than 35 were despatched between December 1917 and March 1919. Many of these small locomotives had long and varied careers after the initial need for them disappeared, and indeed a number have survived into preservation. They were used on a wide range of government supported projects, for example building aerodromes, home grown timber forestry work, operations in connection with inland harbours, docks and ironstone mining. Some of them passed almost immediately into commercial use, with military activities diminishing; many of them not being delivered until after the cessation of hostilities. Several later came back to Stafford, in some instances after being purchased by other companies from the Ministry of Munitions Disposals Board, and sometimes by the Company itself. In the case of the ones the Company purchased, after refurbishment, sometimes accompanied by alteration of track gauge and perhaps other modifications required by a customer, they were resold as almost new locomotives. In the case of the ones purchased by others, attention would be given as required, again often requiring alteration to the track gauge, and in a number of cases the refurbished

Not many Bagnall locomotives were exported to France, but this is one of them. Manufacturer's number 2057 was an example of the standard-gauge six-wheel saddle tank shunting engine, with 14x20in cylinders and 3ft 6½in diameter coupled wheels - a basic type that remained in production for many years. Ordered by the French Ministry of Munitions in February 1917, it was not despatched until January the following year, for use by Schneider & Cie, at its Le Creusot works - later Societe Des Forges Et Ateliers Du Creusot - where it lasted until January 1952. We do not know who the two fellows are, but the one in the cab has a French look about him - could he be an official making a pre-delivery inspection one wonders?

locomotives were exported. As well as those ordered by government departments, others of the same basic type were ordered around the same time by a number of other customers, including a batch of four, manufacturer's numbers 2092 to 2095 of late 1919, which went to Belgium. These were the first Bagnall locomotives to be exported directly to that country, and one of them later turned up later in France, and survives in preservation.

During the war Reg Gard, supported by Edwards, initiated some quite detailed redesign work on the small narrow-gauge circular firebox Mercedes type of locomotive, the design that perhaps more than any other, was the arch-typical Castle Engine Works product. Notwithstanding the basic nature of this design, and the comparatively low price at which engines of the gene could be made, if was felt they could be constructed at an even lower cost and using less raw material. The reason for the need was two-fold, the war-time shortages of labour and raw materials, with an eye on post-war competitiveness in view of the high levels of inflation. If less raw material was required, and less man-hours were occupied, in particular if a smaller number and less complicated castings could be employed, with reduced machining times, considerable economies could be achieved. Bear in mind too, that at the time machine shop capacity was constantly in demand for the machining of shell cases and other munitions work.

Mention was made in the last Chapter of the retirement of Samuel Price as works manager, and how Walschaerts valve gear replaced Bagnall-Price valve gear as a standard feature on these small locomotives. This in itself is interesting, as one of the principal benefits in the use of Bagnall-Price valve gear was the lack of an outside return arm which on small locomotives was so liable to hit trackside obstructions. This would be especially the case in so many of the places, mines and quarries for example, where locomotives of this type habitually operated. Whilst the payment of Royalties to Price may have been a factor in the equation, a far more significant one concerned construction costs. Bagnall-Price valve gear requires an eccentric on the driving axle, resulting in four separate castings - two for the eccentric sheaves and two for the straps - a complicated casting to take the oscillating shaft, a large casting for the motion bracket and a

number of other parts both complicated and time consuming to machine. Clearly, whatever its disadvantages, Walschaerts valve gear is much simpler to manufacture, required almost no castings, less machining time and therefore raw material and labour. Nevertheless, the Company continued to have a soft-spot for Bagnall-Price valve gear, and it continued to be specified for a whole range of other types of locomotive, and right until the end of steam locomotive production. One suspects that Sydney Edwards might have had a hand in the design of this gear; remember he was chief draughtsman when it was designed, despite his name not being directly connected. This being the case, one can perhaps understand why it continued to be used on so many locomotives.

The last of the standard narrow-gauge locomotives to have the Bagnall-Price patent gear was manufacturer's number 2052, supplied in parts between June and August 1916 to the United Alkali Company Limited, for use at its mines at Sotiel Coronado, near Hueleva in Southern Spain. This locomotive was built for 2ft 6in gauge and had 7x12in cylinders; it was one of those mentioned in the proceeding Chapter which, according to the drawing office register was: 'Delivered in parts, the boiler and firebox was finished and tested and the frames, stays and plates were machined and finished by ourselves, the other parts were supplied as rough forgings and castings to be machined by the buyers'. It was quite usual to dismantle locomotives for shipment, but not to supply the parts unfinished - an earlier engine for the same customer, number 2040 of February-March 1916, was also supplied under the same conditions. One if left wondering, especially as in both cases the parts were sent out in two separate batches, if this was not perhaps, a war time exigency to save machining time at Stafford.

The first engines of the modified design mentioned above, and there were a number of other modifications as well as the valve gear, all in efforts to help reduce production time and costs, were manufacturer's numbers 2042 to 2044 despatched in December 1917, followed by numbers 2045 to 2050 of March the following year. The reason why these locomotives took earlier numbers than 2052 mentioned in the last paragraph, which along with number 2051 had Bagnall-Price valve gear, is that whilst these two were ordered in 1915 and 1916, numbers 2042 to 2050 were not ordered

The last of the small circular firebox narrow-gauge locomotives fitted with Bagnall-Price valve gear was number 2052 of 1916. It is seen here in April 1961, very much out of use at mines belonging to Compania Espanola De Explosivos at Sotiel Coronado, which is near Hueleva in Southern Spain. This is one of the locomotives described in the text, originally supplied to the United Alkali Company Limited, and despatched to Spain as a kit of parts to be erected on site. By the time this picture was taken it was named MILANO - which is Spanish for a bird like a Falcon - and was numbered 13.

NAMCHIK, number 1962 of June 1913, is an example of the last variation in design of the narrow-gauge circular firebox saddle tank locomotives fitted with Bagnall-Price valve gear. A 7x12in cylinder engine, one of 15 small locomotives of this basic type supplied between 1894 and 1931, to the Assam Railways & Trading Company. They were all for use at coal mines and ancillary operations at and near Ledo and Tipong Pani in the extreme east of Assam, and some of them were still in use until a few years ago. In comparing this locomotive with the one in the next photograph, along with views of earlier examples of the same basic type in previous chapters, a comparison can be made as design changes were implemented over the years.

The locomotive in this picture makes an interesting comparison with NAMCHICK, as it is a later version of the same basic design, but after the change from Bagnall-Price valve gear to Walschaerts. Notice how the same size 7x12in cylinders are wider, the line of motion with Walschaerts valve gear being outside the main crank, whilst with Bagnall-Price it is inside; this is one of the disadvantages with Walschaerts gear, especially where loading gauge restrictions are an issue. The locomotive illustrated is one of a batch of three, three-foot gauge and new in December 1917 and January 1918, numbers 2058 to 2060. Ordered by the War Office Timber Supply Depot, they were for use on forestry work by the Canadian Forestry Corps - hence the designation CTS 1 on the bunker side - Canadian Timber Supply. These engines had varied lives, initially used in connection with the war time efforts to exploit home grown timber, for which the Canadians were drafted over to help. This particular one, number 2058, was new for forestry works at Corbridge in Hexhamshire, and finished its life with the Consett Iron Company Limited at Butsfield limestone quarry in Durham - it was not scrapped until 1951.

Walschaerts valve gear in close-up, as applied to the small narrow-gauge locomotives and shown with the valve in mid-gear - die in the middle of the link slot. The locomotives is number 2088 of 1919, a 6x9in cylinder version new to the Birmingham Tame & Rea District Drainage Board at Minworth in Warwickshire, although originally part of an order for six, numbers 2087 to 2092, placed by the Ministry of Munitions in June 1918. It currently resides on the Bredger & Wormshill Railway in Kent, where this picture was taken on 23 June 1994. The mechanical lubricator is a later fitting.

until 1918, and were allocated the numbers left vacant in the list originally allocated to the cancelled 0-6-2 side tank locomotives mentioned earlier, ordered by McLeod, Russell for use in India.

Before continuing with the main part of our story, this is perhaps a good point to pause a while and consider just how Bagnall would go about building a locomotive. It has to be remembered, that is those days a company like WG Bagnall Limited, would build a locomotive almost from scratch, and with very few bought-in components, whereas today most locomotive and train builders often do little more than erect vehicles, sub-contracting a whole host of parts, including in many cases complete sub-assemblies.

The process would start in the drawing office, and if the locomotive was of a customers design, like for example the Indian Railways Standard designs discussed earlier, then a complete set of drawings would

be supplied. The drawing office would study the drawings supplied and see if any modifications were required, due to the production facilities available, which on occasions was necessary. For example, frame plates might have to be made in two sections due to the size of the slotting machines available, whilst the drawings called for one piece plates. Any changes would of course, have to be discussed and approved by the customer, but usually issues of this nature would have been identified and resolved to both parties satisfaction at the tender stage. If on the other hand the locomotive was of the manufacturer's design, then a complete set of drawings would be needed and these might consist of several hundred for a large tender locomotive, or a much lesser number for small narrow-gauge tank engines. If the locomotive was basically to an existing design, then the drawings would be available and only an odd new one might be required for any

Another example of the re-designed 6x9in cylinder two-foot gauge version of the small narrow-gauge locomotives is PIXIE, number 2090 of April 1919, from the same batch as the engine in the pervious photograph. This one was sent on Ministry of Munitions instructions to the Staveley Coal & Iron Company, for use at ironstone quarries at Pilton in Rutland. It later had a varied career at various ironstone mines in Rutland and adjacent counties, and this photograph was taken on 28 July 1951 at the Cranford quarries in Northamptonshire. PIXIE became quite famous in preservation as for a long time it was in the ownership of the late Rev. Teddy Boston, and used on the railway around the Cadeby Rectory near Market Bosworth in Leicestershire. Today it is part of the Hollycombe Steam & Woodland Collection in West Sussex. (Late Ralph Russell Collection - Industrial Locomotive Society)

KITTY, number 2085 of March 1919, is one of the larger 7x12in cylinder engines, in this case built to suit three-foot gauge. The photograph was taken in March 1953 at the Hartshill granite quarries of Charles Abell Limited, near Atherstone in Warwickshire. One of a batch of six locomotives ordered in November 1918 by the Ministry of Munitions, it was originally employed on forestry work by the Canadian Forestry Corps. Some time after the war it was purchased by the maker's and in May 1923, after overhaul sold for use at Hartshill; it remained there until scrapped in 1958. Notice the missing cylinder lagging and other bumps and bruises resulting from many years hard work. (Frank Jones Collection -Industrial Locomotive Society)

modifications specified, perhaps a slightly smaller water tank capacity to reduce the axle-load, or different drawgear and couplings etc. Even if it was a completely new design, to reduce as far as possible the drawing office work, earlier drawing would be called up where it was felt existing designs of components, or indeed complete arrangements, valve gear for example, could be used, either for the odd part, or complete sub-assemblies. This would not only reduce the drawing office work, but also perhaps, the number of new patterns and manufacturing jigs required. Whatever the case, the chief draughtsman would ensure that wherever possible, the 'house style' was adhered to and he would personally check each and every new drawing adding his signature before production copies were released for the workshops. A new list would be started in a register under the individual manufacturer's number or numbers, listing all the relevant drawings for future reference.

Where a new design was felt appropriate, the usual practice would be for particular parts of the locomotive to be designated to individual draughtsman/designers; for example one man might be allocated the frames, wheels and axles; another cylinders and valve gear; another the boiler, and yet another the cab, tanks and bunker. The chief draughtsman and his deputy would keep an eye on progress, checking each drawing as it was completed, and ensuring they all came together as a complete locomotive. On completion of the

drawings, which could spread over several months, a schedule of material would be drawn up and an engine material order list started, so a record could be kept of what material was ordered, from whom and when.

In continuing this description it is perhaps best to use an actual example, and we have selected the material order list for the Indian W class mentioned earlier, as a typical example of what the Company would manufacture itself, and what it would buy in. The list would have details added of the external orders placed, for both raw material, castings, forgings and any complete components. Physical work in the shops would not necessarily wait until all the drawing were complete, or all the material was on-hand, and depending on the workload in the shops and the material available, drawings would be sent down for work to start. This would be particularly so with components having long production times, for example the amount of machining of a cylinder block after casting. If a large number of new patterns were required, then obviously, it would be logical to get the relevant drawings to the pattern shop as soon as possible. At the Castle Engine Works almost all the patterns were made in house as there was a very well equipped pattern shop, and any iron castings would be made in the similarly well equipped iron foundry, so the works was pretty well self contained in these respects. As the patterns were made available, whether new ones or existing ones called up by the drawings, the casting

D' HUBERT, a 7x12in cylinder 1ft 11⅝in gauge locomotive of the standard type, new in July 1919 for the Liverpool engineers and agents Bolling & Lowe Limited; this was a company that purchased a number of locomotives over the years. Designed to burn wood fuel was the reason for the rack on the saddle tank. Despatched to Liverpool Docks on 11 July 1919, unfortunately it missed the ship it was intended for and was sent back to Stafford! Redelivery was on 29 August, but the engine's final destination has gone unrecorded in surviving records. However, as it was sent all the way back to Stafford, rather than being held in storage at the docks, might suggest that wherever it was going ships did not sail there very often from British ports. There is a note in one of the order-books to the effect that when it arrived back, an instruction was issued to change the plates on the engine which had Bolling & Lowe's name on them and not Bagnalls, to ones with the lettering R Hamilton & Co Liverpool - a further note mentions that in order to do so the packing case would have to be opened! Notice that the wording on the plate on the cab side in the illustration has been etched out on the negative; under a glass it looks like the Bolling & Lowe plate originally fitted. Something of a mystery but a nice picture showing well the handsome lines of these locomotives.

would be made. Similarly, drawings of those components requiring forging would be sent to the forge. Registers were kept of all the patterns for individual types of locomotive, and the patterns themselves were individually numbered so that they could be traced and located with ease, as would be the case with any templates used in the forge.

The finished castings after fettling along with the forgings and many other component parts, for example boiler plates after rolling and flanging, as well as much of the raw material, would then go to the marking-off tables situated in the machine, boiler and plate shops. Here, once the machining drawings had arrived, the very important and skilled process of marking-out the areas to be machined and drilled etc, would take place as of course, the finished locomotive would only be as

good as the machining, and the machining would only be as good as the marking-out. After this process the parts would go to the machine shop for machining, or wherever else they were required next. The Castle Engine Works never had a steel foundry, so any steel castings would be bought in, but the patterns would be supplied by the Company, and the finished castings would be machined at Stafford. In the case of castings and forgings provision would have been made on the drawings for machining allowances. It is worth emphasising at this juncture, despite already perhaps, being obvious to the lay-reader, that steam locomotives at Stafford were very much hand built, even when orders consisted of quite large batches, and there was never a production line in its later accepted sense.

Among the components that would be sub-contracted would be most of the non-ferrous boiler fittings, gauge glass fittings, safety valves and injectors for example. Where locomotives were fitted with vacuum or air brake equipment this would be ordered in its entirety from the established manufacturers of this type of equipment, and there are other examples like propriety sanding equipment, oil firing equipment and electric lighting to name but a few. The Company kept a list of approved suppliers for this sort of equipment, as well as of course, all the raw material, nuts and bolts etc.

The boiler would be among the components with the longest construction time, so it would be important to get the material ordered and the relevant drawings passed to the plate and boiler shops as soon as possible. Again, only the finished steel, copper plates and the tubes (brass or steel) would be bought-in, all the

cutting, rolling and flanging being undertaken in the shops, followed by riveting the complete assembly - even the stays would be made in the machine shop. Wherever possible the drawing office would have to ensure that existing flanging blocks were suitable for flanging the plates, although of course, on occasions new ones would have to be made. In some cases where engines were built to customer's designs, the main line railways for example, flanging blocks and patterns might be loaned as a part of the contract arrangements. As all the various parts started to become available, cylinders and valve gear components after machining for example, they would be sent to the fitting shop where the various sub-assemblies would be put together, such as complete cylinders with valves and pistons, or bogies and trucks. Plate work for the frames, cab, tanks and

This photograph was taken on 2 April 1956 at the Briton Ferry Works near Swansea in Glamorgan. The locomotive is manufacturer's number 2062, BFW No 5, new in April 1918, although it had been ordered a year earlier. This locomotive is especially interesting as despite being one of the first of the standard narrow-gauge types to be fitted with Walschaerts valve gear; in November 1932 parts were supplied to convert it to Bagnall-Price valve gear! Notice that in order to retain the same cylinders with the off-set line of valve gear, the rod from the crosshead and the fulcrum lever are mounted outside the connecting rod, rather than inside as on the conventional arrangement. To accommodate this arrangement the fulcrum lever can be seen to have a distinct set in it. We do not know why this conversion was undertaken, except perhaps that the Company had an earlier engine fitted with Bagnall-Price valve gear - number 1787 of 1905 (see page 184) - and may have wanted standardisation, or maybe the return arm and combining lever arrangement did keep striking line-side obstructions! BFW No 5 was a large 9x14in cylinder version of the circular firebox design, in this case with 2ft 3½in diameter wheels and on 2ft 4½in gauge. For some strange reason Bagnall chose a photograph of this locomotive, taken at Briton Ferry and before the change of valve gear, for one of its publicity cards; the only known example of a locomotive appearing on one of these cards that was not new and photographed in the works yard. (Industrial Railway Society - Bernard Mettam Collection)

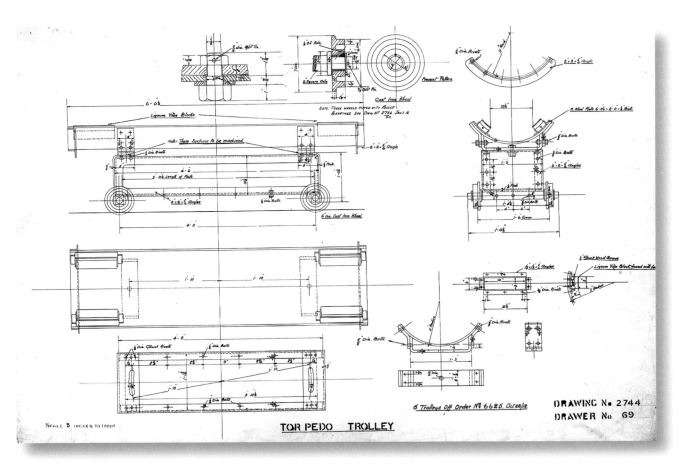

TORPEDO TROLLEY

Drawing of a 1ft 6in gauge torpedo trolley, one of several built in late 1918 and early 1919 - notice the drawing is dated 28 October 1918. The trolleys would have been too late to assist in the hostilities, and we do not know exactly how many were made or where they were delivered to, but there was an extensive 1ft 6in gauge system serving the Royal Arsenal at Woolwich.

bunker, footplating etc., would be cut out in the frame and plate shops, and in some cases - tanks for example - assembled there too. Remember that at this period in history there would be little welding work undertaken, and the tanks, bunkers and other plate work would be of riveted construction.

Once enough parts were to hand the erecting shop would start work, and a chargehand fitter/erector would be appointed to manage, with his gang, the erection of the engine, and this team would see the engine right through to it steam tests. The first job would be to get the frame plates placed on stands and properly aligned, and then, using rivets and fitted bolts as appropriate, the buffer beams and various frame stretches would be put in place, along with the horn plates, spring and brake hangers, smokebox saddle and all the other parts directly fixed to the frame. Cylinders would follow along with motion brackets, and then the axle-boxes,

wheels and axles. The wheels and axles would have been assembled in the wheel shop, together with any eccentric sheaves, and the axle-boxes would have been mated with the axles. Depending on the weight of the various parts, sometimes engines would be wheeled before the boiler was mounted, but on other occasions they would be wheeled afterwards. Among the later jobs would be setting the valves, lagging the boiler and fitting all the non-ferrous components. Perhaps the most significant part of the planning process was ensuring that all the parts came together at the right time, so that construction of the locomotive was not delayed, but on the other hand of course, minimising the amount of material on hand at any one time and keeping the costs associated with work in progress as low as possible. A close eye was always kept on the cash-flows associated with both buying in material and components as well as direct-labour and overheads.

When all was complete, the engine would be hauled outside, mated with its tender if it had one, and the fire would be lit, and steam raised. All the necessary tests would be undertaken, sometimes with the customer's inspecting engineer in attendance.

When all the necessary tests had been undertaken, and any minor adjustments made, and any painting required, arrangements would be made for the engine's despatch. As a general rule engines for customers in this country would be delivered fully erected, if narrow-gauge ones often loaded onto main-line wagons, but in the case of standard-gauge engines on their own wheels, and if they were not going very far - say up to about 25-30 miles - sometimes under their own steam. In these cases a crew would be sent from the customer, and along with a pilotman from the main-line railway and a Bagnall fitter, off they would go. On other occasions, the motion would be removed and either placed in the cab, or on an accompanying wagon, and the engine would be despatched to its destination in a goods train. On these occasions it would also be necessary for a Bagnall fitter to accompany the engine to attend to any lubrication issues en-route, and reassembly of the motion on arrival with the customer. He would also help to put the engine to work and if necessary, undertake any training of the customer's men.

Engines for export, depending on how big they were and how far they had to be moved from the port of disembarkation, would very often be dismantled after testing. Small engines could often be almost completely packed in cases - perhaps with just cabs and chimneys removed - but larger ones would be broken down to three main components; the boiler; the frames; wheels and cylinders; the cab and other parts. Tenders usually went complete, as did on occasions the medium sized engines, again with perhaps just chimneys, cabs and other extraneous components removed. The responsibility of the builder would vary depending on the type of purchase contract entered into with the customer. If the arrangements were free-on-board (FOB), then Bagnall would only have quoted to deliver the engines alongside at the port of embarkation; thereafter the responsibility would pass to whichever shipping agent the customer had appointed. Alternatively, the arrangement could have been on the basis of carriage-insurance-freight (CIF), in which case Bagnall would have quoted, and undertaken to be

responsible for movement of the engine to either the port of disembarkation, or even its final destination. In such cases a shipping agent would have been appointed to make all the necessary arrangements from loading onto railway wagons at Stafford, to the final agreed destination. It was not unknown too, for the arrangements to include the services of a Bagnall fitter going with the locomotive(s) to superintend erection if shipped dismantled, and to assist in putting them to work.

Glancing through the material orders for the first members of the W class, we find that the forged steel axles were bought-in machined, whilst the steel axle boxes which were also bought-in, were not machined, neither were the wheels or any other of the steel castings. These comprised the crossheads, fly cranks and tyres, although unusual as a general rule, in the case of these locomotives the piston rods and slidebars were also bought-in as un-machined forgings. Steel plate to a range of sizes was ordered for the boiler, smokebox, frames, tanks, cab, framing etc., and copper plates for the firebox. Other finished components bought-in were the trailing truck side control springs (these were spiral springs, which the Company did not make, though it did have facilities to make leaf springs), drivers brake valve, gun metal boiler fittings, clack boxes, cylinder cocks, boiler clothing, injectors, lamps, lubricator, copper pipes, boiler tubes, pressure gauge, whistle, and safety valves. This brief description illustrates that the greater part of the locomotive and tender was built at Stafford, from little more than cast iron, finished steel and copper plate bought direct from stockholders; only the steel castings - but with patterns supplied - copper pipes, boiler tubes, tyres, gunmetal fittings and a few other parts were bought-in. Nuts, bolts, rivets, washers and other fixings of course, were generally bought direct from a propriety supplier, but any special types of fixing would be made at the works.

By and large, arrangements on these lines continued for the duration of steam locomotive construction, although as time went on there was an increased use of welding techniques, in lieu of rivets, and to a lesser extent other types of fastenings. As the types of locomotives the firm built got larger and more complex, additional equipment often had to be sub-contracted, and the examples of train brake equipment - which really was a specialist activity - along with turbo-generators and electric lighting, superheater equipment and articulated drawbars are cases to point, some of which have already been mentioned. There were however, some notable exceptions with the Company designing and manufacturing its own specialist equipment. For example superheater headers and steam reversing gear. In the latter case during the Second World War no less, and despite propriety equipment being on the market, although perhaps not readily available.

At a general meeting of the Locomotive Manufacturers Association (LMA) on 19 July 1918, WG Bagnall Limited was elected a member - the Company had applied to join the previous month. Before discussing this membership, it is perhaps worth exploring a little of the history and purpose of this trade association, as the Company was to become heavily involved in its activities, and for the remainder of its independent existence. The origins of the LMA go back to 1870s, when the London & North Western Railway (LNWR) was in negotiations with the Lancashire & Yorkshire Railway (L&Y) regarding a possible amalgamation of the two companies. In the years 1871 to 1874 the LNWR supplied the L&Y with no less than 65 of its standard Ramsbottom designed DX class 0-6-0 goods tender engines, of which no less than 59 were built new at Crewe for this purpose. As events turned out Parliament refused to allow the amalgamation to go ahead, but word got around the private locomotive builders regarding this supply of locomotives between the two companies and they were not pleased. Even less so when they heard that the LNWR were going to be asked by the L&Y to tender against the trade, for additional new locomotives.

Following these concerns a meeting took place in London on 29 April 1875, when a number of the private builders representatives got together, seemingly under the auspices of E Lucie Sacie of the Yorkshire Engine Company of Sheffield, who had written to 12 of the private locomotive building firms. At this preliminary meeting the chair was taken by John Robinson of Sharp Stewart & Company Limited, and on a motion made by JH Kitson of Kitson & Company Limited, and seconded by Lucie Sacie, it was agreed that each company should contribute a sum of money so that counsel's opinion might be obtained. The issue was the legality of the main-line railway companies building new locomotives in their own workshops for sale to other railway companies. A sub-committee was appointed to this end, and having briefed counsel it met at the Midland Hotel in Derby on 4 May 1875; this was in effect, the first meeting of the LMA. At this meeting the following firms were represented: Avonside Engine Company; Vulcan Foundry; Neilson; Manning Wardle; Dubs; Kitson; Beyer Peacock; Sharp Stewart. Counsel's opinion was that the main-line railway companies did not have powers under their various acts of incorporation, to make either locomotives or rolling stock for external sale. The committee therefore, agreed to apply to the Court of Chancery for an Injunction to stop them doing so.

There was a further meeting on 4 June 1875, when the resolution was actually passed to form what was referred to as an Association of Locomotive Manufacturers, and the initial members were: Sharp Stewart; Neilson; Nasmyth Wilson; Kitson; Avonside; Yorkshire; Beyer Peacock; Manning Wardle; Dubs. Subscriptions were based on the number of men employed by each company, and at the next meeting on 16 July, R&W Hawthorn Leslie and the Hunslet Engine Company joined, followed in November by Fox Walker coming to the party. At the railway jubilee celebrations held in Darlington that summer (1875), a number of discussions took place between J Hawthorn Kitson, of Kitson & Company, and Sir Richard Moon, the domineering chairman of the LNWR. This resulted in a letter from Sir Richard to Hawthorn Kitson, making clear that it was never the intention of the LNWR to supply locomotives on a routine basis to other railway companies, but it was only helping out the L&Y at a time when that company found itself in great difficulty in view of a shortage of locomotives. Notwithstanding this, the case for the manufacturers went before the High Court of Chancery, Justice Sir J Jessel sitting on 16 December 1875, and he found in favour of the manufacturers. It was 83 years before this restriction was lifted from the main-line railway workshops, under provisions of the Transport Act 1968.

The committee met again on both the day of the hearing (doubtless with some rejoicing!), and on 31 March 1876, when it was decided to make the Association permanent, as there were a number of other issues that concerned the manufacturers. Not least among these were the various bills before

Parliament at the time, regarding working arrangements between the main-line railway companies, and the use of locomotives belonging to one company by another. By 1879 Robert Stephenson & Company and Vulcan Foundry had joined the fold, but Fox Walker was by then in liquidation and soon left. The LMA with a permanent secretary appointed continued its activities in protecting the interest of its members, but it was some years before any more firms joined. Kerr, Stuart became members in July 1914, and Andrew Barclay, Hudswell Clarke and Peckett in December 1916; as we have seen WG Bagnall Limited joined in 1918.

We do not know exactly what prompted WG Bagnall Limited to join, but it may have been a number of the concerns that were exercising the minds of the industry generally, as the First World War drove inextricably on. A special advisory committee of the Association had met on several occasions between November 1917 and March 1918, to consider the concept of a central selling agency for the industry, and as a possible prelude to this member firms agreed to circulate among themselves details of enquiries and orders received. There was a dissenter to this arrangement, and Kerr, Stuart & Company resigned as a consequence. At a meeting on 12 April 1918, it was agreed to establish a scheme whereby a certain percentage of profits, or of contract prices, should be pooled for the future benefit of members. There was also a suggestion to consider a complete fusion of member company interests (whatever that might have entailed), and once again the concept of establishing a central selling agency. In the event only the concept of a levy was enacted, and this excluded orders under £1,000, along with any spare parts supplied - including boilers. The intention was for the money accumulated to be used not only to further the interests of the industry, but also to help individual firms obtain contracts by in effect, and as opportunities arose, subsidising tender prices.

It will come of little or no surprise to readers to find that WS Edwards became the Bagnall representative at the LMA, and he appears to have attended his first meeting, which was held in London, on 24 January 1919. This meeting was a special one convened in the light of intelligence that some of the armaments firms were rumoured to be considering entering the locomotive building market, as their traditional business collapsed on the cessation of hostilities. There

was at this time a substantial need for new locomotives, both for home and export markets, as the railways of the world started to overcome backlogs of both capital investment, and maintenance after the years of hostilities. The meeting decided to request an audience with Sir Henry Fowler (of Midland and LMS Railway fame) who was at that time in charge of the railway material department of the Ministry of Munitions. A meeting with Fowler was convened when he was questioned as to whether in his opinion, the entry of the armament firms of William Beardmore of Glasgow, Vickers of Barrow and Armstrong Whitworth of Newcastle, and not least the government's Woolwich Arsenal, into the locomotive building industry was permanent, or just to help clear a back log of demand. He answered that he felt that the three private companies might indeed consider it permanent, depending on the success they had, and any profits made.

It was pointed out to Sir Henry by the committee, that locomotive building had been restricted during the war, and men had been drafted away from the locomotive builders to armaments firms, and that if they were released the existing builders might be able to cope with the projected workload. The essence of the issue was the fact that locomotive production by the 'home' builders had been reduced by 50% at Ministry instigation, so that the industry could concentrate on munitions and weapons manufacture. To add insult to injury during these discussions a Mr Valentine Stewart, who accompanied Sir Henry at the meeting, and it seems was in some way connected with Beardmore's, asked if patterns might be loaned by the existing companies to those wanting to join the industry; he got a very stormy reception! In 1921 William Beardmore applied for membership of the LMA, as did Armstrong Whitworth in 1924, but that is another story of which brief details will be found in Chapter Eight.

Some time later Edwards was appointed to the standing committee of the LMA, and he attend his first meeting on 19 February 1920, and thereafter took a very prominent part in the activities of the Association. Moreover, there was an issue concerning the Company on the agenda for that meeting, and this seems to have been the first time the Company was directly involved with the LMA on a specific issue. The question was a potential order for five 2ft 6in gauge Indian W class

0-6-2 tender engines; they were the same design as those mentioned earlier. Clearly Edwards was anxious to get this particular order, as his company had done all the detail design work, and indeed built all the previous members of the class. What he wanted was protection for his tender against other companies bidding, as both Hudswell Clarke and R&W Hawthorn Leslie, had expressed an interest. In exchange for such protection the members at the meeting wanted Bagnall to forfeit to the LMA, 2½% of the value of the order if they were

successful, such a sum to be paid into the LMA funds. This sort of arrangement was in the sprit of the principles that had been developed to help protect members, and ensure they did not undercut each other, but at the same time help to ensure contracts were not awarded to manufacturers in other countries. In this particular case, agreement was not reached on the lines mentioned above, but with one exception (unfortunately not mentioned by name) all the members agreed not to undercut the Bagnall tender. In

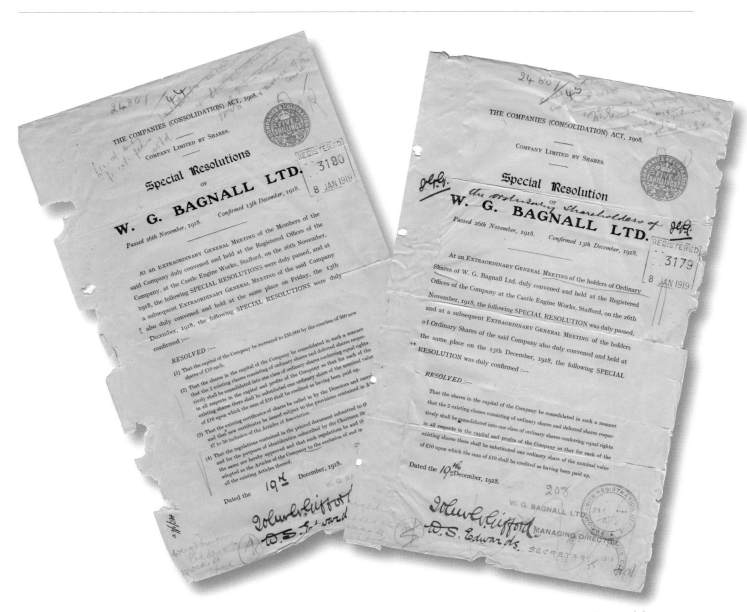

The two Special Resolutions passed on 26 November 1918 and confirmed on 13 December, concerning the consolidation of the two types of shares mentioned in the text, the increase in capital to £35,000, and the adoption of new Articles of Association. Notice that WS Edwards has signed these as the Secretary of the Company, John Gifford being the only Director.

the event the Bagnall tender was accepted, and the Bombay Baroda & Central India Railway placed the order on 10 February 1920, at a price of £2,375 per engine, dismantled and packed for shipment free-on-board. The completed locomotives were manufacturer's numbers 2138 to 2142; the first two were sent to Birkenhead Docks on 1 July 1921, the second two to the same place on 8 August, and the last one to Salford Docks in Manchester on 24 August - all consigned to Bombay. We shall return to the activities of the LMA, and the Bagnall involvement, in subsequent Chapters.

The war years saw the introduction of what became a regular series of social activities for the employees, doubtless engendered by the war-time team-sprit prevalent at the time. One of the first events was a whist drive held in the Borough Hall on 6 August 1918, the proceeds being donated towards a new operating theatre at the Staffordshire Infirmary. This was followed by a social evening at the Central Hall on Friday the 11 January the following year, when over 90 members of staff and their wives were present. Once again there was a whist drive and in this case followed by dancing. Sydney Edwards wife Elizabeth appears to have largely taken charge of organising these activities, as well as a Christmas and new year party, and a Christmas party for the children of the staff, all of which became annual events. She continued to take the lead in organising these activities and was the life-line behind them until shortly after her husband died in 1946.

With the end of hostilities, it is opportune to start a new Chapter in the history of the Company, but before doing so there are a few financial matters to outline. First of all, at some point during the war, George Fletcher, the company secretary retired; Fletcher had been with the Company from its earliest times, and his position was taken by WS Edwards, who having for some time combined the positions of general manager and chief draughtsman, now added this responsibility to that of general manager! During the war years the firm did return to making an annual profit on its activities, the first in 1916. Both 1914 and 1915 had continued the loss making trend, £1,196 and £2,149 respectively, whilst the average profit in the years 1916 to 1919 was £3,479, rising from £285 in 1916 to £7,832 in 1919. It 1920 it climbed further to a figure of £19,137 on a turnover of £122,557 - the 1914 turnover was £57,798.

At an EGM of the Company attended by Gifford and Edwards on 26 November 1918, two special resolutions were passed, confirmed at a second EGM on 13 December the same year. The first resolution consolidated the two types of shares in the Company; ordinary and deferred, into one class of share having a value of £10 - the value of both classes of shares hitherto. The second resolution increased the share capital of the Company from its existing figure of £30,000, by £5,000 to £35,000, achieved by the creation of 500 new shares of £10 each. At the same time revised articles of association were adopted, much simpler than the original ones and in compliance with the various Companies Acts enacted between 1908 and 1917. For the year 1919, and with some consistency thereafter, Edwards was allocated shares in the Company as a bonus to his salary; the first allocation was 57 shares of £10 each, considered as fully paid, on 20 December 1919. Later, at a general meeting of the Company dated 31 October 1921, WS Edwards and John Gifford's brother James Caldwell Gifford were elected directors of WG Bagnall Limited; hitherto, as outlined in an earlier Chapter, since 11 April 1911, John Gifford had been the sole director of the Company.

Chapter Seven

Post War Expansion

I n the last Chapter we saw considerable expansion of the works, its equipment and facilities, both just before and during the war, partly resulting from a policy to enable larger locomotives to be constructed. The balance sheet value of the machinery and plant in 1915 was a little over £10,000 and by 1919 was no less than £30,000. Although inflation had a part to play in this, the Ministry of Munitions loan outlined in the last Chapter, along with the two debenture issues, were the principal factors. The first debenture issue was dated 8 August 1912 for £11,000, and the second one on 15 May 1914 for £7,000: in both cases with Barclays Bank Limited. However, in the period since the death of WG Bagnall, the profitability of the Company had been far from what might be considered acceptable, for example 1908 was but a break-even year, and in the years 1909 to 1914, the annual profit averaged only £1,339. However, in the years 1915 to 1919 the average increased to £3,257, and in the following two years - 1920 and 1921 - there was a noticeable increase to an average of £21,393, and this enabled the Company on 21 November 1921 and 31 December the following year, to redeem the two debenture issues.

In this Chapter we shall explore how the Company was able to continue its expansion into new markets, and in particular the increasing demand for metre-

gauge locomotives for the railways of India, as that country improved and extended its railway communications. The influence of Sydney Edwards in the ongoing developments and how instrumental he was in the firm's expansion, as well as getting the initial foothold in the Indian market through Rendel & Robertson, has already been outlined. The Giffords assumed a lesser role in the day to day running of the Company over the next few years, by and large leaving the day-to-day control in Edwards's hands. By this time the brothers lived in a large house called 'Crossfields', a little south of the town at Weeping Cross, and neither of them ever married. John Gifford is remembered as a rather kindly sole, he would arrive at the works in the summer months on his push-bike, in his tweeds and cycle clips, generally not staying very long! On Saturday mornings before work stopped for the weekend, he would usually make a tour of the workshops, often accompanied by Edwards, and whilst speaking to most of the men rarely made a comment on the work itself. The 15 years or so since Gordon Bagnall had ceased to be involved in the day-to-day management of the Company, and the close working relationship, and indeed friendship, built up between John Gifford and Sydney Edwards, was beginning to work to Edwards's advantage. As a result of John

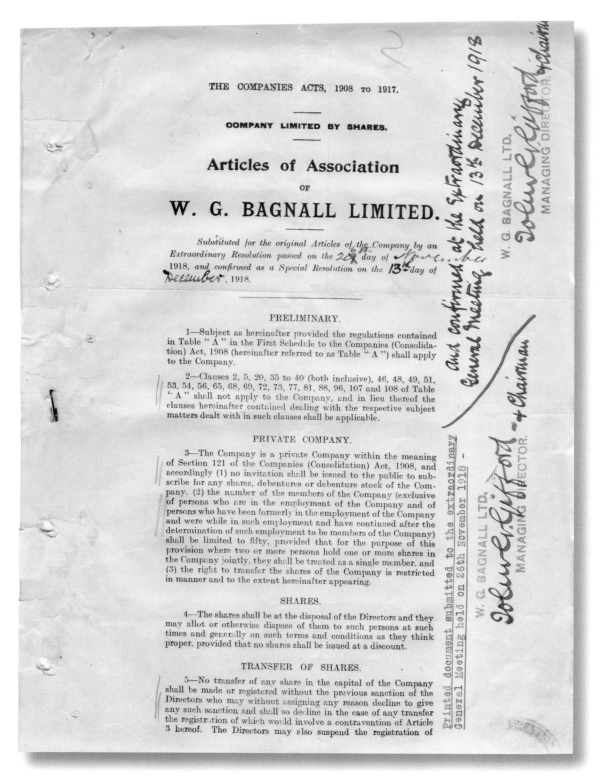

THE COMPANIES ACTS, 1908 TO 1917.

COMPANY LIMITED BY SHARES.

Articles of Association

OF

W. G. BAGNALL LIMITED.

Substituted for the original Articles of the Company by an Extraordinary Resolution passed on the 26th day of November 1918, and confirmed as a Special Resolution on the 13th day of December, 1918.

PRELIMINARY.

1—Subject as hereinafter provided the regulations contained in Table " A " in the First Schedule to the Companies (Consolidation) Act, 1908 (hereinafter referred to as Table " A ") shall apply to the Company.

2—Clauses 2, 5, 20, 35 to 40 (both inclusive), 46, 48, 49, 51, 53, 54, 56, 65, 68, 69, 72, 73, 77, 81, 88, 96, 107 and 108 of Table " A " shall not apply to the Company, and in lieu thereof the clauses hereinafter contained dealing with the respective subject matters dealt with in such clauses shall be applicable.

PRIVATE COMPANY.

3—The Company is a private Company within the meaning of Section 121 of the Companies (Consolidation) Act, 1908, and accordingly (1) no invitation shall be issued to the public to subscribe for any shares, debentures or debenture stock of the Company, (2) the number of the members of the Company (exclusive of persons who are in the employment of the Company and of persons who have been formerly in the employment of the Company and were while in such employment and have continued after the determination of such employment to be members of the Company) shall be limited to fifty, provided that for the purpose of this provision where two or more persons hold one or more shares in the Company jointly, they shall be treated as a single member, and (3) the right to transfer the shares of the Company is restricted in manner and to the extent hereinafter appearing.

SHARES.

4—The shares shall be at the disposal of the Directors and they may allot or otherwise dispose of them to such persons at such times and generally on such terms and conditions as they think proper, provided that no shares shall be issued at a discount.

TRANSFER OF SHARES.

5—No transfer of any share in the capital of the Company shall be made or registered without the previous sanction of the Directors who may without assigning any reason decline to give any such sanction and shall so decline in the case of any transfer the registration of which would involve a contravention of Article 3 hereof. The Directors may also suspend the registration of

Front page of the revised Articles of Association of the Company as presented to an EGM of the on 26 November 1918, and confirmed by Special Resolution dated 13 December 1918. Although these Articles gave powers for the Company to have between two and five Directors, provided John Gifford Gifford was a Director, he could in fact still be the only one. They also established Gifford's remuneration as £750 per annum and that of the other Directors at £100 (this applied to WS Edwards and John's brother James when they were appointed Directors in October 1921), along with a bonus for John Gifford equal to 15% of the annual net profits provided that this figure combined with his salary did not exceed £2,000. Note his signature as both Chairman and Managing Director.

Gifford relaxing his daily commitment to the business, over the next few years Edwards's power and influence over almost everything that went on increased considerably, and not only in the day-to-day activities, but the longer term strategy too. John Gifford had however, been much more active in earlier times, and a copy of one of the firm's catalogues that had clearly been his personal copy still exists. It is well worn and full of hand written notes with additional pages stuck in containing extra information on prices and other issues; obviously one he had kept with him as a sort of aid memoir, perhaps when visiting customers, old and new, and otherwise promoting the firm's products.

In the last Chapter mention was made of Edwards becoming a shareholder in 1919, and in each of the following six years his share holding increased by the allocation of new shares as a bonus, in addition to his salary, such that by 1927 he held 719 shares in the Company, against the Giffords total of 3,281. At an extraordinary general meeting (EGM) of the Company held on 31 October 1921, a special resolution was passed for an alteration to the articles of association, such that any undistributed profits could be capitalised in the form of additional shares, and that such additional shares could be apportioned pro-rata, to the shareholders. This resolution and change of articles was confirmed at a second EGM held on 17 November 1921 and the revised articles also empowered the Company to raise its maximum share capital, from the existing figure of £35,000, to £40,000, by the issue of 500 additional £10 shares. These additional clauses in the articles, had the effect in subsequent years, of enabling additional shares to be allocated to the shareholders, that is the Gifford brothers and Edwards, out of otherwise undistributed profits.

Like all other parts of manufacturing industry, WG Bagnall Limited had to contend with the enormous increase in rates of pay during, and just after the war years. The last of the increases were however, closely followed by the significant depression in manufacturing industry as the enormous war-time engineering needs declined; as a result, the rates of pay went down again, and even more rapidly than they had increased. The basis of a substantial component of the company's method of costing was the rates of pay paid to its staff, and for this purpose whatever the fitters rate was at a particular time, became the key factor. In 1914 the fitters rate was £1 15/- (£1 75p) for the 50 hour week the Company worked, but by December 1918 as a result of various war bonuses, and no less than seven of what were called 'Ministry of Munitions Awards', it had increased to £3 3/ 6d (£3 17½p). Subsequently, following a series of national wage awards within the engineering industry generally, the fitters rate peaked at £3 17/ 6d (£3 87½p) in June 1920. A little over a year later on 20 July 1921 it started to fall, slowly at first to £3 14/ 6d (£3 72½p), but by September 1922 it was down to £2 15/ (£2 75p), remaining at around that figure for a long time. However, by August 1927 it had crept up again to £2 17/- (£2 85p). To help illustrate the effects these wage rates had on the firm's products, let us take the example of the 2ft 6in gauge Indian W class 0-6-2 tender locomotives. The first examples built before the war and despatched in 1913, were sold for £1,315 each. Two more ordered in June 1922 had a selling price of £3,275, whilst a series of six tank engine versions ordered in August 1925, were sold for £2,250 each; it kept the cost office pretty busy continually adjusting rates.

Our knowledge of some of the key individuals involved in the Company not unexpectedly increases in more recent times, and your authors were able to personally interview a number of them. Other important people in the Company, who we were not able to meet, had in many cases been quite well known to those individuals we were introduced to. As well as the Gifford brothers, Sydney Edwards, Reg Gard and Bill Parkinson who have already been mentioned, listed below are some of the other key individuals on the salaried staff in 1924: The erecting shop foreman was Fred Ewington, and the other shop foreman included Jack Dale in the fitting shop; Jim Woollems in the machine shop; Charlie Homer the foreman smith; Harry 'Dick' Walker in the boiler shop; Arthur Slinn in the joiners shop; Jim Robinson in the tool room; George White in the pattern shop; Bill Brown in the foundry; Oliver Jennings the foreman painter; Joe Duckers in the wagon shop; Fred Schofield in the stores; Stan Fisher in the power house. Among the draughtsman were Reg Machin, Victor Bill, L Jones, Percy Godfrey and Geoff Owen. The buyer was Percy Critchley, the chief cost clerk Fred Parker, and his assistant for a number of years was Horace Lorton. The chief cashier was Charlie Tunnicliffe, the chief wages clerk was Harold Coates and Alice Evans (later Alice Lamb) acted as the secretary to John Gifford and Sydney Edwards.

It is perhaps worth saying a little about Frank Percy Critchley, as he claimed in later years to have been only the second indentured apprentice the Company employed. Remember however, that as far back as Gordon Bagnall's time, 'premium' apprentices had been on the books, and in those cases fees had been paid. Percy was a native of Stafford, where he was born on 4 March 1901, joining Bagnalls in September 1916; he was bound until March 1922. Percy studied theory at Stafford Technical College and the latter part of his training was undertaken in the drawing office. In August 1920 Edwards proposed him for graduate membership of the I Mech E, and he took the graduate entrance examination on 19 November 1920; he was elected an associate member in November the following year. After spending some time as a draughtsman, in 1924 he took up the position of buyer, but in about 1933 left the Company to join the Austin Motor Company at Longbridge. Percy also claimed that CA Poulson was the first indentured apprentice the Company employed, and of course, a contemporary eventually replacing him as the buyer; hitherto he had been employed in the drawing office as a draughtsman. Obviously a popular character around the works, Poulson gave a party for the staff at the Vine Hotel in Stafford on the evening of Friday 26 June 1920, to celebrate his 21st birthday and the completion of his apprenticeship. Sydney Edwards presented him with a suitably inscribed silver cigarette case on behalf of his colleagues.

Emphasising Edwards's interest in the progress of the firm's apprentices, at the annual staff Christmas dinner held on 23 December 1922, along with the festivities a presentation was made. Six apprentices were awarded prizes consisting of technical books, with John Gifford and Mrs Edwards making the presentations. The lads were W Evans; P Godfrey; G Gandy; A Summers; C Thorpe and L Jones. Jones in fact, had had no less than five presentations of books during his apprenticeship and later became a draughtsman, as noted above. In his short talk Edwards mentioned that at the time 500 men and boys were employed and that despite the depression that was beginning to seriously effect manufacturing industry, the works was fully employed and he pointed out how important he felt it was for the apprentices to improve their education at the technical college, and

how the firm would give them every encouragement. Mention of this encouragement and full support by Edwards in the training and further education of the firm's apprentices has already been made in the last Chapter, and he never faltered or wavered in promoting it both verbally and more importantly in practical support. He personally conducted recruitment interviews, and saw the boys individually as their apprenticeship progressed, and despite the pretty awesome front he might have presented to those impressionable young men, he could in fact be a very understanding mentor.

The first few years following the cessation of hostilities resulted on the one hand orders for locomotives and rolling stock to replace the depredations of the war years, whilst on the other, the first signs of the onset of a long and wearing period of depression in manufacturing industry generally. The orders about to be described graphically illustrate these two strands that were to be so much a feature of business over the next 15 years or so, as the Company very often struggled to keep its head above water. The first order was a substantial one, a further 20 of the Indian railways metre-gauge F class locomotives were ordered in January 1919. Seven locomotives were for the Rohilkund & Kumaon Railway, manufacturer's numbers 2110 to 2116, and the remainder for the Bengal & North Western Railway, numbers 2118 to 2129; they were all delivered between March 1920 and May 1921. In February 1920 five more of the 2ft 6in gauge Indian W class 0-6-2 tender engines were ordered by the Bombay Baroda & Central India Railway, numbers 2138 to 2142, and these are the engines mentioned in the last Chapter in connection with the involvement of the Locomotive Manufacturers Association (LMA) in the placement of orders. They were despatched in July and August 1921. To illustrate the other side of the coin, the home market was not nearly as lucrative and a batch of four of the standard-gauge 0-4-0 saddle tank industrial shunting locomotives with 14x20in cylinders and 3ft 6½in diameter wheels were laid down to a stock order dated November 1918. This order was placed both in the anticipation of British firms wanting to renew their shunting locomotive fleets after years of intensive use and little maintenance during the war, along with the need to keep the work force employed. In the event the four locomotives found customers quite slowly, and the last one was not despatched until October 1923. The manufacturer's numbers were 2105 to 2108; the first two went to the Barrow Hematite Steel Company at Barrow in November 1919, number 2107 was sold to the Birchenwood Colliery at Kidsgrove near Stoke-on-Trent in September 1922, whilst the last one, number 2108, not sold until October 1923, went to the Burton-on-Trent Brewers Worthington & Company Limited. There is an interesting story surrounding the Birchenwood engine, as this company had an older Bagnall locomotive, number 1402 of 1892, mentioned in an earlier Chapter. In June 1922 this locomotive was sent to Stafford for overhaul, but on examination was found to be in such a poor condition, that a deal was struck for the new locomotive, whilst a scrap value was given for the old one. The new one took the name of the old one - ALEXANDER - and the old name plates were transferred; it lasted until a later coking plant on the Birchenwood site at Kidsgrove closed in 1973, after which it was scrapped.

The small 6in and 7in cylinder circular firebox four-wheeled saddle tank design for the narrow-gauge, remained a popular product in the immediate post war years, and a number of pre-war customers came back with repeat orders. Another particularly significant order was for three 2ft 6in gauge 2-6-2 tender engines ordered by a firm of Indian managing agents, Forbes, Forbes Campbell & Company, for the Larkana Jacobabad Railway. This was a 53 mile long line situated west of the Indus, in what is now Pakistan, and although sanctioned in March 1916, completion was delayed due to the hostilities, and even then it only opened in sections between February 1922 and October

W. G. BAGNALL, LTD., CASTLE ENGINE WORKS, STAFFORD.

2-6-2 LOCOMOTIVE.
For dimensions see other side of card.

So far as is known the Company only produced four colour advertising cards like this one, for which colour illustrations were commissioned. Larkana Jacobabad Railway No 3 as depicted here was manufacturer's number 2152 of 1921. The three engines were extremely neat and handsome locomotives and at the time to an advanced design for the Indian narrow-gauge railways. Piston valve cylinders and superheaters were fitted, in fact the first superheated locomotives built by the Company; notice the high pitched boiler and Belpaire wrapper - the former to allow for a large fire grate and ashpan. Other modern features included Ross Pop safety valves, a mechanical lubricator and a variable blast-pipe top.

The fourth engine supplied to the Larkana Jacobabad Railway was number 2210 of 1923, seen here on 25 January 1945 at the Jullundur Military Railway, where it had migrated in 1940 when the line was converted to broad-gauge. Carrying its North Western Railway number 169, as this railway had taken over operation of the Larkana Jacobabad by the time the engines were delivered. Notice the engine is still in quite nice external condition, has been fitted with the vacuum brake - the engines were not fitted when new - and the addition of a tender-cab. The 45 gallon oil drum on the tender may be serving as a vacuum brake reservoir. This design is thought to have been the genesis of the later quite numerous Indian standard 2ft 6in gauge ZB class.

1923. To work the line Reg Gard and his team designed from scratch a very handsome locomotive with 13x16in outside cylinders and three-foot diameter coupled wheels. Walschaerts valve gear drove 6½in diameter piston valves with a full gear travel of 3½in; the lap was ¾in and the lead ⅛in. The superheated boiler had a Belpaire top firebox, and these were the first engines built at Stafford to be both superheated and fitted with piston valves. The superheater was a propriety 10 element Schmidt unit, the working pressure was 160 psi, and the weight in working order for the engine and tender was 42 tons. Molesworth & Molesworth were the consulting engineers appointed by the managing agents, conducting a watching brief on the design work, construction and testing. As might be expected, the Company were very proud of the completed locomotives, manufacturer's numbers 2150 to 2152, even to the extent of having a coloured publicity card produced, one of only four. Despatch was in October

and November 1921, and there was a repeat order for a fourth identical locomotive - number 2210 - despatched in July 1923. These locomotives provide an insight on how the selling prices and manufacturer's margins had reduced in sympathy with the fitters rate discussed above. The first three cost £7,000 each, free-on-board at Birkenhead Docks for Karachi, with the construction costs quoted as £5,834, whilst the fourth one was sold for £3,800, the maker's recording a profit of £667. By comparison remember, the W class supplied before the war, and only slightly smaller, were sold for £1,315 each.

The Larkana Jacobabad Railway was converted to broad-gauge in 1940, and two of these locomotives then migrated to the Jullundur Military Railway on the opposite side of the Indus. Later, in 1961, they found their way to the Kosi Project Railway, which supported a large irrigation scheme in Nepal. Before leaving these locomotives it is worth recording that the later Indian Railway Standards Committee (IRS) 2ft 6in gauge

The only locomotive built by the Company that could in any way be considered a roadside tramway engine was this one, number 2153 of 1921, for the LNWR owned Wolverton & Stony Stratford Tramway. This picture was taken after delivery and shows the side skirts in place. Notice the warning bell and the encasement of the safety valves; this was a later addition and perhaps, to help divert any escaping steam. Later still a tall extension chimney was added to take the exhaust over the top of the double-deck tramcars. Apart from the few concessions for street tramway use, this locomotives was a standard 10in cylinder industrial locomotive.

2-6-2 tender engine of the ZB Class, for which Bagnall was awarded the detail design and prototype build contract, and of which we shall hear more later, was largely based on the Larkana Jacobabad engines.

Until Government intervention as the industrial depression of manufacturing industry continued on its inexorable way, the Company built very few locomotives for the main-line railways in this country. There were however a few exceptions, single orders for small narrow-gauge locomotives that it would have been quite uneconomic for the main-line companies to design, and then build in their own workshops. Before the war the Company had only supplied three small narrow-gauge locomotives for the main-line railways, one for the North Staffordshire Railway in 1901, and two for the London & North Western Railway (LNWR), one in 1893 and another in 1915. However, in October 1921 another locomotive was supplied to

the LNWR, manufacturer's number 2153, for use on the 3ft 6in gauge Wolverton & Stony Stratford Tramway, which the LNWR owned and operated. Being a roadside tramway this line came under the jurisdiction of the various Tramways Acts, which included clauses regarding the wheels and motion of steam locomotives being concealed from public view, ostensibly so as not to frighten horses. The locomotives were also required, in the terminology of the Acts, to 'consume their own smoke', although few of them seem to have been 100% successful in this respect.

Until the Bagnall was delivered specially designed tramway type locomotives had been employed, but as the new locomotive was a conventional 0-4-0 saddle tank with 10x15in cylinders and 2ft 9¼in diameter wheels, the wheels and motion were covered by skirts below footplate level; they hinged upwards for access. While this seems to have satisfied one of the requirements, nothing was done to avoid the emission of smoke!

Fitted with Bagnall-Price valve gear and a steam brake, the locomotive was finished in the standard LNWR black livery with red and grey lining, and was delivered to Mr Trevethick, of the carriage department at Wolverton. One of the tramway's prime functions was to transport the staff to and from Wolverton Works, and as the earlier locomotives were in a poor condition by the time the Bagnall arrived, it seems to have provided the main stay of motive power on the tramway after its delivery. In fact apart from one example, it appears that all the earlier locomotives had already been scrapped, or soon were. Although reputably numbered 5 in the tramway lists, there is no photographic evidence that it ever carried this number. In an attempt to carry the smoke above the double deck tramcars used on the line, a rather crude and tall chimney extension was later fitted - evidence if need be, that this locomotive at least, did not consume its own smoke! The tramway closed on 2 May 1926, ostensibly for the duration of the infamous general strike of that year, but in the event it never reopened. No further employment was found for this comparatively new locomotive, doubtless in view of its relatively unusual track gauge, and the London Midland & Scottish Railway which had absorbed the LNWR in 1923, does not appear to have tried to sell it. Presumably therefore, it would have been scrapped, doubtless after a period of storage at Wolverton Works. This was the nearest the Company ever came to building a tramway locomotive, although they did use an artists impression of the more usual type of tramway locomotive in one of the early catalogues.

W. G. BAGNALL, LTD., CASTLE ENGINE WORKS, STAFFORD.

TYPE E 2154—0-6-0 LOCOMOTIVE.

This is another of the four colour publicity cards produced by the firm. Like the earlier one it illustrates a locomotive in the Company's standard colour of green with red, black and yellow lining. Unless a customer specified something different, this is the livery they got! The engine is one of several to this neat narrow-gauge side-tank design, supplied to both India and Mauritius. Notice the jack and re-railing ramp alongside the smokebox and the double cab roof. Manufacturer's No. 2154, mentioned in the text, was one of a batch, numbers 2154 to 2159, for India.

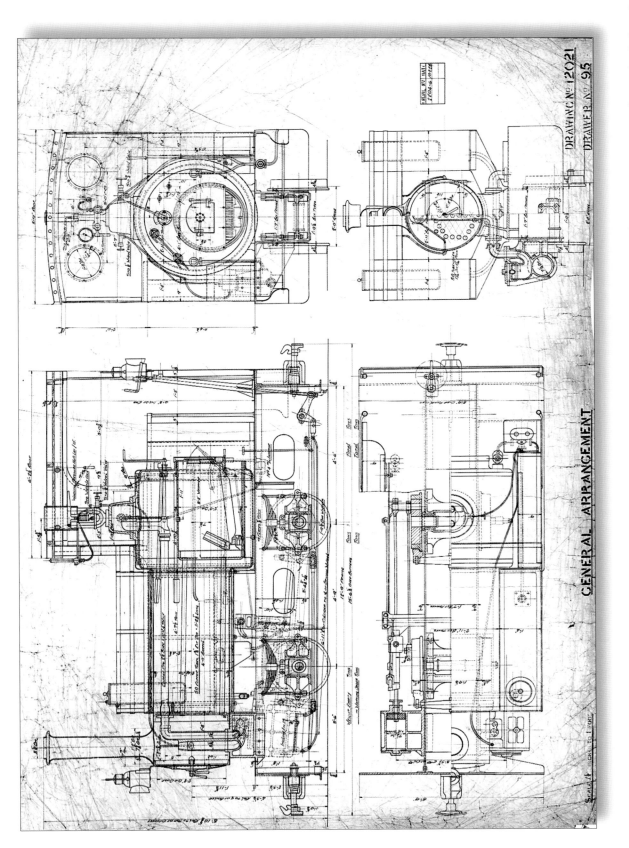

DRAWING No. 12021

DRAWER No. 95

GENERAL ARRANGEMENT

General arrangement drawing number 12021; this illustrates a four-wheel version of the engine in the colour illustration on the previous page - notice the circular firebox. Six locomotives were ordered, numbers 2204 to 2209, delivered in March and April 1923, to the order of the India Office for the United Provinces Public Works Department, Irrigation Branch. There were despatched three each to Bambassa and Shahgarh, both places on the Rohilkund & Kumaon Railway near Pilibit. Two of them later found their way to the Bihar State Sugar Factory at Sakri, and were still there, although out of use, in 1996.

Another of Reg Gard's designs was a neat narrow-gauge 0-6-0 side tank with 7¼in diameter cylinders, 1ft 9½in diameter wheels and Walschaerts valve gear. The first order was for six, manufacturer's numbers 2154 to 2159, despatched between June and August 1921. These six were two-foot gauge, ordered by the India Office for the United Provinces public works department and shipped via Birkenhead Docks to Bombay; their ultimate destination was an irrigation depot at Bareilly. Later a four-wheel version was designed, and 10 of these went to the East Indian Railway between March and June 1922; numbers 2181 to 2190, they were for use on 2ft 6in gauge systems at coal mines owned by the railway company and had slightly smaller 6½in diameter cylinders but were otherwise almost identical. In 1923 a further three six-wheelers and three four-wheelers, numbers 2207 to 2209 and 2204 to 2206 respectively, were delivered to the United Provinces public works department. Some of these neat and tidy little engines, both the public works department ones and those from the East Indian Railway, later found their way into industrial use in India, mainly at sugar factories. The six-wheel version also found favour on the island of Mauritius, four being delivered via the Crown Agents for the Colonies for use in that country between 1922 and 1930; in this case the track gauge was 2ft 6in. Like some of the Indian engines these too, were for public works department use, and again some of them later found their way into the local industry - once again sugar plantations and factories. The builder's were quite proud of this neat design, and it featured in another of the four coloured publicity postcards produced by the Company.

Three rather neat two-foot gauge 0-6-0 tender engines were delivered in June 1921, ordered by the Anglo-Mexican Petroleum Company Limited for use on the FC Cobas A Furbero, a line with a length of no less than 54 miles, near Tuxpan in the Gulf of Mexico; it extended to oilfields at Palma Sola and Furbero. These three locomotives, the first supplied to Mexico since before the war, are especially interesting as they were oil fired, perhaps not surprisingly in view of where they were going, and among the first locomotives the Company built with oil firing equipment. The manufacturer's numbers were 2160 to 2162, cylinders were 7x12in, wheel diameter was 1ft 9½in and they had circular firebox boilers and Bagnall-Price valve gear.

Interesting too, was the use of a copper firebox as otherwise and almost exclusively, the circular firebox boilers had steel fireboxes; the use of copper in this case may have been in view of the oil firing equipment but on later engines equipped for oil burning, steel was usually preferred to copper as a material for fireboxes.

In May 1921 an order was received for two, two-foot gauge 2-6-2 tender engines for the Burma Corporation Limited, for use at silver-lead, zinc and copper mines to the north-east of that country at Bawdwin, in the Federated Shan States of Upper Burma. To serve the mines at Bawdwin and the smelter at Namtu, a curvaceous 46 mile long railway had been constructed, passing through difficult country with a number of steep gradients; it ran from Namyao on the Lashio Branch of the Burma Railway to Namtu, 14 miles and onwards to Bawdwin. In December 1919 the Corporation acquired Burma Mines Limited and in January 1920 was granted a 30 year lease of the mines. The Corporation, a British Company, soon constructed sizable extensions to the plant and equipment, enabling increased output from the mines to be processed, hence the need for additional and more powerful motive power for the railway. Until the Bagnall engines arrived the largest motive power was a series of 0-6-2 tender engines built by the North British Locomotive Company (NBL), and something more powerful was required. To meet this need a very powerful locomotive for such a narrow-gauge was designed, the outside cylinders were 13x16in, the coupled wheels had a diameter of 2ft 6in and the frames were outside. Walschaerts valve gear and piston valves were used and whilst the locomotives had steam brakes, equipment was fitted to operate vacuum brakes on the trains. The weight in working order of the engine and tender was 48 tons, the maximum axle-load six tons 10 cwt, and the tractive effort at 85% of the 180 psi working pressure equalled 13,790lb. By contrast the NBL locomotives had cylinders 12x16in and a tractive effort of 10,440lb. The manufacturer's numbers were 2164 and 2165, and the two locomotives were sent to Birkenhead Docks for shipment to Rangoon in March and April 1922. They cost £6,084 each free-on-board, against which a profit of £948 for the two, was recorded.

The suspension and load transfer arrangements of the leading and trailing trucks was identified as a problem area with these locomotives almost as soon as they started work. It manifested itself in a propensity

This is the second engine from the initial order for two of these two-foot gauge large 2-6-2 tender engines for the Burma Mines - number 2165 of 1922. Points to note are the large boiler mounted sandboxes, Belpaire firebox boiler, vacuum brake and large bogie-tender. Despite problems encountered with the locomotives in service, which were soon rectified, this was one of Reg Gard's most significant designs; such a powerful locomotive on so narrow a track gauge. The little engine behind is one of a batch of 10, manufacturer's numbers 2181 to 2190, supplied to the East Indian Railway for use on light two-foot gauge railways at collieries owned by the railway company. Cylinders were 6½x10in and the wheel diameter 1ft 7½in and, unlike the otherwise similar engines in the previous photograph and drawing, has a conventional locomotive type firebox hence the higher pitch of the boiler. Several of these engines later migrated to sugar factories, two of which were still in existence at the Bihar State Sugar factory at Sakri near Lohat until at least 1996, albeit they were no longer in use. Observe that whilst the Burma engine is finish painted, the Indian one is in primer.

for the trucks to derail on some of the sharp curves on the line and sidings, and the cause was established as individual wheel unloading due to the inflexibility of the suspension. As built the leading truck suspension was via conventional leaf springs mounted inside the engine main-frames, and not on the truck itself; load transfer was via vertical pillars from the spring buckles, which were allowed lateral movement on surface plates that rode on top of extra long axle-boxes. The rear truck, whilst embodying not dissimilar principles to the leading one, had a single inverted leaf spring mounted transversally across the engine mainframe stretcher, and via a beam above it, and vertical pillars at each end, transferred the load in the same fashion as the arrangement at the leading end of the engine. The firebox which occupied almost the entire width

between the frame plates, prohibited exactly the same arrangement at the rear; by these arrangements both trucks were allowed 6½in of movement each side of their central positions. To tackle this problem as early as December 1922, proposals were in hand to modify the suspension arrangements of the trucks. In the case of the trailing truck twin coil springs were added, one set on each side of the spring beam and between it and the axle-boxes, thus both increasing the spring loading slightly, but more importantly acting as a form of damper against individual wheel unloading. For the leading truck the position of the springs was changed from being directly mounted on the engine main frames, to the frame cross stretcher above the truck, and the load transfer was via a system of bell cranks and cross shafts, the two springs being connected to each other at both ends and on each side of the axle-boxes. Both these arrangements were an attempt to improve load transfer between the individual wheels on each truck axle, and in turn reduce cases of wheel unloading on uneven track, leading to derailments.

However, before anything physical could be done, a third identical locomotive was ordered, number 2179, and this one was delivered in August 1922. Kits of parts were shipped out to Burma to modify the locomotives, although it may be that only one was actually modified, as in the event, neither of the revised arrangements was 100% successful. Later engines had a completely different design of truck, with individual coil springs and equalising beams for each wheel, mounted on the trucks themselves, and not the engine main-frames. With this arrangement vertical load transfer between the trucks and the engine main-frames was via twin castings forming bearing blocks, one on the trucks and

one on the main-frames, set at the same radius as the arc of the truck movement, and mechanically lubricated. An order of July 1924, covered the parts to convert the three engines already delivered, and all the subsequent engines had the same arrangement.

Over the next few years a further nine locomotives were supplied to Burma of this general design; however the last three, which dated from 1929, whilst tank engines, were otherwise identical. Indeed, the three supplied in 1925 had been specifically designed such that they could easily be converted to tank engines, and in 1930 parts were supplied for the conversion work on these three, and an earlier one. The boilers had Belpaire top fireboxes and whilst the earlier members were not superheated, later members of the class were, and in 1932 parts were supplied to convert the earlier boilers to superheat. As this was a job of some magnitude, requiring new smokebox and firebox tube-

Although not a particularly good photograph, it is worthy of inclusion as it shows Arthur Burley, Reg Gard's successor, at the Burma Mines in connection with a later scheme to convert some of the locomotives to tank engines as well as superheating the boilers. The engine on the left is a Bagnall, Burma Mines No 37, Bagnall number 2253 of 1925, whilst the one on the right is one of the earlier 0-6-2 tender-engines built by the North British Locomotive Company in 1915. This illustration does show quite well the large but low slung boiler, essential to keep the centre of gravity low for such a big engine on so narrow a track gauge, and the additional supply of sand in front of the smokebox. (Collection Wilf Burley)

One of the Bagnall engines at the Burma Mines survives to this day, and is used for shunting at the main-line end of the mines railway at Namyao. No 42, manufacturer's number 2338 of 1927, it is seen here shunting in January 2001. The picture again illustrates the size and low position of the boiler, but notice the boiler mounted sandboxes have disappeared. (CM Jackson

plates, Arthur Burley, the chief draughtsman at the time - who we shall meet in more detail later in the story - went to Burma in connection with this work as well as that involved in converting the tender engines to tank engines. The vacuum brake appears to have fallen out of use as the later engines were not fitted, but they were equipped with air compressors and compressed air sanding equipment, as well as turbo-generators and electric lighting. As was the case with the superheater equipment, the earlier engines were modified to conform and material was supplied by the maker's. All these locomotives remained in use for many years, and spares were being delivered for them as late as 1977, and one of them remains in use at the time of writing - in this case one of the tender engines.

In 1929 two schemes were drawn up of locomotives proposed to be used at the Burma Mines, and based on the Garratt articulated principle. Had they been proceeded with, they would have employed what were in essence, the same frame, cylinder and wheels as the existing engines placed back to back, but with a much larger boiler. One scheme covered a locomotive with a 2-6-2 + 2-6-2 wheel arrangement, whilst the other was a slightly shorter 2-6-0 + 0-6-2. Just how Bagnall intended to circumvent, or otherwise get around, the various patents covering this arrangement of articulated

locomotive, and held by the Manchester builder Beyer Peacock & Company Limited, had either of the proposals been accepted, has however, gone unrecorded. Neither has it been established if engines to these designs were actually quoted for, or if in fact, they were just schemes for discussion?

In July 1921 the Company received an order for three standard-gauge locomotives from the well established civil engineering contractors Pauling & Company Limited. The requirement called for a light axle-load six-coupled design, for use on temporary railway tracks as Pauling's had just been awarded the contract for the construction of extensive harbour works at Kilindini in Kenya. Situated on the west side of the small island on which the city of Mombasa stands, a harbour claimed to be the finest landlocked anchorage on the east coast of Africa. For this job Bagnall designed a neat 0-6-0 saddle tank with 13x18in outside cylinders and 2ft 9¼in diameter wheels; the wheelbase was 9ft 7in and the weight in working order 25 tons, which gave an axle-load of only 8.33 tons. Bagnall-Price valve gear was fitted along with a copper firebox and brass tubes; the tractive effort at 85% of the 150psi working pressure equalled 11,664lb. The three locomotives were allocated manufacturer's numbers 2167 to 2179 and named MOMBASA, KILINDINI and NAIROBI.

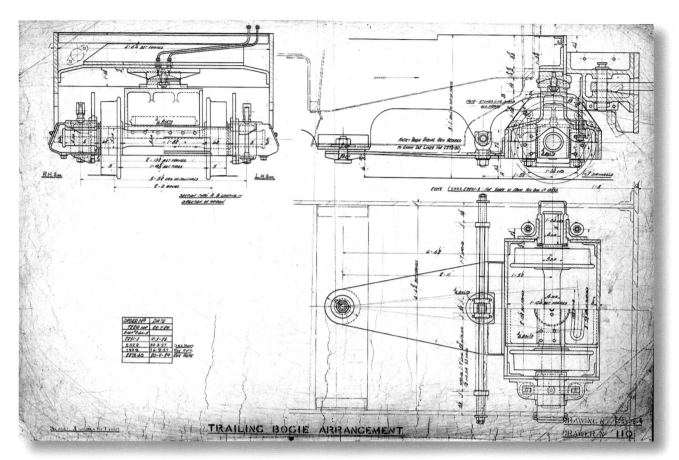

This drawing, number 13313, shows the revised suspension arrangement for the trailing truck on the early Burma Mines engines. Notice the individual coil springs for each axle-box and the method of transferring the load between the engine main frames and the truck. The side-control arrangement is worth a study too, along with the lubrication.

Delivery was spread, the first and last of the trio went to Morpeth Dock at Birkenhead on 23 December 1921 and 23 February 1922 respectively, whilst the second one went to the Royal Albert Dock in London on 13 February 1922. In all cases the locomotives were dismantled for shipment - they cost £2,450 each and the Company recorded a loss of £670 13/ 6d (£670 68p) on the three.

A fourth engine was ordered later, number 2197 THIKA, and this one also went to Morpeth Docks for shipment, in this case on 9 December 1922. Despite quoting a much lower selling price of £1,397, there was a small profit of £39 9/ 5d (£39 47p). As well as these six-wheel engines a slightly smaller four-coupled version was designed for Pauling, in this case with 9x14in cylinders along with a wheel diameter of 2ft 3½in and a wheelbase of five-foot - Bagnall-Price valve gear again being used. Two locomotives of this design were built,

number 2170 KENYA, which was sent to Morpeth Dock on 20 December 1921 and would have been shipped on the same ship as MOMBASA. However, unlike the six-coupled engines the four-coupled ones were shipped fully erected. The second one was number 2198 NYERI, delivered with THIKA on 9 December 1922. For KENYA Bagnall quoted a tender price of £1,750, making a loss of just over £269, whilst NYERI went for £1,300, but with a loss of only £16 14/ 4d (£16 72p). These figures serve to emphasis the points made earlier regarding the reduction in wage rates in the early 1920s. All the locomotives were painted in what was described as a chocolate livery; they were well-proportioned engines ideally suited for use on light axle-load contractors and other temporary railways. On completion of the works in Kenya, except for THIKA, all the locomotives were repatriated and gave many more years service on a whole range of

MOMBASA, number 2167 of 1921, is one of the neat 13in cylinder locomotives supplied to the contractor Pauling & Company Limited, for use on construction works for the harbour at Kilindini in Keyna. The picture however, was taken after the engine returned to this country when engaged on contract work. It shows the engine in February 1939 when on hire by Pauling to another contractor, George Wimpey, and engaged on a contract to widen the GWR main line at Perivale in West London.

As well as the six-wheel engines like MOMBASA, Pauling's also had two of these smaller four-wheel locomotives for use at Kilindini. This illustration is the maker's official photograph of KENYA, number 2170 of 1921. In view of the relatively small diameter cylinders for a standard gauge engine of 9in, notice how the buffer beams are supported against the buffing and drawgear loads by upward extensions of the main frames.

duties. These included opencast coal mining, construction of power stations and during the war construction of Royal Ordnance Factories, along with work on the River Thames rubbish shoots to mention just a few. THIKA eventually came back too, but not before being used on another of Pauling's overseas contracts, the Gebel Aulin Dam construction in the Sudan - it was there by May 1934, and does not appear to have returned to this country until about 1940. No more engines of the four-wheel design were built, but the six-wheel design was perpetuated later for use as a shunting locomotive for the home market. These locomotives were to a large extent a modern design of the sort of low axle-load contractors locomotives that for many years were a speciality of builders like the Leeds based Manning Wardle & Company. That there was much competition for these orders at this rather lean time in the trade, is evidenced by the prices quoted, and the losses made.

A substantial order of August 1921 was for eight

This is one of the eight standard-gauge 0-4-0 saddle tank engines sent to India in 1921 and 1922 for use near Bombay, and one of those later returned to this country. Manufacturer's number 2172 illustrated here at the Kensal Green Gasworks in North-London on 28 October 1954. Notice the engine retains its double cab roof and buffing blocks rather than spring buffers. Note too, the wooden pole on the front buffer beam used for shunting wagons on different tracks, and the large diameter rope on the footplating, doubtless also used for moving wagons on adjacent tracks. Both these shunting practices, long outlawed on the main-line railways, could be accompanied by serious personal consequences for those performing them, unless in the most skilled hands!

standard-gauge 0-4-0 saddle tanks with 12x18in cylinders and 3ft 0½in wheels, to an updated design of this popular size of shunting locomotive. Surprisingly however, especially in view of their track gauge, they went to India - there were not many standard-gauge railways on the sub-continent. Ordered by the India Office for use on the Salsette Trombay Railway, which was owned by the Bombay Development Directorate (BDD), this was a contractor's railway situated to the northwest of Bombay and part of a large scheme to reclaim land for residential development on the island of Salsette. The line was about nine miles in length and had interchange facilities with the Great Indian Peninsular Railway (GIPR) main line at Kurla. The origins of standard-gauge railways in this part of India go back to 1907, when a contractor's line of this gauge was used on the island of Elephanta in connection with building dock extensions at Bombay. When the work there was complete the equipment, or some of it, was

transferred across Bombay harbour to Trombay, where it was put to use by the BDD. The Bagnall locomotives were manufacturer's numbers 2171 to 2178, delivered between December 1921 and September the following year, as STR Nos. 1 to 8. When the development work was complete some of the locomotives were retained to operate a passenger timetable serving the needs of the new communities, trains running from Andheri to the west, and Wadavli to the east, and providing a connecting service with the GIPR board-gauge main-line at Kurla. Later still, this operation was taken over by the GIPR and eventually the lines were converted to broad-gauge when some of the locomotives were scrapped. However, four of them returned to this county in 1929, finding their way into industrial use at gas works, brickworks and a cement works.

Just about the biggest locomotive built at the Castle Engine Works was ordered in April 1922 by the West Cannock Colliery Company Limited, for use at its

W. G. BAGNALL, LTD., CASTLE ENGINE WORKS, STAFFORD.

TYPE E 2193—0-6-0 LOCOMOTIVE.
For dimensions see other side of card.

The last of the colour publicity cards produced by the Company showing locomotives, is this one of TOPHAM. This was the largest industrial shunting locomotive the Company had built to date, number 2193 of 1922, for the nearby West Cannock Colliery at Hednesford.

colliery at nearby Hednesford. To meet the specification the Company designed a large 17x24in outside cylinder 0-6-0 saddle tank, with 3ft 9in diameter wheels and an all up weight of 45 tons; tractive effort at 85% of the 160psi working pressure was 20,962lb. Walschaerts valve gear was fitted and the saddle tank, which covered the full length of the boiler from cab to smokebox, had a capacity of 1,000 gallons. Named TOPHAM, after a director of the colliery company, painted black and lined out in red and yellow, it was delivered under its own steam on 27 November 1922. This was rather unusual, as very few locomotives were delivered under their own steam, more often than not the motion would be removed and they would be hauled to their destinations, either on their own with a brake van attached, or in slow goods trains. In every case a Bagnall fitter would travel with them to ensure all went well, especially in the case of lubrication of the moving parts, and to deal with any other eventualities that might arise. This was a somewhat lonely occupation, and might occupy several days! TOPHAM was partly paid for over a period of time in coal slack, which was delivered to the Castle Engine Works in West Cannock Colliery wagons, to be consumed in the works boilers. Doubtless the willingness to do a deal on these lines had something to do with securing the order in the first place; the equivalent cash price was £3,600. An interesting issue concerning this locomotive was the fact that it was erected facing south, whilst it was otherwise almost universal practice to erect locomotives with the chimney facing north. It was built this way in the knowledge of the route by which it would be delivered, so as to arrive at the colliery facing the way the colliery company wanted it; nevertheless, it would have been a simple operation to turn it round on the main-line railway turntable at Stafford shed, which was next door to the Castle Engine Works. The Company were very proud of this locomotive, and it often appeared in publicity material, although as events turned out no more of the design were built, but there were some four-wheel versions of the same basic design built much later, of which more in Chapter Ten. TOPHAM remained in use at West Cannock Colliery until 1972, when it was sold by the National Coal Board to one of the authors. It then spent a number of years on the Foxfield Light Railway near Stoke-on-Trent, but is now located in Kent.

In July 1923 the Company received its first order for a fireless locomotive, a narrow-gauge one for Edward Lloyd Limited, for use on the extensive 2ft 6in gauge system at the Sittingbourne and Kemsley paper mills in North Kent. Appropriately named UNIQUE, manufacturer's number 2216, it had large 18½x18in cylinders and despite being a fireless, was potentially a very powerful machine. The reservoir pressure was 220 psi, but the cylinders were fed via a reducing valve set at 80psi, which gave a tractive effort of 12,600lb provided the pressure in the reservoir was not allowed to drop below 80psi. The driving wheel diameter was 2ft 9¼in and the wheel arrangement 2-4-0. There were some early problems encountered with this locomotive when put to work, particularly with the flexible steam pipes between the reservoir and the cylinders and it came back to Stafford no less than three times for

attention, in 1929, 1930 and 1935. Nevertheless, it eventually settled down to reasonably trouble free operation and remained in use on the narrow-gauge railway system at Sittingbourne until it closed in 1969. Edward Lloyd, and its successor company Bowaters Lloyd Limited, were good and regular customers of Bagnall over many years for both locomotives and narrow-gauge rolling stock, as the railway system at the paper mills developed. Another fireless locomotive was built for Lloyd's in 1929, a much smaller one in this case with 9x14in cylinders, number 2366 VICTOR. The Company also had a standard-gauge Bagnall, a 12in cylinder 0-4-0 saddle tank new in 1936, number 2542 JUBILEE, which survives in preservation, as in fact does UNIQUE, although VICTOR was scrapped in 1967.

It is perhaps worth saying something on the principles of fireless locomotives, which were both popular and economical where steam could easily be made available from stationary plants - paper mills and power stations being classic examples. They were popular too, at locations where there were particular risks associated with fires, munitions factories and oil refineries being obvious examples - there is no danger of sparks emitting from a fireless locomotive! Instead of a conventional boiler, fireless locomotives have large and very well insulated reservoirs which are charged with hot water and steam. Ideally the charging facilities should be arranged so that as the reservoirs are charged,

The first fireless locomotive the company built was UNIQUE (in more ways than one!), manufacturer's number 2216 of 1923, seen here on the 2ft 6in gauge Bowaters Lloyd paper mill railway in Kent. This picture was taken at Kemsley Mill, the engine's usual haunt, on 12 September 1967. Notice the large cylinders and dome together with the rather unusual 2-4-0 wheel arrangement. A six-coupled arrangement had been discounted in view of the curves the engine had to negotiate, but a long main-frame was essential to cater for the size of the reservoir, in view of the work the engine was designed to do and the time allowed between re-charging the reservoir.

a quantity of the steam condenses, such that when the full pressure is attained in the reservoir, is it roughly three quarters full of very hot water, and the rest with steam at the full reservoir pressure. Conventional gauge glasses are provided to indicate to the driver the level of water. In the case of UNIQUE the maximum reservoir pressure was 220psi, but in later locomotives this was successively increased to 300psi. On completion of the charging process, the locomotive would then be ready to work and because the temperature at which water boils varies with the pressure it is under, as the pressure in the reservoir reduces as steam is consumed to power the locomotive, so the water in the reservoir boils, and by these means fireless locomotives can usually complete about four hours almost continuous shunting. By the time the reservoir pressure reduces to the setting of the reducing valve, the reservoir would be about a quarter full of water, as steam was generated as the pressure dropped in accordance with the principle outlined above. Thereafter, whilst the locomotive would be able to continue working, its tractive effort would decline rapidly and a visit to the charging station would be needed to repeat the process. Depending on the capacity of the steam supply, an average re-charge would only take about half an hour, a little longer from cold, and this could easily be accomplished during for example, a meal break for the staff. Cylinders of fireless locomotives were normally placed at the rear, cab end of locomotives built in this country, with the reservoir well towards the front and by these means the overall weight was better distributed; remember there would be no conventional firebox to balance at one end of the locomotive, the weight of the cylinders at the other.

Although producing nowhere near as many fireless locomotives as its largest competitor in the field, the

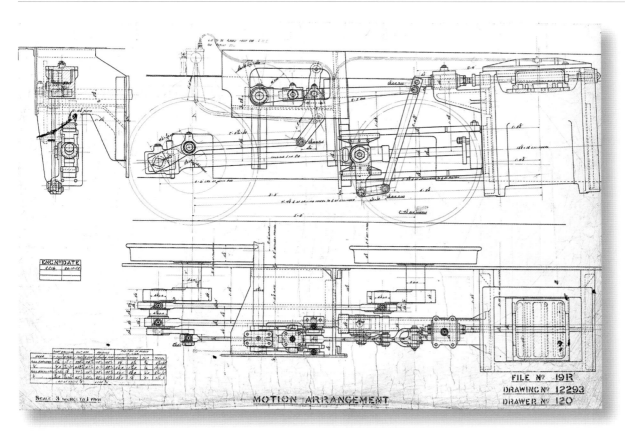

Drawing number 12293 showing the arrangement of the Walschaerts valve gear on the first fireless locomotive, number 2216. Of special interest in the downward extension and the backward set of the expansion link. This was necessary in view of the large diameter cylinders, 18½in, to bring what was in effect the link foot, in a position to enable the swing of the link to be more or less equal each side of its vertical position about its central point. This was a design feature of all the Bagnall fireless locomotives with cylinder diameters as large as, or larger than, the piston stroke, and for the same reason.

W. G. BAGNALL LTD.. CASTLE ENGINE WORKS. STAFFORD.

RIO LOA

TYPE E. 2211. FOR LEADING DIMENSIONS SEE OTHER SIDE OF CARD.

Another of Reg Gard's distinctive designs is this large metre-gauge 2-6-2 tank engine, one of three built in 1923 for use on nitrate railways in Chile. All were named after local rivers and RIO LOA was manufacturer's number 2211. These locomotives were designed to burn oil fuel, with the oil capacity partly where the coal bunker would otherwise have been, and partly in the side tanks - notice the vertical line of rivets alongside the firebox indicating the division between water and oil spaces.

firm did come third in terms of the number built in this country, and publicity material was always emphasising the virtues of the principle. A total of 15 were built over the years, the last one right at the end of steam locomotive production at the Castle Engine Works in 1957, manufacturer's number 3121. The Company that built the most was Andrew Barclay Sons & Company Limited of Kilmarnock, with a total of 114 to its credit between 1913 and 1961, followed by Hawthorn Leslie and later Robert Stephenson & Hawthorns Limited of Newcastle and Darlington, with 17 between 1916 and 1959. Two basic designs were developed for the standard-gauge, a four-wheeler with 18½x18in cylinders and a six-wheeler with 20x18in cylinders, both with reducing valves set at 80psi. The use of such large diameter cylinders (diameter and stroke almost the same - in the 'trade' sometimes referred to as square cylinders!) compensated for the low working pressure of 80psi set by the reducing valve, so that the locomotives could develop a tractive effort similar to a conventional one of roughly the same size. Most of the Bagnall built fireless locomotives were for use at power stations, including one built for 3ft 6in gauge and sent to South Africa; number 2571 of 1937 was ordered by the Electricity Supply Commissioners for use at Coleneso

Power Station in Natal. Another one went to a cement works in the Punjab (India - now Pakistan), number 2536 of 1936, and in this case built to suit a track gauge of 5ft 6in.

Continuing the Company's association with the Chilean nitrate business, in February 1923 an order was received for three quite large metre-gauge 2-6-2 tank engines with 12x18in cylinders and 2ft 9¼in diameter coupled wheels. Baburizza & Company Limited placed the order and the locomotives were for use by the Lautaro Nitrate Company at its Oficina Las Dones, which was a mining complex and smelter. The manufacturer's numbers were 2211 to 2213, and the engines were named respectively, RIO LOA, RIO SABRADOR and RIO SALADO. They were good looking machines with clean exterior lines, outside frames, Walschaerts valve gear, full length side tanks, oil firing and a large balloon stack spark arresting chimney; the fireboxes were of steel construction. All three were despatched in September 1923 via Liverpool Docks for shipment to Antofagasta. They were sold for £1,950 each, making a small loss for the Company of £230 17/6d (£230 88p) on the three, and emphasising the point made earlier in this Chapter, along with the other cases quoted - and there were others - just how competitive the market was at this time. A repeat order of June 1924 was for five more locomotives, identical except built to suit 2ft 6in gauge track, but with the requirement that they could relatively easily be converted to metre-gauge by substitution of longer axles. The manufacturer's numbers in this case were 2238 to 2242, and the locomotives were despatched in October and November 1924 - in this case with numbers and not names - 7/1 through to 7/5. The selling price for these locomotives was exactly the same as the earlier ones at £1,950 each, but on this occasion a profit of £841 was made on the order. A spare boiler to suit all eight engines was supplied in July 1925 at a cost of £600 (profit of £183), but there is no record so far as the authors are aware, to indicate if in fact the second batch were ever converted to metre-gauge. Certainly Bagnall do not appear to have supplied any material for such a conversion.

Towards the end of 1923, new orders were getting harder and harder to come by as the industrial depression in manufacturing industry deepened. As events turned out, for Bagnall this was soon to improve with a large and significant order, but in the meantime on the 19 November 1923, and to help keep the men employed, two stock orders were placed on the works. The first covered two of the light axle-load 13in cylinder standard-gauge 0-6-0 saddle tanks based on those built earlier for the contractors Pauling & Company, whilst the second was for two of the larger 15in cylinder 0-6-0 saddle tank design. Being existing designs little or no drawing office work was necessary, which had an advantage because in fact, the draughtsman were quite busy as although orders were thin on the ground, there was a lot of work in tendering for the potential work that was about. Worth pointing out at this juncture, is the work drawing offices, cost offices and buying departments often had to perform, before any actual orders were received. For every order obtained there would probably be several more where the firm was unsuccessful in its tender, but nevertheless

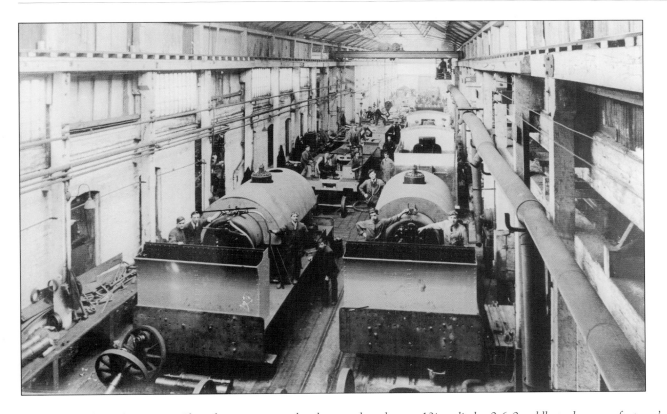

View looking down the Erecting Shop showing nearest the photographer, the two 13in cylinder 0-6-0 saddle tanks, manufacturer's numbers 2221 and 2222, laid down to a stock order in 1923 and worked on in a derisory fashion as and when time allowed, and intended to keep the men busy at slack times. This was a staged picture, hence the men posed on them, one of a series taken in 1925 of which more later, but included here to accompany the description of the locomotives.

at lot of work would have been involved. Obviously, if the tender was for a design of locomotive that had already been built, or one needing only slight modification, the work would be less than if a completely new design was involved. However, the work involved in estimating and tendering should never be underestimated, and when business was slack, and therefore competition strong, as in the case of the period under review in this Chapter and the next, a lot of unproductive work was involved.

In the case of the four standard-gauge saddle tank locomotives it was some time before any positive enquiries were received, so progress on them was undertaken at a very sedentary pace as and when the opportunity presented itself, which was of course, to some extent was why they were laid down in the first place. Once erection actually commenced, as opposed to making individual components, all four were placed at the extreme south end of the erecting shop, and all

those who were employed at the works during the time the engines were located there, and who have been interviewed over the years by the authors, remember them well; they almost became somewhat akin to the furniture at that part of the works! The first to be sold was one of the larger engines, manufacturer's number 2223, for Stewarts & Lloyds Limited, despatched to that Company's Kilnhurst Colliery in Yorkshire on 3 October 1924. Named ELSIE it was sold for £1,800 against a recorded building cost of no less than £2,369, once again illustrating the competitiveness in the business at the time - in this case for industrial shunting locomotives for the home market. This locomotive had a long life, and it came back to Stafford for an overhaul in 1937; it was not scrapped until the early 1970s, by which time it had migrated to Manvers Main Colliery, quite close to Kilnhurst. It had however, been out of use and partly dismantled for some time prior to this.

The second of the four sold was number 2221, but

This is one of the larger, 15in cylinder 0-6-0 saddle tank locomotives laid down to a stock order in 1923. Manufacturer's number 2224 it was not delivered until 1931, to the order of structural steel manufacturer Redpath Brown & Company Limited, for shunting at its Trafford Park Works in Manchester. It is seen in this photograph at Trafford Park on 25 March 1953. (Late Bernard Roberts)

not until 1927, one of the smaller engines, and in this case to the Shropshire Beet Sugar Company Limited, at the time building a new sugar refining factory at Allscott. This was not far from Stafford and adjacent to the main-line between Wellington and Shrewsbury; it was despatched there on 3 June 1927. As with the earlier engine this one too, was sold at a loss, in this case £1,350 against a recorded building cost of £1,861. Named LEWISHAM, it survives today in preservation on the Foxfield Light Railway near Stoke-on-Trent. The third one to find a customer was number 2222, the second of the smaller engines, sold to Burn Craddock & Company Limited for use on the 5ft 6in gauge system at the Howrah Ironworks at Calcutta in India. Despatched on 16 July 1929, it was shipped via the Vittoria Wharf in Birkenhead in a dismantled condition. Yet another significant loss was recorded on

this sale, like the earlier one the building cost was recoded as £1,861, but the sale price was only £1,400. Last of the four was number 2224, second of the 15in cylinder engines lingering on until 5 March 1931, when it was despatched to Redpath Brown & Company Limited for use at its structural steelworks at Trafford Park in Manchester - sale price in this case was but £1,375, against a recorded cost to build, like its earlier sister of £2,369. The similarity in the building costs of these locomotives, despite the long time they were under construction, suggests some creative accounting, to use a more modern term, as they were not actually finished until the orders were placed. Doubtless however, by this time the last one went, the Company was glad to see the back of it! It remained at Trafford Park until 1958, when it was broken up for scrap.

On 1 December 1923, the Crown Agents for the

The Victorias Milling Company 18-BG, is one of two of this unusual design of 0-4-4 side tank, originally supplied to the Kowloon Canton Railway (British Section) in 1924. Specially designed for use on the two-foot gauge Sha Tau Kok Fanling Tramway, unfortunately this line closed in 1928 and the engines migrated to the Philippines where this picture of Bagnall number 2228, was taken in November 1983. There have been several modifications since the engine was built, not least the spark arresting chimney, and it has acquired a tender almost as big at itself, and formerly attached to an American engine of Baldwin build. Returning to Hong Kong in 1995, ostensibly for preservation there, this one has since arrived back in this country and awaits restoration.

Colonies placed an order for two, two-foot gauge locomotives for use on the Sha Tau Kok Fanling Tramway, a narrow-gauge branch of the Kowloon-Canton Railway (KCR) in Hong Kong. This was a roadside tramway dating from the period 1911 to 1912, seven miles long and situated in the New Territories. It was built to help open up the country around Sha Tau Kok and Yuen Long, east of the main-line of the KCR, and at the head of Mirs Bay on the South China Sea. The earlier locomotives were simple four-coupled tank engines, but on this occasion there was a requirement to both improve the riding of the engines in an attempt to reduce the journey times, and in view of the roadside nature of the tramway, give the crews an unobstructed forward vision. These requirements were the result of an increased level of road traffic which was having an effect on both the traffic carried, and the safety of the operation. Against this specification Bagnall designed a neat 0-4-4 side tank specially arranged to run bunker-first, the bogie to help the ride characteristics and the

bunker-first running to assist the crew's vision. The design also embraced some sophisticated drawgear arrangements, again to help improve the ride and in view of the 2½ chain radius curves the engines had to negotiate. As the normal mode of operation was to run the engines bunker-first, the Walschaerts valve gear was arranged so that the die was at the bottom of the link for backward running, rather than the opposite which would normally be the case. Therefore, for the majority of the time the engines were working, the valve gear would give a more direct load-path between the return crank and link, and probably slightly better valve events. The bogie was of an interesting design too, as of course, it would be leading for most of the time the engines were working. The design had combined swing link and spring side control, along with individual leaf springs for each wheel, which between them took the horizontal and longitudinal loads, while the vertical loads were taken by large sliding side bearers; the centre pivot housing took no vertical loads at all, was not fixed

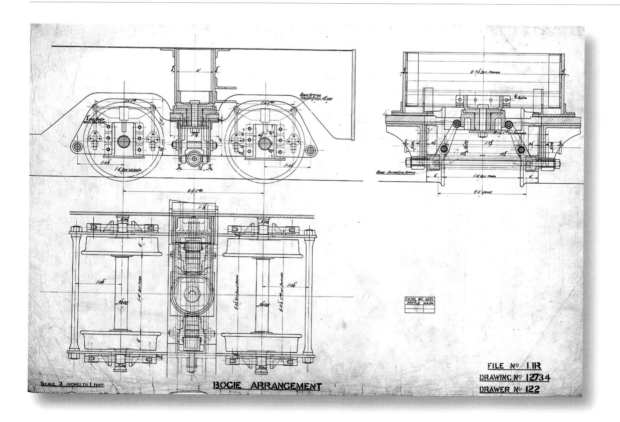

Drawing Number 12734 showing the interesting four-wheel bogie arrangement for the Sha Tau Kok Fanling Tramway locomotives, numbers 2227 and 2228. Notice the system of load transfer via side-bearers, individual axle-box springs, the 'floating' centre pivot and swing links, with associated spring loaded cross beam for centralising purposes.

to the bogie as such, and allowed side to side movement under the control of the swing links. The manufacturer's numbers were 2227 and 2228. Cylinder dimensions were 10x15in, the wheel diameter was 2ft 9in and the weight in working order 21 tons; delivery was to Birkenhead Docks, dismantled for shipment on 13 June 1924.

Unfortunately, through no fault of these engines, the tramway did not have long to live after they were delivered, as the competition from the improving road transport proved too difficult to stem, and it closed on and from 1 April 1928. However, the engines lived on after being sold to the North Negros Sugar Company, and were in use in the Philippines by 1930, where they remained in service until recent times. In September 1995, and before the British moved out of Hong Kong, the Kowloon Canton Railway Corporation negotiated

the return of these two engines to Hong Kong, and they were taken to Ho Tung Lau Workshops of the railway. One of them, number 2227 has been cosmetically restored and placed in the Hong Kong railway museum at Tai Po Market. Sister engine, number 2228, is now back in this country and currently stored awaiting restoration.

On the 24 March 1924, the Company received an order from the Indian Madras & Southern Mahratta Railway (MSMR) for two metre-gauge tender locomotives; the biggest locomotives built by the firm to date. As was to be expected the inspecting engineers were Rendel, Palmer & Tritton, and as each engine was of a different type, this order was almost certainly something of a test, to establish if building such large locomotives was a viable option for the Castle Engine Works. Both were of established Indian Railways

This photograph and the next six were all taken in the works in the early months of 1925, and are part of the first comprehensive collection of views of the workshops and yard. The motive seems to have been the building of the largest locomotives the Company had constructed up to this time, and sets of the pictures were mounted in large leather bound albums. This picture shows part of the Smithy with a brake cross-beam being forged under the steam hammer. The gentleman in the cloth cap is the Smithy Foreman Charlie Homer. Notice the works internal 18in gauge railway track and the higher roof section to accommodate the Massey two-ton steam hammer.

This is the wheel bay, at the extreme south end of the Erecting Shop with the driving wheel-sets of the Madras & Southern Mahratta Railway metre-gauge 4-8-0s in various stages of erection; notice in particular the large wheel press for pressing the wheels on to the axles. The Erecting & Fitting Shop Foreman, Jack Dale, is standing with his hands on his hips, and that is the Fitting Shop to the left - view looks south.

View looking south in the Fitting Shop, which despite its name housed some machine tools as seen here - notice the Stephenson's valve gear expansion link on the bed of the vertical grinding machine in the foreground. This is the larger of the two links seen; the smaller one is for an engine with Baguley valve gear - hence the lug to take the rod to connect the link to the connecting rod - and this would be for a spare part order. There were two link grinding machines, both manufactured by the neighbouring firm of WH Dorman & Company Limited. On the right can be seen the Erecting Shop, and one of the two 13in cylinder 0-6-0 saddle tanks laid down to stock in 1923, numbers 2221 and 2222, in course of construction. Notice how young the apprentices look!

This is the Machine Shop looking north. On the floor in the foreground are two valve chest covers for the Madras engines and that is a cylinder block for one of them hanging from the crane. The Erecting Shop is to the right.

The Boiler Shop with boilers and smokeboxes for the Madras engines in various stages of construction. This picture illustrates well the confined width of the bottom part of a firebox for an inside framed metre-gauge locomotive; this was why, as will be told later, eventually boilers were mounted on the top of the frames on this track-gauge of locomotive to allow for a greater firebox width and grate area. Notice in the left-middle, a circular firebox boiler under construction for a small narrow-gauge locomotive.

A view in the other bay of the Boiler Shop, showing under construction ashpans for the Madras engines as well as in the distance some smokebox tube plates.

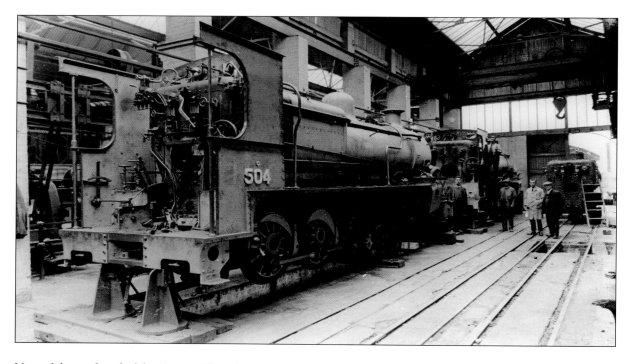

View of the north end of the Erecting Shop showing two of the Madras engines almost complete and ready to be moved outside for steam testing. On the left is No 504, and ahead of it No 503, respectively manufacturer's numbers 2247 and 2246. To the right is a boiler ready for fitting to a third example - there were four in this batch. The gentleman on the right with the cloth cap is the Works Manager Bill Parkinson, together with the Erecting & Fitting Shop Foreman Jack Dale - when Bill retired Jack took over his role. Notice the multi-gauge track on the right hand side and the 18in internal works railway running between the two Erecting Shop tracks. Machine Shop to left.

This is one of the later batch of Madras metre-gauge 4-8-0s, originally MSMR No 413, but by the time this picture was taken at Castle Rock on 28 July 1941, West India Portuguese Railway No 506 - manufacturer's number 2269 of March 1926. (Kelland Collection Bournemouth Railway Club)

British Engineering Standards Association (BESA) designs; a 4-6-0 of the BESA Class PS, and a 4-8-0 of the BESA GS class - in both cases the S indicated a superheated boiler. The 4-6-0 had 16½x22in cylinders and 4ft 9in diameter coupled wheels, whilst the 4-8-0 had 17x22in cylinders and 3ft 7in diameter coupled wheels, respective weights in working order for engine and tender being 65 tons 6 cwt and 71 tons 10 cwt. Despite the fact that basically these two locomotives were of comparatively old BESA designs, they were updated to include among other things, superheaters and piston valves, Wakefield mechanical, Detroit sight-feed lubricators, Goodall articulated drawbars between engine and tender, and steam sanding gear. It is worth noting too, that despite the introduction of the new Indian Railway Standards (IRS) designs of a few years later, some of the older BESA designs updated as in the case of these two, remained popular with some of the Indian metre-gauge railways - and in some cases almost until the end of steam locomotive production.

Despatch of the two engines was in October 1924 for the 4-6-0, manufacturer's number 2234, and January 1925 for the 4-8-0, number 2235, and both of them were later with the Mysore State Railway (MSR) when the lines they were used on were transferred between the two railways. The 4-6-0 was later reclassified as class HPS/1, and with the all India number 31406, lasted until the late 1970s. Some of the 4-8-0s that the Company built later, lasted even longer, into the early 1980s in fact, among the last engines of the class to survive out of the many supplied over the years by several different builders - although the Bagnall engines

were the last ones of the class built. However, latterly the only survivors were employed as somewhat humble works shunters, at the Hubli Workshops on the South Central Railway.

Before either locomotive had actually been delivered, the consulting engineers appear to have been confident of the ability of the works to build engines of this size, as further orders were received for the GS class 4-8-0 goods tender engines. Two more were ordered on 12 September 1924, followed by another two on 27th of the same month, and a further nine on 11 May the following year. Whilst all the orders were placed by the MSMR, some of the locomotives were for use on the West of India Portuguese Railway (WIPR) in Goa, a railway opperated by the MSMR. Goa was a small Portuguese colony on the west coast of India about 270 miles as the crow flies south of Bombay. The 51 mile WIPR railway was built in 1887 and 1888 to connect the British and Portuguese territories and give Southern Mahratta a harbour on the west coast at Mormugao. From July 1902 the line was operated by the MSMR and to a large extent the locomotive fleets of the two lines were used indiscriminately. The line had steep gradients, the Braganza Ghat at 1 in 40, as it descended to the coast, the main reason for these large eight-coupled locomotives, the last examples built of a quite numerous class. The Company made great play of these orders in the technical press, articles appeared in for example *The Locomotive Magazine*, *The Railway Gazette* and *The Railway Engineer*, and the opportunity was taken to have an extensive series of photographs taken in and around the workshops as the locomotives and

Many years later and looking very woebegone whilst eking out its last days as a works shunter at the South Central Railway Works at Hubli, is former MSMR and West India Portuguese No 507. These old engines were never renumbered into the all-India renumbering scheme and this one is Bagnall number 2265 of December 1925, photographed on 24 November 1979.

their component parts were being constructed. This was the first occasion such an opportunity had been taken and the collection forms the earliest comprehensive set of illustrations of the interior of the workshops. Due to the size of the boilers and the facilities available at the time in the Castle Engine Works boiler shop, several of the larger boiler and firebox plates were flanged by Nasmyth Wilson & Company Limited at its Patricroft Works in Manchester. These locomotives were to all intents and purposes, the point of entry by the firm into the market for large metre-gauge locomotive for India, a market that had a significant impact on the Castle Engine Works production right through until the early 1950s.

In 1923 for the first time since before the war, locomotives with internal combustion engines again appeared in the order book. Between April 1923 and September 1926 five were built, the first two, manufacturer's numbers 2220 of April 1924 and 2273 of August 1925, were almost identical to the pre-war P50, described in Chapter Five. The main difference was the use of a Ford four-cylinder 20 horsepower petrol engine instead of the Coventry Simplex fitted to P50, and the first of the two was for the same customer - The Eastern Assam Company - for use on the two-foot

gauge system at tea plantations near Dibrugarh in Assam. The second one however, was a 2ft 6in gauge locomotive built to the order of Norton Griffiths & Company Limited, for use at the British Controlled Oilfields at Maracaibo in Venezuela - it was named BUCHIVACOA. At the time this company held a concession to operate the oil fields. The remaining three were bigger machines, in each case with a 40 horsepower Dorman 4JO four-cylinder engine like the one fitted before the war to P51, and were broadly based on that locomotive. In all these three however, instead of the drive being to an independent change speed gearbox and then a separate final-drive gearbox mounted on the leading axle, a combined gearbox and final-drive unit was mounted behind the trailing axle, and the drive thence by jackshaft and connecting rods to the leading axle - the two axles being connected by conventional side-rods. As a result of these design changes the wheelbase was much shorter than was the case with P51 - 3ft 6in rather than 4ft 10in. These three locomotives were also ordered by Norton Griffiths for the oilfields in Venezuela; the manufacturer's numbers were 2274 and 2275, despatched in October 1925, followed by number 2304 in September the following year. The selling prices for these locomotives

One of the last two petrol locomotives built at Stafford before thoughts turned to diesel powered locomotives - manufacturer's numbers 2274 and 2275 were built in 1925. Notice the Dorman 4JO engine mounted right at the front complete with hand-starting arrangement, with a shaft drive to the combined gearbox and final-drive mounted at the rear and jack-shaft drive to the wheels. The large tank is for the cooling water, a siphon system as there was no conventional radiator, and observe the exhaust through a conventional chimney and the warning bell at the extreme right under the footplate. The two locomotives were for use at oil fields in Venezuela.

together with the profit or loss were: 2220 £400 (loss of £86); 2273 £500 (profit of £20); 2273-2274 £1,320 for the two (loss of £388); 2304 £635 (loss of £283); not a particularly good record! Nevertheless, these interesting small locomotives were the Company's last foray into locomotives with petrol engines, and when internal combustion locomotives again appeared in the order books they were powered by diesel engines

Another large locomotive of the period covered by this Chapter was manufacturer's number 2250, a 3ft 6in gauge 0-8-0 side tank and the first one built with this wheel arrangement. The cylinders were 18x24in, the wheel diameter was 3ft 3in and the wheelbase 13ft 6in; weight in working order equalled 54 tons and the tractive effort at 85% of the 180psi working pressure was 29,651lb. Walschaerts valve gear operated slide valves and the engine was fitted with a copper firebox and steel tubes as well as vacuum brake equipment for train operation. The selling price was £4,025, making a profit of almost £522 10/ (£522 50p) for the builder. Ordered by Light Railways Limited, a subsidiary company of John Birch & Company Limited; both these companies acted as export agents, but more usually on behalf of far eastern customers. In this case however, the engine was for the New State Gold Mining

Areas at Springs on the East Rand of South Africa. It was sent to Birkenhead docks on 19 May 1925 for shipment to Durban. Designed against a specification to haul 40 ton hopper wagons over a curvaceous and steeply graded line, five miles in length running between the mines and the mills, the trains could be loaded to 1,582 tons on level track, 626 tons on 1 in 100, 374 tons on 1 in 50 and 233 tons on 1 in 30 gradients. In 1954 when the mines at Springs closed it moved to the Rustenburg Platinum Mines, located about 60 miles west of Pretoria, where it worked for around another seven years. It is nice to note that this locomotive is still in existence at the South African Steam & Rail Museum at Chamdor, a few miles north-west of Johannesburg; however it could hardly be described as preserved, stored in the open in the condition it finished work. Next to the fireless locomotive UNIQUE, this engine had the largest diameter cylinders used at the time on an engine built at Stafford.

A year or so earlier Light Railways Limited had ordered on behalf of the China Group Commissioners, three locomotives for export to China, the first ones for that country since before the war. Neat and tidy machines another good illustration of the well

A contempory advert of the period covered by this Chapter, appearing in journals like The Railway Gazette, The Locomotive Magazine and The Railway Engineer. The engine at the top is manufacturer's number 2250 of May 1925, the first 0-8-0 tank engine built by the firm, in this case for use at gold mines in South Africa. Notice the flangeless third set of coupled wheels and the vacuum brake equipment - that is the cylinder under the framing and just behind the cab. The Company built a number of not dissimilar engines over the next 15 years or so, mostly for South African mining interests, and it is good to record that this one survives in preservation. In the middle is the first of the batch of Madras 4-8-0s, No 503, manufacturer's number 2246, and at the bottom a typical rolling stock product of the time.

proportioned design features of the Sydney Edwards and Reg Gard era. They were 3ft 6in gauge 0-6-0 side tanks with 12x16½in cylinders and 2ft 9¼in diameter wheels, the manufacturer's numbers were 2230 to 2232 and the consulting engineers appointed were Sir Douglas Fox & Partners. Despatch was on 10 July 1924 to West India Dock in London for shipment to Chin Wang Tao, the final destination was the Chang Cheng Railway at Chin Huang Tao (now Qinhuangdao), in what is now the Hebei Province. Dismantled for shipment erection drawings and working instructions were provided - but whether or not in Chinese has gone unrecorded! Apparently, the Chang Cheng (Great Wall) Railway was about 17 miles long and the specification called for

the locomotives to carry sufficient fuel and water, with ample margin, for a run of 19 miles. The line opened in 1924, so presumably these were its first locomotives, but nothing else is known about either the railway, or the locomotives, not unlike a lot of railway material supplied to China in the period between the wars. Before despatch all three were photographed together and details and illustrations appeared in the railway technical press.

In August 1925 Rendel, Palmer & Tritton commissioned the Company to design a tank engine version of the 2ft 6in gauge Indian W class 0-6-2 tender engines described in some detail earlier. Six locomotives were ordered, a rear bogie being substituted

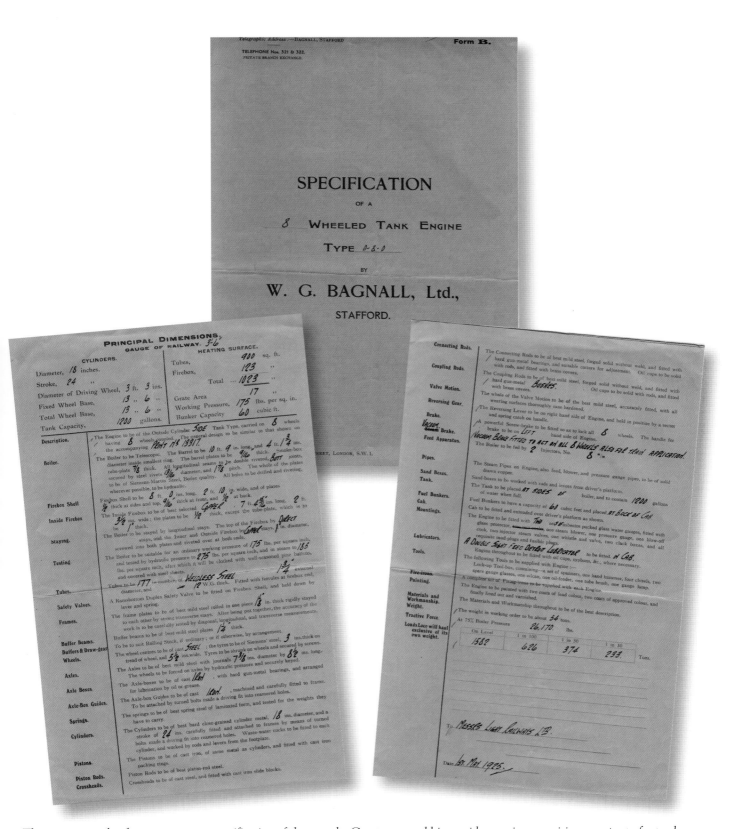

This is an example of a contemporary specification of the type the Company would issue either against enquiries or as part of a tender. It would be accompanied by a diagram of the locomotive showing the principal dimensions and if possible a photograph of a similar engine that had already been built. This particular specification is for one of the engines in the previous illustration of an advertisement, the 0-8-0 side tank for South Africa.

This is one of the Indian Railways 2ft 6in gauge WT class 0-6-4 tank engines, a tank engine version of the W class. No 596, Bagnall number 2280 of December 1925, seen here complete with make-shift auxiliary tender at Petlad on 15 January 1977. Petlad Junction is on the former Gaekwar's Baroda State Railway line from Nadiad to Bhadran, just over 23 miles from Nadiad, where the engine was allocated. Nadiad is on the BBCIR broad-gauge main-line from Baroda to Ahmedabad, about 35 miles north of Baroda, and the line to Bhadran runs south-east from Nadiad and crosses the BBCIR broad-gauge line from Godhra to Cambay (now Khambhat) at Petlad Junction. The plate in front of the smokebox christens the engine in Hindi script, PRECIOUS JEWEL!

for the single axle truck of the tender engines, to accommodate a bunker, making the wheel arrangement 0-6-4. Otherwise the engines had the same basic dimensions as the tender engines - manufacturer's numbers 2278 to 2283 were allocated. The contract price was £12,150 for the batch, and as delivery was actually due by the end of 1925, an overtime night shift was worked between 24 August 1925 and the end of December to help meet the schedule. Moreover, a loss of £983 was made on the contract, and the last three engines were not delivered until towards the end of January 1926. Like many of the tender engines they were for use on the Gaekwar's Baroda State Railway, and remained in use on the narrow-gauge lines of what later became the Western Railway of India, until the early 1980s. One of them, number 2278, latterly Indian Railways No 594, is preserved at the Indian Railways

Museum in Delhi. These were well proportioned locomotives designed specifically for use on some of the shorter lines where water supply was not such an issue, and where axle-loads were not so much of a problem either. Nevertheless, in later years they were used indiscriminately with the tender engines, often accompanied by large water tanks mounted on bogie bolster wagons acting as tenders.

The downturn in the economy of the country, accompanied by the depression that affected manufacturing industry so badly in the years following the First World War, hit the private locomotive builders particularly hard. The traditional markets for many of them, supplying locomotives to Indian and colonial railways, became areas of acute competition from continental and American manufacturers similarly hit by post-war economic issues. We have already seen how the LMA attempted to tackle these issues; nevertheless, as we shall explore later, several British builders were unable to remain viable, closing their doors for the last time as the recession showed little sign of relenting. The country's main-line railway companies were also affected, with reduced levels of traffic, such that in many cases they were unable to generate sufficient funds to maintain their assets at anything like pre-war levels. In an effort to help both the railway companies and the private locomotive and rolling stock building industry, the government of the day agreed to make a series of low interest loans, and there were similar loans to assist other parts of industry too. The loans were on condition that a significant number of the locomotives and rolling stock required were contracted with private industry, rather than built in their own workshops. As a result of this, over the next few years, the four main-line railway companies went out to tender for a whole range of locomotives and rolling stock, and Bagnall was successful in a number of the tenders it submitted.

In the first instance the Company was successful with its tender to the London Midland & Scottish Railway (LMS), covering 15 of the Standard Class 3F (3 Freight) inside cylinder 0-6-0 shunting tank locomotives. The order was placed on 27 January 1926 at a contract price of £49,950, or £3,330 for each locomotive. These were quite large locomotives for the company's resources at the time, with 18x26in cylinders and 4ft 7in diameter wheels, weighing in working order almost 50 tons; they were fitted with vacuum brake gear for train use but not

steam heating. The contract delivery for the first locomotive was between 16 and 18 weeks (therefore, due mid to late June), and thereafter at a rate of two per month, whilst in fact the actual delivery was between 19 August 1926 and 15 June 1927. As the Castle Engine Works had no facilities for forging such a large crank-axle, these were sub-contracted to the Hunslet Engine Company Limited of Leeds at a cost of a little over £92 each. Across the total order a loss of £9152 was recorded, although there were no penalties for late delivery, and all the engines were despatched under their own steam to the adjacent LMS shed at Stafford. The loss made on this order whilst a significant one, was perhaps partly understandable, being the Company's first order for standard-gauge locomotives for the main-line railways in this country. It also illustrates how keen the Company was to get the work, both to keep its employees at work, as well as establishing its name in this sector of the market.

The works numbers allocated were 2288 to 2302, and the original LMS numbers 16535 to 16549, but they were later renumbered 7452 to 7466. After nationalisation of the railways in 1948 they became British Railways 47452 to 47466, with withdrawal from service and scrapping between November 1960 and April 1966. There was one exception however, LMS number 7456, went to the LMS Northern Ireland subsidiary, The Northern Counties Committee (NCC), in August 1944. Before transfer the engine was overhauled at the LMS workshops in Derby, where the

One of the Class 3 shunting and branch line tank engines built for the LMS was re-gauged to the Irish gauge of 5ft 3in, and transferred to the LMS subsidiary, the Northern Counties Committee in 1944. It is seen here shunting at Belfast Docks in 1948, by which time it was renumbered as NCC No 18 - Bagnall 2292 of September 1926. (Frank Jones Collection - Industrial Locomotive Society)

track gauge was altered to the Irish standard of 5ft 3in. As NCC No18, this engine, along with another from a different builder sent to Ireland at the same time, was used for shunting in and around Belfast Docks, and it was not withdrawn for scrapping until 1956.

During the period covered by this Chapter, as well as locomotives, the Company continued to build railway rolling stock and other light railway equipment, in particular turntables, but generally in decreasing quantity, or certainly as a reduced proportion of total workload. The non locomotive aspect of production never again reached the percentage of total workload it had before the war. However, as the years of post-war recession continued the Company was of course anxious to get hold of almost any work it could, and as well as conventional rolling stock and turntables, it branched out into more specialist items. For example skips, buckets and baskets for cranes, along with trolleys and kiln cars for use in the pottery industry at nearby Stoke-on-Trent. There were several orders for ash skips for the main-line railway companies, as well as platelayers trolleys, and even some double deck colliery pit cages for the West Cannock Colliery - no fewer than seven between 1923 and 1931. Cast iron turntables remained a staple diet, and to all types and sizes, and there were also orders for underground mine cars. Spare parts for locomotives provided a steady stream of orders, and the Company was extremely successful in obtaining numerous orders for spares for the BESA design locomotives on Indian railways, and not just the ones it had built itself. In particular, a significant number of orders for spare boilers were obtained, again more often than not for locomotives originally built by other makers, and in many cases the new boilers were fitted with superheaters whilst the ones they were replacing were not. In these cases the Company often supplied the remainder of the equipment to convert the locomotives to superheat, and on occasions this included new piston valve cylinders, valve motion parts and a whole host of other fittings and equipment. These were very lucrative orders, requiring a whole range of the works facilities, and thus providing work for several of the workshops, and not just the boiler shop.

Quite a lot of new plant was added in the period under review; among the bigger items for example, were 10 cwt and two ton Massey steam hammers, a Sentinel

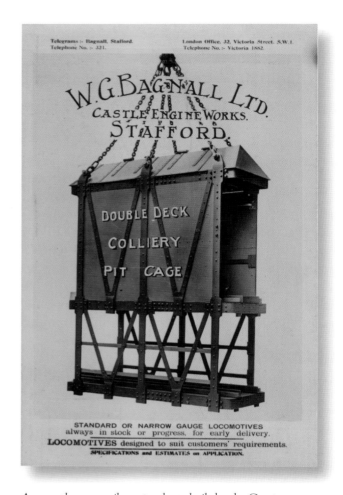

Among the non-railway products built by the Company were colliery pit cages. This is a publicity card depicting one of them, in this case a double-deck variety. The reverse of the card is addressed to JR Howie Limited of Kilmarnock, colliery owners in that part of Scotland, but as it is unstamped and came from the works itself, was obviously not sent. Nevertheless, this helps to illustrate the extent of the firm's efforts to sell it products during difficult trading conditions.

air compressor, a 50 ton riveter for the boiler shop, a 3ft 6in swing wheel lathe and a hydraulic riveter specifically designed for use in the boiler shop to rivet firehole door apertures. For the power house a new 150kW Bellis & Morcom vertical steam generating set, followed in April 1926 by additional steam generating plant in the form of a Tinker & Shenton Lancashire boiler. There were also numerous smaller machine tools along with a variety of other equipment. In regard to the buildings, there were extensions to the boiler shop between May and September 1922, a new pattern shed was erected to hold the ever increasing number of

An example of a wagon built during the period reviewed in this Chapter, in this case a metre-gauge four-wheel side tipper complete with a hand brake and roller bearing axle boxes.

patterns in October 1922, followed by two new bays to the smithy in September 1924, which also benefited from a new overhead crane and a new furnace. The wagon shop also had a new overhead crane and in September 1926 a paint & drying shed was erected in the yard. During the war, despite having moved the bulk of its activities to new and larger premises on the opposite side of the Wellington and Shrewsbury railway line, the Universal Grinding Wheel Company continued to use the facilities on the land it leased as part of the Castle Engine Works site. However, in November 1921, it gave up the lease of the plot of land, but the actual building was purchased by the Company for £250, and became the works canteen and social club. A further building used for similar purposes was purchased from the War Department in August 1920; this was one that had formerly been in use at the military camp on Cannock Chase and came much cheaper, at the princely sum of but £41. In September 1921 the Company invested in its first motor car, a Rover purchased at a cost of £410 10/- (£410 50p), and principally for use by Sydney Edwards.

In 1926 Reg Gard, the chief draughtsman and designer since 1915, left the Company to take up a similar post on the New Zealand Government Railway (NZGR). He had applied for this position to further his career following an advert in *The Railway Gazette* in its issue dated 2 April 1926, and he assumed his new duties on 22 December the same year. The chief draughtsman's position was one of the principal assistants to the chief mechanical engineer of the NZGR, Gilbert Somerville Lynde, who was also recently appointed and had only been in office since April 1925, when he was 36 years of age. Lynde had previously been based in London as the general manager of the Superheater Company Limited, although he trained with the Great Central Railway at Gorton Works in Manchester, prior to distinguished service with the Royal Engineers during the First World War. Commissioned in September 1914, he served with the Railway Operating Division (ROD) and towards the end of the war had charge of all railway workshops under British control in France and Belgium. Mentioned in Despatches no less than three times, Lynde retired with the honorary rank of Lieutenant Colonel in December 1919. As events turned out Lynde did not enjoy great success in his New Zealand appointment, taking the blame for a series of Beyer-Garratt articulated locomotives he specified which turned out to be something of a disaster, although no fault of their builder. The story goes that conscious of his own lack of experience in locomotive design, Gilbert Lynde wanted an experienced locomotive design engineer with a good track record and plenty of recent experience, to take charge of all design and development issues in New Zealand. This being the case, he certainly found what he wanted and unlike his chief, Reg Gard went on to have a very successful career in New Zealand; fortunately he was not involved in the specification for the Beyer-Garratt locomotives. The two would have known each other prior to Lynde moving to New Zealand, as Bagnall had already done business with the Superheater Company.

After Lynde left in 1930, in strained circumstances following the Garratt debacle, the traditional responsibilities of the position of chief mechanical engineer were split, with Reg Gard taking full responsibility for design and development, and Percy Roy Angus the remainder. Reg Gard was therefore, independently responsible for design and development issues and reported directly to the general manager. Among his most significant achievements was the conception and design of the well known, quite famous, and without doubt most successful of all main-line New Zealand Railway steam locomotives, the magnificent K

class 4-8-4s, and J class 4-8-2s. These two classes, including a number of derivatives, were built in large numbers both by the railway's own workshops in New Zealand, and under contract in this country, and they predominated the main-line motive power in New Zealand from their inception, and until the end of steam traction in that country. Reg Gard was left very much to his own devices in designing these and other locomotives, as well as modernising much of the rest of the fleet. The position of chief mechanical engineer, with total responsibility for the department, was not filled until 1941, and until then Angus was in effect the locomotive superintendent, responsible for the locomotive running branch and workshops.

Reg Gard was a great loss to the Company, and whenever he returned to this country, as he frequently did both on leave and in connection with contracts for building locomotives and rolling stock, he never failed to visit the Castle Engine Works. On these occasions Sydney Edwards would accompany him around the works as he was extremely proud of his protégés

This picture and the next four were all taken in the early months of 1925, at the same time as the earlier internal works views when the Madras engines were being built, and are part of the same collection. This first one shows the works yard looking north. Notice the booking-on clock in the lean-to on the extreme right. Machine Shop external walls to the right, and the shops on the left are the Smithy, followed by the Boiler Shop and beyond the chimney the Iron Foundry and the Railway Shop, as it was then termed.

Another view of the works yard, looking south from north of the Smithy and Boiler Shop, with the steel storage shed to the left followed by the Pattern Shop and Stores, with the Wagon Shop to the right. Notice on the left a complete saddle tank can just be discerned, over the steel stockpile and under the shed roof.

The interior of the Works Canteen with the staff waiting their hungry customers. This building was formerly an army hut from the First World War Camp on nearby Cannock Chase.

The Boiler House with three hand-fired Lancashire Boilers and their attendants.

The Works power-house at a time when all the electricity was generated on site. Two of the three Bellis & Morcom vertical triple-expansion enclosed steam sets can be seen, the one on the left coupled to a Siemens alternator, with the site electrical power distribution board to the rear. The gentleman is Stan Fisher, the Power House Foreman at the time.

The management and salaried staff photographed in 1925 in front of one of the Madras 4-8-0 tender engines; the engine is MSMR 503, Bagnall 2246.

Front Row left to right:

W J Lloyd - Draughtsman/Estimator; Miss L Ecclestone; Miss E Bryan; Jack Dale - Erecting & Fitting Shop Foreman;
Fred Parker - Chief Cost Clerk; Reg Gard - Chief Draughtsman; John Gifford - Managing Director;
Sydney Edwards - General Manager; Bill Parkinson - Works Manager; Charlie Tunnicliffe - Chief Cashier;
Harold Coates - Chief Wages Clerk; Miss J Williams; Miss Alice Duckers - Buyer's Typist; ? .

Middle Row left to right:

LL Jones - Draughtsman; Joe Duckers - Wagon Shop Foreman; J Eaton - Draughtsman; Percy Critchley - Buyer;
E Brandrick - Secretary; Miss A Evans (later Alice Lamb) - Secretary to Sydney Edwards; Miss D Plant - Stores Clerk;
Miss E Parker - Tracer; Miss A Beardsley - Tracer; Arthur Owen - Cost Clerk; Reg Machin - Draughtsman;
Victor Bill - Draughtsman; ?; Monty Bruce - Cost Office; ? .

Back Row left to right:

Horace Lorton - Cost Clerk; L Jackson - Deputy Chief Draughtsman; Oliver Jennings - Foreman Painter;
Jim Woollams - Machine Shop Foreman; Charlie Homer - Smithy Foreman; Harry (Dick) Walker - Boiler Shop Foreman;
Arthur Slinn - Forman Joiner; Percy Godfrey - Draughtsman; Jim Robinson - Toolroom Foreman;
George White - Pattern Shop Foreman; W Brown - Foundry Foreman; H Davies - Cost Clerk; Harry Whale - Cost Clerk.

In Cab left to right:

Fred Schofield - Stores Foreman; Stan Fisher - Power House Foreman; Tom (Major) Ryan - Gatekeeper & Time Clerk.

achievements; Gard left Stafford on amicable terms to improve his position and future career prospects, and the two of them remained very good friends with enormous mutual respect for each others qualities and achievements. Reg Gard never forgot his time at Bagnalls, always recalling it with great affection, and by all accounts would regale his new found colleagues in New Zealand for hours on end, particularly after retirement and at various reunions and similar occasions; he had endless tales of life at the Castle Engine Works. Reg Gard took a number of Bagnall design features with him, many he had himself been responsible for, notably the rather angular design characteristics of the cabs, tanks, bunkers and other plate-work along with, what is perhaps the most noticeable part of a locomotive, its chimney. Several of the locomotives he was responsible for in New Zealand, including some older ones modified and rebuilt under his direction, were graced with the very same chimney profile he had designed at Stafford for some of the Indian metre-gauge locomotives. Bagnalls too, continued to use the same chimney profile and one wonders if Gard and Edwards ever talked about this as they walked around the workshops at Stafford! In October 1942, Reg Gard became deputy chief mechanical engineer of the NZGR when Angus finally took full responsibility for the department; he remained in this position until his retirement on 21 May 1949.

After retirement from NZGR Gard worked in a consultancy basis for A&G Price Limited, the New Zealand locomotive builders and general engineers, and among other achievements designed a range of small diesel-mechanical shunting locomotives - they called them tractors. These were quite popular for shunting at various industrial plants around the country, and some were sold to the NZGR. We have expanded on the career of Reginald John Gard, as not only did he achieve so much while at Stafford, stamping his mark very clearly on the locomotive design characteristics, some of which remained until the end of steam locomotive design, but he was also remembered with a great deal of respect by all who knew him. His enormous influence in the design of the New Zealand Railway locomotives, with more than a little bit of influence from the Castle Engine Works drawing office finding its way into them, is a nice story too. Reg Gard passed away after a long and distinguished career on 9

February 1981. As we have seen his most significant achievements were in New Zealand, and examples of the magnificent J and K class locomotives he designed have been kept and are preserved there for all to see. Many of the design features he introduced are still in evidence in this country, also in India, as well as many other countries around the world, on locomotives that have survived into preservation. In particular his chimney lives on as one of the most distinctive features of any steam locomotive. Harold Wood, a much later occupant of the post of chief draughtsman at Stafford, recalled to the authors that whenever a drawing had to be called-up dating from Reg Gard's time as the chief, they could be sure it would be one 100% accurate, which was apparently, a lot more than could be said for drawings undertaken in the tenure of some of the other holders of the post.

Arthur Burley, another of Edwards's old colleagues from Kerr, Stuart, took Reg Gard's place at Stafford. Burley was born in Stoke-on-Trent on 27 August 1888, and served his apprenticeship at the California Works of Kerr, Stuart; coming from a railway family, his father was a driver on the North Staffordshire Railway. In 1910 Burley moved to Scotland to take up an appointment as a draughtsman with the North British Locomotive Company Limited in Glasgow, and in 1915 took up a similar appointment with the Fairfield Shipbuilding & Engineering Company Limited, also located in Glasgow. Towards the end of the war, in 1918, he returned to locomotive work with the Glasgow based shipbuilder and armaments manufacturer, William Beardmore & Company Limited. This was at the time when the enormous reduction in armaments, munitions and shipbuilding work as hostilities were clearly drawing to an end, was causing companies like Beardmore enormous labour and excess resource problems, and a decision to enter the locomotive manufacturing business had been taken. This movement into locomotive building by Beardmore's, along with other traditional armaments manufacturers was briefly discussed in the last Chapter in connection with the LMA, and more will be heard of it in later Chapters. However, as a result, Beardmore were looking for experienced locomotive draughtsman, and Burley took up the offer. Nevertheless he was not with Beardmore very long, before moving south again, to take up an appointment as a senior draughtsman with Robert

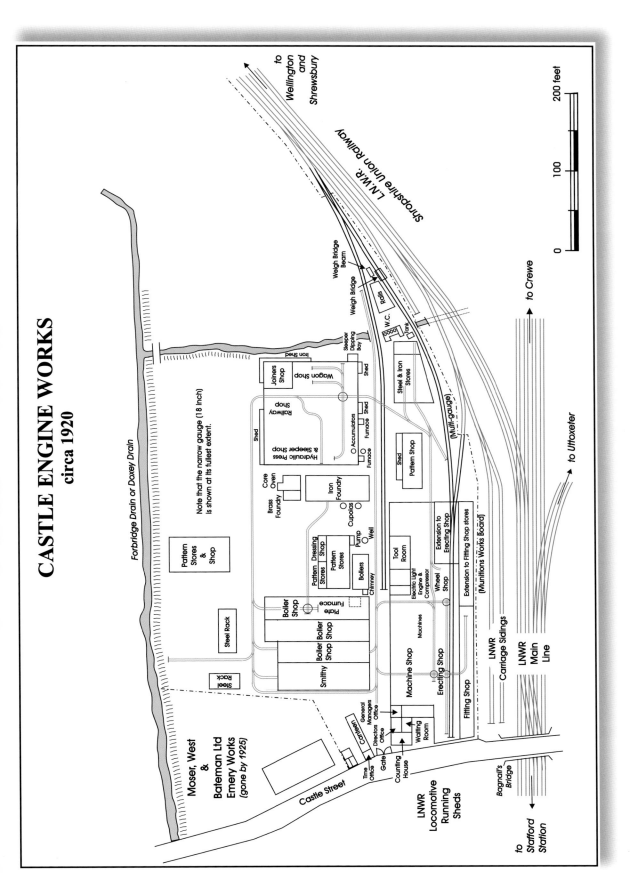

CASTLE ENGINE WORKS
circa 1920

Note that the narrow gauge (18 inch) is shown at its fullest extent.

Forbridge Drain or Doxey Drain

Moser, West & Bateman Ltd Emery Works (gone by 1925)

Pattern Stores & Shop

Steel Rack

Steel Rack

Smithy

Boiler Shop

Boiler Shop

Boiler Shop

Plate Furnace

Pattern Dressing Shop

Pattern Stores

Boilers

Chimney

Brass Foundry

Core Oven

Iron Foundry

Cupolas

Pump

Well

Furnace

Hydraulic Press & Sleeper Shop

Railway Shop

Shed

Accumulators

Furnace

Joiners Shop

Wagon Shop

Shed

Iron Shed

Sleeper Dipping Bay

Electric Light Engine & Compressor

Tool Room

Wheel Shop

Machines

Machine Shop

Extension to Erecting Shop

Extension to Fitting Shop stores
(Munitions Works Board)

Pattern Shop

Shed

Steel & Iron Stores

(Multi-gauge)

Erecting Shop

Fitting Shop

LNWR Carriage Sidings

LNWR Main Line

to Crewe

to Uttoxeter

W.C.

Tank

Rails

Weigh Bridge

Weigh Bridge Beam

W.C.

L.N.W.R.
Shropshire Union Railway

to Wellington and Shrewsbury

General Managers Office

Directors Office

Canteen

Waiting Room

Time Office

Gate

Counting House

Castle Street

Bagnall's Bridge

LNWR Locomotive Running Sheds

to Stafford Station

0   100   200 feet

Plan of the works layout as it was around the year 1920. However, this plan shows the 18in gauge internal works railway at it maximum extent.

Stephenson & Company Limited at Darlington. Throughout this part of his career Arthur Burley seems to have kept in touch with Sydney Edwards, and with Reg Gard's departure Edwards invited him to move to Stafford and take up the appointment of chief draughtsman and designer. Edwards would have kept in touch with Burley, as he was shrewd enough to do with a lot of former colleagues and other acquaintances. Doubtless through his friendship with James Warren, the chief draughtsman at Darlington, he would have been aware of Burley's suitability to take-up the senior post in the drawing office at Stafford.

Before we leave this period of the Company's history, it is opportune to have a brief look at the financial position. Despite all the problems and issues associated with the immediate post-war years, including the fluctuations in wages mentioned earlier, and the losses made on some large contracts, the Company was profitable. In the years 1922 to 1927 the average annual profit after tax amounted to £4,039, against an

Aerial view of the works taken on 3 September 1925. Notice the West-Coast main-line railway running from side to side, London and the south to the right with Crewe and the north to the left. The two branches are at the top, the former Great Northern Railway line to Uttoxeter, and at the bottom the Shropshire Union Railways & Canal Company line to Wellington and onwards to Shrewsbury. In the bottom junction fork can be seen the war-time works of the Universal Grinding Wheel Company, and in the top fork Venables timber yard; the former LNWR Stafford running sheds are to the extreme right. Compare this photograph with the circa 1920 plan, although as will be observed there have already been some extensions, in particular notice that the Smithy and Boiler Shop have been extended westwards towards the bottom of the picture.

average annual balance sheet of £93,534. The average turnover in the years 1926 and 1927 was £129,354. In 1914 the wages and salaries bill equalled £18,510, and by 1926 this had climbed to £38,628, the salaried part of which was £8,411; the following year it rose again to £42,713, a figure which included the salaries at £8,616.

Advert from The Railway Engineer, issue dated July 1925. The locomotives are at the top number 2234 of 1924 for India, in the middle 2216, also of 1924 and the firm's first fireless locomotive named UNIQUE, and at the bottom one of the standard-gauge 0-4-0 saddle tanks built in 1921 and 1922, numbers 2171 to 2178 which were sent to India. All these locomotives are described in this Chapter; observe too yet further examples of narrow-gauge rolling stock the firm built.

This publicity leaflet was issued in about 1925 to help market the four standard-gauge locomotives laid down to stock orders in November 1923, and discussed in detail on page 287. The right-hand illustration is one of the earlier 13in cylinder engines, number 2169 of February 1922 NAIROBI, new to the contractor Pauling & Company Limited, and described on Page 280. The left-hand engine is one of the 15in cylinder locomotives sent to China - see Chapter Four.

Chapter Eight

Difficult Times:
The End of The Era
of The Giffords

James Caldwell Gifford died on 18 October 1925, at his home at 'Crossfields' in Weeping Cross, which he shared with his brother, and like his brother he never married. Although a director of the Company at the time of his death, James took very little interest in its affairs, at least in later years, and was never seen around the workshops. Sixty nine years old at the time of his death, the funeral service was on Wednesday 21 October at St Mary's Castle Church in Stafford, where he was later laid to rest - only a few feet from Gordon Bagnall's grave. His sister Margaret Caldwell Gifford, who never married either and lived with her brothers in Stafford, is alongside him; she died on 28 December 1911 when only 54 years old. His brother John, along with Sydney Edwards and no less than 22 employees of the Company attended the funeral, including almost all the shop foremen. A number of family members were present, as well as several prominent local businessmen. James Gifford left his entire estate to his brother, which included the 259 shares in the Company, and was valued at £9,660. Thereafter, there were but two shareholders in WG Bagnall Limited, John Gifford and WS Edwards.

In 1926 another Kerr, Stuart trained man joined the Company, and once again we can be sure Sydney Edwards had a hand in the appointment. Harry Davies, who eventually became general manager, joined in 1926. Born in 1902, he was a native of Stoke-on-Trent where his father was an senior officer in the local Police Force; eventually rising to the rank of Superintendent. Harry joined Kerr, Stuart in 1918, and after completing his apprenticeship spent some time in the estimating department. As a result of this when Edwards interviewed him for a draughtsman's job, he was persuaded to take on a position that while encompassing some draughting work, also had estimating responsibilities. At the time the chief estimator was WJ Lloyd, who it appears Edwards had taken a dislike to, and within a few months of Harry arriving he left. In fact Harry told the authors that 'Edwards sacked him', leaving Harry at a somewhat tender age in sole charge of the estimating department, and a very crucial one it has to be said!

About the same time too, Hugh R Taylor joined the Company as assistant chief draughtsman; a Glaswegian from the North British Locomotive Company where he had trained, and a former colleague there with Arthur Burley. He came south at Burley's invitation as the previous occupant of this post, L Jackson, about whom we know very little, does not appear to have got on very well with Arthur Burley and left soon after he arrived.

In March 1927 the Company received orders for

eight metre-gauge 2-6-2 tank engines with 15x22in cylinders and 3ft 7in diameter driving wheels, four each for the Indian Bengal & North Western Railway (BNWR) and the Burma Railway (BR). The two lots were almost identical, a standard BESA design which the Indian railways classified as T, and the Burma Railway M. With neat and clean external lines they were typical of the BESA types, fitted with Belpaire fireboxes, in both these cases with steel inner boxes, and as they were not superheated balanced slide valves, as well as vacuum brakes for train operation. The Burma engines also had Lambert wet sanding equipment. These were the largest metre-gauge tank engines built by the Company for the Indian sub-continent by this date. The manufacturer's numbers were 2313 to 2316 for the Indian engines which were despatched in November 1927, BNWR Nos. 343 to 346, and 2317 to 2320 for the Burma ones, which were despatched in December the same year - they became BR Nos.154 to 157. The design of this BESA class had been entrusted by Rendel, Palmer & Tritton (RP&T), to Robert Stephenson & Company Limited (RS) of Darlington, and the drawings used at Stafford were the same as those of an earlier batch of the same type, built by RS for the BNWR; RP&T acted as the consulting engineers. It is perhaps worth mentioning at this point that some years later Bagnall built some similar engines, but in that case to a revised and generally updated design, the Indian Railway Standard (IRS) class TS. In

the redesign a superheated boiler and larger 16½in diameter cylinders were substituted, as well as piston valves. The numbers were 2569 and 2570, built in 1936 for the Rohilkund & Kumaon Railway. Also developed under the IRS auspices was a slightly smaller version with 11½x18in cylinders classified TS/1. Bagnall built eight examples of this class, all for the Mysore State Railway between 1932 and 1935; numbers 2464 and 2465 in 1932, 2481 to 2484 in 1933, and lastly in 1935, 2526 and 2527. The last two had larger, full length side tanks, as opposed to the earlier engines that had tanks stopping short of the smokebox - the respective water capacities being 850 and 1,000 gallons.

In April 1927 an order was received via the Crown Agent for the Colonies on behalf of the Federated Malay States Railway, in this case for five metre-gauge 0-6-2 side tank locomotives. Cylinders were 13x20in and coupled wheel diameter 3ft 3in, the locomotives had round topped fireboxes and Walschaerts valve gear, and as they were not superheated, balanced slide valves were used. Designed in their entirety at Stafford, and unmistakably in the legacy of the Reg Gard design school of the period, particularly in the external features of the cab, side tanks and chimney. An interesting aspect of the order was the shipment of the locomotives from the King George V Dock at Tilbury, as they were shipped completely erected aboard the SS GLENGARRY bound for Selangor, the largest locomotives built at Stafford by this date to be so

Eight engines of this metre-gauge 2-6-2 side-tank design were supplied in 1927, four each to the Indian Bengal & North Western Railway and the Burma Railway. This is the first one, manufacturer's number 2313 for India, later class T/1. Originally BNWR No 343 it was renumbered 135 when it passed to the North Eastern Railway, and 32064 under the all-India renumbering scheme. In 1943 the BNWR and the Rohilkund & Kumaon Railway combined to form the Oudh Tirhut Railway.

Although built in a later period than covered by this Chapter, it is opportune to include this photograph as the class in mentioned in the adjacent text. The engine in manufacturer's number 2464, one of two built in 1932 for the metre-gauge Indian Mysore Railway, class T/S, the S indicating superheated, and in effect an updated version of the engine in the previous photograph. This particular one as Indian Railways 37338 is still in existence at the small railway museum at Mysore. Notice the round-topped firebox as opposed to the Belpaire, piston valve cylinders and a shorter coupled and total wheelbase, making a more compact design, although the driving wheel diameter remained the same at 3ft 7in.

treated, and attracting some publicity as a result. Only the cab roofs had to be removed for them to clear the LMS loading gauge, and they were all transported to the docks as one train load, leaving Stafford on 26 January 1928. The manufacturer's numbers were 2323 to 2327, and a special lifting beam was included in the order to facilitate loading, and whilst this travelled to the docks with the locomotives and went to Malay with the ship to assist in the unloading, it eventually found its way back to Stafford. It lay around the works yard for a long time afterwards. Apart from one member of the class damaged during the war by the Japanese and scrapped in 1948 - works number 2324 - they all remained in use on the duties they were designed for, shunting around Port Swettenham and Kuala Lumper, until the mid 1960s. One of them, number 2327 was converted to burn oil fuel in 1962, whilst another, 2325, was sold in 1965 to a cement factory at Ipoh, which is to the north of the country, and when it finished work there was purchased by the railway authorities, and today resides at the small railway museum in Kuala Lumper.

In October 1927 a new draughtsman joined the Company, one who was to have a significant impact on

its fortunes over the next 10 years or so. Ivor A'Court Farr was a native of Swindon, where he was born on 3 November 1902, and at the age of 16 followed his father and grandfather before him, into the employment of the Great Western Railway (GWR) at Swindon Works. His father was employed in the drawing office where he was responsible for locomotive and rolling stock spares. During his five year apprenticeship Ivor attended evening classes at the local technical college, and in view of his rapid progress, was later awarded a GWR day studentship to read mechanical engineering. Attending Owens College in Manchester, he graduated with a BSc in the subject. Returning to Swindon he

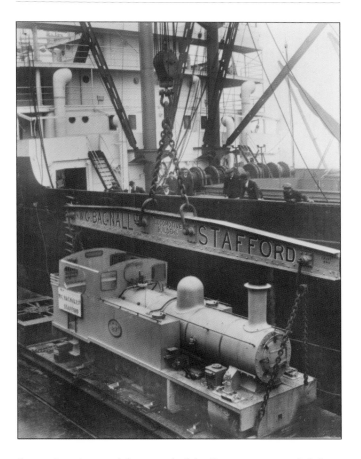

Interesting picture of the second of the five metre-gauge 0-6-2 side tank engines for the Federated Malay States Railway, being loaded on-board ship at the King George V Dock at Tilbury on the River Thames in January 1928 - it had left Stafford on the 26th of that month. At the time these were quite large engines to be shipped fully erected and the lifting beam was also made at Stafford, and whilst it travelled with the engines for unloading at Port Swettenham, it later returned to this country and lay around in the works yards for several years.

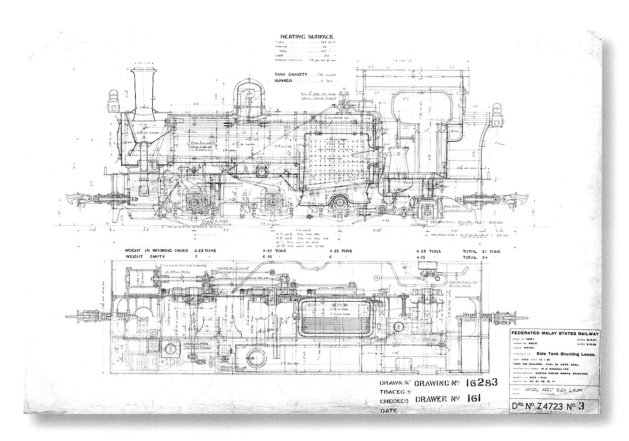

General Arrangement drawing of the Malayan tank engines. It was rare for the Company to produce a general arrangement drawing on its own account, but they were often requested by main-line railways, and sometimes a contract requirement of consulting engineers. In this case it would have been requested by the Crown Agents, who were responsible for the order, and the cost of production would have been allowed for in the tender price.

joined his father in the drawing office, in his case as a junior draughtsman, and remained there until his move to Stafford. Ivor had his reasons for wanting to leave Swindon, despite the prospect of a promising career with the GWR; he was anxious to spread his wings and get involved in more innovative design work, reckoning a small private locomotive builder might just offer him such an opportunity - he was not disappointed. Shortly before he left Swindon for Stafford, FW Hawkesworth, at the time the chief draughtsman there, happened to be talking to Ivor's father, and casually asked why his son was leaving, and where was he going? Ivor used to delight in telling the story that on being told that young Ivor was going to Bagnalls, Hawkesworth in expressing some surprise, said he had never heard of the company - who, what and where were they? Ivor would embellish the story on the lines that Hawkesworth's knowledge being thus enhanced, was the reason Bagnall subsequently got

contracts to build two series of pannier tank locomotives for the GWR! Be that as it may, Bagnall did go on to built no less than 100 GWR design pannier tank locomotives between 1930 and as late as 1954.

In the immediate post war years RP&T were commissioned by the Indian Government to produce a updated range of standard locomotive designs, and on this occasion covering the three principal rail gauges used in that country - broad-gauge (5ft 6in), metre-gauge (3ft 3³/₈in) and narrow-gauge (2ft 6in). In the case of the earlier BESA designs, only the broad and metre-gauges were encompassed. The new designs were known as the Indian Railway Standard Designs (IRS), in some cases little more than updated versions of the earlier BESA designs, but in others completely new - brief mention of some of these designs has already been made in this Chapter. The consulting engineers went about this task is a similar way to the earlier BESA designs, once the range of types needed had been agreed and the broad specifications established, allocating the detailed design work and prototype construction to individual private locomotive building firms. In this scheme of things Bagnall were allocated the detailed design work on two of the proposed 2ft 6in gauge engines; the ZB, which was a light axle-load 2-6-2 tender engine, and the ZD, a much larger 4-6-2 tender engine. In the event no ZD engines were ever built, although Bagnall did complete the detail design work. However, the Company was allocated the contract to build the prototype locomotives of class ZB.

The order for the first two ZB engines was placed on 29 November 1927 by the High Commissioner for India, intended for the North Western Railway (NWR), and this was in fact before any of the design work had started! However, to a large extent the ZB was based on the earlier Larkana Jacobabad Railway locomotives - manufacturer's numbers 2150 to 2152 and 2210 -

described in the last Chapter, and this may have had a bearing on Bagnall being allocated the work. Nevertheless, a complete new set of drawings had to be produced, as once designed, any manufacturer with the right facilities, should have been able to build any of the IRS designs. The opportunity therefore, was taken to improve the design and one of Ivor Farr's first jobs was the lay-out of the valve gear, including cylinders, wheels, axles and associated parts. The locomotives had 12x18in cylinders and a 2ft 10in coupled wheel diameter, Walschaerts valve gear drove seven inch diameter piston valves and the superheated Belpaire firebox boiler had a copper firebox, brass tubes and a drop grate. Vacuum brakes were fitted as well as Lambert wet sanding, Goodall articulated drawbars between the engine and tender, and Sunbeam electric lighting. Sunbeam lighting equipment, including the turbo-generators, was manufactured by the American

Fortunately, one of the Malayan engines has survived in preservation. It is seen here at the small railway museum in Kuala Lumper in May 2001, with its later number 321-01, indicating the first engine of class 321.

Sunbeam Electric Manufacturing Company, of Evansville in Indiana, for which the Baldwin Locomotive Works were the sales agents. The weight in working order of the engine was quoted as 28½ tons, with a maximum axle-load of six tons, the leading and trailing truck springing compensated with the coupled wheels. Total weight in working order for the engine and tender equalled 44½ tons, and the tractive effort at 85% of the 160psi working pressure amounted to 10,039lb. The end result was a very handsome locomotive with a neat six-wheel tender, and over the following years, particularly after the last war, examples were built by several other manufacturers, both in this country and on the continent, as well as further ones from Stafford.

The prototypes were manufacturer's numbers 2339 and 2340, despatched fully erected in October 1928 as NWR Nos. 201 and 202. They cost £8,806 for the pair, plus £385 for the design work and drawings. However, at the request of RP&T, a further £190 of design costs was allocated to a subsequent order. There is an interesting story about these two locomotives, related to the authors several years ago by former employees who were around at the time, and at this distance in time it is perhaps, safe to go into print. When the time came to weigh the first ZB, it was found to be almost two tons over its working order design weight, a discovery only a couple of days before the RP&T inspecting engineer was due to make his final inspection prior to testing in steam, which included accepting the engine as within its design weight tolerances. Obviously there was no time to do very much about it, and after much scratching of heads, and at Edwards instigation, the water level was lowered in the boiler until the weight of the locomotive was within the allowed tolerance. Following this, the bottom water gauge passages were temporarily blocked and the gauge glasses filled with water to half a glass, which was the stipulated level the specification called for in the working order weight calculations. Everybody concerned, threatened with awful consequences by Edwards if the truth got out, then held their breath when the inspector came, that he

The second Indian 2ft 6in gauge ZB, number 2340, just brought out of the Erecting Shop and being prepared to be coupled to its tender and subsequently posing for the official photograph and then steam testing. The gentleman in the suit in front of the tender is the Works Manager, Bill Parkinson, directing operations, and on the left is C R Peach, one of the Draughtsmen. This picture was taken one lunchtime in October 1928, by Ivor Farr who had been heavily involved in the design of the engines.

would not operate one of the gauge glass drain cocks during his inspection. All the time he was on the footplate, accompanied by Edwards and the erecting shop foreman Fred Ewington, the view was that if the inspector opens one of the cocks, then the right fellow is there to do the explaining. Well, to the profound relief of all concerned, he did not, and Edwards related later that knowing the inspector concerned had never before tested the drain cocks unless the engine was in steam, he correctly assumed he would not do so on this occasion. Following this there was some hurriedly arranged machining of some of the component parts, in particular castings, on the other locomotive, to get it within the design weight. But by all accounts, the first member of the class went out to India almost two tons over weight, and nothing more was ever heard about it. Except that is, some of the draughtsman concerned. The engines were for use on the Khushalgarh Kohat Thal line on the North-West Frontier, the same line the earlier 2-4-2 saddle tank engines with auxiliary tenders had been supplied to in the early 1900s, mentioned in Chapter Three.

The second order for ZB engines, in this case two locomotives in December 1928, manufacturer's numbers 2371 and 2372, was for the Bombay, Baroda & Central India Railway (BBCIR); identical in almost every respect to the earlier ones. Despatched to Birkenhead Docks for shipment on 11 July 1929, once again fully erected and two months late on the contract delivery date, the running numbers were 20 and 21. In the post-war all-India renumbering scheme they became 56 and 57 in the Western Railway fleet, allocated to the narrow-gauge lines between Ankleshwar, Rajpipla and Netrang, south of Baroda; they survived until dieselisation of these lines towards the end of the 1980s. Although jumping ahead of our story somewhat, it is perhaps opportune at this juncture to mention three more ZB engines, and the last ones ordered from Stafford before the war. In September 1932 two more were ordered for the NWR, followed by another in November for the BBCIR, all three however, had a fundamental difference in their design. Instead of Walschaerts valve gear and piston valves, they were fitted with Caprotti poppet valve gear driven by a single drive shaft from a gearbox mounted between the frames on the intermediate coupled axle. Ingeniously mounted within the smokebox saddle was a further gearbox, from

which two shafts ran at right angles to the engine frame, one to each of the two cam boxes and valve chests which were mounted on top of the cylinders. The whole of the valve gear including the cam boxes and valve chests, was supplied by William Beardmore & Company Limited, as at the time this Company had the British patent rights for this type of valve gear. They were the first locomotives built at Stafford with any form of poppet valve gear.

There was another design change from the earlier engines, as these three had slightly larger tenders with higher sides, a tender-cab and a water capacity of 1,400 gallons - 100 gallons more than their predecessors - the fuel capacity was also increased, from two tons and five cwt, to three tons. The manufacturer's numbers for the NWR pair were 2476 and 2477, and as NWR Nos 210 and 211, they were despatched in June 1933, once again shipped fully erected to Karachi from Birkenhead Docks. The selling price was £6,767 for the two; one of the old cost books also quotes the price in rupees - Rs103,066! By the early 1970s these two locomotives were still operating on the railway from Kohat to Thal, in what in now Pakistan, and when observed in October 1974, number 2476 was still fitted with Caprotti valve gear. However, when its sister was seen in January 1979, it had been converted to conventional piston valves and Walschaerts valve gear.

The third engine was allocated manufacturer's number 2478, BBCIR No 22, also shipped via Birkenhead Docks, in this case to Bombay in July 1933; it was sold for £3,442, and the maker's recorded a loss of £2,164 9/ 4d (£2,164 46p) on the three locomotives. This one too, lost its Caprotti valve gear on conversion to conventional piston valves and Walschaerts valve gear. When one of the authors saw it as Western Railway No 58, under repair in the railway workshops at Pratapnagar near Baroda on 12 January 1977, he was told by the works manager that the conversion had been done at Pratapnagar in either 1963 or 1964, due to difficulty in obtaining spares. Like the earlier BBCIR engines this one was also allocated to Ankleshwar, and lasted until ousted by diesels in the late 1980s. Although no more ZB class engines were built at Stafford until after the war, the German manufacturer Hanomag (Hannoversche Maschinenbau AG, Hannover) built seven in 1932, presumably having tendered a lower price than any British manufacturer.

Manufacturer's number 2478 of 1933, although from a period covered by a later Chapter, but discussed in the adjacent text, is one of the ZB engines fitted with Caprotti poppet valve gear. Bombay, Baroda & Central India Railway No 22.

Almost certainly, Bagnall would have quoted a higher price than that charged for the three engines it had already built.

It is interesting to speculate why these locomotives were fitted with Caprotti valve gear, an invention of an Italian engineer Signor Arturo Caprotti (1881-1938). As might be expected in view of the concept, Caprotti trained in automobile engineering and would have been more conversant with internal combustion engines rather than steam locomotives. In 1924 he read a paper describing his valve gear - *A New Locomotive Distributing Gear Using Poppet Valves*, to members of the Institution of Locomotive Engineers (I Loco E) in London. A year later the Glasgow based engineering company William Beardmore & Company Limited, acquired the British patent rights for the manufacture of the gear, in the first instance it seems, with a view to its use on marine engines. The equipment was manufactured at Beardmore's Speedwell Works at Coatbridge, but when the plant there closed manufacture was transferred to the main-works at Dalmuir. The equipment for the Bagnall locomotives however, came from Coatbridge, and it would seem from the records that originally it was only intended to

fit the BBCIR locomotive, but at some stage a decision was made to fit all three; RP&T were the consulting engineers in the case of both orders.

At the I Loco E annual dinner on 18 February 1927, Signor Caprotti was presented with the medal of the Institution for his paper by the then president of the Institution, Sir Seymour Biscoe Tritton, and among those present at this event was WS Edwards. One can speculate that the three of them may have discussed the gear during the after dinner socialising. The invention goes back to 1916, but it was not until 1921 that a locomotive of the Italian State Railways was fitted, and 1926 before it was tried in this country. This first application was by the London Midland & Scottish Railway (LMS), on an ex London & North Western Railway Claughton class 4-6-0 express passenger engine, and after an initial period of trial, a further nine members of the same class were fitted in 1928. Subsequently, the gear was fitted to several other classes of locomotive both for use in this country, as well as for export to India and other countries. This was at a period in the history of the steam locomotive when many engineers were attempting to improve its efficiency, and the use of poppet valves was seen as

Footplate layout of a member of the ZB Class, in all probability the first member; only the North Western Railway ones were vacuum fitted. Notice to top left the Detroit sight-feed cylinder lubricator and on the right the Dreadnought Vacuum brake ejector and driver's brake handle. The screw reverse, electric lighting and sand-gun for cleaning the tubes are worth a mention too; that's the latter just above the fire-hole door. Below the footplate can be seen the twin injector water feed hoses, the small steam pipe to the tender brake, the articulated drawbar and the train vacuum brake pipe. If the steam pressure gauge is to be believed the engine is in steam - it's reading about 80 psi!

having a lot of potential. Other forms of ingenious mechanism were developed in the wake of Caprotti, to operate similar types of poppet valves in several different configurations; however, in the event, and by and large, the simplicity of conventional piston valves and Walschaerts valve gear, outweighed whatever efficiency improvements poppet valves gave.

We must now go back a few years and record two more orders from the main-line railway companies, in each case for the LMS class 3F shunting and branch line tank engines. The first order was dated 4 April 1928, for 15 locomotives - manufacturer's numbers 2343 to 2352 - delivered between August and November 1928; they differed from the earlier batch as they were not fitted with vacuum brake equipment for

train use. The original LMS numbers were 16675 through to 16684, but the engines were soon renumbered in the series 7593 to 7601, and finally became British Railways (BR) 47593 to 47601 - all were withdrawn between March 1960 and December 1966. Several of these locomotives were allocated to Stafford and nearby Stoke-on-Trent sheds, and the Stafford ones were a daily sight around the town. Indeed there are photographs of some of them actually shunting in the Bagnall works yard. The second order came in June 1928, but not on this occasion from the LMS, rather for the Somerset & Dorset Joint Railway (SDJR), a railway jointly managed by the LMS and Southern Railway, but with the LMS having responsibly for all motive power issues. Seven locomotives were ordered, numbers 2358

Indian ZB class number 2478 once more, and after conversion to Walschaerts valve gear as described in the text. The engine is seen here as Indian Railways No 57, in the late afternoon sun at Ankleshwar on 1 March 1981, where at the time all the Indian pre-war Bagnall built members of the class were allocated. This was a part of the former Rajpipla State Railway system which was worked by the BBCIR. The system was some 58 miles in extent, opened between 1897 and 1932 and left the BBCIR broad-gauge main line at Ankleshwar (originally Anklesvar), just south Baroda, heading in a easterly direction to Rajpipla. It closed completely to be replaced by road transport on the 10 March 1994.

to 2364, SDJR Nos 19 to 25, delivered in January and February the following year to Bath, where the railway had its motive power headquarters. Unlike the LMS engines which were painted plain black, these engines were turned out in the rather splendid SDJR livery of a prussian blue, and unlike the previous batch of LMS engines, as they were intended for branch line as well as shunting work, they had vacuum brake and steam heating equipment as well as screw, rather than lever reversing gear. When the locomotive stock of SDJR was absorbed into the LMS fleet in 1930, these locomotives became LMS 7150 to 7156, but were later renumbered to the series 7310 to 7316, eventually becoming BR 47310 to 47316. All were withdrawn between September 1959 and June 1967, and No 47313, which survived shunting at Westhouses Colliery in Nottinghamshire until June 1967, was one of the very last of this once numerous class of engine to survive in

Bagnall 2362, SDJR 23, was one of the seven LMS Class 3F shunting and branch line tank engines delivered to the Somerset & Dorset Joint Railway between December 1928 and February the following year. These locomotives were finished in the lovely shade of Prussian Blue, the standard livery of the SDJR, which unfortunately soon gave way to plain black when the SDJR fleet was absorbed into LMS stock in 1930. This particular engine lasted in service until November 1966, when it was allocated to Lostock Hall depot near Preston.

BR service. The LMS engines cost £3,025 each, and the SDJR ones £3,050; the crank-axles for the former came from the Monks Bridge Iron & Steel Company Limited at a cost of £108 each, and for the SDJR engines from Vickers Armstrong at £102 10/- (£102 50p). A combined loss of £5,316 was made on these two orders.

In June 1928 an order was received from the Peruvian Corporation for three large standard-gauge 0-6-0 saddle tank locomotives for shunting work on the Central Railway of Peru, with Livesey Sons & Henderson appointed consulting engineers. To meet the specification a powerful locomotive was designed with bar frames and a very short wheelbase of nine-foot; cylinders were 18½x24in and the wheel diameter four-foot. The locomotives had a steel firebox and were oil fired, the working pressure was 180psi and the tractive effort at 85% equalled 26,182lb. The engines were fitted with vacuum brakes, Lambert wet sanding, Stones electric lighting equipment and although not superheated, eight inch diameter piston valves were used. In view of the short wheelbase the engines had a long connecting rod, and the drive was on the trailing wheelset. The axle-boxes were fitted with adjustable wedges, but interestingly, a specific point on the order was that these should be of British make, and not of the Franklin type. The Franklin was an American design of spring loaded automatically adjustable axle-box wedge, a particularly popular one with North American builders and one wonders if the Peruvians had had problems with them on other locomotives. It was manufactured by the Franklin Railway Supply Company Inc., of New York. The use of bar frames at Stafford was unusual, and this was the first occasion since the two-foot gauge locomotives for South Africa before the war. In this case the main longitudinal sections were cut out at Stafford from two mild steel slabs, 27ft 7in x 2ft 2½in x 4¼in, no mean feat with the equipment available at the time, and the weight in working order of the completed locomotives was 51 tons. Reginald G Machin was the draughtsman responsible for most of the design work, and a neat and tidy job he made in comparison with the American designed locomotives that were more prevalent in Peru. The manufacturer's numbers were 2355 to 2357, and the completed locomotives were despatched to Liverpool Docks for shipment in April 1929, with the running numbers 32, 33 and 34: they cost £3,665 each. In March 1972, at least one of these locomotives was still in use shunting the yards at Callao.

Official Central Railway of Peru photograph of the three large saddle tank locomotives, numbers 2355 to 2357, delivered in 1929. Although carrying the running numbers 32 to 34 when new, at some time they seem to have been renumbered and this picture shows the first member of the class, renumbered as 30. It was still in use shunting the yards at Callao in 1972. Notice the bar frames and the long connecting rod necessary in view of the short coupled wheelbase.

This and the next four photographs were all taken in the workshops in late March or early April 1931, and the second occasion when a comprehensive set of photographs were taken of the complete works. This view looks north in the Erecting Shop and on the left can be seen a standard-gauge 12in cylinder four-wheel saddle tank in the later stages of construction. This is number 2450 despatched in late April 1931 to the Horseley Bridge & Thomas Piggott works at Tipton. At the extreme end on the right hand side is one of the second batch of GWR pannier tanks and behind it the last member of the Assam Railways & Trading Company metre-gauge 4-6-0s, number 2421, which was despatched in early May. On the right and nearest the cameraman is the completed boiler for another pannier tank.

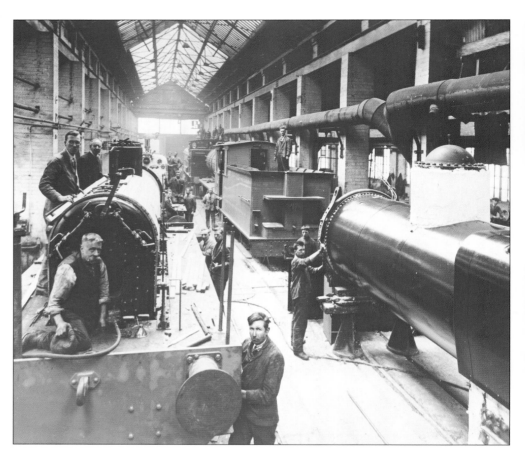

A view further north in the Erecting Shop; the saddle tank on the left is for the Horseley Bridge engine in the previous photograph and there is a set of upturned pannier tank frame plates that can just be discerned in front, whilst at the extreme end is another pannier tank. The boiler alongside is for another Assam engine. The pannier tank in its final stages of erection is almost certainly one of manufacturer's numbers 2433 to 2435, GWR numbers 8736 to 8738, despatched on 23 March, 1 and 13 April respectively. The gent in the smock just in front of the pannier tank is the Works Manager Jack Dale.

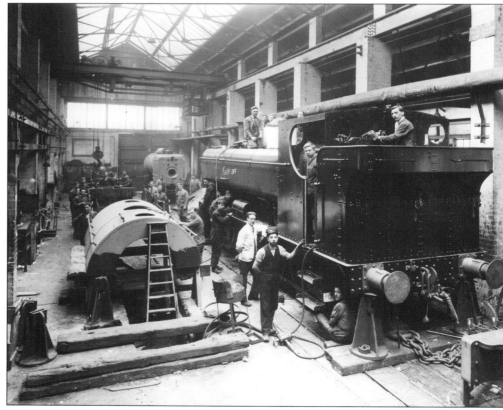

View of the Fitting Shop, situated between the Erecting Shop and the eastern extremity of the works alongside the main-line railway. View looks south; observe to the right the GWR pannier tank and the Assam engine seen in the two previous views. On the benches can be seen motion parts and sand boxes for the pannier tanks as well as some slide bars and metre-gauge axles.

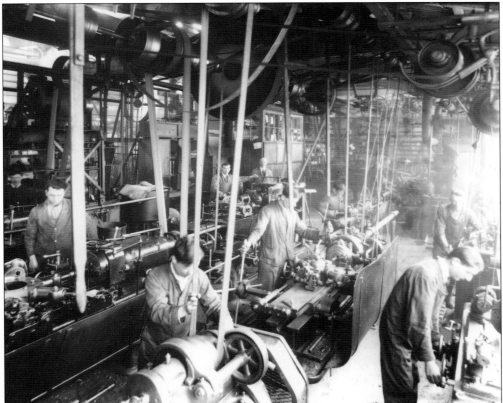

Part of the Machine Shop, situated to the west of the Erecting Shop, in fact Fitting and Machine Shops flanked the Erecting Shop on opposite sides. This picture illustrates the capstan and turret lathes used for the bulk production of components, with a couple of grinding machines to the right. Notice all the machines are driven from line shafting via belts, much of which was soon to be replaced by the machines having individual electric motors. The gentleman with the smock in the centre, and along-side the elevated office he shared with the Machine Shop Foreman, is the Tool Room Foreman, Jim Robinson.

This view shows the Iron Foundry with the men engaged in preparing core-boxes and moulds ready for making castings.

Mention was made earlier in this Chapter of orders from the GWR for pannier tank locomotives, and two such orders were received in the period being discussed. On 15 July 1929, the GWR ordered 25 of its Standard 5700 Class 0-6-0 pannier tanks, at a contact price of £2,745 each, for delivery commencing in 20 weeks, with the first one due on 22 July, and thereafter at a rate of three per month. In fact at this time the GWR ordered from private manufacturers 100 of this class of locomotive, with North British in Glasgow, Yorkshire Engine Company in Sheffield, and Kerr, Stuart at nearby Stoke-on-Trent, each supplying 25. The inside cylinders were 17½x24in and the wheel diameter was 4ft 7½in, and whilst the GWR used this class of engine for both shunting and branch line work, in the case of the ones built at Stafford, as they were only intended for shunting, neither the vacuum brake nor steam heating equipment was fitted. Delivery was somewhat late, and the first one was not despatched until 4 February 1930, and the last one at late as 3 October, but as no penalty was imposed we can only assume, that some form of agreement was reached. The manufacturer's numbers

were 2381 to 2405, and the GWR numbers 6700 to 6724 in the same order. As a part of the contract some parts were supplied free-issue from Swindon, including various standard GWR fittings like the injectors, cylinder lubricator, steam brake valve, regulator stuffing box handle and rod, water gauges, clack boxes and safety valves. In addition, the GWR loaned Bagnall the flanging blocks for the boiler and firebox plates, but as the crank-axles were built-up rather than forged, they were made at the Castle Engine Works.

It appears that the GWR were in no hurry for these locomotives, as the last 15 of them, numbers 2391 to 2405, after a couple of months running-in from South Wales sheds, were placed in store and it was not until two years later, during August 1932, that any of them were permanently allocated to sheds. Most of them seem to have spent their lives at various locations in South Wales; Cardiff East Dock, Duffryn Yard and Swansea East Dock for example, had substantial allocations over many years. Presumably this lack of an urgency to put the locomotives into service was the reason no penalty was imposed for the late delivery, and it may have been the case that the railway company requested delivery be delayed. As the engines were to replace a miscellany of old pre-grouping locomotive types of the various South Wales railways, the GWR could have wanted to ensure the engines being replaced had completed their mileage between heavy repairs, before they were withdrawn. These engines were themselves withdrawn and scrapped by BR in the period from August 1957 and April 1964.

Before delivery of these locomotives was complete, a second order for a further 25 locomotives of the same class was placed on 8 May 1930. Once again they were of the 5700 class, but in this case as they were intended for more general use, they were fitted with vacuum brake and steam heating equipment, as well as screw couplings. Manufacturer's numbers were 2422 to 2446, and contract delivery between 24 November 1930 and 7 July the following year; the price was a little more than the earlier batch, at £2,983. A much better job of complying with the contracted delivery programmes was achieved with this batch, and the first locomotive was delivered on 25 November, and the last on 10 July 1931 - only three days late. The GWR numbers were 8725 to 8749, and a similar free issue of fittings and

other equipment took place, but on this occasion it included the steam heating equipment and some of the vacuum brake gear. Whilst the Company made a loss on building the first batch of these locomotives - no less than £6,240 - on the second lot there was a profit of £3,682. As was the case with the earlier engines, the GWR ordered a total of 100 locomotives from the trade, with Beyer Peacock in Manchester, Armstrong Whitworth in Newcastle, and North British in Glasgow each supplying 25. In the case of the Castle Engine Works the two orders had the effect that from the middle of 1929 when work started, until July 1931 when the last one left, there were always locomotives of this type under construction. Being more versatile, engines of this second batch were allocated all over the GWR system; they were all withdrawn by British Railways between February 1961 and September 1965.

The Assam Railways & Trading Company Limited undertook a range of activities in Upper Assam, operations including coal mines, brickworks, forestry, oil extraction and tea plantations. It also owned and operated the Dibru-Sadiya Railway. Dating from 1882, this metre-gauge line ran 61 miles from Dibrugarh, on the banks of the Brahmaputra, in an easterly direction

In the nick of time! The first Assam engine on exhibition at Wavertree on the occasion of the Liverpool & Manchester Railway Centenary Celebrations between the 13 and 20 September 1930. Doesn't she make a lovely sight and quite a contrast to the standard-gauge engines exhibited by the main-line railways. Some of these can just be discerned behind. The steps were to allow the general public access to the footplate. This is a photograph taken by the late WH Whitworth, a prodigious follower of the contemporary railway scene in those times.

Footplate view of the first Assam engine number 2416. Points of interest are the Dreadnought vacuum brake ejector and drivers brake valves to top right, screw reverse, Detroit sight-feel cylinder lubricator to top left, electric lighting for the gauge glasses and the vacuum brake reservoir to bottom left - unusual for these to be located in a cab. The works multi-gauge test track is worth a study too.

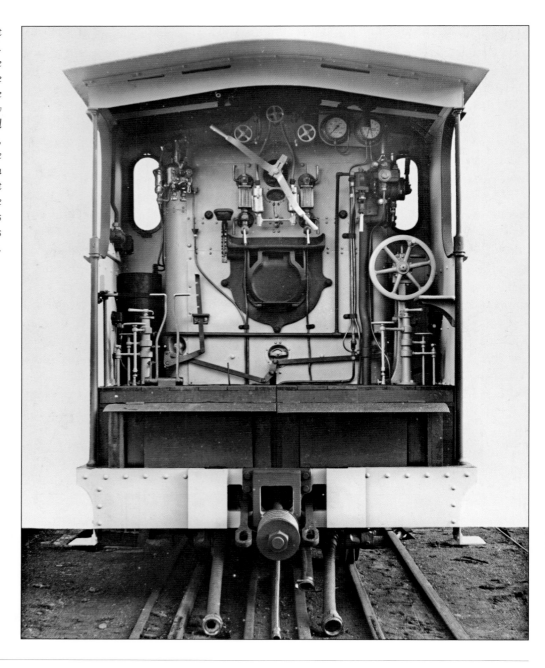

to Margherita. There was a 24½ mile branch to Saikhoa, running due north from about mid-way (Makum Junction) on the main-line, Saikhoa being on the opposite side of the Brahmaputra to Sadiya. A 12 mile long extension of the main-line ran further east from Margherita, and served a number of collieries, brickworks and tea estates at Ledo, Lekhapani and Tipongpani. At Tinsukia, also roughly mid-way on the main-line and two miles west of Makum Junction, connection was made with the Assam-Bengal Railway (ABR), a section of line which opened in March 1903 -

hitherto the Dibru-Sadiya line was isolated from any other railway. The Assam Company had been buying locomotives from Bagnall for many years, as far back as 1894 in fact, but in most cases small two-foot gauge circular firebox saddle tank engines for use at the collieries and brickworks.

On 10 February 1930, an order was received for six metre-gauge 4-6-0 tender engines of a new design for the Dibru-Sadiya Railway, although the Company had supplied 4-6-0 tender engines to the railway earlier. In the case of the earlier engines, manufacturer's numbers

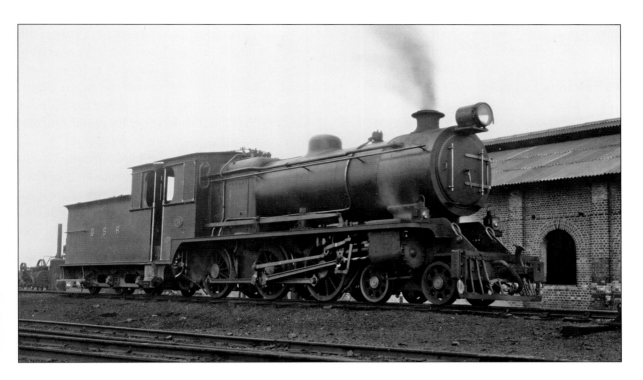

Here we have one of the Assam Railways & Trading Company locomotives in service, manufacturer's number 2418, AR&TC No 55, with the tender lettered DSR - Dibru Sadiya Railway. What a pity we do not have a colour photograph of one of these engines, as they must have looked quite magnificent decked out as they were in the Umber Brown livery, similar to the last colour scheme adopted for the locomotives of the London, Brighton & South Coast Railway. This particular engine eventually became North Eastern Railway No 31859 under the all-India renumbering scheme, and was withdrawn from service in March 1971. (Kelland Collection Bournemouth Railway Club)

2328 and 2329 of 1928, the design was a slightly improved version of the BESA class HC - in this case classified HM - with 15½x22in cylinders and a 4ft 9in coupled wheel diameter. The specification for the new engines called for more power and the ability to burn inferior fuel, so a substantial redesign was necessary. To cater for a significant increase in grate area and firebox capacity, the whole boiler was mounted much higher, so that the bottom of the larger firebox could sit above the main frames, rather than tapering inwards to fit between them, as had been the case hitherto. The frames had to be specially adapted to accept this arrangement, with the result that the Belpaire wrapper firebox had a grate area of 25.5sq ft, as opposed to only 15.5sq ft on the earlier engines; a creditable almost 60% increase. The total heating surface of the boiler increased from 1,063 sq ft in the earlier engines to 1,292.5 sq ft, although it was perhaps surprising, that no superheater was called for. The cylinder dimensions were the same as the earlier engines but the coupled

wheel diameter was reduced to four feet, increasing the tractive effort at 85% of the 180psi working pressure to 16,847lb, against a figure of 14,187lb before. As no superheater was fitted the cylinders had balanced slide valves. The reduction in wheel diameter was necessary on two counts, to allow the increase in the tractive effort without enlarging the cylinder diameter, and for the firebox to sit on top of the frames without the locomotive infringing the loading gauge. An interesting aspect of the specification, issued by the consulting engineers Robert Bruce & Sons Limited, was provision for the cylinders to be bored out to 16½in, but whether this was ever done is not known. Equipment included vacuum brakes for the locomotive, tender and train operation, Sunbeam electric lighting, ABC couplers; the weight in working order of the engine and tender was 64½ tons, and the maximum axle-load 9¾ tons.

The manufacturer's numbers were 2416 to 2421, the railway running numbers 53 to 58, and the selling price was £3,951 each - against which the Company made a much smaller loss than had been the case with some other recent contracts, only £414 10/ 11d (£414 55p). At the time these engines were ordered the LMS were making plans to celebrate the centenary of the opening of the Liverpool & Manchester Railway, the first public passenger railway in the world, which started operations in 1830. The celebrations included an exhibition of locomotives and rolling stock in the goods yards at Wavertree Park, in Liverpool, held between 13 and 20 September 1930. As well as a collection of older locomotives, each of the Big Four main-line railway companies exhibited examples of its latest designs, accompanied by a selection of locomotives built by private industry for the export market. Edwards was partly instrumental in both the idea of including locomotives from the private manufacturers in the exhibition, and making the arrangements. As a member of the Council of the Institution of Locomotive Engineers (I Loco E), he had been involved in the organisation of the exhibits for the earlier, 1925 Railway

Centenary Celebrations at Darlington, where the omission of examples of any locomotives from private industry for the world-wide export markets, was considered to have been a serious omission. As British built locomotives had inaugurated railways in almost every country of the world, it was quite significant that nobody on that occasion, thought to include a few! Along with his former colleague James Warren, and a few others prominent in the industry supported by the I Loco E, and of course his extensive network of contacts in the private locomotive building industry, arrangements were made for a representative collection of exhibits from the private builders.

One of the locomotives selected was the first of the Assam order, number 2416, but first of all it had to be completed in time. To encourage the staff because time was tight, it was arranged by Edwards that provided the first engine was ready in time, he would take the entire workforce on a day trip to the exhibition on Saturday 20 September. By all accounts it was touch and go, and the

Perpetuating a very old design of the Glasgow builder Neilson, dating from 1887 in fact, in 1931 the Company supplied three of these metre-gauge saddle tanks to the Bengal & North Western Railway, following two earlier ones back in 1907. They were a successful design and specifically for shunting trains on and off the train ferries that crossed the Ganges. As they only weighed 17 tons in working order, their light axle-load made them ideal for the temporary tracks that frequently had to be re-laid at short notice, connecting land with ferry, in view of the vicissitudes and varying nature of the river. The manufacturer's numbers were 2461 to 2463, running numbers 67 to 69, later renumbered as North Eastern Railway 35107 to 35109. Notice the transverse safety valves, single slide-bar and Detroit sight-feed lubricator in the cab.

engine and its tender, loaded on two LMS well wagons, were despatched to Liverpool where they were unloaded using two LMS breakdown cranes, and placed on a short length of track. It was only necessary to remove cabs from both the locomotive and tender to clear the LMS loading gauge, and the Bagnall fitters that were on hand to oversee the unloading, helped to replace the items and generally make the locomotive ready to receive visitors. True to his word, Sydney Edwards chartered a train and the entire workforce and their families had a day out visiting the exhibition as well as Liverpool. The engine came back to Stafford after the exhibition to be made ready for shipment along with the other five, which in the event was via Birkenhead Docks and not Liverpool, in all cases for unloading at Chittagong. From there they could travel on their own wheels via the ABR to the Dibru-Sadiya line at Tinsukia. These were very handsome locomotives, as will be seen from the illustrations, finished in what was described as 'Umber Brown similar to LBSCR locomotives', and whilst they were being built the opportunity was taken for the second time, to have a comprehensive set of photographs taken in and around the Castle Engine Works. These were the last new locomotives built for the Dibru-Sadiya Railway, designated class K, they all passed to the Bengal & Assam Railway when the Assam Railways & Trading Company sold the Dibru-Sadiya Railway to the Indian Government on 1 April 1945. However they all continued to operate in the same part of Assam, and apart from one that was written off after an accident in 1949, as Indian Railways Nos 31858 to 31862, lasted until 1970 and 1971.

Although we have no concrete proof, it was certainly the intention of the Company to exhibit a second engine at Wavertree. This was one of manufacturer's numbers 2406 and 2407, 2ft 6in gauge 2-6-2 side tanks ordered by the London agents Kilburn Brown & Company, for the Singri Panchnoi River Tramway in Assam. This short 20 mile long line ran from Singri, which is west of Tezpur and on the banks of the Brahmaputra river, due north to Panhnai, where it met the ABR metre-gauge line from Lalmanirhat to Rangapara. At Rangapara by the way, the ABR made connection with the Tezpur-Balipara Tramway mentioned in Chapter Five. The engines had 11x16in cylinders and 3ft 0½in diameter driving wheels and

whilst they were both ordered in October 1929, and the first one was delivered in December the same year; it was not until 18 October 1930 that the second one was despatched. This might suggest it was held-back for the exhibition. The first one was sent dismantled and the second one complete, again perhaps suggesting it went from the exhibition direct to Birkenhead from where it is known to have been shipped, and without returning to Stafford. The engine appears in the list of exhibits in the official programme of the event, but not in a report in *The Locomotive Magazine*, issue of 15 October, whilst in *The Railway Gazette* of 19 September 1930, it is mentioned as being present. Of all the members of staff we have interviewed over the years and who were around at the time, none of them ever mentioned this locomotives as being at Wavertree, although we have to add we never asked the specific question - but they all recalled the 4-6-0; neither do any photographs seem to exist. Before leaving the exhibition it is worth mentioning that The Hunslet Engine Company of Leeds also exhibited two locomotives, a standard-gauge 0-6-0 saddle tank destined for harbour works at Haifa in Palestine, along with a metre-gauge 2-6-2 side tank for Tanganyika. Nothing much appears to be known about the two Bagnalls in Assam, but a replacement boiler was supplied in January 1946.

Despite these and other large locomotives being designed and built by the Company, the small standard design of circular firebox narrow-gauge locomotive continued to be built, and occasionally, when work was slack, a stock order might be placed on the works for this type of locomotive. Having said that, the demand for small narrow-gauge steam locomotives was fast diminishing, in fact for the home-market it never recovered after the immediate post-war years. The need for new locomotives of this type was not helped by the large numbers available second-hand, many having seen little work and surplus from the whole range of operations connected with the war and its aftermath. This was the case not only with locomotives Bagnall had built, but several from other builders too. They could be purchased quite cheaply, flooding what was already a declining market with petrol and diesel locomotives also becoming available. Additionally there was a general decline in the use of narrow-gauge railways in industry, as road based equipment was developed. Between 1930 and the outbreak of the

Second World War, only five narrow-gauge locomotives were built for the home market.

Further additions to the plant were undertaken in the period covered by this Chapter. For example additional electricity generating plant in the form of a Brovett & Lindley 200 kW vertical compound steam set, complete with a 200 volt 900 amp generator in June 1927. Whilst this plant was new, in April the following year a second-hand 500 cub/ft/min Bellis & Morcom steam driven air compressor was acquired. There were also quite a lot of new, and in some cases second-hand machine tools, including a new planning machine with a 12ft bed, a new crank pin quartering machine and a large second-hand flanging press. Further generating plant arrived in July 1930, a 220 kW Bellis & Morcom steam set and a Lawrence Scott generator. The buildings also saw improvements and additions, a new timekeeper's office was completed in September 1929, and there were extensions to the foundry in December the same year, along with extensions to the main offices in January 1930. Several new overhead cranes were provided in a number of the shops, and others upgraded to lift greater tonnages; the boiler shop roof was substantially rebuilt in June 1930. But these were difficult times, as will have been gathered from the losses made on a number of the contracts, so money for plant and machinery improvements was tight.

It is important to discuss at this point the demise of the nearby competitor, Kerr, Stuart & Company Limited, a company which had over the years provided Bagnall with so many of its people, as it has significant implications for the rest of our story. Despite the obvious competition, relatively cordial relations always seem to have existed between the management of the two companies, and over the years men of all grades moved about between the two companies, on occasions several times. In June 1930, a number of banks having considerable debt, foreclosed on Kerr, Stuart & Company Limited, and before the autumn was out the California Works at Stoke-on-Trent had closed its doors to railway engineering for the last time. This was particularly bad news for Stoke-on-Trent and surrounding district, as the previous two years had witnessed the almost complete closure of two very large iron works and colliery complexes, both large employers of labour, as a consequence of which the number of men out of work was enormous. At the time Kerr, Stuart

employed over 1,200 people, roughly double the number employed by Bagnall, and potentially it had a relatively large order book. A few of them did find work at the Castle Engine Works, but not many. The boiler shop at Stafford was quite busy at the time, with a number of contracts for spare boilers, as well as for example, the GWR pannier tanks, and some men with the right trades and experience were found employment. Whilst elimination of a competitor was bound to help those companies remaining in the trade, in this case it went a significant way to avoid a similar fate befalling WG Bagnall Limited, and in a number of less obvious ways to be discussed later in the story.

It goes without saying that Sydney Edwards would have dearly liked to have obtained the Kerr, Stuart goodwill, but as we have seen at the time cash was tight at Stafford, and in the event it was acquired by the Hunslet Engine Company of Leeds. The plant and equipment meantime, was sold piecemeal by auction and some machine tools and other loose equipment were purchased. These included a large Readham planer with a nine-foot bed along with some smaller machine tools and other equipment. The chief draughtsman at Kerr, Stuart, a well known personality in the private locomotive building trade, was FHB Harris, who had occupied that position for many years and a mentor of Edwards during his training there - we shall hear much more of him later in our story. Suffice it to say at this juncture, that among the items purchased at the auction were several large chests of draws and other office furniture, and when these arrived at Stafford, low and behold, they were stuffed full of drawings and all sorts of other literature appertaining to Kerr, Stuart products! Also acquired and apparently under the guise that in fact they were something else, were a number of flanging blocks, patterns, templates and gauges. Several old employees have related to the authors the events surrounding these acquisitions, which at this distance in time it is perhaps safe to divulge! Trips to and from Stoke-on-Trent with motor transport, clandestine and under the cover of darkness, with these and similar missions in mind! Harris would have had a lot to do with this, and Edwards was instrumental in getting him a position with RP&T - but as will soon be revealed, only until he was able to find a position for him at Stafford.

An early manifestation of the demise of Kerr, Stuart

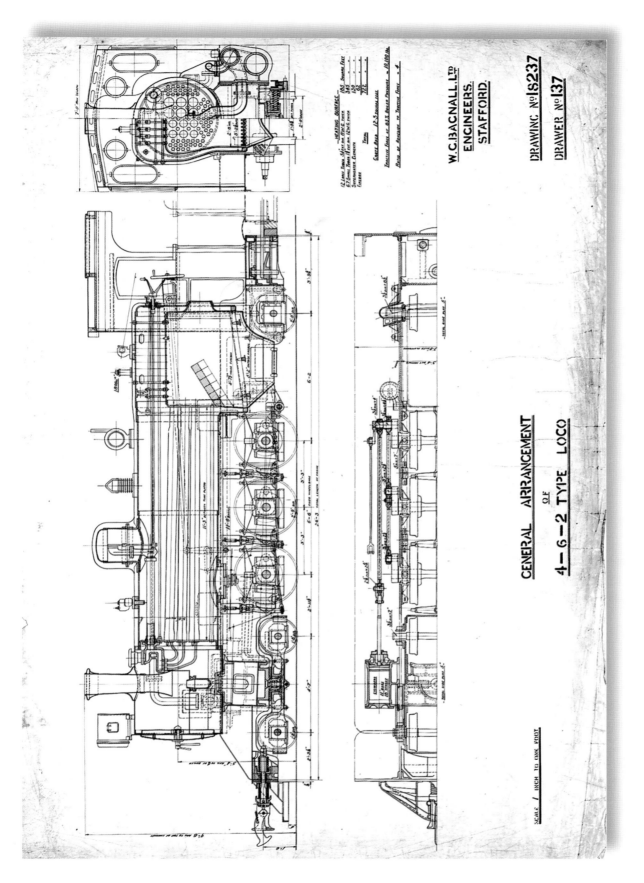

General Arrangement drawing of the Gwalior two-foot gauge Pacific's. Notice the 'Cortazzi' trailing axle with its angled horn-guides.

was an order for eight two-foot gauge Pacific tender engines for the Indian Gwalior State Railway, as hitherto, and since just about the time of its inception, almost the entire motive power needs of this railway had been supplied by Kerr, Stuart; as was the case with much of its rolling stock too. The railway dates from the early 1890s, when the Maharaji Madhava Roa Scindia, built in the grounds of his palace and private estate at Gwalior, a two-foot gauge railway. Gwalior was one of the Indian Princely States, some 170 miles or so due south of Delhi. Later the Maharaja decided to extend the line so it could be of use for public traffic, part of a scheme to open up and develop the State, such that by 1909 the system consisted of some 253 miles radiating from Gwalior in three separate directions. Between 1895 and 1928 Kerr, Stuart supplied no less than 35 locomotives and four steam railcars, as well as substantial quantities of both passenger and goods rolling stock. As late as March 1932, a forth line was opened, running 42 miles from Ujjain to Agar, completely isolated from the remainder of the system and 250 miles south-west of Gwalior, in a small part of the State that was completely separate from the rest. In was in part to work this new line that a requirement arose for additional locomotives, and four of the eight ordered from Bagnall were specifically intended for it. The use of two-foot gauge was comparatively rare in India, most of the narrow-gauge railways were 2ft 6in gauge.

The Maharaja was clearly a keen railway enthusiast, he had an electrically driven model railway which ran around the top of his dinner table and by these means the condiments and the like, were moved around between his guests. Until he died in June 1925 he took a great interest in the railways, being personally involved in purchasing new equipment, and developing the system. As might be expected he had his own personal carriage, which along with other vehicles was kept exclusively for his use, and that of his friends and guests. He was succeeded by his son Prince Jiwaiji Rao Scinda, who was only nine years old when his father died, but nevertheless he grew up to take a similar paternal interest in the railways.

The order for the Bagnall pacifics was received on 25 August 1931, and the consulting engineers appointed by the railway were Robert White & Partners. The later designs of Kerr, Stuart locomotives were of the 2-8-2

and 4-6-4 wheel arrangements, the last ones delivered as late as 1928, and whilst successful in their own right, Bagnall designed a much more modern machine with a superheated boiler and piston valves. Cylinders were 11x18in, driving wheel diameter was 2ft 9in, and a weight in working order for the engine and large double bogie tender 47¼ tons - the maximum axle-load was six tons. The completed locomotives were very handsome machines, with a range of modern refinements, including for example: hopper ashpans, Wrench restrained piston valves (an invention of JMD Wrench, chief mechanical engineer of the Great Indian Penisular Railway), and because of poor quality of water where they were to operate, Filterator linseed water softening equipment. The Belpaire top firebox boiler was particularly large, the total heating surface was 722 sq ft, of which the superheater contributed 62 sq ft, and the grate area was 12.3 sq ft. The large bogie tender necessary in view of the length of the lines and scarcity of water, contained 1,500 gallons of water and four tons of coal. Another interesting feature of the design was the Cortazzi radial axle-boxes on the trailing carrying wheels, the engines being designed to traverse three chain radius curves. Nicely finished with a typical Bagnall chimney complete with a polished copper cap, and stainless steel boiler lagging bands, articles, photographs and drawings appeared in the railway and technical press at the time they were despatched. Ivor Farr was largely responsible for this design, as he had been for the Assam engines mentioned earlier. The manufacturer's numbers were 2453 to 2460, the running numbers were 34 to 41, and the eight locomotives were despatched via Birkenhead Docks between January and March 1932 at a total cost of £23,370 - a loss for the builder of £6,073. They all survived until the Gwalior lines were dieselised in the early 1980s - the Ujjain to Agar line closed earlier, after which all the engines were concentrated at Gwalior. Two of them have returned to this country and are currently in store awaiting restoration.

Unfortunately, getting this order was not all good news for the Company. The chief draughtsman Arthur Burley, visited Gwalior on two occasions for discussions and negotiations in connection with the order, helping to develop and agree the exact specification. He died there of sun stroke on 11 June 1931 when only 44 years old. Arthur Burley is buried at Gwalior, in what was

First of the Gwalior Light Railway Pacific's, manufacturer's number 2453 of January 1932, Gwalior No 760 stopped specially for photographs when en-route from Gwalior to Bhind, and just short of Nonera, which is 33 miles from Gwalior, on 30 December 1976. What a splendid sight she made too!

then a small British settlement at Morar, about three miles from the town itself. Keith Pearson, the firm's London agent went to India to supervise the funeral arrangements, both on behalf of WG Bagnall Limited and the family - Pearson's son Kenneth, was in fact with Burley at the time of his death. The grave stone at Morar records the fact that at the time of his death, Arthur Burley was the chief draughtsman of WG Bagnell (sic) Ltd. Among those sending condolences to Burley's wife and family was George Glass Hooper, for many years a director, and later chairman and managing director of Kerr, Stuart. Glass Hooper knew Gwalior very well, as he had visited many times in connection with the business Kerr, Stuart had conducted there. He was therefore, able to describe in a letter to Mrs Burley, her husband's last resting place, and the relevant extract from the letter is worth quoting. 'Three miles from the city of Gwalior lies a British settlement consisting of the British residency, post office, club, church and cemetery wherein are laid non but British subjects of the King. The church is as pretty as it is

small with a little square tower standing just back from the road and in the midst of the cemetery, covered with roses, and it is there that your husband will be lying now, borne reverently to his last rest by English people who know that sometime their own hour may come. I have often thought that had it been my lot to die in a foreign country I could wish for no happier resting place than this little cemetery at Morar, for that is the name of the little settlement'. Glass Hooper of course knew Arthur Burley, and in a casual meeting with Sydney Edwards in London, had heard of his death. Before leaving the Gwalior engines it is worth recording that Geoffrey Owen, one of the draughtsman who had been involved in the design, went to India with the locomotives to assist in putting them into traffic, and to explain all the various modern features which the railway staff would be unfamiliar with.

Arthur Burley's two sons were both employed by the Company. Richard, the eldest, completed his training at Stafford and became a draughtsman, whilst his younger brother Wilfred, who commenced his

*View of the interior of the Drawing Office taken at the same time as the other internal works scenes illustrated in this Chapter. The people are; from left to right: Reg Machin - Draughtsman/Designer; Ivor Farr - Draughtsman/Designer; Miss Alice Duckers - Buyer's Typist; R Walton - Draughtsman; CH Peach - Draughtsman; Percy Critchley - Buyer (Standing in corner); Miss P Bassett - Tracer Miss S Jones - Tracer; Hugh Taylor - Deputy Chief Draughtsman; Arthur Burley - Chief Draughtsman; CR Bromage - Draughtsman; Miss K Boyisset - Typist to Chief Draughtsman.
There was a further row of desks to the left.*

apprenticeship in 1936, accompanied his mother when she returned to her native Glasgow in 1938. James Black, the chief draughtsman of the North British Locomotive Company at the time, after an introduction by Sydney Edwards, arranged for the transfer of young Burley's apprenticeship, as of course, Black had known his father. Wilf Burley had an interesting career, and after being invalided out of the Royal Navy in 1943, returned to North British as a draughtsman before joining the Crown Agents for the Colonies in January 1946, as an inspecting engineer. He remained with the Crown Agents in positions of increasing responsibility, in particular an involvement with the inspection of locomotives and rolling stock, and being based in

Glasgow, often at his old company - North British. Arthur Burley's position of chief draughtsman at Stafford was filled by his deputy, Hugh Taylor.

This is perhaps an opportune juncture to introduce Keith Pearson, mentioned briefly earlier, who had been the Company's London agent since 1910, although he also acted independently as a consulting engineer. Ian Keith Fredrick Pearson had been a pupil of William Adams, locomotive superintendent of the London & South Western Railway at Nine Elms, and on completion of his training went to work for Sir Alexander Rendel, eventually becoming an assistant to Seymour Biscoe Tritton in the locomotive & rolling stock department of RP&T. Later he went to work for another company of consulting engineers, Caruthers & Elliot, which acted for the New Zealand Government Railways, subsequently going into business on his own as a consulting engineer, and taking the Bagnall London agency in 1910. Pearson remained as the London agent of the Company until his retirement in 1948, latterly working from an office at 33 Victoria Street, SW1 - he died in January 1951. His son Kenneth, who as we saw earlier had been involved with his father in the Bagnall agency business, continued to represent the firm for a few years after his father's death.

As well as the specific orders for locomotives mentioned above, in the period covered by this Chapter other engines of various types and sizes were despatched to a number of countries. Examples are for Nigeria, several 3ft 6in gauge 0-6-0 side tanks to an existing Hunslet design ordered by the Crown Agents; for Natal in South Africa, in a continuing relationship with the two-foot gauge lines of the Tongaat Sugar Estates, 4-4-0 side tanks similar to earlier orders; for Tanganyika, a metre-gauge 2-6-2 side tank ordered via the Crown Agents, along with other locomotives for Mauritius, the Gold Coast, Egypt, China, New Zealand, Malaya, as well as of course, India and the home market. Of the Indian railways not so far mentioned in this Chapter locomotives were built for the Eastern Bengal, Morvi and Cutch State Railways, as well as a number of industrial customers. For the home market, whilst as outlined earlier orders for narrow-gauge locomotives were very much on the decline, there were a few orders for standard-gauge saddle tanks with 12in or 14in cylinders, along with some fireless locomotives.

Sydney Edwards was not only successful in building up good relationships with the consulting engineers

Although from a later period than covered by this Chapter, this is a typical member of the large fleet of 4-4-0 side tanks supplied over the period 1906 to 1946 (although actually the very first one was a 2-4-0) to the Tongaat Sugar Company for use on its estate in Natal, South Africa. This one is manufacturer's number 2599 of 1939, WJ MIRRLEES, bringing a fine load of sugar cane in from the fields for processing - the enormous spark arresting chimney was a later addition! The picture dates from 1945; notice the pile of sand on the front buffer beam and the two fellows ready and waiting to poor it on the rails by hand, as the engine blows-off impatiently awaiting the pleasure of the photographer!

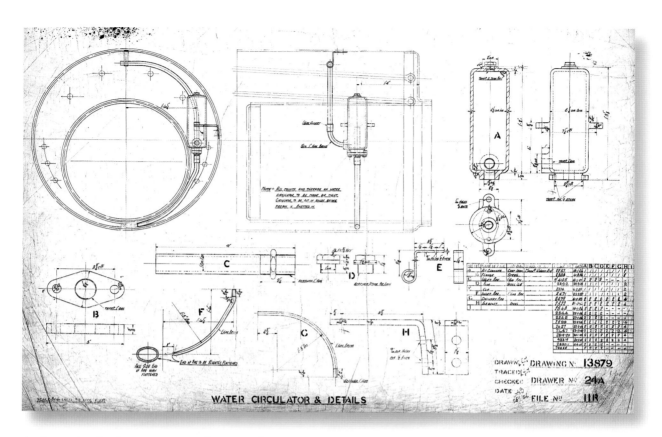

WATER CIRCULATOR & DETAILS

DRAWING No. 13879
DRAWER No. 24A
FILE No. 11R

An interesting development to try and improve the water circulation in the circular firebox boilers was the arrangement shown in this drawing. These boilers were notoriously slow in raising steam from cold, the water underneath the fire-grate remaining at a consistently lower temperature from the remainder, until the locomotives had been working for some time. The principle of thid device was to try and improve this situation by promoting a circulation of water below the fire-grate, but it seems to have met with little success. This drawing dates from January 1926 and shows the particular arrangement as first used on one of the earlier Tongaat engines, number 2287 of that year. The last new locomotives fitted in accordance with this drawing were two articulated locomotives built in 1946, also for use on a Natal sugar estate, and there was a spare boiler for an earlier articulated locomotive in use in Natal - number 2545 of 1936. In some other cases two of these circulators were fitted, one on each side of the firebox, but it would seem with no more success than the single version. The theory of the arrangement was in placing the cast iron tank in the water space at the centre-line of the firebox, and below the lowest working water level, and close to the firebox wall, the water heated by radiation from the fire, would expand, discharging through the outlet pipe into the steam space and thus, promoting movement of the colder water from below the firebox into the tank (item A on the drawing), and so on.

RP&T, but other partnerships of consulting engineers as well at the Crown Agents for the Colonies. Frequently in London, he often managed to combine his business with the activities of the learned institutions, and he missed no opportunity to advance the facilities available at Stafford to meet the requirements of agents and consulting engineers. Indeed, there is circumstantial evidence, supported by the memories of some of those who were around at the time and who worked alongside him, that in helping RP&T with the IRS designs, Edwards was able to exert sufficient influence in some of the designs to ensure that the Castle Engine Works could actually build a number of the larger metre-gauge engines, despite the comparatively limited facilities there.

Rolling stock and turntables, as well as many of the other products already mentioned, continued to feature in the works production, and a few examples of the more significant orders are outlined below. In January 1931, six large 3ft 6in gauge bogie vans for the Barranquilla Railway & Pier Company in Colombia; this was another railway that had been a long standing customer of Kerr, Stuart. The Imperial Chemical Industries ordered no less than 220 two-foot gauge 27 cub ft capacity drop side-tip wagons in November 1931, followed by a further 55 in April the following year; unfortunately however, no record appears to have survived regarding where they were despatched to. The Haunchwood Brick & Tile Company of Nuneaton ordered 50 1ft 11½in gauge double-deck kiln drying cars in July 1931, and in April 1929 no less than 420 3ft 6in gauge four-wheel fruit wagons were despatched to the South African Railways & Harbours - an order worth £2,919, returning a profit of £366. In October 1929 the Company built both 30 and 75 ton standard-gauge transformer trucks, respectively for the Hackbridge Electrical Construction Company and the British Thomson Houston Company Limited. Lastly, and on a smaller scale, in May 1931, the Company made six five-foot diameter cast-iron turntables for the Admiralty which were despatched to the Torpedo Factory at Greenock in Scotland. These are just a few examples to give a flavour, but there were many others, usually it has to be said, for much smaller quantities, and the small drop side-tip wagons for two-foot gauge,

and the various sizes of wagon turntables, were frequently laid down to stock orders so that a quick delivery could be promised when enquiries were made.

For locomotives, and to a lesser extent other products that had already been built and delivered, there was a continuous flow of orders for spare parts, and this provided a staple diet of workload. It was also a profitable workload, much more of a sellers market than new products, and very rarely were losses made on spare part orders. The Company was also quite successful in tendering for spare parts for locomotive made by other builders, in particular, as has already been mentioned, in tendering for replacement boilers, particularly where the engines concerned were examples the Indian BESA and IRS designs. Between 1921 and 1932, over 160 spare boilers were supplied, and as a large proportion were for metre-gauge locomotives, they were quite large boilers representing a steady workload for the boiler shop, irrespective of any new locomotive orders. This success in boiler shop workload was one of the reasons why Bagnall was able

This is one of six large 3ft 6in gauge 30ft long bogie vans supplied in 1931 to the Barranquilla Railway & Pier Company Limited, a company operating a 26 mile long railway in Columbia. It ran from the port of Barranquilla on the River Magdalena, in the north of the country, westwards to Puerto Colombia on the Caribbean coast. Not only was it the first railway in the country, but it was also the only one of this gauge - dating from 1871 it closed in 1946. The Company had been staunch customers of Kerr, Stuart, and this order coming Bagnalls way was partly a result of its demise. The order number was 9900 and the six vans were sold for £2,130, against a total works cost of £2,161 6/ 3d (£2,161 31p).

to provide employment for some of the boilermakers and riveters made redundant when Kerr, Stuart closed. In 1931 and 1932, 26 superheated boilers were supplied for the various BESA B, P and R class metre-gauge 4-6-0 tender engines, in all cases in connection with converting the engines concerned from saturated to superheated steam. In many of these orders the boilers were accompanied by a whole range of other fittings and equipment. The various Indian railways included the Bengal & North Western, South Indian and Eastern Bengal Railways, and in some cases the equipment included new cylinders and motion parts to convert the engines from slide valves to piston valves - it combined to make a substantial workload. Another interesting order of November 1928 covered the supply of sufficient parts to construct a metre-gauge MS class 4-6-0 tender engine, everything except a boiler that is. Along with a complete tender, the whole lot was despatched to the Mysore State Railway workshops at Mysore, between November 1928 and February 1929, and the locomotive became Mysore State Railway No 39 - later in the all India list No 31248. Presumably the railway company had a spare boiler on hand to complete the locomotive, but Bagnall did supply most of the boiler fittings, including a set of vacuum brake equipment and piping, and the clothing and lagging plates for the boiler. However, why this rather unusual practice was adopted appears to have gone unrecorded, and for many years the presence of this locomotive in the Indian railways lists, provided enthusiasts with somewhat of a mystery.

Before we move on to discuss a number of people, financial and general management issues, and in view of the firm's significant involvement in the supply of metre and narrow-gauge locomotives for the Indian railways, it might help readers if the structure of railways in the sub-continent is briefly outlined. The Indian Government has throughout history, had a significant involvement in the country's railways, notwithstanding the actual owners and operators. A gradual process of the State acquiring ownership of the main-line railways goes back a long time, and at the time of Partition in 1947, there was a decision to take into State ownership the bulk of those remaining in private hands. At that time there was also of course, the issue of dividing the ownership of those lines that penetrated the borders between India and what became East and West Pakistan. A good example of the government's earlier

Another example of a contemporary wagon product is this bogie platform wagon show inside the Wagon Shop. Notice the particularly heavy bolster arrangement and the detachable stanchions.

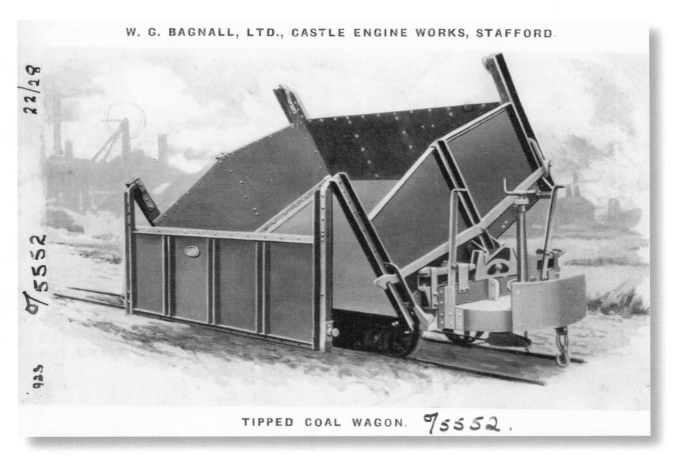

W. G. BAGNALL, LTD., CASTLE ENGINE WORKS, STAFFORD.

22/28

5552

923

TIPPED COAL WAGON. 5552.

This is the last of the colour publicity cards issued by the Company, and the only one not showing a locomotive. Order number 5552 of 1923 was for 20 of these all steel side-tip coal wagons ordered by Edward Lloyd Limited for use on the 2ft 6in gauge system serving the paper mills at Sittingbourne and Kemsley in Kent. Fitted with roller bearings and with a capacity of 3½ tons the total selling price was £2,210, which gave a profit of £477 14/10p (£477 75p). The handwriting is Horace Lorton's, a member of the Cost Office staff at the time.

involvement, whether the railways were state owned or not, is the BESA and IRS standard locomotive designs, and how by these means, it exerted its influence on the types of locomotives the individual railways should buy. For the Castle Engine Works, designing and building locomotives for the Indian metre and narrow-gauge railways provided its biggest market in that country. It also ensured much of the business success the firm achieved in the inter-war years, and was largely its salvation; it would not have survived the recession without this Indian market. It is also worth mentioning at this point, the brief hang-over of orders in the immediate post-war years, as the railways in India, like so many countries, struggled to get back onto a peace time footing. Bagnall was a beneficiary of this 'Indian Summer' too.

In view of the bulk of the locomotives the firm built for India being in the years between the wars, it is adequate for our purposes to describe the situation with the Indian railways in that period. For statistical purposes the railways were divided into three classes, based on gross earnings. The Class One lines - at 1939 rates - were those with annual earnings in excess of 50 lakhs Rupees. These were of course the bigger operations; largely, but by no means exclusively, broad-gauge. For example the Great Indian Peninsular, Bombay, Baroda & Central India, East Indian, Bengal Nagpur, North Western and Madras & Southern Mahratta Railways, in many cases operating lines on all three gauges. The Class Two lines had earnings of between 10 and 50 lakhs, and were exclusively metre or narrow-gauge. Examples are the Barsi Light, Bengal

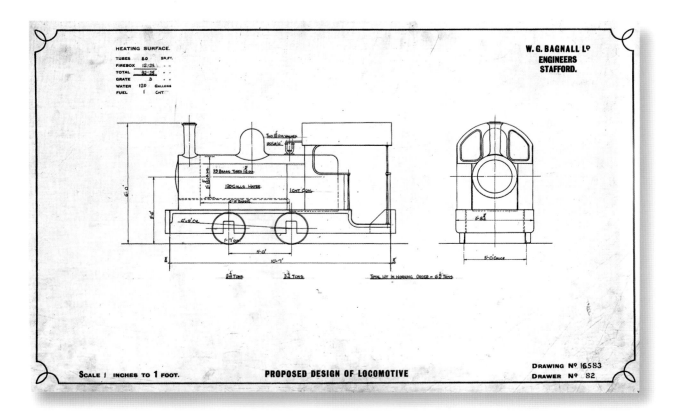

HEATING SURFACE.

TUBES	8.0	SQ.FT.
FIREBOX	12·25	" "
TOTAL	32·25	" "
GRATE	3	" "
WATER	120	GALLONS
FUEL	1	CWT

W. G. BAGNALL L⁰
ENGINEERS
STAFFORD.

SCALE 1 INCHES TO 1 FOOT.   PROPOSED DESIGN OF LOCOMOTIVE   DRAWING N⁰ 16583
DRAWER N⁰ S2

For every locomotive order the firm received, it probably made proposals, and in some cases tendered, for on average three others. To give one example, this drawing accompanied a proposal to the South Metropolitan Gas Company for the three-foot gauge system at its Bridgefoot Gas Works at Vauxhall. The proposal was for an updated version of earlier locomotives supplied, manufacturer's numbers 1354, 1415 and 1536 of the period 1891 to 1898. By the time this drawing was undertaken in November 1928, one of the earlier locomotives had already been scrapped and another was on its last legs. Unfortunately the Company was undercut by Peckett, the Bristol based builder, which is illustrative of the competition in the industry at the time, and a locomotive of not dissimilar design came from the Peckett stable. Peckett was also successful the following year in tendering to rebuild one of the Bagnalls. See page 147.

Dooars, Dibru-Sadiya, Gaekwar's Baroda State, Junagadh State and Morvi, and in several cases with lines of both metre and narrow-gauge. Lastly the Class Three railways with earnings of less than 10 Lakhs, and with the exception of the port railways at Bombay and Madras which had broad-gauge tracks, and the Udaipur-Chitorgarh which was metre-gauge, they were all narrow-gauge. Examples are the McLeod lines around Calcutta discussed in some detail in the last Chapter, several lines operated by the managing agents Martin & Company, again mainly in and around Calcutta, the Bengal Provincial, Cutch State, Dholpur State, Gwalior Light and Tezpore-Balipara.

Actual ownership of the railways is a very complicated area, as outlined above very much tied-up with the involvement of the state, many lines going through several changes of ownership. There were also

cases of the railway companies operating by agreement, lines they did not own, but suffice it to say in this brief description, that generally ownership fell into three classifications. Many of the Class One railways were both owned and operated by the state, although in most cases this had not always been the case. Examples are the Great Indian Peninsula Railway, taken over by the State in 1925, the North Western Railway which had been State owned and operated since as long ago as 1866, and the Eastern Bengal Railway, similarly from 1884. Other lines like the Bombay, Baroda & Central India and the South Indian, whilst owned by the State, were operated by private companies under agreements embracing for example, their financial structure, investment, operating ratios and division of earnings. In all these cases the companies were registered in this country and were listed on the London Stock

Exchange. Last of all are those lines, mostly the smaller ones in the Class Two and Three categories, but with notable exceptions like the Bengal Nagpur, which were also owned and operated by private companies, generally registered in this country, and listed on the London Stock Exchange. Several of the Class Three lines had been built under state guarantees by private companies, and were operated under similar guarantees by managing agents, like the McLeod and Martin companies mentioned above. Others like the Gaekwar's Baroda State, Gwalior Light and the Jodhpur, were the property of the Princely States, although in some cases they were operated by the bigger companies - for example until June 1913, the Gwalior Light Railway was operated by the Great Indian Peninsula Railway, after which it was taken over by the Gwalior Durbar.

Mention has already been made several times in earlier Chapters, regarding the involvement of consulting engineers by the various Indian railways in the procurement of locomotives. Whilst in many cases following its involvement with the BESA and IRS designs, RP&T were involved, this was not always the case and many of the smaller lines used other companies. In the case of the state managed railways the actual purchasing body with the Governor-General in Council, for locomotives ordered from British builders, via the India Office based in London. However, in the case of those lines not state managed the consulting engineers might in some cases also act for the procurement, but in others either the railway itself would act, or a specific purchasing agent would be employed. All the consulting engineers had to a greater or lesser extent standard specifications against which tenders would be invited, specifying for example, all the various types of material to be used in the component parts, how the parts should be marked, how the locomotives should be tested, painted and packed for shipment. In fact a whole plethora of issues; the one issued by RP&T for the Indian State Railways, and others would not be much different, runs to no fewer than 86 foolscap pages plus an Index. In leaving almost no stone unturned, it gives details how the drawings should be prepared, how many copies should be submitted, how many photographic views should be taken and at what angles, as well as how the spare part lists should be compiled.

It is now time to discuss a number of people issues and staff changes. Bill Parkinson, the works manager since 1915, retired in 1930, and his place was taken by John (Jack) Dale, another Kerr, Stuart trained man. Known to Edwards Jack Dale had been recruited some years earlier as erecting shop foreman, and his replacement in this post was Fred Ewington who was Bagnall trained. Harry Davies, who we met earlier in charge of estimating, returned to Kerr, Stuart in 1929; he was there when the firm ceased trading. Subsequently he worked for Sir WG Armstrong Whitworth & Company Limited at Newcastle - anxious to recruit experienced locomotive engineers at the time - and then the Air Ministry, before becoming London representative for Babcock & Wilcox Limited. He returned to Stafford in 1940, so we shall meet him again later in our story.

At this juncture it is opportune to look at the Companies continuing involvement in the activities of the Locomotive Manufacturers Association (LMA), and in particular the involvement of Sydney Edwards. First we must retread our steps a little to the mid 1920s, a time when all the member companies were struggling to keep their heads above water and their staff and assets employed. Mention was made earlier of the concerns within the industry after the war when the big armament firms decided to enter the locomotive building and repairing business. The Glasgow based William Beardmore & Company enquired about becoming a member of the LMA, but in the event never did, whilst Armstrong Whitworth of Newcastle-on-Tyne joined in June 1935. One of the particular concerns of all the manufacturers was the capital depreciation allowances granted by the Inspector of Taxes, for wear and tear of the machine tools used in the manufacture of locomotives. The argument centred on the fact that as locomotive building was in effect a heavy industry, machine tools had a relatively short life. Around 20 years was cited, with the additional proviso, that after around 10 to 15 years, accuracy was such, that even if the machines were retained, they would be used on less accurate work - apprentice training was mentioned as an example. The argument was supported by the very fierce competition within the industry, particularly from European and American builders, making it essential for the British manufacturers to employ every tactic possible, to reduce production time and manufacturing costs so as to remain competitive. This resulted in the machine tools being used not just far more intensely than hitherto, but also at higher levels of productivity, as more metal was removed per cut, to reduce machining times; in some cases individual machines were double and even treble shifted. As a result the economic life of the machines was on average much shorter, than had been the case before the war.

As a result of the forgoing, the LMA membership decided to elect a sub-committee to deal exclusively with the Inspector of Taxes on this issue, in an attempt to improve the allowances. The machinery depreciation sub-committee had its first meeting on 23 April 1925, with WS Edwards, along with AH Browning of the North British Locomotive Company, as its founder members; a decision having been made to commission Messrs Wheatly, Kirk, Price & Company, well established accountants and valuers, to act in the matter on behalf of the Association. The employment of professional advisors was a decision of the main committee, as an earlier attempt in August 1922 to get the tax situation relaxed, in that case by the members acting for themselves, had been unsuccessful. There were some concerns expressed by several of the member companies; for example, as it was assumed the inspector would want to visit at least some of the workshops to view the machine tools, and as Armstrong Whitworth (at that time) and Beardmore were not members, those two companies might not be happy if approached by the inspector. However, after some correspondence the two firms concerned agreed to support the LMA if approached by the inspector, and in any event, as noted above, Armstrong's eventually joined the LMA, while Beardmore's management decided to exit the locomotive business on completion of what became its last orders in 1931.

It was not long before the sub-committee became disappointed with the performance of Wheatly, Kirk, Price & Company, in particular its representative John Place, and at the suggestion of Edwards, Messrs Dean & Son, accountants and sharebrokers of Stafford, were appointed in their place on 9 June 1926. This was a company already acting for WG Bagnall Limited, and Mr Herbert Owen, one its principals, took over the case. At a general meeting of the LMA on 9 June, with incidentally AH Gilling in attendance - we met him

earlier as general manager at Stafford prior to Edwards appointment - representing the Yorkshire Engine Company, FS Walley of the Vulcan Foundry was appointed to the sub-committee. Dean & Son prepared a very comprehensive case on behalf of the LMA, and this was submitted to HM Inspector of Taxes on 23 December 1926. The submission articulated the argument for the existing allowance of 5% to be increased to 7½%; running to several pages it pointed out that inter alia, whilst at 5% it would take 40 years to write down machine tool values, at 7½% this would be achieved in 29 years. In the submission the capital value of the plant and machinery at the Castle Engine Works as at December 1928, was quoted as £25,964, whilst the figure for the Vulcan Foundry, by way of comparison, was £297,017; one indicator of the difference in size between one of the largest builders in the country and one of medium size. In the Bagnall Company books the aggregate value of the plant and machinery in the years 1914 to 1924 totalled £249,587, and in the same period the individual annual value increased from £11,255 to £25,886. Against the aggregate sum a figure of £23,690 had been provided for depreciation, which was equal to 9.49%.

As a result of the LMA submission, and as predicted visits were requested on behalf of the inspector, and these were arranged to both the Castle Engine Works at Stafford and the Vulcan Foundry at Newton-le-Willows in Lancashire. These two works were considered as being at almost opposite ends of the scale in terms of size, were a good representation, and of course, the two managing directors were members of the sub-committee; there is no evidence that any other works were visited by the inspector. Some delay was occasioned in arranging the visits as both Bagnall and Vulcan were anxious to ensure the works were at, or near, maximum production as the aftermath of the industrial action taken by the coal miners in 1926, was still causing material supply problems for the industry. The visits eventually took place early the following year - 1927 - on 28 February at Stafford, and 1 March at Newton-le-Willows. The Tax Inspector was represented by Mr A Snook, and on both days he was accompanied by Messrs Dean, Edwards and Walley. According to the report, which was dated 9 March, Edwards stated that there was not a single machine tool at Stafford more than 20 years old. Over the next few months there followed a number of further submissions, and several meetings took place with Edwards, Herbert Owen and FS Walley - sometimes represented by Benjamin Isaac Greenwood, also of Vulcan Foundry (and at the time president of the LMA) - in attendance. The inspector was represented by AC Alcock, the chief inspector himself, and Mr A Snook. Forceful arguments were presented, along with numerous statistics, and the last meeting appears to have taken place on 29 January 1929. However, it was not until 24 February the following year (1930) that a decision was given, delayed to some extent by individual LMA members with particular local concerns; for example R&W Hawthorn Leslie & Company of Newcastle-on-Tyne, in view of the amount of marine, as opposed to locomotive work it undertook.

The decision however was a good one for the industry, and whilst not agreeing all that had been asked for, it went a long way to address the concerns. In essence it gave a 7½% allowance for light machinery, and the definition used in the agreement encompassed the vast bulk of the machine tools used in locomotive manufacturing, leaving the allowance at the existing figure of 5% for the heavy equipment, for example boilers, overhead cranes and power generating plant - it was also backdated to the financial year 1928-9. At the LMA main committee meeting of 5 June 1930, as well as discussion on the generally favourable decision of the Inspector of Taxes, FS Walley made it very clear to the assembled company, and ensured his comments were recorded in the minutes: 'that by far the greater part of the work which had been involved in bringing these matters to a successful conclusion had been arrived through the efforts of WS Edwards'. Unfortunately Edwards was not able to attend the meeting - he was represented by Keith Pearson - but nevertheless a special tribute was paid to him by the members and the whole meeting expressed its regret that he was not able to be present in person.

One other issue regarding the LMA is worth a mention in this Chapter. For reasons that need not detain us, but in connection with proposals to erect a locomotive building facility in India, Kerr, Stuart & Company Limited had resigned its membership in 1919. When this particular issue - building a factory in India - was no longer of a concern to the LMA, efforts were made to encourage Kerr, Stuart to rejoin, but to no

avail. At a meeting of the general committee on 28 October 1926, the subject of the Kerr, Stuart membership was again raised, and Edwards volunteered to use his influence in that direction. In this he appears to have been successful, and Kerr, Stuart once again became members in November 1928, with Mr Langham Reed, the then managing director as the representative. This is again illustrative of the cordial relationship that existed between the management of Kerr, Stuart and WG Bagnall.

As we come towards the end of the period in the history of the Castle Engine Works covered by this Chapter, we have to record the end of an significant era too, for on Monday 17 October 1932, at his residence of 'Crossfields' at Weeping Cross, John Gifford Gifford passed away at the age of 72 years. He had been unwell for some time, and despite suffering from angina continued to visit the works until only a few weeks before he died. His doctor incidentally was Fredrick N Cookson, a step-brother of Jessie Bagnall, and coronary thrombosis was stated as the actual cause of death. Sydney Edwards was with Gifford at the time of his death, a boss he had known and worked with for almost 30 years - they were great friends and colleagues. John Gifford had been involved with the Company for almost 46 years, and for the last 25 its managing director, and for most of this time, in effect the sole owner of the Company. In his will he did not forget his employees, and to each member of the staff who was in employment at the date of his death, he bequeathed a sum equal to four weeks salary, and to each member of the wages grades an amount equal to two weeks wages. To William Sydney Edwards he left 1,000 £10 shares in the Company, along with £1,000 in cash, and he also made the following cash bequests in addition to those mentioned above: to Charles Tunnicliffe the cashier £250; to HE Coates and Miss AE Evans, both clerks, £15 and £10 respectively - all in addition to the four weeks salary mentioned above. The will was proved at £46,630 gross, and there were a series of other bequests to local hospitals and nursing societies as well as the domestic staff at 'Crossfields'. Being a life long enthusiast of the game of golf, and a founder member of the Cannock Chase Club in 1893, he left his debentures in the club to the Brocton Hall Golf Club, as the two clubs had later joined forces. The remainder of his shares in WG Bagnall Limited, a majority shareholding

A photograph taken in 1930 or 1931 at the firm's annual Christmas and New Year staff party held in the Works Canteen and Social Club. The three gentlemen in the centre at the rear, with party hats but looking decidedly glum, are from left to right Jack Dale the Works Manager, Sydney Edwards and John Gifford, and the rest of the gentlemen to the right are Hugh Taylor the Chief Draughtsman, Percy Critchley the Buyer and Arthur Owen the Chief Cost Clerk, whilst to the left of Jack Dale is Charlie Tunnicliffe the Chief Cashier. Just below Jack Dale with the large moustache is Jim Woollams the Machine Shop Foreman, and to his immediate right Fred Ewington the Erecting Shop Foreman. On the extreme left is Jim Robinson the Tool Room Foreman and sitting at the table from left to right are Fred Schofield the Chief Storekeeper; Joe Duckers Wagon Shop Foreman, Charlie Homer Foreman Smith (with large moustache), George White Pattern Shop Foremen, Stan Fisher Power House Foreman, and Geoffrey Owen the Chief Estimator. Geoff Owen incidentally, went on to have a very successful career and was eventually appointed Managing Director of the North British Locomotive Company in Glasgow, the country's largest locomotive builder. Of course most, if not all the gentlemen have their ladies accompanying them! If this is the 1931 party, and the balance of evidence suggests it is, then this would be the last such event John Gifford would attend.

in the Company, he left to his two nephews, twins Eric William MacLeod Maitland and Richard MacLeod Maitland. The shares were to be divided in two equal parts, but in trust until the boys reached their majority at the age of 21 years - they were 10 years old at the time. The trustees were their parents, John Gifford's niece and her husband, Charles and Norma Agnes Maxwell Maitland.

The funeral took place on Friday 21 October at St Mary's Castle Church, although unlike his brother and sister, he is not buried there. John was almost the last of a long line of Giffords and therefore, there were few family mourners, but they included his cousin Patrick Gifford, along with his niece Norma Agnes Maitland and her husband Charles. As was to be expected there was a very large contingent of mourners, including over 200 employees of WG Bagnall Limited, six of them acting as pall bearers; HR (Dick) Walker the boiler shop foreman; Arthur Slinn foreman joiner; Jim Woollams machine shop foreman; R (Fred) Schofield stores foreman; E Wilkes and F Taylor. Most of the other senior staff were present including of course, WS Edwards; Charles Tunnicliffe the cashier; Keith Pearson; Geoffrey Owen the chief estimator; Hugh Taylor; Jack Dale; Percy Critchley the buyer and Albert Owen the chief cost clerk. They were accompanied by a number of prominent businessmen from the Stafford and Stoke-on-Trent area and the staff at 'Crossfields' were represented by the gardener, Albert Groucott. There were floral tributes from Mrs WG Bagnall and Mrs Jessica Gordon Alsop (WG Bagnall's daughter), and as yet another link with the past, his physician Dr. Fredrick Nesfield Cookson was there too.

The end of an era indeed. From the inception of the original partnership back in 1875, until John Gifford's death in 1932, the firm had been very much a family one, successively managed by the rather fatherly figures of William Gordon Bagnall and John Gifford; latterly however, with increasing responsibilities falling to William Sydney Edwards. The First World War and its aftermath, the almost continuous deepening recession in manufacturing industry during the 1920s, along with the strive for new markets if the firm was to remain in business, along with an increasing need and ability to build larger locomotives, had not been achieved without enormous effort. The trading environment encountered by the firm in the post-war years was not only common with its competitors, but to manufacturing industry generally, and in so many cases firms were unable to compete - especially the smaller ones - and went into liquidation. Adapting the Company and its facilities to conditions of the time had largely fallen on the shoulders of Edwards, and it is to his credit that the firm weathered the storm, and despite the pressures worsening in the next few years, continued to do so. But for WG Bagnall Limited at least, the days of the traditional family firm were rapidly coming to an end, life and management of the Castle Engine Works was about to take on a new, but no less interesting, turn.

But before leaving John Gifford, and at the expense perhaps of a little repetition, it is worth recalling how he was best remembered by those who knew and worked with him. He was without doubt the archetypical gentleman bachelor - with a capital G - spending much of his time on the golf course, he would nevertheless, take a weekly walk around the workshops on Saturday mornings shortly before work ceased for the weekend. Knowing many of the staff personally, and in the case of the older ones over many years, he always had an encouraging words to say, and in times of personal hardship could be relied upon to be as humanitarian as possible. His bequests are evidence of his regard for those who worked for him, as well as his staff at 'Crossfields', and the local charities and other organisations mentioned in his will. Although largely a part of the story going forward, it is perhaps opportune to mention at this juncture, that for all the ruthlessness of Sydney Edwards's management, as necessary as it was, the firm never quite lost the fatherly attitude to its staff. Each Christmas there was a staff party, although sometimes held early in the new year, and a separate children's event in the works canteen for which Mrs Edwards always organised and took charge. At this event every child of a member of staff attending, including those who for whatever reason could not, was given a present paid for by the Company along with a bag of sweets. As well as the excursion to the Liverpool & Manchester Railway centenary celebrations at Liverpool in 1930, all the staff and their immediate families were taken to the British Empire Exhibition at Wembley in 1924, where the firm had a stand in the palace of engineering. As in the case of the Liverpool event, a special train was chartered.

Photograph taken of the salaried staff just before the first Assam engine was sent to the exhibition in Liverpool in September 1930. The people are, from left to right:

Front Row:

Jim Woollams - Machine Shop Foreman; Harry Skelton - Welding Shop Foreman; Fred Ewington - Erecting Shop Foreman; George White Pattern Shop Foreman; Dick Walker - Boiler Shop Foreman; Bill Brown - Foundry Foreman; Arthur Burley - Chief Draughtsman; John Gifford - Managing Director; Sydney Edwards - General Manager; Jack Dale - Fitting Shop Foreman - Designate Works Manager; Charlie Tunnicliffe - Chief Cashier; Bill Parkinson - Works Manager - on verge of retirement; Jim Robinson - Tool Room Foreman; Hugh Taylor - Deputy Chief Draughtsman; ? - Office Boy.

Middle Row:

Unfortunately, it has not been possible to identify any of the ladies, but they would be employed as secretaries, typists and tracers in the Drawing Office, also the boy at the extreme right. However, the gentlemen are: Stan Fisher - Power House Foreman; Reg Machin - Draughtsman; ?; Oliver Jennings - Foreman Painter.

Back Row:

Albert Slinn - Foreman Joiner; ?; Charlie Homer - Foreman Smith; Geoffrey Owen - Chief Estimator; ?; Horace Lorton - Cost Clerk; ?; Ivor Farr - Draughtsman/Designer; Charles H Peach - Draughtsman; Harold Coates - Chief Wages Clerk; CA Poulson - Buyer; Albert Owen - Chief Cost Clerk; ?; Fred Schofield - Stores Foreman; Tommy Ryan - Timekeeper.

To end this Chapter in the history of the Company, a brief look at the financial situation will not go amiss. Despite the heavy losses outlined on a number of the contracts for locomotives, the Company had been profitable overall, and a net trading profit was made in the years 1928 to 1931, averaging £2,248. Brief mention has been made of the profitability of spare part orders, as was the case with almost all the other work the Company undertook. There is also more than a suggestion that for internal reasons, the actual works overheads allocated to the locomotive contracts was overstated. Nevertheless, in 1932 there was a trading loss of no less than £4,618, reducing the average profit for the five years from 1928 to 1932 to £1,094. In 1929 the turnover was £149,891, but by 1932 had reduced to £105,990, with the wages bill similarly dropping over the same period from £34,985 to £25,669 - the salaried pay bill account remained roughly the same at around

As well as the salaried staff, the opportunity was taken to photograph all the other members of staff in front of the first of the Assam locomotives, and prior to everybody visiting the exhibition at Liverpool. They were photographed on a shop by shop basis, and we have selected three of the groups to represent them all. This one shows the men from the Boiler Shop with the foreman, Dick Walker, seventh from the left in the front row.

This photograph has the staff from the Smithy duly assembled with the foreman, Charlie Homer, fourth from the right in the front row.

In this third picture of members of staff along side the Assam engine, are men form the Pattern Shop, Foundry and Wagon Shop. In the front row respectively sixth, seventh and eighth from the right are; Bill Brown the Foundry Foreman, George White the Pattern Shop Foreman and Joe Duckers the Wagon Shop Foreman.

£10,000 for the same period. Despite the difficult trading conditions already prevailing, it was getting even more difficult with the recession in manufacturing beginning to bite even harder. Up until this time there had been little short time working except in the aftermath of the 1926 coal industry industrial action, and the reduction in staff wages was a result of less overtime and natural wastage, rather than any policy to lay men off; this was a situation that was soon to change.

These were extremely difficult times, and not only for this country. In January 1924, the conservative party was defeated in Parliament and whilst it still had a majority, it was not an overall one and the labour party, having the second largest number of MPs, in alliance with the liberals, formed a government with Ramsey McDonald as the country's first labour Prime Minister. This situation did not last long and the conservatives swept back to power in August, the government having been defeated over its attempt to patch up relations with Russia. The coal industry industrial action followed by the short lived general strike - as it become known - of 1926, further dented the economy and between 1921 and as late as 1938, unemployment was never less than one million. The May election of 1929

again resulted in the conservatives not having an overall majority, and whilst the Prime Minister, Stanley Baldwin, might have hung on in an alliance, the party having settled its differences with the liberals, in effect Ramsey McDonald was again appointed Prime Minister. However, labour did not have an overall majority either and within a month the infamous Wall Street crash occured in America, and in this country unemployment rocketed.

In March 1930 almost half a million more people were unemployed than had been the case a year earlier, and this combined with a lack of confidence in the government's spending plans, brought about its collapse. As a result, at the King's invitation McDonald was invited to form a National Government consisting of all three principal parties, which he did in August 1931. There followed a general election in October, confirming the King's inititive. On a wider front German economic problems combined with political instability gave Hitler his chance of power, and Japan invaded Manchuria, whilst some years later in 1935, Mussolini's Italy attacked Abyssinia (now Ethiopia). The outlook for the locomotive and rolling stock building industry was no more promising than for most other industries, as we shall explore in the next Chapter.

Chapter Nine

EDWARDS IN CONTROL: YEARS OF INNOVATION

Following probate on John Gifford's will on 10 March 1933, the shareholding of the Company from 12 May that year was: WS Edwards 1,719 shares consisting of the 719 he already held, plus 1,000 bequeathed to him in the will; Charles & Norma Agnes Maxwell Maitland, upon Trust for Eric William MacLeod Maitland and Richard MacLeod Maitland in equal parts and until they each attained the age of 25 years - they were twins, and only 10 years old at the time of Gifford's death - 2,281 shares. This gave the Maitlands, who resided at Frimley Place, Frimley in Surrey, a majority shareholding, and Charles Maitland became a director of the Company to represent the interests of his sons. Thereafter, the two directors of the Company were Edwards and Maitland. Incidentally, John Gifford left his house and estate at Weeping Cross to his niece, Norma Agnes Maxwell Maitland.

Norma Maitland was the daughter of John & James Giffords sister Jessie Caldwell Gifford. Jessie was born in 1854 and on 18 December 1877 married Norman MacLeod, six years her junior; she was the eldest of three sisters and the only one of the five children of William & Jane Gifford (nee Gibson) to marry. Norma married Charles Maitland of St Andrews in Fife, where he had been born in 1880, and their two sons were born there in 1922. According to family legend Jessie's

husband Norman MacLeod was a 'bad lot', despite the Royal connections of his father as recounted in Chapter Two, who would disappear for months or even years on end. As a result Jessie and her children - as well as Norma there were two boys, Norman MacLeod and Richard MacLeod, both of whom later joined the army - lived for much of the time with her mother Jane. However, when Jane died in 1897, they went to live with her brothers and sister in Stafford, at Burton Manor and later 'Crossfields'. After Jessie died in 1901, the children continued to live with their uncles and aunt, as a result of which the Gifford brothers became very attached to Norma and her brothers, both of whom died quite young. As the only child to have children, Norma's sons were the last surviving issue of the Gifford family, and for this reason it would seem, John Gifford left them in trust the bulk of his estate.

We do not know if the Maitlands had any inclination of the content of John Gifford's bequests prior to his death, but in any event, they do not seem to have had any plans as to how they might discharge the responsibilities placed on them as trustees on behalf of their sons. Moreover, initially they do not appear to have taken a lot of interest in the affairs of WG Bagnall Limited, at least until the following year, when Herbert Owen of 'The Firs', 22 Newport Road Stafford, a locally

Mention has been made of how good a customer the Sittingbourne and Kemsley paper mills of Edward Lloyd Limited eventually became, although hitherto this firm had favoured Kerr, Stuart locomotives. This photograph illustrates the first of three 2ft 6in gauge 10in cylinder 0-6-2 side tanks, in this case manufacturer's number 2472 of 1932 ALPHA. The company ran its own passenger trains to take its people to and from the various locations as the main-line ran some four miles from Sittingbourne to Ridham Dock on the River Medway. ALPHA is approaching the dock on a winter afternoon in December 1967.

based accountant, was appointed as a director to look after their interests. Owen was a partner in Dean & Son, the Stafford based accountants who had in the past acted for the Company, and as we saw in the previous Chapter also acted for the Locomotive Manufacturers Association (LMA). To comply with the articles of association of the Company Owen had to have a minimum of five shares, the minimum requirement for qualification as a director. At the time of John Gifford's death the entire authorised share capital of the Company was issued, consisting of 4,000 shares of £10 each nominal value. As noted above Edwards now had 1,719 shares and the Maitland boys 2,281, from this latter holding five shares each were transferred to Owen and Charles Maitland, so that the two them could qualify as directors.

After John Gifford's death Sydney Edwards was appointed managing director, and very soon exerted his influence in the appointment of his old friend and mentor FHB Harris, to a senior position in the drawing office. We met Harris earlier as the chief draughtsman of Kerr, Stuart, when on that Company's collapse, he was able to help Edwards in acquiring various items of equipment, and in turn Edwards helped secure him a post with Rendel, Palmer & Tritton (RT&P). His appointment to a position at Stafford was a major coup

for the firm, and would only appear to have been delayed in view of John Gifford's concerns. Getting Harris to come to Stafford had been an objective of Edwards ever since Kerr, Stuart closed its doors, as his influence with loyal and long standing customers of his old company was considerable. As briefly mentioned in the last Chapter he was one of the most accomplished designers in the private locomotive building industry in the country, and extremely well connected. It will be obvious perhaps, what Edwards had in mind, but clearly whatever success the firm might have going forward with Kerr, Stuart's former customers, it was not likely to please the Hunslet Engine Company of Leeds, which had bought the good-will. John Gifford would have been very wary of this, but Edwards was far less concerned and although one might hesitate to refer to him as unscrupulous, as we shall explore later the Company ran very close to the wind on a number of issues. Be that as it may, Harris arrived at Stafford in the early months of 1933, and whilst the obvious position for him was chief draughtsman, this post was already filled by Hugh Taylor, following Arthur Burley's untimely death in India. In the words of Harold Wood (a later occupant of the post of chief draughtsman) Harris was referred to as 'The Old Man, and his standing in the eyes of Edwards was very much higher than that of Taylor'. As might be expected this resulted in a very uncomfortable situation, not only for Hugh Taylor, but Harris himself, and indeed the rest of the drawing office staff. It was not long therefore, before the situation became untenable for Taylor and he left early in 1937, to take up an appointment with GWB Furnaces Limited, a company based in West Bromwich. Thereafter, Harris reigned supreme as the chief draughtsman.

Francis Henry Barham Harris was born in Walthamstow on 4 February 1871, the son of a mercantile clerk, Francis Alexander Harris, and his wife Emma Jane (nee Taylor). His father was appointed to a position of manager with the London silk merchants D&J Bradwell in 1876, and sent to manage its mills and warehouse at Macclesfield in Cheshire. Young Harris attended dame school in Congleton, and in January 1881 went to the Xaverian Brothers Public School at All Saints Square in Manchester. He boarded there until the summer term of 1886, and did particularly well in the sciences and engineering-based subjects, later obtaining a first class certificate at the South Kensington examinations. He was successful in a range of subjects including mathematics, chemistry and science. On leaving school he was apprenticed to Messrs Hartley, Arnoux & Fanning of the California

Works at Stoke-on-Trent, where he came under the charge of John William Hartley, senior partner in that Company and a well-known engineer of the time. Earlier he had been chief draughtsman of the North Staffordshire Railway at Stoke. On completion of his training Harris spent some time in the pattern shop before leaving the Company for a few months in 1892, when it was in financial difficulties. But he was soon back when Kerr, Stuart & Company Limited took over the California Works in 1893. Up till then Kerr, Stuart, whilst dealing in locomotives and rolling stock, had sub-contracted the physical design and construction work to a series of engineering companies of which Hartley, Arnoux & Fanning were one of the principals. In acquiring the California Works the Company was in fact taking over the design and manufacturing activities of one of its major sub-contractors, initiating the design and manufacturing activities itself. George Glass Hooper, managing director of Kerr, Stuart, was well acquainted with Harris from earlier times, and he appointed him to the drawing office in early 1893. From that time onwards, in one form or another, Harris was involved with just about everything the firm built, and in 1901 took over from John MacFarlane Galt as chief draughtsman. Galt went north to assume a similar position with Robert Stephenson & Company at

Huntley & Palmers biscuit business was the first customer for what became the standard type of four-wheel fireless locomotive. Two were built for use at its Reading factory in 1932, numbers 2473 and 2474, and this view shows the first of the pair on 22 August 1959. Notice the two safety valves, the one by the cab on the low pressure side and the one on the reservoir on the high pressure side. Observe too, the extension of the expansion link to bring its point of swing more in line with the centre-line of the cylinder, necessary in view of the large diameter cylinders - this principle is discussed in some detail in Chapter Seven.

Darlington. Although comparatively young for such responsibilities, he was only 31 years of age, Harris took charge of all design work and the Company were far more than just locomotive and railway rolling stock builders. Products of the California Works encompassed a quite amazing range of mechanical engineering. Harold Wood, who eventually took over from Harris as chief draughtsman at Stafford, testifies to the fact that he 'certainly knew his way around the drawings that WGB found they had'! These are the drawings and other literature mentioned in the last chapter, acquired from Kerr, Stuart by various means, and in some cases under what might be termed clandestine methods.

With the master stroke of getting Harris to Stafford, a combination of his vast knowledge, experience and standing in the private locomotive building industry, along with all those drawings, put the Company in an excellent position to pick-up orders that might otherwise have gone to Kerr, Stuart, had it still been in business. Discretely at first, Edwards and Harris started to make it known that WG Bagnall Limited was ready and willing not only to build locomotives to Kerr, Stuart designs, but also to supply spares parts for those already built. John Gifford would not have liked this, and when this got to the ears of the Alcock family, principals of the Hunslet Engine Company, as can be imagined they were very annoyed. They had bought the Kerr, Stuart goodwill, and felt they had paid a fair price for it. Nevertheless, as we shall see Bagnall made a significant impact in the area of what had traditionally been seen as Kerr, Stuart business. Not only did the Company build locomotives to former Kerr, Stuart designs, but significant quantities of spare parts were supplied to former Kerr, Stuart customers all over the world! Bagnall also managed to sell locomotives of its own designs in otherwise well established Kerr, Stuart markets, for example the two-foot gauge pacifics for the Gwalior Light Railway in India described in the last Chapter. The Gwalior Light Railway had almost been an exclusive Kerr, Stuart customer for over 30 years, and its business provided a constant supply of orders for spare parts of one sort or another, so this particularly galled the Hunslet fraternity! At one stage Hunslet threatened legal action, and relationships within the Locomotive Manufacturers Association (LMA) of which both companies were members, were strained.

But nothing ever came of it, and with the country's rearmament programme gaining momentum in the late 1930s, as the possibility of hostilities against Germany loomed large, Hunslets order books were as full as Bagnalls; the tension eased. However, we are jumping ahead of our story somewhat and as we shall explore later, Hunslet got some redress during the war, and for a few years after. John Alcock, managing director of Hunslet after the war, once told Harold Wood when he was chief draughtsman at Stafford, that whilst his company got the goodwill of Kerr, Stuart, Bagnall got the better part of the deal, as it got the people!

We must now look at some of the locomotives built during the period under review in this chapter. In December 1932 the Company received an order via RP&T for six metre-gauge 4-6-0 tender engines for the Gaekwar's Baroda State Railway (GBSR) in India. This was the same railway that the Company had earlier supplied 2ft 6in gauge locomotives for, as it operated a whole network of lines on the two gauges in the Baroda State. These locomotives are especially interesting as despite being ostensibly an updated version of the older British Engineering Standards Association (BESA) design, they were not to an Indian Railways Standards (IRS) design, as in the event there was no 4-6-0 in the IRS range. The engines had the same wide Belpaire top wide firebox as the Assam engines mentioned in the pervious Chapter, sitting on top of the frames rather than between them. Although partly based on some earlier engines supplied by the German manufacturer Hanomag (manufacturer's numbers 10364-8 of 1924), in that case for the Madras & Southern Mahratta Railway and also under RP&T inspection, a lot of redesign work was necessary. Cylinders were 15½ x22in, driving wheel diameter four-foot, and the coupled wheelbase 11 foot. Unlike the Assam engines in this case the boiler was superheated, the Stirling twelve-element superheater contributing 123 sq ft to the total heating surface of 854 sq ft; the working pressure was 160psi. Walschaerts valve gear drove eight inch diameter inside-admission piston valves with a travel of 4$\frac{13}{16}$ inches, and the engines were fitted with electric lighting, vacuum brakes, self-emptying hopper ashpans and Clyde soot blowers. The total cost was £18,213 for the six free-on-board at Birkenhead, against which a loss of £4,565 was recorded. The manufacturer's numbers were 2488 to 2493 and

A view looking north in the Erecting Shop in the early months of 1933. The four locomotives in various stages of construction comprise part of the batch, numbers 2488 to 2493, metre-gauge 4-6-0 tender engines for the Indian Gaekwar's Baroda State Railway. Note on the extreme right a set of main-frame plates stacked against the wall and ready for erection once the far locomotive was complete and pushed outside for testing, also the ashpan and in the bottom right corner a set of tender wheel sets. Notice too, how the boilers of these engines sit on top of the frames allowing a larger firebox width and ashpan capacity - this is discussed in the adjoining text. Multi-gauge track on right hand road with the 18in gauge works internal railway along the centre of the shop.

delivery to Birkenhead Docks was in April and May 1933. There were three repeat orders from the GBSR for this design of locomotive; three were delivered in 1935 - numbers 2531 to 2533 - and after the war four in 1948 - numbers 2852 to 2855, and a further seven in 1951 and 1952 - numbers 2964 to 2970. These were handsome well proportioned locomotives and the only noticeable difference in the later builds was a distinctive type of cow-catcher at the front. They were all still operating the lines for which they were originally built, by then part of the Indian Western Railway, well into the 1980s, and until the encroaching dieselisation overtook them.

Brief mention was made earlier that the IRS range of metre-gauge locomotives did not include a 4-6-0 design, instead a light nine ton axle-load Pacific was developed - class YA. In the event however, none of the

railways requiring a light axle-load passenger locomotive considered it had sufficient traffic to justify a pacific, with the result that no locomotives of class YA were ever built. This ensured the survival of the 4-6-0 type, and as well as Bagnall, several builders designed and supplied what were in effect, updated versions of the BESA design - in all cases with larger boilers - of which the GBSR engines were one example. Mention was also made in the last Chapter that significant numbers of the earlier BESA 4-6-0 engines, were modified with superheated boilers and in some cases piston valve cylinders too, and Bagnall was not alone in participating in the supply of boilers and other parts to complete these modifications. There were two other IRS metre-gauge pacific designs, the YB with a 10 ton axle-load and the YC with a 12 ton axle-load, and engines of both these classes were built, the YB in large

Taken from a similar vantage point and at about the same time as the previous photograph, but in this case looking in the opposite direction, this view shows the tenders for the Gaekwar's locomotives and on the right the next set of locomotive main frames. The same tender wheel sets in the previous view are on the left with the extreme rear of the main-frame plates stacked against the wall. Fitting Shop to left with a cylinder for one of the locomotives being prepared for fitting - bogie centre casting in right foreground.

numbers, many of which lasted until almost the end of steam on the metre-gauge railways in India.

In November 1932 the Company received another interesting order, three 2ft 6in gauge tank engines specially designed for a fast shuttle suburban service, fast by narrow-gauge standards that is, on the Mysore State Railway line between Bangalore City and Yelahanka, a distance of almost eight miles. To meet the specification submitted by RP&T, Bagnall designed a comparatively small and neat 2-4-2 side tank with 8x12in cylinders and three-foot diameter coupled wheels. The design included a range of modern fittings, for example grease lubrication for the axle-boxes and motion parts along with Lentz rotary cam poppet valve gear; the only Bagnall locomotives ever built with this gear. One of the principal differences between Lentz poppet valve gear and Caprotti, as fitted to some of the ZB class engines mentioned in the last Chapter, is the positioning of the valves themselves. In Caprotti gear they are mounted vertically, whilst in Lentz they are horizontal. Whilst consideration had been given to the use of diesel railcars for this new service, as Bangalore expanded its boundaries, steam locomotives were eventually chosen in view of their simplicity, the existing maintenance facilities, and first cost. The engines were manufacturer's numbers 2485 to 2487; they were sold for £1,650 each (a loss of £936 on the three was recorded) and despatched to Birkenhead

A completed member of the Gaekwar's Baroda State Railway locomotives under steam test outside the Erecting Shop; fitter attending to some minor adjustments.

Photograph taken on 16 January 1977 at Mahesana Junction on the Western Railway of India, showing Indian Railways 31022, Bagnall 2492, and former Gaekwar's Baroda State Railway number 89. This engine, along with all its sisters built between 1933 and 1948, were still in use at that time on the sections of railway they had originally been built for.

Under steam tests outside the Erecting Shop is one of three 2ft 6in gauge 2-4-2 side tanks with Lentz poppet valve gear built in 1933 for the Mysore State Railway; they were specifically designed for working fast suburban passenger trains at Bangalore. Manufacturer's numbers 2485 to 2487 this one is complete except for final painting.

docks in September 1933. On test in Mysore with a trailing load of 26 tons, one of them covered the 62 miles from Bangalore City to Chintamani - the ruling grade is 1 in 100 - in four hours including stops for water and examination. The engine was easily able to maintain a steady speed of 20 mph, despite the grades, and with the valve cut-off at 20% it was reckoned the fuel consumption was 16lb per train mile, as compared to 28lb for the earlier engines in similar circumstances. The three engines seem to have operated the service successfully until eventually it succumbed to motor bus competition, and whilst one of them was scrapped in the period 1953-1954, the other two survived on other duties until about 1960.

In late 1932 the Company tendered for the supply of a two-foot gauge diesel powered locomotive for the Ashanti Goldfields Corporation Limited, for use at its mines in the Gold Coast. The specification was a complicated one, the locomotive had to work on grades as steep as 1 in 25 and round curves of 60ft radius, very often the sharpest curves being on the steepest gradients. The Corporation was having problems with its existing wood-burning rigid framed steam

locomotives, frequent derailments seriously effecting production. It was quite brave for Bagnall to tender against this specification, especially as its first attempt to enter the market for diesel powered locomotives; nonetheless it was successful and the order was received in January 1933. Messrs Rhodes & Windeler were appointed consulting engineers by the Corporation's London office. To meet the tender specification a double-bogie articulated locomotive had been offered, and the contracted delivery date was 5 April; a tall order for such a new and complicated design by a builder with little experience in the field. Edwards had delegated to Ivor Farr the job of formulating most of the technical aspects of the tender submission, and he was subsequently put in charge of the design work. An easy decision was the selection of a suitable diesel engine, the Gardner 6L2, a six-cylinder vertical in-line four-stroke rated at 62½ bhp @ 1100 rpm, an existing and well-proven design that had already been successfully used in rail traction. However, as the locomotive was to have two power bogies a suitable and proven transmission was not so readably available in the market, and the brave decision had been made at the

First of the double-bogie diesel locomotives and the first diesel locomotive built by the firm, number 2494 of 1933. Described at length in the text, this is Ashanti Goldfields Corporation No 1 outside the Erecting Shop and alongside the wooden board used as a backcloth for the official photographs.

tender stage, to design a suitable gearbox from scratch. The design was based on the epicyclic principle, delivering two road speeds with the gears being in constant mesh, along with a dog-clutch reverse mechanism combined within the one housing, such that a separate reversing gearbox would not be necessary. As a result of this decision, the final drive arrangements on the outward axles of each bogie, could be simple propriety worm gearboxes without the need for any reversing mechanism; the drive thereafter, to the inward pairs of wheels was via conventional side rods.

The significant elements of the gearbox's unique design were three fold. In the first instance the gear train brake bands were situated outside the gearbox, so that any brake band particles that became detached as normal wear and tear took place, would not contaminate the lubricating oil in the box itself. This was important as the dog-clutch reverse arrangement was at the bottom of the gearbox, where any loose particles might otherwise deposit themselves. Secondly, as the brake bands were outside the box they were not, as would be the case in a conventional epicyclic gearbox, liable to oil contamination with consequent reduction in braking friction; it also allowed them to be much smaller than might otherwise be the case. Lastly, and perhaps the most innovative, was an ingenious arrangement whereby two separate epicyclic gear train

ratios were combined within one gear train assembly by means of a second annulus wheel in the centre of the assembly, and a second set of what were referred to as idler planet wheels. The second annulus was a conventional gear wheel, rather than the accepted form of an annulus wheel in an epicyclic gearbox, and was located in-line with the sun wheel of the other gear train. However, it was connected to a separate output shaft, the two shafts revolving one within the other and therefore, connected separately to the two brake band assemblies situated outside the gearbox as described above. The idler planet wheels, and the planet wheels for the conventional gear train, were of course connected to the gearbox output shaft via the reverse mechanism, and depending on which annulus was braked depended on which set of planet wheels drove the gearbox output shaft. The fact that the brake bands were external to the gear train itself made this arrangement practicable, as it would not have been possible to brake the second gear train by the method used in conventional epicyclic gearboxes. The output speed ranges were 3½ to 4 mph in low gear, 10 to 12 mph in high gear, and the tractive effort at 3½ mph was 5,350lb.

This gearbox was designed in its entirety by Ivor Farr, and very largely built at the Castle Engine Works, including cutting some of the gears and the authors well

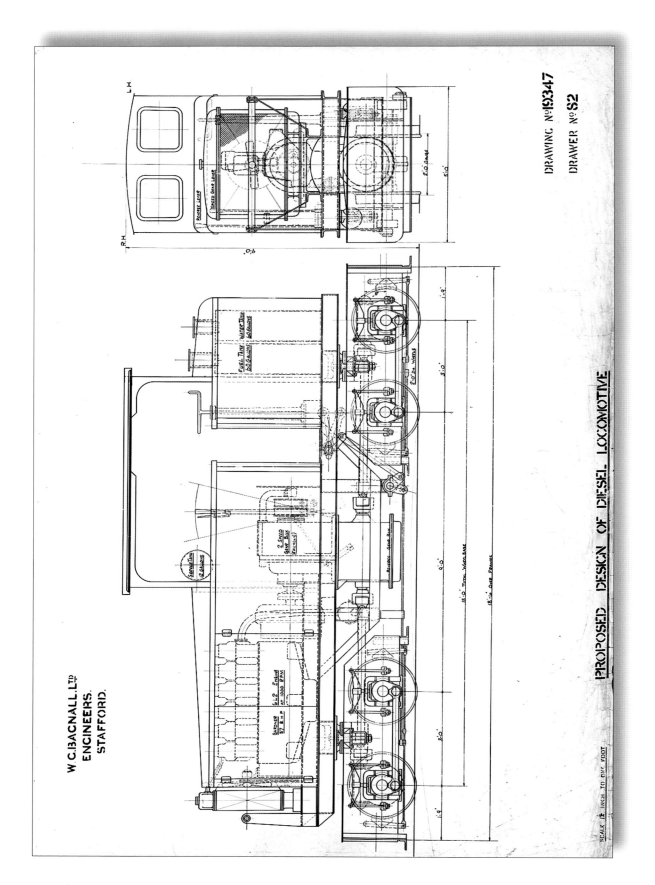

Although described as a proposal, this is in fact a diagram of the Ashanti diesel locomotives and to all intents and purposes as they were eventually built. Although not dated, the entry in the drawing register for this diagram is 13 July 1932. Notice the arrangement of drive train from the Gardner diesel engine to the gearbox and thence the final drives on the bogies.

remember Ivor describing the apparent incredulity of such operations being undertaken in the machine shop of a steam locomotive builder! But they did it, and it worked. It was Ivor's view that because of the design of the gearbox any sort of clutch between engine and transmission was unnecessary, but the consulting engineers 'raised their eyebrows' of having no conventional clutch between engine and gearbox, and as a compromise a Vulcan-Sinclair hydraulic flywheel was fitted. All the gearbox bearings, including those of the planet wheels, used Hoffmann roller or ball bearings, the actual type depending on the thrust load patterns, and the lubricating oil was circulated by a gear-driven pump. There was an ingenious arrangement to ensure that only one brake band could be applied at any one time, and it was impossible to change the direction of the locomotive if either gear was engaged. Ivor's main aim in designing this gearbox was to make driving the locomotive as simple as possible, as part of the specification was for the locomotive to be driven by unskilled labour, and this was yet another reason why he wanted to avoid the need for a conventional clutch.

Before being despatched the locomotive was tested in the works yard in the presence of Horace Morgan of the Ashanti Goldfields Corporation, representatives of Rhodes & Windeler, along with members of the technical press and other consulting engineers who had been invited. By somewhat ingenious methods, using the multi-gauge test track it was found possible to couple the locomotive to a load of around 200 tons, consisting of loaded standard-gauge wagons, and the locomotive hauled them with ease. The impossibility of stalling the engine, even when selecting high gear on starting with the 200 ton load, amazed the spectators; the smoothness of the gear change and the ability of the locomotive to move less than an inch at a time when moving to couple to its train, was also commented on favourably. The locomotive proved easy to drive and it was impossible to carry out gear or direction changing in anything other than the correct order.

Although this gearbox employed well established and proven epicyclic gear train philosophy, the design of the brake bands and the combination of two-speeds within one gear train, along with the integral reversing mechanism, were sufficiently innovative to be patented. A patent was taken out in the name of the Company and WS Edwards; patent No 427,879, it was accepted on 25 April 1935 and titled: *Improvements in and relating to Gearboxes for Power Transmission on Locomotives and other Mechanically Propelled Vehicles*. The completed

This is a view of the innards of the innovative epicyclic gearbox, subject to British Patent number 427,879 of April 1935, as fitted to the Ashanti diesel locomotives and fully described in the text. Notice the single epicyclic gear train partly in its own case at the top centre, with the twin brake drums, one for each speed range, external to the box itself to the top right. The dog-clutch reversing mechanism is at the bottom with the twin output shafts, one each side. The input shaft is at top left.

Another view of the Ashanti diesel locomotive illustrating the cab interior and layout of the driver's controls. The lever looking like a steam locomotive reversing lever does the same job, whilst the lever transverse to the frames is the change speed control shown in the central, neutral position. Movement one way or the other applied pressure to the respective gearbox speed range brake bands, which can themselves be seen immediately in front of the lever. By use of the ratchet mechanism on the quadrant pressure could be applied to the brake bands and this arrangement took account of the bands wearing with use. Additionally, the bands were easily accessible when it was necessary to renew the linings. The throttle and brake controls can also be seen and notice where a manufacturer's plate has been fitted, although there were two others in more conventional positions on the cab sides.

locomotive, manufacturer's number 2494, was delivered to Liverpool Docks on 14 June 1933, which whilst late on the contract date, was nonetheless a commendable achievement bearing in mind the design work involved. The selling price was £1,950 free-on-board and there was a small profit of £35 16/ 5d (£35 82p). When the locomotive was put to work at Ashanti it was found that whilst it easily achieved the design requirements, indeed it exceeded them in some areas, there was a problem that had not been anticipated at the design stage. Because the drawbars were located on the bogies rather than the locomotive frame, an unequal distribution of the total load was experienced between the individual bogie drives, with whichever bogie was coupled to the train taking the greater load. This resulted in uneven wear on the worm final drives, and to overcome the problem a differential gear was embodied in the design of the gearboxes of subsequent

locomotives. After some more clever design work by Ivor, it proved possible to encompass the modifications within the existing gearbox housing.

A second locomotive was ordered in January 1934, number 2514, despatched in October at the same selling price as the earlier one. A replacement gearbox for the first locomotive, complete with the differential gear modification was delivered at the same time. A further two locomotives were ordered later, but before they were delivered the fluid flywheel on the first locomotive was found to be leaking fluid badly, and Ashanti asked Bagnall if it would be possible to fit a conventional flywheel, as a spare one was to hand for another Gardner engine in use at the mine as part of a stationary power plant. While Sydney Edwards was unsure about this, Ivor assured him it would 'be okay'; remember he never felt an hydraulic coupling was necessary in the first place! According to Ivor, all

Edwards said in his reply was: 'It had better be'. The solid flywheel was then fitted to the engine at Ashanti and the locomotive worked satisfactorily; Ivor was vindicated, and the last two locomotives had conventional flywheels instead of fluid couplings. Incidentally, this did not stop the Hydraulic Coupling & Engineering Company Limited of Isleworth, manufacturers of the Vulcan-Sinclair coupling, using a picture of the Bagnall locomotive in its publicity material for several years afterwards. The gearbox from the first locomotive came back to Stafford to be modified with the differential gear, and was then fitted to a later locomotive; there were two more, number 2546 of August 1936, and 2568 of January 1937. Bagnall were quite rightly very proud of these locomotives and they featured in its advertising material for many years.

One more articulated diesel locomotive was built and with the same gearbox arrangement, but first another significant development needs to be chronicled. In April and May 1933, the Company entered into an agreement with the German manufacturer of locomotives and diesel engines, Humboldt-Deutz Motorenwerke AG., of Cologne, to build under licence in this county locomotives and railcars of Deutz design, with Deutz diesel engines and transmissions. The Humboldt-Deutz Company had been formed in 1930 by an amalgamation of Moterenfabrik Deutz, a pioneering company in the design and manufacture of internal combustion engines, and Maschinenbauanstalt Humboldt, one of Germany's oldest manufacturers of mining machinery and, in earlier times, steam locomotives. As well as designing and building diesel engines the new company developed a range of diesel locomotives and railcars, along with a other products. This agreement was a significant coup for the Company, as rail vehicles with diesel engines were increasing in popularity with a significant number of operators, as advances in the design of the engines grew apace. There was a lot of activity around this time in the locomotive building industry, with many traditional builders dipping their feet into the design and development of diesel powered rail vehicles. Edwards was shrewd enough to realise that his Company could ill afford to spend large amounts of cash on the development of the newer forms of traction; experience with the gearbox outlined above had already taught him

a lot. By tapping into the established Deutz designs he could avoid the otherwise high development costs.

Sydney Edwards first introduction to the Deutz and Humboldt people would have been during the Institution of Locomotive Engineers annual summer visit of June 1928, when a party of about 100 members visited Germany, although on that occasion they did not actually visit the Deutz works. The agreement came at a time when locomotive orders were at their lowest ebb, not just at Stafford but with all the private locomotive builders both in this country and on the continent. Several manufacturers had already been forced into liquidation due to the enormous reduction in demand whether at home or abroad. The situation was aggravated by continental and American builders increasing their foothold in what had been seen as traditional British markets; in particular India and some African and South American countries. They achieved this by undercutting the prices the British manufacturers were able to offer, sometimes by quite large margins. The old established and well-known firm of Manning Wardle & Company of Leeds went under as far back as 1926, and as we have already related Kerr, Stuart & Company closed it doors for the last time in 1930, albeit in that case for different reasons. In 1934 the Bristol based Avonside Engine Company packed up, and before the decade out two other famous names in the trade disappeared. Nasmyth Wilson & Company of Patricroft, one of the oldest in the business built its last locomotive in 1938, followed by no less than the one-time giant in the industry, Kitson & Company of Leeds, with a history going back to 1837. Another Leeds builder, John Fowler & Company, whilst continuing in business built its last steam locomotive in 1935. In 1937 two other old established firms in the trade, R&W Hawthorn Leslie & Company of Newcastle and Robert Stephenson & Company of Darlington, amalgamated their locomotive building departments, trading thereafter as Robert Stephenson & Hawthorns Limited, in an attempt to be better equipped to tackle the declining market. Mention has been made in Chapter Six, of how the traditional builders reacted to the big armament firms of Armstrong Whitworth and William Beardmore, along with Woolwich Arsenal, building locomotives in the post-war years. In the case of the Arsenal, its activities in this direction did not last very long, but Armstrong Whitworth and Beardmore persevered, and with some success. Nevertheless, William Beardmore dropped out as early as 1931, and Armstrong Whitworth followed in 1937. As an illustration of how hard times were, the largest of all the manufacturers in this country, the North British Locomotive Company with its three works in Glasgow, had been forced to close one of them as far back as 1923 - the Atlas Works - or at least stop locomotive production there. This Company had employed no fewer than 8,262 folk in 1919, by 1932 the figure was as low as 389, about 150 less than Bagnall; in 1932 the two works that were still open delivered not a single locomotive. In fact, in 1932, the total number of locomotives delivered by the British private locomotive industry was only 39, and of this number just over half came from the Castle Engine Works. All things considered, Bagnall managed to do reasonably well during these lean years, and it was Edward's proud boast in Stafford that 'Bagnalls chimney never stopped smoking', which was almost, but not quite the whole truth, as there was some short time working.

The LMA were heavily involved in the discussions concerning the closure of some of the private builders works, and Edwards, as the representative of WG Bagnall Limited, had much to contribute at the various meetings. In the case of Sir WG Armstrong Whitworth & Company Limited, it was agreed at a meeting of the LMA on 14 January 1937, that the Association should buy the locomotive manufacturing goodwill of that company, which it did for £125,000. It is worth pointing out that neither Armstrong Whitworth nor William Beardmore designed steam locomotives in the way of the traditional builders, rather they built locomotives to existing designs, usually those of either main-line railway companies or consulting engineers. They would on occasions undertake the detail design work to produce manufacturing drawings, but would not design a locomotive from first principles, as for example, Bagnall did. These two companies did however invest in the development of diesel traction, in these cases designing and building locomotives from first principles, albeit with indifferent success. Later in the same year, at a meeting on 16 December 1937, the LMA agreed to purchase for as little as £70,000 the goodwill of Nasmyth Wilson, and the sale was completed on 25 January the following year. There was more to come when at its meeting of 5 April 1938, the question of the

goodwill of Kitson & Company Limited was considered by the LMA. In this case a receiver had been appointed as far back as 1934, and operations had continued on a limited scale. The Kitson goodwill, along with the freehold of the once world-famous Airedale Foundry, was secured for as little as £45,000. How are the mighty fallen!

When Manning Wardle had closed down in 1926, its goodwill had been acquired by Kitson, and on closure of the Kitson Airedale Foundry for locomotive purposes it was agreed by the LMA at its meeting on 28 October 1938, that the Manning Wardle industrial locomotive business which Kitson had continued, should be transferred to Robert Stephenson & Hawthorns (RSH). However, there was a proviso that should RSH build any industrial shunting locomotives to either an existing Kitson or Manning Wardle design (which in the event it did), a levy of 10% of the contract price would be paid to the LMA - the agreement to operate for 10 years from 1 July 1938. Part of the deal to acquire the Kitson goodwill from the receiver, was a lease back of the Airedale Foundry at a peppercorn rent, on condition it was no longer used for either building locomotives or supplying their component parts. The Airedale Foundry had a modern and very well equipped steel foundry, as Kitson was one of the few private builders in this country that made its own steel castings. The firm had done good business in the supply of steel casting to other builders in the trade, as well as on occasions to the main-line railway companies. In particular the London & North Eastern Railway (LNER) had been a regular customer for cylinder castings, at times when its own foundry capacity was stretched. Some time after the arrangements were put in place the receiver requested permission from the LMA to supply steel cylinder castings to the LNER; the LMA however, insisted on adherence to the agreement. With the onset of hostilities against Germany in 1939, some locomotive work was undertaken at the Airedale Foundry, but this is outside the scope of these notes, and the Company was finally wound-up in December 1945.

Ever since 1930 the government had been applying pressure of one sort or another on the coal mining industry to both restrict production and become more productive. The coal owners had been encouraged to amalgamate colliery companies in the hope that this would improve the economics, and whilst some action had been taken it was not of a significant nature taken as a whole. As with coal mining there was government pressure for rationalisation within the locomotive and railway rolling stock building industry, again with suggestions that companies should voluntarily reduce capacity. The pressure was applied both directly on some of the individual builders, and also through the LMA, in neither case being particularly welcomed. The industry felt it was doing all it could reasonably be expected to in the progress it had made in acquiring the goodwill of those companies that had ceased trading, ensuring a continued supply of spare parts, and should they be required, locomotives of the specific designs of those manufacturers that had ceased trading. Independently of the activities of the LMA, the Hunslet Engine Company of Leeds had acquired the goodwill of the Avonside Engine Company along with that of Kerr, Stuart. The one initiative that did perhaps stem from the Government's concerns was the amalgamation of the locomotive business of Hawthorn Leslie with that of Robert Stephenson Company referred to earlier. In the late summer of 1937, the LMA did take a further initiative in forming a new company, the Locomotive Manufacturing Company Limited, which was registered on 1 September 1937 to better manage the goodwill of the companies it had in effect absorbed. The onset of the country's rearmament programme soon provided the remaining companies with all the work they could handle, and the whole question of excess capacity, along with the procedures the LMA had put in place to ensure an even distribution of workload, were to a large extent negated. But we are jumping ahead of our story again, and we will return to the activities of the LMA and its members later in this Chapter.

We must now explore the Deutz agreement and its implications. Sydney Edwards had made the acquaintance of Marcel Porn, a Romanian born in Ploesti on 27 January 1884, with a varied and interesting career prior to coming to this country in 1919. Educated at the Evangelical Realschule at Brasso in Hungary, after some practical experience in the works of Messrs Julius Teutsch in the same town, he attended the well established German technical college at Mittweida. On graduation with a diploma in both mechanical and electrical engineering, Marcel Porn worked for several engineering companies in Bucharest and Ploesti, and in 1904 undertook his military service

which was compulsory at the time. Between 1909 and 1916 he worked on his own account as a consulting engineer and as well as an involvement with the Serbian Railways, represented several companies including Marconi and Franco Tosi. By 1914 he owned his own engineering works in Bucharest, prior to being commissioned into the Romanian Army as an engineering officer in 1916; he came to this country on cessation of hostilities. Marcel Porn later became a naturalized British subject and once settled in this country established a small workshop in Tiverton Street, London SE1, specialising in lift installations, which were then becoming popular. In April 1927, in conjunction with a business partner and financier Thomas Archer Dunwoody, a limited company was formed, Porn & Dunwoody Limited, of which he was both chairman and managing director. Soon after this larger workshops were acquired, known as the Union Works, still in south-east London at Southwark. Initially the firm continued to specialise in lift installations, acquiring the British agency for Stigler lifts, but later branched out into the diesel engine market through a subsidiary company, the West Cambrian Power Company Limited, formed by Porn in 1929 with its base in Fishguard. Through his numerous business contacts Porn negotiated the British agency for Deutz diesel engines, at a time when Humboldt-Deutz Motorenwerke AG., was promoting its new range of diesel engines world wide.

The business connection between Porn & Dunwoody and Deutz became Marcel Porn's principal interest for much of the rest of his life, as although the formal connection between the two companies was broken on the outbreak of the Second World War, his practical involvement with the Deutz diesel engines continued. It was also the reason he and Edwards got together in a business relationship. At the Union Works in Bear Gardens, under licence from Deutz facilities were established to overhaul Deutz engines as well as the manufacture and supply of spare parts. Deutz diesel engines were particularly popular in this country as a result of Porn's activities, for in-shore fishing vessels and other small costal craft. This was at a time when sail was rapidly giving way to power in small vessels, and the Deutz range of engines were admirably suited for this type of application. Marcel Porn was instrumental during the 1930s in the design and installation of diesel power plants for marine use, as well as in a number of other industries, and the firm became particularly adapt at converting small and medium sized sailing vessels to diesel power. By the time war broke-out in 1939, large numbers of Deutz diesel engines were in service in this country, and the facilities of Porn & Dunwoody were of significant importance when the supply of spare parts from Germany dried-up. Worth a brief note is the fact that during the war Bagnall supplied Porn & Dunwoody with a number of castings and forgings for the repair of Deutz engines fitted in small inshore craft.

An extremely accomplished engineer, a man of enormous energy and business acumen, Marcel Porn was instrumental in forming a number of other companies involved in power generation, shipping and the production of high grade suede leather. In April 1936 he was elected an associate of the Institution of Mechanical Engineers (I Mech E), and became a full member in November the following year. It should come as no surprise that Sydney Edwards proposed Porn's application to become an associate, and along with Archibald Kay Bruce of the consulting engineers Robert Bruce & Partners, he was a supporter later for his election to full membership.

After the last war Porn & Dunwoody Limited developed a range of small horizontal diesel engines, up to 15 horsepower, known as the Uniporn range. They were so successful that additional manufacturing facilities soon became necessary, and large numbers were built under licence by the Damiler Company, better known for its cars, in Coventry. The Company also built a range of in-line vertical, and V form engines with horsepowers up to 72, and these were equally successful. As well as being a member of the I Mech E., Marcel Porn was a member of the Institution of Marine Engineers, a master of the Worshipful Company of Gardeners and a member of the City of London Livery. A man of enormous talent, vitality and vigour, Porn had a profound love for his adopted country and was held in high regard in government circles during the war, due to his special knowledge of engineering activities in occupied Europe; his advice was frequently sought. Marcel Porn passed away at his home, Little Kingshill Grange, at Great Missenden on 21 April 1949, leaving a wife and three daughters, the eldest of whom, Alice Porn, was a director of the company. In later years Porn & Dunwoody concentrated on its original activity of

specialising in lifts, and under the title of P&W Lifts Limited, was still in business as late as 1991.

Despite high aspirations when the Bagnall-Deutz agreement was entered into, it did not in the event, result in an enormous number of orders for locomotives. Between November 1933 and January 1938, ten locomotives were built under the agreement, along with one of an otherwise Bagnall design which was fitted with a Deutz engine. The external lines of the first few Bagnall-Deutz diesel locomotives, as they were known, were modelled on the German Deutz designs; they had the characteristic and distinctive rounded cabs with other parts of the superstructure being quite curvaceous - typical features of the builder. After the first few had been built Harris set the drawing office to work, with the result that the later locomotives had less curves and more straight lines, and as a result looked much more like a product of the Castle Engine Works. The outbreak of the Second World War brought an end to the agreement, as was the case with Porn & Dunwoody too, but it had helped in a limited way to consolidate the firm's entry into the market for diesel locomotives.

The Bagnall-Deutz locomotives fell into three basic types. There was a small narrow-gauge four-wheel machine with a single-cylinder engine of about eight horsepower, a slightly larger 0-4-0 of about 25 horsepower with a two-cylinder engine, and a much bigger version that could be of either an 0-4-0 or 0-6-0 wheel arrangement. In this case a two-cylinder engine rated at 75 horsepower was used in the 0-4-0, and a three-cylinder engine developing 120 horsepower in the 0-6-0; they could be made in gauges from metre upwards. There was also a design of locomotive for use in underground mining operations, and unlike all the others which had two-stroke engines, this one had a four-cylinder four-stroke rated at 45 horsepower; as events unfolded only one example of this type was built. In all cases the engines, gearboxes and final-drives were manufactured in Germany and delivered to Stafford as complete assemblies. Porn & Dunwoody were involved in this process and also acted on occasions as selling agents for the complete locomotives. The basic Deutz engine was an airless injection water cooled two-stoke with a scavenge pump driven directly off the crank-shaft; the individual fuel pumps were regulated by a conventional centrifugal governor. Engine starting was by compressed air, with part of the engines exhaust gases being diverted via a non-return valve to charge a large air bottle. If this bottle was completely discharged, an external supply of compressed air was necessary to start the engine. The gearboxes were of the constant-mesh type, continuously running in oil with either two or four speed ratios, and the final-drive incorporated a dog-clutch reversing arrangement. Integral with the gearbox in the larger designs was a double-disc friction clutch actuated by oil pressure, arranged such that slipping could be controlled over a wide range, allowing the locomotives to take up trailing loads with ease. In the case of these locomotives the drive was via a jack-shaft and conventional side-rods, whilst in the smaller designs the gearbox was mounted directly on the trailing axle. In these cases the final-drive was combined within the gearbox and the clutch was a conventional plate type operated by a foot pedal in the cab. The very smallest of the designs had a chain drive between the axles, whilst the larger ones had side-rods. Radiators and associated equipment were supplied by the Spiral Tube & Components Limited of Derby.

Before describing the Bagnall-Deutz locomotives in more detail, the fifth articulated locomotive briefly mentioned earlier needs to be discussed. Although this locomotive had a Deutz engine, it was otherwise to a Bagnall design, manufacturer's number 2498, a smaller version of the Ashanti Gold Mines design. The engine was a two-cylinder vertical two-stroke rated at 22 to 24 horsepower and the transmission system a smaller version of that fitted to the earlier articulated locomotives. Ordered by the Halkyn United District Mines Limited, for use underground at its Penbryn lead line at Halkyn, which is near Holywell in North Wales. The track gauge was 1ft 10½in and despatch on 31 March 1934. Ordered with the locomotive were several items of rolling stock, comprising 51 mine cars of 18½ cub ft capacity, 12 bogie passenger trolleys and one four-seater inspection car, which might suggest that some expansion of the operations at the mine was underway. The locomotive was sold for £1,325; the Deutz engine cost £176 13/- (£176 65p) plus a duty of £33 19/- (£33 95p), and a profit of a little over £67 was generated on the whole transaction. In service the same problem arose with this locomotive as the Ashanti one, unequal loading of the worm final-drives, but in this case in September 1934 the whole locomotive came back to the works for attention. The contract stipulated that the final 20% of the price was payable in two instalments, 10% on entry into service, followed by 10% after six months successful operation; so it was some time before all the money was paid. When the locomotive came back the gearbox was modified with the addition of the differential gear, and it was despatched back to Halkyn on 8 October. As it was necessary to dismantle the locomotive so it could be lowered end-on down the mine-shaft, part of the

The second design of double-bogie diesel locomotive, number 2498; in this case somewhat smaller and with a German Deutz engine, but the same arrangement of gearbox and final drive. New to the Halkyn United District Mines for use underground at its lead mine at Hollywell in North Wales, the track gauge was 1ft 10½ ins. Notice the sand boxes mounted on the bogies and the balance weight on the brake lever in the cab.

The Halkyn District Mines also ordered some rolling stock including 12 of these man-riding 'trolleys' - as they were described - and like the locomotive for use underground.

contract covered Bagnalls men assisting this process as well as descending the shaft to re-erect the locomotive underground. In the event they had to do this twice, also dismantling the locomotive when it had to come back to Stafford for the differential gear to be fitted. All this backwards and forwards movement of men between Stafford and Halkyn was quite a talking point around the works at the time, flavour being added when it was discovered the locomotive's overall dimensions were such that it was too big to fit into many of the underground tunnels where it was intended to operate. The dimensions were checked and it was confirmed that whilst it had been built entirely to specification, the customer's calculations were wrong, and apparently a lot of work was necessary at the mine to enable it to operate successfully. Be that as it may, it did not have a very long life, and would appear to have been scrapped in about 1939.

The first two orders for Bagnall-Deutz diesel locomotives were in January 1934, with Robert Bruce & Sons appointed the consulting engineer in both cases. Sydney Edwards, Marcel Porn and AK Bruce, had already been busy in developing the designs, and canvasing for orders. One locomotive was ordered by RG Shaw & Company Limited, managing agents for a number of tea plantations in Assam, and the other by the Assam Railways & Trading Company. The locomotive for RG Shaw was from the smaller range, a 2ft 6in gauge 22 to 24 nominal horsepower 0-4-0 for use by the Budla Beta Tea Company on its Pengaree Degboi Trolley Line. Manufacturer's number 2506, it was fitted with a Deutz OMZ 117 two-cylinder engine rated 24 horsepower at 700 rpm; the cylinder dimensions were 5x6¾in. Transmission was via a double-disc oil operated friction clutch and four-speed constant mesh gearbox mounted on the trailing axle, and this gave road-speeds of: 1.87; 3.24; 5.42 and 9.68 mph. The frames were inside and the drive to the leading axle was by side-rods; weight in working order was 4½ tons. Despatch was on 17 May 1934 and the selling price

What would appear to be the first advertisement issued by the firm indicating its ability to built Bagnall-Deutz diesel locomotives; from The Railway Gazette of 16 June 1933. Note reference to 9,000 locomotives already built, selling agents Porn & Dunwoody Limited and London agents KR Pearson & Son. The three locomotives illustrated are ones built in Germany, but it is interesting to compare them with the locomotives built at Stafford in the following illustrations. Notice too, in the bottom left illustration the Bagnall name on the building, a bit of trick photography as under a glass on the original print the remainder of the writing is in German!

£595; there was a loss of £3 18/ 2d (£3 91p) - not bad for a first effort! A similar locomotive was supplied to the same agents for the Budla Beta Tea Company in May 1938, but with a smaller 11 to 12 horsepower engine suitable for hand, as opposed to compressed-air starting. In this case the locomotive was built to suit two-foot gauge track and was presumably for use at a different tea estate; the number was 2595 and as events turned out it was the last Bagnall-Deutz diesel locomotive built.

First member of the smaller design of Bagnall-Deutz diesel locomotive, number 2506 of May 1934, with the engine compartment doors removed to expose the two-cylinder vertical engine. Notice the conventional whistle mounted on the engine exhaust pipe, and blown using the engine's exhaust gasses!

Manufacturer's number 2506 again, this time on test in the works yard with a rake of small bogies that were delivered with the locomotive to the Budla Beta Tea Company in Assam. Notice the large compressed air cylinder in the cab; this was charged by exhaust gases from the engine and used for engine starting. The driver is Fred Ewington, Erecting Shop Foreman at the time. The railway lines immediately behind the fence are the former Shropshire Union Railways & Canal Company's line to Wellington, with the former LNWR west-coast main-line behind the building; the large arrays of signals were for movements on the approach to the station. The far chimney to the extreme left is beyond the main-line and belongs to Venables timber yard; the other one is part of the Universal Grinding Wheel factory.

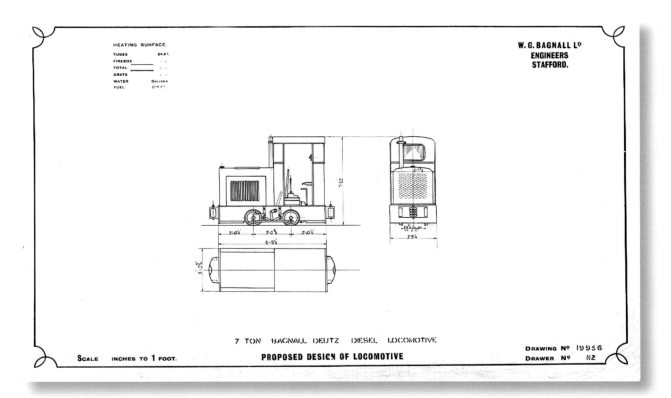

HEATING SURFACE.

TUBES	SQ.FT.
FIREBOX	" "
TOTAL	" "
GRATE	" "
WATER	GALLONS
FUEL	CUB.FT.

W. G. BAGNALL Lᴅ
ENGINEERS
STAFFORD.

7 TON BAGNALL DEUTZ DIESEL LOCOMOTIVE
PROPOSED DESIGN OF LOCOMOTIVE

SCALE   INCHES TO 1 FOOT.

DRAWING Nᵒ 19956
DRAWER Nᵒ 82

Bagnall drawing number 19956, undated but with a date of February 1933 recorded in the drawing register, illustrating in diagram form a proposal for a Bagnall-Deutz locomotive for 1ft 11⁵/₈in gauge track and very similar to number 2506.

The second locomotive was from the larger range, a metre-gauge 0-4-0 of 50 to 55 horsepower and intended for shunting duties on a main-line railway. Manufacturer's number 2507, it had the larger OMZ 125 two-cylinder engine rated at 55 horsepower at 500 rpm - the cylinder dimensions were 7x10in. The gearbox, of similar characteristics to the smaller locomotive but obviously much bigger, was mounted behind the trailing axle and there was a jackshaft and rod drive to the wheels; the four road-speeds were: 3; 5; 7.75 and 12.5 mph. Weight in working order was 11½ tons and the locomotive was designed to start a load of 300 tons on level track, and 130 tons on a 1 in 30 gradient. Despatch was in May 1934, although it is worth pointing out that both these locomotives were actually contractually due in March. This one was sold for £1,387, at a loss of £35 15 4d (£35 76p). In February 1935 a repeat order was received from the Assam Railways & Trading Company, but in this case for a slightly larger locomotive with an engine developing 70 to 77 horsepower - but at a reduced speed of 430 rpm - this was Deutz type OMZ 130, and as a result the

weight in working order went up to 14 tons. Manufacturer's number 2530, despatch was in September 1935 and the selling price £1,625. The change in the design of the external characteristics of these diesel locomotives is apparent in comparing this one with its predecessor.

Two locomotives from the smallest range were built at Stafford and these differed from all the others in having horizontal, rather than vertical engines. The Deutz type MAH 514 was a single-cylinder engine rated at 8 to 8½ nominal horsepower and running much faster than the vertical ones, in this case at 1,200 rpm. The drive was through a two-speed gearbox mounted on the trailing axle which like the bigger versions was combined with the final drive, and thence by chains - the frames were outside. The first one was manufacturer's number 2499, two-foot gauge for the Oakley Slate Quarries at Bleanau Festiniog in North Wales, where it was sent in March 1934 at a selling price of £298 - which included £48 for extra ballast requested by the customer to take the working order weight from 2.8 to 3.75 tons. Apparently intended for

These two illustrations show the first member of the larger of the initial Bagnall-Deutz designs, in this case number 2507 of 1934. Notice once again the air reservoir for engine starting and the whistle blown by the engine's exhaust gasses. Unlike the smaller locomotive where the final-drive was mounted on the trailing axle, in this case the drive was via a jack-shaft.

This photograph shows one of two Bagnall-Deutz locomotives built to this design, the smallest of the range, and in this case driven by a single-cylinder - hence the large flywheel - horizontal Deutz engine; the only design of Deutz locomotive built at Stafford embodying a horizontal as opposed to a vertical engine. Manufacturer's number 2499 of 1934 was for the Oakley Slate Quarries in North Wales.

underground use at the quarry this locomotive does not seem to have been a great success, and was later confined to shunting on the surface. It came back to Stafford for an overhaul in April 1937, and the last spare parts were delivered as late as October 1945. The second locomotives of this design, number 2524, was ordered in November 1934 by the New Consolidated Goldfields Limited, a South African based company for use at mines in that country. Despatch was free-on-board to Liverpool Docks on 28 January 1935, consigned to Lagares Tin Mines (1933) Limited. This locomotive had a modified clutch arrangement and there was no requirement for any additional ballast - the selling price was £294 15/- (£294 75p).

Two six-wheeled Bagnall-Deutz diesel locomotives were built, the first, number 2567 of February 1937 was for the African Manganese Company Limited for use on a 2ft 6in gauge system in the Gold Coast, and a second, number 2573 of September 1937, for Sir JL Hulett's two-foot gauge system at the South African Darnall Sugar Estate in Natal, South Africa. These two

locomotives had the larger three-cylinder engine of Deutz type OMD 130, rated at 110 to 130 nominal horsepower at 450 rpm, and a four-speed gearbox giving speeds of: 4.35; 6.8; 11 and 17.3 mph. The drive was via a jack-shaft at the rear of the locomotive and rods, and both locomotives were fitted with Westinghouse air brake equipment. Designed to haul in bottom gear 385 tons on the level and 120 tons on a grade of 1in 50, frictional resistance in both cases was based on 20lb per ton. These two were respectively sold for £2,095 and £2,360, in the first case free-on-board Liverpool and in the second, carriage, insurance and freight paid to Durban. Only one Bagnall-Deutz locomotive was built to suit standard-gauge, number 2577 of October 1937, fitted with the two-cylinder engine of type OMZ 130 rated at 70 to 77 nominal horsepower, and a four-speed gearbox. The weight in working order was 22 tons and the selling price £1,875. Despatched in October 1937 it had been ordered by FH Lloyd & Company Limited for shunting at its Darlaston Steel Foundry, where it remained in use until 1957. FH Lloyd by the way,

The solitary standard-gauge Bagnall-Deutz diesel locomotives was number 2577 of 1937, seen here at the Darlaston steel works of FH Lloyd & Company Limited some time in the early 1950s. Notice in the case of this locomotive the whistle is blown directly by air from the engine starting cylinder.

were one of the principal suppliers of steel castings to Bagnall.

There remains to be described the solitary underground mine locomotive of Deutz design that was built at Stafford, manufacturer's number 2516, a two-foot gauge 0-4-0 for the Coltness Iron Company Limited. Despatched on 22 January 1935 for use at Kingshill Colliery in Lanarkshire, unlike the other Bagnall-Deutz locomotives this one had a four-stroke rather than a two-stroke engine, Deutz type A4M 317, a four-cylinder vertical, airless injection water cooled unit rated at 40-45 horsepower at 1,000 rpm. The engine was equipped with a special arrangement to reduce exhaust emissions underground, along with 'Delbag' air intake filters to protect the engine from any dust and grit in the underground air. Transmission was via a single-disc friction clutch, cardan shaft and a

totally enclosed Deutz four-speed gearbox complete with reversing arrangement and a jackshaft drive to side-rods - the speeds were: 2.3; 3.5; 5.6 and 9 mph. The minimum speed gave a drawbar pull of 4,200lb, and the maximum load that could be hauled on level track was approximately 120 tons. Compressed air start was employed, but unlike the two-stroke engines that used exhaust gases, this one had a separate air compressor and there was a 12 volt flame-proof electric lighting system supplied from an engine driven dynamo. The arrangements for cleaning the exhaust, essential underground in a coal mine to prevent sparks, are worthy of some detail. Small jets of water were directed against the exhaust valves and passages to cool them, and the exhaust itself was then directed to a 'scrubber' which extracted soot, oil vapours and any un-burnt fuel. A screen of stainless steel was fitted in the exhaust

This is one of the later Bagnall-Deutz locomotives of the larger design, number 2530 of September 1935, mechanically identical to the prototype number 2507, and also for the Assam Railways & Trading Company. Notice how the external design has evolved taking on much more of a Bagnall, as opposed to a Deutz, appearance. The photograph is particularly interesting as Marcel Porn is on the footplate with a member of the staff of Robert Bruce & Sons, the consulting engineers, alongside. In all probability this is Archibald Kay Bruce.

Two views of the sole member of this design of underground mining locomotive and the only Bagnall-Deutz locomotive with a four-stroke, as opposed to a two-stroke engine. Number 2516 of 1935 for the Coltness Iron Company at Kingshill Colliery in Scotland. Notice in the top picture the air cylinder for engine starting with the dynamo below, the handbrake wheel, electric lighting and motor-car type horn. The engine exhaust pipe passes inside the frames just in front of the leading wheelset, as the exhaust scrubber was situated between the frames. The bottom view shows the opposite, right-hand side of the locomotive, with detail of the engine and drive to the gearbox.

DIESEL LOCOMOTIVES BUILT WITH 30 YEARS EXPERIENCE BEHIND US

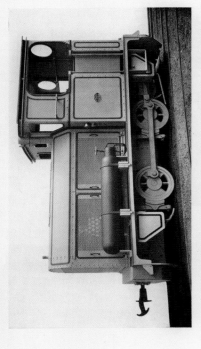

Photograph shows a Double Bogie Articulated Diesel Locomotive supplied to Ashanti Goldfields, Ltd., fitted with 70 h.p. Gardner and Two-speed Epicyclic Gearbox, absolutely fool-proof, and easy to handle, with great flexibility. Weight of above Locomotive 14 tons.

W. G. BAGNALL LTD. CASTLE ENGINE WORKS, STAFFORD

Photograph shows standard Bagnall Deutz Diesel Locomotive, 77 h.p., fitted with a Bagnall Deutz Two-stroke Engine and Four-speed Gearbox, and Oil operated clutch. Weight in working order 15½ tons, to give speeds of 3, 5, 8, 13 miles per hour, maximum tractive effort 7,000 lbs. The Engine and Gearbox are very robustly constructed, and weigh 5½ tons. The Two-stroke Engine is most suitable for Locomotive work, of generous proportions, simplest construction combined with low speed and long life having minimum of maintenance.

Photograph below shows the Engine and Gearbox of the above Locomotive.

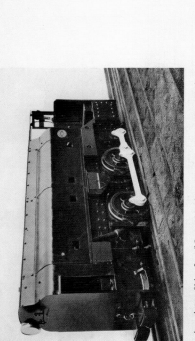

Photograph above shows a 50 h.p. Bagnall Deutz Mining Locomotive, Weight in working order 8 tons. Fitted with a Four-cylinder Bagnall Deutz Four stroke Diesel Engine, with a Four-speed Gearbox, can be designed for working either in Firedamp Mines or any Underground Works, without danger from fire or fumes.

W. G. BAGNALL LTD. CASTLE ENGINE WORKS, STAFFORD

W. G. BAGNALL LTD. CASTLE ENGINE WORKS, STAFFORD

Inside pages of a brochure issued in 1937 in connection with the Bagnall-Deutz diesel locomotives. The locomotives illustrated are top left number 2494, bottom left 2516, top right 2530. The remaining illustration is a Deutz two-cylinder type OMZ 125 55 horsepower engine and gearbox combination as delivered from Germany; this is a slightly smaller engine than alluded to in the brochure description.

system in order to extinguish any flames in case the water jets failed, and lastly the exhaust gasses passed through a mixer, where they were mixed with fresh air at a ratio of 1:20. Although perhaps sounding quite crude by today's standards, the design would appear to have been quite advanced technology at the time. The locomotive weighed 8½ tons in working order and cost £1,300. Unfortunately, nothing is known of its subsequent history, but spares were being despatched for it until January 1938.

This locomotive for the Coltness Iron Company was an early example of a diesel locomotive for use underground in a coal mine in this country, and before regulations were introduced by the Mines Department of the Government, to regulate the use of diesel locomotives in such circumstances. It was 1937 before tests were undertaken at the Mines Department's underground testing station at Buxton, to establish the standards for exhaust emissions from locomotives fitted

with diesel engines used underground in gaseous mines. Locomotives that met the standards imposed were granted what was called a 'Buxton Certificate'. The Hunslet Engine Company of Leeds, along with Ruston & Hornsby of Lincoln, were the first companies to design locomotives to meet the new standards and be granted certificates. The Bagnall-Deutz locomotive was built at a time when locomotive haulage by diesel locomotives underground was only just becoming a viable option anywhere in the world, as developments in cleaning engine exhaust systems were developed. This was a brave attempt by Bagnall, using the Deutz design, to break into the market in this country, but this locomotive was the only one of the type built.

Obviously the Company made great play in the trade press and in advertising material, by means of articles, adverts and leaflets, of its ability to build diesel locomotives and some extraordinary claims were made. For example one leaflet claimed that 15,000 Bagnall-

An example of one of the smaller locomotives built in the period covered by this Chapter. Manufacturer's number 2495 was one of four of these small two-foot gauge 0-4-0 side tanks with 7¼x12in cylinders, ordered by the Indian agents McLeod & Company (Calcutta) Limited, for use on the docks at Vizagpatnam (now spelt Visakhapatnam) which is on the east coast of India. Two were delivered at this time, July 1933, followed by a third in 1935 and a post-war one in 1953. This picture shows the first one as Port Trust No 1, busy shunting iron-ore skips ready for loading onto a ship on 9 January 1977; the little engine is sporting a rather gaudy livery - at the time all four of them were named after Walt Disney cartoon characters!

Deutz diesel locomotives had already been built, and in a *Railway Gazette* advert that first appeared in its issue dated 16 June 1933, there was a claim that 'Over 9,000 locomotives constructed'! Doubtless even Deutz had not made that many by this date! The selling agents were quoted as Porn & Dunwoody Limited, with an address of 72-78, Fleet Street London EC4, which was its office, as opposed to a workshop address. Although jumping ahead of the story somewhat, after the last war the Deutz franchise passed to a new company, British Deutz Limited; formed in September 1946 this Company was part of the Associated British Oil Engines Group that was headed by Alan P Good; we shall have much to say about this gentleman later in the book.

In September 1933 an order was received via one of the Company's Indian Agents, Greaves Cotton & Company of Bombay, for the design and construction of three metre-gauge 2-8-0 tender engines for use on the ghat (hill) section of the Udaipur Chitorgarh Railway. The design called for the locomotives to haul a 300 ton

trailing load up a 1 in 50 gradient, compensated for curvature. This railway, owned and operated by the Mewar Durbar, was situated in Rajputana, Western India, and eventually extended some 145 miles. The first section had opened as far back as 1895, it connected Chitorgarh on the Bombay Baroda & Central India (BBCIR) metre-gauge main line from Ajmer to Ratlam, with the old city of Udaipur. In the period 1930 to 1932 it was extended 65 miles due-north from Mavli Junction, which was 40 miles from Chitorgarh, to Khambli Ghat, on the high ground above the plains towards Jodhpur. In February 1936 a further 13¼ mile section was opened to Phulad; this line descended the ghats from Khambli Ghat at ruling grades of 1 in 50. Connection was made at Phulad with the metre-gauge Jodhpur Railway, and via this railway, connection was made with the BBCIR metre-gauge main line from Ajmer to Ahmedabad at Marwar Junction. It was for the ghat section that the Bagnall locomotives were specifically designed, hence the wheel

Another of the smaller locomotives, in this case one of the standard circular firebox saddle tank design. Number 2497 of 1933, together with an earlier sister, 2466 of the previous year, were for use on the four-foot gauge system of the Steetley Lime & Basic Company at the Whitehaven limestone quarries at Porthywaen near Oswestry. Notice the home made cab sides. An interesting point about these two locomotives is that they had a wheelbase six inches smaller than the track gauge - an unusual design feature. Picture taken on 2 July 1949; both engines were scrapped in 1953. (Late Ralph Russell - Frank Jones Collection Industrial Locomotive Society)

Udaipur to Phulad passenger train at Lawa Sardargarh on the Indian Udaipur Chitorgarh metre-gauge railway on 12 October 1940. The locomotive is Bagnall 2502 of 1934, one of five engines of this type built by the Company, and the only metre-gauge 2-8-0 tender engines in India. The requirement for eight-coupled wheels was in view of the gradients on the ghat section of the railway between Khambli Ghat and Phulad. (Kelland Collection - Bournemouth Railway Club)

arrangement, and the design was the only one of this wheel arrangement on the metre-gauge railways in India.

In the design Bagnall adopted similar principles to those of the previously described GBSR and Assam 4-6-0s, the boiler being mounted high enough to allow the firebox to sit on top of the frames and embody a large grate area, in this case 25.5 sq ft. The boiler centre line was 7ft 6in above rail level, and the barrel diameter 4ft 9in, a rocking drop grate was fitted together with a hopper ashpan and the working pressure was 180psi. Cylinders were 16¾ x 22in, piston valves eight inch diameter with a full gear travel of 4 $^{27}/_{32}$in, and the maximum cut-off was set at 75%. The driving wheel diameter was 3ft 7in and the weight in working order of the engine 44.35 tons; complete with the tender which carried 4½ tons of coal and 2,500 gallons of water, the all-up weight was 71.1 tons and the maximum axle-load was 9.6 tons. The engine springing was part compensated in two separate groups; the leading truck was compensated with the two leading pairs of coupled wheels, whilst the two trailing pairs of coupled wheels were compensated between themselves. Manufacturer's numbers were 2500 to 2502 and the selling price £4,542 each, which resulted in a total loss on the contract of £1,014. Delivery was carriage, insurance and freight (CIF) paid to Bombay, dismantled in parts via Birkenhead Docks for shipment in February 1934. These locomotives were another handsome and well thought out design, and another example of Bagnall designing and building locomotives that were either variations on the IRS designs, or as in this case specialist ones. Worth a special note is the fact that the railway company did not appoint any consulting

A much later view of one of the Udaipur 2-8-0s; this is the same locomotive as in the previous photograph seen here outside Khambli Ghat shed on 23 January 1977; it was being serviced ready for its next turn of duty. Notice the ladder against the tender used for loading coal by hand. Forty three years since they were built, in 1977 the engines were still at work over the ghat sections, albeit by this time only on goods and mineral trains.

engineers to oversee either the design or building of these locomotives; being a relatively small railway it would appear to have been content to rely on the builder.

There was a repeat order from the Udaipur Chitorgarh Railway in March 1936, again via Greaves Cotton, for two identical locomotives, numbers 2548 and 2549 being allocated, and despatch was in December 1936, on this occasion to Alexandra Dock Liverpool. In the case of these two the selling price was £4,302 each CIF, again indicating how competitive the business was at this time. That the locomotives were successful in their intended use on the steep ghat section is evidenced by the fact that they continued to be employed there until the late 1970s. Eventually displaced by the ubiquitous post-war Indian standard YG class 2-8-2s, although initially only on the passenger trains, this was in any event for but a few years before

the diesels took over. In 1977 when one of the authors visited this part of India, all five were still allocated to Khambli Ghat Shed and still working freight traffic over the ghat section to Phulad.

In January 1934 the Company received an order from the Bhavnagar State Railway in India, for two large 0-8-0 metre-gauge tank engines, another unusual wheel arrangement for the metre-gauge in that country. Like the tender engines just described these too, had a boiler mounted high to allow a large firebox to sit on top of the frames, in this case with a grate area of 15½ sq ft. Although not superheated the engines had piston valves for the 14½x20in cylinders along with drop grates, hopper ashpans and arch-tubes which gave an extra 7¼ sq ft of boiler heating surface. The weight in working order was 34 tons, the maximum axle-load was 8½ tons and the tractive effort at 85% of the 180psi working pressure equalled 16,496lb. Inspection was by

Robert White & Partners, the manufacturer's numbers 2509 and 2510, and delivery to Birkenhead Docks in June 1934. Intended for shunting around the docks at Bhavnagar on the Gulf of Cambay in Gujarat, some years later the side tanks were removed and mounted on bogie wagons that were semi-permanently attached. This had the effect of reducing the axle-load and allowed them to work on some very light track around the docks; both locomotives remained in use until the early 1970s and were still at Bhavnagar when one of the authors visited in January 1977, although by that time no longer in use.

The principle of mounting the boiler on top of the frames on metre-gauge locomotives to allow the designer to provide a larger firebox and grate area, was not confined to completely new designs. When the Indian Junagadh State Railway ordered three 4-6-0 tender engines in July 1934, ostensibly to an earlier design based on the British Engineering Standards range, a boiler of this type was fitted. Some limited redesign was necessary, including a cast iron smokebox support saddle combined with the frame stay, and a circular drumhead-type smokebox. Despite this, the engines retained slide valve cylinders and were not superheated, but firebox arch-tubes were fitted to give an extra nine sq ft of heating surface, and on one of the locomotives the firebox material was steel, as opposed to the more usual copper. Other advantages of the wide firebox with parallel sides was the ability to put the inner box in to the boiler from the bottom, and after the back plate had been riveted in place - a particular advantage when repairs necessitated removing the inner box - and of course all the stays were accessible without having to lift the boiler clear of the frames. Cylinder dimensions were 14½x22in, driving wheel diameter was four-foot and the weight in working order of the engine and tender 60 tons 10 cwt. The manufacturer's numbers were 2518 to 2520, Junagadh State Railway numbers 19 to 21, and inspection by the London based consulting engineers Robert White & Partners. Despatch from Stafford was in January and February 1934 to Alexander Dock in Liverpool for shipment to Veraval, which is on the southern tip of Gujarat and actually served by the Junagadh State Railway. This railway eventually consisted of some 230 metre-gauge route miles radiating from the town of Junagadh. These neat and handsome engines

eventually became Indian Railways class P2 numbers 31167 to 31169 in the all-India renumbering scheme, and survived until the mid 1970s.

Mention should be made at this point of a proposed double-bogie locomotive ordered by the LNER from the Sentinel Waggon Works at Shrewsbury, as Bagnall were involved. The railway company had been having some success in reducing costs of shunting by using small Sentinel shunting locomotives, and of operating branch lines by Sentinel-Cammell railcars. All these Sentinel rail-vehicles were powered by high-speed enclosed steam engines with geared drive and water tube boilers, either vertical or horizontal three-drum type designs. The Sentinel Company had considerable commercial success after the war with its design of locomotives and railcars, with the Nottingham factory of the Metro-Cammell Company building the coach portion of the passenger vehicles. Based on the principles of its long established and very well known steam road vehicles, the new rail designs were finding their way to railways all over the world. Following the success of its designs this innovative firm was busy developing more sophisticated locomotives with enclosed engines of a new design driving directly onto the wheels, rather than via a chain or shaft transmission system as hitherto. In 1933 three quite big metre-gauge locomotives were built on this principle with twin six-wheel bogies and a Woolnough three-drum water tube boiler. There were six engine units, two cylinder compounds, with one mounted on each axle in the style of axle-hung traction motors on diesel-electric and electric locomotives. The new locomotives were for the Societe Nationale de Chemins de Fer Colombe (Colombian Railways), but prior to delivery one of them was taken over to Belgium to be tested and put through its paces, partly as a publicity exercise, on the metre-gauge lines of the local provincial railways - the Vicinal (SNCV). During the course of these trials any number of distinguished guests were invited to observe the locomotive in operation, including officials from the LNER, and Nigel Gresley, the chief mechanical engineer of that railway attended in person. Following this demonstration the idea would appear to have germinated for a somewhat smaller machine on the same principles for the LNER. It was thought that such a locomotive might be both more suitable and offer economies on branch lines where the passenger loadings were too high for the railcars, whilst on the other hand uneconomical when a conventional locomotives and coaches were employed.

To meet the specification Sentinel designed a locomotive with four-wheel as opposed to six-wheel bogies and four engines - two on each bogie - developing a total of 600 horsepower. The Woolnough three-drum water tube boiler it was planned to use would have had a working pressure of 375psi. A contract for the mechanical parts, and it would appear from surviving records final erection, was placed with Bagnall in November 1934, when manufacturer's number 2521 was allocated. A significant amount of design work was completed at both Shrewsbury and Stafford, with the Castle Engine Works drawings dated between 14 November 1934 and 22 February the following year. Unlike the Colombian locomotives which had compound engines with cylinder diameters of 7¼in and 4¼in with a 6in stroke, on the LNER locomotive the engines were two-cylinder simples with a 6in diameter and stroke. In the event, the exact reasons we know not, nothing physical seems to have been done, at least at Stafford, although some material does appear to have been ordered, before the job was cancelled. Neither do we know why Sentinel wanted to sub-contract the mechanical parts, as it appears with the exception of the boilers the Colombian locomotives were built in their entirety at the Shrewsbury works. There is a suggestion that the Colombian locomotives were not the success the maker envisaged, and conscious of its reputation suggested to Gresley that it might be better if the proposed locomotive was not proceeded with. As mentioned above the LNER was having a lot of success with the Sentinel designed railcars and locomotives, in both cases providing economy over conventional types, and the maker would not want its reputation tarnished. In one of the surviving order books the following note appears: 'Not proceeded with due to unfortunate conditions of trading', whatever can be inferred from that.

During the 1930s the Company managed to get a stronger foothold in the relatively lucrative market for standard-gauge locomotives for industrial service in this country. However, as we have already seen, the firm had its fingers burnt a little in an attempt to make inroads in that trade in connection with the four locomotives laid down to stock in November 1923. In 1931 one of the senior draughtsmen, Reg Machin, was given the job of updating the four-wheel 12in cylinder standard-gauge shunting locomotive while at the same time reducing the cost of construction. In the redesign a lot of effort was put into simplifying the manufacturing processes, in particular the cab and bunkers, by reducing the amount of riveting needed, and secondly in the number and complexity of castings required; making them easier and less labour intensive for both the patternmaker and moulder. Apart from the cylinders just about every major component was redesigned. The boiler was of a completely new design too, smaller than the earlier version but due to improved design principles was estimated to have the same steam raising capacity, and a circular drum-head smokebox replaced the wrapper type. The overall height of the locomotive was reduced, but the overall weight went up by a ton. Two locomotives to this modified design were soon ordered, both in 1931, manufacturer's numbers 2450 and 2451. The cylinder dimensions were 12x18in, the wheel diameter was 3ft 0½in and the wheelbase was 5ft 6in; weight in working order with 550 gallons of water and 18.5 cub ft of fuel was 22 tons, and the tractive effort at 85% of the 160 psi working pressure 9,600lb. The first one went to the Horseley Bridge & Engineering Company Limited at Great Bridge near Tipton, and the second to a local firm of porcelain manufacturers at nearby Stone - Taylor Tunnicliffe & Company Limited. Very keen prices were quoted to get these orders: the Horseley Bridge locomotive, which was named JT DALY, was sold for £1,185, and the Taylor Tunnicliffe one for a little less at £1,125 - the latter deal included taking an old locomotive in part exchange; despatch dates were 20 April and 18 August respectively and a loss of £447 was recorded against the two orders. With but minor alterations this design remained in production almost until the end of steam locomotive production, 17 more being built including one for use on metre-gauge in Africa, and another for use on 5ft 6in gauge in Ceylon. Some of them had a slightly larger cylinder diameter, either 12½in or 13in. JT DALY is still in existence and can be found at the Pallot Heritage Museum on the island of Jersey, but the second engine was scrapped in October 1963.

Other customers for standard-gauge shunting locomotives in the period covered by this Chapter included Glascote Colliery at Tamworth, which had a

This is the first example of a design of 15in cylinder six-coupled saddle tank for industrial shunting, a type which became particularly popular during the war-years in the ironstone mining industry. This one, number 2508, was despatched in April 1934 to the Glascote Colliery Company for use at its Amington colliery near Tamworth - it lasted until 1964. Picture taken outside the Erecting Shop.

quite large 15in cylinder 0-6-0 saddle tank in April 1934, number 2508, a design which with minor alterations over the years became a standard. Customers included the Butterley Company for use at collieries in Derbyshire and Nottinghamshire, and during the war the Ministry of Supply were instrumental in ordering several for use in the ironstone quarrying industry resulting from the war-time emphasis on increased home mined iron ore. The Cransley Iron & Steel Company from Northamptonshire had a 14in cylinder 0-4-0 saddle tank in October 1934, number 2517, and a similar engine went to Metropolitan Vickers Limited for its factory at Trafford Park in April 1938, number 2591. As well as these The British (GKN) Iron & Steel Company Limited had a much larger four-wheel saddle tank for its Margam Works in South Wales. Designed to handle heavy loads in and around the blast furnaces, the locomotive was to all intents and purposes a four-wheel version of TOPHAM, number 2193 mentioned in Chapter Seven. Cylinders were the same size at 17x24in, as were the wheels at 3ft 9in diameter; the weight in working order was 43 tons, giving a maximum axle-load of 21 tons 16

cwt. With the name KENFIG, number 2515, it was despatched on 24 August 1934. There was a repeat order for Margam in May 1940, three locomotives numbers 2630 to 2632, despatched between December 1940 and March 1941, followed by one more, number 2768 of April 1944. These four differed from KENFIG in having inside Stephenson's link motion rather than outside Walschaerts valve gear - apparently Walschaerts gear had been problematic with all the various external obstructions laying around a steel works which the return arm was apt to strike. In this re-design to retain the same cylinder arrangement, and for the wheel-sets to be interchangeable with the earlier engine, the valves were operated by rocking shafts from the inside motion and the crankpins on the driving axles had squared ends, with the rods retained by what were in effect foreshortened return arms. By this means the conventional return arm of Walschaerts valve gear could be fitted if the wheel-sets were used under KENFIG, and spare wheel-sets could all be of the same design. To give an idea of price escalation, KENFIG was sold for £1,850, the 1940 trio at £3,650 each, and the 1944 one at £5,430. All these locomotives remained in

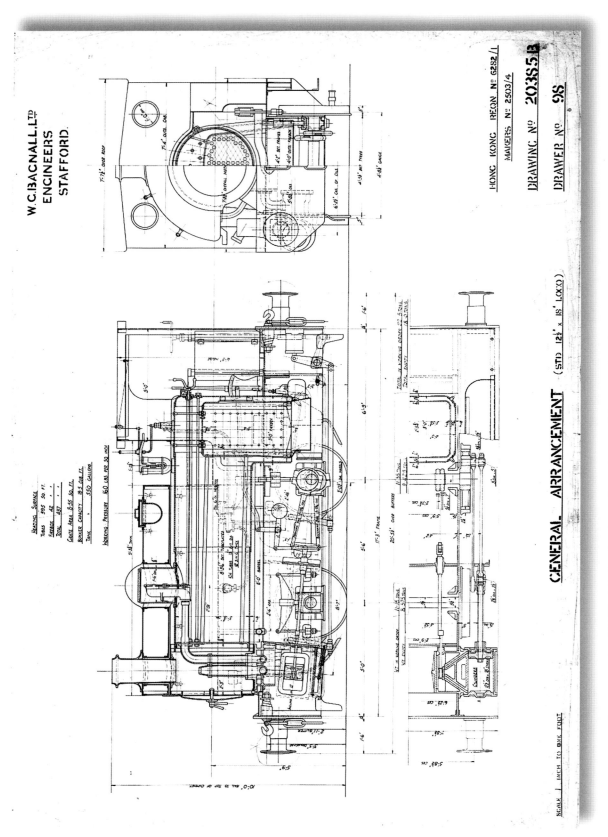

General arrangement drawing number 20385 of 11 October 1933, drawn by one of the senior draughtsmen Cyril Poulson, illustrating the redesign of the 12in cylinder four-coupled industrial saddle tank shunting locomotive as described in the text. However, in the case of the locomotives this drawing applies to, the cylinders were slightly enlarged to 12½in. Numbers 2503 and 2504 were ordered by the Crown Agents for use in Hong Kong on the construction works of the Shing Mun Valley reservoir and associated water works; despatch was in December 1933. After the reservoir works were complete the engines passed to the Kowloon Canton Railway (British Section), where they were used for shunting and lasted until about 1949.

use at Margam until displaced by diesels in 1957, and the diesels also came from Stafford, as we shall see later in our story.

Another interesting standard-gauge locomotive was one specially designed to be used for instructional purposes by the War Department, at the Royal Engineers training establishment at Longmoor Camp in Hampshire. Manufacturer's number 2587 was an 0-6-2 side tank with 18x24in cylinders, 4ft 3in diameter driving wheels, a weight in working order of 58½ tons and a tractive effort at 85% of the 180psi working pressure equal to 23,325lb. In view of its intended use for instructional purposes fitted bolts were used in most applications rather than rivets, which would have been normal practice, so that the locomotive could be easily dismantled and re-erected. Also for instructional purposes it was fitted with all number of items of specialist equipment, including both air and vacuum brakes, electric lighting, Lambert wet sanding, LMS-pattern continuous boiler blow-down, hopper ashpan and a GWR style jumper blast pipe top. Walschaerts valve gear and piston valves were employed and the boiler had a copper firebox and steel tubes; the selling

price was £4,432. Appropriately named KITCHENER - the name plates were supplied by the WD, suggesting that they came from an earlier locomotive of the same name - and painted in 'War Office Green' with black and white lining, it was despatched to Longmoor on 30 April 1938. This was a very handsome locomotive with a varied history. After the war, displaced by the numerous locomotives specially built for war-time use and available in large numbers, it was sold in 1948 to the Appleby Frodingham Steel Company Limited for use at the Frodingham Iron & Steel Works. Being a non-standard type at the steel works, once other locomotives were available, by 1950 it was in the hands of the well-known Sheffield based machinery dealer Thomas W Ward Limited, and sold in the same year to the National Coal Board for use in South Wales at Garw Colliery in the Maesteg area. Later it worked at one or two other collieries around Measteg until falling out of use at Duffryn Rhondda Colliery, where it was scrapped in May 1967. Not surprising perhaps, this rather special locomotive was not completely successful in everyday industrial operation, with most of its special fittings soon falling out of use. Before we leave this locomotive

KITCHENER, number 2587 of 1938, outside the Erecting Shop posed for its official photographs and prior to despatch to the Longmoor Military Railway on 30 April 1938. Notice the vacuum and air brake fittings as well as electric lighting and not least the superb external condition, a requirement of the order as the engine was intended for instructional purposes. The nameplates, not of Bagnall design, were supplied by the WD having previously been carried by an earlier engine of the same name

an interesting story is worth recalling. When the time came for it to be moved out of the erecting shop for testing, as it was not designed with a view to operating over the main-line railway system in this country, its external dimensions were not constrained to the somewhat restricted British main-line loading gauge. The erecting shop doorway however, was only big enough to suit the main line loading gauge and KITCHENER would not fit through the gap. So there had to be some hasty alterations!

The Mysore State Railway in the south-west of India has already been mentioned in an earlier Chapter. The Railway was the property of the Government of His Highness the Maharaja of Mysore, and over the years operated a number of Bagnall locomotives. The system was a relatively small one, largely metre-gauge but with several sections of 2ft 6in gauge, along with a very short two-foot gauge line. The metre-gauge system which eventually consisted of a little over 609 route miles was roughly centred on Arsikere, 103 miles due-north of Mysore, and the system also served the City of Bangalore, 58 miles to the north-east of Mysore. The last sections opened as late as 1938, although the system was largely complete four years earlier. The railway is especially interesting because as well as operating several of the BESA and IRS designs, it had some specially designed tank engines for suburban passenger services around Mysore and Bangalore. Eight in number, whilst all of the 2-6-2 wheel arrangement the last two differed in having a larger water capacity with the side tanks extended alongside the smokebox - 1,000 gallons as opposed to 850. Cylinder dimensions were 11½x18in, wheel diameter 3ft 7in; the weight in working order 34¼ tons for the earlier engines and a little over 35½ tons for the pair with the bigger water tanks. These locomotives were of a modern design and although not an IRS standard, embodied similar design characteristics including superheaters and piston valve cylinders, Sunbeam electric lighting, Lambert wet sanding and in the case of the last two, grease lubricated axle-boxes. RP&T were the consulting engineers, and the first two locomotives were despatched in March 1932, numbers 2464 and 2465, the second batch of four in March the following year, numbers 2481 to 2484, and the final two, numbers 2525 and 2526, in May 1935; the earlier engines were classified TS and the last two TS/1.

To illustrate how orders for locomotives were obtained and the time scales involved, the last of these Mysore engines represent a typical example. The invitation to tender was published in the *Railway Gazette* - issue dated 1 June 1934 - by the Stores Purchasing Committee of the Government of India, and the tender documents were obtainable through the consulting engineers, with completed tenders due on or before 6 August. Bagnall would have responded to this notice and doubtless there would have been discussions with the consulting engineers in the period before the tender was submitted. Doubtless too, further discussions would have taken place after submitting the tender, clarifying various issues, as there would also have been with other companies tendering. Bagnall had an advantage in the case of this order, having built the earlier engines; putting together the tender submission would have been quite a straightforward process. The contract was let on 22 November 1934, indicating perhaps, some lengthy and complicated discussions between the consulting engineers, the Purchasing Committee, and those companies submitting tenders. Sydney Edwards would have been a busy man.

The influence of FHB Harris became particularly apparent in 1935, when a locomotive was built exactly to the well established Kerr, Stuart Moss Bay design. The Moss Bay type was an 0-4-0 industrial saddle tank with 15x20in cylinders and 3ft 6in diameter wheels, first introduced early in the century and taking its name from the Moss Bay Iron & Steel works in Cumberland where the first examples worked. Locomotives of this type with small modifications over the years, had been a standard product of Kerr, Stuart for industrial locomotives of this size. Often laid down to stock orders, a number of them were still on hand when Kerr, Stuart closed, eventually being sold by Hunslet. Nevertheless, it has to be said that by the time Bagnall built a locomotive of the design, it was becoming somewhat outdated in a number of its design characteristics - use of Ramsbottom safety valves for example. Bagnall built a locomotive of this design, manufacturer's number 2537, 5ft 6in gauge ordered by Killick Nixon & Company Limited, long-time customers of Kerr, Stuart, agents acting for Indian companies and well know to Harris. The locomotive was despatched on 20 December 1935 via the Royal Albert Docks in London for the Punjab Portland

Bagnall 2537 of 1935 was a fragrant copy of a Kerr, Stuart design, known as the Moss Bay and described in detail in the adjoining text. As if to add insult to injury, so far as the Hunslet Engine Company of Leeds were concerned, as that company had acquired the Kerr, Stuart good-will, WS Edwards had the locomotive painted as shown here and this picture was widely used for publicity purposes!

Cement Limited, for use at its factory at Wah, between Rawalpindi and Campbellpore in what is now Pakistan. Although the customer requested the locomotive be named RICHARD, prior to despatch Edwards had it painted with the name MOSS BAY on the saddle tank, exactly in the style Kerr, Stuart used. Photographed in this guise the illustration was subsequently used in publicity material and it has to be added that the Hunslet Engine Company were not amused. One more Moss Bay was built at Stafford, number 2597 of March 1939, also 5ft 6in gauge and for use in India, in this case by the Indian Army for its Jubbulpore Gun Cotton factory - delivery was via Liverpool and Bombay. There was a view within the industry that Edwards was 'sailing very close to the wind'!

At about the same time that Killick Nixon ordered RICHARD, a 5ft 6in gauge fireless locomotives was ordered for the same cement factory. This engine was one of the larger design of fireless locomotive, an 0-6-0 with 20x18in cylinders and a reservoir pressure of 200psi, although it was specified that the reservoir should be designed to suit a pressure of 250psi. Named PETER, an interesting requirement of the specification

was that the locomotive should be both as powerful as a Moss Bay, and embody as many similar components as possible. Perhaps somewhat bizarrely, there was also a requirement for it to be designed so that it could be easily fitted at a later date with Moss Bay design cylinders, motion and a boiler, to convert it to a conventional locomotive! Despite this requirement the locomotive was built to the standard Bagnall six-wheel fireless design of the period. In terms of power compatibility, and taking tractive effort as a yardstick, the Moss Bay at 85% of the 160psi working pressure gave a figure of 14,500lb, and the fireless at 85% of the 80psi setting of the reducing valve, 15,645lb. In terms of theoretical power output therefore, the two locomotives were roughly compatible

More of the Harris influence was evident in a new design of 15in cylinder 0-4-0, in fact an updating of the Moss Bay, with 3ft 6½in diameter wheels and a full length saddle tank. Bagnall did not have a 15in cylinder four-wheel industrial locomotive in its standard product range, and this was an obvious attempt to both plug the gap as well as bringing the Moss Bay design up to date. The first one was manufacturer's number 2590 of December 1937, new to the South Wales Coalite Company Limited, for use at Wern Tarw Colliery at the foot of the Rhondda Valley. The design was a great improvement on the Moss Bay, with a 920 gallon water-tank capacity, a drum-type smokebox mounted on a cast saddle, and a boiler pressed to 180psi, which gave a tractive effort at 85% equal to 17,800lb. A number of engines to this design were built over the next few years, and the design retained an unmistakable, and typical Kerr, Stuart design of cab. To reduce the overall height later members of the class had a lower cab roof and a cheeky little stovepipe-type chimney. Examples went to the Royal Arsenal at Woolwich, number 2606 of May 1939, the Butterley Company for use at its collieries in Derbyshire and Nottinghamshire, numbers 2607 of May 1939, 2619 of September 1939 and 2622 of October 1940, ICI Limited at Heysham, number 2620 of September 1940, and finally one for the Shelton Iron & Steel Works at Stoke-on-Trent. The last one, number 2623 of November 1940, named HAWARDEN, survives in preservation on the Foxfield Light Railway which is just south of Stoke-on-Trent, and of course, not too far from where it spent its working life. The authors, acting together, were responsible for saving this engine from the furnaces at Shelton when it finished work in 1972.

One other standard-gauge design, although not for use in this country, is worth a mention here. In March 1937 the Company was successful in its tender to supply two locomotives to the order of Braithwaite & Company (Engineers) Limited. This firm of constructional and civil engineers had been awarded the contract to build, on behalf of the Turkish Government, an integrated iron and steel works at Karabuk. Karabuk is roughly in the central-northern part of the country and about 60 miles south of the Black Sea port of Zonguldak. The order was for two large 18x24in cylinder 0-8-0 side tank engines with 3ft 9in diameter wheels and a weight in working order of 57 tons. The large water tanks held 1,500 gallons of water and the cylinders had slide valves driven by Walschaerts valve gear; tractive effort at 85% of the 180psi working pressure equalled 26,432lb. Manufacturer's numbers were 2578 and 2579 and the selling price £3,320 each; despatch was in September and October 1937. These were the largest standard-gauge locomotives the Company built, and were still in use at Karabuk until about the year 2000. There were some not dissimilar locomotives built about the same time, but somewhat smaller and for 3ft 6in gauge, for use at various mining operations in the Transvaal province of South Africa. The supply of large side tank engines for the South African gold mining industry had for many years previously been almost the sole preserve of the North British Locomotive Company of Glasgow, along with its earlier constituents. However, Bagnall was able to penetrate the market with a very modern looking 16x24in cylinder 0-8-0 with 3ft 3in diameter

Second of the two large 18in cylinder eight-coupled side tanks built in 1937 for the Karabuk iron and steel works in Turkey, numbers 2578 and 2579. At the time these were the largest standard-gauge locomotives the firm had built.

wheels and a 180psi working pressure which gave a tractive effort at 85% equal to 24,200lb. Two were built in 1935 for Springs Mines Limited, numbers 2534 and 2535, and later the design was elongated into a 4-8-2, of which five were built between 1937 and 1939. The firm had recently appointed an agent in South Africa, Baldwins (South Africa) Limited which was responsible for all these orders. The 4-8-2 version had a weight in working order of 58 tons compared to 41 tons for the 0-8-0, but in view of a bigger capacity boiler and larger water and fuel capacities, 1,500 vice 800 gallons and 3½ tons vice a little over one ton, the axle-load remained the same at just over 10 tons. Designed to work on 60lb per yard rail the larger engines were intended for line work as opposed to shunting, and the respective selling prices were £3,895 and £4,925, in all cases carriage insurance and freight paid.

Another agent operating in South Africa was A&H MacNay Limited of Durban, also acting as consulting engineers, specialising in the sugar industry in Natal. Arthur MacNay was an interesting character, born at Shildon on 29 November 1865, he attended King James 1st grammar school in Bishops Auckland and afterwards Darlington technical college, where he took the South Kensington science and art examinations. MacNay served his apprenticeship between 1882 and 1888, initially with the Darlington Wagon & Engineering Company, but later with the North Eastern Railway at its Darlington Works, completing his training in the

drawing office. In July 1888 he joined Blair & Company, marine engineers, and spent much of the next 15 months at sea. In February 1890 he emigrated to South Africa and entered the locomotive carriage & wagon department of the Cape Government Railways at Salt River, moving to the drawing office three months later. In January 1898 MacNay became district locomotive superintendent at Salt River, and in June 1890 was promoted to the position of district locomotive superintendent at De Aar in the Cape, roughly mid-way between Cape Town to Kimberley. After a succession of further promotions, he retired as acting chief mechanical engineer of the South African Railways in 1925. On retirement he commenced business with his son Harold, trading as A& H MacNay Limited, with an engineering workshop in Durban, and the company acted as agents and consulting engineers for a number of manufacturers as well as the sugar industry. Arthur MacNay was elected a member of the I Mech E in February 1902, and he passed away on 16 October 1946, his son unfortunately having predeceased him. Remaining actively involved in the business as governing director almost until the time of his death, the company he helped to form continued to trade and we will come across it again later in our story.

In view of the distances covered by some of the light railways connecting the sugar factories and cane fields in Natal, and the loads that had to be hauled over indifferent track, articulated locomotives were

Somewhat smaller than the Turkish engines, but otherwise similar, an 0-8-0 design was developed for the South African mining industry and two were built in 1935. This is the second, number 2535, 3ft 6in gauge with 16in diameter cylinders. Notice the vacuum brake equipment and electric lighting.

This is one of the large 3ft 6in gauge 4-8-2 tanks, also built for use in the South African mining industry, and developed from the 0-8-0 design in the previous illustration. Photograph taken in 1968, number 2583 of 1938 as East Daggafontein Mines No 1 illustrates well the long and rather ungainly lines of this design. Notice the steep inclination of the cylinder in view of the bogie, long connecting rod and small driving wheel diameter - only 3ft 3in.

becoming popular with several of the estates. Before its demise the Avonside Engine Company of Bristol had some success in this direction, and Bagnall decided to have a go too. Once again Ivor Farr was involved with the design work and a double-bogie articulated locomotive on the Meyer principle was decided on. The two bogies had outside frames and were arranged with the cylinders at the inward ends, this served to keep the total wheelbase as short as possible, help towards equal weight distribution and enable the steam and exhaust pipes for the trailing bogie to be as short as possible. The closely spaced bogies and the need to keep the centre of gravity as low as possible in view of the narrow track gauge, while at the same time providing a large enough firebox, prohibited the use of a conventional boiler. There was no room for the firebox to sit partly below the frames, and for it to sit on top of the frames the centre of gravity would be unacceptable. In view of these restrictions a Bullhead circular firebox boiler was employed, the first time boilers of this type were fitted with superheaters, and as events turned out the boilers of these locomotives became the achilles heal of the design. Piston valve cylinders were used with Walschaerts valve gear, cut off and reversing being under a single control for both engines.

Avonside had overcome some of the problems of an articulated locomotive - in particular, how to retain a sufficiently large firebox - by using a V form enclosed high-speed engine on the lines of the American Heisler design. The engine was mounted transversally across the frames, beneath the boiler, in the middle of the locomotive and between the cab and front side tanks. The drive was through cardan shafts to worm drive gearboxes on the bogie inner axles, and then by conventional side rods. In the case of the Bagnall design the main-frame consisted of a series of rolled steel joists (RSJs) riveted together and embracing the bogie pivots. The bogies had of necessity flexible steam and exhaust connections to the main frames, and these were of the Flextel patent design manufactured in Stafford by WH Dorman & Company Limited. This Company had at the time the sole manufacturing rights for the Flextel patent system, and we shall explore later how at one period manufacture took place at the Castle Engine Works.

Initially two locomotives of the articulated design were built, both for two-foot gauge and one bigger than the other. The first, manufacturer's number 2544 had 7¼x12in cylinders and two-foot diameter wheels; it was despatched on 2 September 1936 to the Illovo Sugar Estate in Natal. The boiler had a total heating surface of 402 sq ft, of which the eight superheater elements contributed 60 sq ft; the working pressure was 180psi and the grate area nine sq ft. Tractive effort at 85% equalled 8,600lb, and the weight in working order was 17 tons eight cwt. The second and larger locomotive, which became the prototype for five more built later, had 9x12in cylinders and the same size wheel diameter, but the boiler was larger, with a total heating surface of 501 sq ft, the superheater contributing 70 sq ft and the grate area was 11½ sq ft. Tractive effort at 85% of the 180 psi boiler pressure equalled 12,400lb, and the weight in working order 28 tons - a much more powerful locomotive. With the name and number RENISHAW No 5, manufacturer's number 2545, the completed locomotive was despatched on 21 May 1936, to the order of Crookes Brothers Limited for use on its Renishaw Sugar Estate in Natal. Both these locomotives were ordered via MacNay's, and the smaller one was fitted with the vacuum brake for train operation. The purchase price in the case of the smaller locomotive was £2,235, and for the larger one £2,350, in both cases CIF to Durban. To give an indication of shipping and insurance costs at the time the locomotives were built, for the larger one Bagnall was also asked to quote a price free on board at Liverpool Docks, and this was £2,100, a difference of £250. Whilst the design was by no means an unqualified success, a further four locomotives of the same basic design were built for use in the Natal sugar industry, the

last ones as late as 1953, together with one for use in this country. The subsequent history of all these locomotives will be covered in a later Chapter, but it is worth mentioning at this point that RENISHAW No 5 returned to this country in August 1969; purchased privately, it is currently in store awaiting restoration.

We must now describe what was perhaps the most spectacular achievement of the company to date; the design and construction of two of what were at the time among the largest rigid-framed metre-gauge locomotives ever built. The order was received on 29 January 1935 from the Parana Plantations Limited, the engines for use on the Sao Paulo-Parana Railway, a lengthy metre-gauge undertaking owned and operated by the plantation company some 218 miles north-east of Santos in Brazil.

The railway dated from 1925, running westwards from Ourinhos (itself on the Sorocabana Railway) to serve the Parana plantations, and from 1928 it was gradually extended from the original 18¾ miles for a further 100 miles. This westwards extension towards the River Parana was to serve coffee plantations east of the River Tibagy, although it never did get as far as the Parana River which was the border with Paraguay. It did, however, get as far as Cianorte, making the line some 118 miles in length, along with a branch of 31¼ miles south from Apucarana to Ponta Grossa, where

Second of the articulated locomotives for the Natal sugar estate lines was this one, number 2545 of 1936, for the Renishaw estate of Crookes Brothers Limited. This, the larger of the two designs, was the basis of five more built after the war. Points to note are the piston valve cylinders positioned at the inner ends of both bogies, steam and exhaust pipes between the tank and the framing, along with the circular firebox boiler which facilitated close spacing of the bogies and a low centre of gravity.

This is the sole example of the smaller of the articulated designs, number 2544 of 1936, for the Illovo Sugar estate in Natal. Picture taken in 1945 showing the locomotive at work and apart from some general knocking about, in pretty much as-built condition. Despatched on 4 September 1936, the locomotive was shipped to Durban from Alexandra Dock at Liverpool aboard the Clan Line steamer SS CLAN McKENZIE - carriage, insurance and freight paid. It was scrapped in about 1954.

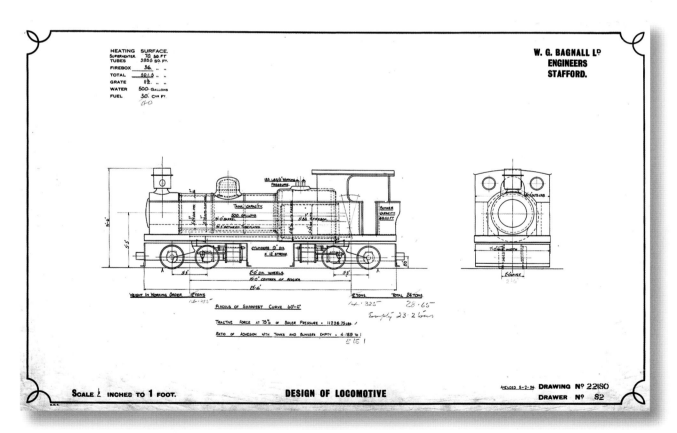

Outline drawing of a proposal for the larger design of articulated locomotive with 9x12in cylinders. Drawing number 22180 dated 3 December 1935, it differs little from the first locomotive as actually built.

View looking south in the Erecting Shop with the frames of one of the San Paulo locomotives in the foreground. This illustrates well the arrangement of extending the frames to accommodate the wide firebox boiler and trailing truck. Notice the extension piece cantilevered out from the forward section of frame helping to support the rearward frame extension. Behind can be seen a tender frame for the same locomotive and beyond that a fireless locomotive in advanced stage of construction - this is number 2536, a 5ft 6in gauge 0-6-0 for the Punjab Portland Cement Company. Fitting Shop to left.

connection was again made with the Sorocabana system. This was the last metre-gauge main line railway to be constructed in Brazil, and to work the extended system larger locomotives were required, as hitherto a series of Hunslet built 4-6-0 tender engines were the largest available. To meet the need Bagnall designed a truly magnificent 2-8-2 tender engine to the latest design standards with a number of interesting features. The design specification, drawn-up under the direction of the appointed consulting engineer Clement G Hodgson (one time locomotive superintendent, and later chief mechanical engineer of the Sudan Government Railway), called for the locomotives to haul 500 tons at 15mph on gradients of 1 in 55 with curves of 16 chains radius; the weight of the rail was 60lb per yard.

The cylinders were 19x24in, the biggest Bagnall had made to date, and the driving wheel diameter was four-foot. The total length of the locomotive and tender was 56ft 2½in over the frame plates, and the total weight in working order no less then 95 tons eight cwt. The superheated round-top firebox boiler had a total heating surface of 1,766 sq ft, the grate area was 32.33 sq ft and the 180psi working pressure gave a tractive effort of no less than 27,616lb. The engines had one inch thick frame plates stayed by steel castings, but because of the maximum size of frame plate that could be cut, slotted and drilled at the Castle Engine Works, there was an ingenious arrangement at the trailing end. The main frames themselves were terminated behind the trailing coupled axle, and riveted extension frames extended to the rear buffer beam. To ensure sufficient strength bearing in mind these extensions had to encompass the drag box, and therefore take the total trailing loads, a second and parallel set of extension frames were cantilevered out from the main-frames, and they too extended to the buffer beam to form in effect a double frame arrangement.

Years after the event the late Vic Betteley recalled to the authors how he had watched one of the most experienced of the Bagnall boilersmiths, Charlie Burghall, bending - or more correctly setting - these extension frame plates prior to fitting on the engine. As a young apprentice at the time he particularly remembered the skill involved in getting the 'set' just right, and at the first attempt (Charlie by the way, who died in 1958 was still employed by the firm at the time of his death; latterly the boiler shop foreman, Vic recalled Charlie as a great loss to the Company, a first class craftsman and an excellent foreman. He was also a first class shot in his hobby of rifle shooting). These extension frames, which also took the weight of the

What a magnificent beast! Second of the two metre-gauge 2-8-2 tender engines, numbers 2528 and 2529, for the San Paulo Parana Railway in Brazil. Notice the lovely finish complete with copper capped chimney. The gentleman standing alongside is Fred Ewington, the Erecting Shop Foreman.

Another view of the second of the San Paulo locomotives, in this case taken at the north end of the works yard. Points to note include the Worthington-Simpson boiler feed pump on the framing, electric lighting generator and bell. The two hand-operated valves alongside the smokebox are in connection with the patent superheater by-pass arrangement described in the adjoining text.

firebox were 1½in thick, and in principle this design characteristic was not unlike the method used by WA Stanier, chief mechanical engineer of the LMS, for the pacific locomotives he designed and introduced a few years earlier. The 21 element MeLeSco superheater was fitted with an arrangement whereby the elements could be bypassed in the event of an element failure, and steam supplied direct from the boiler to the cylinders. This was a Bagnall design patented in the names of WG Bagnall Limited and WS Edwards as managing director. Patent No 422,630 was accepted on 16 January 1935: *Improvement in and relating to Superheater Steam Headers for Locomotives and similar Vehicles.* Referred to as The Edwards-Type Superheater Header, although it is doubtful if Sydney Edwards had much to do with the design. A similar arrangement was used on the articulated locomotives described earlier.

Other features were an Owen double-beat balanced regulator valve, nine inch diameter piston valves with a full gear travel of 4¾in, electric lighting, vacuum brakes, a soot ejector in the smokebox and a Worthington-Simpson horizontal duplex boiler feed pump, as well as two nine m/m injectors. The springing was arranged so that the two trucks, front and rear, were compensated with the adjacent coupled axles, which were themselves compensated as a coupled axle group, and there was an ingenious arrangement so that the vertical load transfer onto the trailing truck, was always central on the axle bearings. As might be imagined the maker's were extremely proud of these two locomotives, numbers 2528 and 2529, and a number of photographs were taken of them both under construction and when complete. They were finished in a livery described as super Indian red, with lining consisting of a 2½in surround of black with a ⅜in chrome yellow stripe. The frames were also painted red and all the external brass and copper work was polished, the chimney having a copper cap. Both locomotives were dismantled for shipment, which was via Canada Dock Liverpool to Santos, the first on 30 and 31 October 1935, and the second on 27 November; the selling price was £5,400 each free-on-board. Unfortunately little is known about their later history, but they were still operational until at least the early 1960s. The railway appears to have been satisfied with these locomotives as a repeat order for two more was received in 1940. This order will be discussed in the next Chapter, as in the event the

completed locomotives were diverted to India as a war-time contingency.

Before leaving these two locomotives, which were so significant in the history of WG Bagnall Limited, it is perhaps worth telling a story as related to the authors by a number of employees of the period. Because of the size of the boiler and the height available under the overhead cranes in the erecting shop, the boiler had to be mounted on the frames prior to the driving wheels being fitted When the time came to wheel the first of the two engines, the fact that the total weight to be lifted was in excess of the overhead cranes safe-load capacity, as stated on the plates on the cranes themselves, became an issue of some consternation among the staff. Of course many of them had already realised this would be the case, and had been wondering how the situation would be handled! Anyway, as events turned out when work stopped one Saturday lunch time, the first job scheduled for Monday morning was fitting the wheels to the first locomotive - 'wheeling' as it is called in the trade. All the erecting shop staff then went home for the weekend. On Sunday the millwrights were busy, and after some very minor alterations and some paint, the safe working load on the smaller of the two cranes was increased! On the Monday the locomotive was wheeled without a hitch, or so the story went! Moreover, the men stood outside the frames guiding the axle-boxes into the horns, rather than in their more customary position between the frames!

It is opportune at this juncture in our story, to return to the activities of the LMA. At a general meeting of the Association on 2 August 1934, discussion took place following reports of the Southern Railway repairing industrial shunting locomotives in its workshops. Though there was no restriction on the main-line railway companies in this context, since the restrictions applied only to building new locomotives for immediate sale, such activity clearly denied potential work to the private builders, bearing in mind they were all in the business of repairing and overhauling locomotives as well as building them. As a result of the discussions it was agreed that WS Edwards and John W Vaughan, Secretary of the LMA, should seek an interview with the chief mechanical engineer (CME) of the Southern Railway in an attempt to persuade him to cease undertaking this type of work. We have not been able to locate details of any such meeting in the surviving LMA papers, but John Vaughan does mention the issue in his report of the activities of the Association for the period August 1934 to May the following year. In the report he refers to 'a successful interview by himself and WS Edwards, with the CME of the Southern Railway, regarding repairs done on private locomotives, when the CME agreed not to do so in future', the interview presumably with REL Maunsell, the Southern Railway CME at the time. Edwards would know Richard Maunsell quite well; he was president of the I Loco E., in the session 1928 to 1929, at a time when Edwards was a vice president. They also sat together for several years on the council of the Institution, and this would be one of the reasons why Edwards was the nominated representative to address this issue.

On 9 October 1935 the LMA made a very lengthy submission to the government, through the Rt. Hon W Runciman, President of the Board of Trade. At that time, with the exception of Peckett & Sons Limited of Bristol (who resigned from LMA membership in October 1921), all the country's private builders were members. The submission was an attempt to get financial incentives to help the industry, not least to compete with the American and European builders for overseas orders, but also to help the main-line railways replace ageing locomotives by placing orders with its members. Some interesting statistics were quoted in the submission. For example it was calculated that at the time of the submission the industry had a capacity to build 1,900 modern locomotives per annum, having a capital employed of no less than £7,250,000. Slightly over 9,000 men were employed in the industry, compared with 23,000 in 1914. In the period 1930 to 1934, on orders for locomotives and spare parts which included boilers, for which British builders had tendered and been unsuccessful, the continental manufacturers had undercut to a total figure of £193,862. This was against a total contract price from the continental builders of £1,546,970, and an aggregate tender price by the British builders of £1,740,832. In 1933 the industry had supplied 160 locomotive and 171 spare boilers to a valve of £356,580. By the end of 1935 the figures for that year were 218 locomotives and the same number of boilers to a total contract value of £3,215,881. Clearly there was large

redundancy in the manufacturing capability of the industry at the time, and it was spread across the 13 member firms.

Emphasis was placed on the home railway companies lack of support for the industry, and the example was given of how orders had shrunk since the 1923 grouping of the railway companies into the Big Four. A specific case cited was that of the several small Welsh railways which had all been absorbed into the Great Western Railway (GWR). Traditionally, and almost exclusively, these companies had bought new locomotives from the private builders, but this was a market that had all but dried up, being serviced from the GWR workshops at Swindon. The workshops of the larger pre-grouping companies like Swindon - others being Crewe, Derby, Doncaster, Darlington and Eastleigh to give but a few examples - had more than enough capacity to serve the routine needs of their respective railways. There had been Government support to the Big Four railway companies since 1923 to assist in locomotive renewal programmes, albeit somewhat spasmodically, and this had allowed significant numbers of locomotives to be built by private industry. The last such case was an order placed by the LMS in 1935, and the private manufacturers were now asking for something similar. In both America and Europe the building of locomotives by the main-line railways in their own workshops was almost non-existent, and this ensured that private industry in those parts of the world had an ongoing base workload, which enabled them to keep overheads much lower. It was for this reason the manufacturers contended, that in so many cases the overseas builders were able to undercut the tenders of the British firms. In 1913 it was stated that a total contract value of £4,330,000 was attributed to the export locomotive business in this country. In 1920 the equivalent figure was £5,573,000, but by 1925 it had dropped to £2,534,000, reaching its lowest level in 1931 at £296,000, but by 1934 had climbed again to £1,248,000. In addition to financial inducements to the main-line railways to help them renew locomotive fleets, the Association were asking for substantial export credit facilities, and help in the area of exchange currency values with some countries, in particular South America.

It is not clear what, if anything the government did following this submission, but as mentioned earlier the onset of the rearmament programme had the effect of filling the order books of the member companies. However, the submission did upset the LMS, when details got into the national press. The LMS board took the view that the submission gave misleading and inaccurate statements regarding the railway companies post-war policy of locomotive construction, in particular its own situation. In trying to get hold of a copy of the submission, under the signature of Sir Josiah Stamp, its chairman, the LMS wrote to all the private builders asking for a copy. The letter, which was dated 8 November 1935, also asked for any comments or observations the builders may care to make. WS Edwards was quick to reply as he was anxious to maintain 'the excellent and amicable relationship between your company and ourselves'. However, in his reply, dated 11 November, he appears to have been somewhat economical in the truth, stating that no representation had been made either to the government or the LMA by his company. He went on to say that a

representation had been made by the standing committee of the LMA to the President of the Board of Trade regarding the state of the industry, but that WG Bagnall were not members. What he was saying was that his company was not a member of the standing committee, which had instigated the submission, but WG Bagnall Limited were of course, members of the LMA, and he was personally a member of the general committee. It goes without saying, therefore, that he was well aware of what was going on, but the letter was crouched in terms that implied he was not!

There is one more locomotive order to describe in this Chapter, and one of great importance to the Company, for it came at a time when the order book was just about at its lowest ebb. It was also one that was tendered for under extremely fierce competition from the continental manufacturers. At meeting of the general committee of the LMA on 6 June 1935, the levy placed on members on orders received was amended to 1%, and this included any spare parts supplied below a

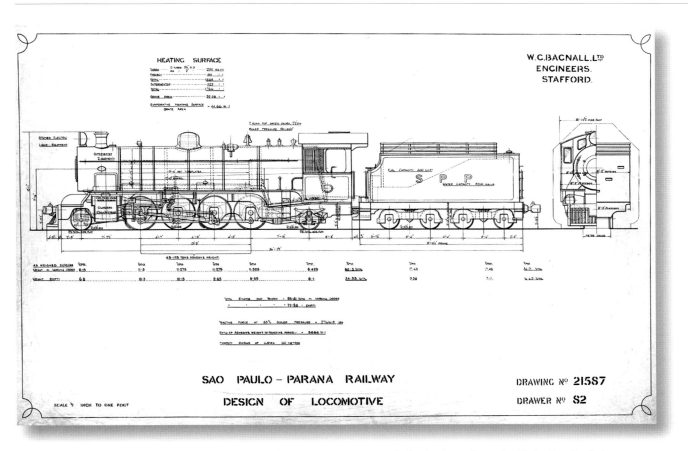

Drawing 21587 of 18 February 1935 is a diagram drawn in connection with the firm's tender to build the San Paulo locomotives; it shows the engines pretty much as built.

value of £1,000, which had been excluded hitherto - the revised figures to apply from 1 July. A new scheme was put in place on 1 December 1936, known as the LMA 1936 Scheme, and the levy was increased to 2½% on new locomotives and 7½% on spares. On 16 December 1937 it was again increased to 3%, and 10% respectively, and from 17 July 1937 WS Edwards became one of the trustees of the scheme. Payments were made quarterly by member firms, the additional capital to be used by the LMA in both subsidising orders where this was felt desirable, and in negotiating with the continental builders attempting to put in place 'working agreements', thereby avoiding loss-making contracts by any company. It was also agreed to 'ring fence' £5,000 as a contribution to a national locomotive testing station, an issue engaging the minds of the main-line railway companies at the time, in particular the LMS and LNER.

On 16 March 1936 the Company was successful in its tender for no fewer than 15 standard-gauge 2-4-2 side tank engines for use on light agricultural lines of the Egyptian State Railways. The quoted price was £2,477 each, CIF to Port Said from Birkenhead. However, this price was subsidised to the extent of £3,000; that is £200 per locomotive, under the arrangements outlined above, and due to competition by German and Czech builders. The design was a new one, cylinders were 13½x20in, driving wheels 3ft 8in diameter and the weight in working order 42 tons 15 cwt. The leading and trailing wheels were not swivelling trucks in the accepted sense, but rather radial axles with the axle-boxes running in radial guides within the frames. Readers may recall that a similar arrangement had been employed on the earlier standard-gauge locomotives of the same wheel arrangement sent to Egypt in 1907. The new engines were for use on the Minieh Auxiliary Railways in Upper Egypt, and a water lifter was fitted so water could be taken from streams and rivers en-route. The fifteen locomotives, manufacturer's numbers 2550 to 2564, were designed and built in a very commendable time frame, and were all delivered between 6 July and 28 October 1936 - but the works had little else to do at the time. As these locomotives were standard-gauge they were moved to Birkenhead on their own wheels with motion removed, usually two at a time. There had been a period earlier in 1936 when most of the workshop staff were laid off, as there was

very little work on hand, only the foreman and apprentices being kept on to progress the odd spares orders. Indeed, it has been suggested by several of those who were employees at the time, that but for this Egyptian order the Company may well have had to go into receivership, and this was probably the basis on which Edwards was able to agree the subsidy with the LMA.

In 1937 Bagnall was unsuccessful in its tender for the second batch of four of these locomotives, despite being a Castle Engine Works design; the original contract had stipulated that the intellectual property right of the design be vested in the Egyptian State Railways. On this occasion the contract went a Czechoslovakian Company, the Skoda Locomotive Works at Prague, one of the principal contenders for the earlier order. According to the *Reuters* news agency, reporting in the *Railway Gazette*, issue dated 7 January 1938, Skoda had quoted £3,383 each for these locomotives, against the lowest British tender of £4,097, although quite how it came by this information is a mystery. The higher figure is the Bagnall one, not on this occasion subsidised by the LMA, and at a time when the order book was quite healthy. Nevertheless, after the war in August 1946 the Company was successful in its tender of eight more locomotives of the same design. Despatched between April and June 1948, numbers 2880 to 2887, they differed from the earlier engines in being equipped for oil, rather than coal fuel. To illustrate the increase in prices after the war, they were sold for £6,900 each plus an extra £142 for the Laidlaw Drew oil-firing equipment, free-on-board at Liverpool; like the earlier engines they were moved to the docks in special trains on their own wheels with motion removed. In March 1949 kits were supplied to convert the 19 existing engines of the class to oil firing.

It is now time to investigate a number of other products the Company tried its hand at in efforts to remain viable during the difficult times of the 1930s, and before the country's re-armament programme started. One idea was the development of a small petrol-paraffin engine that could be used to power a small water pump, a dynamo or for other similar purposes. This was at a time when small portable internal-combustion engines were becoming popular on farms, for example, where the use of mechanical rather than animal power was taking hold. Despite the fact

Two of the 15 Egyptian State Railway standard-gauge 2-4-2 tank engines being shunted away from the works and towards Stafford station, on the first stage of their journey to Birkenhead Docks for shipment to Port Said. This procedure was quite unusual, as the Company did not build many standard-gauge locomotives for export, but whenever it did, provided they would clear the main-line loading gauge, in those days it was more economic to despatch them on their own wheels rather than load them onto wagons. It is interesting to note that the LMS Class 3 tank doing the shunting is one built at the Castle Engine Works, number 2350 of 1928, originally LMS 16682 and later 7599. It was allocated to Stafford shed at the time and remained there for many years, until 1950 in fact.

that there were numerous specialist manufacturers in this field, with well proven products and well established reputations, a brave attempt was made by Bagnall to compete. We do not know at this distance of time whose idea it was, but as might be expected Ivor Farr was put in charge, and in 1936 he designed a five horsepower single-cylinder vertical engine that could be built with the facilities at Stafford. There is a nice story concerning the early development of this engine, Ivor going along to the local Austin car dealer in Stafford, the Gaol Square Garage, to purchase a piston and connecting rod and then designing the engine round them! Be that as it may, he also designed all the jigs and tools to allow batch production, catalogued all the parts and even prepared hand-coloured sectional drawings to allow publicity material to be produced and for spare-part ordering. Known as the Bagnall-Demon, a totally enclosed four-stroke water-cooled engine with a single-cylinder running at 750 rpm, it had an inbuilt

centrifugal governor and a seven inch diameter and six inch face pulley for the power take-off. Ball and roller bearings were used throughout, and there was an Amal float-feed carburettor and a Wico magneto. Overall dimensions were 1ft 7in x 2ft 6in x 2ft 5in, and engines could be supplied mounted on a small four-wheeled hand truck, and/or coupled to pumps, generators or as complete lighting sets - in fact you name it. The basic price was £33 complete with tools, some spares and instructions, and £4 extra for the truck. In its standard format a ready to run engine but without fuel or water, weighed 3½ cwt, had a fuel tank capacity of 2¾ gallons and a water tank capacity of 50 gallons for cooling purposes. A very nice badge was designed by Ivor for the engines, complete with a Demon and his spear, and circumstantial evidence would suggest that just one batch of 50 engines was made.

Over a period of several years, in one configuration or another, most of the 50 Demon engines seem to have been sold. There is evidence however, that at least one completed engine was left lying around the works and could be found in the electricians store as late as the early 1950s. Whether the relatively small number built paid back the design and tooling costs has gone unrecorded, and it would seem that more parts were made than were actually used, as members of staff recall finding odd bits lying around the works for years afterwards! This is another example of the workshops becoming involved with engineering as far removed from the rugged simplicity of the steam locomotive as is possible to get, and the whole exercise was a credit to all concerned. Joe Owen was the fitter selected to assemble the engines at his bench in the fitting shop as and when orders were received.

Another attempt to keep the order books full was a venture in 1932 with a company called Furnival-Victor, to manufacture a concrete mixer with a drum that was rotated by hand. The arrangement consisted of a series of handles around the perimeter of the drum so that it could, in the words of the publicity, be: rotated on the ships wheel principle. The bowl was 32in diameter and 22in deep, mounted on a two-wheel trolley that could be tipped, complete with the bowl, to empty out the mix. They were sold for £13 15/- (£13 75p) ex works, or £15 15/- (£15 75p) free-on-board for export, but there is no surviving record of exactly how many were built.

In the period covered by this chapter there were of course significant numbers of spare parts supplied for locomotives and rolling stock, including a large quantity for Kerr, Stuart locomotives. Word had got around regarding the ability of the Company to supply parts for locomotives made by Kerr, Stuart, and Harris would have been instrumental in many of these orders; his contacts with former Kerr, Stuart customers and agents were extensive. Between 1932 and 1938 around 200 spare boilers were supplied, many of them quite large ones for metre-gauge locomotives in India, and in the same period some 27 industrial shunting locomotives, many of other builders manufacture, came in to the works for attention of one sort or another. One of these spare boiler orders is worthy of special mention, as it was one of the first instances within the industry of a levy being applied, under the then new arrangements with the LMA. Such levies were at that time only payable when it was confirmed that the order

would be placed in this country, and in some cases competition was avoided from other LMA members by a payment from the LMA to part compensate them for not bidding. Such an order was one for the Iraq Government, and as it was initially placed with the Crown Agents for the Colonies it was one that would go to a British builder. Iraq was not, of course, a British colony, but it came under British rule from 1919 until 1927 and retained considerable ties for many years after, hence the Crown Agents involvement. The order was for six superheated boilers for metre-gauge BESA Indian HGS class locomotives working on the Iraq Railway; large numbers of this class had been transferred to Iraq from India during the First World War. The order number was 8008 of 28 November 1934, and the levy was £100 per boiler. It is worth noting that the company had already supplied three boilers of the same type to Iraq earlier in the year. A particularly large order for boilers was order number 7345 of July 1934, consisting of no fewer than 17 boilers for the Indian Eastern Bengal Railway's metre-gauge BESA design P class 4-6-0 tender engines.

Among other diverse jobs undertaken were repairs to steam road rollers for Staffordshire County Council, machines not just from the Stafford division but Gnosall, Stoke-on-Trent and Newcastle-under-Lyme divisions too. Between May 1929 and November 1935 eight rollers, variously of Aveling & Porter of Rochester, and John Fowler of Leeds manufacture, came in for attention of one sort or another. On other occasions men were sent out to attend to the rollers wherever they were working, and local farmers occasionally had a similar service provided for their steam traction and ploughing engines.

In 1933 the Company supplied the Gardner-Edwards Railcar Company Limited of 3, Brunswick Street Belfast, with an underframe, bogies and other mechanical parts for a three-foot gauge railcar being built for the South American Antioquia Railway in Colombia. The design of this vehicle was not too dissimilar from the railcars built by Walker Brothers (Wigan) Limited, of the Pagefield Iron Works in Wigan, although there does not seem to be any connection in this case, no more with Sydney Edwards. The consulting engineers were Messrs Robert W Hunt & Company of Ludgate Hill in London and Dr. A Lopez, of the Colombia Consul-General also based in London.

In this vehicle, unlike the Wigan built cars, the engine was mounted on the main-frame, and not as in the case of the Walker vehicles on the power-bogie, and there was a rather curious wheel arrangement. A four-wheel power-bogie at the rear and a single-pair of wheels at the front arranged to pivot about a centre, but with no lateral movement. The power equipment consisted of the well-proven Gardner 6L2 six-cylinder vertical diesel engine, which although designed to develop 74 horsepower at 1,300 rpm, as it was intended for use at heights of around 6,000ft, its output would be much lower. Transmission was via a four-speed gearbox and propeller shaft to the trailing axle of the power-bogie, and thence to the other pair of wheels by conventional side-rods. The car was designed to seat 30 passengers,

climb grades of 1 in 25 around curves of four chains radius, and haul a trailer; the weight in working order was 10½ tons. When complete the railcar was successfully tested in June 1933 on the Ballymena to Larne section of the LMS (Northern Counties Committee), where it attained a maximum speed of 43 mph with a fuel consumption of a little under 21 mpg. It was stated at the time that this was the first rail vehicle built in Ireland, north or south, for service abroad. The Bagnall order number was 5457.

Nothing seems to be known of this vehicle after delivery, the FC De Antioquia is situated in the centre of Colombia and eventually connected Puerto Berrio on the River Magdalena, westwards with Medellin on the opposite side of the Andes via a tunnel and the La

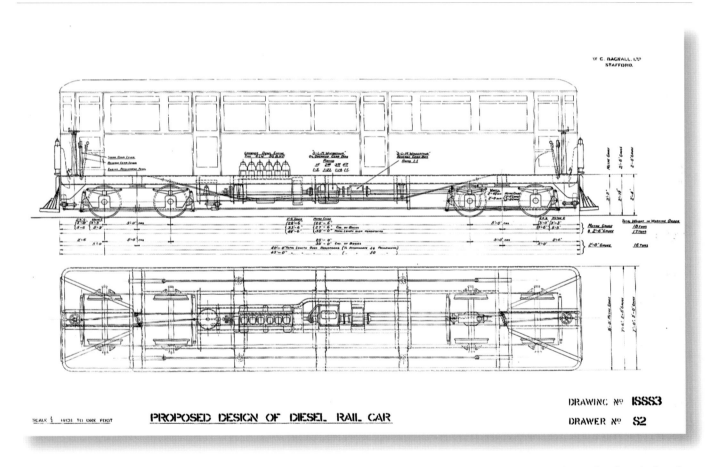

Although this diagram of a Gardner-Edwards diesel railcar is not the same one the Company built an under-frame for, described in the adjacent text, it is nevertheless an interesting proposal dated 12 February 1932, suggesting perhaps, additional business of this nature might have been in the offing. The engine for this design was a Gardner 6LW, not dissimilar to the one in the railcar that was built, but in this case rated at 90 horsepower, and the gearbox, of Swiss design and manufacture, giving four-speeds, which via a separate reversing gearbox were available in both directions. The track gauge is shown on the diagram as metre, but the drawing register suggests that the car could also be built to suit both two-foot and 2ft 6in gauge.

"BAGNALL DEMON"
BALL AND ROLLER BEARING
TOTALLY ENCLOSED ENGINES

TYPE B.C.C. PUMPING SET.
An invaluable combination for all duties involving large quantities at moderate heads. Complete with centrifugal pump delivering 15,000 galls. per hour at 30-ft. head as illustrated.
Alternative quantities and heads to suit individual requirements.
Prices on application
COMPLETE WITH TOOLS, SPARES & INSTRUCTIONS
Mounted on 4-wheel truck complete with drag handle, extra £5.
Dimensions 50″ × 30″ × 34″

TYPE BRV. Stationary Engine. The ideal agricultural and industrial unit. As illustrated.
Price: £33
COMPLETE WITH TOOLS, SPARES & INSTRUCTIONS
Dimensions 19″ × 30″ × 29″

TYPE B.C. 2 K.W. Electric Generating Set. The most economical source of light. Direct Lighting System.
Battery Lighting System, As illustrated.
Prices on application
COMPLETE WITH TOOLS, SPARES & INSTRUCTIONS
Dimensions 50″ × 30″ × 34″

5 B.H.P., PARAFFIN, PETROL, GAS OIL, OR TOWN'S GAS

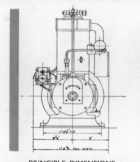

DUST-PROOF
OIL-PROOF
with a
MINIMUM
OPERATING
ATTENTION

CORRECT LUBRICATION !
  Automatic oil sump system.
EASY STARTING !
  "Wico" Impulse Starter Rotary Magneto.
UNIFORM SPEED !
  Sensitive throttle governor.
CORRECT IGNITION !
  Automatic advance and retard.
MINIMUM RUNNING COST !
  "Amal" variable jet fully compensated carburettor.
MAXIMUM POWER !
  10% more power if required for short periods.
LONG LIFE !
  Ball and Roller Main Bearings.

PRINCIPLE DIMENSIONS.
Revolutions per minute	750
Weight (bare engine)	3½ cwt.
Fuel Tank capacity	2¾ gallons.
Water Tank ,,	50 ,,
Hopper Tank ,,	5 ,,
Water Pipes ..	¾″ gas.
Exhaust Pipe ..	1¼″ gas.
Foundation Bolts	½″ diameter.
Standard Pulley	7″ dia. × 6″ face.

Starting Handle—Pulley side clockwise rotation—(Timing side anti-clockwise if required)

TYPE BRVT TRANSPORTABLE ENGINE
The most powerful light engine available for the farmer or road contractor. As illustrated, fully equipped and self contained, mounted on wood skids.
Price: £35
Complete with Tools, Spares and Instructions.
Mounted on 4-wheel truck complete with drag handle, extra £4.

NOTE: ALL PRICES (EXCEPT TYPE B.R.V.) INCLUDE FOR FUEL AND WATER TANKS AND PIPES (HOPPER OR TANK COOLING OPTIONAL)

GUARANTEE.
In lieu of any warranty or condition implied by law, we guarantee that the materials employed in the manufacture of these engines are of the best quality and if through any latent defect or workmanship any part or parts become broken or suffer undue wear within twelve months, (or where machinery is run continuously day and night within six months) from delivery, we undertake to replace any such part or parts free of charge to destination within the British Isles, or if abroad free to port of exportation provided that the defective part or parts are sent to our works, carriage paid, within the specified period ; all the replaced parts to become our property.
Save as aforesaid we are to be under no liability in respect of machinery which we supply whether as regards design, material, workmanship, or otherwise, or as regards any matter arising directly or indirectly from any defects therein.
Accessories or machinery supplied, which are not of our own manufacture, are subject to the warranty of the maker thereof only and are not covered by this guarantee.
N.B.—Whilst every care is taken in the preparation of this folder, which cancels all previous editions: illustrations, specifications and dimensions must not be taken as binding until confirmed by us, alterations being found necessary from time to time. Any variation from our standard specification may involve increase in price and delay in delivery.

This is the inside of a brochure for the Bagnall-Demon petrol-paraffin engine described in the adjoining text.

An example of the Bagnall-Demon petrol-paraffin engine coupled to a water pump and mounted on a hand trolley; the large tank is for engine cooling purposes. Notice the Demon badge designed for use on these engines and located on the side of the single-cylinder.

Quiebra pass; 150 miles long it was built in sections between 1880 and 1929. The journal *Diesel Railway Traction* in its issue dated 16 June 1933, describes and illustrates a range of railcars ostensibly available from this Belfast company, some similar to the one described above and others with twin-bogies; in one case a six-wheel bogie with an engine rated at 400 horsepower mounted on it. However, as there are no vehicles built by this company known to have been used in Ireland, and as the one described above is reckoned to be the only one exported at the time it was built, along with no records of any others, we are left to assume it was a one off venture. In fact the Company may never have had much in the way of manufacturing facilities of its own.

In 1933 for the GWR Bagnall built 66 six and four ton railway sleeper creosoting trolleys for its Hayes Creosoting Plant, and a further 12 were ordered in December the following year.

A significantly contract of August 1936 was the supply of parts to the Midland Uruguay Railway to convert five standard-gauge 2-6-0 locomotives from slide valves and none superheated boilers to piston valves and superheating. As this order included some quite complex design work, once again it was entrusted to Ivor Farr, with the boilers, cylinders and some motion parts being supplied as kits of parts for the conversion work. The engines involved had slide valves and Stephenson's link motion between the frames, so converting them to outside eight inch diameter piston valves, whilst retaining the inside motion resulted in some quite ingenious scheming by Ivor. Cylinder dimensions were 16½x24in and the boiler pressure 200psi, which was a high pressure for a boiler built at Stafford - they were quite big locomotives. Two more sets of parts and boilers were supplied in October 1939, one more set in 1941, and another in 1946. The 1941 order was quoted as being a replacement and one is left wondering if perhaps, one of the 1939 sets was lost at sea during the war. The locomotives concerned had originally been built between 1905 and 1915 by the Manchester-based Beyer Peacock & Company Limited.

Yet another stream of work was the supply of Owen patent balanced double-beat poppet valve regulators, to the design of Arthur Eugene Owen, their inventor. Owen was born in the Headingley district of Leeds in 1887, where his father was employed by one of the private locomotive builders based in that city. After an apprenticeship and training in the Leeds private locomotive industry he moved to Barrow-in-Furness and joined the Furness Railway, rising to the position of chief locomotive draughtsman by the time of the 1923 amalgamation of the railways. Shortly after this he moved to Derby where the newly formed LMS was establishing its principal drawing office, and by 1927 was the deputy chief locomotive draughtsman. In 1937 Owen was appointed to the position of chief locomotive draughtsman at Derby, a post he held until late 1942, when having fallen out of favour with his boss, Tom Coleman, the chief draughtsman for all locomotive and rolling stock issues on the LMS, he left the railway soon after. Over the period 1921 to 1934 Arthur Owen, on the last two occasions along with his two-year older brother Henry, had four patents granted for regulator valves, all of them employing the poppet valve principle. The first one, patent number 171,510 was accepted on 24 November 1921, and titled *Double Beat Equilibrium Regulator Valve for Locomotive Type of Boilers*. This was in AE Owen's name alone and gave his address as 27 Salthouse Road Barrow-in-Furness. The valve was unique, as although like some other double-beat regulator valves it employed two separate valves; the top valve had a piston at its lower extremity which fitted into a hollow cylinder in the lower valve; the piston had a set of piston rings to make the internal cylinder steam tight. In operation the bottom valve would open first by mechanical linkage, and as the opening increased it would come into physical contact with the top valve as the piston was moved in its cylinder, and gradually open that valve too. As the diameter of the twin passages in the header casting on which the valves seated were the same diameter as the internal cylinder in the bottom valve, it follows that the action of the valve was completely balanced. Additionally, as one valve opened a small amount before the other, it enabled drivers to achieve very fine control of locomotives so fitted. Because the two valves could move in relation to each other, this arrangement had the added advantage of avoiding any leakage that might be caused by differential expansion when steam was being raised in the boiler.

The second patent, also solely in the name of Arthur Owen, and still with a Barrow address, was granted on 11 October 1923, patent number 204,830, *Improvements in Double Beat Equilibrium Valves of Piston Type*. The design in this case, as its title suggested, was an improvement on the earlier one which as well as a general simplification of the design, eliminated a particular problem with the earlier version. In the first design, because both valves were of the same size, to enable the bottom one to be removed from the header casting it was necessary for the top valve seat to be removable from the casting, so as to make a hole large enough to remove the bottom valve. This not only complicated manufacturing, but also made running shed maintenance of the bottom valve almost impossible. To allow the bottom valve to be smaller, whilst retaining the balanced principle of the original invention, an ingenious solution was adopted. The bottom valve has a series of holes so that steam at boiler pressure is admitted to the underside of the piston, and thus the bottom valve, despite being smaller than the top one, is balanced, even when it is closed, as steam at boiler pressure is applied on both sides. The top valve is prevented from opening as the steam pressure, applied to its underside via the integral piston in the cylinder, covers a smaller area than the top valve. To summarise, in the case of the top valve, whilst this is slightly out of balance when in the closed position for the reason given, as soon as the bottom valve opens, which it does first for the same reason as in the original arrangement, then steam at boiler pressure is admitted to the total area of its underside, and it too becomes perfectly balanced. This patent also covered alternative arrangements in the design of headers so that both the valves could still be the same size, and there was an arrangement to use the valve for marine purposes, in which case it would be located external to the boiler.

The third patent was in the names of both Arthur Owen and his brother Henry. Arthur, having moved to Derby gave an address of 'Oakdene', 107 Palmerston Road Derby, whilst Henry was still living in Leeds and gave his as 4 Manor Terrace Headingley. Patent number 373,273 was granted on 23 May 1932, *Improvements in Regulator Valves*. The main purpose of this patent was to allow the use of the regulator in a smokebox situation, rather then in a dome. To facilitate use of the Owen valve as a smokebox regulator, clearly it was desirable for the valve to be operated from above rather than below, and several methods of achieving this are outlined. These included fitting the valve to existing headers without disturbing any of the air tight joints in the smokebox. Additionally, as it was possible to get very fine movement of regulator valves of this type, there was an arrangement of linkage that could be applied to regulator handles in locomotives cabs so that drivers would be able to place the handle in a drifting position. It is good practice to keep a small amount of steam flowing to the valves and cylinders even when locomotives are coasting; it improves lubrication, helps eliminate knocks and bangs in cushioning any wear in the bearings, and it gives a smoother ride all round. The arrangement of mechanical linkage was such that a small notch in the quadrant indicated to the driver a very small opening of the bottom regulator valve.

The last of the four patents, again in the joint names of the brothers, was dated 6 September 1934 and the patent number was 415,857. This covered a more sophisticated arrangement to allow drifting steam to be

applied to locomotive cylinders. Obviously, having a large valve open a very small amount and for potentially long periods was not particularly good engineering practice - scouring of the valve and seat was a likely result over time. In the case of this patent the bottom valve was arranged such that a small movement opened an annular chamber underneath the valve itself, but without fully opening the valve to the main steam pipe. This was possible as the valve itself was a close fit in the circular aperture in which it moved at the bottom of the header. The chamber had a series of passages allowing boiler steam in small quantities to escape. Arrangements could then be made for these passages to be connected, via internal and external steam pipes, to

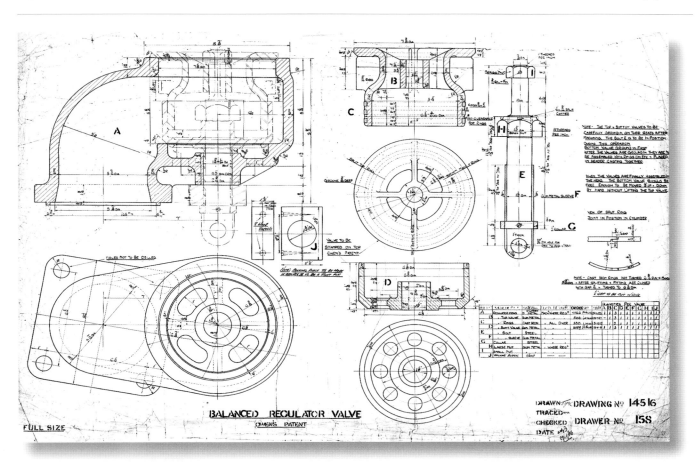

This drawing illustrates an example of the Owen double-beat poppet valve regulator as built by the Company. It covers four orders for in total 21 valves supplied between January 1926 and April 1928, none of which were for locomotives the Company was building. The type of valve shown is in accordance with the second (1923) of the four patents, and embodies the basic principles of all the designs. The following two patents of 1932 and 1934 were refinements, in the first case to allow use of the valve in a smokebox superheater header situation, and in the second provision for a small amount of steam to by-pass the main valve when it was in a particular position, so that drifting steam could be supplied to the cylinders when the main valve was closed. This could facilitate both improved cylinder lubrication and when fitted on the wet side of a superheater allow small quantities of steam to pass through the elements to prevent them overheating.

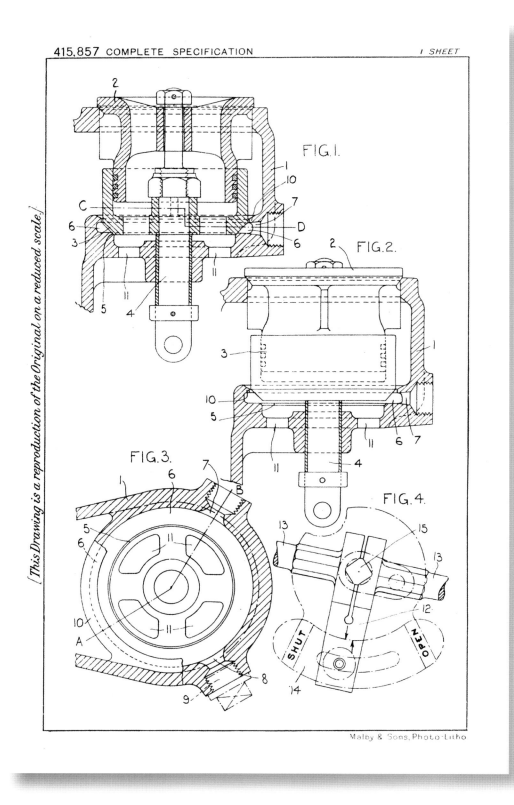

I SHEET

FIG.1.

FIG.2.

FIG.3.

FIG.4.

[This Drawing is a reproduction of the Original on a reduced scale.]

Malby & Sons, Photo-Litho

This drawing is from patent specification number 415,857 dated 6 September 1934, and shows the final design of Owen poppet valve regulator with the by-pass arrangements for drifting steam. The chamber and escape port for the steam can be seen in Figs 1, 2 & 3, as respectively numbers 6 and 7. From this and the previous drawing, along with the description in the adjoining text, readers should be able to follow the principles of the operation of these valves.

reach either the steam chests and thence the cylinders, or, if required, items like superheater dampers, by-pass or relief valves, lubricator atomisation valves; and in the case of engines with Caprotti and other poppet valve gears, to move the valves onto their seats before any steam admitted by opening the regulator reached them. Of course, it was possible for steam to escape to the main steam pipe past the bottom valve, as there would be a limited clearance between it, and the circular aperture in which it moved, but this would be a very small amount. When this arrangement was applied to locomotives there had to be a method of showing the driver the position he needed to have the regulator handle in for drifting, and this could either be the one outlined in the earlier patent or some similar arrangement.

It is worth noting that the Furness Railway does not appear to have had any form of condition of employment in place, with regard to its employees applying for patents in their own names involving their professional activities. It was often the case for patents granted under these sorts of conditions to be in the joint names of the individual and the railway company. However, this does appear to have been the case and moreover, there does not appear to be any evidence that regulators of the type designed by Owen were ever used on Furness Railway locomotives. Perhaps even more interesting is that the LMS does not seem to have had any such conditions either, but the inclusion of brother Henry in the last two patents, with his name appearing first in the applications, doubtless has a bearing on the issue. Unlike the Furness Railway Owen was able to interest the LMS in his second patent, and in 1927 four members of the numerous LMS and former Midland Railway design of Class 4 0-6-0 freight engines were fitted with the valves - numbers 4432 to 4436 built at Derby. It is not known how successful or otherwise the LMS considered them to be, or for how long they remained fitted however, two particularly interesting orders came direct from the LMS to Bagnall. These involved fitting the regulator valves to three Royal Scot class 4-6-0 express passenger engines of the railway's latest design. The first order was in January 1929 for two valves, and the second in April the same year for one valve. One of these valves was fitted to the engine by Bagnalls men, but as the locomotive was too big to traverse the tightly curved rail connection into the

Castle Engine Works, the work was undertaken in the nearby Stafford running sheds. Unfortunately there does not appear to be any surviving record of which individual locomotives of the Royal Scot class were fitted or, as with the Class 4 freight engines, what the experience with them was.

Although there never appears to have been a formal agreement, Bagnall seems to have been the sole supplier of this regulator valve against orders obtained by Owen, except perhaps those fitted to the Class 4 freight engines at Derby mentioned in the previous paragraph. Arthur Owen left the LMS shortly after his dismissal as chief locomotive draughtsman, and died at a comparatively early age, but his brother Henry - later trading as Henry Owen, and later still H Owen & Company Limited from a Headingley Leeds address - continued the business well into the 1960s. There was a nephew, also named Henry, who was for many years a draughtsman at the Castle Engine Works, and this seems to have been at least one of the reasons why Bagnall was chosen to manufacture the valves.

For the reasons already mentioned, this type of regulator was particularly popular for locomotives fitted with the various types of poppet valve gear. It was also popular with the Indian railways, and large numbers of the valves were supplied to manufacturers in both this country and on the continent, when fitment was specified by the end customers. Stan Baxter was the specialist fitter who did most of the assembly work at Stafford, and it seems that in recognition of Bagnall manufacturing the valves, no royalty was paid if they were fitted, as they often were, to Bagnall-built locomotives. They remained in production until the late 1950s, and there was always a healthy spare part business connected with them. To give some idea of the extent of this workload, between 1925 and 1929, there were 18 separate orders, and in most cases several valves for each order. The authors can personally testify to the ease of operation when regulators of this type are fitted - almost no muscular effort is needed at all. However, for anyone more used to conventional arrangements, one has to be very careful!

Although very much on the decline, there was a steady stream of orders in this period for wagons of all shapes and sizes, turntables and other equipment, along with a small amount of track-work. The orders included kiln and transfer cars for potteries and the iron

Another type of wagon from the period under review is this drop-side bogie vehicle embodying three-piece diamond frame bogies and a hand brake. The 3-8-0-0 chalked on the end, indicates three tons and eight cwt as the vehicle's unladen weight.

and steel furnace industry, also wagons for sleeper creosoting depots belonging to the main-line railway companies like the GWR ones mentioned earlier, as well as more conventional wagons and skips. There were also orders for colliery pit cages, brick dryer cars, wagon tipplers and transformer trucks, to name but a few. There was even a 20 ton self-standing traversing gantry hand-crane, supplied to the Gwalior State Railway in 1932. So the wagon shop was moderately busy throughout most of the 1930s. In November 1931 a large order came from Imperial Chemical Industries (ICI) for no fewer than 220 dropside tip wagons of 27 cub ft capacity; two-foot gauge they were delivered at a rate of 25 per week from 8 January the following year. There is no surviving record of where they were delivered to, but they were numbered 2650 to 2869 and painted in red oxide. The Bagnall order number was 3996, and the value of this order was £2,772. ICI were quite a good customer at this time for narrow-gauge wagons, for example it ordered 30 of the same type for ICI (Lime) Limited, to order 4231 of March 1932; contract value was £383. As these were stipulated to be the same as the others, we can assume that they too, were for the lime works subsidiary, and they were

numbered consecutively - 2870 to 2899. There were another 55 in April, order number 4367 costing £693, followed by 24 later on in 1932, and 50 in May 1933. No running numbers were quoted for these last two orders. Incidentally, a few of these skips were noted in use at Redburn Mine, at Rookhope in County Durham in the mid 1960s, so it is possible they were all delivered there.

We must now turn our attention to some people, and first of all two apprentices who commenced their training with the Company in the period we are here reviewing and who were to have a significant influence in the years to follow. Albert Henry Victor Betteley, known to family and friends as Vic, commenced his training at the Castle Engine Works on 15 June 1934, where his father had worked before him. Thomas Charles Betteley (1883-1968) was a native of Stoke-on-Trent where he was born in 1883, but began his apprenticeship with Bagnall in 1897, his first job helping to cut out the brass chimney numerals for the 4-4-0 locomotives building at the time for the Egyptian Delta Light Railways - manufacturer's numbers 1540 to 1549. Some years after completion of his apprenticeship he went to work for Kerr, Stuart at

Stoke-on-Trent, but came back to the Castle Engine Works a year or so before the First World War. He left the railway industry in the early 1920s when he moved to the nearby English Electric Works. We shall meet his son Vic again later in our story, as he eventually became production engineer.

In August the following year Fredrick Harold Wood joined the Company, always known as Harold, another native of Stoke-on-Trent and, like WS Edwards educated at Hanley High School. Harold was persuaded to make a career in locomotive engineering by Guy Leslie Murray, a former works manager of Kerr, Stuart. Murray was born in Trentham, Stoke-on-Trent, on 12 April 1888, and went on to a distinguished career in both practical and academic terms. Having been top of Queensbury High School at Longton and a gold medallist (top of school) there in 1903, he later distinguished himself at Fenton Technical College, which he attended between 1903 and 1910 and where he became a part-time lecturer in machine construction and applied mechanics for two years from 1910. Between March 1903 and August 1906 Guy Murray served his apprenticeship with Kerr, Stuart, and was then employed in the drawing office under FHB Harris until appointed assistant works Manager in January 1912 - and he was still only 24 years old! In March 1914 he became works manager, but soon moved on to further significant appointments. In the following year he joined Joshua Buckton & Company, machine tool makers in Leeds as general manager, and later still was the works manager of Manning, Wardle & Company, the well known Leeds locomotive builder, subsequently being appointed as works superintendent of the Sudan Government Railways. Later, on returning to this country he was with Kirkstall Forge, and in 1939 joined the teaching staff of Cheltenham School and led the development of an engineering syllabus there; he died in October 1955. One of Harold's uncles introduced him to Murray, and it was Murray who introduced Harold to Edwards, whom of course, he knew well. So young Harold got good career advice, and went on to a very successful career, eventually taking over from his mentor, FHB Harris, as chief draughtsman at Stafford. We shall meet him again later in our story.

An unfortunate casualty of this period was Ivor Farr, who it seems had a problem getting along with Harris. Whilst known in the drawing office as the Old Man, he was less favourably referred to around the works as Boggie Harris; when not in earshot of course. As we have seen Ivor Farr had an extremely fertile and active mind, and as is sometimes the case with people of this disposition, he was also something of a prankster, always game for a joke, or some horseplay. It seems that after a number of incidents with Harris, Ivor stormed out of the office one day and went home refusing to return unless he had an apology. Edwards intervened as he was anxious not to loose his services, eventually managing to calm things down. However, it was not long before there was a repetition, and Ivor left for good, Edwards feeling that his intervention on a second occasion would not be good for drawing office moral generally. Harris was well known as a strict disciplinarian, and it was obvious that the two of them were never going to hit it off again. This would be in September 1938, and Ivor straight away got a placement at the English Electric factory in Stafford, where he remained until retirement in December 1967; a great loss to locomotive engineering. Ivor Farr died on 18 May 1990, and among the things he left was a quantity of very early 9.5 m/m movie film, all very professionally taken and edited. It includes shots taken in the drawing office and around the works at Stafford. He and Harold Wood became good friends, and before Ivor met his future wife Kathleen, he occasionally visited Harold at his Burslem home in Stoke-on-Trent, and on one occasion, along with Harold's sister, they went boating on Rudyard Lake near Leek in the Staffordshire Moorlands. There is footage of this excursion on one of Ivor's films.

Ostensibly to help restore discipline in the drawing office after the departure of Farr - which in Harris's opinion had been far too lax in Taylor's time - Thomas Stockton arrived in 1937 as a leading draughtsman. Tom Stockton was the son of Alexander and Ellen Stockton, born on 26 December 1892 at Silverdale near Newcastle-under-Lyme, where his father was an ironstone miner. Serving his apprenticeship with Kerr, Stuart he was of course, well known to both Harris and Edwards. After serving in the Royal Navy during the First World War where he became a Chief Petty Officer (Engineering Artificer), he joined the Bristol locomotive builder Peckett & Sons Limited. He may however, have initially returned to Kerr, Stuart for a period after the war. As a native of North Staffordshire,

Full page advert from The Railway Gazette dated 29 November 1939 - this was the Annual Overseas Railway Number published over many years in which the Company invariably advertised. Notice the reference to the various agents as well as the Company sharing its London Office with the Keith Pearson agency. The locomotives illustrated are: top - 2529 for Brazil; middle left - 2557 for Egypt; Middle right - 2575 for South Africa - these locomotives are all described in this Chapter. At the bottom is number 2600 for the Barsi Light Railway in India, discussed in the next Chapter. Note A&H McNay should be spelt A&H MacNay.

Tom Stockton was happy to return north when Harris sounded the recall. During the war he served on a ship that was in the fleet at the Battle of Jutland, as was Charlie Jones a turner in the machine shop; Tom always made a point of having half an hour's chat with Charlie on each anniversary of that great battle - the 31 May. We shall meet Tom Stockton again later, as in 1945 he became works manager.

In regard to Harris's reputation as a disciplinarian there is a good story worth telling of his time at Kerr, Stuart. Among those who trained under Harris was Reginald John Mitchell, the famous aircraft engineer and designer of the celebrated Spitfire. Reg Mitchell was a native of Stoke-on-Trent, and another old boy of Hanley High School, serving his apprenticeship at Kerr, Stuart between 1911 and 1917. There were two drawing offices at the California Works, one for locomotives and another, situated on the floor above, for everything else. At the time Mitchell was working in the upper one, and often used to make a lot of noise, banging closed the large drawing cabinet drawers for example, only of course, when the Old Man was downstairs! Harris would rush up to see what was going on, but Mitchell would in the meantime have persuaded his colleagues to deny any knowledge of who the culprit was, or even being conscious of any great noise, such that when a puffing and panting Harris arrived, all would be quite with everybody hard at work at their drawing boards! By all accounts this annoyed Harris out of all proportion, and he was glad to see the back of Reg Mitchell who he had suspected all along, but was only confirmed as the guilty party after he had left. It is worth mentioning in concluding this story, that years later Harris often proudly told the story of how he had trained the famous designer of the Spitfire!

The relationship between WS Edwards and the Maitlands was never going to be easy, but as they were the major shareholders, some cognisance of their views was necessary. During the difficult financial period following John Gifford's death, there would seem to have been regular arguments about the profits generated (or lack of them), the directors fees and the dividends paid, or not, as the case may be. In the years 1932, 1933 and 1934, the Company made a loss on its trading of a little over £4,500 in each of the first two years, reducing to £655 in the third, and there were suggestions that matters with the Inland Revenue were

not what they might be. During the 1934 Company Christmas dinner and dance at Maer Hall, which is between Newcastle-under-Lyme and Market Drayton, there was a visitation by Inland Revenue officials and the festivities ended somewhat abruptly! The issue concerned a claim by the Inland Revenue for underpayment of tax in connection with excess profits, corporation and income tax, to in its view, the tune of £14,449. However, quite why the officials felt it necessary to descend on the evening festivities has gone unrecorded, but it might have been considered that embarrassing Edwards in such a way and in front of his staff would have been beneficial to their case. Whatever the reasoning behind the visit, there had obviously been discussions at which no agreement had been reached. No further summery action was taken but in that year's accounts the Company made a preliminary provision of £10,000 as a liability to the Inland Revenue, and after further discussions this figure was agreed with payment made in November 1936. This is however not quite the end of the matter as it raised its head again in late 1943, and we shall return to it in the next Chapter. By all accounts it was not long after this event that Edwards health started to deteriorate, and as the war years loomed there was even more pressure from the Maitlands, who were convinced that, with the country's re-armament programme underway and the order book filling up, profits should have been higher. Actually, in the years 1935 to 1938 the annual profit averaged £4,570, but 1936 was a bad year and the figure was only £460 - and remember this was the year when almost all the staff were laid-off for a period of weeks.

At this stage in his career Edwards was a prominent personage both in Stafford and North Staffordshire generally, living with his wife in a large house called 'Enville', at 190 Sandon Road. He had a chauffer driven car (actually there were two Company owned Daimlers) and Tommy Upton, one of the tool room fitters acting as the driver as and when necessary. Edwards and his wife had a country retreat at Fairbourne near Barmouth in North Wales, a bungalow also called 'Enville' where the couple frequently disappeared at weekends and holiday times - Tommy often doing the driving and having to do one of the journeys 'light'. Edwards had married Eliza Williams (although latterly as least, she was known as Elizabeth), another native of Hanley, at Hanley Parish Church on 26 February 1906 - they were both 23 years old at the time. Eliza was the daughter of William Williams, a retired Police Sergeant; she was an accomplished singer and for many years in the choir of St Mary's Castle Church in Stafford. There were never any children. By the mid to late 1930s, as well as his activities with the professional engineering Institutions, Edwards was vice-president of the North Staffordshire Engineering Employers Association (from 1938), vice-president of the Birmingham, Wolverhampton & Staffordshire District Engineering & Allied Employers Association (appointed president in January 1936), and a member of the council of the Engineering & Allied Employers National Federation; he was also a member of the general council of the North Staffordshire Chamber of Commerce. A prominent notice in his office read: 'Be Concise, Be Brief, Be Gone', which in many ways was so typical of him.

On the occasion of the Silver Jubilee celebrations of the reign of King George V, May 6 1935 being designated Jubilee Day, along with the other employers in Stafford the Castle Engine Works employees, consisting at the time of some 400, were given a day off with pay. At the 1936 Christmas & new year party held on a Friday evening 1 January 1937, with the annual children's party the following day, Edwards made mention that despite the problems still facing the industry, full employment had almost been maintained throughout the year, locomotive production in percentage terms consisting of: 63% for Egypt; 20% for India; 13% for South Africa and 4% for the home market, illustrating just how important the Egyptian order had been. Mention was also made that during the year two old employees had passed on, former works manager Bill Parkinson and yard foreman A Lawrence. Charlie Homer, the foreman blacksmith, as the oldest employee with over 40 years service, proposed the toast to the Company, and Sydney Edwards responded.

It was through his many business connections that Sydney Edwards became acquainted with the Cadman family who, like Edwards originated from Hanley and were influential in coal mining, general engineering and other associated industries in Staffordshire and Shropshire. In earlier times the Cadmans had been heavily involved in the mining and iron making activities in and around Silverdale, near Newcastle-under-Lyme. The Cadman Brothers, James and John, were the sons of James Cope Cadman (1851-1914), a very famous North Staffordshire mining engineer and for many years general manager of the extensive collieries and iron works at Silverdale. Both sons followed their father into the mining industry. John the elder (9/1877-5/1941), eventually forsook coal mining for the embryo oil industry and went on to become very well known in that industry - at the time of his death he was chairman of the Anglo Iranian Oil Company Limited and the Iraq Petroleum Company Limited, as well as being a director of the Suez Canal Company and the Great Western Railway. However, along with his brother and eldest son John Basil Cope Cadman (born 1909), he also maintained many interests in North Staffordshire. John Cadman was in fact a man of many and varied interests, created First Baron Cadman of Silverdale in 1938; he died in May 1941 and was succeeded as the Second Baron by his eldest son John Basil Cope Cadman. However, his younger brother James Cadman DL; DSC; JP (1878-9/1947) of Walton Hall near Eccleshall, remained in North Staffordshire and became very prominent in local industry, not only in Staffordshire but in Shropshire too, and particularly, but by no means exclusively, the mining industry.

In January 1929 James Cadman had been instrumental in acquiring from the liquidator of the very old-established and well-known firm of North Staffordshire and Yorkshire iron and coal masters, Robert Heath & Lowmoor Limited, the North Staffordshire colliery undertakings of that former combine. The collieries were at Ford Green (Norton Colliery) and Black Bull near Biddulph (Victoria Colliery). As events turned out this was almost all that was salvaged from the tragic demise of this very large employer of labour in and around Stoke-on-Trent, which was reputed to have been in its day the largest producer of bar iron in the world. Reformed as Norton & Biddulph Collieries Limited, the two collieries at Ford Green and Black Bull became a successful mining operation. Later, in May 1931, Cadman almost pulled off a similar operation by the acquisition of Kidsgrove Collieries Limited, which consisted of the large Birchenwood Colliery and associated coking and by-product plant at Kidsgrove, just north of Stoke-on-Trent and on the Staffordshire-Cheshire border. This time, however, though he was unable to

One more interesting design of locomotive built in the period under review must suffice to conclude this Chapter. Manufacturer's number 2572 of September 1937 was a special design for the Port of Par in Cornwall, as the locomotive had to clear a very low bridge taking the Great Western Railway main-line to the west, over a line from the works to a quay - maximum height was 7ft 6in. Cylinders were 10x16in and the weight in working order 16½ tons; the engine was fitted with Bagnall-Price valve gear. With the name JUDY it is seen here shunting at Par in 1968, and its height can be judged in contrast with the covered vans it is hauling. In 1953 JUDY was joined by an identical twin, ALFRED, number 3058.

save the collieries, he did manage to form a consortium with two other local colliery companies to rescue and keep in operation the coking oven and chemical by-product part of the plant. Somewhat earlier, in March 1925, he had rescued from the receiver an old established company of North Staffordshire general engineers, Cowlishaw Walker & Company Limited, which had latterly specialised in the manufacture and repair of mining machinery, holding a number of associated patents with workshops at Eturria. With the acquisition of the Victoria Colliery at Black Bull came the extensive Robert Heath & Lowmoor engineering workshops, and into these he expanded Cowlishaw Walker, which went on to become a very successful company of mining and general engineers. WS Edwards became a director of this company, and later joint managing director through his association with the Cadman family.

Edwards managed to persuade James Cadman and his brother's eldest son, John Basil Cope Cadman, to acquire the Maitland interests in WG Bagnall Limited. However, before this there were a number of changes in the directorship of the Company, partly it would seem in view of increasing concerns of the Maitland family in the way it was being run, but equally to ensure the best deal possible in any sale of all or part of their shareholding. First, on 8 March 1938, Leslie William Rose Robertson was appointed a director, and secondly on 12 July, Charles Maitland resigned to be replaced by his wife Norma Agnes Maxwell Maitland, and finally, on 3 December 1938, Colonel RG Lockhart Jervis was elected to the board. Both Robertson and Lockhart

Jervis described themselves as consulting engineers, and were clearly there to ensure the best possible valuation of the Company. Robertson was the son of the engineer Leslie Stephen Robertson, author of that paper read before the I Mech E, at its summer meeting in Derby in 1898: *Narrow-Gauge Railways, of Two Feet Gauge & Under* - and described earlier in our narrative. This was the paper Gordon Bagnall had made a written contribution to in the published proceedings of the Institution. LWR Robertson was born in Wimbledon in 1896, and became a distinguished locomotive engineer who would have been well known to Edwards, and there was by all accounts not a little friction between the two of them. At the time Robertson was living in Rugeley, so he was not far away from Stafford. He installed himself in an office next door to Edwards, and there was trouble for any employee found talking to him. As can be imagined these were very difficult times for all concerned, not least Edwards himself, as the two of them tried to double-guess each other on a whole range of issues.

Robertson had been a pupil of Sir Henry Fowler, chief mechanical engineer of the Midland Railway at Derby, interrupted by distinguished wartime service in which he rose from the Territorial Army to the regular rank of Captain in the Royal Artillery. After completing his training at Derby in September 1921 he joined the then newly formed locomotive department of Sir WG Armstrong Whitworth & Company Limited, as personal assistant to the general manager, and later represented the company at its London office. This was at a time when Armstrong Whitworth were breaking into the locomotive building business, as discussed earlier, in attempts to maintain the large organisation established to serve the war-time armament and munitions needs. In April 1927 he moved to Kitson & Company Limited, the Leeds locomotive builders, as general manager. Elected a member of the Institution of Mechanical Engineers in January 1931, (associate 26 January 1922) at the time of his appointment to the Bagnall board he was also engaged as a consultant to the Coventry Pneumatic Tyred Railcar Company Limited.

His colleague Lockhart Jervis was not around for long, and would appear to have only been appointed to assist in the sale of the shares, for on 13 December 1938 the Maitlands sold their entire share holding to James Cadman in a cash transaction. On that day Agnes Maitland, Herbert Owen, Lockhart Jervis and Robertson all resigned their respective directorships, and James Cadman was elected a director and chairman of WG Bagnall Limited. A further era in the history of the Company was about to begin, and one no less eventful than those that had proceeded it.

INDUSTRIAL LOCOMOTIVES FOR ALL PURPOSES

All sizes of Locomotives built and designed to suit customers requirements. Photograph above shows 0-4-0 Loco supplied to Messrs. British Guest Keen Baldwins Iron & Steel Co. Ltd., Port Talbot. Weight in working order 43 tons Cylinders 17" dia. × 24" stroke.
Tractive effort at 85% boiler pressure=20962 lbs.

Photograph above shows standard range of Shunting Locomotive, we have designs for all sizes, types and wheeling arrangements, and shall be pleased to quote for any requirements. Loco above was supplied to Spring Mines Ltd., South Africa. Weight in working order 42 tons. Cylinders 16" dia. × 24" stroke.
Tractive effort at 85% boiler pressure = 24,200 lbs.

Photo above shows a standard 4 wheeled Loco, weight in working order 22 tons. Cylinders 12" dia. × 18" stroke.
Tractive effort at 85% boiler pressure=9675 lbs.

Photo above shows a heavy 0-6-0 saddle tank loco, supplied to Messrs. Amington & Glascote Colliery Ltd,, Tamworth. Weight in working order 40 tons. Cylinders 15" dia. × 22" stroke.
Tractive effort at 85% boiler pressure = 18,650lbs.

W. G. BAGNALL LTD. CASTLE ENGINE WORKS, STAFFORD   W. G. BAGNALL LTD. CASTLE ENGINE WORKS, STAFFORD

Part of a publicity leaflet issued in about 1937 illustrating some of the industrial locomotives recently built. Top left is number 2515 of 1934 for Guest Keen & Baldwins Limited at Port Talbot; bottom left number 2450 of 1931 for The Horseley Bridge & Engineering Company Limited at Tipton; top right number 2575 of 1937 for Springs Mines in South Africa, and bottom right number 2508 of 1934 for Glascote Colliery at Tamworth.

Chapter Ten

THE ERA OF THE CADMANS

For a few months after the acquisition of the Maitland shares by James Cadman, he and Edwards were the sole shareholders and only directors of the Company. In the 'deal', Edwards's shareholding went up from the 1,719 shares he held hitherto, to 2,000, with James Cadman holding the other 2,000 making them equal partners. Unfortunately, we do not know if Edwards bought the extra shares or if in fact Cadman purchased the entire holding of the Maitlands and passed some on to him as part of the acquisition arrangements. In December 1938 Cadman's nephew John Basil Cope Cadman, who lived at his father's residence Shenley Park, Bletchley in Buckinghamshire, became a director, and 50 shares were transferred to him by his uncle. In June 1939 there was a further re-distribution of the shares held by James Cadman as he undertook to reduce his individual investment, but almost certainly part of the original agreement between Edwards and himself. In the first instance a number of shares were transferred to individuals; 50 shares to his son James Simon Cadman (always known as Young Jimmy), 50 shares to Hesketh Ramsden and 50 shares to Fredrick William Carder. Secondly, two financial organisations were enlisted to invest in the Company; Branch Nominees Limited of 15, Bishopsgate London EC2, taking 450 shares, and Bishopsgate Nominees Limited, an associated company of the same address taking 225 shares. This left James Cadman with 1,125 shares.

Hesketh Adair Ramsden of Market Drayton, and FW Carder of 'Garth', Milford near Stafford, were business associates of the Cadmans, and held a number of directorships in other companies that the Cadmans were involved with. Ramsden was a mining engineer, and Carder a chartered accountant and partner in F Green & Company, chartered accountants of Victoria Chambers, Stoke-on-Trent; a partnership of which Carder was a principal, and which acted for all the Cadman interests. Both were directors of the Stoke-on-Trent based Norton & Biddulph Collieries Limited, and Cadman was chairman of no less than 19 companies, most but not all local to North Staffordshire, as well as being a director of a number of other companies including the National Provincial Bank.

It is perhaps worth saying a little more about Ramsden, as he had served his country in the First World War, and been awarded the Military Cross. Although only 18 years old he had volunteered in August 1917 and was commissioned as a 2nd Lieutenant on 29th of that month, with the Kings Royal Rifle Corps. He went to France with his regiment in January 1918 and, with the rank of Acting Captain from

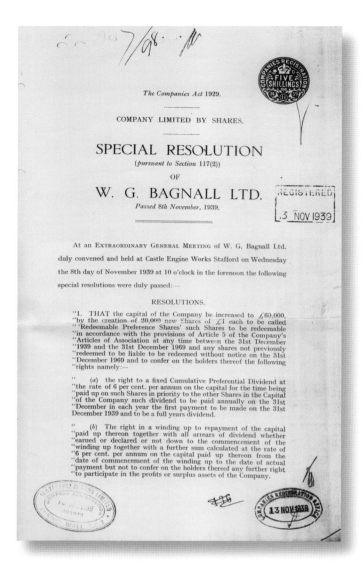

The Companies Act 1929.

COMPANY LIMITED BY SHARES.

SPECIAL RESOLUTION
(*pursuant to Section 117(2)*)

OF

W. G. BAGNALL LTD.
Passed 8th November, 1939.

REGISTERED
3 NOV 1939

At an EXTRAORDINARY GENERAL MEETING of W. G. Bagnall Ltd.
duly convened and held at Castle Engine Works Stafford on Wednesday
the 8th day of November 1939 at 10 o'clock in the forenoon the following
special resolutions were duly passed:—

RESOLUTIONS.

"1. THAT the capital of the Company be increased to £60,000,
"by the creation of 20,000 new Shares of £1 each to be called
"'Redeemable Preference Shares' such Shares to be redeemable
"in accordance with the provisions of Article 5 of the Company's
"Articles of Association at any time between the 31st December
"1939 and the 31st December 1969 and any shares not previously
"redeemed to be liable to be redeemed without notice on the 31st
"December 1969 and to confer on the holders thereof the following
"rights namely:—

"   (a) the right to a fixed Cumulative Preferential Dividend at
"the rate of 6 per cent. per annum on the capital for the time being
"paid up on such Shares in priority to the other Shares in the Capital
"of the Company such dividend to be paid annually on the 31st
"December in each year the first payment to be made on the 31st
December 1939 and to be a full years dividend.

"   (b) The right in a winding up to repayment of the capital
"paid up thereon together with all arrears of dividend whether
"earned or declared or not down to the commencement of the
"winding up together with a further sum calculated at the rate of
"6 per cent. per annum on the capital paid up thereon from the
"date of commencement of the winding up to the date of actual
"payment but not to confer on the holders thereof any further right
"to participate in the profits or surplus assets of the Company.

*First page of the notice of the Special Resolution passed on 8
November 1939, at an EGM of the company increasing the
capital to £60,000 by the creation of 20,000 new shares
of £1 each.*

April 1918, won his MC in action there in the summer.
Discharged in December 1918 Ramsden remained a
reserve officer and was called to serve his country again
in the next conflict, joining the Royal Leicestershire
Regiment in January 1940 at his substantive rank of a
2nd Lieutenant. He was gazetted as Acting Captain
again from 1 February 1940, and as a member of the
1/Fifth Battalion of his Regiment went to Norway in
April 1940, following the German occupation of
Denmark and invasion of Norway. The Leicestershires
disembarked at Andalnes south of Trondheim, with the

ill-fated object of stemming the tide of the German
advance from Olso. As events turned out this abortive
mission was very much a loosing battle from the start,
and despite some advances it was a hopeless situation.
With our forces vastly outnumbered and out flanked,
the operation was eventually abandoned, and we were
lucky to have been able to recover as many of the troops
and equipment as turned out to be the case. Ramsden,
known in his regiment as 'Heckie', was in command of
C Company, and prior to the decision to abandon the
campaign some progress was made, and a stand was
achieved at Tretten. The Battle of Tretten, as it became
known, being in effect, the last stand of the British
Army in Norway. Here on the night of April 23
positions were lost and regained, only to be lost again,
and over a period of some time. Heckie Ramsden led a
bayonet charge which effectively silenced a German
machine gun nest which had been menacing the entire
C Company position for some time. In doing so he gave
his life in extremely gallant circumstances.

At an extraordinary general meeting (EGM) of the
Company held on 13 October 1939, two special
resolutions were passed, one to adopt revised articles of
association, and the second to convert the 4,000 shares
of £10 each into 40,000 shares of £1 each; each £10
share being sub-divided into 10 £1 shares. As well as
establishing this change in the share values, the new
articles allowed for the issue of preference shares that
could be redeemed out of any surplus profits generated,
as well as a number of other minor changes that need
not detain us here. At a second EGM held at the Castle
Engine Works on 8 November 1939, with WS Edwards
in the chair, another special resolution was passed, in
this case to increase the capital of the Company by the
creation of 20,000 new shares of £1 each, to be called
redeemable preference shares. This was in accordance
with the changes in the articles mentioned above. The
resolution also covered the payment of a 6% per annum
cumulative preferential dividend on any such shares
issued, and in priority to any other shares. Last, and
most significant, was the capitalisation of £17,000 of
undivided net profits held by the company, the articles
stipulating the 17,000 redeemable preference shares
created as a result of this be allocated to the existing
shareholders on a pro-rata basis, and based on the same
criteria that would have applied had the £17,000 been
declared as all or part of a dividend. The result of this

issue of new shares gave the shareholders the following individual holdings: -

Name of Shareholder	Ordinary Shares	Preference Shares	
WS Edwards	20,000	8,000	(2,776)
James Cadman	11,250	4,781	(6,247)
Hesketh Adair Ramsden	500	212	(500)
James Simon Cadman	500	212	
Fredrick William Carder	500	212	(500)
John Basil Cope Cadman	500	212	
Branch Nominees	4,500	1,912	(4,500)
Bishopsgate Nominees	2,250	956	(2,250)
Surplus Shares	-	3	
Total Shares	40,000	17,000	

The Articles allowed for the chairman, James Cadman, to hold the surplus shares on trust.

On 23 November 1939, there was a further change in the allocation of the preference shares when 5,724 of those issued to WS Edwards were transferred viz: - 2,588 to Branch Nominees; 1,294 to Bishopsgate Nominees; 1,466 to James Cadman; 288 to FW Carder; 288 to HA Ramsden. This resulted in the figures given in brackets in the table, and was to address a correct balance of ownership rather than the strict distribution as determined by the articles, Edwards signing individual renunciations in favour of each transfer. However, it maintained Edwards as the largest single shareholder, although he did not hold a controlling interest.

Before we move on to the physical activities of the Company over the next decade, it is worth taking stock

Increasing responsibilities and advancing years with the onset of hostilities, persuaded Jim Woollams that his position as Machine Shop Foreman was becoming untenable. However, he agreed to continue working for as long as he felt able during the war but in a lesser role, albeit still in the Machine Shop. This group picture is thought to have been taken to record the occasion of him stepping down as Foreman and includes the Machine Shop staff. That is Jim with his characteristic moustache on the extreme left with Jack Dale the Works Manager at the extreme right. To Jim's left is Jim Robinson the Toolroom Foreman.

of some other people involved. The individual shop foremen were: fitting & erecting Fred Ewington; machine Albert E Somers; pattern shop George White; foundry Cliff Jenkinson; smithy Charlie Homer; boiler shop Arthur Vine: wagon shop Joe Duckers; joiners Arthur Slin; painters (there was no paint shop as such) Oliver Jennings; storekeeper Fred Schofield; toolroom Jim Robinson; power house Stan Fisher; yard gang Harry Rogers. Fred Ewington left the Company shortly after this, going to work for a company in Coventry. Fred was Bagnall trained and quite a loss, his place was taken by another Bagnall trained man, Albert (Bert) Emery. Jack Dale was still the works manager (he became a member of the I Loco E., in September 1941) and FHB Harris the chief draughtsman. Harold Shaw was the buyer and Geoffrey Thorold Owen (not related to the Owen of regulator fame) the chief estimator; Shaw was Kerr, Stuart trained and Owen had taken over as estimator in 1929 when Harry Davies left the Company in 1929.

Geoffrey Owen was a native of Stafford educated at Rossall School and the local technical college, a student apprentice with the Company from 1922 to 1926, later being employed in the drawing office. He was a very useful employee and on various occasions attended to the Company's business on trips to India, Egypt and South Africa - indeed we have explored in an earlier Chapter his involvement with the two-foot gauge pacifics built for the Gwallior Light Railway. In 1939 he left to join Newall's Insulation Company as a contract manager, but Edwards persuaded him to return the following year as his personal assistant. However, in 1940 he joined Associated Industrial Consultants and in 1942 was appointed supervising engineer covering its business in Scotland. As a result of this he became involved with the North British Locomotive Company in Glasgow, joining it as general manager in 1951; he was elected to the board the following year and became managing director in September 1957. In 1958 he was elected president of the Locomotive & Allied Manufacturers Association, as the LMA had become, and remained with North British until his retirement on its demise. Geoff Owen was elected an associate member of the Institution of Locomotive Engineers in 1929, becoming a full member in April 1952.

The demise in early 1938 of the Manchester (Patricroft) locomotive builder Nasmyth Wilson &

Company Limited brought an order to Stafford from one of its regular customers, the Indian Barsi Light Railway. For this famous 2ft 6in gauge railway which extended some 202½ miles from Latur, via Barsi Town and Kurduvadi to Maraj, south of Bombay on the western side of the sub-continent, Nasmyth Wilson had designed a handsome 4-6-4 tender engine for passenger traffic. The design dated from 1928, and there was a contemporary 2-8-2 for goods traffic; Nasmyth had supplied seven of the former and 10 of the latter. The 4-6-4 locomotives had 15x18in cylinders and 3ft 6in diameter coupled wheels, the boilers were superheated and the tractive effort at 85% of the 160psi boiler pressure was 13,114lb. It was because the Barsi line had a maximum axle-load of only seven tons that a 4-6-4 wheel arrangement had been chosen against the original idea of a Pacific, thus enabling a more powerful locomotive to be designed. They were the only design of 4-6-4 tender engines to run of the narrow-gauge lines in India; the total weight in working order of the engines was 35¾ tons, and with the large bogie tender no less than 58¾ tons. Prior to the introduction of these engines the line had been worked by large tank engines, but as the line was extended in length a tender engine, in view of the water problems in that part of India, became essential. Bagnall built two, manufacturer's numbers 2600 and 2601, and these were the last members of the class built. Inspection was by the consulting engineers Sir John Wolf Barry & Partners with despatch in May and June 1939.

The Barsi Light Railway dates from 1897, when the first section between Kurduvadi, on the Great Indian Peninsular Railway main line south from Bombay to Raichur, and Barsi Town was opened in March that year. The almost 89-mile section south-west to Maraj, where it met the Madras & Southern Mahratta Railway metre-gauge main line south from Poona towards Bangalore, was not completed until November 1927, hence the design of the 2-8-2 and 4-6-4 tender engines as mentioned above. The line served the very important pilgrimage centre of Pandharpur and traffic was heavy at certain times of the year. The Bagnall locomotives remained in use until diesels took over in the late 1980s.

Also in 1939, the Company made yet another blatant copy of a Kerr, Stuart design, in this case the narrow-gauge 0-6-0 side tank known by Kerr, Stuart as the Haig class. This class name came from General (later Field Marshall) Sir Douglas Haig, commanding officer of the British Army in France for much of the First World War. The class dated from that period and was in fact a development of an earlier design first supplied for use by the British Army in France. After the war the design became quite popular with the sugar estate industry on the island of Mauritius, and Kerr, Stuart supplied them to a number of customers there. Bagnall built four Haigs between 1938 and 1947, all for former Kerr, Stuart customers in Mauritius, although the Company had in the past done good business with a number of the same sugar plantations (as well as others) supplying locomotives and rolling stock of its own designs. The only changes to the Kerr, Stuart design were a slightly different arrangement of smokebox saddle, the axle springing, Ross Pop safety valves on the firebox rather than Ramsbottom on the dome, and substitution of Bagnall-Price valve gear for Walschaerts. Cylinders were 8¼x12in (the Kerr, Stuart design had 8½in diameter cylinders) and the wheel diameter 1ft 11 ⁵/₈in. The first, manufacturer's number 2603, was despatched in March 1939 for use on the 2ft 5½in gauge system of the Breton Estate of Mon Desert Alma Limited, with the appropriate name BRETON. The others followed: number 2675 in 1943, which was the odd man out as it was built to a different track gauge of 2ft 7½in; number 2827 in 1946, and finally in 1948 number 2894. While the second engine was photographed and used in publicity material, in this case the Company did not

Photograph taken a little before seven o' clock on the morning of 6 November 1979, one of the best times of day to take pictures in India, at Kurduvadi on the famous Barsi Light Railway. The engine is one of the two Bagnall built 4-6-4s, number 2601 of June 1939, and by this time Central Railway class G number 733. The engine is about to leave with the seven o'clock train to Latur.

The Company built two of these neat 0-6-2 tank engines for the Mufulira Copper Mines in Northern Rhodesia, largely based on the earlier 0-8-0 design for South Africa. This one is manufacturer's number 2611, photographed in primer although prior to despatch to Alexander Dock in Liverpool on 27 November 1939, it was painted green and lettered MCM Ltd in 18in high gold letters. The cost was £3,465 free-on-board Liverpool fully erected; although in the event an extra £75 was charged for dismantling and packing. The second engine was built after the war, number 2909 of 1949.

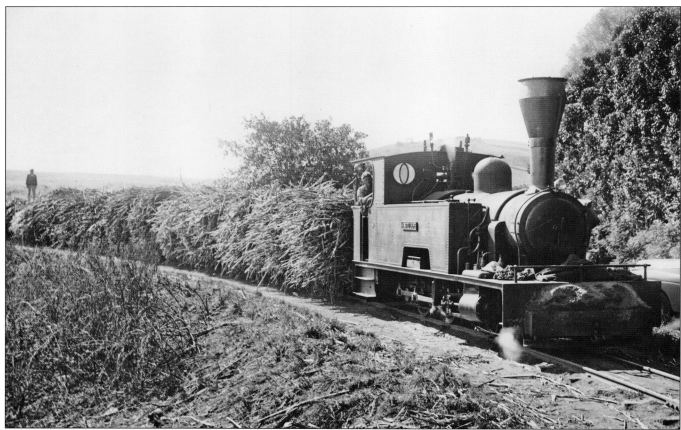

This is one of the later two-foot gauge 4-4-0 side tanks for the Tongaat Sugar Estate in Natal. Manufacturer's number 2627 A BOULLE, sent to Vittoria Dock Birkenhead for shipment on 17 February 1941 - it cost £2,100. Along with several of its sisters this engine is now back in this country, under restoration in the north-east; this photograph however, was taken on location in Natal about 1950. Note the rather impressive spark arresting chimney, twin whistles and the way the sugar cane is loaded on the otherwise invisible wagons!

Manufacturer's number 2675 was one of four 0-6-0 tank locomotives of this design, almost an exact copy of the Kerr, Stuart Haig class of First World War vintage. In fact the only significant difference was the use of Bagnall-Price valve gear rather than Walschaerts. This one was ordered by London based agents Frank Ross & Company, and like the other three was destined for a sugar estate in Mauritius - it was despatched to Liverpool docks for shipment on 22 November 1943.

perpetuate the MOSS BAY idea, and paint the name HAIG on the side tanks! Perhaps discretion was considered the better part of valour, following the Hunslet murmurings after the episode described in the last Chapter.

Yet another significant order in 1939 was for three 4-8-0 tender engines for the 5ft 6in gauge Ceylon Government Railways (CGR), the order coming via the Crown Agents for the Colonies in June. Prior to this order the Company had not built many broad-gauge locomotives, and these were by far the largest, those built earlier being confined to comparatively small tank engines. It was not a new design but one from the Hunslet Engine Company of Leeds stable, going back to 1928: CGR Class A3. Cylinders were 17x22in, driving wheel diameter four-feet, the boiler was superheated and the tractive effort at 85% of the 180psi working pressure equalled 20,266lb. Steel fireboxes were fitted and the cost for the three £20,900 free-on-board Liverpool, although in fact they were shipped from Birkenhead. The all-up weight in working order of the engine was almost 50 tons and with the tender 84 tons and 18 cwt, making them among the biggest engines built to date. Manufacturer's numbers were 2608 to 2610 and despatch in June and July 1940; because of the war the first one was shipped separately from the

other two and they all arrived safely. The running numbers were 334 to 336, and they lasted until displaced by diesels in the period 1970 to 1972. After the war there was a repeat order for a slightly updated version of the design, as a stopgap until diesels could take over, but we will deal with this order in a later Chapter.

One more 1939 order is worthy of special reference, as it was the first obvious sign of the Government, via the Ministry of Supply imposing its will on locomotive production - we shall however, see more this Ministry's influence later. On 10 August 1939, the Company received an order from Eregli Kozmurlerli Isletmesi (ETI Bank - this was a Turkish Government trading organisation) for five metre-gauge 0-6-0 tank engines for use at coal mines in and around Zonguldak, on the Black Sea coast of Turkey. For this order Bagnall designed a very handsome 13x18in outside cylinder pannier tank, with 2ft 11½in diameter wheels; a very modern design with a 180 psi working pressure and Walschaerts valve gear. In view of the type of tank, boiler supply was via a top-feed, and the engines turned the scales at 28½ tons in working order, with a tractive effort at 85% of the boiler pressure of 13,110lb. *The Stafford Newsletter* reported that in securing this order the firm had faced world-wide competition, including

In 1940 the Company delivered its largest broad-gauge locomotives, although to a design of engine supplied earlier by the Hunslet Engine Company of Leeds; three of these 5ft 6in gauge 4-8-0 tender engines for the Ceylon Government Railways, manufacturer's numbers 2608 to 2610 and railway numbers 334 to 336. They were sent to the West Float at Birkenhead, dismantled for shipment in June and July 1940 and were recorded 'on-line' in Ceylon in August, September and November respectively.

German and Belgium manufacturers. It is interesting to speculate why this design was developed, a medium-power six-wheeler with a relatively light axle-load; to some extent it was a modern and much more sophisticated replacement for the earlier 13in cylinder design as supplied to the civil engineering contractor Paulings back in 1921, with other examples built later for stock.

In any event, on 17 July 1940 the Ministry of Supply intervened and stopped the delivery to Turkey of four of these five locomotives, and they were completed to standard rather than metre-gauge. It should be noted nevertheless, that unlike the First World War when Turkey was on the German side, in the Second World War it was neutral, and efforts were made by the Allies to ensure it either stayed that way, or joined them. One of the five locomotives was therefore allowed to go to Turkey, and a replacement order was placed for four more locomotives to replace those commandeered. It may be of course, that the one that was allowed to be exported was in such an advanced stage of construction that an alteration of track gauge would have been very expensive. Nonetheless, as manufacturer's number 2617 it was sent to Langton Dock Liverpool on 30 October 1940, en-route to Zonguldak. The other four, numbers 2613 to 2616, which were completed to suit standard-gauge, went to the Royal Navy. The first one,

number 2613 was sent on 17 September 1940 to the old Kerr, Stuart California Works at Stoke-on-Trent, part of which was being used as an Admiralty machinery and armament storage depot. The other three, numbers 2614 to 2616, were sent between September and November 1940 to Rosyth Royal Dockyard on the River Forth in Scotland. Worth a brief mention here, the Admiralty store at the old Kerr, Stuart works was used to house, among other items, the spare turrets and 14, 15 and 16in gun barrels for the main armament of the Royal Navy's battleships and battle cruisers.

The replacement order was dated 3 September 1940, four locomotives of the same type, the numbers 2639 to 2642 being allocated. These four were sent for shipment in May and June 1941, three to Birkenhead and one to Hull, and due to war-time exigencies they were shipped in three different vessels. Tradition in the works had it that at least one of the five locomotives sent to Turkey was lost at sea, and certainly enthusiasts who have visited Turkey from the early 1970s, including one of the authors, were never able to locate them all. This was despite two, and perhaps three, being dismantled and some of the parts used to build standard-gauge locomotives, all of which have been observed. It is perhaps worth mentioning at this juncture that a Trade & Payments Agreement had been established between the British and Turkish

At Catalagzi, near the Black Sea port of Zonguldak in Turkey, are situated coal mines and this is where some at least, of the metre-gauge Bagnall pannier tanks described in the adjoining text worked. This is one of the engines delivered as replacements for those commandeered by the Government, number 2640, colliery number 23, on 25 June 1976 waiting to take a train of empty wagons from the exchange siding with the Turkish Railways to the mine. Notice to the left, one of the vehicles that were used at shift change times to transport the miners to and from the colliery!

Governments on 3 February 1940, which was refined by a subsequent agreement of December the same year. The prices charged for these locomotives are interesting. The price quoted to Eti Bank was £1,966 free on board Liverpool, which was the selling price for both number 2617, and the four replacements. The Admiralty however, paid £2,500 for the engine that went to Stoke and £2,566 for the three that went to Rosyth. As these prices were free-on-rail at the destination, the extra £66 in the second case presumably covered the longer distance to Rosyth.

There was a further order from EKI in October 1945, as clearly the Turkish coal mines must have liked the design, in this case four more locomotives, manufacturer's numbers 2845 to 2848, despatched in September and October 1946. Price escalation since the earlier engines were built resulted in this batch being sold for £3,780 free-on-board Liverpool. Despite the design being, ostensibly at least, specifically for Turkey, three more engines of the same type were built, one for use in this country and two, quite amazingly, for use in India. It may be that these three were laid down to stock at the same time as the replacement engines for Turkey, as they were built at the same time, but if that was the case the surviving records are silent. The one for use in this country, manufacturer's number 2643,

was ordered on 12 November 1940 by the Ministry of Supply and intended for the War Department (WD) camp at Tidworth in Hampshire. In the event it was sent in September 1941 to Meole Brace, for use on the Shropshire & Montgomery Railway, a light railway running from Shrewsbury north-west some 18 miles to the Welsh border town of Llanymynech, that had been commandeered by the WD. This locomotive had a varied career and finished its life with the National Coal Board at Morton Colliery in Derbyshire; it was scrapped there in June 1964.

The two for India, like the Turkish ones, were built to suit the metre-gauge and were ordered on 13 September 1940 via the consulting engineers Robert White & Partners. Manufacturer's numbers 2645 and 2646, for the Jaipur State Railway, which classified them as its class TJ. Despatched in November 1940, they were sent to Birkenhead Docks for shipment to Bombay. When one of the authors visited Junagadh and Bhavnagar in Gujarat during January 1977, he found both these locomotives, though they were not actually in use. One of them, number 2646, had by 1982 migrated to the Indian Railways Museum at Delhi, whilst one of the British examples has also been preserved. This is the original class member originally ordered for Turkey, number 2613, and now carrying the

Western Railway of India No 643 of class TJ, manufacturer's number 2646, was one of two engines to the basic Turkish design, sent to India in 1941. It is seen here at Junagadh on 20 January 1977, and although it had recently been taken out of service, the kindly Loco Foreman had it hauled outside the shed for photographs, and as can be seen it was in excellent external condition. This locomotive is now in the Indian Railway Museum in Delhi, whilst its sister, which was out of use at Bhavnagar on the same date, was later scrapped.

name BROOKFIELD, after the Brookfield Foundry & Engineering Company, which had acquired the former Kerr, Stuart California Works from the Admiralty after the war. The WD engine cost £2,599 and the Indian ones £3,012 free-on-board Liverpool; in the event as noted above, they went via Birkenhead.

A special design of 1940 was a 700m/m gauge 0-6-2 tender engine with 10x12in cylinders, outside frames and 1ft 7in diameter driving wheels. A modern and quite good looking machine with a neat six-wheel tender its total weight in working order 22 tons and 10 cwt. The engine had a commodious cab with a double roof, twin Worthington-Simpson horizontal boiler feed pumps, one on each side foot plating alongside the smokebox, piston valve cylinders and Walschaerts valve gear. The order came via British agents Guthrie & Company Limited of Dorking in Surrey, and delivery was on 6 February 1941 to Birkenhead for shipment to Singapore. The engine was destined for Oil Palms of

Malay Limited, for use at its Ulu Remis palm oil plantation in Central Johore. Brass plates with the designation SL No 4 (Steam Locomotive No 4) were fitted on each cab side, as well as being painted on the tender sides; a large balloon stack spark arresting chimney completed the picture. The Oil Palms of Malay Company had been formed in June 1930, and among its interests had acquired the Merlimau Rubber Plantations, which was where, as related in Chapter One, the late Richard Gordon Bagnall had worked prior to joining the army in 1915. The estate where the engine worked was approximately 12 miles south of Kluang, with the actual factory two miles east of Layang Layang station on the Malayan Railways. Dating from 1930, until the Bagnall was delivered it had relied on German built locomotives which of course, were not available in war-time. This engine would only have reached the estate a short time before the Japanese invasion of the peninsular commenced in December

1941; the advance was comparatively fast and Layang Layang was the site of some very strong resistance. It was reported that the retreating army placed a hand grenade in the firebox of the Bagnall locomotive, as well as others used on the plantation, to prevent them being used by the occupying Japanese. Be that as it may, the engine was later repaired - doubtless after the occupation ended - and it continued in use until replaced by diesels in about 1956.

It is interesting to consider why a completely new design of locomotive was developed for this order, coming at the time with the war time constraints. It may be that Bagnall were attempting to adopt some continental design practices, as the completed locomotive certainly resembled one of perhaps, German manufacture, and as mentioned earlier the previous locomotives on the estate were of German build. The engine had a large firebox with a Haycock raised outer wrapper, and to allow for a big grate area - it was 10 sq ft - the boiler was mounted high, such that the firebox sat on top of the frames. The boiler barrel had large inspection covers just ahead of the firebox, which was another German design feature. Clearly the engine was intended to burn inferior fuel. The cylinder dimensions are interesting too, with the comparatively short stroke of 12in for a 10in bore. Perhaps surprisingly Ramsbottom safety valves were fitted, but there was a modern Owen poppet valve double-beat regulator in the dome. The manufacturer's number was 2628, and the tender price was £2,999 free-on-board Liverpool,

although actually shipped from Birkenhead. After the end of hostilities, despite being a British company, further engines came from German builders. However, the design was chosen again at Stafford for the last steam locomotive order the Company received, but the story of this one will have to wait until Chaper Fourteen.

Two orders that were subsequently cancelled are worth a brief mention. The first, allocated manufacturer's number 2636, for an 18in gauge four-wheel saddle tank for the Royal Arsenal at Woolwich. The order was placed on 28 May 1940, and the design work was completed by late September. Bagnall proposed one of its standard circular firebox 7x12in cylinder machines, but as no engines of this type had been built for some time, a lot of new design work was undertaken. The engine would have had outside frames in view of the narrow track gauge, and a saddle tank encompassing the smokebox, a design feature not hitherto used on these small locomotives. Walschaerts valve gear was specified and the engine was designed to burn oil fuel. Some material was ordered and some parts were made when, for whatever reason we know not, the order was cancelled on 12 November 1940. The quoted price was £1,070, and delivery was due on 1 October, but only if the material required for construction was available in four to five weeks of the order being placed. Unfortunately we do not know at this distance in time if this was achieved, and if perhaps a projected late delivery was the reason for cancellation.

Number 2628 is the 700m/m gauge 0-6-2 tender engine described in the text and sent to Malaya in February 1941. Notice the duplex boiler feed-pump on the foot framing at the front, the steam turbine alternator on the boiler for electric lighting and the design of firebox - this was particularly large as the engine was designed to burn just about anything combustible as coal was in short supply in the part of Malaya is was destined for.

In any event it was a shame, as this engine would have been the last 18in gauge steam locomotive built for commercial use in this country, and the last steam locomotive to be built for use on the very old 18in gauge internal railway system at Woolwich. Those parts that were made were later incorporated in manufacturer's number 2841, of which more anon.

The second order came from the Indian Jamnagar & Dwarka Railway for a P class metre-gauge 4-6-0 tender engine. This order was placed on 28 August 1940, with Robert White & Partners the consulting engineers. Very little if anything was done to progress the order, as not much in the way of material was made available. It has to be remembered that by this stage of the war all raw material was being allocated by the Ministry of Supply to ensure that the wartime needs of the country and its allies were best addressed. Obviously in this case material was not available, which is perhaps surprising, because as noted above, material was made available for other engines that were sent to India around the same time. It has not been possible to trace the actual date of cancellation, and the manufacturer's number allocated - 2644 - was left blank in the order books. After the war two engines of this class, but with superheated boilers (class PS) were built for this same railway, manufacturer's numbers 2843 and 2844 being despatched on 15 September 1947, to an order dated 27 October 1945. It would seem from surviving records that these two PS class locomotives were in fact a part replacement for the earlier order.

It was not only material that the Ministry of Supply concerned itself with during the war, but also the allocation of man-power. Ministry inspectors would regularly visit the works, as they did all other engineering establishments, to ensure that the man-power met the work-loads, or not as the case may be. Men were often arbitrarily transferred, and in the case of Bagnall some men were moved to the new ordnance factories at nearby Swynnerton (ROF No 5), and somewhat further away to the Radway Green Factory near Crewe; this was designated as a Small Arms Factory. In addition some of the younger members became 'Bevin Boys', and were transferred to work in the coal mines around Stoke-on-Trent, whilst others joined the forces as outlined later in this Chapter.

Yet another Kerr, Stuart design perpetuated at the Castle Engine Works was for very small narrow-gauge engines that had originally been specifically designed for

This is one of the two Indian class PS metre-gauge tender engines built for the Jamnagar & Dwarka Railway in 1947, but in effect partly a result of the cancelled war-time order mentioned in the text. Numbers 2844 and 2845, as railway numbers 19 and 20. The design was an interesting combination of old and new, a boiler with a narrow firebox to fit between the frames was to the old school, whilst the superheating and piston valve cylinders were new; Sunbeam electric lighting was fitted. The engines later became Indian Railways 31649 and 31650, and remained in use on the Western Railway in Gujarat until the late 1970s. They were both despatched, dismantled for shipment to Vittoria Dock at Birkenhead on 15 September 1947, and the selling price was £9,572 each free-on-board.

use at the various Glasgow Gas Works. The design had actually originated way back in 1893 with the Scottish builder Sharp Stewart, but Kerr, Stuart built by far the largest number, and for other gas works in Scotland as well as those in Glasgow. We do not know exactly why Bagnall became involved, especially as the orders were placed during the war years, but its known ability to build to Kerr, Stuart designs may have had a bearing on the decision. Two were built, manufacturer's numbers 2618 of June 1940 and 2662 of June 1942, the first for Dalmarnock Gas Works and the second for Tradeston Gas Works. These were very small two-foot gauge locomotives with a low overall height of no more than five feet and no cab as such; this was to enable them to shunt small wagons within the gas retorts. Cylinder size was 6½x9in and the wheel diameter 1ft 8in, the meagre 22 gallon water capacity being held in a small well tank which Bagnall referred to as a frame tank, located between the frames at the front. Because of this position for the tank, there was no room between the frames for the valve chests, so these were on top of the

outside cylinders, but as the Stephenson's link motion was inside the frames, the valves themselves were actuated via rocking shafts. The grate-area was only 2.5 sq ft and the weight in working order four tons; tractive effort at 85% of the 140 psi working pressure amounting to no more than 2,262lb. The first engine cost £648, but the cost of the second, doubtless due to war time inflation, escalated to no less than £1,098. These two locomotives were the last of the gene built, and engines of this type, modified slightly over the years, were a familiar sight for many years around a number of Scottish gas works. The two Bagnall-built examples lasted until March 1957, when they were both scrapped. As well as these two locomotives two spare boilers were supplied for the earlier examples built by Kerr, Stuart, the first one in late 1939, and another in 1949.

It was during the war years and those immediately preceding them that Bagnall made its first significant inroads into the supply of standard-gauge locomotives for the British industrial market. As has already been

Another of the Kerr, Stuart designs perpetuated by the firm was this small two-foot gauge 0-4-0 well-tank, a very popular type with various Glasgow gasworks. Two were built during the war; this is the first, number 2618 of June 1940, sent to Dalmarnock Gasworks - the initials stand for Glasgow Corporation Gas Department. The simplicity of the design will be apparent and the gentleman standing alongside is the chargehand erector responsible for the engines erection, Bert Emery, posed here to give an idea of scale to the illustration.

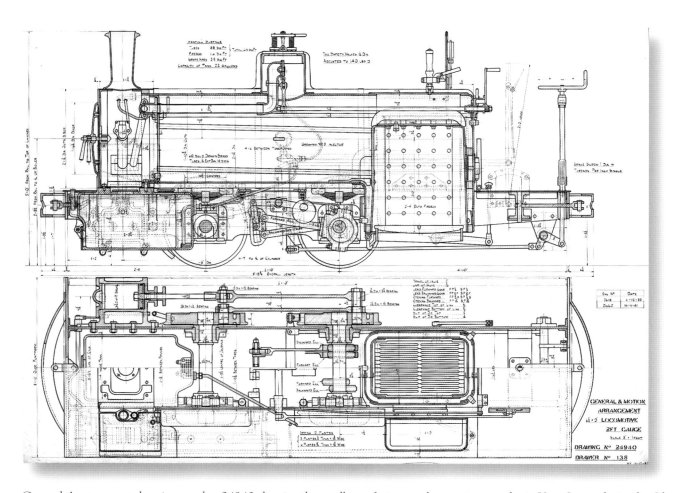

General Arrangement drawing number 24940 showing the small two-foot gauge locomotives to a basic Kerr, Stuart design for Glasgow gasworks. The drawing covers numbers 2618 and 2662, dated 11 December 1939 and 14 November 1941 respectively. Notice the small size and position of the well tank between the frames at the front and the general simplicity of the design.

pointed out, the Company was never a prolific supplier in this arena. Along with its other activities, the Ministry of Supply involved itself in trying to ensure that the best possible use was made of production facilities around the country, and this had, for Bagnall, the unfortunate effect of allocating the building of diesel locomotives to those builders who had the most experience in that field. We have already seen that the Bagnall production of diesel locomotives had been quite small, and the Deutz connection for the supply of the engines and transmissions was of course, severed with the onset of hostilities with Germany. The Hunslet Engine Company and John Fowler & Company, both Leeds based, along with a number of other builders, had made much more progress before the war in developing ranges of diesel locomotives and were therefore, allocated a lot of the diesel shunting locomotive market.

As a result Bagnall concentrated on steam. It should be mentioned nevertheless, that this did not stop the Company from continuing to advertise in the trade press its ability to design and build diesel-engined locomotives, and a picture of the first of the double-bogie locomotives built for the Ashanti Goldfields adorned its adverts throughout the war years.

Mention has already been made of how the 12in cylinder four-wheel saddle tank design had been updated, to both reduce construction time and material content. Just prior to the war the slightly larger, 14in cylinder four-wheel saddle tank industrial shunting engine had also been redesigned, on generally similar lines, and with the same objectives in mind; the opportunity being taken to increase the cylinder stroke from 20 to 22in at the same time. Significant numbers of both the 12in and the 14in cylinder engines were

Two of the 14½in cylinder four-coupled saddle tanks built during the war on behalf of the Ministry of Supply, posed outside the Erecting Shop in August 1942. The occasion was a visit by members of the Canadian armed forces, prior to their involvement with the famous Dieppe engagement later that year. During the war there were frequent visits of this nature to factories all over the country, moral boosters so that members of the armed forces could meet the people and see activities in the civilian sector, and for those not serving in the forces to meet those who were. Fourth from the right, partly hidden between the solders and the fellow with the trilby is Tom Stockton, assistant works manager at the time, while eighth from the right with hands in pockets is Jack Dale the works manager. The other gentlemen in plain clothes are officials of the Ministry of Supply. The locomotives are to the left, number 2671 new to Vickers Armstrong at Elswick, and to the right, number 2672 new to Thornhill Power Station near York.

ROF No 15 No1 is one of the nine 14½in cylinder four-wheel saddle tanks supplied to Royal Ordnance Factories in 1941 and 1942. This picture was taken at the Patricroft Factory near Manchester, which was ROF No 16. This engine was originally delivered to the Bescot Factory in Birmingham which had the designation ROF 15 - it moved north in 1947 with a spell en-route at the factory at Swynnerton, south of Stoke-on-Trent. The Patricroft Factory was the former works of the locomotive builder Nasmyth Wilson, mentioned in this Chapter in connection with the Barsi Light Railway locomotives - it ceased locomotive production in 1938. The engine appears in the not untypical unkempt external condition that was the lot of many industrial shunting locomotives - the photograph dates from the early 1950s.

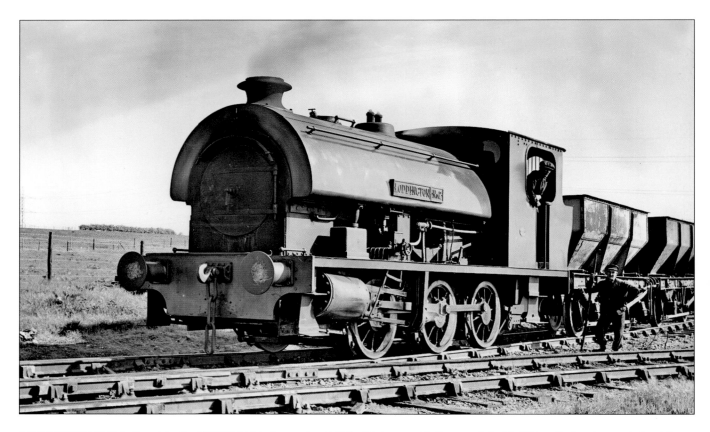

LODDINGTON No 2, originally BYFIELD No 2, number 2655 of February 1942, one of six 15x22in cylinder six-coupled saddle tanks of very clean and neat lines built during the war, at Ministry of Supply instigation, for use at various east midlands ironstone quarries. Although new to the Byfield Quarries the engine is seen here on 24 May 1957 after transfer, although not directly, to the quarries at Loddington; both are situated in Northamptonshire.

supplied just before and during the war, and to a whole range of customers including for example, power stations, gas works, chemical works and dockyards. A slightly larger version with 14½in diameter cylinders found favour with the Royal Ordnance Factories (ROF) during the war, and nine were supplied in 1941 and 1942 for use at its factories around the country. For the higher power range a 15x22in cylinder 0-6-0 saddle tank was developed, based on a pre-war design of 1934 (manufacturer's number 2508 for Glascote Colliery at Tamworth), and at Ministry of Supply instigation a number were built for use at east midlands ironstone quarries. During the war it was essential to develop the extraction of home-mined iron ore to its maximum, hence the need for additional railway motive power in both existing, and newly developed ore fields. The first of these locomotives, manufacturer's number 2629 of February 1941 and named STAVELEY, was for the Staveley Coal & Iron Company's quarries at Pilton,

near Luffenham in Rutland. The design presented an extremely good-looking locomotive with a full-length saddle tank, large cab and an ample coal bunker. Five more were supplied to various ironstone quarries in the east midlands between February and July the following year, and they all had long lives, some of them moving around between different quarries several times. The six locomotives lasted until the home-produced iron ore mining industry in this country effectively disappeared in the early 1970s, although four of them have survived into preservation.

As mentioned above several of the 12in cylinder four-wheelers were built in this period too, and again for a whole range of customers. One of them, manufacturer's number 2588 of May 1938, was built to suit a track gauge of 3ft 6in and went to South Africa - for Stewarts & Lloyds Limited at its factory at Vereeniging near Johannesburg. The order for this locomotive came via another the firm's South African

TELEPHONE Nos. 321 & 322.
PRIVATE BRANCH EXCHANGE.
Telegraphic Address:
"BAGNALL, PHONE, STAFFORD."

CONTRACTORS TO THE ADMIRALTY, WAR OFFICE, INDIA OFFICE AND FOREIGN GOVERNMENTS.

ALL COMMUNICATIONS TO BE ADDRESSED TO THE COMPANY, NOT INDIVIDUALS.

PRIVATE.
CODES { A.B.C. 5TH EDITION.
ENGINEERING.
BEDFORD McNEIL.
WESTERN UNION.

W. G. BAGNALL Ld.,
LOCOMOTIVE BUILDERS & RAILWAY ENGINEERS.

LONDON OFFICE:
32, VICTORIA STREET, WESTMINSTER.
TELEPHONE No.:
1882 ABBEY.

YOUR REFERENCE

OUR REFERENCE
GTO/PL

Castle Engine Works.
Stafford.

16th March, 1940.

SPECIFICATION

of a
0-6-0 TYPE SADDLE TANK LOCOMOTIVE.

For Messrs. The Staveley Coal & Iron Co. Ltd.,

1, Queen's Road,

NOTTINGHAM.

The whole of the material used in the construction of this Locomotive to be of the highest quality procurable, and to conform to the latest Specifications of the British Engineering Standards Association for Railway Rolling Stock Material. The workmanship to be of the best description.

SUMMARY OF LEADING PARTICULARS.

Gauge of Railway		4' 8½"		Heating Surface of Tubes	601.5	sq. ft.
Wheeling Arrangement		0-6-0		" " Firebox	65.5	sq. ft.
Diam. of Cylinders		15	ins.	" " Superheater	----	sq. ft.
Stroke of Pistons		22	ins.	Total Heating Surface	667	sq. ft.
Diam. of Driving Wheels	3 ft. 4¼	ins.	Grate Area	13.75	sq. ft.
" Leading "	3 ft. 4½	ins.	Working Pressure	180	lbs. per sq. in.
" Trailing "	3 ft. 4½	ins.	Bunker Capacity	60	cb. ft.
Rigid Wheelbase	10 ft. 6	ins.	Tank	800	galls.
Total	10 ft. 6	ins.			
Maximum Height	11 ft. 0	ins.	Weight when empty (approx.)	30¼	tons.
" Width	8 ft. 2	ins.	" in working order "	38½	tons.
" Length } excluding Buffers }	23 ft. 5¾	ins.	Tractive effort at 85% B.P.	18,650	lbs.
			Ratio Adhesion/Tractive Effort	4.6 to 1.	

Description	The Engine to be carried on **six** wheels, and to be of the 0-6-0 type, with outside cylinders and **Saddle** Tank, the general design to be similar to that shown by the accompanying **Photograph type E.2508.** and Drawing No. 20954.
Boiler and Firebox Casing.	The Boiler casing to be of best Siemens Martin open Hearth Acid Steel Plates. The barrel to be **9** ft. **1** ins. long, in **2** rings, the smallest being **3** ft. **7** ins. diameter inside, **1/2** ins. thick; the longitudinal seams to be double rivetted **butt** joints; circumferential seams **single** rivetted. Smokebox Tube-plate **3/16** ins. thick. The Firebox to be of the **Round Top** type, the Shell to be **4** ft. **6** ins. long by **4** ft. **1** ins. wide outside at foundation ring. The top and side Plates to be **1/2** ins. thick, the throat plate **1/2** ins. thick and the back plate **1/2** ins. thick. The whole of the rivets in the Boiler Casing to be **3/16** ins. diam. 1⅜ ins. pitch, hydraulically rivetted wherever possible. A Steam Dome to be securely rivetted to the Boiler Barrel with a heavy strengthening ring inside the barrel directly underneath. A liberal supply of Mud Plugs and wash out facilities to be provided, the Boiler Plates to be suitably stiffened where mud plugs are screwed in. The Foundation and Firehole Rings to be forged from best selected scrap iron or welding quality mild steel.

Front page of the specification as quoted to the Staveley Coal & Iron Company Limited, for the first member of the 15in cylinder six-coupled saddle tanks for the ironstone industry. The engine delivered as a result of this particular specification was number 2629 of February 1941, which went to the Company's Pilton quarries at Luffenham in Rutland. This is a typical example of a specification as sent to customers, potential and otherwise, at this period.

This is an illustration of an unusual example of the 12in cylinder four-wheel saddle tank design, built to suit a very low loading gauge, the overall height was only eight-feet, doubtless to clear some obstruction at the Park Gate Iron & Steel Works at Rotherham, where it was despatched on 4 April 1942. The works had older engines built to suit the same loading gauge, but these were not built by Bagnall. The manufacturer's number was 2659. In January 1957 this engine was moved to the Charwelton ironstone quarries near Banbury, also owned by the Park Gate Company, where it remained until December 1963 when it was scrapped.

agents, Baldwins (South Africa) Limited with offices in Johannesburg. This engine cost £1,750 carriage, insurance and freight paid to Durban, and was fully erected and not dismantled for shipment. A slightly larger version with 13x18in cylinders, but of the same basic design, was manufacturer's number 2592 of June 1938, in this case for Forsters Glass Company Limited at St Helens. With the name POCKET NOOK, the customer was very particular about how the engine was painted and reserved the right to inspect it before delivery; it also had the cab slightly altered with rounder corners and half-round beading. Other 12in cylinder four-wheelers were for the Admiralty at Portsmouth, George Richards Engineers from Altringham, the North Thames Gas Board, Park Gate Iron & Steel Company Limited at Rotherham - in the latter case especially cut-down in height to clear a low loading gauge - and there were a number of others too. To give an idea of how costs increased as war time inflation began to bite, the engine for Forsters Glass was sold for £1,560 delivered to St Helens, whilst the Park

Gate engine, manufacturer's number 2659 of April 1942, was sold for £2,433 delivered to Sheffield.

A slightly larger design of six-coupled saddle tank was introduced in 1942, in this case with 16x24in cylinders and 3ft 6½in diameter wheels, again partly based on a pre-war design. In June 1936 Bagnall had delivered manufacturer's number 2547 to the British War Department for use in Singapore, where the Royal Artillery had a standard-gauge system to serve the gun battery at Changi. In this case the cylinder stroke was 22in, and the wheel diameter 3ft 4½in, nevertheless this engine was the prototype for the new locomotives. Other engines similar to the Changi one had been supplied to the Butterley Company for use at its collieries in Derbyshire and Nottinghamshire, in this case in 1939 and 1940. However, a significant amount of redesign took place in 1942 and one of the innovations was a saddle tank with partly vertical sides, rather then being completely rounded, which not only enabled the water capacity to be increased slightly, but also assisted the crews forward vision. Three were built

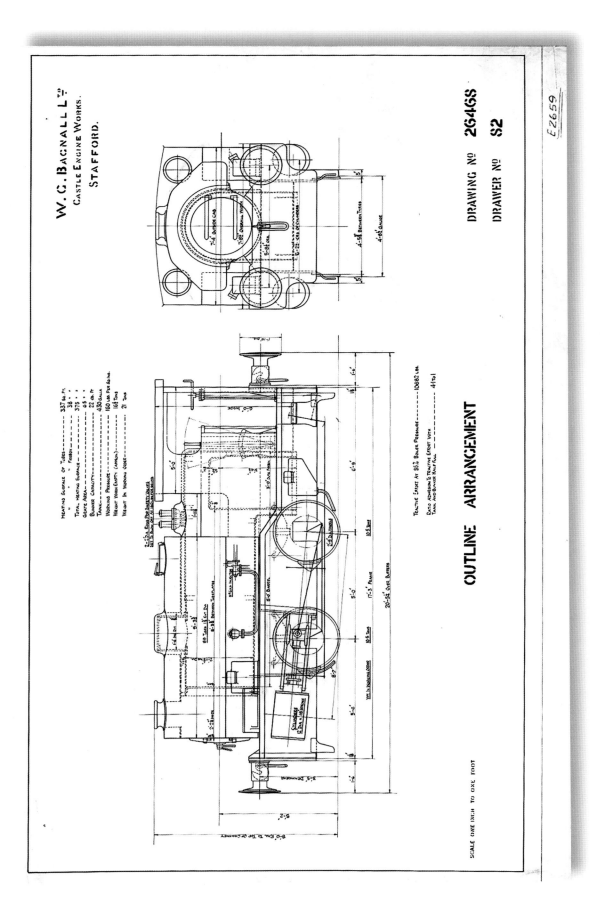

Outline diagram of the cut-down Park Gate locomotive number 2659. Notice the low overall height of eight-feet.

Another variant of the 12in cylinder four-wheel saddle tank was this one, number 2657, one of two despatched in March 1942 to the North Thames Gas Board for use at the enormous Beckton gasworks, on the north bank of the Thames in Essex. The manufacturer's numbers were 2657 and 2658, and this photograph shows the first engine, works No 7. Notice the single slide bar as these locomotives had smaller driving wheels than usual on a 12in cylinder engine, 2ft 9in diameter as opposed to 3ft 0½in. Observe too, the lack of a cab and the solid, rather than spring buffers.

This is the first of the 16x24in cylinder six-coupled industrial shunting locomotives to the slightly revised war-time design. Manufacturer's number 2680 it was new in December 1942 for the Birchenwood Coking Plant at Kidsgrove, north of Stoke-on-Trent, where it is seen at work on 8 June 1970. As plant No 4, it remained in use there until the plant closed in 1973, and whilst now in preservation, it is currently in store. When new it cost £3,960.

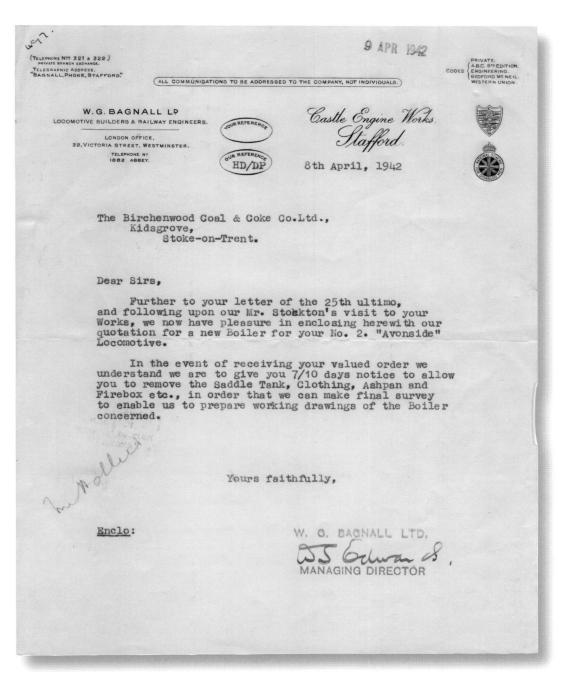

A contemporary example of the firm's letter heading is this letter dated 8 April 1942, and signed by WS Edwards as the managing director - his signature differed little over the years. The text is in connection with the new boiler for the Birchenwood Coal & Coke Company's Avonside 0-6-0 saddle tank mentioned in the text. Following receipt of the quotation for a new boiler, it was decided to send the complete locomotive to Stafford for a full overhaul, but not until the new locomotive in the previous illustration had been delivered. Mr Hollies, whose name appears in pencil on the letter, was the manager of the coking plant.

in 1942 and 1943, manufacturer's numbers 2680 to 2682, one each for the Birchenwood Coking Plant at Kidsgrove near Stoke-on-Trent, Sneyd Colliery at Burslem in Stoke-on-Trent, and Preston Docks. This design became a standard one after the war, with Preston Docks taking no fewer than six more, three in each of the years 1946 and 1948. Another eight were built for use in the North Staffordshire coalfield, along with one for use at Rawdon Colliery in Leicestershire.

The last two were supplied as late as 1955, and were the last conventional steam locomotives built by the Company for the home market. One more was laid down to a stock order but never completed, those parts built which included the boiler, being sold to the North Staffordshire Area of the NCB for use as spares.

A particularly interesting order of May 1940 was for three metre-gauge 4-4-0 locomotives, which were a slightly updated version of a very old, and indeed a pre

Western Railway of India OJ class metre-gauge 4-4-0 tender engine number 639, at Bhavnagar Para shed on 17 January 1977. One of three despatched in late 1943, the basic design was a very old one, dating back to 1883, but clearly favoured by the Jaipur State Railway for which the engines were built. Obvious modifications to the original design are a superheated boiler and piston valve cylinders. The manufacturer's number is 2633, and by the time the photograph was taken one of the trio had already been withdrawn, although still in situ, while the other two were eking out their mileage on shunting duties. The last of the three, number 2635, is now preserved on a plinth outside Jaipur railway station.

British Engineering Standards Association Indian design - going back to 1883 in fact! This was the O class, and the three built by Bagnall, manufacturer's numbers 2633 to 2635, were classified OJ, and among other refinements had piston valve cylinders and superheated boilers. The order was via consulting engineers Robert White & Partners and the locomotives were despatched in December 1940 for the Jaipur State Railway, a railway that quite obviously liked this aged design. As with the pannier tanks mentioned earlier in this Chapter, when one of the authors visited Bhavnagar in January 1977 all three of these locomotives were still in existence, two of them being used as works shunters - a less suitable locomotive for

shunting it would be hard to imagine - and one of them was is steam and working.

It is worth mentioning at this juncture that, through the Cadman connection, WS Edwards took up an additional appointment as a member of the board of directors of Cowlishaw Walker & Company Limited, and because of this there was on occasions an exchange of workload between the two companies. For example, Cowlishaw Walker at its Black Bull Biddulph works, which was north of Tunstall in Stoke-on-Trent, fabricated the tender tanks for the three Jaipur locomotives, and there were a number of other instances of tanks, cabs and other plate work being thus sub-contracted. In return Cowlishaw Walker, which on occasion contracted to repair and rebuild industrial shunting locomotives, in particular, but not exclusively, from local North Staffordshire collieries, sub-contracted much of this work to Bagnall. Not surprisingly some of the locomotives came from the Cadman-owned Norton & Biddulph Collieries. Sometimes the complete locomotives would come to the Castle Engine Works for attention, while on other occasions only parts of them. This usually including the boilers, often for new fireboxes to be fitted along with other repairs, and on a number of occasions complete new boilers were supplied too. The Cadman connection with the Birchenwood coking and chemical by-product plant was doubtless the reason why the new 16in cylinder 0-6-0 locomotive mentioned above was supplied there. Later there was a similar locomotive built new for Norton Colliery, and one of the earlier

Birchenwood locomotives came to Stafford during the war for a new boiler and complete rebuild. This was an Avonside six-wheel inside-cylinder saddle tank dating back to 1897.

In July 1940 yet another interesting order arrived, in this case from The Engineering Company of Portugal, for two very large 600 m/m gauge 2-8-2 side tank locomotives for the Cia do Caminho de Ferro de Porto Amboim. This railway ran some 90 miles inland from Porto Amboim on the coast of Portuguese West Africa, to coffee plantations at Gabela, on the Amboim plateau at an altitude of some 3,300 feet - all the climbing being in the last 50 miles or so. Dating from 1925, Henschel of Germany had been the traditional supplier of motive power to this railway, but because of the war this source of supply was not available, hence the order coming to Bagnall. Nevertheless when additional locomotives

First of the two large 600m/m gauge 2-8-2 tank engines despatched in 1941 to Portuguese West Africa (now Angola), numbers 2637 and 2638, and to some extent based on earlier six-coupled engines for the Burma Mines. Notice the large wood rack for fuel, Belpaire firebox wrapper, sand boxes on the boiler, enormous oil headlamp and the position of the mechanical lubricator behind the trailing coupled axle. Quite magnificent beasts they were too, and indeed they may still be in existence, although nothing has been heard of them for several years.

This is one of the 16 15 ton bogie vans ordered at the same time as the locomotive in the previous illustration, for the Cia do Caminho de Ferro de Porto Amboim. The tare weight was 6096 kilos (6 metric tons - almost 6 imperial tons) and the gross weight 23,336 kilos (23 metric tons - almost 23 imperial tons). Points to note are the American design three-piece diamond frame bogies and the corrugated iron roof.

were required after the war, the railway returned to Henschel as its supplier. For such a narrow-gauge these were big locomotives with cylinders 13x16in, wheels 2ft 6in diameter and the weight in working order of 42 tons. The boilers were superheated and the vacuum brake was fitted; tractive effort at 85% of the 180 psi working pressure was 13,790lb. Designed to burn wood fuel, they had additional fuel capacity on top of the tanks and boiler, and when out on the line it seems that a bogie wagon was semi-permanently attached to carry even more fuel supplies. To some extent these locomotives were based on the earlier 2-6-2 tank engines built for the Burma Mines. Manufacturer's numbers 2637 and 2638 were allocated and the cost was £10,570 for the two. Delivery was protracted due to the war, and they were sent for shipment in a dismantled state, the first one to Bramley Dock Liverpool on 3 November 1941, and the second to No 8 Dock at Salford in Manchester on 24 January the following year. However, the first one was not shipped on this occasion; instead it was moved on 2 January 1942 to Newport Docks and shipped from there. These

were quite magnificent machines and became the staple motive power on the railway for the weekly passenger train, which took 12 hours in each direction! The railway was reported as closed in October 1975, and nothing appears to have been heard of the railway or the locomotives since. Delivered with the locomotives were 16 15-ton covered bogie goods wagons, a further six being ordered in July 1947. As was the case with the locomotives, these wagons were all fitted with the vacuum brake.

In February 1940 the Company had received a repeat order from Parana Plantations Limited for two more of the 2-8-2 metre-gauge tender locomotives that had been supplied back in 1935, manufacturer's numbers 2528 and 2529. A price of £8,720 each was quoted, free-on-board Liverpool with delivery in 10 months. There were a few differences from the earlier engines; for example the tender had a larger fuel capacity and the engines had steam operated reversing gear. As this was the first time the Company had been asked to supply locomotives thus fitted, it is surprising that rather than purchase proprietary equipment, it chose to design and build with its own resources. Due to the war and the control of work-load by the Ministry of Supply, progress on these two locomotives went on in an extremely derisory fashion, as and when material and man-power became available, and this continued until early 1943. At that time as will be related later in this Chapter, there was a reduction in the Ministry of Supply work due to some cancelled orders, so work proceeded again, but then, when the locomotives were almost complete, they were requisitioned by the Ministry of Supply and diverted to India. Actually they were allocated to the War Department and even given nominal WD numbers, but in the event were initially loaned to the Director General India Stores Department.

With the manufacturer's numbers 2625 and 2626, delivery of the locomotives was to the Bombay Baroda and Central India Railway, and shipment from Birkenhead Docks in May and September 1943 respectively. Eventually the engines were sold to Indian railways, number 2625 to the Jodhpur Railway and number 2626 to the Mysore Railway. As none-standard types under the later government ownership of almost all the Indian railways, the two engines were concentrated together on the South Central Railway and given the classification Modified YD, the YD design being the Indian Railway Standard (IRS) metre-gauge 2-8-2 design, albeit a much smaller engine. One of the authors found one of these two Bagnall locomotives as Indian Railways number 30253, and still in use on stone trains at Tadepli, near Vijayawada (formerly Bezwada) in November 1978. The men there reckoned it was some 75 tons better in load hauling than a YD - not surprising perhaps, with two inch more cylinder diameter.

Deep in the Belgian Congo (now Zaire) was one of the world's longest 600m/m gauge railways, the Chemins de Fer Vicineaux de l' Uele, usually abbreviated to the simple Vicicongo Railway. Dating from 1924, it eventually extended some 521 miles in the northeast of the Congo, the main-line running east between the valleys of the Congo and the Nile, from

At Tadepli on 12 November 1979, metre-gauge Indian Railways (South Central Railway) number 30253, manufacturer's number 2626, poses for its photograph having been specially painted for the occasion, albeit in colours one of the authors might not have chosen himself! This is one of the two locomotives ordered in 1940 for Brazil, but diverted to India by government decree and despatched in 1943; along with the earlier engines for Brazil, these were the largest locomotives the firm built. As seen here the locomotive was substantially in as-built condition with the exception of the steam reverser, which had been replaced by a conventional manually operated screw.

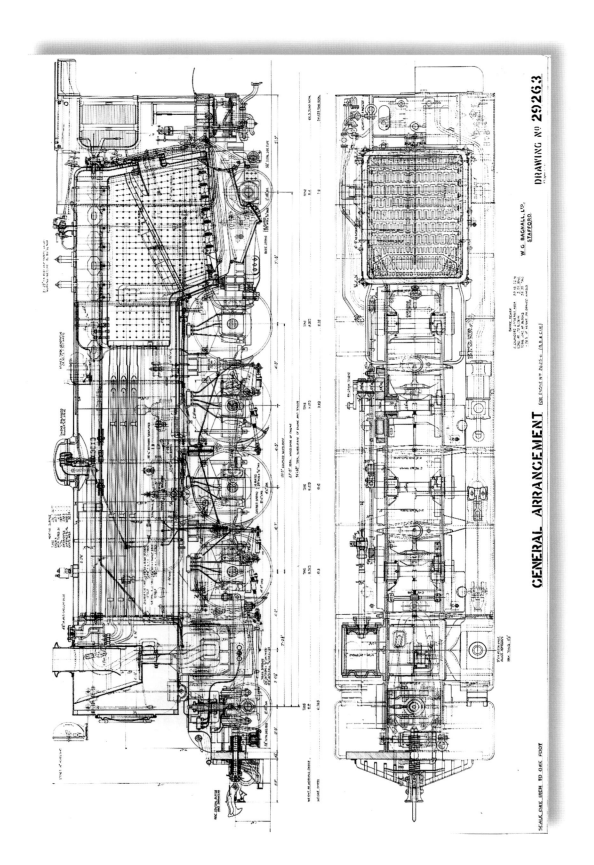

GENERAL ARRANGEMENT FOR ENGINE N°S 2625... (N.M. GUE)

SCALE ONE INCH TO ONE FOOT

DRAWING N° 29263

W. G. BAGNALL, LT.D
STAFFORD

General Arrangement drawings on this and the next page of the large metre-gauge 2-8-2 engines numbers 2625 and 2626, ordered for Brazil but in the event sent to India. These wonderful examples of the draughtsman's art were drawn by the late Ray Stephens, and notice they are dated 11 July 1947, long after the engines were despatched. As mentioned in the text general arrangement drawings were not, as a general rule, commissioned, unless there was a specific need, usually at the request of the customer or consulting engineers. Ray had been an apprentice with the Company and became a good friend of the authors - needless to say he treasured a copy of these drawings.

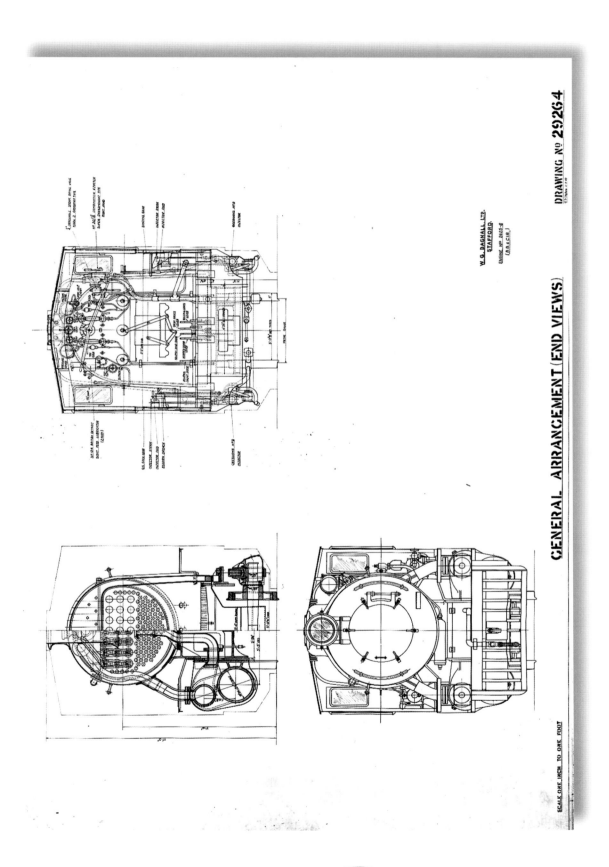

Manufacturer's number 2686 was the fourth member of the 600 m/m gauge 2-8-2 tank and tender engines built for the Vicicongo Railway in the Belgium Congo, and described at length in the text. Seen here without its bogie tender, points to note are the electric lighting, air reservoir, position of sand boxes just behind the cylinders and the air brake cylinder for the engine under the bunker; as a Belgian design the lack of a Belpaire firebox is perhaps surprising. Standing alongside from left to right are: Keith Pearson the firm's London Office Manager; an official from the Ministry of Supply; WS Edwards and Tom Stockton the Assistant Works Manager. Observe how Edwards has aged considerably from earlier photographs as his debilitating illness took hold.

Aketi in the west and on the Itimbirt River (a Congo River tributary), to Mungbere in the east - there were a couple of shorter branches too. During the last war, when this country was engaged in fighting the German Army under the command of Field Marshall Erwin Rommel in North Africa, the British Eight Army under the command Field Marshall Bernard Montgomery, was experiencing enormous difficulties in its supply lines. Despite the magnificent efforts of the Royal Navy's Mediterranean Fleet under Admiral Andrew Cunningham, the supply ships were suffering severe losses from German and Italian U Boats as well as the Luftwaffe and Italian Air Force. Somebody had the brainwave of extending the Vicicongo Railway from Aketi, south to Bumba on the main Congo River, and building a lengthy extension northwards from Mungbere to join up with the Sudan Railways. This would have allowed supplies to be landed on the west coast of Africa and, by a combination of the Congo River, Vicicongo and Sudan Railways, reach the entrenched Eight Army in North Africa. It was a very brave scheme which would have required the construction of some 500 miles of 600m/m gauge railway. Moreover, who ever it was who had the brainwave, thought the campaign was going to be a very long one.

As a part of this plan a fleet of 48 locomotives were ordered from Bagnall in two separate orders, the first on 2 May 1942 for 18 locomotives and the second on 27 July for a further 30, manufacturer's numbers allocated were 2683 to 2700 followed by 2707 to 2736. The selling price was £8,950 for the first batch and £8,920 for the second, free-on board-Liverpool, a total cost of £428,700, by far and away the largest contract the firm had ever secured. There was also a substantial order for spare parts to accompany the locomotives. The design was one already in use on the railway, a 2-8-2 side tank with 15¾x17¾in cylinders and 3ft 1¹³/₃₂in diameter driving wheels, a large double bogie tender completing the picture as the engines were designed to burn wood fuel. As might be expected the design was that of a Belgian builder, Ateliers Metallurgiques Tubize, and several of the draughtsman at Stafford had an interesting time converting the Tubize drawings, which were of course in metric, to imperial dimensions before sending them to the shops! The chief draughtsman at the time, the strict disciplinarian FHB Harris, would not allow any rounding up or down, the conversions had to be accurate, hence the driving wheel diameter noted above! These were big locomotives, the weight in

working order for the engine alone was 42.33 tons, with the tender 55.63 tons; the maximum axle-load was 7.87 tons, water capacity 2,222 gallons between the engine and tender, and the fuel 247 cub ft. The boiler was not superheated, the firebox was steel and the grate area some 24.2 sq ft; tractive effort at 85% of the 170 psi working pressure equalled 16,907lb. Other equipment included air brakes, Lambert wet sanding and Stone's electric lighting. The engines were designed to haul loads of 300 tons at speeds up to 28 mph, around curves of 10 chains radius and on gradients as steep as 1 in 66 - the two centre pairs of driving wheels had no flanges.

As events unfolded with the victory of the Eight Army under Montgomery at El Alemain, the reason for the railway link disappeared overnight, resulting in only five of the locomotives being completed before the

Another design developed around the time of the war and discussed in the last Chapter was a 15in cylinder four-wheel saddle tank for shunting purposes. This was a size of locomotive otherwise missing from the maker's range, albeit size for size it was similar to the Kerr, Stuart Moss Bay type, and although a completely new design the influence of FHB Harris is obvious in for example, the design of cab, which was pure California Works practice. A total of seven engines of this type were built, and this is the last, number 2623 of November 1940, despatched to the Shelton Iron, Steel & Coal Company's works at Etruria in Stoke-on-Trent, where it is seen on 24 August 1970. Unlike the earlier examples the last two - the other one was for the Butterley Company - were slightly cut-down in overall height, improving in the authors opinion, their appearance and resulting in the distinctive small chimney. Named HAWARDEN after the Shelton parent company works at Shotton on the English-Welsh border west of Chester, it was both the last new steam locomotive delivered to Shelton and appropriately, the last in use there being saved for preservation by the authors in March 1973. It was then moved to the Foxfield Light Railway south of Stoke-on-Trent, where it can still to be found regularly at work on operating days.

order was given to cease work. These five were delivered in May and June 1943, as WD numbers 4000 to 4004, Vicicongo Railway numbers 56 to 60. However, a lot of material had been ordered for the remainder and many parts had been batch produced, in particular wheel-sets and motion parts, castings and forgings - there were even some part-completed boilers. Work was stopped very abruptly and all the material and the parts made, whether complete or not, were shipped off in railway wagons to the WD depot at Sinfin Lane in Derby. Some of the staff involved recall that the long reversing rod posed a particular problem when shipping the parts to Derby, as it was longer than the packing cases sent by the WD; the Bagnall answer was to apply heat to the rods and bend them into a U shape to fit into the cases! Employees at the time recalled to the authors years later what an extremely melancholy sight this was, wagonload after wagonload and how empty the shops were for a period afterwards, until that is work got going on other orders - like the Parana engines mentioned above. The sadness was tempered later as the knowledge gradually sifted through with regard to what the engines had been intended for, and why the order was cancelled. Whilst there is evidence that some of the completed parts were eventually shipped out to the Congo as spares, for the vast majority it was the scrap heap; and in any event the reversing rods would not have been of much use! A financial settlement was eventually agreed with the Ministry of Supply and the figures are worth quoting as they give an indication of the amount of work undertaken before the order was terminated. For the five locomotives completed and delivered, a figure of £44,099 was agreed (£8,820 each), for the five numbers 2688 to 2692 which were partly completed £20,882, for the five numbers 2693 to 2697 on which less work had been undertaken £15,469, and for numbers 2707 to 2736 £14,068. There was also the sum of £3,900 for the spare parts already manufactured. There was no payment made for numbers 2698 to 2700.

This is perhaps a good juncture to describe some of the other work the Company got involved in during the war years as, like all engineering companies, a lot of work was allocated by the Ministry of Supply far removed from the traditional workload. Among the diverse jobs undertaken were a large number of cordite presses and reeling machines, along with Bofers anti-aircraft machine gun platforms. Boom hurdles and skates for aeroplanes were made in 1940 and 1941, and in May the same year 18 six-wheeled bogies were designed and made for standard-gauge gun trucks to carry 9.2in diameter guns. The wagons themselves, and presumably fitment of the guns, was entrusted to the Metropolitan-Cammell Carriage & Wagon Company at Saltley in Birmingham. It was not unusual in wartime for contracts to be split like this, with several different manufacturers making components, and it has to be added with individual companies not always knowing what the final product was. Quantities of gun carriages for 4½in guns were also made. The wagon shop had what might be termed its Indian summer during the war years in so far as railway wagon and turntable construction was concerned, as there were significant orders for railway rolling stock and other equipment, a lot of it for various government establishments around the country. There were also other unusual orders - for example in November 1941 a 5ft 6in gauge bogie coke car was built under sub-contract from the Stockport-based coke oven manufacturers Simon Carves Limited, for the Indian Tata Iron & Steel Company. Another one for the same customer followed in April 1942 and, it is perhaps worth mentioning here, yet another as late as April 1951. These were the only coke cars the company built.

Other war-time work included gun cradles for Canning Town Glass Works, a company presumably making some other components connected with the cradles, likewise tank axles for Armstrong Whitworth & Company, and revolving port housings for Metropolitan Cammell. For Fairy Aviation there were latch pins, whatever they were, and a lot of machining of components, as well as building manufacturing jigs and the like for a host of other companies. For example AV Roe & Company, the Stockport-based aircraft builders had wing assembly jigs manufactured for the Manchester and later Lancaster heavy bombers they were building. For the British Thompson Houston Company there were transformer trucks, for Ransomes Sims & Jeffries of Ipswich relieving gear, the Brush Electrical Engineering Company of Loughborough ordered transformer trucks, and there were many other orders of a not dissimilar nature. Along with orders of the nature just described where the firm in effect acted as sub-contractors, there were other contracts direct

During the war, in April 1944, the Company supplied this large 17in cylinder four-wheel saddle tank to the Port Talbot iron and steel works of Richard Thomas & Baldwins Limited. Number 2768 it was identical to three earlier examples supplied in 1941, and based on the Kenfig design of 1934, although differing in having Stephenson link motion between the frames rather that Walschaerts gear outside the frames. However, to retain the same design of cylinders as KENFIG, the valves were operated by rocking shafts which can just be discerned behind the cylinders - see page 383. As fleet No 6, the engine was photographed on 3 September 1949. (Late Ralph Russell - Frank Jones Collection Industrial Locomotive Society)

with the Ministry of Supply and other Government departments. For example a steady stream of orders for conventional railway rolling stock was maintained, hence the Indian summer for the wagon shop mentioned above. There were orders for both this country and overseas, old customers like the Kent paper maker Edward Lloyd Limited, the Anglo Iranian Oil Company, the Mauritius sugar industry, Gibraltar Dockyard, and the Gas Light & Coke Company to name but a few. Bagnall even managed to undertake some work, mainly castings and forgings, in connection with spare parts for Deutz diesel engines to the order of Porn & Dunwoody Limited. It will be recalled from the last Chapter that before the war this Company acted as the British Deutz agency, and it continued to help as best it could, owners and operators of Deutz engines after the agreement was abruptly terminated on the outbreak of hostilities. In view of the pre-war

connection between Porn & Dunwoody and Bagnalls, and the personal friendship between Sydney Edwards and Marcel Porn, the Castle Engine Works did its best to assist where it could.

In March 1944 the Company received a substantial order from the War Department for modifying and equipping a fleet of standard-gauge railway mobile workshop units. The order consisted of 10 each generator vans; workshop vans type A; workshop vans type B; welding plant vans; stores vans and no less that 26 compressor vans, some of the work being sub-contracted to Cowlishaw Walker. The vehicles themselves were 20-ton four-wheel vans brought over from America and the completed trains, each consisting of six vans (one of each type plus some spare compressor vans) were for use by the Royal Engineers on the continent of Europe. Bagnall were responsible for modifications to the vans themselves to suit the

An example of a Bagnall built war-time Austerity design of six- wheel coupled saddle tank with 18x26in cylinders, built in large numbers by several manufacturers to assist the war-effort. Bagnall built 52 engines of this class, to a Hunslet design in 1944 and 1945, and this is one of the last, number 2787 of October 1945. After a brief period on the Longmoor Military Railway this particular one went on loan to the Southern Railway and, as it turned out, was the only one made by any of the builders involved, to be used by the Southern Railway. The engine betrayed this fact for the rest of its life as it was fitted with the multiplicity of headlamp brackets peculiar to that railway. Repaired at Eastleigh Works in January 1946, it was used from Eastleigh shed until sold to the National Coal Board in 1947, moving to Foxfield Colliery in North Staffordshire. This picture was taken after a later move in 1965, to Holditch Colliery near Newcastle-under-Lyme on 18 August 1970. The engine was scrapped at Holditch in October 1972, replaced as it happens by Bagnall built diesels, redundant from another local colliery.

European loading gauge and operating constraints, as well as ordering and fitting all the equipment. This included generator sets and fuel tanks, compressors, benches, machine tools and lockers etc. It appears that most of the vans were actually located at the Cowlishaw Walker works at Biddulph, but with a lot of the material and equipment supplied from Stafford.

Returning to locomotives, the Company built a 52 of the standard 18x26in cylinder Hunslet design Austerity saddle tank shunting locomotives, as built by several

other builders. Thirty were ordered by the Ministry of Supply for the War Department on 7 May 1943, and a further 32 on 27 July. Manufacturer's numbers allocated were 2738 to 2767 and 2773 to 2804. Apart from the last 10 (2795 to 2804), which in the event were cancelled, they were all delivered between May 1944 and February 1946. Many of the later deliveries, initially at least, went into store at Longmoor Camp in Hampshire as by the time they were delivered hostilities had ceased, and the urgent need for them was no longer there. This was prior to a substantial number being offered for disposal, and in the event most of the ones sent to Longmoor were sold to the London & North Eastern Railway (LNER). The earlier deliveries of these locomotives, like those from other builders, found employment in a whole range of locations, and not only at Army establishments in this country; for example on loan to the main-line railways both in this country and on the continent. Significant numbers from a whole range of builders also found their way on loan to opencast coal mining sites, as these were developed to help increase the country's coal production, and there were other users too. Indeed, anywhere to assist the war effort. After the war along with sales to the LNER numerous examples were sold to a whole range of industrial establishments in this country, some of them having returned from working on the continent, although a significant number of those that were shipped overseas never returned. In this country the National Coal Board was perhaps the largest single user, and examples could be found at collieries all over the country. Several of the Bagnall-built examples survive in preservation.

The reason for the cancellation of the last 10 of the engines was the transfer of that part of the order to the Scottish builder Andrew Barclay Sons & Company Limited of Kilmarnock. This was part of an arrangement brokered by the Ministry of Supply to move the building of 10 2ft 6in gauge 4-8-0 tender engines from Kilmarnock to Stafford. These engines were part of an order of 20 for the Sierra Leone Government Railway, ordered by the Ministry of Supply, and the order for the completion of the contract was placed with Bagnall on 20 October 1943. Manufacturer's numbers allocated were 2805 to 2814 (the Barclay numbers were 2171 to 2180), and they arrived in a partly completed state at Stafford. Andrew Barclay were having problems completing the order to the time scale required, while of course, there was less urgency for the standard-gauge saddle tanks at this stage of the war. The locomotives had 12x16in cylinders and very small 2ft 4in diameter wheels, and were actually based on a German design of the builder Hanomag, Bagnall having built some similar engines before the war for the Indian railways. This was a difficult order for the Castle Engine Works, picking up where others had left off, and it was a commendable effort to get the first three locomotives completed and

A nice action shot of one of the Sierra Leone Government Railway 2ft 6in gauge 4-8-0s, a relatively unusual wheel arrangement on any gauge. This one is manufacturer's number 2811, railway number 180, photographed at Cline Town in February 1946, while working the 3.15 pm train from Water Street (Freetown) to Songo. These engines were based on a German design originally supplied for 2ft 6in gauge railways in India, although British builders had built examples for India too, including Bagnall. In the case of the Sierra Leone locomotives the design was selected by the consulting engineers on behalf of the Ministry of Supply. (Late Bernard Roberts)

despatched on 12 February 1944. The engines arrived in varying stages of construction, but in many cases little erection had taken place, and in the case of some locomotives no work had been undertaken although most, if not all the material had been ordered and was shipped down from Kilmarnock. In the event all 10 were despatched by the end of March 1944.

It is interesting to investigate the reasoning in connection with the allocation of the orders for the Austerity locomotives, and the transfer of the orders between Bagnall and Andrew Barclay. At the time Robert A Riddles, formerly a senior executive of the London Midland & Scottish Railway, had been appointed to head the Government Directorate of Transportation Equipment, and he later became deputy director-general Royal Engineers Equipment, with responsibility for all military railway requirements, both in this country and wherever there were British responsibilities abroad. His remit extended to railway requirements for what were otherwise main-line railway systems, where a military requirement existed. It is well known that in this position Riddles was responsible for the design of the Austerity 2-8-0 and 2-10-0 heavy freight locomotives that were built in large numbers during the war, and for both military use and in assisting the home railways. He was also responsible for selecting the Hunslet Austerity design of six-wheel saddle tank for lesser military duties, and for allocating the orders for the locomotives and overseeing their construction and subsequent dispersal. In discharging some of his responsibilities Riddles had, as might be expected, the need to enlist the support of the Locomotive Manufacturers Association (LMA). At a meeting of the general committee of the LMA on 16 June 1943, with both Riddles and WS Edwards in attendance, a requirement for an additional 22 of the 0-6-0 saddle tank engines was tabled, which was over and above the 100 already authorised to be built by various builders in 1944. It was decided at the meeting to leave the allocation of this additional order to the discretion of LMA, but an earlier decision to allocate the building of some of this type of engine to Peckett & Sons of Bristol was rescinded. Remember, as mentioned earlier, Peckett were not members of the LMA as such, but wartime contingencies brought them under its umbrella in the overall allocation of orders directed by the Ministry of Supply. This decision was based on the

facilities available at the Peckett works, which were somewhat restricted for such large locomotives; it was thus decided to allocate Peckett orders for smaller shunting locomotives. Riddles also mentioned at this meeting that Andrew Barclay was behind with the order for the Sierra Leone engines, proposing that no further orders be placed with that company for the time being. There was mention too, of an order from Ceylon for six 5ft 6in gauge B1 class 4-6-0 tender engines; these were big engines with 18½x26in cylinders and 4ft 5½in diameter driving wheels, and it was suggested that this order could be placed with Bagnall.

After Riddles left the meeting the members agreed to allocate the requirements for the 0-6-0 engines to be built in 1944 as: 50 to Hunslet, 20 to Hudswell Clarke, 20 to Robert Stephenson & Hawthorns (RSH) and 20 to WG Bagnall. This left 12 unallocated, and it was agreed to place this order at a later date depending on the individual manufacturer's progress with the locomotives, along with their other workloads. Edwards expressed the view that the Ceylon engines were really too big for the Castle Engine Works to build in any sensible time frame, and it was agreed to place this order with RSH (RSH numbers 7152 to 7157 delivered between September and November 1944). At the next meeting, exactly one month later, with Riddles and Edwards again in attendance (as was Keith Pearson, also representing WG Bagnall Limited), it was agreed to place the order for the unallocated 12 saddle tank locomotives with Bagnall, making its complement 32. At a further meeting on 30 November 1943, attended by Brigadier Griffiths of the WD, seemingly representing Riddles, an earlier agreement reached in correspondence was ratified; to reduce the Bagnall order to 22 locomotives, by transferring 10 to Andrew Barclay, and in return transferring completion of 10 of the Sierra Leone locomotives to Stafford. Andrew Barclay claimed an acute shortage of men, and Bagnall agreed to complete the Sierra Leone order by the end of February 1944 - in fact as we saw earlier the last engine of this order was sent to the docks on 18 March, a commendable effort none-the-less. The last of the Sierra Leone locomotives built by Andrew Barclay were not despatched until August 1944, and it was June 1946 before it completed delivery of the 10 Austerity saddle tanks. At the same meeting Edwards agreed to deliver 45 of the saddle tanks by the end of 1944; in the event the Company managed 38 by this date. One more meeting is worthy of mention, held on 2 November 1944, with the Brigadier again in attendance when Edwards claimed that Bagnall needed further orders of one sort or another and by June 1945, to ensure continuity of production. By then of course, peace was in sight, and the Company was able to concentrate on a number of orders that it had previously had to hold back due to the Ministry of Supply requirements.

With the end of hostilities things gradually started to return to normal, but the order book remained quite healthy. Among the orders were several for industrial shunting locomotives for use in this country as industry started to address overage assets that had been kept in service in the years of austerity. A number of these orders had actually been placed during the war, but were not completed until some time afterwards. Other orders placed towards the end of the war included two 2ft 6in gauge 0-6-2 side tanks with 10x15in cylinders for the Anglo Iranian Oil Company Limited; as would be expected they were oil burners with steel fireboxes, although to a new design. Manufacturer's numbers were 2824 and 2825 and the order was dated 2 September 1944 for delivery within six to eight months, but in the event they were not despatched until February 1946. The cost was £6,770 for the two free-on-board at a British port, including a quantity of spares. Two more of the two-foot gauge articulated locomotives were built for the South African sugar industry, manufacturer's numbers 2830 and 2831 ordered in July 1945. They were of the larger, 9x12in cylinder design, and were despatched in May the following year to Sir John L Hulett & Sons Limited, Darnall Estate in Natal, and once again the agent was A&H MacNay. The cost was £9,160 for the two, plus an extra £60 each for speedometers to be fitted, but one is left wondering why engines engaged in hauling sugar cane should need such sophistication! These two differed from the earlier engine (number 2545) in having shorter side tanks which stopped short of the smokebox, but nevertheless by some re-design, the water capacity remained the same at 500 gallons.

Egypt featured again in the order book when on 30 January 1946, the Company received an order from the Sucreries et de la Reffinerie d'Egypt (Egyptian Sugar Refineries) for two 1ft 11⁵/₈in gauge 0-6-2 side tank engines, which were almost two years in the making. A neat design was produced, not dissimilar to the Kerr, Stuart Haig design in outline, but with 10x14in cylinders and 2ft 2in diameter driving wheels. Designed to burn either coal or oil fuel, they were actually equipped as oil burners when delivered, and once again the boiler was pitched high to allow the firebox to sit on top of the fames, thus giving 9.72 sq ft of grate area. Walschaerts valve gear was used along with piston valve cylinders, and as well as twin injectors there was a boiler feed pump mounted on the left-hand side by the smokebox. The engines were complemented by large balloon stack spark arresting chimneys, sand boxes mounted on top of the side tanks and a water lifter so that water could be taken from line side streams and the like. Given manufacturer's numbers 2703 and 2704 they were not delivered until 31 December 1948. A lot of new design work was undertaken for this order, and one wonders why more existing design work was not incorporated; perhaps it was felt an updated design of locomotive around this size and power output would be a useful post-war addition to the product range. In the event, no more of the type were built, and surprisingly no official photograph appears to have been taken. Unfortunately, nothing is known of these two locomotives after delivery.

In the case of the locomotives mentioned above, the long time between the orders being placed and delivery taking place, will have been noted. This was the result of a general shortage of raw materials, as for some years after the end of the war allocation of some material, in particular steel, was still under central government control. There were particular shortages in iron, steel and copper, as well coal for fuel, as the country gradually returned to peace time production. The two metre-gauge superheated PS class 4-6-0 tender engines mentioned earlier for the Indian Jamnagar & Dwarka Railway, were a case to point: ordered in October 1945 they were not delivered until September 1947. As before the war, Bagnall continued to supply replacement boilers, cylinders and other parts to convert many of the older Indian P, H and M class metre-gauge 4-6-0 locomotives to superheater boilers and piston valve cylinders. For example the Assam Bengal Railway had four boilers and other parts for M class engines ordered in May 1939, and four more for the H class in May the following year. For the Bengal & North Western Railway for P class engines five each in

May 1939 and November 1941, along with two more in October 1943. Jumping ahead a little, a further seven for P class engines were supplied in January and July 1947; in this case part of a general order for the Indian Government owned railways placed by the India Stores Department. It can thus be seen that the boiler shop continued to be quite busy, and there were other spare boiler orders for overseas too, as well as a small backlog of orders for boilers and fireboxes for British customers. These were for a variety of industrial shunting locomotives that had doubtless been kept going with boilers in poor condition during the war, or others that had been put aside until replacement parts could be obtained.

During the war a significant number of industrial shunting locomotives were sent to the works for overhaul, no less then 34 in fact, and from a whole range of customers. This was in addition to the boilers, fireboxes and other parts supplied to Cowlishaw Walker, mentioned earlier, for locomotives that were being repaired at its works at Biddulph. Some of the locomotives that arrived for repair had been built in the works in earlier times, but the majority were the products of other manufacturers. At lot of this type of work was directly for the Ministry of Supply, the engines coming from ordnance and munitions factories, or other

locations under Ministry control. There were others too, belonging to for example, the Gas, Light & Coke Company at Beckton Gas Works, the Butterley Company, Port of London Authority, Guest, Keen & Baldwins Iron & Steel Company, Dunlop Rubber Company, Liverpool Gas Company and many others. The level of work varied, ranging from complete rebuilding, often including a new boiler, to less extensive work, for example fitting new tyres to wheel-sets, overhauling axle-boxes and motion parts. Incidentally, the locomotives that came from Beckton Gas Works had been damaged by enemy action during the infamous London blitz of 1940. A listing of all the locomotives that are known to have been overhauled or repaired at the Castle Engine Works, appears in Appendix III.

No fewer than 48 locomotives of all shapes and sizes were ordered in 1946, including a number for the Indian railways which, like many of the world's railway systems, were embarking on quite extensive programmes to replace equipment, and make good some of the lack of investment that had been necessary during the war. But the initial five or six post war years were to a considerable extent the Indian summer, and in more ways than one, in the market for metre and narrow-gauge locomotives for India. This was a market

In February 1945 the firm supplied to the almost new design illustrated here, two metre-gauge four-wheel saddle tanks with 9x14in cylinders. Ordered by the Admiralty as early as June 1943, it is unclear from the surviving records where they were originally delivered to, although it is presumed to have been Gibraltar. By early 1957 they had both been transferred to the Singapore naval base. This picture of manufacturer's number 2770 - the other one was 2769 - was taken in the naval yard at Gibraltar in February 1957.

Another new design of the period under review was this 0-6-2 pannier tank specially designed to meet the requirements of the Anglo Iranian Oil Company for use in Iran. Two of these engines were supplied in February 1946, along with a large quantity of spares, manufacturer's numbers 2824 and 2825. Cylinders were 10x15in and they were, as might be expected, oil fired. Built for use on the 2ft 6in gauge Darkhazineh Railway, a large system serving the oil fields near Ahwaz and dating from 1923, they were fleet Nos. 7 & 8.

that had provided the Castle Engine Works with a regular workload for the best part of the previous 30 years. Within a few years indigenous production facilities for locomotives became available in India, and the loss of this market was one that the Company never fully recovered from. Nor was it alone among the British manufacturers in the respect. At the 1934 annual Christmas dinner and dance that the Company arranged for its staff, Edwards in his customary after-dinner address mentioned the Indian market for locomotives that had provided them with work for so long, and went on the say that while this may have been obvious to most of them, it was nonetheless extremely poignant. He talked about how dependent the Company had been, and indeed at that time still was, on its Indian market. He suggested to his audience that they should seriously consider voting for whichever political party advocated retaining the Indian Empire (the issue of independence being topical at the time), as without the market for railway material that it supplied, the long-term future prospects for a company like WG Bagnall Limited did not look bright. How true that prophecy turned out to be.

The average time to delivery of the 48 locomotives mentioned in the proceeding paragraph was around two years, indicative of how the raw material supply issue outlined earlier was holding production up. As a result, and despite the healthy order book, many delivery promises were broken. It has to be mentioned though,

that delivery were usually quoted only on condition material was available.

This is perhaps an opportune juncture to bring this Chapter to a close in so far as works production is concerned, but before doing so we must catch up on a number of personnel and other issues leading up to a further change in ownership. The locomotives ordered in 1946 will therefore be dealt with in the next Chapter, which will cover the period when they were actually delivered.

The period of the Second World War, as might be expected, brought with it a number of improvements around the works itself. The erecting shop, for example, which was flanked by the fitting shop to its east and machine shop to its west, was extended northwards. As we have seen in earlier Chapters, this shop had been gradually extended and the 1941 extension was to be the last; the machine shop was extended at the same time. When further additional erecting shop capacity was needed after the war, a completely new shop was built, but that is jumping ahead somewhat. The boiler shop's twin bays were also extended, in this case westwards, whilst the wagon shop was extended north. Along with these fixed asset building improvement there were additions and replacements to the fixed plant and equipment, extra machine tools for example, and a gradual movement away from the use of line shafting and belt drives to power the machine tools to individual electric motors. Around £6,500 was spent on

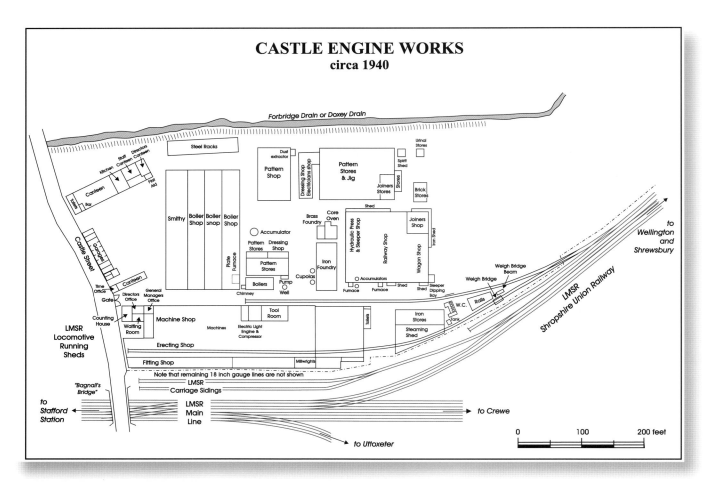

CASTLE ENGINE WORKS
circa 1940

The Castle Engine Works as it would have been in about 1940, but including the war-time, and as it turned out, final extensions of the Erecting and Machine Shops; this building work was not completed until the following year.

additions to the buildings during the war, and almost £15,000 on machinery, plant and tools. There was a serious fire in the power generating plant in 1942 which completely stopped production for a few days, and most of the employees had to be laid off. However, connection to the mains supply was soon effected, and from then on the firm ceased to generate its own electricity. The power plant was dismantled for scrap soon afterwards.

As would be expected a number of the firm's men served in the armed forces during the war, including those who were already members of various Territorial Army units, while others enlisted into the regular army. Among those remembered are Edgar Bailey, Tom & Alf Buckley, Bill Potts and Alf Narroway from the erecting shop; Pat Fallon, JPH Jacob and Cyril Stanton from the machine shop and Cyril Booth who was a wages clerk. After the war some of those who fought for King &

County returned to the firm, whilst others did not, and at least two, Pat Fallon and Alf Buckley, remained in the forces.

Despite the war-time austerity the firm managed to continue to host its annual staff Christmas and new year party, along with the children's event. Mrs Edwards, as had been her custom since their inception during the First World War, was very much in charge on such occasions, and not only of the catering but the amusements too. At the children's event it had been the practice to give every child a present, but at the 1943 party as nothing suitable could be obtained, each child was given a small sum of cash. Considering that on average during the war years the attendance was around 120 children, these were quite sizable events, and one of the children always made a presentation to Elizabeth Edwards. At the 1942 party, a young Joyce Griffiths, the daughter of a member of the staff, presented a bouquet of chrysanthemums that had been grown by her father. In April 1942 there was a special fund raising event in the form of a dance, the organising committee being chaired by Elizabeth, in aid of the Sneyd Colliery Disaster Fund, when £45 16/- (£45 80p) was raised. Sneyd Colliery in nearby Stoke-on-Trent had been the scene of a terrible explosion on new years day 1942, when 57 men and boys lost their lives. Over 350 people attended the event.

Brief mention was made earlier of a deterioration in health of Sydney Edwards, which became quite serious during the war years. He suffered from a coronary problem and as a result lost a lot of weight, and there were times when he had to have an external supply of oxygen, cylinders being delivered to the works and a constant supply being available in his office. However, by the accounts of those who were involved at the time, he lost little of his vigour and none of his tenacity. Harold Wood tells the story of his office at the foot of the stairs that led from the workshops to the drawing office, and how the door would usually be open. Any member of the works staff who made their way to the drawing office, or similarly any member of the drawing office who did the reverse, would be accosted by Edwards and an inquisition would take place. This apparently had the effect of making the draughtsman careful, and the shop floor thoughtful - in Harold's words. It was during the war that Jack Dale the works manager began to fallout of favour with Edwards, and there were a number of disagreements. The story goes that during a particular bad time for Edwards health in 1943, Jack formed the view that he had not long for this life, and had a very nice coat dyed black in anticipation of the funeral! Mrs Edwards, always something of a matriarch and becoming more and more influential and dominant in Company matters as her husband's heath deteriorated, got to hear of this, and that, so the story goes, was the end of Jack! Be that as it may, Jack Dale left the Company in 1943 and took up an appointment with FH Lloyd Limited, the Wednesbury steel castings manufacturers. FH Lloyd were the principal suppliers of steel casting to WG Bagnall Limited and had been for many years, so Jack would have been well known to the management there. Tom Stockton, whom we met earlier, an old colleague of Edwards and Harris from Kerr, Stuart days, who had been gaining in favour, took over from Jack Dale as works manager.

To bolster the management team, back in 1940 Edwards had managed to persuade Harry Davies to return to the fold. Readers will recall Harry had been with the Company in the late 1920s, and after a period back with Kerr, Stuart with whom he had earlier trained, he had been first with Sir WG Armstrong Whitworth & Company Limited, and subsequently the London representative of Babcock & Wilcock Limited. Later still he worked for the Air Ministry. It would seem that some 'back room' work was necessary by Edwards to get Davies released from his Air Ministry job, but released he was, and he came back to Stafford with the dual role of chief estimator and personal assistant to Edwards. Geoffrey Owen, who had been in charge of estimating for a number of years, moved on to Associated Industrial Consultants (AIC) about the same time. It was Harry, incidentally, who was responsible for the costing in connection with the Vicicongo locomotives mentioned earlier. Obviously this was a difficult estimating exercise, building locomotives to another builder's design, and having to convert all the measurements from metric to imperial. He was very proud that his estimate came out spot-on, and he remembered the exact figure 30 years later when interviewed by the authors. Similarly, costing the Sierra Leone locomotives, when some parts had already been made, and most of the material was supplied free of charge, made estimating not an easy task. However, once again Harry's estimates were accurate.

In December 1942 there were some changes in the shareholding of the Company, largely involving the Cadmans, with the transfer of a significant number of shares held by James Cadman to his son - Young Jimmy - along with a smaller number of preference shares to his nephew. At the same time two new shareholders were introduced, both members of the Cadman family, and Edwards reduced his holding of preference shares from 2,776 to 2,000, by transfer to the new shareholders, who were Cynthia Marriott and Una Nancy Clarke. Both these ladies were daughters of John Cadman. Cynthia was the wife of Lieut. Colonel Ian A Marriott, of whom we shall hear a lot of in the next Chapter, as he later became managing director of WG Bagnall Limited. Una Nancy was the widow of the late Colin Clarke; Marriott was, and Clarke had been, business associates of John Cadman. Hesketh Ramsden, as noted earlier, was killed killed in action on 23 April 1940; his will, proved on 4 October 1941, transferred his shares to his executors, which were his wife, Joan Passmore Ramsden and James Cadman. His instructions were for his shares to be disposed of or retained as the executors saw fit in complying with, and discharging the other terms and bequests of his will. After these changes the allocation of shares was:-

Name of Shareholder	Ordinary Shares	Preference Shares
WS Edwards	20,000	2,000
James Cadman	6,750	250
Executors of		
Hesketh Adair Ramsden	500	500
James Simon Cadman	2,000	2,500
Fredrick William Carder	500	500
John Basil Cope Cadman	500	500
Branch Nominees	4,500	4,500
Bishopsgate Nominees	2,250	2,250
Una Nancy Clarke	1,500	2,000
Cynthia Marriott	1,500	2,000
Total Shares	40,000	17,000

By this time John Basil Cope Cadman, having succeeded to the Baronetcy on his father's death in June 1941, took the title Lord Cadman of Silverdale.

In the period 1939 to 1946 the average net profit was £5,642, and the annual turnover increased from £167,000 in 1939 to £354,450 in 1946. In 1939 the wages costs were £38,000 and the salaries £8,200, whilst by 1946 these figures had increased to £60,000 and £16,700 respectively. The 1938 Balance Sheet showed a figure of £45,800 and the 1946 figure was £90,646. It will therefore be seen that the years of the Second World War significantly increased the financial position of the Company. The same period saw total figures of £40,065 and £44,056 respectively, expended on loose and fixed plant and equipment, along with £22,450 on the works buildings. The total income from sales between 1938 and 1946 was £1,806,188, peaking at £291,708 in 1945.

Mention was made in the last Chapter of an issue over tax payable raised by the Inland Revenue in 1934. As a result in November 1936 the Company offered to pay the sum of £10,000 in full settlement, although this was not accepted until September the following year, when the payment was made. This issue raised its head again in 1943, and a case was heard at the Kings Bench Division, where the Inland Revenue made a claim against the Company for excess profit duty, corporation and income tax. It appears that whilst a sum of £14,449 was considered to have been payable at 1 January 1935, the offer to pay £10,000, which had been accepted in September 1937, was considered by the Company to have been a debt under the terms of the later Finance Act of 1939, and should therefore, have been allowed as a deduction in computing its capital for the period of this new Inland Revenue claim. Whilst at the time this was accepted by the Commissioners after an appeal had been lodged by the Company, the Crown was now appealing against the Commissioners decision on the basis that the £10,000 was not a debt prior to September 1937 within the meaning of the 1939 Act, and that a further sum of £2,400 was owing for the year ending 31 December 1939. Mr Justice MacNaughton presiding, gave judgment for the Crown, on the basis that there had been a default by the Company and this had in effect been admitted, in the light of the agreement to pay the £10,000. The question was he opined, at what date was the new debt established, and as there was no evidence the Commissioners could find that a debt existed at 1 January 1935, there was no liability until after the offer of £10,000 was accepted in September 1937. It follows therefore, that a debt did exist at the present time and the Company had to pay. This long running affair with the Inland Revenue, raising its head again at this point, is further considered by those who were around at the time, to have contributed to the deterioration in the health of Sydney Edwards.

On Saturday 28 December 1946, in the evening and at his home 'Enville', 190 Sandon Road Stafford, at the age of 64 and after a long and debilitating illness, William Sydney Edwards passed away. As we have seen Edwards had been in increasingly serious ill-heath for some time, suffering from coronary thrombosis; the final death was the result of a cerebral haemorrhage and arteries sclerosis. He had continued to conduct his business affairs until about a week before he died, largely from his bed and assisted by supplies of oxygen. Managers from the works would be summoned to

'Enville', first having to negotiate the rather formidable Elizabeth Edwards which would include a close inspection of whatever it was they were wearing, least the slightest sign of them having been in the house be apparent after they had left! The furniture was always very highly polished, as Mrs Edwards ran the household with the proverbial 'rod of iron', and there were clear instructions that visitors from the works were to avoid touching anything. They had to stand around their master's bed and were not allowed to sit down! Tom Stockton was the clear favourite of Edwards at this time, and the one most frequently summoned. This fact was made so obvious to all and sundry around the works, not least by Tom himself, and with the notable exception of FHB Harris, everybody was subservient to Tom. In the words of Harold Wood: 'whilst Tom made it obvious he was the chosen one, he was able to lord it over everybody except the Old Man'; that is FHB Harris.

At the time of his death as well as being the managing director of WG Bagnall Limited and holding the single largest number of shares, Edwards was also joint managing director with Ian Marriott - a son-in-law of Cadman - of Cowlishaw Walker & Company Limited. Sydney Edwards has featured extensively in our story so far, as he was involved with the Company for almost 45 years, in senior positions of responsibility for 43 of them, and to all intents and purposes in control for the last 31 years of his life. Like his wife he was a formidable person with a very strong character, and an extremely experienced and knowledgeable engineer; indeed he could be said to have been of the most senior class of locomotive engineers in the country at the time of his death. He had given his life to the railway rolling stock engineering business, and most of it to WG Bagnall Limited seeing, and indeed for much of the time presiding, over the growth of the Company from one employing a couple of hundred people and producing 25 or so small narrow-gauge locomotives and associated rolling stock in a year, to one with a turnover of almost £300,000. It was a company at the time of his death capable of building 50 or so medium-sized locomotives in a year, along with about the same number of additional boilers, as well as much else - the staff totalled about 500. Remember that among the locomotives built were four which ranked at the time among the largest rigid-framed metre-gauge

Portrait of William Sydney Edwards - albeit a picture taken somewhat earlier in his life. There is little doubt that this man, a giant in the industry in which he spent all his working life, did more for the firm, its people and its reputation than anybody else, including perhaps, even its founder. If any man gave the company the right to call itself: 'Builders of Locomotives for the World's Railways', this is him.

locomotives in the world. It was an amazing achievement, for while he was by no means universally liked by all his people, his nickname in the workshops being Nutty, he was nevertheless, very much respected.

Mention was made in an earlier Chapter, but it is well worth repeating here, that in the years between the wars when unemployment in the engineering industries was at its lowest ebb, it was his proud boast in Stafford that whilst others stopped, 'Bagnalls chimney never stopped smoking'. And whilst some short-time was worked, for the majority of the time there was full time working at the Castle Engine Works. This was in no small measure due to the indefatigable efforts of

Edwards, and all those employed at the time had cause to be grateful to him. In his vast knowledge of the industry the Company operated in, in the contacts and influence he brought to bear, in his acute judgement of those he gathered around him in support, his tremendously shrewd business acumen, and last but by no means least, in his love of the Company he gave almost all his life to, this is his epitaph. Tall and erect until illness took control of him, he always wore a Homburg, such that some of the staff though he slept in it. When confined to a wheelchair he would propel himself around the workshops every week to view progress and keep a close eye on all production issues, and many who were there at the time confirm that he never missed anything. Those who knew him closely testify that he did in fact have a kindly streak, taking a great personal interest in the recruitment and training of apprentices; and for those of his people with personal problems there were frequent friendly gestures of a kind that went very much unadvertised. As late as December 1944, he had personally made presentations of technical books to eight of the firm's apprentices following their success at various technical colleges. The individuals were Derek Rowley (later a senior draughtman); Ray Stephens (later a draughtsman); P Walker; Roy Brunt; Bill Brownsword; W Hatierid; Jim Webberley (later chief draughtsman); John Reynolds. The fees too, were always refunded by the Company.

Although from a slightly later period, it is worth quoting at this point the words of Derek Cobby, who was an apprentice in the early 1950s, as of course, nothing much had changed in the way locomotives were built, or apprentices trained, by that time from the methods and systems established in Edwards's day. Derek had been turned down by British Railways for training at Swindon, failing his medical (the main-line railways were extremely strict on medical conditions in those days), and instead went to Bagnalls. He goes on: "With the benefit of hindsight I am firmly of the opinion that the Bagnall training was superior to Swindon, and probably Crewe, Doncaster or any other main-line works. The accuracy of machining was somewhat inferior, mainly due to obsolete machine tools; however, the deficiencies were mainly in areas of brake gear. The critical stuff was still overseen by highly skilled old timers who had been around for donkeys years. Where Bagnalls really excelled was in the subtle way in which

William Sydney Edwards lies in the small and pleasant grave yard of St Cynon's church at Fairbourne, which is some three miles from the church itself. Both his bungalow in Fairbourne and his house in Stafford were named ENVILLE. There is a village of this name which features in the Doomsday Book, south-east of Bridgenorth, near the border with Shropshire. A large hall there was the one time seat of the Earls of Stamford & Warrington, and it is assumed that this village or its surroundings are the source of the name, having some significance with Edwards and his wife.

the training was implemented by Chargemen, etc. To paraphrase an old friend, they only had two methods, 'bouquets and rollockings'; between those two you had to listen, learn and get on with it on your own. The result far more self reliance". These few words tell us a lot about Edwards and help an understanding of how the firm achieved so much with so little, except that is, a highly skilled body of craftsmen who in most cases had themselves been trained at the Castle Engine Works.

At the time of his death as well as all his other commitments already outlined, Edwards was the chairman of the Stafford County & District Building Society, and a prominent member of various committees under the auspices of the LMA. We have already seen how he had been instrumental in a number of initiatives under the LMA umbrella, and of course WG Bagnall Limited was one of the comparatively early members of the Association. As was to be expected the funeral was exceptionally well attended, and eight of the older employees of the firm acted as pall bearers: C

Jennings; H Walter Skelton; W Banks; Tommy Dawkes; George Banks; C Clewlow; George Norwood and William Biddulph. The funeral service was conducted by the Reverend PV Appleton at St Mary's Church in Stafford, where Edwards and his wife worshiped, on Wednesday 8 January 1947. The family mourners along with his wife Elizabeth were his nephews Thomas and Anthony Stone, George Horne and his niece Dorothy Horne, whilst James Cadman DSC DL, chairman of the Company, accompanied them. Representing WG Bagnall Limited were Lord Cadman, a fellow director, Tom Stockton the works manager; FHB Harris chief draughtsman; Harry Davies chief estimator; Harold J Shaw chief buyer; Arthur E Owen chief cost clerk; Harold E Coates chief cashier; Keith F Pearson and Mrs A Moss, the last two representing the London office. Cowlishaw Walker & Company Limited were represented by James Cadman Jnr, who had been joint managing director with Edwards, Major GC Neilson a fellow director; FJ Smith the secretary; R Petrie works manager; JW Bedson; F Cooke and J Bradshaw.

No lesser personage than RA Riddles, a vice president, represented the London Midland & Scottish Railway Company along with Tom Coleman the chief draughtsman at Derby, and a fellow apprentice with Edwards at Kerr, Stuart. Others attending and the companies they represented were: John Alcock the Hunslet Engine Company; Kenneth Pearson (son of KF) Robert Stephenson & Hawthorns Limited; JWD Milligan representing Sir George Nelson, chairman and managing director of the English Electric Company Limited; GC Saunders of WH Dorman & Company Limited; JF Button of the British Reinforced Concrete Engineering Company Limited; JF Phillips and BA Morris Universal Grinding Wheel Company Limited - all prominent Stafford businessmen. Also paying their last respects were: JT Slaley of Brereton Collieries Limited; JW Vaughan of the LMA; RS Hoddler of the Crown Agents for the Colonies; JC Shedell of Billington & Newton Limited; RC Moss of the United Steel Company; WC Bryan Hartleys Stoke-on-Trent Limited; HF Walker Ministry of Supply; RD Metcalfe Davies & Metcalfe Limited. Dr. WA Chapman the principal, represented the Stafford Technical College, with which Edwards had a number of connections, and CW Todd the captain, represented the Brocton Hall Golf Club of which Edwards was a member (he had himself been

captain earlier - appointed in 1933). Many others were present both as personal friends and colleagues, or representing his many business associations, along with a very large number of the staff and employees of WG Bagnall Limited - life would never be the same again for any of them. There were numerous floral tributes.

After the funeral service the body was taken to the small North Wales seaside village of Fairbourne, in Merioneth, where from about 1920 he and his wife had enjoyed a small bungalow, and where they had spent so many happy times together. As was the case at Stafford, Edwards was quite prominent in local affairs, and with his wife worshiped at St Cynon's Church in the village. After a short service at St Cynon's, William Sydney Edwards was taken to his last resting place, and in accordance with his wishes laid to rest in the grave yard of St Cynon's, which is some three miles south of Fairbourne on the coast road to Llwyngwril. The grave stone reads: 'In Loving Memory of William Sydney Edwards M I Mech E of 'Enville' Stafford and Fairbourne Died December 28 1946'. Sydney Edwards was very proud of his membership of the Institution of Mechanical Engineers, as rightly he should have been.

By the standards of the day Edwards was a rich man. His will was proved on 1 March 1947 at £61,339 8/ 3d (£61,339 31p), a lot of money in those times, and as there were no children he left his entire estate to his wife of 40 years, Elizabeth - this of course included the major shareholding in WG Bagnall Limited. There can have been no other man at the time within the British private locomotive building industry who had given so much to a single company, and notwithstanding the wealth this had generated for him, it was a career of which he could be justifiably proud. The achievements of the company, never a big one in the league of British private locomotive builders, were legendary with the facilities available; almost nothing was too much for it. We shall see in the next Chapter details of an analysis concluding that a number of the contracts the Company took on in Edwards's time were really beyond the capability of the facilities at the works, such that it was decided that work of a similar size should not be tendered for in the future. But taken on they were - and completed to time and budget too, to coin a phrase of more recent times. But in those dim and distant inter-war years the Company needed all the work it could get, having no external financial support, until that is the

Cadmans arrived on the scene; it had little capital to invest, but Edwards made it his business to ensure survival, and survive it did.

One has only to compare the lists of locomotive built, the diversity of types, sizes and range of customers, along with all the other activities we have been at pains to describe, and compare them with their contempories among the smaller locomotive builders in this country, to understand that this was a company with no equal. William Gordon Bagnall would have had no reason but to be very proud of the Company he had started all those years ago. A close study the photographs in this book will give an appreciation of the points we have tried hard to make, in particular the scenes within the workshops, the cramped conditions, the state of the buildings, the old and often outmoded machinery and

equipment. But study too, those craftsmen at work - almost 500 of them by 1946 and to a man known to Edwards by their names - and the locomotives they are designing and building. Locomotives built by the Company could be found all over the world and the Bagnall name a household one within the industry - rarely can there have been such achievements. This then should be the true epitaph of William Sydney Edwards, whose name within the industry was synonymous with that of the company he had served so well and for so long. He was a giant within the private locomotive building industry in this country, well respected in the railway industry generally - and not only in this country - and he was greatly missed by all who knew him. The Company would never be quite the same again.

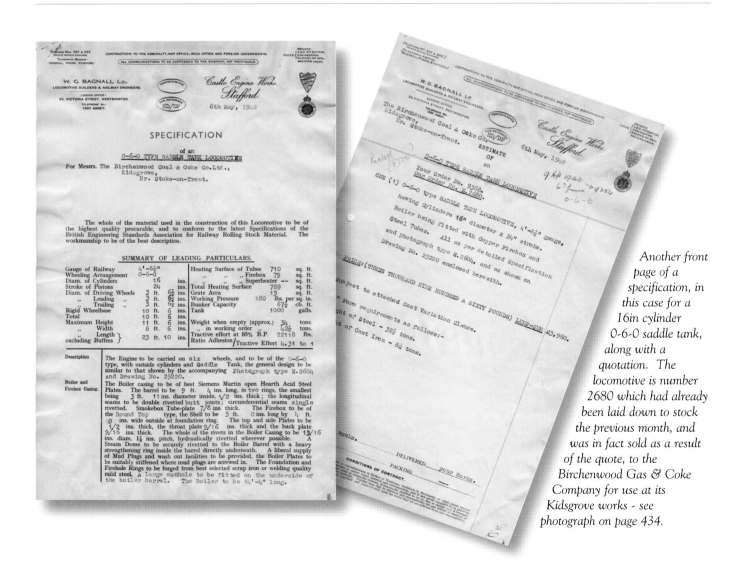

Another front page of a specification, in this case for a 16in cylinder 0-6-0 saddle tank, along with a quotation. The locomotive is number 2680 which had already been laid down to stock the previous month, and was in fact sold as a result of the quote, to the Birchenwood Gas & Coke Company for use at its Kidsgrove works - see photograph on page 434.

Chapter Eleven

Alan Good Takes Over: The Early Post-war Years

In the last Chapter mention was made that Sydney Edwards, having no children, left his entire estate which included the shareholding in WG Bagnall Limited, to his wife Elizabeth. Elizabeth had little or no interest in retaining any involvement in the Company, and with Edwards dead, James Cadman's interest was no longer as strong as before. In addition, Elizabeth had taken a dislike to Cadman's son, Young Jimmy, and was determined that he should not acquire control from his father as the latter reduced his business commitments. Mention was also made in the previous Chapter that Cynthia Marriott, one of Cadman's daughters, had become a shareholder, and we introduced her husband Ian Marriott. This is then an opportune time to have a closer look at Marriott, as he has a significant part to play in the story. But first it should be mentioned that James Cadman did not long outlive Sydney Edwards. On Sunday 7 September 1947 he was driving alone along Middlemoor Hill, near Pateley Bridge in Yorkshire, when he was involved in what turned out to be a fatal accident. No other vehicles were involved, and it seems he got into some sort of skid, lost control and his car left the road. Apparently he had been on a shooting expedition and was on his way back to his hotel in Harrogate; he died as a result of his injuries at the General Hospital in Harrogate the following day.

James Cadman was 69 years old and was laid to rest on 12 September at Silverdale, near Newcastle-under-Lyme, where he was born. His will was proved at a little over five million pounds, an enormous sum in those days.

Ian Arthur Marriott was born in London on 25 March 1911, a son of Hugh Fredrick Marriott, one-time governor of the Imperial Institute and a president of the Institution of Mining & Metallurgy. For 40 years Hugh Marriott was a director of the Magadi Soda Company Limited, as a nominee of the Kenyan Government. Young Marriott was educated at Rugby and later at New College Oxford, where he studied modern languages. In 1930 he joined Messrs Frazer & Chalmers Limited at Erith in Kent as a pupil apprentice, initially in the millwrights department, but later he was involved with heavy oil engines. At the same time he attended Erith technical college and studied mechanical engineering. Between 1933 and 1939 Marriott was on the engineering staff of ICI Limited Alkali Division (ICI owned almost all the share capital of Magadi Soda), initially involved in the maintenance and construction department at Winnington in Cheshire, and subsequently became personal assistant to WH Demuth, the production director. Marriott was a founder member of the British Institute of Management.

Although taken a couple of years later when Ian Marriott left Stafford to take up a new appointment, this is nevertheless a very good likeness of him, as well as WA Smyth and Harry Davies. Left to right at the presentation, which was held during the annual smoking concert on 20 April 1950 are: WA Smyth; Ian Marriott; Harry Davies; Reg Moon - the works trade union convenor who is making the presentation of a carriage clock - and the Mayor of Stafford Councillor L Dobson.

In April 1932 Ian Marriott enlisted in the Territorial Army as a 2nd Lieutenant in the Royal Engineers, 48th South Midland Supplementary Reserve, and in April 1935 was promoted 1st Lieutenant. From July 1936 he was posted with the 41st (5th North Staffordshire Regiment) Anti-Aircraft Battalion and on 28 April 1936 was promoted to the rank of Captain. In 1932 he had attended the School of Military Engineering at Chatham for a field engineering course, and later the School of Anti-Aircraft Defence at Biggin Hill, qualifying in 1939 at the intermediate staff course. Serving throughout the war in the Royal Engineers. Marriott's first war-time posting was with the Allied Expeditionary Force in Europe, but later he served with the Chemical Industries Division of the Control Commission for Germany. Gazetted Acting Major in March 1942, he was then attached to the Imperial General Staff, Director of Weapons & Vehicles, being promoted permanent Major in November 1943. In February 1945 Marriott was made Acting Lieutenant-Colonel and on demobilisation in April 1946, was given the honorary rank of Lieutenant-Colonel. Thereafter, he always insisted on being addressed as Colonel Marriott. Moreover, he retained his involvement in the Territorial Army and for several years commanded the 176 Transport Workshop Squadron Royal Engineers (Supplementary Reserve).

On leaving active service Marriott was appointed by his father-in-law (James Cadman) to the position of general manager of Cowlishaw Walker & Company Limited, where of course, he came into close contact with WS Edwards, a director of that Company, and through Edwards WG Bagnall Limited. Ian Marriott was therefore a somewhat obvious contender to take over from Edwards at Stafford, and as we shall see this is exactly what happened. However, before this move took place we have to introduce another character, one who had a considerable influence and plays a very significant part in the story. Alan Paul Good was an Irishman born at Foxrock near Dublin on 9 April 1906, the son of a prominent surgeon in that city. Educated at Marlborough, he studied law at Oxford, subsequently qualifying as a lawyer. Good arrived back on this side of the Irish Sea in 1935 to make his fortune with but a few hundred pounds in his pocket. He once told WA Smyth he had but £500, nevertheless in an amazing short space of time he acquired an interest in a formidable portfolio of companies. Alan Good was a physically big man, 6ft 6in tall, who dominated every collection of people he ever came into contact with. WA Smyth went on to say he had a brilliant intellect, believed in his superiority over all other individuals, trusted implicitly in his own destiny, and lived in great style on a large estate at Glimpton, near Woodstock in Oxfordshire.

Practicing law in London with Pennington & Son of Lincoln's Inn, Good soon established contacts with the

Alan Paul Good (1906-1953); a picture taken in 1949. Good was the founder, and at the time Deputy Chairman of the Brush Group of Companies.

Hambro family, and with the financial backing of Hambros Bank Limited, where for a short time he worked as a solicitor, one of his first moves was to acquire control of Petters Limited. This was a relatively small and ailing Yeovil-based manufacturer of small and medium-sized diesel engines. He subsequently acquired an interest in the Brush Electrical Engineering Company Limited, with extensive workshops - the Falcon Works - at Loughborough in Leicestershire; Hambros being the Brush company bankers. Good soon arranged to transfer the Petter business to better and otherwise under-utilised facilities at Loughborough, along with a rationalisation of the product range. This included a gradual discontinuation of engines in the medium-power ranges, which worked on the two-stroke principle and were the less successful of the firm's products. This rationalisation was in conjunction with Good's expanding interest in the manufacture of diesel engines in the medium and high-power ranges. In November 1948 Good arranged the transfer of the bulk of the Petter business from Loughborough to premises rendered vacant at Staines in Middlesex, as among other things, he wanted production of the smaller range of engines to be nearer London. This move was facilitated because in September 1947 he had acquired the almost defunct Lagonda Car Company, which he eventually closed down, vacating the premises for Petters. However, the manufacture and supply of spare parts for the larger and otherwise discontinued range of Petter engines remained at Loughborough. WA Smyth maintained that Good made a significant amount of money in a subsequent sale of the stock of spare parts for the Logonda cars!

In 1938 Alan Good founded Associated British Engineering Limited (ABE) as a holding company for Petters along with any other companies he acquired. He then went on to acquire interests in several other diesel engine manufacturers, all of which came under the ABE umbrella. The Leeds-based J&H McLaren Limited joined the fold in 1943, followed by Mirrlees, Bickerton & Day of Hazel Grove the following year and, in January 1946, Atlantic Engine Company (1920) Limited of Wishaw in Scotland. Later in the summer of 1946 interests were acquired in the National Gas & Oil Engine Company Limited of Ashton-under-Lyne (became a controlling interest in June 1949, the Company being bought outright by Brush in August

1951), and Crossley Brothers Limited of Openshaw in Manchester. These were all big-names in the field of design and manufacture of diesel engines, and not just in this country. Independently of the ABE operation, Good also acquired interests in numerous other companies, such that by 1946 he was on the boards of no fewer than 28 companies, and chairman of 23 of them.

Among these other companies was Associated Locomotive Equipment Limited, which held the manufacturing rights for British Caprotti valve gear (from February 1945); Fielding & Platt Limited and Heenan & Froude Limited, both based in Worcester, the latter firm well known for its hydraulic machinery. Another company in which he held an interest was Sir WG Armstrong Whitworth (Engineers) Limited. On 21 November 1945 a new private company was registered, Associated British Oil Engines Limited (ABOE), to coordinate the activities of the various companies under Good's control that were involved in the manufacture of diesel engines, and not least to act as a central sales agency. The initial directors were Good himself and FS Mitman, and in the following year Oil Engines (Coventry) Limited was added to the portfolio, although this company was already owned by the Brush group. Henry Meadows Limited of Wolverhampton followed in March 1949, but in this case total ownership was not until April 1952.

Alan Good's master plan was two-fold. In the first instance, in acquiring interests in a number of diesel engine manufacturers the ABOE group could supply engines across the complete power and utilisation ranges. The more subtle scheme however, was for various manufacturers to each concentrate on a smaller range of engines, in which they had both a better skill-base and reputation, thus improving manufacturing productivity, along with product performance, combined with more competitive selling prices. At the same time it was envisaged that across the whole ABOE Group engines could be supplied to meet just about all the market requirements. Secondly, Good saw a large market for diesel-powered locomotives as the world's railways re-equipped after the ravages of the recent war; he was shrewd enough to realise that in many cases, following the North American example, many of the railways would move away from the steam locomotive to more modern forms of traction. We saw above how

the Brush Electrical Engineering Company Limited was one of Good's first interests, and he became deputy chairman and managing director in 1938.

We must now return to Ian Marriott, who joined ABOE in late 1946 as commercial director and became a director of Brush in January 1947; he was known as a 'local director' and was responsible for sales. Marriott's remit was to direct the sales teams of the two companies, Brush and ABOE, trading from February 1948 as the Brush-ABOE Group. About this time too, a number of subsidiary ABOE companies were put in place to promote export sales in different parts of the world; for example British Oil Engines (Export) Limited in March 1946 with Captain RC Petter as its first managing director, British Oil Engines (Australasia) Proprietary Limited in March 1947, and Scottish Oil Engines Limited in October 1947. In October 1946 Good, the Hon. AC Geddes - who we shall meet again later - and Mitman also formed British Deutz Limited to supply spares and effect repairs to engines of this builder, with workshops at Thalia Works, Governor Road at Hanwell in London. The Brush-ABOE Group established a London office at Dukes Court, 32 Dukes Road St James, which was also the Brush Electrical Engineering Company London office.

An obvious move by Good to assist his aspiration of breaking into the market for diesel locomotives, and in particular diesel-electric locomotives, was the acquisition of an established locomotives builder. Marriott of course, knew Elizabeth Edwards, and her views on the future of her shareholding in WG Bagnall Limited, in particular her dislike of Young Jimmy Cadman. He was therefore able to broker a deal between Alan Good, Elizabeth Edwards and James Cadman for the sale of WG Bagnall Limited. Good used the financial resources of Heenan & Froude Limited, of which he was chairman, to acquire the entire share capital of WG Bagnall Limited, and the Company changed hands on 22 July 1947. We do not know for certain why Good used Heenan & Froude in this transaction, as it made WG Bagnall Limited a subsidiary of that company, rather than Brush, despite a clear vision of a future working relationship between Bagnall and Brush. However, at the time Heenan & Froude had a cash surplus in its general reserve of £100,000 (at 31 August 1946), and this could well have been the reason. Before proceeding to detail the changes that took place following the sale, it is opportune to mention that after Edwards's death a business associate of Cadman replaced him on the Bagnall board. This was George Charles Neilson, a director and chairman of the Goldendale Iron Company Limited with works at Tunstall in Stoke-on-Trent, a gentleman also well-known through her late husband to Elizabeth Edwards; he represented, at least in part, her interests during the sale process.

The existing directors of WG Bagnall Limited resigned en-block on 22 July 1947 and a new board was appointed. It consisted of Alan P Good as chairman; Francis James Fielding; The Hon Alexander Campbell Geddes; Charles Loraine Hill and Ian Marriott. Good we have already met, Fielding was managing director of Heenan & Froude, Geddes was managing director of ABOE and a director of Brush, while Hill was a director of both Heenan & Froude and Brush. At this stage Ian Marriott was commercial director of both Brush and ABOE, but soon after the acquisition he was appointed managing director at the Castle Engine Works, an appointment effective from December 1947. It was generally recognised at the time that this was Alan Good's way of rewarding Marriott for his involvement in brokering the deal that led to the acquisition by Heenan & Froude of WG Bagnall Limited. The secretary under the new regime was William Oliver John Urry, who held a similar position with Heenan & Froude, and on the 16 September 1947 the registered office was moved to the parent company's works at Shrub Hill in Worcester. At the same time the London office of WG Bagnall Limited was moved to Dukes Court, the Brush offices; hitherto it had been at 32 Victoria Street Westminster. After the sale the District Bank Nominees Limited (successors to Branch Nominees Limited) retained a sizable shareholding, and by a special resolution dated 29 November 1947, it was agreed to convert the Company's 20,000 £1 redeemable preference shares (17,000 of which were issued and fully paid) into 20,000 ordinary shares of £1 each. The first trade announcement of the change of ownership would seem to have been in *The Railway Gazette*, issue dated 26 July 1947.

Before moving on to discuss the firm's products at the time, it is worth covering in some more detail the people issues. Ian Marriott never seems to have endeared himself to the workforce, was seen as somewhat of a flamboyant character - he was very much a Ladies Man - and not always perceived as completely interested in the Company's future, as perhaps he might have been. Harold Wood described him as: 'a bright and breezy good-looking guy, who was able to charm Elizabeth Edwards and James Cadman that Alan Good was the best outlet for their shares'. The late WA Smyth, who eventually took over from Marriott, was much more scathing, and reckoned he hardly knew one end of a locomotive from the other! Studies of Ian Marriott in the various photographs will perhaps give the reader a not altogether dissimilar impression. Marriott never moved home to live in the area, retaining his large house called 'Priory of Lady St Mary', at Wareham in Dorset. Initially he stayed during the week at various hotels in Stafford, but later arranged for the Company to purchase Highfield Manor, a large house in Newport Road Stafford, as a club-house for senior members of staff and a flat for himself. He remained a member of the Brush board and became representative of that Company on the Internal Combustion Group of the Locomotive Manufacturers Association (LMA), Brush having recently been elected members. An early appointment of Marriott's was the promotion of Harry Davies to the position of general manager, as, unlike Edwards, he had no intension of shouldering the day-to-day activities of the workshops, as well as that of managing director - he saw himself much more as a figure-head! In any event Harry Davies, along with Tom Stockton, had largely run the business in the interregnum between Edwards's death, the transfer of ownership and until Marriott was appointed, so this was a well-deserved promotion. However, both Davies and Stockton had by all accounts, had rather a rough time from Mrs Edwards! Harry Davies continued to represent the Company at the LMA.

Ian Marriott was not long in taking a dislike to a number of senior members of the staff, and an early casualty was FHB Harris, who was after all 76 years of age at the time of the change in ownership. Just how long Harris would have carried on had Edwards remained in charge is anybodies guess, but as he had lost a lot of money when Kerr, Stuart went into liquidation, he was by no means a rich man. It appears he had over the years taken a large number of shares in Kerr, Stuart, in lieu of both salary and bonuses, and it was a widely held view that he continued to work to such a ripe old age for necessity, as much as any other reason. Edwards of course, had an extremely high respect for Harris and would have been well aware of his financial circumstances, and be sympathetic to his cause. Harris used to show Harold Wood and others his then worthless Kerr, Stuart share certificates. Harris retired in late 1948 and went to live in retirement with his daughter at 'Court Cottage', Waltham near Canterbury; his family had roots in that part of Kent, in particular the nearby village of Barham, hence his middle Christian name. FHB Harris lived to the ripe old age of 82 years and passed away on 7 December 1953. As the trade press recorded of his death at the time, he was 'The Grand Old Man of the Private Locomotive Building Industry in the Country'. Harold Wood, of whom he was the mentor and who became his successor, told the story "that although his mathematical analysis of stress problems was self-taught, and although it had its limitations, it was very sound", and if evidence of this were needed one only has to look at the long lives of many of the locomotives he was responsible for designing, many of which are still around today.

Tom Stockton the works manager, known around the works as Freddie Fox, was in 1949 another casualty, as was Harold Coates the chief cashier - they both had to go but found alternative employment at the English Electric Company works in the town. Tom soon became second in command there in the buildings and plant maintenance department, and after retirement in 1955 took on part-time teaching of technical subjects at the local technical college. He passed away on 3 November 1960 at his home, 72 Baswich Street in Stafford, at the age of 65. Tom Stockton, a 'favourite' in the latter days of Edwards's tenure, was put under enormous pressure by Ian Marriott and, in his turn and through him, by Harry Davies, such that life became quite intolerable. Tom Stockton had made life pretty difficult for other senior members of the staff when he had the confidence of Edwards during the period when the latter was largely incapacitated, such that he had few friends among the management team. The general view was that his demise was but a matter of time once Edwards had gone.

The departure of Harris and Stockton obviously left two important gaps in the senior management structure. The position of chief draughtsman was filled by Harold Wood, who, it will be recalled, had left the Company in September 1946, as he recalled many years later, 'to let Edwards do his dying'! Wood went to work for FW Langley & Company, a firm of general engineers based in Clough Street at Hanley in Stoke-on-Trent. At the time this company was heavily involved in helping to rebuild and modernise the local pottery manufacturing industry after many years of war-time neglect. Many of the pottery firms had been forced to close down during the war because of staff or equipment shortages, and the opportunity was being taken before recommencing full production to re-equip and modernise the production facilities. In many cases outmoded steam plant was being removed and replaced by electrically-driven machinery, with supplies from the National Grid. Harold Wood was involved in the design work for this type of change. However, knowing of the impending retirement of FHB Harris and the other changes at the Castle Engine Works, Harry Davies approached Harold Wood as early as March 1947, with a view to him coming back to Stafford as chief draughtsman designate, which he eventually did in September that year. Harold also told the story that towards the end of Edwards's life, and in the period before the change of ownership, Elizabeth Edwards started to take an increasing interest, and indeed in his words 'interfere', in the day-to-day activities at the works, and in particular the running of the works canteen. As a result a number of regular users of that establishment, Harold included, started to go into town for lunch rather than use the canteen!

The replacement for Tom Stockton was Sydney Ridgway, who arrived in May 1950 having previously been with Beyer Peacock & Company Limited, the well established locomotive builders from Gorton in Manchester, world famous for its articulated locomotives on the Garratt principle. Sydney Ridgway (always known at Stafford as Sam) was born on 10 June 1914, a native of Crewe, where he was educated at the county secondary school. He commenced an engineering apprenticeship with the London Midland & Scottish Railway (LMS) in Crewe Works, where at the time his father was the machine shop foreman. Young Sydney attended the local technical college and was awarded the Whitworth prize in 1937; he went to Manchester College of Technology between 1936 and 1939, taking his BSc in mechanical engineering at

London University in 1939. During this time Ridgway was employed as a draughtsman at Crewe, and among his jobs was assisting in the design of the projected joint LMS and London & North Eastern Railway (LNER) locomotive testing station, in which WA Stanier chief mechanical engineer of the LMS, and Nigel Gresley his counterpart on the LNER, were collaborating. In the event, as is widely known, the commencement of hostilities put a stop to this project, and it was not until after the war that work started again. Feeling well qualified but underpaid, Ridgway decided to seek his fortune elsewhere, and in 1939, under the auspices of the India Office, took up the appointment as assistant works manager of the Saidpur metre-gauge locomotive carriage & wagon workshops of the Eastern Bengal Railway in Assam. Moreover, before departing these shores he got married.

After the commencement of hostilities with Japan, and when it looked as if Assam would be invaded as the Japanese advanced through Burma, Sydney's wife, and a daughter who had been born in Assam, returned to this country. Sydney was transferred to the Indian Engineers and posted to Badarpur, where he took charge of around 300 miles of railway from Akhaura, which is north-east of Lumding, and onwards to the various ferry crossings of the Brahmapurta River. In January 1942 the Eastern Bengal and Assam-Bengal Railways had been combined to form the Bengal & Assam Railway, and the main-line of the hill-section was the part controlled by Ridgway. In view of the gradients this line was worked by Garrat articulated locomotives, and it was in view of his experience with this type of locomotive that he joined Beyer Peacock as assistant works manager on returning to this country after the war. Before taking up his new duties in August 1950 as works manager at Stafford, Ridgway was sent by Alan Good to America to gain experience in the manufacture and maintenance of diesel-electric locomotives. At the time diesel locomotives were becoming very popular on that side of the Atlantic and for the next few years the experience and knowledge he gained stood the firm in very good stead. As in fact it did for other companies in the Brush Group. In particular at the various American Locomotive Company (ALCO) workshops, Sydney Ridgway gained valuable knowledge and experience in heavy-duty arc welding, and this initiative was another example of

Good's business acumen and forethought. In the building of locomotives on the other side of the Atlantic, welding was largely replacing the earlier practice of riveting, with enormous savings in both production time and material, and of course man-power and total costs.

During the period between Tom Stockton leaving and Sydney Ridgway taking up his appointment, Arthur James Woollams as the chief foreman had covered the responsibilities. When Albert Somers, the machine shop foreman, left the Company in 1948, Woollams had been promoted to a position of superintendent of the fitting, erecting and machine shops, making him in effect, the senior foreman, and this was considered by many of the staff, as a typical Bagnall money-saving move! On his arrival Ridgway met with some hostility among the staff, as many of them felt that Arthur Woollams should have been appointed; however, it soon became clear to Ridgway that in fact Woollams did not really want the job, and was content to remain in his existing, and already expanded role. Woollams father Jim, by the way, had been the machine shop foreman in earlier times, and his brother Walter was also employed in the machine shop. Jim Woollams had 50 years service with the firm in 1935, but stayed on in a lesser role as a turner in the machine shop after reaching the normal retirement age of 65, and he died while still in the service of the Company just after the war. The Woollams family had as splendid a history of service with WG Bagnall Limited as any other.

Sydney Ridgway's popularity was soon on the upward, as he was able to very quickly sort out a whole range of production problems, such that productivity and hence output increased, and with them the men's earnings! To use his own words: 'it was soon sweetness and light'. In 1950 the other senior members of staff were: Harold J Shaw the buyer; Arthur Owen cost accountant; George Brown chief estimator; Vic Betteley progress engineer. The various shop foreman were: Albert (Bert) Emery fitting & erecting; Arthur Vine boiler: George White pattern; Cliff Jenkinson foundry; J Brownsword smithy; Ben Lee machine; W Skelton wagon; Bill Monaghan joiners & painters; W Pittard tool room; Albert Appleton storekeeper; E Williams power house; H Rogers yard gang.

There is one more character to be introduced at this stage, and another gentleman who was to have a very significant influence over the Company's affairs during the next decade. This was William Addison Smyth (pronounced Smith), who always insisted on being referred to as WA Smyth, except in close personal relationships. WA Smyth became a personal friend of one of the authors, but nevertheless, we shall respect his wish, and will refer to him as either WA Smyth, or plain Smyth, throughout this book. He was born in Dublin on 12 July 1902 of a railway family, his paternal grandfather had joined the service of the Midland & Great Western Railway (M&GWR) of Ireland at an early age, and his father was its chief accountant. Educated at Mountjoy School in Dublin, followed by the Municipal Technical College and then the Royal School of Science for Ireland, WA Smyth became a pupil of WH Morton, the locomotive engineer of the M&GWR, at Broadstone Works in Dublin on 7 September 1920. In 1923 he went into the drawing office to complete his training and in May 1925, on completion of his pupillage, was appointed locomotive foreman at Ballina. This was a small shed almost at the end of the branch from Manulla to Killina on the north-west coast of Ireland, with a couple of engines allocated for branch line work. The staff consisted of but 12, and as there was neither a fitter nor boilermaker, Smyth had to attend to such necessities himself, assisted as appropriate by one or more of the cleaners! This was of course ideal training for an up and coming locomotive engineer, and in March 1925 he was sent to Limerick to take up the appointment of assistant district locomotive superintendent for the Western Division of the Great Southern Railway (GSR), into which the M&GWR had been amalgamated in 1924. Among his other tasks whilst holding this appointment, it fell to his lot to undertake, as he described it, 'the very melancholy task' of supervising the closure of the West Clare Railway workshops at Ennis in County Clare. This three-foot gauge railway, for which Bagnall had supplied the initial batch of engines, had also been absorbed by the GSR, and a decision had been taken to concentrate all heavy repairs of locomotives and rolling stock at the better facilities in Limerick. He was reminded of this years later as one of the engines that came to Limerick for repairs during his time there was one of those built at Stafford. In June 1928, on further promotion, Smyth came back to Dublin, to Inchicore Works on this occasion, to take up the appointment as designate

Portrait of WA Smyth, taken about the time he was appointed Managing Director at Stafford. More than any other individual, Smyth was responsible for keeping the firm viable in the period after Alan Good's death, and until the Dorman take-over.

assistant works manager. Inchicore had been the workshops of the Great Southern & Western Railway of Ireland, and became the principal workshops of the newly formed GSR; Smyth took up his substantive post a few months later. Elected a student member of the Institution of Mechanical Engineers in May 1923, he became an associate member in October 1927 and a full member in March 1936.

After a couple of years at Inchicore, and seeing few opportunities of further advancement for several years within the GSR, Smyth decided to look elsewhere. In October 1929 he entered the colonial service and took up the appointment as assistant locomotive engineer (manufacture) on the Ceylon Government Railway

(CGR), at Ratmalana Workshops near Colombo. In April 1931 he became assistant mechanical engineer for the CGR and in 1934 was appointed to the most senior mechanical engineering position, as chief mechanical engineer. Two years later, in Colombo, he married Meriol Margaret Irwin, whose father was also in the colonial service based in Ceylon. Whilst in the service of the CGR WA Smyth was responsible for several pioneering developments in the introduction of diesel-electric traction, including some interesting railcars and shunting locomotives. The CGR was, relatively speaking, in the forefront of a number of areas with diesel-electric traction in the colonies, not least because of the problems with water supplies for steam locomotives on many of the Ceylon routes, and Smyth played a large part in these developments. Unfortunately a period of ill-health prompted a decision to leave Ceylon, despite excellent career prospects and enormous job satisfaction, and although offered the position of chief mechanical engineer of the railways in Palestine, where it was felt the climate would suit him better, he decided against acceptance. This decision was the result of a chance meeting while in Palestine considering the possible appointment, with Charles Eugene Bedaux. Bedaux had achieved fame as the originator of the work-study concept of the 'standard minute'; a result of the meeting was Smyth joining Bedaux's British company, British Bedaux Limited (which later became Associated Industrial Consultants Limited - AIC), and with his wife Smyth came to live in this country.

Charles Bedaux was an interesting and complex character and although he is not strictly part of our story it is worth mentioning that as well as lending his French chateau to the Duke of Windsor and Mrs Simpson, where they were later married, he worked during the last war for the Vichy French and German Governments. This was despite having become an American citizen, although he was actually of French-Canadian extraction. Captured by the Americans in 1941, during lengthy legal proceedings while in captivity, in 1944 he managed to commit suicide. Despite Bedaux's political leanings Smyth always spoke highly of him, emphasising that he was an inspiration to work for, was the father of modern-day workstudy practices and, as mentioned earlier, was the originator of the 'standard', as opposed to the 'clock' minute, the cornerstone of all production work measurement ever since. With British Bedaux and later AIC, Smyth undertook a number of assignments to help engineering manufacturing companies improve productivity. These included the Iraq State Railways and the North British Locomotive Company in Glasgow. At the time he was involved, North British were engaged in building the war-time Austerity 2-8-0 and 2-10-0 locomotives, required in large numbers to assist the war effort and Smyth was able to help the company improve the time taken to build each locomotive. His role during the war years was an essential one, and he was also able to help make significant improvements in the production of aircraft at the Leven Aircraft Works, and in ship building with Lobnitz Limited in Renfrew.

It is both significant and interesting to mention at this juncture that in April 1942 Smyth was approached by Edger C Bredin, general manager of the GSR, and asked if he would return to Inchicore as deputy chief mechanical engineer. Added to the request was a promise that he would succeed to the existing occupant of that position, MJ Ginnety, when he retired in September the following year. Obviously Smyth gave this offer serious consideration, but to his lasting credit, and despite being an Irishman, he decided that the work he was doing to help wartime production in this country was of greater importance than his personal career. WA Smyth's last job with AIC was at the Guest Keen & Nettlefolds Limited (GKN) Screw Division in Birmingham, as a result of which he joined that Company in 1943 as deputy general manager, and became general manager of the Screw Division in 1945.

With the return of peace Smyth felt the urge to return to his roots in railway engineering, and he joined the London & North Eastern Railway (LNER) - soon to become a part of British Railways - in 1947 as chief production engineer. Based in Doncaster he reported to the chief mechanical engineer, which at the time was Arthur H Peppercorn. This was a newly created job, with the principal objective to improve what was considered very low productivity in the LNER locomotive, carriage and wagon workshops. Smyth found this an extremely difficult task, as although the position was in his own words pretty desperate, especially at Stratford in East London, there were so many vested interests that he made little headway. Not surprisingly he did not find this job a very happy appointment, but his name had come to the notice of Alan Good via Sir Ronald Matthews, who was at the time chairman not only of Brush, but the LNER too. We shall explore later how Good had been able to win a contract to supply the CGR with a fleet of diesel-electric locomotives, and it was Smyth's knowledge of the railways of Ceylon, along with his railway engineering and production experience that was the attraction. Good was able to persuade Smyth to join his group, and with an obvious objective of appointing him managing director of WG Bagnall Limited. However, with Marriott in position at Stafford, in July 1949 Good appointed Smyth as director & general manager of Henry Meadows Limited, the diesel engine builders in Wolverhampton, which at the time was about to be acquired by the Brush-ABOE Group. Moreover, at the same time Smyth joined the Bagnall board; he was not at Meadows long, and in March 1950 took up the appointment of managing director of WG Bagnall Limited. Marriott was all intents and purposes sacked; he was awarded £2,500 compensation for loss of office and allowed to purchase his company Jaguar for £931. Alan Good, perhaps with a twinge of his conscious, arranged his appointments to a similar position with Parsons Engineering Limited of Southampton, of which they were both directors. This was much nearer his home in the New Forest and turned out to be an amicable arrangement all round.

This is perhaps the place to say a little more about Ian Marriott, before he leaves our story. In July 1953 he left Parsons in Southampton and took up an appointment with Wellworthy Limited, the well-known makers of piston rings at the Radial Works at Lymington in Hampshire, which was even nearer to where he lived than Southampton. However, he seems to have later come onto rather hard times, as Harold Wood recalled when he met him many years later. By this time, which would be about 1960, Marriott had married a second time and was working for a company making curtain rails and associated fittings! He passed away on 15 December 1985 after a long illness - he was 74 years old. The notice in the *Daily Telegraph* dated 23 December noted that he had lived his '74 years of life with a capital L'. Whatever else he achieved in life, it is a fact that few people shed a tear when he left the Castle Engine Works.

The appointment of WA Smyth to lead the Company

at this time in its history was an excellent one. With his knowledge and experience of railways and in particular locomotive engineering, coupled with his expertise in production management and not least his knowledge and experience of working in Ceylon, made him an ideal choice. Despite Heenan & Froude cash having been used to acquire the Company, and therefore, being the parent, Good made it very clear to all concerned that WG Bagnall Limited should take its lead from Brush in all matters. At the time of the acquisition the directors of Brush were: Sir Ronald Matthews as chairman; AP Good as deputy chairman and general manager; Charles L Hill; Captain RC Petter; DB Hoseason; Sir Richard Arthur Pease Bt; RW Richards; AC Geddes. As noted above Sir Ronald Matthews was also chairman of the LNER, and it was through him that Alan Good came to meet WA Smyth, and become acquainted with his experiences in Ceylon and dissatisfaction with life on the LNER. Charles Hill we have already met as a director of both Heenan & Froude and Brush. Hill had a number of other interests, most of them in other companies in the Good empire, but additionally he was a majority shareholder in the Bristol City Line of Steamships Limited, a family concern whose ships sailed under the name of The Hill Line. Richard Cecil Petter was of the Petter engines family, whilst Hoseason was a manager at Brush. Donald Bright Hoseason was born in 1899 and spent his entire career, until joining Brush, with Metropolitan Vickers (formerly British Westinghouse) based at Trafford Park, latterly as chief engineer of the motor department, joining Brush in 1940. A vice president of the Institution of Electrical Engineers, Hoseason left Brush in July 1947 to take up an appointment as director of studies at the Administrative Staff College, Henley-on-Thames, but he died rather tragically in a motor accident on 16 July 1948. Sir Richard Pease was a member of the famous north-east family of coal-owners and a director of Pease & Partners Limited, as well as East Hetton Collieries. RW Richards was involved in a number of Good-controlled companies, in particular those involved with the manufacture of diesel engines. The Hon. Alexander Campbell Geddes OBE MC (Lieut-Col Royal Artillery Rtd.) was a son of Baron Geddes and a great nephew of Sir Eric Geddes MP, wielder of the infamous Geddes Axe of 1922. Sir Eric, who had chaired the post-war committee of national expenditure, had been heavily involved in munitions supply during the war, was one time First Lord of the Admiralty and before that deputy general manager of the North Eastern Railway. Nominally Alexander Geddes was a sort of roving ambassador for the Brush-ABOE Group, and other Good companies. WA Smyth recalled that it was Geddes who 'vetted' him on Good's behalf for the appointment to Henry Meadows, and in doing so at the Travellers Club in London, gave him one of the best lunches he ever had! A keen fly fisherman, Smyth was soon able to get parts of his flies made at the Castle Engine Works!

In July 1950 Alan Good put in place what was in effect a new company, to act as a marketing and selling agency for the diesel-electric locomotives it was proposed to build. To achieve this he used an existing almost 'shelf' company that was a part of his holdings. This company, Flather & Company Limited, had been registered on 4 December 1945 to 'sell or otherwise deal in motors, machinery etc', with its registered office at the Falcon Works (this was the Brush Works in Loughborough), having a capital structure of £1,000 divided into 1,000 shares of £1; the principal shareholder was Brush Coachworks Limited, another member of the Group. In fact the Flather Company was a re-construction of an earlier company of the same name, registered as long ago as 1894 and based in Leeds. It is perhaps best remembered today as a manufacturer of dynamos, many of which can still be observed fitted to preserved showmans steam road locomotives that can be seen at traction engine rallies around the country. Brush had acquired Flather & Company in 1945, and its electrical machine business continued for a few years under the name of Flather (Leeds) Investments Limited. However, the manufacture of electrical machines was soon discontinued at Leeds and what remained spread around various other companies both within and outside Alan Good's interests.

Anyway, so far as we are concerned on 11 July 1950 the name of the Flather Company was changed to Brush Bagnall Electric Traction Limited (it was changed again on 20 November 1950 to Brush Bagnall Traction Limited), and the capital increased by the addition of 24,000 shares of £1, to equal in total £25,000; in this case all held by Brush Electrical Engineering Company Limited. At the same time the articles were altered to encompass: 'to manufacturer, buy, sell or hire diesel engines, locomotives etc', and the initial directors were: Donald Hoseason and Ronald Wall. However, a new board was soon appointed consisting of: Alan Good as chairman; AC Geddes; JWC Milligan; Rex Bate; EW Martin; James Calderwood; PC Sharp; JT Rymer; WA Smyth. Milligan was the managing director of Brush, Bate was the sales manager there, Martin was the managing director of Associated Locomotive Equipment Limited, Calderwood was the technical director at Brush and Rymer was the managing director of Mirrlees, Bickerton & Day Limited. Calderwood by the way, who joined Brush in January 1949, had been manager of Sulzer Brothers (London) Limited, but spent most of his career, and undertook his training with Swan, Hunter Wigman Richardson & Company Limited, the north-east shipbuilders. However, he had been in the RAF during the war.

Whilst all this activity was under way, and behind the scenes so to speak, Good shocked the industry in March 1950 by announcing an order for 25 main-line diesel-electric locomotives for Ceylon, at the time the largest single export order placed in this country for diesel locomotives - and right from under the noses of his competitors, and the 'big-boys' in both the locomotive building and electric traction equipment manufacturing industries. It caused shock waves to rumble around the industry for some time afterwards, and was without doubt a major coup in which WG Bagnall Limited were to play a significant part. Good's initiative in getting Smyth to lead the team at Stafford was now to pay off handsomely, as Smyth knew personally the principal individuals in Ceylon who were, and would be, involved with the order.

Before moving on to describe some of the activities of Brush Bagnall Traction Limited, it is necessary to return to the orders on hand in the last year or so of the Edwards's regime, as many of them were not completed until after the change of ownership. This is also the place to mention that Elizabeth Edwards continued to live in Stafford, at 'Enville', until her death on 12 January 1969. Her will was proved on the 18 March 1969 at £303,271, a large sum of money in those days, and she was very generous in her bequests. In addition to her housekeeper Dorothy L Plant, to whom she left no less that £45,000, there were bequests to St Mary's Church in Stafford where she and her husband had worshipped (and remember where WG Bagnall and his

The advertisement reads:

128   *OVERSEAS RAILWAYS, A Railway Gazette Publication*

A general purpose locomotive

**For full availability and ease of maintenance
A Bogie Shunting Locomotive is the answer.**

The illustration shows the latest **BRUSH BAGNALL** design of Diesel Electric Locomotive — 500/750 H.P. This type of locomotive has been specifically designed for heavy duty shunting; switching and transfer work, and for secondary main-line duties. Locomotives can be arranged for multiple operation from a single cab. **BRUSH BAGNALL** Locomotives are powered by MIRRLEES Diesel Engines and BRUSH electrical equipment with mechanical parts by W. G. BAGNALL LTD.

the best answer is **BRUSH BAGNALL**

All enquiries concerning Diesel Electric Locomotives should be addressed to :—
BRUSH BAGNALL TRACTION LTD., LOUGHBOROUGH, ENGLAND
A member of the BRUSH ABOE group

15.102

Contempory advertisement for Brush Bagnall Traction Limited, as appeared in the Railway Gazette, annual publication Overseas Railways, 1952 edition. The locomotive illustrated while an artists impression, is not unlike some locomotives built later by the Company for the Steel Company of Wales.

wife Jessie where married), to the Institute of Cancer Research at the Royal Cancer Hospital in Fulham, and the local branch of the Salvation Army. Also, and perhaps not surprisingly, a bequest to St Cynon's Church at Fairbourne where her husband was buried, some of such monies to be spent on maintaining the graveyard; the residual monies were to be used to help local residential homes for the elderly. Strangely perhaps, in asking to be cremated she left the disposal of her ashes to the discretion of her executors, and did not request them be placed with or near to her husband's grave in Fairbourne. The bungalow in Fairbourne incidentally, which also went under the name 'Enville', was not mentioned in the will and had presumably, been disposed of at some earlier date. It may be that the memories it brought back had caused her to dispose of it soon after her husband's death.

It is worthy of a mention too, that despite her husband's death in December 1946, the annual Christmas & new year children's party went ahead as planned on Saturday 4 January the following year, at which she presided in her usual inimitable fashion. Elizabeth Edwards felt very strongly that it would have been what her husband would have wanted, as despite having no children of their own, and both being quite formidable characters, they had a soft spot for children. These annual children's Christmas and new year parties

by the way, continued until the end of the Company's independent existence.

Not unexpectedly after the years of hostilities, once peace returned several orders were placed for industrial shunting locomotives - and not just for the home market. Examples are two of the standard 16in cylinder six-wheelers for the Butterley Company collieries in Derbyshire and Nottinghamshire, manufacturer's numbers 2816 and 2817 despatched in May 1945. Also ordered were two 14in cylinder four-wheelers for the Staveley Coal & Iron Company Limited, numbers 2821 and 2822 of April 1945, and a 12in four-wheeler for Frazer & Chalmers of Erith in Kent; this was number 2826 of April 1946. A particularly interesting order came from the North West Midlands Joint Electricity Authority for two 14in cylinder 0-4-0 saddle tanks, as they were for use at what became the first new power station to be commissioned in this country after the war. Manufacturer's numbers 2828 and 2829 despatched in November 1945 and April 1946 respectively, to Meaford Power Station at Barlaston near Stoke-on-Trent. For overseas there was a metre-gauge 12in cylinder four-wheel saddle tank for the Admiralty in Ceylon, number 2823 of November 1945, and two more of the two-foot gauge articulated locomotives for Sir John L Hulett's sugar estates at Darnall in Natal, numbers 2830 and 2831 of May 1946. Additionally two

MURIEL, No 2 in the pair of 14in cylinder locomotives supplied in 1946 to Meaford Power station near Stoke-on-Trent. This was the first new power station commissioned after the war. The locomotive is manufacturer's number 2829 and the picture was taken on 7 January 1970, the last occasion the locomotive was used prior to withdrawal. It was subsequently sold for scrap.

more of the two-foot gauge 4-4-0 side tanks so popular with the Tongaat Sugar Company, also in Natal. Manufacturer's numbers 2819 and 2820 of March 1946; as events turned out the last new locomotives ordered by Tongaat.

In July 1945 the Crown Agents ordered six metre-gauge 2-8-2 tender engines for the Tanganyika Railway, the design being a development of an earlier one, and latterly class 25 of the East African Railways (EAR). The Bagnall engines were designed to have a maximum axle-load of 10 tons and be able to negotiate curves with a radius of five chains and cope with grades of 1 in 45. The EAR classification was class 26, and a rather handsome engine was designed with 17x23in outside piston-valve cylinders and 3ft 7in diameter driving wheels. Because at the time the engines were ordered it was contemplated that the railway might at some time in the future be converted to the standard South African gauge of 3ft 6in (known locally as the Cape Gauge), the wheel centres were so designed to allow new tyres to be fitted to suit the wider gauge. Likewise the brake gear and couplings were arranged so that they could easily be altered to suit. The boiler was superheated with a smokebox mounted MeLeSco multiple-valve regulator complete with the Edwards patent by-pass arrangement, and there was a large firebox with a grate area of 27 sq ft, to allow for either wood or coal as a fuel. Boiler feed was via a Weir vertical single-cylinder pump mounted on the right-hand side foot framing along with a feed water heater on the left, as well as a No 9 m/m live steam injector. Other fittings included electric lighting, vacuum train brakes, roller bearing axle-boxes on the leading and trailing trucks and a large eight-wheel tender with a capacity of 4,200 gallons of water and 250 cub ft of coal; an additional 530 cub ft was available for the wood. The complete engine and tender turned the scales in working order at 98.2 tons, and the tractive effort at 85% of the 180 psi boiler pressure equalled 23,651lb. The six engines and tenders, manufacturer's numbers 2832 to 2837, were despatched between December 1946 and May 1947, as Tanganyika Railway numbers 700 to 705, and later EAR 2601 to 2606; they were all shipped from Birkenhead to Dar-es-Salaam and cost £16,515 each free-on-board. In the event the engines were never converted to 3ft 6in gauge, but some of them were still working on the EAR in the late 1970s allocated to Dar-es-Salaam and Tabora. Being among the biggest metre-gauge locomotives the firm built, a colour painting was commissioned showing one of them hauling a train, and this was used for publicity purposes, including the cover of the only catalogue, as opposed to a brochure, produced by the Company after the war.

The London-based consulting engineers Fox & Mayo placed an order in November 1945, on behalf of the Bolivar Railway (not Bolivia note) Company Limited, for two 3ft 6in gauge 2-6-2 side tank engines. The design was based on earlier engines the Company had

Official photograph, along with a painting that appears on the next page, undertaken for publicity purposes, of the metre-gauge 2-8-2 tender engines supplied to the Tanganyika Railway, numbers 2832 to 2837 of 1946 and 1947. Notice the feed-water heater and tender side extensions to provide additional fuel space for wood to supplement coal.

OVERSEAS RAILWAYS, A Railway Gazette Publication   123

2-8-2 LOCOMOTIVE SUPPLIED TO THE TANGANYIKA RAILWAY

W.G. Bagnall LTD   CASTLE ENGINE WORKS STAFFORD

" Bagnall Built " is synonymous with faithful service and economy under all working conditions, and the locomotive shown here is no exception. Designed to special requirements and weighing 98.2 tons, this locomotive with its eight-wheeled tender will negotiate minimum curves of 330 feet radius and gradients of 1 in 45.

CODES : A.B.C. 5th EDITION, ENGINEERING, BEDFORD McNEIL, WESTERN UNION

LOCOMOTIVES FOR EVERY PURPOSE

dm BL 44

Artists impression of the Tanganyika Railway 2-8-2 locomotives, used for publicity purposes.

built with the same wheel arrangement for India: cylinders were 15x22in and the coupled wheel diameter 3ft 7in. A Belpaire firebox boiler was fitted with a steel firebox and steel tubes, but there was no superheater. The engines were intended for the Puerto Cabello & Valencia section of the Bolivar Railway and the price quoted was £8,025 each, free-on-board Liverpool. The proposed destination of these engines can be a little confusing, as the railway, the Puerto Cabello & Valencia Railway Company Limited was in Venezuela and not Bolivia, and ran some 34 miles inland from the port of Puerto Cabello on the Caribbean Sea, directly south to Valencia, and in the process crossed the Las Trincheras mountain range and associated valleys. It was to all intents and purposes a freight only railway, and never seems to have operated a timetabled passenger service; dating from 1888 it was built and operated under a concession from the Venezuelan Government, but was in fact a British Company. In December 1944 operation was taken over by the Bolivar Railway Company Limited, one that takes its name from the famous South American liberator Simon Bolivar, who was born in Caracas the capital of Venezuela. The route included a rack section of two-and-a-quarter miles at 1in12½, and the majority of its small fleet of locomotives dated from around the time it opened, and it was struggling to survive by the end of the war, hence its acquisition by the larger company.

The rack section was operated by three large 0-4-2 rack tank engines built by Beyer Peacock of Manchester and dating from 1887 and 1895; they were fitted with Lange & Livesey's patent arrangement of rack engine and gearing. Special equipment specified for the Bagnall engines included both the Le Chatalier and Heberlein brakes, as the engines were to operate over a section of the line where the gradient was 3.5% for around two-and-a-half miles, and where it crossed the valley of the Las Trincheras. As these requirements for special braking equipment had not been part of the specification against which Bagnall had tendered, when Fox & Mayo made mention of it, there was some consternation in the drawing office! Moreover, Fox &

Mayo themselves, in a letter to Bagnall dated 21 February 1946, appeared equally perplexed as to exactly what was required. The Le Chatelier brake, sometimes referred to as the Riggenbach brake, is a counter pressure arrangement where the cylinders act as air compressors during braking, water being admitted at the same time for cooling purposes, later discharged as steam. This was quite a common arrangement of braking locomotives used on steep gradients, and almost a standard fitting on locomotives used on both pure-rack and rack-assisted railways, and for this reason the engines had slide, rather than piston valves. The requirement for the Heberlein brake was much less usual, however, as by this date it was generally considered a completely outmoded system, consisting of a series of ropes or wires passing along the entire length of a train with weights at intervals to keep them in tension. This arrangement kept the brake blocks off the wheels, and releasing the tension allowed the weights to apply pressure onto the brake blocks, and thus apply the brake, or a brake of sorts! It was a train brake, rather than a locomotive brake, and in any event the locomotives were also fitted with a direct acting steam brake. However, it seems that the Beyer Peacock rack engines were fitted with the necessary equipment for the operation of a Heberlein type of train brake, or at least they were when they were delivered. Additionally the locomotives had rail washing equipment, steam

Official photograph of number 2850 of 1947 completed and ready for delivery to the Bolivar Railway in Venezuela. As described in the adjoining text, in the event the order was cancelled due to non-payment, and this engine and its sister, after some modifications, went to Nigeria.

sanding and electric lighting and were oil fired. The manufacturer's numbers allocated were 2849 and 2850, and the locomotives were completed in November 1947, lettered and numbered as FC Bolivar 31 and 32, with No 32 posing for the official photographs. The engines also carried plates indicating that actual ownership was vested in the Securities Agency Limited, a London finance house; Fox & Mayo by the way, gave its address as 155 Dashwood House, Old Broad Street, which was the same as the Bolivar Railway Company Limited. This was the first and only occasion Bagnall were involved with this firm of consulting engineers, one that seems to have done most of its business with various South American railways.

For whatever reason we know not, but doubtless due to financial issues and the agreement between Securities Agency and the Bolivar Railway, the order was cancelled before the engines could be despatched; they were therefore left on the maker's hands. The Puerto Cabello & Valencia Railway had been in

liquidation since 1946, and along with the Bolivar Railway Company Limited, which as we have seen had taken over its operation, were acquired by the Venezuelan Government soon after. It closed in 1959, but seems to have managed with its existing motive power up until that time. Eventually an arrangement was entered into with the Crown Agents for these two engines to go to Nigeria, following some alterations, and an order for them was placed in January 1948. The alterations included conversion from oil to coal fuel, and the fitment of rocking grates and hopper ashpans. The special brake equipment was removed and vacuum train braking equipment fitted; the rail washing gear was also removed. As Nigerian Railways 41 and 42, they were eventually despatched fully erected to Queen's Dock Liverpool, for shipment to Apapa on 5 April 1948.

What became the last order for the very smallest type of locomotive was received in May 1946. Ten two-foot gauge 0-4-0 saddle tanks with cylinders no more than

One of the 10 diminutive 4½in cylinder two-foot gauge 0-4-0 saddle tanks built in 1948 for coal mines in and around the Black Sea port of Zonguldak in Turkey. These were the smallest locomotives built post-war and although a re-design of the much earlier standard design embodying Bagnall-Price valve gear, in this case conventional locomotive type firebox boilers were fitted - notice how high the boiler sits on the frames. Photograph taken on 25 May 1976 at Uzulmez colliery near Zonguldak, long after the locomotive had fallen out of use. Manufacturer's number 2863, fleet No 4.

Photograph taken at Mahesana Junction on 25 February 1948, illustrating one of the successful A class metre-gauge 4-6-0 tender engines much liked by the Gaekwar's Baroda State Railway. This is one of the post-war batches, almost identical to the pre-war engines of the class, but in this case designated class A1. Indian Railways 31029, formally GBSR No 96, Bagnall number 2854 of 1948. Mahesana was the point on the metre-gauge main line from Baroda to Delhi where several of the former Gaekwar's lines converged, and where all the engines of this class were allocated for most of their lives.

4½ x7½in and a wheel diameter of 1ft 3¼in, ordered by the British Geco Engineering Company Limited for use at state-owned coal mines and associated operations near Zonguldak in Turkey. For this order Bagnall developed a variant of the popular engines of earlier times, complete with Bagnall-Price valve gear, but in this case a conventional locomotive type boiler with a copper firebox and brass tubes. Because this boiler was designed to burn inferior coal, the design called for small 'tailings' with an ash content of 25%, the firebox was relatively large, and as it would not fit between the frames the engines had rather a tall-looking appearance. They also had special firebars and hopper ashpans; could these be the smallest engines ever fitted with such a luxury? Designed to haul an 85-ton trailing load on the level, the boiler pressure was quite high at 170 psi, and this gave the engines a tractive effort at 85% equal to 1,439lb. Manufacturer's numbers allocated were 2860 to 2869, and with an overall height of 6ft 6¾in and a weight in working order of four tons and five cwt, the engines were shipped fully erected and each in its own packing case! Due to their small size

and the Company's full order book at the time, these little engines were erected in the wagon shop and not the erecting shop, the wagon shop being otherwise somewhat under-utilised at the time. They cost £1,115 each free-on-board Liverpool, were despatched in April 1948, and carried the running numbers 1 to 10. Several of them were still to be found around Zonguldak in the late 1970s although not, unfortunately, in use.

In the immediate post-war period there were a number of orders for both metre and 2ft 6in gauge locomotives for the Indian railways, as India started to re-equip its railways after the ravages of the war years. Indeed, the few post-war years were very much an Indian summer for the building of steam locomotives in this country for the Indian sub-continent. In fact as at March 1948, the Company had no fewer than 117 steam locomotives on order along with an invoice value of £166,000, for boilers, spares parts and other equipment. In April 1945 Rendel, Palmer & Tritton were involved with two orders for the Gaekwar's Baroda State Railway, four more of the A class metre-gauge 4-6-0 tender engines, actually designated A1, although

Another of the Gaekwar's Baroda State Railway metre-gauge 4-6-0s provides the backcloth for this group photograph taken on 15 February 1948, on the occasion of a visit to the Castle Engine Works by the Ministry of Supply, GR Strauss. From left to right the personalities are: Eric Bridges Erecting Shop Foreman; Ian Marriott Managing Director; Tom Stockton Works Manager; Mr Williams-Thomson Chief Information Officer Ministry of Supply; Ruth Turney Mayor of Stafford; Captain Stephen Swingler MP for Stafford; GR Strauss Minister of Supply; Miss Nadya Turney Mayoress of Stafford; Messrs SA Davies, LB Hutchinson, JM Wilson and FC Limbrey, respectively Under Secretary, Private Secretary, Regional Controller Midlands and his Deputy, of the Ministry of Supply; Mervyn Talbot Public Relations Officer of ABOE; Harry Davies General Manager; Harold Wood Chief Draughtsman. The locomotives in number 2855 - GBSR No 97.

Indian 2ft 6in gauge W1 class 0-6-2 tender engine, a post-war development of the popular W class. This one is Indian Railways No 591; Bagnall 2857 of 1948, one of four supplied at this time and photographed busy shunting on 2 March 1981 at Ankleshwar, on the Western Railway just south of Baroda - now known as Vadodara. Notice the Walschaerts valve gear substituted for Bagnall-Price on the pre-war engines of this class.

First member of the four rather splendid metre-gauge pacifics despatched in early 1949 for the Morvi State Railway; a specific design for this railway. Notice the copper caped chimney and stainless steel boiler bands along with the arrangement at the rear end of the frames to accommodate the wide-firebox boiler. Manufacturer's number 2872.

they were little different from the pre-war batch. These engines carried manufacturer's numbers 2852 to 2855 and were despatched in January and February 1948. In addition there were four modified versions of the W class 0-6-2 tender engines, designated class W1, the principal difference was the substitution of Walschaerts valve gear for Bagnall-Price, and the tenders had small cabs. In this case the numbers allocated were 2856 to 2859 with despatch in November 1948. All of these engines were still at work well into the early 1980s.

A particularly interesting order of the period, in May 1946, came from the Morvi Railway in India. This railway was a comparatively small system consisting of but 132 route miles of metre-gauge built at the expense of, and operated by, the Maharaja Sahed of Morvi. The main-line ran from Wadhwan on the Bombay, Baroda & Central India Railway to Rajkot Junction on the Gondal Railway, and was entirely in the State of Gujarat. For this order, because of the low axle-loads required, Bagnall designed a very handsome pacific, a singular departure from the various 4-6-0 classes otherwise favoured by the smaller Indian metre-gauge railways. Indeed, we saw in Chapter Nine how the design of the proposed Indian Railway Standards (IRS) lightweight pacific was for various reasons not proceeded with. Four engines were ordered and Sir John Wolfe Barry & Partners were the consulting engineers appointed. These locomotives were exceptionally good-looking,

their appearance marred only by a comparatively small tender essential to enable them to be turned on the existing turntables; this was a great pity. Cylinders were 15x22in and the coupled wheel diameter four-feet, the superheated boiler had a wide Belpaire firebox mounted on top of the frames was equipped with arch-tubes. Walschaerts valve gear drove nine inch diameter piston valves with a full gear valve travel of $5\,{}^{11}/_{16}$ in at the maximum 80% cut-off. The engines had rocking grates and hopper ashpans, Lambert wet sanding, electric lighting and vacuum brakes for both engine, tender and train. The trailing truck was of the same design as the earlier 2-8-2 engines built for South America and India, where the springs were arranged such that they sat centrally over the axle journals, thus ensuring the best possible load transfer, and the truck springing was part compensated with the trailing coupled axle. Tractive effort at 85% of the 180psi working pressure was 15,778lb, and the weight in working order of the engine equalled 44.925 tons, and complete with the tender 70.275 tons - the maximum axle-load was nine tons. The manufacturer's numbers were 2872 to 2875, the Morvi Railway numbers 28 to 31; the engines were beautifully finished complete with copper-caped chimneys and polished brass boiler bands. Despatch was in February and March 1949 and they cost £12,780 each, free-on-board Liverpool.

By the time these engines got to India the Morvi

Railway had been absorbed by the Saurashtra Railway, and it is a matter of speculation as to whether a special design would have been contemplated had this change of ownership taken place earlier. Be that as it may, the engines eventually became Indian Railways class NIS numbers 960 to 963, and were latterly allocated to Bhavnagar shed and continued in use on some of the lightly-laid branch lines thereabouts until the early 1980s. Like so many of the numerically small metre-gauge classes these engines were displaced by the standard Indian post-war YP 4-6-2, and YG 2-8-2 classes, as the lines over which they worked were upgraded to take the heaver axle-loads, and the latter engines were gradually replaced on the main-lines by diesels. As it turned out this was in itself for but a few years as diesels continued to be built in large numbers, or the lines themselves were converted to broad-gauge, which has been the lot of many of them.

The orders mentioned above were not the only

orders for the Indian sub-continent and in June 1946 Greaves Cotton & Company Limited, a company acting as one of the Bagnall agents in that part of the world, ordered three metre-gauge 4-6-0 tender engines for the Mewar State Railway. This railway was one and the same as the Udaipur Chitorgarh Railway - renamed in 1940 - as it had originally been constructed at the cost of the Mewar Durbur, and was in fact operated by the Durbar from 1897. Like the 2-8-0 engines delivered before the war, manufacturer's numbers 2500 to 2502 and 2548 and 2549, these engines were intended to work over the ghat section at Khambli Ghat, but why a six-coupled design was chosen rather than more of the successful 2-8-0s is a mystery. The engines were yet another variety of the various 4-6-0s built for the metre-gauge railways in India just after the war, and in deference to the gradients to be climbed had four-foot diameter driving wheels rather than the 4ft 9in of the standard British Engineering Standards Association

Almost 30 years since it left Stafford, this photograph is of former Morvi Railway No 31, as Western Railway of India 963, Bagnall 2876, at Dhola Junction on 18 January 1977. At that time the four engines, designated class NIS, were allocated to Bhavnagar shed in Gujarat and worked passenger and mixed trains on branch lines in and around the area they were originally built for. Despite its rather unkempt external appearance, the locomotive still displays its handsome lines only marred by the rather small tender, essential to enable the engines to fit the turntables that were in use when they were supplied.

An obvious posed view looking south in the Erecting Shop in the early months of 1949. On the left is one of three metre-gauge 4-6-0 tender engines in its final construction stages being built for the Indian Mewar State Railway, numbers 2876 to 2878, despatched in April and May. On the right is a set of frames for one of the first members of the 50 0-6-0 pannier tanks being built for British Railways and described in the next Chapter. Behind the frames can just be discerned the frames of the next of the Mewar locomotives and behind them the engine's boiler. There are two more locomotives under erection at the extreme end of the shop. The gentleman in the cloth cap by the tender of the left hand engine is the Erecting Shop Foreman, Eric Bridges, and this photograph illustrates well the somewhat cramped conditions in the shop, but where nevertheless, over the years, so much was achieved.

(BESA) passenger engines of classes HP and HPS, and indeed most of the other 4-6-0 classes. Cylinders were 16¾ x22in, larger than the BESA designs but the same as the 2-8-0s, and the boiler was superheated. An interesting aspect of the design was the use of Sekflo self-aligning roller bearings on the driving coupling rod crankpins and the connecting rod big ends, as well as where the eccentric rod coupled onto the return arm. Numbers allocated were 2876 to 2878, and the running numbers were 25 to 27 of the Rajasthan Railway, which the Mewar State Railway had been renamed before the engines arrived. They left Stafford in April and May 1949 and cost £31,950 for the three, free on board Liverpool. Like the 2-8-0s they remained in use on the section of railway they were built for, latterly Indian Railways class BR, and with numbers 31038 to 31040, until the early 1980s. Their last couple of years were spent shunting around Ajmer; local shunting duties were the lot of many Indian railway locomotives as they eked out remaining boiler life.

There were some narrow-gauge locomotives for India too, and in 1946 the Company designed a neat two-foot gauge 0-4-2 side tank with outside frames and 9x14in cylinders. This was in fact an updated version of earlier engines of this wheel arrangement which had been popular in pre-war days for plantation type railways, mining operations and the like. This wheel arrangement with a trailing truck and longer coupled wheelbase, as opposed to an 0-4-0, gave a steadier riding locomotive where longer runs were required, as well as reducing the axle-load and at the same time allowing for increased fuel and water supplies to be carried. The engines had 2ft 3½in diameter coupled wheels, a fixed wheelbase of five-foot, a total wheelbase of 11 foot, and Bagnall-Price valve gear was used. Four engines of this design were built at this time, two for India and two for South Africa. The Indian engines were two-foot gauge, manufacturer's numbers 2896 and 2897 of July 1948, and went to the Goalpara Forest Tramway in Assam, via agents McLeod & Company of Calcutta; nothing however, has been heard of them since. The South African engines were ordered by Baldwins (South Africa) Limited, Bagnall agents, and were also two-foot gauge and with numbers 2870 and 2895, were delivered together in July 1948; despite

having been ordered separately. They were for use at the Rustenburg Platinum Mines in the Transvaal, and were followed by two more for the same customer, numbers 3023 and 3050 of March 1953. All four have survived, the first one, 2870, in the Johannesburg Mining Museum; the second, 2895, in a private collection in this country, while the other two are on the Welsh Highland Railway at Portmadoc in North Wales.

In August 1946 the Company received an order from the Egyptian Government on behalf of the Egyptian State Railways, for eight standard-gauge 2-4-2 side tank locomotives, a repeat order of the engines delivered in 1936. However, in this case they differed slightly in being designed to burn oil, rather than coal fuel. The manufacturer's numbers allocated were 2880 to 2887 and delivery was free-on-board Liverpool, between

It was usual practice on Indian railways for engines to eke out their last days on shunting duties, and this is one such. Former Mewar State Railway No 25, Bagnall 2876 as Indian Railways 31038, at Mewar Junction Shed on 24 February 1981, not far in fact, from where it spent most of its working life. Mewar Junction is on the former Bombay Baroda & Central India Railway metre-gauge main line from Baroda to Delhi, and it was from here that a short branch headed due south to make an end-on connection to the Mewar State system.

Official photograph of manufacturer's number 2896 of 1948, one of two small two-foot gauge nine inch cylinder 0-4-2 side tanks built for the Goalpara Forest Tramway in Assam. These engines were almost identical to others supplied at about the same time for the Rustenburg Platinum Mines in the Transvaal. Notice the Bagnall-Price valve gear.

Egyptian Western Oases Railway 2ft 5½in gauge 2-8-2 tender engine, one of two built to this much earlier Nasmyth Wilson design, manufacturer's numbers 2888 and 2889 despatched in August 1950. The motion skirts are an attempt to keep the desert sand away from the moving parts. Notice the oil fuel filler lid at the front of the tender.

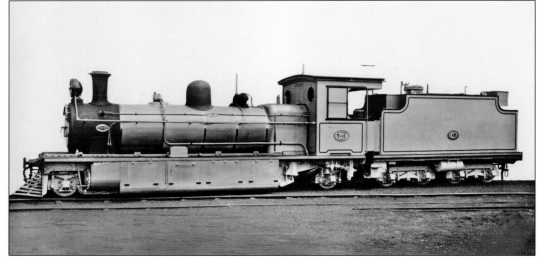

April and June 1948, at a cost of £6,900 each. As with the earlier engines they travelled to the docks on their own wheels with the motion removed, and also like the earlier ones were for use on the old Auxiliary Railways in Upper Egypt.

A month later the Egyptian Government ordered two more locomotives, in this case for the 75c/m (2ft 5½in) gauge Western Oases Railway. This railway, which left the main-line of the Egyptian State Railway at Oases Junction (Nag Hammadi), a few miles north of Farshut and some 340 miles south of Cairo, took a westerly route across the Libyan Desert to Kharga and adjacent settlements in the fertile Oases. The total length was 121 miles of which the desert stretch was 65 miles. In view of the absolute sterility of the desert there were no stations between Gara in the Nile Valley and Mehrig, a distance of 102¾ miles, but there were crossing stations every 10 miles or so. Oases Junction is 226ft above sea level, the summit of the line reached 1,265ft, and the gradual descent to Kharga - 10 miles - was at an average gradient of 1 in 40 with some cork-screw curves. The railway dated from 1908, and two years after opening was taken over, and subsequently operated by the government. From the forgoing it will be seen that this was by no means an easy line to work, and the earlier engines had been designed and built by Nasmyth Wilson of Patricroft in Manchester, two being supplied in 1933. The engines Bagnall built were

Fireless locomotives became quite popular in the post-war years, presumably as companies strove to minimise operating costs and with the scarcity of coal. Bagnall built several to this basic four-wheel pre-war design and the one illustrated, manufacturer's number 2898, was supplied in September 1948 to a new woollen mill being built for Paton & Baldwins Limited at Darlington. It was sold for £4,121 plus £55 for the steam charging equipment and it remained in use until rail traffic ceased at the factory in about 1970; today it is preserved in Darlington. Photograph taken on 6 July 1967; notice the dummy chimney as the exhaust is actually through the large diameter pipe at the rear - this enhancement of dubious effect on the engine's appearance, was not part of the original specification. It was in fact fitted in 1959 during an overhaul of the locomotive by the local builder, Robert Stephenson & Hawthorns Limited. The locomotive is painted light blue.

This small 7x12in cylinder circular firebox four-wheel saddle tank was an updated version of the popular pre-war design. Notice the full length saddle tank and re-designed cab. Manufacturer's number 2841 it was ordered by the Ministry of Supply and despatched in September 1946 to the United Nations Relief & Rehabilitation Administration (UNRRA); shipment was to Yugoslavia. The track gauge was 1ft 11⅝in and some of the parts used in its construction came from an earlier cancelled order for a similar locomotive, in this case number 2636 which would have been for the 18in gauge railway at Woolwich Arsenal. It cost £1,464 free-on-rail at Stafford, but unfortunately no information has ever come to light to the authors knowledge, of what the locomotive was used for in Yugoslavia.

Photograph was taken at the 1948 Smoking Concert, which became an annual event, and in this case held at the town's Borough Hall on 20 May. The individuals are, left to right:

Back Row: *Arthur Roberts later Boiler Shop Foreman; Harry Rogers Yard Foreman; Jack Pettit Bagnall Club Steward (former crane driver); ? .*

Middle Row: *George Carless Foundry Foreman; Don Metcalfe Erecting Shop Chargehand; ?; Alf Homer Pattern Shop Foreman; Albert Appleton Head Storekeeper.*

Front Row: *Walter Skelton Wagon Shop Foreman; Ian Marriott Managing Director; Freddie Boult Toolmaker; Joan Duffy Secretary; Harry Owen Toolroom (later managed the short lived Apprentice Training School); Harry Chambers gateman; Harry Walker machinist; Harry Davies General Manager.*

largely to the Nasmyth Wilson design, which was itself a development of a 1911 engine with a 2-6-2 wheel arrangement. The Bagnalls were 2-8-2 tender engines with 15x20in cylinders and three-foot diameter coupled wheels, a Belpaire top firebox boiler was fitted with a steel inner firebox and steel tubes, doubtless as they were designed to burn oil fuel. Surprisingly in view of the long waterless desert section the engines had to operate, the boilers were not superheated, but the large bogie tender had a capacity for 2,000 gallons of water and 750 gallons of oil fuel. However, because of the desert section the whole of the motion was covered with skirting, with hinged access doors to allow for lubrication and inspection. The manufacturer's numbers were 2888 and 2889, and at a cost of £26,720 for the two; they were sent to Liverpool Docks free-on-board for shipment on 14 August 1950 - the running numbers were 2002 and 2003, displayed on large brass plates on the cab sides in Arabic script. Unfortunately, the Western Oases Railway closed in 1960, and one presumes these engines were at that time, or soon afterwards, scrapped.

A social event for the staff introduced in Ian Marriott's time was what was referred to as a smoking concert, intended as a gathering for employees and friends of the Company - a title one might hesitate to use in this day and age! The first such event was held at the Borough Hall on the evening of Thursday 20 May 1948, with over 400 in attendance, when Marriott introduced what was referred to as 'The 30,000 Scheme', a commitment agreed by the board of directors two months earlier, to spend a sum of £30,000 on new machine tools, rebuilding the wagon shop with power rather than hand operated overhead cranes, a new erecting shop, canteen and extensions to the

offices along with some other general improvements. Around the same time the opportunity was taken to surrender the lease of the site from Lord Stafford, which had 24 years to run, while negotiating for another 99 years from 25 March 1948, at an annual rent of £350. This ensured longevity of the operations and followed unsuccessful attempts to persuade the owner to sell.

This was all part of the scheme to re-equip the works for the manufacture of diesel-electric locomotives. Marriott also presented to the Company a silver cup to be awarded annually for an interdepartmental football competition, which for the first year had been won by the boiler shop. The second of the smoking concerts, which became an annual event thereafter, was held on Wednesday 2 February 1949, and on this occasion Marriott mentioned in his introduction that the previous year had seen an increase in turnover of 73% on the year before, as the country returned to normal trading after the difficult immediate post-war period. He went on say that that the current number of people employed was 450, which was a 14% increase over the

At the 1948 Smoking Concert the retirement presentation was made to FHB Harris the Chief Draughtsman, and Keith Pearson the London Representative. Here is Ian Marriott on the extreme right shaking hands with FHB Harris, while Keith Pearson looks on; on the extreme left is the General Manager Harry Davies.

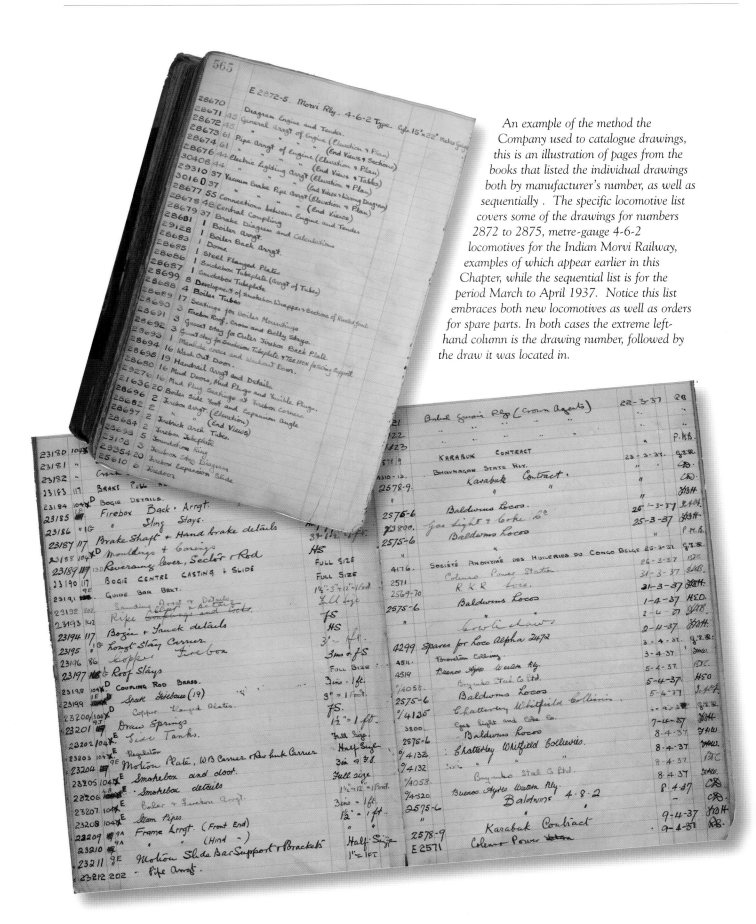

An example of the method the Company used to catalogue drawings, this is an illustration of pages from the books that listed the individual drawings both by manufacturer's number, as well as sequentially . The specific locomotive list covers some of the drawings for numbers 2872 to 2875, metre-gauge 4-6-2 locomotives for the Indian Morvi Railway, examples of which appear earlier in this Chapter, while the sequential list is for the period March to April 1937. Notice this list embraces both new locomotives as well as orders for spare parts. In both cases the extreme left-hand column is the drawing number, followed by the draw it was located in.

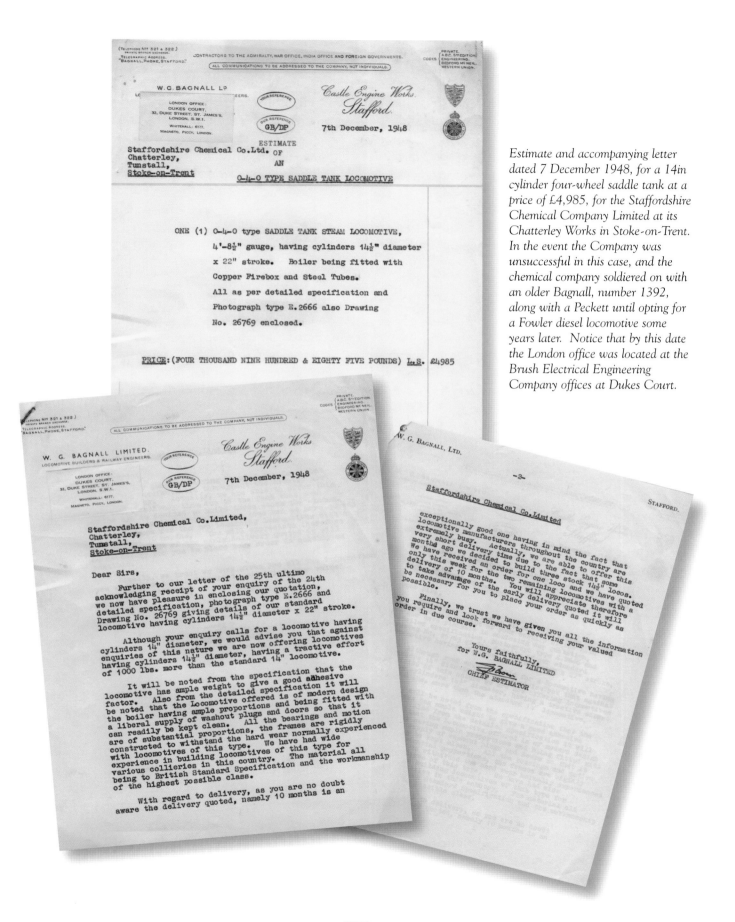

Estimate and accompanying letter dated 7 December 1948, for a 14in cylinder four-wheel saddle tank at a price of £4,985, for the Staffordshire Chemical Company Limited at its Chatterley Works in Stoke-on-Trent. In the event the Company was unsuccessful in this case, and the chemical company soldiered on with an older Bagnall, number 1392, along with a Peckett until opting for a Fowler diesel locomotive some years later. Notice that by this date the London office was located at the Brush Electrical Engineering Company offices at Dukes Court.

last year of the war. At the 1948 concert the opportunity was taken to make presentations to two long serving members of staff who had recently retired, and cheques along with other gifts were presented to FHB Harris and Keith Pearson, who it will be remembered had been the Company's London representative since as long ago as 1910. Like Harris his retirement had been part of the Marriott restructuring.

Mention was also made of the new canteen and improvements to the office buildings which were nearing completion, and a proposal to hold an open day, not just for families of the staff and their friends, but the general public too, to celebrate these new facilities. A small ceremony was held at the works on the morning of Friday 20 May 1949, when Alderman Mrs Ruth Turney formerly declared the new canteen open, along with improvements and extensions to the office block, after which the open day was officially declared as open! There followed that evening an event for the staff and their families in the new canteen, which also served as a works sports & social club, when Harry Davies formally opened the bar in the traditional and time-honoured way of such events!

As well as his commitments to WG Bagnall Limited, Keith Pearson operated an independent business as consulting engineers, and in this role acted as agents in this country for the French company of Freins Jourdain Moneret and among other things the British agency for Lambert wet sanding equipment. After Keith's death on 24 January 1951, his son Kenneth, with offices at 32 Victoria Street in London, continued the business and the company later became known as Kenneth R Pearson & Son. However, soon after his father died Kenneth sold out the Bagnall agency element of the business to a fellow called Ash. By a quirk of fate William James Ash had been the chief draughtsman at the Broadstone works of the Midland & Great Western Railway of Ireland when WA Smyth started his pupilage there, and one of Smyth's first actions on becoming managing director at Stafford was to buy out this agency agreement as he soon found it was costing a lot, and delivering little. Henceforth, Associated Locomotive Equipment Limited, another member of the Heenan Group, acted at the firm's London representative. Kenneth Pearson by the way, was appointed a director of The Vulcan Foundry Limited in late 1951, and was

later involved in the locomotive business of both the Vulcan Foundry and Robert Stephenson & Hawthorns, at the time when both these companies became part of the English Electric Group in 1955. He was also prominent in the activities of the LMA and for several years served on its finance committee.

A particular serious problem in connection with the firm's workload was the availability of skilled labour, as those who had served in the forces gradually returned to civilian occupations, and other demographic issues settled down following the enforced redistribution of labour to meet war-time requirements. In mid 1947 the total staff amounted to 344 against a requirement to meet commitments of around another 150. Difficulty was experienced in filling the gap and the Ministry of Labour could not see a way of assisting in the short or medium term. Thoughts turned to providing housing to encourage men to move from other parts of the country and a scheme was developed to buy or lease additional land from Lord Stafford, to the west of the works site, and finance a medium sized housing estate. The scheme provided for 76 dwellings, a combination of houses and flats, and was perused to a point where work could have commenced, only for the Borough Council to refuse planning permission at the eleventh hour. While offering a potential alternative site elsewhere in the town, in the event, the labour situation began to ease, such that by April 1950 there were 477 people on the books, and the question of providing housing was quietly dropped.

In this Chapter we have covered in some detail a number of the more significant orders for locomotives that had been ordered under the old regime, but not delivered until after the Company had changed hands. Mention has been made of an Indian summer for steam locomotive orders, which it clearly was, and not just with this builder, but others both in this country and other major locomotive building countries of the world. It was not quite at an end yet either, as we shall see in the next Chapter, with the enormous backlog of requirements as the world's railways came to terms with the arrears following the war years. It is now time to move on and see how the Company managed under its new management, along with Alan Good's aspirations to enter the market for diesel-electric locomotives.

Chapter Twelve

THE BRUSH BAGNALL
PARTNERSHIP

Before proceeding any further it is perhaps opportune to briefly explore the position of the British private locomotive building industry in the immediate post-war years, and Bagnalls position within it. We saw earlier the contraction that had taken place among the traditional builders in the late 1920s and 1930s, along with the post First World War entrants to the field, William Beardmore and Armstrong Whitworth, ceasing to build locomotives. Also outlined was how the Locomotive Manufacturers Association (LMA) had been instrumental in a number of the firms either going out of business completely, or in any event dropping out of the locomotive building trade. Additionally in 1937 the amalgamation took place of the locomotive building activities of R&W Hawthorn Leslie & Company Limited, with Robert Stephenson & Company Limited. Moreover, during the 1930s under government pressure aided and abetted by Montague Norman, governor at the time of The Bank of England, other similar amalgamations of locomotive building companies, or at least their locomotive building activities, had been discussed. In the event none were accomplished, the efforts being largely frustrated by the intransigence of the North British Locomotive Company, the biggest played in the market, and despite paying no dividend on its ordinary shares throughout

the 1930s. In 1944 R&W Hawthorn Leslie & Company Limited disposed of its remaining interest in Robert Stephenson & Hawthorns Limited (RSH), when this company was jointly acquired by The Vulcan Foundry Limited and the North British Locomotive Company Limited, although in the following year North British sold its interest to Vulcan.

In order to get a fuller picture of the locomotive trade in the years between the wars, the early moves towards diesel traction have to be explored. The introduction of electric traction to railways, dating back to the last years of the 19th century, naturally involved the then relatively infant manufacturers of electrical equipment in the locomotive building business. British companies like British Westinghouse and Siemens Brothers got involved in designing and building locomotives, and we saw earlier how several companies specialising in electrical equipment teamed up with Bagnall to build electric locomotives, and there were other similar partnerships. Some of these partnerships between traditional locomotive building firms and electrical machinery manufacturers later designed and built diesel-electric locomotives. Some of the partnerships were medium or long term agreements, while in other cases locomotives were built on an order by order basis. For example in 1926 the Vulcan Foundry entered into an agreement with the Danish company A/S Frichs of Aarhus, and a number of diesel-electric locomotives of joint design were constructed in the years leading up to the Second World War. The English Electric Company established a working relationship with R&W Hawthorn Leslie, which continued after the formation of RSH, and much later in 1944, Beyer Peacock & Company Limited joined forces with Metropolitan Vickers (successor to British Westinghouse) and established a new company based in Stockton-on-Tees to build diesel locomotives. This was the Bowsfield Works of Metropolitan Vickers - Beyer Peacock Limited. There were other initiatives too, including the already explored Bagnall agreement with Deutz, which, like the Vulcan/Frichs arrangement was terminated on the outbreak of hostilities in 1939.

One of the results of the years of hostilities was an enormous back-log of orders for steam locomotives, both for the otherwise natural replacement of life expired assets, and to assist the railways of the world repair the ravages of war-time. Many locomotives had been kept running far longer than might have been the case in times of peace, both on main-line railways as well as in all sorts of industrial undertakings. This resulted in a plethora of orders for steam locomotives being placed with all the builders, both in this country and wherever else they were built. Some of the orders had actually been placed prior to the commencement of the war, while others had been placed during the war, but not proceeded with due to what were considered at the time more pressing war-time commitments. All the British steam locomotive builders were very busy, consisting at the time of North British, Vulcan, RSH and Beyer Peacock, as in effect the big-boys of the trade, with companies like Bagnall, Hunslet, Hudswell Clarke, Yorkshire Engine and Andrew Barclay in the medium range, along with the comparatively smaller Peckett & Sons.

There was also the relatively new entrant into the market, and in a more specialist field, Sentinel (Shrewsbury) Limited, brief mention of which has been made earlier. This company specialised in locomotives and railcars having three-drum water-tube and vertical boilers with high-speed steam engines with a geared drive, and considerable success had been achieved. Both locomotives and railcars built on these design principles, which evolved from the firm's earlier steam

road vehicle practice, date back to the mid 1920s, and significant inroads were made into the home market after the war for shunting locomotives. Indeed at a meeting of the LMA on 28 January 1954, mention was made of the severe competition being encountered by the traditional manufacturers in the market for 14 to 16in cylinder four and six-wheel coupled industrial shunting locomotives from the Sentinel company. As a result it was agreed to reduce the LMA levy on these types of locomotive from 3% to 1%, and to write and invite Sentinel to become members of the Association. An invitation was send but Sentinel never became members. Worth noting is that in an earlier incarnation as Sentinel Waggon Works (1936) Limited, in November 1943 it had actually applied to become a member but, as no agreement was forthcoming from Sentinel on its adherence to the terms for admittance, membership was not granted.

The locomotive trade was not confined to the builders mentioned above, and there were a few others specialising in small and medium-sized diesel shunting locomotives; for example John Fowler (Leeds) Limited, FH Hibberd & Company Limited based in London, EE Baguley Limited of Burton-on-Trent, Motor Rail Limited of Bedford and Ruston & Hornsby Limited of Lincoln. The last three companies were particularly successful in the market for narrow-gauge diesel locomotives, both for use above ground and in mines. Jumping ahead of our story somewhat, in March 1955 English Electric acquired the remaining share capital of the Vulcan Foundry and its subsidiary RSH, following a steady stream of share acquisitions over the proceeding few years. This put it in an excellent position to tender for, and obtain contracts of, both diesel-electric and electric locomotives as well as electric train-sets and diesel railcars.

As would be expected during the first few years after the war, with full order books all the companies were quite profitable. For example RSH made a dividend payment for the year ending 31 December 1953 of 10%, plus a bonus of 3%, the net profit for the year amounting to £21,067 (£50,152 before tax). In the case of Beyer Peacock for the same year the dividend was 3½% with an added bonus payable of 8½%; the pre-tax profit being £569,438. The North British Locomotive Company had a record turnover for the same year, with 97% of output for export, the net profit amounting to

£196,749 and the declared dividend 5%. In terms of men employed in 1950 North British topped the league with some 4,800 at its two works, followed by the Vulcan Foundry at Newton-le-Willows with 2,400. Of the somewhat smaller builders Beyer Peacock employed 1,600 and RSH 1,450, while at the lower end of the scale Hunslet had 650 men, Bagnall at 475 and Andrew Barclay 400; the smallest employer in terms of men employed was Peckett with 180. The combined total for the industry of traditional steam locomotive builders was 12,325. From the foregoing few paragraphs it can be understood why the industry considered itself at the time to be in a strong position, in particular to return to the pre-eminence it had enjoyed from time immemorial in the export markets. In this aura of comfort WG Bagnall Limited, and the Brush Bagnall Traction Limited partnership, were no exception. The large Ceylon order for diesel-electric locomotives briefly mentioned in the last Chapter gave a significant boost and confidence in the new venture.

We must now explore some of the Castle Engine Works share of the large number of orders for steam locomotives placed in this country and noted above. But first of all mention needs to be made of the significant amount of orders for spare boilers, some in significant quantities, along with a number of locomotives that were sent in to the works for overhaul. For example in 1948 over twenty spare boilers were ordered, and for a variety of customers both in this country and abroad. Much of this work was the result of war-time neglect, boilers having been kept in service long after they should have been replaced, and industrial shunting locomotives literally run into the ground. Of course there was always a steady and continuing supply of other spare parts for locomotives that had been supplied earlier to countries all over the world. This included regular orders for spare parts for Kerr, Stuart built locomotives.

In July 1947 the Mysore Iron & Steel Works at Bhadravati in what became the Karnataka State of India, about 140 miles northwest from Bangalore, ordered four two-foot gauge 2-8-2 tender engines for use on what it referred to as its tramways. There were three of these tramways radiating from the works to

What a lovely sight - No 13 in the Mysore Iron & Steel Works narrow-gauge fleet photographed at Bhadravati on 22 November 1979. Presumed to be Bagnall number 2905 of 1950; because the manufacturer's plates on these locomotives were located on the smokebox, and as the company had a spare boiler, interchange of boilers had the effect of making the identity of the individual locomotives difficult. By the time this photograph was taken the works had been renamed Visvesvaraya after its founder.

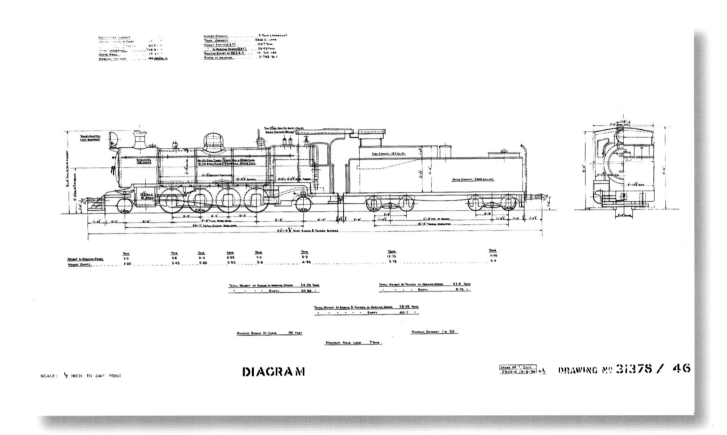

DIAGRAM

SCALE: ½ INCH TO ONE FOOT   DRAWING Nº 31378 / 46

Outline drawing No 31378 dated 13 June 1950, with the principal dimensions of the Mysore Iron & Steel Works two-foot gauge 2-8-2 tender engines.

serve ironstone, limestone and quartz quarries. That the lines these engines were designed and built to operate could hardly be described as tramways in the accepted sense is evidenced by the size of the truly magnificent machines Bagnall designed. Loosely based on some earlier and smaller engines built by Kerr, Stuart as long ago as 1922, there is little doubt that this order came to Stafford due to the influence of FHB Harris. Doubtless the last significant one in which he was personally involved, and unsurprisingly the completed locomotives had a distinct Kerr, Stuart look about them! The longest of the tramways was over twenty miles, and the staple diet of the engines was hauling large bogie wagons, empty from the works and loaded on the return journey. Cylinders were 13½x18in, the frames were outside and the driving-wheel diameter was 2ft 9in. The total engine wheelbase was 20ft 7in and with the large bogie tender which had a capacity of 2,800 gallons of water and almost three tons of coal, the complete wheelbase was no less than 44ft 2⅞in. The

total weight in working order for the engine and tender was 58¼ tons. Walschaerts valve gear was used and although the engines were superheated, they had slide rather than piston valves and the firebox had a Belpaire top. It can be seen from these dimensions that these were very big locomotives for a two-foot gauge tramway. Tractive effort at 85% of the 180psi working pressure was 15,200lb. Manufacturer's numbers were 2903 to 2906 and the running numbers 11, 13, 14 and 15; despatch was in April and May 1950 at a cost of £9,930 each free-on-board Liverpool. As the painting and numbering instructions arrived too late for the first two engines, they were despatched to the docks on 11 April in grey primer. The second pair, despatched on 10 May were painted black, and with the initials MISW on the tender sides one of them posed for the official photograph incorrectly numbered 12 - as noted above, in the numbering instructions given there was no number 12, although subsequently one of them did carry that number.

One of the authors had what he still describes as his most remarkable journey ever on a narrow-gauge train behind one of these engines, which is saying quite something bearing in mind some of his journeys before and since. A fascinating and absorbing day had been spent at the limestone mines at Bhandigund, where the engines had to descend into the quarry by a series of zigzag lines due to the depth, taking empty wagons to the loading points and bringing the full ones out. After some time engaged in these operations, and after assembling the loaded train for the return journey, there was a problem over the payment of wages. The outward train from the works had included the pay (wages) coach complete with its numerous guards, and a shortage of cash was rumoured! The small party of which one of the authors was a member were anxious to get back to Bhadravati to catch the evening metre-gauge train to Bangalore. Judging by the time it had taken to get to Bhandigund in the morning all seemed lost, but the problem was eventually sorted and the train left in complete darkness with eight loaded wagons in tow, along with the pay coach, and another one which had been added for the party's convenience. This was despite the party consisting of but three, albeit accompanied by the grandiosely titled superintendent tramways.

The train proceeded to make its way back at what seemed like breakneck speed, the coaches were at the back of the train and the line twisted and turned in all directions, the engine running tender first with its massive electric headlight picking out more of the forest than of the track ahead in view of the curvature. The big Bagnall had a lovely deep-tone hooter which the driver blew vigorously, and frequently. The sight and sound of that magnificent locomotive tearing through the night, large headlamps fore and aft, twisting and turning with its long train, was indeed a sight for sore eyes. It was literally pitch black, not a light anywhere apart from the engine headlamps and the two coaches at the back of the train, and the glow from the engine's fire when the fireman opened the door to add coal, was usually accompanied by a display of fireworks from the engine's chimney. The 12-mile trip was accomplished in less than half an hour, the outward trip having taken over two hours - with some photographic stops it has to be added - and of course, the connection with the main line train was made with ease. In bidding the new-found friends goodbye, it was vowed to visit them again after a trip for which this description hardly does justice and one that will remain in the memory for all time.

The engines at Bhadravati were kept in lovely condition, particularly by Indian standards of the time, and were exceptionally well maintained and clean inside and out. But when the tasks they had to perform day in and day out are considered, it was quite obvious that high standards were essential. The earlier Kerr, Stuart engines which were somewhat smaller tended to be used for shunting around the works area and on the shorter line to the quartz mines at Bilikalbetta. On a second trip in November 1979 the twenty-odd mile route to the ironstone mines at Kemmangundi was explored, but that is another story. Unfortunately, narrow-gauge rail operations appear to have ceased in the mid 1980s, being replaced by road transport, and as far as is known all these magnificent locomotives, together with two others to be described later, found their way into the melting furnaces of the steel works.

On 7 January 1948 the Company received its biggest single order for locomotives, 50 six-coupled pannier tanks for the British Transport Commission, Railway Executive, to the former Great Western Railway (GWR) 9400 class design. This was a taper-boiler version of the well known and popular GWR penchant for six-wheel coupled pannier tank locomotives for branch line work and shunting. The class was a development by FW Hawkesworth, the chief mechanical engineer, of earlier designs (in particular, the 5700 class, of which Bagnall had built examples before the war), and the first examples were built at Swindon and completed the previous year. Following these 10 home-built engines orders were placed with private industry for no less than 200 more, which only differed in having non-superheated boilers, the boiler otherwise being the GWR Standard No 10. Orders for these locomotives were also placed with RSH (80), The Hunslet Engine Company (20), Yorkshire Engine Company (30) and Hudswell Clarke & Company (20). In the event both Hunslet and Hudswell Clarke sub-contracted their orders to Yorkshire Engine and RSH respectively, so that Yorkshire actually built 50, and RSH 100. Of all those ordered from contractors Bagnall was the first company to make a delivery, and No 8400 arrived at Swindon for commissioning on 27 July 1949. All the Bagnall built examples were hauled

BRITISH RAILWAYS - WESTERN REGION

8400

Publicity illustration of the first of the 9400 class pannier tanks for British Railways, No 8400, manufacturer's number 2910.

to Swindon for commissioning with the motion removed and sometimes in pairs.

To no small extent the orders for these locomotives very soon became somewhat of an embarrassment for the Railway Executive. There were two reasons for this; in the first case an early decision after nationalisation of the railways to invest in large fleets of diesel-powered shunting locomotives in efforts to gain economies in shunting operations. In the second, there had been a not dissimilar decision regarding the operation of branch lines with the investment in large fleets of diesel-powered multiple unit trains; somewhat ironically this was a concept pioneered by the GWR before the war. Therefore much of the type of duty that these new steam locomotives were intended to be used for disappeared, in many cases even before they had all been delivered. As a result of this and despite the original contracted delivery dates, agreement was reached with all the builders, and to one extent or

another, to delay delivery. It could be argued that this just made the situation worse, as even more diesels had been built when they were delivered, but there were other issues involved too. In Bagnalls case the contracted delivery programme was for the first locomotive to be ready by October 1948 followed by delivery at a rate of two every month with completion in October 1950. In the event it was 2 July 1954 before the last one was despatched. Not surprisingly the LMA got involved with the contracts to build these locomotives; as outlined above all the builders had quite healthy order books at the time as they strove to overcome the backlog of orders after the war, while the newly nationalised coal industry was placing a lot of orders with most of the builders for new shunting locomotives. There was also a post-war shortage of steel, effectively delaying the delivery of this material. The otherwise healthy order books were among the reasons why Hunslet and Hudswell Clarke sub-contracted their orders, a move accomplished in conjunction with the LMA. Bagnall was criticised by the British Transport Commission in December 1951 for the late delivery of the engines it was contracted to build, but it was able to point out that some 18 months earlier, its subsidiary The Railway Executive, had actually asked for delivery to be delayed!

The contract price was £8,260 each; a total of £413,000 for the 50 locomotives, which followed on from an earlier quote to the GWR on 29 May 1947, but this final price was not agreed until 12 December 1947. The contract included provision of completed boilers from Swindon (Bagnall never made a taper boiler) and a number of other standard GWR fittings, and as noted above the engines were delivered to Swindon and painted plain black. At Swindon the GWR automatic train control (ATC) apparatus was fitted before the engines entered service. Also provided on loan from Swindon and for the duration of the work, were the flanging blocks for the smokeboxes and doors. The

engines had vacuum train brake and steam heating equipment and the manufacturer's numbers allocated were 2910 to 2959; the running numbers were 8400 to 8449 (see Appendix X).

In the event, delaying the delivery of these engines gave the Castle Engine Works a partly stable workload for over four years, also providing a number of price escalation clauses in the contract, such that the last locomotives delivered were charged at £10,117. Unfortunately these engines had very short lives and the first withdrawals took place as early as the week ending 11 July 1959, British Railways (BR) numbers 8412 (Bagnall 2922) and 8432 (Bagnall 2942), these two having been delivered on 26 September 1950 and 14 February 1953 respectively. The last members to be taken out of service were BR 8403 (Bagnall 2913), 8415 (Bagnall 2925) and 8436 (Bagnall 2946) during week ending 11 July 1965 - some members of the class never had anything more than intermediate repairs in BR workshops. In their short lives however, the 50 engines

First member of the post-war 2ft 6in gauge Indian Railways ZB class, Bagnall 2977 of 1952 with the Chief Draughtsman, Harold Wood, standing alongside. There were a few modifications from the earlier engines, for example roller bearing axle-boxes on the carrying and tender wheels and an extension of the cab mounted on the tender. Rather unusually this locomotives was erected facing south, while the more normal practice was for erection to take place with the engines facing north, which was the case with the remainder of this batch. Photograph taken at the north-end of the works yard, near to where rail connection was made with the main-line. Notice the white painted boards behind to assist the photographer when masking the photograph for publicity purposes. The buildings behind are beyond the main-line to Wellington and part of the Universal Grinding Wheel Company.

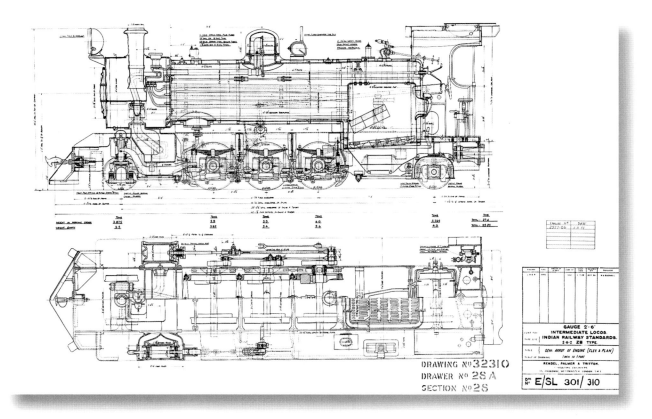

General Arrangement drawings of the post-war Indian ZB class engines.

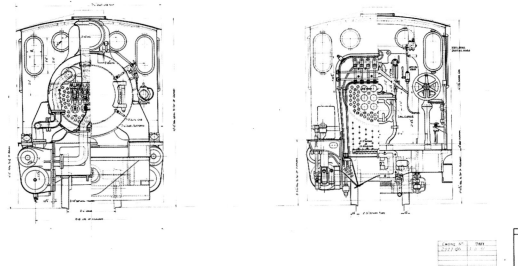

built by Bagnall were widely spread over the Western Region of BR, and a number of them finished their days, and achieved some notoriety, after been transferred to the London Midland Region for use in banking trains up the famous Lickey Incline at Bromsgrove in Worcestershire. The first transfers for this banking work took place in January 1957, numbers 8400 to 8406, and although the individual engines changed somewhat over the next few years, around six of them were engaged on banking duties on the Lickey until steam locomotives ceased to be used on this job. In fact the last engine to be so used was BR number 8415 on Saturday 26 September 1964, after which Bromsgrove shed closed and diesels took over.

Seven more of the metre-gauge 4-6-0 tender engines were ordered in February 1948 for the Gaekwar's Baroda State Railway (GBSR), again via Rendel, Palmer & Tritton (RP&T) the consulting engineers.

Manufacturer's numbers 2964 to 2970 were allocated and delivery was between October 1951 and March the following year; the cost was £12,509 each dismantled and packed for shipment free-on-board Liverpool. Under Indian Railways ownership these engines became class B2, and the earlier batches B and B1 respectively, although there was very little difference between them. Like the earlier engines, these seven also continued to be used almost exclusively on the lines they were built for, until displaced by the Indian standard post-war YP pacific, and YG 2-8-2 engines, themselves displaced by dieselisation of the main-lines in the early 1980s.

In July 1948 another order was received from the GBSR, in this case 10 more of the 2ft 6in gauge ZB type 2-6-2 tender engines which, it will be remembered, Bagnall had before the war designed and built the first examples. The order was for a slightly updated version with, for example, a cab on the front of the tender to

This photograph shows one of the post-war ZB class engines, manufacturer's number 2979, Western Railway of India No 61, in a typical narrow-gauge Indian railway shed scene at Dabhoi on 1 March 1981. Dabhoi was the junction of no fewer than five lines of the former Gaekwar's Baroda State Railway, and the station had an air of a main-line railway about it. There were frequent arrivals and departures throughout the day and it even boasted a public address system - not many 2ft 6in gauge systems anywhere in the world could manage that. In more recent times most of the narrow-gauge lines in this part of India have either been closed completely or converted to broad-gauge.

afford the crews more protection. Large numbers of ZB class engines were ordered by the Indian railways in the immediate post-war years, and from several builders both in this country and in Europe; some by Eastern European manufacturers. As with the earlier engines RP&T were involved with all the orders, and in the case of the Bagnall engines the numbers allocated were 2977 to 2986. The drawings used for this slightly updated version issued by RP&T came from Hudswell Clarke of Leeds, as this company had been engaged in the revision, and had built a batch of the engines itself. Despatch of the Stafford built locomotives was between June and December 1952. For whatever reason now lost in the mists of time, the first member of this batch of 10 locomotives was built facing south, whilst it was almost universal practice to erect locomotives at Stafford the other way round, and there would not appear to be any logical reason for this departure. The boiler shop at Stafford was particularly busy at the time these engines were being built, so to affect as early delivery as possible the boilers were sub-contracted to Societe Franco Belge de Material de Chemins de Fer, at Raismes in Belgium, an arrangement put in place by the consulting engineers. In fact, in view of the heavy boiler shop workload, and the need for the type of skills employed there on the Brush Bagnall diesel electric locomotives, in particular the Ceylon order, the boilers for the GBSR 4-6-0s numbers 2964 to 2970 were also sub-contracted to Franco Belge. However, as in this case all the material was on hand, lengthy and expensive negotiations ensured getting the necessary export and import licenses resulting in a loss of around £1,300 on each locomotive, while for one of this size a profit of something like £600 would have been expected.

It would appear that most manufacturers boiler shops were busy at this time and we have seen how the boilers for the GWR pannier tanks were built at Swindon. In fact all the boilers for the 200 pannier tanks were built either at Swindon, or by RSH (at both its Newcastle and Darlington works), irrespective of the actual builder of the locomotives. The cost of the ZB engines was £13,874 each, and in this case the engines were despatched fully erected and free-on-board Birkenhead.

After a lapse of many years Henry Rogers Sons & Company Limited, the Wolverhampton agents again appear in the order book when on 18 August 1948, two locomotives were ordered. These were large metre-gauge eight-coupled tank engines with 14½x20in cylinders and a 3ft 3in wheel diameter; indeed very much bigger than anything supplied before to this customer. Manufacturer's numbers 2987 and 2988 were allocated and the engines were named BARREIROS and RIO FORMOSO; despatch, dismantled for shipment, was in November 1950, to one of Roger's oldest customers (over three generations), Cia Acucareira Santo Andre do Rio Una, in Pernambuco (Recife). In 1981 both these engines were still in use at Usina Barreiros, a sugar plantation railway and factory, but to reduce the axle-loading they had been converted to tender engines. The cost was £8,820 each plus an extra £226 for electric lighting; this seems to have been an afterthought and was fitted after the painting was finished in a livery of black and green with gold lining and brass nameplates. One of these two engines - BARREIROS - was embarrassingly derailed in the works yard when under test and driven by JA Twentyman - we met this family in Chapter Five - a director of Henry Rogers. Subsequent correspondence between Rogers and Barreiros would indicate this was by no means the last occasion a derailment of one of these locomotives occurred, and doubtless this may have had something to do with the owners later converting them to tender engines.

We now have to turn our attention to the activities of Brush Bagnall Traction Limited; but first let us explore the activities of the Brush Company in diesel-electric traction before Alan Good acquired an interest in WG Bagnall Limited. Mention was made earlier of Sir Ronald Matthews being on the boards, and indeed chairman of both the London & North Eastern Railway (LNER) and Brush, and this was a significant element in introducing Brush to building diesel-electric locomotives. In 1944 and 1945 the LNER at its Doncaster Works had built four diesel-electric shunting locomotives, based on the successful 0-6-0 English Electric design which had become popular with the London Midland & Scottish Railway (LMS), and later became the standard shunting locomotive with BR - the Class 08 to give it its later designation. The four locomotives built at Doncaster had, like their LMS counterparts, English Electric engines and electrical equipment, but authority to build a fifth locomotive in April 1945, specified alternative power equipment.

This locomotive was equipped with Brush electrical equipment and a Petter type SS4 four-cylinder two-stroke 360 horsepower diesel engine, and here we can see more of the Matthews influence - and remember that by this time Brush owned the Petter Company. On completion of the mechanical parts in December 1947, it was moved from Doncaster to the Brush works at Loughborough for installation of the engine and electrical equipment along with subsequent testing. Originally intended to carry the LNER number 8004 (following on from the earlier three), it appears never to have done so and instead took the number 15004 (the earlier locomotive being renumbered 15001 to 15003) in the BR list. Apparently it was while the locomotive was at Loughborough that the Brush design office staff took the opportunity of a detailed study of the mechanical parts, the results of which were soon plain to see. In November 1949 the former GWR works at Swindon turned out a similar locomotive which also had Brush equipment and the same Petter engine as 15004, but in this case complete erection was at Swindon - it entered traffic as BR number 15107.

In 1946 Brush received an order for five sets of diesel engines and electrical equipment for shunting locomotives to be built by the Irish Railways (CIE) at Inchicore Works in Dublin. The order was actually via Associated Locomotive Equipment Limited, a company of which Alan Good was chairman and deputy managing director. In this case the engine was a Mirrlees TLD6 six-cylinder in-line four-stroke developing 487 horsepower, as by this time this company too, was a member of the Brush Group. Having many similarities to the earlier locomotives and a clear lineage to the English Electric design, these Irish locomotives entered service in 1947, and most of them remained in use until the early 1970s. This was the first time that a Mirrlees engine had been used for any rail traction application.

An interesting development on 11 March 1948 was the election to the board of WG Bagnall Limited of John Fredrick Alcock, joint managing director (later in March 1951 he became sole managing director and chairman) of The Hunslet Engine Company Limited of Leeds. While at first sight this might appear a strange move, the appointment of a senior member of what was in effect a rival firm; this was yet another appointment fostered by Alan Good, who felt strongly a need for some additional knowledge and experience of locomotive manufacturing among the Bagnall board members. The two men knew each other through Good's involvement in the Leeds based J&H McLaren Limited, a member of the ABOE Group, as McLaren engines had been used in Hunslet locomotives. Good had a pretty low opinion of engineers in general, making it clear in a letter to Alcock that he felt with a few exceptions, Alcock included, most of them made the easiest problem more difficult.

Earlier, in December 1947, Alcock had been appointed chairman of the LMA, a position he relinquished in February 1951, but he later became its president - a much less onerous position - in May 1953. John Alcock was born in September 1905 and was with Hunslet all his working life following his father, Edger Alcock's footsteps; Edger was chairman and managing director prior to his son. Mention has already been made that following a direction by the Ministry of Supply, all diesel locomotive enquiries and orders during the war years were channelled via the LMA to those builders which had been most prolific in the field, as a result of which no diesel locomotive were built at Stafford after 1939. Any enquiries for diesel locomotives that came Bagnalls way were therefore directed via the LMA to other builders.

Hunslet was one of the builders that had made significant inroads into the design and development of diesel locomotives before the war, deriving great benefits from this policy when hostilities ceased, understandable as it was in view of the contingences of war time production. The significance of this to Hunslet as diesel locomotives increasingly replaced steam should not be underestimated. It was also significant for Bagnall, albeit in a negative way. As the Company was now involved with Brush in the development of diesel-electric traction as opposed to locomotives with mechanical transmissions, a result of John Alcock joining the board of Bagnall was that any enquiries for diesel-mechanical locomotives were channelled to Hunslet. This was a most perverse situation for the Castle Engine Works to find itself in and one can imagine WS Edwards, to coin the proverbial saying, turning in his grave. Edwards had not been at all popular with Hunslet following the demise of Kerr, Stuart, and one can imagine that John Alcock had more than a smile on his face when each and every enquiry for diesel-mechanical locomotives - and there were quite a few - passed completely unfeted from Stafford to Leeds! Needless to say over the next few years this appointment caused some friction between Alcock and Smyth, but the two were nevertheless good friends. It seems Good's motives were largely as a result of his experiences when Marriott was managing director at Stafford, Marriott having no locomotive experience at all when he was appointed to that position. Smyth continually pressed Good to rescind the arrangement but nothing happened until after his death - it was eventually terminated on and from 10 July 1953.

One of Smyth's early actions was to have the registered office of WG Bagnall Limited moved from Worcester to Stafford - this took place on 2 October 1952 - and to get Norman Stokes, an employee of the Company appointed at the same time as company secretary; he was also made a board member. Hitherto the secretarial function had been undertaken by Alexander C Hayes by a form of remote control from Worcester, as he was secretary of all the Heenan Group companies; he replaced WOJ Urry who died suddenly in November 1948. Another of Smyth's achievements, albeit one started in Marriott's time, was to enhance the image of the Company with a completely new logo, along with an impressive range of literature, altogether introducing quite a striking new style. Part of this policy coined the phrase Builders of Locomotives for the World's Railways. A new catalogue was produced; the last one issued by the Company and indeed the only completely new one since before the First World War. This was a splendid effort consisting of 56 pages printed on high quality art paper, spirally bound with a specially commissioned colour painting on the cover - as mentioned in the last Chapter - this depicted one of the 2-8-2 locomotives built in 1946 for Tanganyika. Included among its pages were illustrations of many of the locomotives built since the First World War, along with their main dimensions and details of the information required when ordering locomotives. In addition it contained several fold-out diagrams of the standard 16in cylinder industrial steam shunting locomotive, designed to facilitate the ordering of spare parts. This very well designed and produced publication was largely the work of Harold Wood the chief draughtsman at the time, and he was very proud

of the result. There was also a rather splendid brochure illustrating the vast majority of types of locomotive the Company had supplied over the years to the Indian sub-continent; it opened out to a size of no less than 20x18in. Much more adventurous adverts than hitherto appeared in the trade journals with a whole range of imaginative themes, and as had been the case in earlier times the firm lost no opportunity to get its products featured in articles in a whole range of technical journals, and not just those directly related to railways.

This is a good point to continue the story of the official photographer of the Company, CE Fowke, with a studio in Victoria Road at Stafford. Charles Edward Fowke is briefly mentioned in Chapter Two, when in 1904 in partnership with Paul Weiss, the local photographic business of Harold Tilley was acquired. Although Weiss left in 1915, to form his own Castleberg Studio, also in the town, it was the Fowke business that undertook almost all the official photography of the locomotives and rolling stock built, and the original prints can usually be identified by the imprint C E Fowke Stafford, in the bottom right hand corner. During the First World War, in June 1916, George Fowke joined the forces, initially in the Experimental Tank Corps, but later in an occupation more in line with his knowledge and experience, as an air photographer. His business however, continued in his absence, which he rejoined on demobilisation. In 1934 a young prize winning photographer, Bertram Sinkinson, joined Fowke and when the latter retired in 1938, Sinkinson acquired control. The business continued to trade under its original name and closed when Sinkinson retired in the early 1970s. Fowke was an Alderman of the town from 1948 and it's Mayor in the period 1951 to 1953; retiring from the council in 1955, he lived to a ripe old age and passed away in his 89th year in 1965. In 1951, its centenary year, Bertram Sinkinson was president of the Royal Photographic Society and chairman of the Society of Staffordshire Photographers.

WG Bagnall Limited initially used a Halifax based firm called Lilywhite Limited, to reproduce in quantity, with a sepia tone, 'postcards' of locomotives and other items of rolling stock etc., for publicity purposes. These cards, which used as their basis the Fowke original prints, had the principal dimensions of the locomotives on the rear, or brief descriptions in the case of rolling stock and other products, along with the name of the Company on the front. Later the cards were produced by The Valmer Photo-Works in Leicester. Between 1905 and almost when the last locomotive was built, over 200 of these cards were produced, most a little over postcard size, but with the odd ones of different sizes, both smaller and larger. A number of them are reproduced in these pages; they can be identified as they have the firm's title on the top and the E No at the bottom - that is the manufacturer's number, to which ostensibly at least, the picture refers, although care is needed as in some cases the number quoted is not the correct one for the locomotive illustrated, rather a similar one.

It is worth mentioning here that in 1950, at the instigation of the Anglo-American Council for Productivity (what today one supposes would be termed a quango - it was formed in the autumn of 1948), a Diesel Locomotive Productivity Team was nominated. Under the auspices of the LMA and led by Ian Marriott, the team made an almost seven week visit to the USA, excluding the time travelling, outward by the famous Cunard liner RMS QUEEN MARY, returning on its sister RMS QUEEN ELIZABETH. The Team's purpose was to study the entire field of diesel locomotive manufacturing and maintenance in that country. Marriott was nominated to lead the team by Alan Good and the remit included the design, planning, manufacturing, productivity and human relations issues. The members consisted of representatives from a cross-section of the private manufacturers at management, supervision and blue-collar staff level; the secretary was AR Robertson of the LMA. In the USA from 10 January to the 23 February 1950, the group visited a whole range of workshops including those of locomotive manufacturers and railway companies undertaking diesel locomotive maintenance, sub-contractors making component parts, research establishments, technical colleges and trades union headquarters. There were also a number of official receptions. On its return the team produced a detailed and comprehensive report entitled *Diesel Locomotives - Report of a visit to the USA in 1950 of a Productivity Team representing the Diesel Locomotive Industry*, which, although it is dated November 1950, was launched at a reception and luncheon held at the Dorchester Hotel in

London on 13 December that year. This event was sponsored by the Internal Combustion Group of The LMA and one of its outcomes was a decision to hold a conference the following February. This took place at Blackpool in June 1951, and John Alcock as the LMA chairman took the chair. The conference considered the findings of the report in more detail, and how the industry in this country might benefit. The trip and conference was the swansong of Marriott at Stafford as on his return from the USA he took up an already agreed appointment as managing director of Parsons Engineering Limited in Southampton (which has already been mentioned) and his place at Stafford was taken by WA Smyth.

In the last Chapter we saw how Alan Good had formed what was to all intents and purposes a new company, Brush Bagnall Traction Limited, as a marketing and selling agency for the locomotives to be built by the combination of Bagnall mechanical parts, Brush electrical equipment and diesel engines by other companies in the Associated British Oil Engines Limited (ABOE). Once again the first directors were:

Alan Paul Good - chairman.
Hon Alexander Campbell Geddes - commercial director Brush.
John Whitfield Cumming Milligan - managing director Brush.
Rex Bate - sales manager Brush.
Ernest William Marten - managing director Associated Locomotive Equipment Limited.
James Calderwood - technical director Brush.
Percival Clifford Sharp - Brush.
Jesse Talbot Rymer - managing director Mirrlees, Bickerton & Day Limited.
William Addison Smyth - managing director WG Bagnall Limited.

The sales manager was PJ Martin and the registered office was at Loughborough.

Apart from Rymer we met all these characters in the previous Chapter, so there is no need to go into any detail about them here. Rymer was on the board to address the interests of ABOE of which he was a director, but in April 1953 he left the Brush Group to take up an appointment as managing director of

Sentinel (Shrewsbury) Limited. Jumping ahead a few months, in May 1951 Kenneth Newton Eckhard joined the Brush Bagnall board as general manager; he was formally chief electrical engineer of the General Mitre Railway in Argentina. Eckhard had served his apprenticiship with London United Tramways and on completion of his training in 1909 worked for the London Electric Railways. However, in 1912 he joined the Central Argentine Railway (FCCA - later the General Mitre Railway) and was engaged on the suburban electrification schemes around Buenos Aires, becoming resident engineer of the electrification section of the chief mechanical engineer's department in 1920. When this section became an independent one in 1926, Eckhard was appointed chief electrical engineer and in that position later became responsible for diesel traction too. In 1945 he was a member of the committee of the British owned railways in Argentina which visited America to study the latest developments

in diesel-electric traction in that country. Elected a member of the Institution of Locomotive Engineers as far back as 1920, he was prominent in the activities of its South American centre. Eckhard retired from the General Mitre Railway in 1949 and returned to this country.

A few months later in July 1951, Harry George Ivatt, the last chief mechanical engineer of the LMS joined the Brush Bagnall board in a part-time and non-executive capacity, with a remit to provide technical advice. Latterly he had been mechanical engineer of the London Midland Region of BR. In July 1951 Miles Beever JP joined the board as deputy chairman; he was also the deputy managing director of the main Brush Company. A nominee of Matthews, Beever was formerly secretary to the British Transport Commission and before that solicitor and chief legal advisor to the LNER - he was of course, a lawyer by profession. However, from June 1947, and for the last few months

A view taken at the extreme south-end of the Erecting Shop with two of the Brush Bagnall Steel Company of Wales 0-6-0 diesel-electric locomotives under construction, the one in front only as far as what was termed 'deck-level', but with an air compressor placed on top. Wheel-sets for these locomotives can be observed to the left with the Machine Shop Foreman's office to the right. Photograph probably taken very early in 1951.

of the existence of the LNER, he had been its acting chief general manager. Educated at Winchester and Oxford, Beever joined the LNER as its chief legal advisor in 1925; he also served with distinction in the RAF Volunteer Reserve during the war with the acting rank of Flight-Lieutenant. John Humphrey Russell Nixon was another new board member elected in July 1951. In 1952 WA Smyth spent a few weeks in Brazil on behalf of Brush Bagnall Traction Limited undertaking market research, but no orders came the way of the new Company from that part of the world.

At its meeting on 26 January 1951 Brush Bagnall Traction Limited was admitted to membership of the LMA. It appears that originally there had been an intention that at the same time WG Bagnall Limited and the Brush Electrical Engineering Company Limited should cease to be individual LMA members. In fact in the case of Brush this is what happened, although WG Bagnall Limited retained its separate membership. Brush Bagnall was represented at the LMA by WA Smyth and PJ Martin. Martin incidentally left the group in late 1951 to take up an appointment as mechanical engineer of the Jamaican Government Railway, taking up his new responsibilities on and from 1 February 1952. One or two other LMA matters are worth a mention at this point. In November 1951 a Technical Advisory Committee was appointed and WA Smyth was a founder member. In March the following year a further committee was established to cover the particular interests of the industrial locomotive builders, and WG Bagnall was again represented by Smyth. The other builders represented on this committee were Andrew Barclay; Hunslet; Hudswell Clarke; Yorkshire Engine; RSH and Peckett (Peckett had rejoined the LMA after the war). Smyth was a founder member of yet another committee, the General Purpose Committee formed in July 1952; needless to say, the members of these various committees elected to meet whenever possible on the same day! From April 1951 Harry Davies represented the LMA at the Federation of Associations of Colliery Equipment Manufacturers meetings.

On 16 February 1948 and some time before the formation of the new marketing company Brush placed an order on Bagnall for five sets - later altered to six - of mechanical parts for diesel-electric locomotives, with the intension that the locomotives be fully erected at Stafford. Much of the mechanical design work was actually shared between Stafford and Loughborough, but in general terms the design was based on the earlier LNER locomotives and once again bore a striking likeness to the English Electric locomotives supplied to the LMS. The locomotives had an 0-6-0 wheel arrangement with outside frames, the wheelbase was 11ft 6in and the wheel diameter was four-foot; the engine was a Mirrlees TLT6 normally aspirated six-cylinder in-line vertical four-stroke delivering 355bhp @ 720rpm. This was among the first applications of a Mirrlees engine for rail traction purposes; as mentioned above the Irish locomotives were the first. The electrical equipment consisted of a Brush main generator with a capacity of 280kW, and two axle-hung and nose-suspended traction motors rated at 174 horsepower each driving the leading and trailing axles - conventional side rods coupled all the axles together. The weight in working order was 51 tons and the manufacturer's numbers allocated were 2971 to 2976. While these locomotives were being built Brush was actively canvassing the newly formed Steel Company of Wales (SCOW - incorporated 1 May 1947), which was constructing a new and very large integrated iron and steel works, to be known as the Abbey Works, at Margam near Port Talbot in South Wales. The existing and adjacent Margam works was being modernised at the same time; the net result a burgeoning need for a new fleet of shunting locomotives.

The SCOW was a consortium of Guest Keen & Baldwins Limited (owners of the existing Margam works), John Lysaght Limited, Llanelly Associated Tinplate Companies Limited and Richard Thomas & Baldwins Limited; it had made known as early as 1948 that it was likely to want to employ diesel locomotives at the new works rather than steam. The Margam works was an old customer of Bagnall. Chris Wordsworth, who was in charge of internal transport at the new works, was heavily involved in decisions on any new locomotives. In expressing his interest in the new diesel-electric locomotives being built at Stafford, he considered that not only was more installed horsepower necessary, but additionally heavier mechanical parts were essential, not just to support a more powerful engine, but in view of the rough and tumble that was the everyday life of locomotives in a steel works. In particular he wanted much deeper and stronger buffer

Photograph was taken on 23 January 1951, on the occasion of the launch to the press and other interested parties of the first Brush Bagnall diesel-electric locomotive, manufacturer's number 3000, Steel Company of Wales No 701.
The gentleman are, from left to right:

Standing: *Ted Beeston Shop Steward (Boiler Shop); Reg Moon Works Convenor (marker-out);*
George White Pattern Shop Foreman; Harry Owen Shop Steward (Tool Room); Harry Cooper (leading-hand Erecting Shop);
Ben Lee Machine Shop Foreman; Fred Millward Shop Steward (Foundry); Albert Appleton Chief Storekeeper;
George Carless Foundry Foreman; Bill Pittard Tool Room Foreman; Harry Rogers Yard Foreman; Bert Lowe Maintenance Foreman;
George Dumbleton Shop Steward (Smithy); Harry Millward Packing Shop Foreman (no relation to Fred);
Bert Emery Erecting & Fitting Shop Foreman; Bill Monaghan Foreman Painter; Alf Homer Shop Steward (Pattern Shop);
Jack Brownsword Foreman Smith; Charlie Burghall Boiler Shop Foreman;
Bob Dilley Brush Electrical Engineering Company Representative; Les Arnold Shop Steward (Fitting Shop);
Eric Williams Power House Foreman.

Sitting: *Les Brown Chief Cashier; Arthur Woollams Assistant Works Manager; Harold Shaw Buyer;*
Norman Stokes Company Secretary; Sydney Ridgway Works Manager; WA Smyth Managing Director;
Harry Davies General Manager; Harold Wood Chief Draughtsman; Arthur Owen Chief Accountant;
George Brown Chief Estimator; Mr Brunton (on loan from Brush); Vic Betteley Contracts Engineer.

beams, right down to almost rail level, so as to restrict damage if and when the locomotives derailed. The requirement was to achieve a starting tractive effort of 34,000lb @ 26% adhesion and a maximum speed of around 20 mph. Also worthy of mention at this point is that Wordsworth wanted to give steam a last chance to compete with any new diesels, and as a result the

SCOW ordered directly from Bagnall three very modern steam locomotives for comparison purposes and these will be described later in this Chapter.

In view of Wordsworth's requirements a revised mechanical design was developed and on 19 January 1949 the SCOW ordered four locomotives from Brush, once again to be completely erected and delivered from

Steel Company of Wales No 703, Bagnall 3002 of April 1951, at the Abbey Iron & Steel Works about a year or so after delivery. Notice the deep buffer beams referred to in the text and the poor forward vision for the crew.

Stafford; manufacturer's numbers 3000 to 3003 were allocated. These locomotives had the bigger Mirrlees engine, turbo-charged and rated at 480bhp @ 720rpm - the type TLST6 - and the weight in working order of the locomotives was 55 tons. The frame plates were 1½in thick as opposed to one inch on the earlier locomotives and the buffer beams were three inches thick - the stock order locomotives weighed some four tons less. Three of these locomotives, given SCOW numbers 701 to 703, were despatched between February and April 1951, but not before a significant publicity event was staged at the Castle Engine Works. On 23 January 1951, a large contingent of the press, both local and technical, along with other interested parties including representatives of the SCOW, descended on the works. Along with the deputy mayor of Stafford Alderman CE Fowke (the Mayor himself, Alderman L

Dobson, being ill) and other members of the town council the party toured the workshops, and after a number of group photographs in front of locomotive number 3000 (SCOW No 701), the participants repaired to the Swan Hotel in Stafford where a reception was held. The fourth locomotive of the series - number 3003 - was sent on 30 June 1951 to the Trostre Tinplate Works at Llanelli, an associated operation to Margam, and another new SCOW development. This one was designated TROSTRE No 1 and the plant there started production in the same year the locomotive was delivered.

Returning to the stock order for diesel-electric locomotives mentioned earlier, there was a real possibly in late 1949 that all six might have been sold to the Egyptian Government Railways, which would have required some modifications to the design, vacuum brakes and drawgear for example. In the event this did not happen and the Egyptian order went to the Germany builder, Arn Jung Lokomotivfabrik GmbH, of Jungenthal. The first of the batch, manufacturer's number 2971, was eventually sold to an order of 3 January 1950 from Lever Brothers Port Sunlight Limited, for use at its extensive works at Port Sunlight near Birkenhead. Named MONTGOMERY of ALAMEIN, it was not delivered until 22 October 1951, which illustrates that not a lot of work had been undertaken on its construction since the SCOW indicated the changes it wanted for any locomotives supplied to Margam. Indeed of the six locomotives ordered for stock, as no work had been undertaken on the last two, numbers 2974 and 2975, they were cancelled and these numbers were not used again. However the other three, numbers 2972 to 2974, were eventually sold against two separate orders to the SCOW. The first order came to Stafford from Brush on 18 February 1952 for one locomotive, number 2972 being supplied as running number 713 - it was despatched on 18 August 1952. The second order for the other two locomotives arrived on 10 December 1952, and they were despatched to Margam on 11 May and 20 July 1953 respectively, as SCOW numbers 711 and 712. The mechanical parts for these three locomotives, including final erection at Stafford but excluding the engines and electrical equipment, cost

Brush £9,033 for the first one and £9,250 each for the other two. In August 1956 an exchange took place between the locomotive that had been sent to Trostre, works number 3003, and works number 2974; this was to concentrate the higher-powered locomotives at Margam - it then became fleet number 704. All three of the lower-powered locomotives were modified before leaving Stafford with deeper buffer beams, but they retained the thinner frame plates and smaller engines, although these were later up-rated to 390 horsepower.

These seven locomotives were the only 0-6-0 diesel-electrics to be used by the SCOW at Margam, as for reasons to be outlined later subsequent orders were for either four-wheel or double-bogie locomotives. Nevertheless the 0-6-0s had comparatively long lives and some of the batch with the smaller engines later had the intermediate wheels and side rods removed, making them in effect four-wheel machines. This modification enabled them to better negotiate the seven chain radius curves around the plant when they were used turn-and-turn-about with the double-bogie locomotives built later. Whilst this modification reduced the propensity for derailment it increased the axle-load by no small amount - from just over 18 tons to 25½ tons. A particular problem anticipated by Chris Wordsworth arose from the length of the main-frames, and they suffered with the frame spreaders fracturing and the rivets working loose. The locomotives that were

Similar to the Steel Company of Wales diesel-electric locomotives were two for the Consett Iron Company in Durham, one of which is seen here much later in its life in July 1967. Consett No 5, Bagnall 3020 of February 1952.

not converted to four-wheelers had the flanges removed from their intermediate wheels, and whilst this not only helped reduce derailments it also increased tyre life by reducing flange wear on the leading and trailing wheel-sets. This particular modification was undertaken on both batches of locomotive; in the case of the lower-powered ones prior to them being converted to four-wheel machines. All seven of these 0-6-0 locomotives had comparatively long lives, lasting until the early to mid 1970s.

On 16 February 1950 two more sets of mechanical parts for this same design of six-wheel locomotive were ordered by Brush to be erected at Stafford and fitted with the smaller of the Mirrlees engines, the TLT6 rated at 355 horsepower. Allocated manufacturer's numbers 3020 and 3021, these two were for the Consett Iron Company Limited for use at its iron and steel works at Consett in Durham. This company had been buying diesel-mechanical locomotives from Hunslet, and the decision to acquire these two diesel-electrics followed reluctance by Hunslet to build a 300 horsepower diesel-mechanical locomotive. As a matter of interest, subsequently Consett designed and built with its own resources two 300 horsepower diesel-mechanical locomotives based on the Hunslet design. Hunslet seem to have been concerned with the reliability of a suitable transmission system but the engineer in charge of the locomotives at Consett, George Cowell, had formerly worked for Hunslet! In the event the Brush Bagnalls were the only diesel-electric locomotives used

Framework for the New Erecting Shop under construction in November 1952. The steel work was second-hand and formerly a turbine hall at Whitebirk power station in Blackburn. It was impossible to get a licence for new material, in view of the post-war steel shortage, and the offer of £2,600 was accepted by the demolition contractors in June 1949. The new Tank & Frame Shops are to the left, rebuilt from the old Wagon Shop, and in the foreground are boiler flanging blocks and foundry casting boxes.

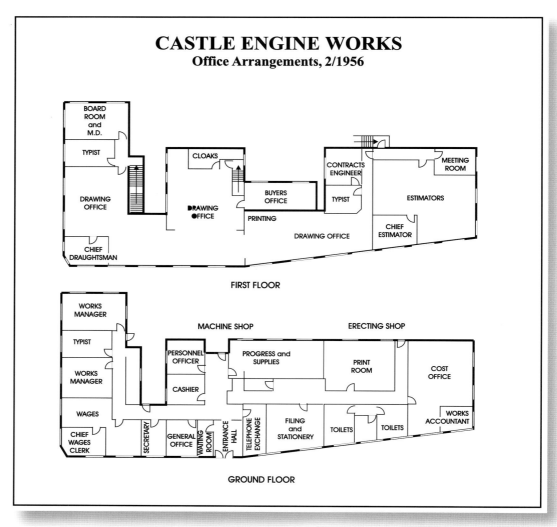

Plan of the new offices showing the function of each. Although this plan dates from a later period, the offices were in fact completed in 1950.

CASTLE ENGINE WORKS
Office Arrangements, 2/1956

FIRST FLOOR

GROUND FLOOR

at Consett, and one presumes in preferring the mechanical transmission Consett elected to standardise on that type after the successful development of the 300 horsepower locomotive outlined above. Despatch from Stafford was on 22 February and 26 May 1952 respectively, and the running numbers were 5 and 6.

A problem arose as these locomotives were approaching completion, when an injunction was taken out against Brush Bagnall by the English Electric Company (EE) for infringement of its patents in the design of the traction motor suspension and reduction gears. It will be recalled from earlier in this Chapter that Brush had in fact largely copied the EE design in many respects, when the LNER locomotive was being built at Doncaster and its equipment fitted at Loughborough. The result was the need to redesign the offending parts and in the case of the three stock

locomotives, numbers 2972 to 2974, a significant amount of work had to be scrapped, and replaced by the new design, involving some delay in completing them, and hence their sale to the SCOW.

The mechanical parts for the Consett locomotives including final erection cost £7,316 each. One of them, No 5, lasted until May 1970 when it was scrapped at Consett, whilst sister No 6 was transferred in August 1971 to the Trostre Tinplate works in Camarthenshire. This concentrated the surviving members of the class employed in the steel industry in South Wales, and was possible after nationalisation of the industry.

There were more locomotives of this basic design built under the Brush Bagnall umbrella, but in their case to a slightly modified specification, and these will be described later. But first of all it is necessary to describe the improvements and alterations to the plant and buildings at the Castle Engine Works to accommodate the new workload. It is also worth mentioning here, that at this period Brush did not allocate any specific manufacturer's numbers to the locomotives it supplied the electrical equipment for, even when they were erected at Loughborough, and all the ones so far described had the Bagnall numbers on their identification plates, which nevertheless had the words Brush Bagnall on them, and not WG Bagnall Ltd or Brush.

Most significant among the improvements was the erection of a completely new erecting shop - to be colloquially known by the staff as the new bay. This large building was situated to the west of, and slightly north of, the original erecting shop and consisted of a building of part brick and part steel construction 175ft long, 43ft wide and 40ft high. Two tracks ran the whole length, one of which had mixed-gauge rails to suit 5ft 6in, 4ft 8½in, 3ft 6in, and metre-gauge; the other road originally only catered for standard-gauge, but later had two-foot gauge added (this was to help with the construction of manufacturer's numbers 3124, 3125 and 3205). Twin 50-ton electric overhead travelling cranes traversed the entire length of the shop, 30ft

above rail-level, and the completed shop was brought into use towards the middle of 1953. Part of the structural steelwork for this building was second-hand, and had been on site for some time prior to construction starting. A few years before construction of the new bay, as mentioned in the last Chapter, the old wagon shop had to all intents and purposes been completely demolished and replaced by a new building consisting of three bays with a floor area of 9,000 sq ft, the plan being to use much of this area for the increased level of sheet metal work anticipated in the construction of the diesel locomotives. The new shop, known as the tank and frame shop, was completed in late 1949 and the wheel-bay, which had occupied the southern end of the erecting shop, was moved there. This was a much more satisfactory arrangement and released much needed space in the erecting shop to allow more locomotives to be under construction at any one time. These improvements, along with an almost completely rebuilt general office accommodation, a part rebuilt and extended drawing office and the large canteen building and works social club (opened in June 1949), were all completed and commissioned by mid-1950.

A significant number of new machine tools were

Interior of the light and airy drawing office on the top floor of the new office building. Compare with the earlier drawing office illustrated in Chapter Eight.

Exterior of the new office building as seen from 'Bagnalls Bridge', which took Castle Street over the main railway line. The works entrance in through the gates beyond and that is the canteen and social club building in the yard further-on. All the buildings are still in existence although the offices are currently vacant (February 2008).

acquired including a Cincinnati Hypro boring machine in the wheel shop, a cylindrical and surface grinding machine and a lot of smaller machine tools. A Tilghman's of Broadheath Manchester, sand blast and exhaust plant was installed in the iron foundry along with a Brayshaw annealing furnace, and for the fabrication shop a Unionmelt submerged arc-auto welding machine was purchased. Other mew machinery included a Waldrich open side planner, a Schmaltz axle-grinder and a 60in Webster-Bennett boring mill. However, perhaps the most impressive item of new equipment was a large Fielding & Platt 450-ton hydraulic press which could handle plate up to $1\frac{1}{8}$in thick and 10ft x 8ft 6in in overall size. The stores facilities were improved and extended and for use in the yard a six ton capacity Coles road crane was purchased. Once the new bay was complete almost all the erection of diesel locomotives was transferred there, although manufacturer's numbers 3066 to 3072 were an exception, leaving the older erecting shop by and large for building steam locomotives and other general engineering items. In total, but excluding the building works, over £100,000 was spent on new equipment and

other improvements, and by this time the number of people employed by the Company had risen to a little under 500 (see Appendix X).

Brief mention was made in the previous Chapter of the order Good was successful in obtaining for 25 5ft 6in gauge main-line diesel-electric locomotives for the Ceylon Government Railways. The order from Brush for the mechanical parts for these locomotives was placed with Bagnall on 7 June 1950 (the order from the Crown Agents to Brush was dated 13 March) at £41,500 each, with final erection undertaken at Loughborough. As well as Bagnall, Brush had also been busy constructing a new erecting shop for the increased workload anticipated with its entry into the locomotive market. At the time the Ceylon order was obtained the price announced to the technical press was considered to be extremely competitive, and the industry in general questioned how any profit could be derived from the order at such a figure. The work allocated to Stafford consisted of the complete under-frames and bogies along with the fuel tanks and a number of other items - mechanical parts to what was referred to as 'deck-level' - the superstructure being made and fitted at

Loughborough. The traction motors were supplied from Loughborough but fitted to the bogies at Stafford. Delivery of the first two sets of equipment from Stafford to Loughborough was contracted to be no later than March 1951, and thereafter at a rate to be decided; inspection on behalf of the customer was by Crown Agents of the Colonies inspectors. In the event the initial delivery to Loughborough was not until May 1952, and the last set of mechanical parts left the works in October 1955. The locomotives had an A1A-A1A wheel configuration with nose-suspended and axle-hung traction motors on the leading and trailing wheels

Underframes in course of construction in the Frame Shop for the Brush-Bagnall A1A-A1A diesel-electric main-line locomotives for Ceylon. The frame in front is upside down; notice the housings to take the bogie pivots. Just beyond the bed of the large slotting machine on the left, can be seen one of the box section bogie frames for the same locomotives. These were the bogie frames that suffered fractures when the locomotives were in service, as described in the adjoining text.

First member of the Brush Bagnall main-line locomotives for Ceylon, manufacturer's number 3025, Ceylon No 539. Initially the Brush Bagnall locomotives were given numbers in the Bagnall list; only later did Brush also allocate a number in its own series. Although the first numerically, this was not the first one despatched. The photograph was taken at the Brush works in Loughborough.

of each bogie; the intermediate wheel-set being unpowered. The engine was the Mirrlees JS12VT, a 12-cylinder V form supercharged four-stroke rated at 1,000bhp @ 850rpm. The main generator had a continuous rating of 652kW and each traction motor was rated at 196 horsepower. The wheel diameter was 3ft 7in, the bogie wheelbase was 10ft 6in and the total wheelbase 37ft 6in; top speed was 55mph and the weight in working order 87 tons. Starting tractive effort @ 26% adhesion was 33,700lb, and continuous tractive effort 24,600lb @ 11.7mph. The locomotives were arranged so that they could be worked in multiple formations with one crew and they were fitted with straight air brakes and vacuum train brakes.

The total contract value to Brush Bagnall amounted to £1,038,500 with delivery free-on-board Liverpool or Birkenhead. Allocated manufacturer's numbers in the Bagnall list in the series 3025 to 3049, the locomotives carried Brush Bagnall plates with these numbers and the running numbers were 539 to 563. BD Rampala the chief mechanical engineer (CME) of the Ceylon Government Railways was heavily involved in the specification and outline design; he was in this country in March 1950 and again in 1952. Bamunuarachige Don Rampala was well known to the managing director at Stafford, in fact he had been one of Smyth's pupils when he was in charge in Ceylon. Born in 1910, a student apprentice with the CGR, obtaining his BSc in

mechanical engineering in this country in 1936. Appointed CME in 1949, and elected a member of the Institution of Mechanical Engineers in 1936, on the proposal of Smyth. The first locomotive was handed over to the High Commissioner of Ceylon, Mr EAP Wijeyaratne, at Loughborough during a ceremony on 20 November 1952; actually it was the second locomotive numerically - number 3026 - CGR 540 - as the first one had already left for Birkenhead Docks. At a press conference that accompanied the handing over ceremony, a point picked up by the journal *Diesel Railway Traction*, was that at £33 per brake-horsepower and £500 per ton of empty weight, the price of these locomotives, if such levels could be maintained, would stand the Brush Bagnall partnership in a very good position for future orders. Delivery of the total fleet was complete by the end of 1955. The journey to the docks was by rail with the locomotives temporally fitted with standard-gauge accommodation bogies for the trip, their own bogies being loaded into adjacent wagons. The accommodation bogies, which had also been made at Stafford, were then returned to Loughborough to be used time and time again. Marshalled in freight trains the locomotives when en-route to the docks were on trains that were routed via Stafford!

Whilst the long delivery timescale may seem excessive, it was in fact deliberate and intended to allow service experience with the locomotives delivered earlier to be analysed and any resultant improvements and modifications to be embodied in the later locomotives. The original quotation was for a delivery period for the entire fleet of 30 months, but Ceylon pressed for earlier delivery and in the end agreement was reached to complete the delivery in two years. On further pressure being applied it was arranged to supply one locomotive in 18 months and a second one in one month later. As things turned out the first delivery was late, and the locomotive in question did not arrive in Ceylon until early in January 1953; it entered traffic two weeks later. After two locomotives had been delivered further deliveries were held back whilst service experience was gained, but after a few months three more locomotives were delivered. A number of problems did manifest themselves once the locomotives entered service, most but by no means all associated with the Mirrlees engines.

Mention has already been made that the Brush Bagnall locomotives were among the first applications of a Mirrlees engine of any description for rail traction purposes, and they had what might be considered more than their fair share of problems. In the case of the Ceylon locomotives it was also the first use in any application of what was a completely new design of twin-bank V form engine. It is also worth mentioning at this point that when the same 12 cylinder engine was fitted into locomotives supplied to BR, although at a higher rating - of which more later - the engines were eventually replaced by those of a different maker due to acute in-service problems. The problems were not confined to the engines either, and for example the electrical circuitry also proved problematic, but perhaps the most serious from the point of view of the Castle Engine Works was fracturing of the bogie frames. The cause in this case was eventually established as excessive stress concentrations in the areas where the manganese liners for the horn guides had been welded into position, and increased strengthening of the thrust transoms was necessary to cure the problem. Remedies were eventually developed for a number of other cases of in-service problems, and modifications undertaken, either on site in Ceylon, in the manufacturing process where work had started, or in the case of the later locomotives before construction commenced. Once it was felt that the bulk of the initial problems had been identified and appropriate action taken, arrangements

were made to commence the delivery of the remaining 20 locomotives and the first of these arrived in Ceylon on 18 May 1954; they had all arrived by early 1956.

Despite the initial problems and consequent late delivery, the locomotives gave good service and two of the earliest ones delivered hauled the Royal Train on a number of separate journeys when the Queen and Duke of Edinburgh visited Ceylon in April 1954. On one of the trips on 14 April, as the train had to travel between Moho Junction and Polonnaruwa where the track was of very light construction, it was instead hauled by two light axle-load steam locomotives, and by a happy coincidence these were both built by Bagnall, of which more later. Ceylon was of course at this point in its history, still a British colony - later on independence becoming Sri Lanka. The locomotives all remained in service until the early 1980s - they were withdrawn in the period 1980 to 1984 - and No 551, Brush Bagnall 3037, is preserved in the Ceylon Railway Museum at Ratmalana, but does see occasional use at times of special events.

As the first main-line diesel locomotives used on the CGR the Brush Bagnall locomotives after the initial teething problems settled down to return good performance, and led the way to the complete dieselisation of the railways in that country. That they were a success is evidenced by the design being in effect the prototype for the later BR Type 2 (Class 31) locomotives; the first examples of this numerous class were ordered from Brush Bagnall in November 1955. In London on 14 March 1956, a paper by BD Rampala was read before the Institution of Locomotive Engineers titled *Diesel Electric Traction in Ceylon*. Most unfortunately Rampala was unable to be present to deliver it in person, having recently been appointed general manager of the CGR and thus unavoidably detained in Ceylon. However, among the audience was his old boss and mentor WA Smyth, who entered into the discussion and played tribute to his former colleague and friend. Subsequently the paper was read at the various branches of the I Loco E around the country, and when it was read in Derby on 21 March, among those contributing to the discussion was Harold Wood, chief draughtsman at Stafford when the locomotives were being designed and built. A film was made of these locomotives covering both their construction and while in service in Ceylon, and this was first shown at the British Council Theatre in Hanover Street, London, on 15 February 1955. Among those who accepted invitations to attend was the High Commissioner of Ceylon Sir Claude Corea, along with Sir Brian Robertson chairman of the British Transport Commission, and many others involved in the railway industry in this country.

In the early months of 1951 Alan Good went on a 25,000 mile tour of the commonwealth and the USA, in an effort to both establish the Brush Bagnall Company, and more importantly to secure orders for locomotives. During his time in Australia a new company was formed there, Brush Electric (Australia) Pty Limited, as a marketing organisation to cover the antipodes. One order Good seems to have obtained was from the 3ft 6in gauge Queensland Government Railways, a diesel-electric locomotive which it was envisaged would have been the prototype for a potential and significant follow-on order. The mechanical parts for this locomotive, which it is assumed would have been based on the Ceylon A1A-A1A locomotives - it was certainly

going to have the same Mirrlees JS12VT engine - was placed with Bagnall on 29 May 1951, only to be cancelled on 29 August the following year and before any physical work had been undertaken. Unfortunately we do not know the full story behind this, and it may be that Alan Good was in fact jumping the gun, and that there was no firm order from Queensland in the first place. There is also a suggestion that he had promised delivery in March 1952, and in view of the problems being encountered with the Ceylon locomotives, it was in fact Brush who decided to get out of the contract. Perhaps significantly, in May 1951 the Queensland Government Railways placed an order with the English Electric Company for 10 1,500 horsepower diesel-electric locomotives, and the following month went out to tender for 10 more main-line diesel locomotives.

About this time there were also thoughts that it might be a good idea if in fact a prototype main-line locomotive was built speculatively for demonstration purposes, probably adaptable for both 3ft 6in and metre gauge, with the South African Railways as a potential

Former Steel Company of Wales and now Corus No 902, Bagnall number 3064 of 1955, still at work at Margam on 26 June 2007. Like the surviving four-wheel locomotives most of the double-bogie ones have also had replacement engines fitted, but otherwise the power equipment is as originally built. However, this particular locomotive has been fitted with the type of bogie designed for a later batch of similar locomotives, but with higher horsepower engines. Notice the equalising beams and compare with the next illustration.

This photograph illustrates one of the bogies built at Stafford for the first order from the Steel Company of Wales for Bo-Bo diesel-electric locomotives. Complete with traction motors and exactly as it would have been delivered to Loughborough, where final erection of the locomotives took place. Compare with the later design of bogie seen under the locomotive in the previous illustration. The gentleman looking at the photographer is Jim Webberley, the Chief Draughtsman.

market. It was Alan Good's firmly held view that if Brush Bagnall did not make significant inroads into the market, English Electric would have a free-hand in tendering for diesel-electric locomotives so far as this country was concerned. About this time too, Brush Bagnall tendered for a possible 17 locomotives for the north-east steel maker Dorman Long, which was at the time considering replacing its steam fleet (in the event it was some years before this happened), and there was a very large potential order from Argentina, no less than 180 locomotive in three types covering the horsepower range 400 to 1600.

Problems with the six-wheel shunting locomotives built for the SCOW, not least in the poor visibility from the cabs and the awkward arrangements for the shunting staff to travel on them, led to the design of a double-bogie locomotive as briefly alluded to earlier. Actually the SCOW already had five locomotives of this wheel arrangement, Bo-Bo diesel-electric machines built by the American Locomotive Company (ALCO) of Schenectady and delivered in March 1950, which apart from war time imports were among the first American diesel locomotives to be used in this country. Difficulty was encountered in getting an import licence for these ALCO locomotives, and it was only the

inability of British manufactures to meet the time scales, along with the need to get the new Abbey Works in production as quick as possible, that prevailed. However by the time more locomotives were needed the manufacturing situation in this country had improved and the British Government refused to grant an import licence for any more American locomotives. The ALCO locomotives had an engine rated at 660 horsepower, a starting tractive effort of 59,430lb at 30% adhesion, and a weight in working order of 88½ long tons - maximum speed was 30mph. Apart from the buffers and drawgear they were a standard product of the builder.

On 10 March 1953 Bagnall received an order via Brush Bagnall Traction Limited for the mechanical parts for three Bo-Bo diesel-electric locomotives specifically designed to meet the SCOW requirements. A Mirrlees six-cylinder normally aspirated four-stroke vertical engine rated at 515bhp @ 875 rpm - type JS6 - was specified and of course the electrical equipment was of Brush manufacture. The four traction motors coupled in series-parallel across the compound-wound main generator each had a rating of 78 horsepower. The starting tractive effort was 47,000lb @ 30% adhesion, and the maximum speed 28mph. Bogie

An illustration of one of the four-wheel diesel-electric locomotives built under the Brush Bagnall name for the Steel Company of Wales, Bagnall numbers 3066 to 3072 of 1954 and 1955. Awaiting final painting the locomotive is in the works yard at Stafford; notice the low engine compartment to give the crew good vision and the excellent access provision for shunting staff.

wheelbase was eight feet, total wheelbase 26ft 6in, bogie centres 18ft 6in and the weight in working order 79 tons; they were therefore, somewhat smaller than the ALCO locomotives. To assist vision from the cab in the forward direction the engine and generator compartment was lowered towards the cab end. The mechanical parts of these locomotives, which included the bogies complete with the axle-hung and nose-suspended traction motors, were despatched to Loughborough between December 1954 and April 1955, where final erection took place. The completed locomotives were given the Bagnall numbers 3063 to 3065 and carrying Brush Bagnall plates with these numbers they were delivered in late 1955. The SCOW running numbers were 901 to 903, and the cost of the parts made at Stafford £6,750 for each locomotive. The Mirrlees engines in these locomotives, like the bigger variant in the Ceylon locomotives, could never be considered a complete success, and they suffered numerous problems ranging from excessive cylinder liner and piston wear to warped and fractured cylinder blocks and crankcases. As a result the locomotives were later fitted with new engines, in this case a Rolls Royce 12 cylinder V form engine type DV8TCE,

rated at 515bhp @ 1,800 rpm, similar to the Mirrlees but running a lot faster and requiring a step-down gear ratio.

On the same day that the Bo-Bo locomotive mechanical parts were ordered a second order was placed for seven 0-4-0 diesel-electric locomotives, also for the SCOW and in this case for less arduous duties around the new Abbey steel works. This was another new design specially to meet the SCOW requirements; in this case however, complete erection was at Stafford. Allocated numbers 3066 to 3072 and supplied with Brush Bagnall plates carrying these numbers, a neat design emerged with outside frames and excellent cab visibility. It was to help achieve good visibility for the crews following experience with the 0-6-0 locomotive, that a different engine was selected. In designing a locomotive with a much lower engine compartment, an engine physically smaller than, and in particular not as tall as, the Mirrlees was essential. The achieve the required horsepower rating but at the same time limit the overall physical size, meant a high-speed engine and the choice fell on the National type M4AAU6, as by this time National were also in the Brush/ABOE group. This engine chosen was rated at 300bhp @ 1,200rpm, a six-cylinder in-line four-stroke with exhaust pressure charging. As a result of this engine choice, and unlike the later 0-6-0 and the Bo-Bo locomotives, there was no necessity to lower the engine compartment at the cab end as the whole compartment was at the same level as the bottom of the cab windows. The Brush main-generator of type TG 78-43 was a compound-wound machine rated at 272kW and each axle had an axle-hung and nose-suspended traction motor rated at 150 horsepower; the wheel diameter was 3ft 6in, the wheelbase eight-feet, and the weight in working order 43 tons and 3 cwt. Starting tractive effort was 24,000lb @ 25% adhesion, and the maximum speed 20 mph. These locomotives carried SCOW numbers 501 to 507 and were despatched between December 1954 and June 1955.

Subsequently several were fitted with Rolls Royce DV8N engines, a V form eight-cylinder unit, rated at 335bhp @ 1,250rpm, and in about 1972 works numbers

3066 and 3067 were rebuilt as a master and slave unit, semi-permanently coupled. In this configuration and with 3066 as the master, the cab and controls were removed from 3067 and the combination became in effect, a 600 horsepower locomotive. Others were similarly converted later, but the arrangements were never completely successful as it proved impossible to get 100% synchronisation between the two units, resulting in buffing shocks and broken drawbars. With reduction in the level of locomotive work at the Abbey Works, the opportunity was taken to phase out the slave units and several have been converted into brake-tenders, with all the power equipment and the superstructure removed, ballast weights being added where the engine compartment and cab used to be. In this form they are semi-permanently coupled to the remaining locomotives of the same type, and this enables the combinations, as they have similar brake power as the Bo-Bo locomotives, to undertake the

A recent photograph of one of the four-wheel locomotives at what is now the Corus steel works at Margam in South Wales. No 501, Bagnall 3066, first member of the class, coupled to the remains of sister 3067, cut-down with ballast weight added to assist the braking capability, a picture taken on 14 August 2007. Notice the side-rods have roller bearings, when new this batch of locomotives had plain bearings in these positions. However, a subsequent batch of similar locomotives did have roller bearings side-rods, so clearly over the years some swapping of wheel-sets and rods has taken place. At the time this photograph was taken the locomotive had given over 50 years service, the only major modification being a new engine, retaining it's original electrical equipment.

remaining locomotive duties around the works. This is due to the weights that have to be hauled, the sharp curves and steep gradients. These combinations, one four-wheel locomotives and one brake-tender, are of course less powerful than the larger locomotives, but nevertheless the arrangement has been relatively successful as a stop-gap pending the delivery of new locomotives.

Having described the early diesel-electric orders built under the Brush Bagnall regime we must now backtrack slightly and discuss the other locomotives built in the period under review. In the early post-war years the company had a significant measure of success in selling fireless steam shunting locomotives. Many of them were for use in electricity generating stations as a number of new power stations were built and commissioned in the immediate post-war years. But others were supplied to, for example, the Prince Regent Tar Distillers Limited for its refinery in east London, number 2851 of September 1947, and the Gloucester Carriage & Wagon Company Limited for its works in Gloucester, number 2871 of December 1947. All the post-war fireless locomotives with one exception were of basically the pre-war 0-4-0 design with a few modifications to bring them into line with current best practice. The exception was a six-wheeler, number 3019 of 1952, for Shell Refining & Marketing Company

Limited, for use at Middleton works at Heysham in Lancashire. Mention has already been made of how ideal a fireless locomotive is for shunting at plants where there is a large supply of steam available from stationary plant, power stations being excellent examples, or alternatively where fire presents a risk, oil refineries for example. The Shell locomotive was based on the pre-war design too, but with a number of modifications and a higher reservoir pressure of 300psi. Although ordered in September 1949 this locomotive was not despatched until 16 May 1952, another illustration of how the heavy work-load and healthy order book was affecting delivery schedules. The cost was £8,425 plus £85 for a set of charging equipment and this locomotive is still in existence.

Several more of the standard-gauge 16in cylinder six-coupled saddle tank shunting locomotives were built, all except one for local North Staffordshire collieries, and there was a four-wheel version of this design developed too. Only two of these were built, manufacturer's number 2907 supplied 1 October 1949 to the Staveley Iron & Chemical Company Limited, and number 2993 of November 1950 for Glasgow Corporation Gas Department. This second one was for use at Dawsholme gas works and was specially adapted to enter the restricted clearances of the gas retorts; as a result it had an overall height of just 9ft 9in.

This was the sole six-wheel fireless locomotive built post-war, all the others were four-wheelers. Manufacturer's number 3019 new in May 1952 for the Shell Refining & Marketing Company, for use at its refinery at Heysham in Lancashire. A standard design feature of fireless locomotives built at Stafford was, as seen here, a cover over the crossheads and slide-bars. With the cylinders at the cab end and adjacent to the cab footsteps, this was felt to be an important safety consideration.

Only one of these four-wheel versions of the 16in cylinder 0-6-0 design was built; DNT, the initials of David Neville Turner a director of the Staveley Coal Iron & Chemical Company in Derbyshire, which was where the locomotive worked. Manufacturer's number 2907 of October 1949, it turned the scales at 40 tons. Photograph taken at Staveley on 27 July 1950 when the locomotive was less than a year old. There was one other locomotive with similar main dimensions, but built to suit the restricted loading gauge of a Glasgow gasworks. (Late Ralph Russell - Frank Jones Collection - Industrial Locomotive Society)

MEOZAMA, No 13 in the fleet of Sir John R Hulett's Darnall sugar estates in Natal, South Africa, was one of two of these articulated locomotives despatched in June 1953. The two locomotives, numbers 3014 and 3015, were to the basic pre-war design but with shorter side tanks and a lot of welding employed in their construction rather than riveting. This one is number 3014 outside its shed at Darnall in 1967.

To help the Ceylon Government Railways recover from the ravages of the war years, and prior to the arrival of the Brush Bagnall diesels mentioned earlier, an order was placed by the Crown Agents in March 1949 for six of the 5ft 6in gauge A3 class 4-8-0 tender engines. These were very similar to those supplied in 1939, manufacturer's numbers 2608 to 2610, but in this case classified A3D, the most noticeable difference being a redesigned and larger tender and a different cab design - much more welding at the expense of rivets in both cases. These locomotives were specifically intended for use on the hilly Batticaloa to Trincomalee section which had a very restricted axle-loading, where additional motive power was needed to assist with works in connection with a large irrigation scheme at Gal-Oya. It was two of this batch of locomotives that

hauled the Royal Train mentioned earlier when the Queen and Duke of Edinburgh visited Ceylon. So far as the authors are aware, along with the diesels, these are the only occasions when Bagnall locomotives have been used to haul Royal Trains. The six locomotives were the last new steam locomotives built for CGR and they were despatched from Stafford in June and August 1951, free on board Liverpool, and the cost, £16,348 each. The manufacturer's numbers were 3004 to 3009 and the CGR numbers 357 to 362. As with their earlier sisters they lasted until the bulk withdrawal of the remaining steam locomotives in Ceylon in the period 1970 to 1972.

Three more of the narrow-gauge articulated locomotives were built; two of them were repeat orders for Sir John L Hulett's South African sugar estates in

The last articulated steam locomotive built and the only one for use in this country was MONARCH, number 3024, new in July 1953 for Bowaters Lloyd Pulp & Paper Mills Limited, for use at Sittingbourne in Kent. This picture was taken at Kemsley Mill shortly before the locomotive went into preservation on the Welshpool & Llanfair Railway in Mid-Wales. The large sandbox mounted on the smokebox is not original, and not a very good idea either, as it only applies sand to the wheels on one side of the engine. When sand was applied by this method in times of less than 100% adhesion, the axles would experience excessive torsional (sheer) stresses for which they were not designed.

Natal and ordered via the Bagnall South African agents A&H MacNay. These two, manufacturer's numbers 3014 and 3015 were two-foot gauge and although ordered in July 1949, were not despatched until June 1953; they cost £10,142 each. The third engine was for use in this country on the extensive 2ft 6in gauge system at the Sittingbourne and Kemsley paper mills in Kent of Bowaters Lloyd Pulp & Paper Mills Limited; delivered in July 1953 it appropriately named MONARCH. Apart from the track gauge it was to all intents and purposes identical to the South African engines and cost £10,092; the number was 3024. Bowater Lloyd was an amalgamation of Bowaters Limited and Edward Lloyd Limited, Lloyd's being the previous owners of the Sittingbourne and Kemsley operation and over many years good customers of Bagnall, not only for locomotives but rolling stock too. This was Bowaters last new steam locomotive, and in fact, the last new narrow-gauge steam locomotive built for industrial use in this country. Unfortunately the engine was by no

means as successful as had been hoped, and whilst it could and did manage the work of two of the smaller engines, which was the specification against which it was ordered, there were a number of problems encountered in service. Some of these were quite serious; the men at Sittingbourne never completely mastered the management of the circular firebox boiler for example, and there were problems with the boiler itself, including the superheater. This was the only superheated locomotive ever used on the system at Sittingbourne so perhaps this was not altogether surprising. A lot of time and effort was expended at both Sittingbourne and Stafford, including modified parts being supplied and men sent to fit them, but the engine was never considered 100% successful. As a result of these and other issues, when traffic levels on the narrow-gauge system started to decline Bowaters Lloyd decided to dispose of this engine.

Fortunately when MONARCH fell out of use it came to the notice of the late Ralph Russell, an enthusiast

Official photograph of the last member of the three large shunting engines, numbers 2994 to 2996, in this case 2996, supplied to the Steel Company of Wales in 1951. These locomotives were without doubt the most advanced industrial steam locomotives to work in this country; despite their success however, they could not stem the tide of dieselisation at the Margam Iron and Steel works. Notice in particular the piston valve cylinders, roller bearings for the motion and the large balance weight on the reversing-shaft lifting arm - an average sized man could manually reverse these engines while comfortably sitting down.

This view looks south in the Erecting Shop in the early months of 1951; probably taken at the same time as the view of the diesel-electrics on page 502. On the right are the three Steel Company of Wales locomotives nearing completion and in front of them a set of frames, with its boiler alongside, for one of the 0-6-0 pannier tanks for the Western Region of BR. There is another pannier tank to the left, looking just about complete and probably undergoing finish painting. To the right background is one of the Steel Company of Wales six-wheel diesel-electrics. This picture, taken as it is from one of the overhead cranes, quite comprehensively illustrates the rather cramped conditions in this shop, but nevertheless, where over the years so much was achieved. Fitting bays to the left and Machine Shop to the right.

who had built up a strong relationship with the management at Sittingbourne and who was heavily involved in the early days of the Welshpool & Llanfair Railway Preservation Society. This delightful railway in Mid-Wales was in need of additional locomotives as its activities expanded, and Ralph arranged to personally purchase the engine from Bowaters, and in effect present it to the Welshpool & Llanfair Railway. The engine was moved to Llanfair in May 1966. Unfortunately, despite seeing some use at Welshpool over the next few years it appears to have achieved no more success there than it had at Sittingbourne, very

soon earning as bad a reputation with the crews in Wales and those in Kent! As a consequence the engine spent a lot of time out of use and was eventually sold to a group connected with the Festiniog Railway at Portmadoc, whence it migrated in February 1992. The intention was to convert the engine to 1ft 11½in gauge for use on the Festiniog Railway, but in the event little progress was made, largely it seems in view of extensive repairs found to be necessary to the boiler. As a consequence the engine languished for several years in a partly dismantled state, and with parts in several different locations. Happily however, it has since been sold to a group of members of the Welshpool & Llanfair Society and moved back to Llanfair. The intention is that one day it might be possible to put the engine back into working order, while in the meantime it has at least, been reassembled for exhibition purposes.

Mention was made earlier that as well as introducing diesel-electric locomotives at the new Abbey Works the SCOW also ordered some new steam locomotives. They were for use at the adjacent and reconstructed Margam works where a new blast furnace plant was built, and primarily for hauling the molten metal and slag ladles associated with operations around these furnaces. Chris Wordsworth, whom we met earlier in this Chapter, and who had charge of the rail operations around the two works complexes, was anxious that steam be given a chance to prove the economics or otherwise of diesel traction. He felt strongly that hitherto, in comparing steam against diesel in industrial plants it had always been a case of new diesel locomotives pitted against old steam locomotives - old, that is, both in age and design. Following on from this analysis he was of the view that a steam locomotive specifically designed for the duties he had in mind, and embodying all the modern refinements possible, would give the diesels a very close run for their money. The requirement was to haul 450 ton loads up gradients of 1 in 70 and around curves of 2½ chains radius, the loads consisting of 65 ton blast furnace bogie slag ladle wagons. An order was placed with Bagnall on 17

November 1948 for three 0-6-0 saddle tank locomotives to meet the requirements specified above, and fitted with a whole range of modern refinements. The design team at Stafford led by Harold Wood set about designing what were without any doubt the most modern and sophisticated industrial steam shunting locomotives ever built for use in this country.

The three locomotives had 18x26in outside cylinders, 4ft 3in diameter wheels and a wheelbase of 11 foot; the boiler pressure was 180psi and the weight in working order 52½ tons. Whilst these dimensions might not in themselves appear in any way special, it was the range of special features that set these locomotives apart from any of their predecessors. All the axle bearings were of the double-row self-aligning roller type and there were self-aligning roller bearings on the side rods and the connecting rod big ends. Needle roller bearings were fitted on the motion parts including the little ends, with the sole exception of the eccentric rod return cranks which also had self-aligning roller bearings. Piston valves of eight inch diameter actuated by Walschaerts valve gear was used and the sidebars were hardened by the Shortersing process. The locomotives had rocking grates, hopper ashpans, self-cleaning smokeboxes, Lambert wet sanding, an Owen balanced regulator, balanced reversing gear and manganese steel liners on the axle-box horn guides. All the moving parts were either grease lubricated or fed by a mechanical lubricator. It will be seen therefore that

Steel Company of Wales No 401, Bagnall 2994, at work at Margam when quite new. Just discernable to the left is one of the large bogie ladle wagons, the movement of which was the staple diet for these locomotives.

considerable thought was put into reducing the servicing requirements, increasing times between overhaul and easing the lot of the drivers. The balanced reversing gear allowed the engines to be easily put into backward gear by an average-sized driver sitting down. To improve visibility the saddle tanks were designed with part straight sides and were full-length with a capacity of 1,500 gallons. The boilers had a steel firebox and steel tubes, but, perhaps surprisingly in view of the other refinements, were not superheated; the view was taken that in the light of the comparatively short runs the engines would undertake the added efficiency possible from a superheater would hardly justify the extra cost both in installation and maintenance. To complete the picture the piece de

resistance of the engines was a large five inch diameter tri-tone chime whistle. Harold Wood and his team were very proud of these engines, and rightly so, and Harold felt strongly that they needed to be heard wherever they went! Hence a magnificent sounding whistle which the company designed and made itself.

Costing £9,887 each and given the manufacturer's numbers 2994 to 2996, the SCOW numbers were 401 to 403; they were despatched on the 12 February, 16 February and 13 March 1951 respectively. Painted in a pleasing shade of what was called midland red with lemon lining they were put to work immediately on their intended duties. It was soon found that these locomotives could comfortably exceed their design loads and in the period to 1955 it was only necessary to

VICTOR, Bagnall 2996, after acquisition in 1957 by the Austin Motor Company for use at its Longbridge works in the West Midlands. This picture was taken on 4 April 1970; two of the engines migrating here with the onslaught of diesels at Margam. The story goes that members of the Austin staff saw the Brush Bagnall diesels being delivered as they passed the Longbridge plant on their journey south. They had large signs on their sides stating where they were destined for, and the conclusion was drawn that they must be replacing steam engines. As the Austin locomotive fleet was due for some modernisation, phone calls elucidated that locomotives in otherwise good condition had recently been sold to a South Wales dealer - the rest, as they say, is history.

take any of them out of service, with the exception of boiler washouts and servicing, on two occasions, and this was for attention to the tyres. Washouts were every two weeks and otherwise they were in use 24 hours a day and seven days a week. On the second occasion when they were taken out of service for attention to the tyres, the opportunity was taken to make a detailed study of any wear that may have taken place on the moving parts. As a result of this inspection it was considered that nothing like a heavy repair would be needed for some considerable time; indeed as events turned out such a repair was never necessary while the locomotives were in use at Margam. In the words of Chris Wordsworth: "these locomotive handled all the traffic they were given with conspicuous success, and four years after delivery they could be heard taking their regular load of 450 tons up a 1 in 70 grade without any trouble and with an absolutely regular beat".

However, at the end of the day the accountants made the decisions and while the steam locomotive costs over a three-year period compared reasonably favourably with the diesels, especially in terms of depreciation where they were in fact better, the diesels won. The costs were worked out on a 'per shift hour in service' basis and included the cost of the crews. In the case of the steam engines this equated to £1 0/ 6d (£1 5p), whilst the figure for the diesels was almost half, at 12/2½d (65p); however, these costs were for the entire SCOW steam fleet and one would have expected the Bagnall engines on their own to return somewhat better figures. Availability figures were 88% for steam and 94% for the diesels. As a result of this analysis these magnificent locomotives along with the remainder of the steam fleet were taken out of service in early 1957, but not surprisingly all three found further use. Two of them, numbers 2994 and 2996, became VULCAN and VICTOR at the Austin Motor Company plant at Longbridge, whilst the third engine, number 2995 went to the NCB at Ogilvie Colliery. This locomotive was eventually scrapped in 1967, but the other two after

A scene at Katwa, north-west of Calcutta, with Burdwan-Katwa Railway No 13 about to leave on the afternoon mixed-train to Burdwan on 2 January 1977. This was one of three of these 2-6-2 side tanks supplied to the McLeod Railways in 1953, an updated version of the First World War design originally ordered for Egypt and described in Chapter Six, several of which were in the event, delivered to the McLeod Railways. This one is Bagnall number 3053.

finishing work at Longbridge in 1973, passed into the preservation movement. Initially they went to the West Somerset Railway, but despite subsequently somewhat varied lives, it is good to know that two examples of this last significant development in industrial steam locomotive design in this country are still around for all those who are interested to see and study.

Mention was made earlier of the comparatively large orders for metre and narrow-gauge locomotives for India that the Company had on hand in the immediate post-war years, and this was referred to as an Indian summer of steam, and in more ways than one. Indeed, no more orders of the type and size described earlier came the way of the Castle Engine Works; or for that matter any of the other British locomotive builders. One of the very last orders for steam locomotives for India, and the last one for more than a single locomotive, came from the managing agents McLeod,

Russell & Company Limited for the 2ft 6in gauge railways they still managed in, and not far from, Calcutta. This company ordered three 2-6-2 side tank locomotives in May 1951, which were an updated and improved version of locomotives supplied earlier, a development of the Delta class which it will be recalled, Bagnall had originally designed for the Egyptian Delta Light Railways before the First World War - manufacturer's numbers 2022 to 2033. As related in Chapter Six because of the First World War some of the engines ordered for Egypt were diverted to India and used on the lines McLeods managed. Later, more of the type were ordered by McLeods - numbers 2411 and 2412 of 1930 - and this post-war order was in effect a continuation of this policy. The other Bagnall engines used on the lines were larger 0-6-4 side tanks, but the 2-6-2 design was preferred at this time as they were kinder on the track. Manufacturer's numbers 3053 to

The Phalton Sugar Works is situated near Daund, not far from Pune (formally Poona) in central-west India, and until about 1980 operated an extensive two-foot gauge system to serve the cane fields. In April 1952 Bagnall supplied three of these rather delightful 4-4-0 side tanks with 10in cylinders, numbers 3016 to 3018 - they were ordered by one of the firm's Indian agents, Greaves Cotton & Company of Bombay. This one is Bagnall 3016, Phalton S1, busy at work in the cane fields in April 1979. Unfortunately the railways closed down shortly after this picture was taken, replaced by road transport, and as far as is known the locomotives were subsequently scrapped. (Frank Jux)

3055 were allocated and the engines were despatched in October 1953 at a cost of £10,958 each.

The first two were destined for the Burdwan Kawta Railway, and the third the Bankura Damooder River Railway, although there was some swapping around later. In 1929 and 1930 McLeods had purchased a number of Sentinel Patent vertical-boiler chain-driven locomotives of that companies design with high-speed vertical engines - mention was made of this type of locomotive earlier in this Chapter. These locomotives were to supplement the conventional engines in catering for increased traffic levels, and in view of their light weight, help to reduce track maintenance. It was these Sentinel locomotives falling out of use, because of their high maintenance costs and low availability that prompted this order for conventional locomotives from Bagnall, and to a tried and tested design. In 1957 the McLeod railways passed to the control of the nationalised Indian railways, and these new locomotives along with most of the earlier ones remained in use until the lines they operated were converted to diesel traction in the late 1980s.

In the period covered by this Chapter the amount of work for other than locomotives was comparatively small, both in terms of rolling stock or general engineering, thought the odd couple of turntables were produced. But the supply of spare boilers and fireboxes kept the boiler shop very busy as there were significant orders for metre and narrow-gauge locomotive boilers for India. For example over 100 spare boilers were built in the period from the change of ownership to the end of 1953. A number of industrial shunting locomotives came into the works for overhaul during the same period too, and these often required replacement boilers or at least heavy boiler repairs and new fireboxes.

Another period of uncertainty in the fortunes of the company resulted from the death of Alan P Good. Before we discuss this issue and its aftermath in more detail it is worth having a look at some of the other people issues, along with the financial position of the company. Dealing with the latter first, at an EGM held of 32 August 1949 it was agreed to increase the capital of the Company to £100,000 by the issue of 40,000 new £1 shares. This was achieved by a re-evaluation of the leasehold land and buildings along with the capital reserves, and the new shares were allocated on a pro-rate basis among the existing shareholders. There was

a further increase in share capital following another EGM held on 18 December 1950, this time by the issue of 50,000 new £1 shares and this took the share capital of the Company to £150,000. In this case the increase was achieved by diverting profits and reserves rather than declaring a dividend, and once again the new shares were allocated on a pro-rata basis to the existing shareholders. As the District Bank Nominees of Manchester were still the largest shareholder, they were allocated the majority - 45,800 new shares - with Heenan & Froude as the second largest shareholder being allocated 1,650 new shares. There was yet another increase in capital, this time to £250,000 by the issue of a further 100,000 £1 shares, and this was agreed at an EGM held on 28 August 1951. The share capital of the Company remained at this figure for the remainder of the time it was part of the Heenan & Froude Group.

In 1949 the Company had declared a trading profit of £45,063, a net profit of £23,247, and a profit after tax of £9,749. In 1953 the comparative figures were respectively: £44,584, £15,845 and £6,498. The totals for the years 1948 to 1953, again respectively, were £211,420, £102,076 and £45,831, and the averages, once again respectively, £42,284, £20,415 and £9,166. The year 1952 had in fact been a record one for the company in terms of physical output.

There were a number of changes in the directorships of WG Bagnall Limited as opposed to Brush Bagnall Traction Limited in the period covered by this Chapter. We saw earlier that John Alcock had joined the board in March 1948 and he was followed by Alexander Chetwynw Hayes, elected on 3 February 1949. WA Smyth discussed in some detail earlier joined on 12 September 1949; James Calderwood on 31 August 1949; Hubert Harry Wheeler on 26 September 1949; Edward Maurice Benjamin on 19 December 1949; Ernest William Marten on 24 April 1950; Charles Loraine Hill on 28 July 1952 (Hill had earlier been elected on 22 July 1947, and resigned 3 November 1949); Norman Alfred Stokes on 1 October 1952. There were also a number of resignations, Marriott as already mentioned on 24 March 1950, along with Alcock on 10 July 1953; Wheeler and Benjamin did not stay on the Board long and both resigned on 18 December 1950. We have already met most of these characters except Wheeler and Benjamin. These two

The order for this locomotive, number 3013 of February 1952, almost certainly came the firm's way as Hugh F Marriott, after whom it was named, was the father of Ian Marriott the Bagnall Managing Director when it was ordered in July 1949. Built to suit metre-gauge with 12in cylinders, the specification called for a relatively easy conversion to suit 3ft 6in gauge. Ordered by the ICI Limited subsidiary, The Magadi Soda Company Limited, for use at its plant by Lake Magadi in Kenya; Hugh Marriott was the Kenyan Government nominee on the Magadi Company board. There was a proposal at the time for the gauge of the national rail network in Kenya to be changed from metre to 3ft 6in, hence the specification, although this never took place. Notice the twin couplers and double cab roof, although the locomotive is otherwise of the standard 12in cylinder design. It is currently preserved in the National Nairobi Museum where it has been since 1975.

were as WA Smyth described them, "itinerant aides of Alan Good", and while he had little to do Benjamin, Wheeler was a chartered accountant who had a habit of turning up unannounced and demanding to see all the accounts. However, as can be seen from the dates quoted above, neither were on the Bagnall board for very long. Hayes incidentally was secretary of the Heenan Group at the time of his appointment. Stokes, who took over from Hayes as secretary of WG Bagnall Limited on 1 October 1952, originally came to the Company from Bright Westland, accountants in Stafford.

Alcock, in a parting letter to Charles Hill of Heenan & Froude, the Bagnall chairman, made the point that being as he called it 'somewhat of a collector', if Heenan ever wanted to part with the Bagnall steam locomotive

goodwill, he hoped his collecting tendency would not be overlooked. This was a reference to Hunslet already having the Kerr, Stuart and Avonside goodwill.

On 9 July 1952 Harold Wood was loaned to Brush, initially for three months, to assist in the design work of the diesel-electric locomotives, and soon after took up a permanent appointment there as chief mechanical designer - he resigned from Bagnall on 31 October 1952. His place at Stafford, initially on an acting basis but from the following year permanently, was taken by Arthur James Webberley. Whilst Jim Webberley, a native of nearby Stoke-on-Trent, had started his apprenticeship at WH Barker & Company, engineers at Fenton, he came to Stafford in 1943 when quite young, and was to all intents and purposes Bagnall-trained. At the same time William Alfred Brooks became in effect the deputy chief draughtsman, appointed 30 December 1953, as he was the senior section leader. Bill Brooks was born at Dunston near Stafford on 9 August 1920 and joined the company as an apprentice in August 1934. He went into the drawing office in May 1937, becoming a junior draughtsman in August 1941 and a designer in September 1945, remaining in the drawing office for the remainder of the history of the company. Both Webberley and Brookes had been appointed section leaders on 19 March 1951. On 20 October 1952 Vic Betteley was appointed to the new position of Contracts Engineer. Changes among the foreman in the period being covered included the retirement of the pattern shop foreman George White on 31 July 1953, his place taken by Alfred Homer. In the same year George Carless became foundry foreman and following the departure of Bert Emery, JM (Mac) Durber assumed control of the fitting & erecting shops on 2 January 1952. The yard foreman Harry Rogers left the company in July 1951, and his position was taken by Leo Fielding.

Highfield Manor in Newport Road, which readers will recall had been acquired by the Company in Marriott's time as a residence for him during the week, as well as a potential club house for senior managers, was conveyed to the Company on 9 February 1953. Originally, in 1949, it was only on lease, and even then only the ground floor, but after Marriott moved on it was converted in April 1950 into four flats. This was an idea of Smyth's, to help senior members of staff with living accommodation, and for much of the time the flats were occupied by Sydney Ridgway, Vic Betteley, Jim Webberley and Arthur Jacob (a draughtsman), along with their families. Eric Parkin, another draughtsman, moved in when Ridgway left. Stan Ponting, a former Bagnall apprentice was appointed assistant buyer in September 1955 - he was promoted to the position of buyer in September the following year. Vic Betteley by the way had married Doris King in Stafford in 1950; they met during the war when Doris, who hailed from Stamford Hill in London, was serving in the RAF and was posted to the RAF Maintenance Unit (16MU) based in Stafford. Moving in to the Manor in 1950, their four children were all born there. The grounds of the Manor were looked after by a Mr Carter, who lived in the lodge, and various out-buildings were rented to EFW Wilkinson who owned a café in the town and used the paddock and stables for several

horses he owned and raced. An annual summer fate, which the company held for its staff and friends for a few years in the mid 1950s, was also held in the grounds.

The Manor incidentally, which dated from the late 19th century, had been built for a wealthy Stafford shoemaker David Hollin and his wife Emma. Hollin, the son of a railway guard, was born in 1844 and did rather well for himself establishing his own shoe manufacturing business in the town. However, the freehold of the Manor appears to have belonged to Lord Stafford as a part of his Castlechurch estate. Hollin died in 1911 but his wife continued to live there until she passed away in 1926, and a Fredrick Harris had the lease latterly. The Manor has since been demolished and the land used for housing, but the lodge and the main entrance drive gate-posts remain. It is interesting to note that Castle Hill House, former home of the Bagnall family described at length in Chapter One, was next door to Highfield Manor, albeit the two buildings were well separated by the extensive gardens of both properties. Unlike the Manor however, Castle Hill House still stands, well back from the Newport Road and obscured from a view off the main road by more recent property occupying what had been part of it's grounds.

For all his energy charisma and gravitias, Alan Good was taken seriously ill in late 1952 and in September resigned his managing directorship of Brush. But he remained a director and stayed on the Brush Bagnall and WG Bagnall boards, but lessened his other business responsibilities considerably. His health had in fact started to deteriorate as far back as 1950, as a result of which he paid frequent visits to the south of France where the climate helped. In a further effort to improve his health he went to South Africa early in 1953, but died there on 10 February. We have seen how Good as the father figure engineered the strong business connections between WG Bagnall Limited and the Brush Group, and how he was the founder and principal player in the Brush Bagnall Traction Limited partnership. Moreover we have seen how despite WG Bagnall Limited being owned by the Heenan & Froude group, under Good's direction Bagnall took its leadership from Brush. With Good no longer in control these relationships changed overnight, and with the connection severed it is time to move on to the next Chapter in the history of the Company.

Bagnall advertisement from The Railway Gazette Annual Overseas Number of 1950. The locomotive is one of the two metre-gauge 2-8-2s for the San Paulo Parana Railway, built in 1935, numbers 2528 and 2529.

Chapter Thirteen

LIFE AFTER ALAN GOOD:
INDEPENDENCE - BUT AT
WHAT PRICE

Although Alan Good did not influence the overall diesel locomotive market to an enormous extent, he did become a figure of considerable dominance in the control of diesel engine manufacturers in this country with his objective to acquire complete control of this market. Since he started his work in 1938, and in no small measure helped by the financial interests of Hambros Bank, and using his exceptional legal prowess and understanding of the financial markets of the day, he came a long way towards achieving his goal. How much more successful he might have been had he lived longer is hard to say, but we can be sure that more progress would have been made. When he gained his first controlling interests it was through Associated British Engineering, a company with a capital at the time of but £20,000. Alan Good attempted to centralise the oil engine building industry and control it for financial and commercial ends, which was not always to the good of the industry and its products. However, he was able to pour money into a number of firms that they would never have been able to find themselves, and so increase production. Having said that, it is a fact that during the war he worked tirelessly to increase production of the concerns he then had interests in, and it is on record that for weeks on end he lived on the premises at the Brush Works in

Loughborough working almost night and day. Some would say that for an Irishman this was not only noteworthy, but a wonderful example of loyalty to his adopted country. His loss in so far as WG Bagnall Limited was concerned was to have significant consequences. Good was succeeded by Miles Beever, and Ian T Morrow became deputy managing director of the Brush Group; Sir Ronald Matthews remained chairman.

As a direct result of Good's death the only tangible connection between the Brush and Heenan & Froude groups no longer existed, as he was the common denominator. Nevertheless for a few years Brush Bagnall Traction Limited survived as a joint marketing company, with Bagnall benefiting from the mechanical parts orders for most of the locomotives built. The two companies therefore continued to work together as though nothing had changed, although as was the case before, the entire share capital of Brush Bagnall Traction Limited, amounting to 25,000 £1 shares, was held by Brush. Here it is perhaps worth discussing the continuing story of Brush Bagnall Traction Limited and until its demise as such. In late 1955 Brush decided to end the formal joint arrangement and on 19 December that year the name of the Company was changed to Brush Traction Limited, and at that time WA Smyth

Mention has been made several times in these pages of the good business the firm did over many years in the supply of spare and replacement boilers. This picture of a not untypical example posed for its official photograph in the Erecting Shop, clearly illustrates that in some cases it was not just a boiler supplied, but complete will many fittings including in this particular case a smokebox and ashpan. Order number 6543 of July 1951, a spare for the Jodhpur State Railway T Class engines, large metre-gauge 2-6-2 side tanks built in 1925 and 1926 by Nasmyth Wilson. The boiler supplied however was of Class T/2, a superheated version. Bagnall had earlier built engines of both classes for the Rohilkund & Kumaon and Burma Railways.

and EW Marten left the board. Shortly afterwards on 16 January 1956, the Brush representative James Calderwood left the board of WG Bagnall Limited. A couple of years earlier on the 6 December 1951, Harry Davies, the general manager at Stafford, had been elected a board member of WG Bagnall Limited. Despite these formal changes close collaboration continued between the two companies. Before leaving the Brush connection it is worth mentioning that in April 1957 the Brush Group, along with all its subsidiaries, was acquired by the Hawker Siddeley Group Limited, although it remained largely independent. Today what has for many years been the principal Brush business of designing and manufacturing electrical machines and transformers, along with the more recent business of locomotives, remains in operation at the Falcon Works in Loughborough, still under the Brush name, and as a part of the FKI Engineering Group.

The board of directors of WG Bagnall Limited then consisted of:

Charles Loraine Hill chairman
(chairman Heenan & Froude Group - in succession to Alan Good).
WA Smyth managing director.
Francis James Fielding
(managing director Heenan & Froude Group).
Alexander Chetwyne Hayes
(secretary Heenan & Froude Group).
Ernest William Marten
(managing director Associated Locomotive Equipment Limited).
Harry Davies general manager
Norman Alfred Stokes secretary/accountant

The principal members of staff were: Sydney Ridgway works manager; Harold Shaw buyer; Vic Betteley

Company letter heading from the period under review in this Chapter. The three motifs to the top right are, left to right: Federation of British Industry; National Scheme for Disabled Men; Engineering Allied Employers National Federation.

contracts engineer; George Brown chief estimator; Jim Webberley chief draughtsman. And the principal assistants in the various functions: Stan Ponting buying; Les Brown accountancy; John Cartlidge contracts; Arthur Woollams works management; Bill Brooks drawing office; E Parkin progress; Bernard Lunt personnel. The Shop Foremen consisted of: JM Durber fitting & erecting; Ben Lee machine; Alf Homer pattern; Charlie Burghall boiler; George Carless foundry; Eric Williams electrical; Bill Pittard tool room; Bill Monaghan paint; Bert Lowe millwrights; Jack Brownsword smithy; Albert Appleton stores and Des Ponting welding technologist. In April 1956, the Company's London office was moved from the Brush offices at St James Square, to Imperial House, Dominion Street London EC2.

By 1954 orders for steam locomotives were getting few and far between so it is perhaps best to discuss them first. The last member of the family of narrow-gauge saddle tank engines so typical of the firm's products since the days of Ernest Baguley left the works in November 1953 - although on this occasion with a normal, rather than a circular firebox. Manufacturer's number 3051, it was a 7x12in cylinder 0-4-2 on 2ft 5½in gauge. The customer was the United Africa Company Limited with offices in London and the engine was destined for the Huleries du Congo Belge, for use at the Alberta Estates in the Belgian Congo; this was a Unilever Company with a palm fruit plantation near Leopoldville. The engine was painted green, lettered HCB, and shipped fully erected via Liverpool at a cost of £4,519 free-on-board; some difference from

The last of the long-line. This locomotive, number 3051 of 1953, for the Belgian Congo, was the last member of the small narrow-gauge saddle tank locomotives built. A generic type that more than any other design of the builder typifies a Castle Engine Works locomotive, with an unmistakable likeness going back over 60 years.

Another view of number 3051, in this case outside the Erecting Shop ready for steam testing prior to finish painting. Notice the fitter undertaking some minor adjustments.
(Peter Dyer)

the few hundred pounds some of its predecessors had cost! This locomotive was a repeat order of one sent to the Alberta Estate some years earlier, number 2890 of June 1949, but in that case the wheel arrangement was just four-coupled wheels with no trailing truck; it also cost less at £1,949 free-on-board.

Manufacturer's number 3052 was a small two-foot gauge 0-4-0 side tank with 7¼x12in cylinders and a circular firebox boiler, being in fact almost a side tank version of the engine just mentioned. It was also the last locomotive built with a circular firebox boiler, although two spare boilers for the same customer were the last

boilers of this type built. This was the fourth engine of this design sent to India for the Visakhapatnam Port Trust; it was despatched fully erected on 3 December 1953. The earlier engines were numbers 2495 and 2496 of July 1933, followed by number 2541 of December 1935; in the case of all these locomotives the orders were placed by the Company's Indian agents McLeod, Russell & Company. In January 1977 one of the authors saw all four of these engines, three of which were in steam and in use hauling specially designed wagons that carried iron ore skips. The skips were loaded with ore from main-line railway wagons and then transhipped on

SALT RIVER, number 3056 of 1954, the last of the numerous 14in cylinder four-wheel saddle tanks, in this case modified to suit 3ft 6in gauge and fitted with vacuum brake equipment and South African Railway couplers. New to Salt River Power Station in the Cape Province of South Africa. This locomotive has been preserved at a working railway museum at Epping in Cape Town.

the narrow-gauge to the harbour at Visakhapatnam. This port is on the east coast of India and the ore was shipped to iron and steel works in other countries. These small engines continued to be used on this operation for a few more years but they had fallen out of use by the mid 1980s, and despite attempts to sell them to enthusiasts in this country, nothing has transpired ~ see page 377.

In July 1951 Merz McLellan, as consulting engineers for the a new power station in the Cape Province of South Africa, the Salt River Power Station, ordered one of the standard design of nominal 14in cylinder 0-4-0 saddle tanks on 3ft 6in gauge. Actually the engine built, manufacturer's number 3056, had 14½x22in cylinders, was named SALT RIVER, but not despatched until 7 April 1954, which helps to illustrate how busy the Company was at this particular time, and despite the contract delivery being 18 months after the order was placed. As this was the first engine of this size built for some time the design was slightly modified with, for example, more rounded edges on the cab roof and more extensive use of welding for the plate work, rather than rivets as used before. It was also fitted with South African Railways type centre couplers and equipment to operate vacuum train brakes; the cost was £7,662 free-on-board. A particularly interesting order placed in August 1951 was one by Sellick Nicholls & Company Limited for a 0-4-0 saddle tank locomotive,

the specification calling for an extremely restricted overall height. The engine was to operate on the railway system at Par Harbour in Cornwall and was a repeat order of one supplied in September 1937, number 2572 JUDY; the overall height was restricted to 7ft 6in as the engines had to pass under a very low bridge that the took the harbour lines under the Great Western Railway main line at Par. The two engines had 10x16in cylinders and 2ft 9¼in diameter wheels and were fitted with Bagnall-Price valve gear, and in the case of the second one, number 3058 ALFRED, it was the last engine so fitted and was despatched on 15 January 1954. These two locomotives have achieved immortality in the writings of the late and lamented Reverend W Awdrey with his well-known children's books in the *Thomas The Tank Engine* series. Both passed into preservation when no longer needed at Par Harbour, and ALFRED has been known to masquerade as Awdrey's BEN in more recent times touring preserved railways in the south-west ~ see page 413.

The National Coal Board (NCB) ordered more of the 16x24in cylinder 0-6-0 saddle tanks for collieries in North Staffordshire, along with one for the Leicestershire area. In late 1951 and early the following year two were ordered, one for Florence Colliery at Longton and another for Sneyd Colliery at Burslem, and they were despatched respectively on 29 January 1954 to Florence Colliery, manufacturers number 3059

ALFRED, number 3058 of 1954, sister to JUDY discussed in Chapter 9, and the last locomotive fitted with Bagnall-Price valve gear. Photograph taken outside the Erecting Shop and prior to finish painting.

This is one of the later 16in cylinder 0-6-0 saddle tanks for the National Coal Board, in this case number 3059 of 1954, which had been new to Florence Colliery in Stoke-on-Trent, as FLORENCE No 2. Photograph taken at Cadley Hill Colliery near Swadlingcote on 24 April 1976, where the engine had migrated in January that year, and following a new coat of paint. Notice the Giesl oblong exhaust ejector chimney; when fitted to this and two similar locomotives at Florence, it was reckoned it enabled them to haul two empty wagons more, around 16 tons, on a long uphill gradient between the colliery and the main-line exchange sidings. This locomotive has survived into preservation on the Foxfield Railway, south of Stoke and not far from where it originally worked.

FLORENCE No 2, and on 10 February 1954 to Sneyd, number 3060 No 4. Number 3061 was despatched to Rawdon Colliery in Leicestershire in October 1954, followed by number 3075 to Berry Hill Colliery in November 1954. The final two were ordered in February 1954, numbers 3077 and 3078, and although intended for Hem Heath Colliery at Trentham in Stoke-on-Trent, which was being extensively developed at the time, in fact they went to nearby Stafford Colliery in June and July 1955 respectively. One more engine of this type was laid down to a stock order on 20 February 1954, allocated manufacturer's number 3089 it was never completed. However, some parts were made, including the boiler, and these were eventually sold to the NCB North Staffordshire Area as spares. On

average these later 16in cylinder locomotives cost around £9,500 each and it is nice to record that two of them have survived into preservation.

In January 1956 the Company delivered a very neat 2-6-2 side tank of a completely new design to the Natal Sugar Estates in Natal, South Africa. Built to suit a track gauge of 2ft 0½in the engine had 12x16in cylinders, a 2ft 7in coupled wheel diameter and a 5ft 10in fixed wheelbase. This was a very modern design with Walschaerts valve gear and a steel firebox, boiler pressure 180psi; electric lighting and a spark arresting chimney were fitted and the engine was designed to traverse curves of one and a half chains radius. Water-softening equipment was fitted and while it was originally intended to fit piston valves, in the event slide valves were used. The Natal Estate railway system was one of the longest sugar estate railways in the province and at the time the locomotive was delivered consisted of some 75 miles; there were gradients as steep as 1 in 50, one of which was three miles long. The manufacturer's number allocated was 3090 and the engine was named CAMPBELL; it was despatched on 25 January which was a commendable achievement as it was only ordered on 16 September the previous year, especially when one bears in mind the design work necessary. The engine was named after WA Campbell, the son of Sir Marshall Campbell, the founder of the estate. The order was placed by the agents A&H MacNay Limited and the cost £14,588 free-on-board.

There is an interesting story concerning CAMPBELL and one of the authors involvement with it. The engine was being steam tested at Stafford one day when lunch time intervened, and he was left in charge whilst his seniors partook of their refreshment, having first left strict instructions as to how they wanted to find the water level, steam pressure and the fire when they returned an hour later. It was with some trepidation that he went about looking after his charge - he was only an 18 year old apprentice at the time - as this was the first occasion he had been left in sole charge of a steam locomotives which was actually in steam! However, it was with much relief that all was found to be well at the conclusion of the lunch break, as he went off for his somewhat delayed refreshments.

WA Smyth was extremely enthusiastic on the virtues of fireless locomotives and he went to considerable efforts to promote their use. We saw in the last Chapter that the Company had some success with its four-wheel fireless design in the immediate post-war years, and Smyth attempted to build on this success. He had a rather nice brochure produced as late as December 1959 specifically covering the fireless designs the Company had built, and it included extracts of letters from satisfied customers. He also wrote several articles

The penultimate conventional steam locomotive built at Stafford, number 3090 CAMPBELL, new in 1956 and a direct result of the managing director, WA Smyth, visiting South Africa. This view shows the engine after unloading from the ship at Durban, on a South African Railway flat-wagon for its journey to the Natal Sugar Estates at Mount Edgecombe. Notice the overall dimensions chalked on the bunker, while some wag had added under the name plate 'The Campbells are Coming'!

Last of the fireless locomotives built was this one, number 3121 of 1955, to the earlier design but with a modified cab based on the firm's diesel-mechanical locomotive designs of the time. New to English Clays at its Plympton Works near Plymouth, this photograph was taken on 8 September 1972, by which time the locomotive was spare to a diesel.

for a range of journals, for example *British Engineering* in January 1954; *The Steam Engineer* in April 1954 and *Mine & Quarry Engineering* in September 1956. As events turned out only one more order for a fireless locomotive came the firm's way when in December 1955 English Clays Lovering Pochin Company Limited ordered one. This was another of the standard four-wheel design, for use at its Marsh Mills Drying Works at Plympton near Plymouth. The only difference from the earlier examples was an almost completely enclosed cab which rather interestingly used the same window designs as the contemporary diesels. The manufacturer's number was 3121 with delivery in April 1957; the cost £9,993. This locomotive survives today ostensibly in preservation, although it is in a pretty rough condition having had little or no work undertaken on it.

Last of the long line of steam locomotives came in January 1956 when the Mysore Iron & Steel Works ordered a repeat of its earlier engines, another of the magnificent two-foot gauge 2-8-2 tender engines for use on the so called tramways at its Bhadravati iron and steel works in Mysore. With manufacturer's number 3126 and running number 15, it was despatched on 15 July 1957 and cost £21,120. Some time after this engine was delivered the ingenious people at the Mysore works,

which later became known as the Visvesvaraya Iron & Steel Works after its founder, managed to construct another engine of this type, which took the logical fleet No 16. Over the years the company had ordered considerable quantities of spares, both to keep the other engines running, as well as providing a float for maintenance purposes; they included a complete boiler, cylinders, wheel-sets and motion parts, along with many other items. With the parts on hand a new locomotive was constructed and notwithstanding how many priority parts they had, the feat of actually building a locomotive was no small achievement. One of the authors can testify from personal observation what a splendid job had been made as the engine was undistinguishable from its sisters. There is no evidence that any main-frames were ever supplied as spares from Stafford, or even just frame plates, or indeed any specific tender parts. Hence the conclusion has to be that the frames, the complete tender along with many other parts must have been made in their entirety locally. The workshops at Bhadravati were well equipped but at the expense of repetition, and despite the items on-hand, the actual building of a complete locomotive and tender to such a high standard was a wonderful achievement. The completion of number 3126 was not the end of steam locomotive activity at

Last steam locomotive of a long and noble line covering a period of 81 years, number 3126 of 1957.
This was another of the magnificent Mysore Iron & Steel Works two-foot gauge 2-8-2 tender engines, en-route from the limestone
quarries at Bhandigund and passing another of the class outward-bound with empty wagons; 6 February 1978. One of the authors
was travelling on the outward-bound train, hauled by fleet No 11 - Bagnall 2903 - and it was the return run of this trip that is
described in Chapter Twelve.

the Castle Engine Works, as much work was still undertaken in supplying spare parts, rebuilding and repairing exiting locomotives, but before discussing this work it is time to return to the progress being made on designing and building diesel locomotives. An interesting interlude is nevertheless worth a paragraph first.

In 1953 the company acquired for preservation one of its early locomotives. Between 1896 and 1922 the Cliffe Hill Granite Company of Markfield in Leicestershire had purchased nine Bagnall locomotives for a two-foot gauge system serving its works and quarries. Changing patterns of quarrying and transport resulted in the railway system gradually closing down from just after the last war, until final closure of the remaining sections in 1948. Not only locomotives, but wagons and track-work had been supplied over the

years, and the Fitzmaurice and Preston families, both involved in the management of the company, became quite friendly with Gordon Bagnall and Ernest Baguley. In fact Baguley, a keen cyclist, sometimes called at the works when on holiday and cycling in the area as the original railway equipment and locomotives had been supplied from Stafford. Fortunately many of the locomotives were not scrapped at that time the system closed, but were just laid aside, and this came to the notice of Harry Davies, the general manager, who thought it would be good idea to bring one of the engines back to Stafford. It could then serve as a sort of memorial to all the locomotives that had been built at the Castle Engine Works, and of course the men who had designed and built them. Needless to say WA Smyth was in full agreement and in negotiation with the Cliff Hill Company, which was more than happy to see

Two pictures of ISABEL, the first in the condition it arrived from the Cliffe Hill, and the second after restoration by the apprentices mounted on a plinth in the works yard. (left-hand photograph Peter Dyer)

one of its faithful little locomotives saved, an agreement was reached to donate one of them. The engine chosen was the oldest survivor, ISABEL, manufacturer's number 1491 of 1897. ISABEL was a 7in cylinder 0-4-0 saddle tank with a circular firebox boiler and Baguley valve gear, typical of the firm's products in its early days. It was an extremely fitting choice and the engine arrived back at Stafford in March 1953. Cosmetically restored by the apprentices, ISABEL, which took its name from the daughter of Peter Preston, the manager of the quarry, was mounted on a plinth in the works yard late in 1953 and a cast-plaque was mounted alongside. This paid tribute to what was claimed to be the 3,000 locomotives built by the Company and the men who had designed and built them. The actual figure was in fact much less than 3,000 (nearer 2,000), as somebody decided to conveniently forget all the numbers in the works list that were either not locomotives, or had not been used - they just used the highest number in the list.

The decision to design and develop a range of diesel-mechanical shunting locomotives was taken locally late in 1952, and discussed formally at a meeting of the board on 9 February the following year. Note that this was before the death of Alan Good, although it was known he was extremely unwell, and perhaps in anticipation that he might not survive. WA Smyth was ever conscious of the firm's future prospects should the link between Heenan & Froude and Brush be lost, and had long wanted John Alcock off the board. Alcock

was absent from the meeting, out of the country in Africa at the time, and the decision in effect, forced his resignation on his return. Jim Fielding was delegated the difficult job of telling him.

The design team under Jim Webberley and his assistant Bill Brooks started work on a series of diesel-mechanical shunting locomotive designs. They were assisted by GT Todhunter, who had some knowledge and experience of diesel locomotives with mechanical transmissions; he was specifically employed at the time to act as a technical assistant in this area. This range of locomotives was first introduced to the trade press in January 1954, articles appearing in *The Railway Gazette*, issue dated 15 January 1954, and *The Oil Engine*, issue dated January 1954; there were also trade advertisements and a neat and concise brochure. Two basic types were envisaged, an 0-4-0 and an 0-6-0, both with jackshaft and side rod drive and in the case of the 0-4-0 in engine horsepowers of 75,100 and 150, and in the case of the 0-6-0 150, 200 and 240. Mention was also made that locomotives of any wheel arrangement or power could be made for any track-gauge from two-foot upwards. The type of diesel engines quoted were from the McLaren M series range and transmission via a Vulcan-Sinclair fluid coupling and a constant mesh gearbox, although mention was also made that a hydraulic transmission could be fitted if desired. In the event it was some years before the Company used a hydraulic transmission in a locomotive; all the diesel-mechanical locomotives had an epycyclic gearbox.

INDUSTRIAL DIESEL LOCOMOTIVES

W.G. Bagnall LTD.
DIESEL MECHANICAL LOCOMOTIVES

W. G. BAGNALL LTD. CASTLE ENGINE WORKS, STAFFORD

Front page of a publicity brochure dated November 1953 to promote the new range of diesel-mechanical locomotives. However, as at this date the actual designs were not finalised, when built the locomotives differed in many respects from this artist's impression. Similar impressions appeared in trade press advertisements and about the same time Tri-ang, a well established supplier of model railways, introduced into its range of OO gauge equipment an 0-4-0 dock-shunter which would seem to have been based on the external lines of this artists impression.

Like Alan Good, Ernest Marten had also undertaken a world tour, in his case in the summer of 1951 visiting Australia, New Zealand, India, Pakistan and Egypt on behalf of both the Heenan & Froude and Brush groups, making some useful contacts. This was especially so in New Zealand and in October 1953 WA Smyth also visited New Zealand, in his case on behalf of both WG Bagnall and Brush Bagnall Traction. At this time the New Zealand Government Railways (NZGR) were investing heavily in diesel traction to replace steam, initially on shunting duties, and already had some Drewry Car Company (actually built under licence by the Vulcan Foundry) and Hunslet built diesel-mechanical shunting locomotives in service, with more on order. Locomotives from both these suppliers were fitted with the well proven in rail traction Gardner 8L3 engine, an eight cylinder in-line four-stroke unit rated at 204 horsepower. Smyth was able to develop the already established relationships with the officials of the NZGR and this proved to have been well worth while soon after his return. He also arranged the appointment of Russell Searle Limited of Wellington to act as agents to represent WG Bagnall Limited in New Zealand. As events turned out it was not long before

View inside the New Erecting Shop looking north. On the left are the frames with the National diesel engine and final-drive already in position, for the first diesel-mechanical locomotive, number 3076, new in 1955 for the Tasman Pulp & Paper Company in New Zealand. Notice the battery along side the engine to enable it to turn-over for test purposes. Beyond are the frames for the first of 10 similar locomotives, in this case for the New Zealand Government Railways, number 3079. At the far end is one of the Brush Bagnall 0-4-0 diesel-electric locomotives for the Steel Company of Wales, while on the extreme left is a box-section side-member, part of a bogie for one of the Brush Bagnall A1A-A1A main-line locomotives for Ceylon.

Searle obtained an order for Bagnall when the Tasman Pulp & Paper Company Limited placed an order for what became the first of the new range of diesel-mechanical locomotives to be built at Stafford. The order was placed on 10 December 1953 and the locomotive was for use at a paper mill at Kawerau on the North Island.

A couple of interesting points are worth a mention at this juncture. In the first instance in making friends with Russell Searle WA Smyth arranged for Searle's son Brian to come to this country and spend a few months in the summer of 1955 undergoing engineering training at the Castle Engine Works. Secondly, on his return from New Zealand Smyth called at Ceylon where he

was able to both renew his personal acquaintance with the country and the friends and colleagues from his time there, but also on behalf of Brush and Bagnall to report on the performance of the main-line locomotives that had been supplied. His report covered both the Brush Bagnall diesel-electrics and the Bagnall steam locomotives all of which were, by and large, operating satisfactorily bearing in mind the technical issues with the diesels outlined in then last Chapter.

The design of the diesel-mechanical locomotives was a neat and tidy one, but nothing particularly outstanding from a technical point of view; in fact they employed the already well established power train used in the Drewry Car Company designs. The arrangement

First of the post-war diesel-mechanical locomotives, number 3076, posed for its official photograph and prior to finish painting. The neat and tidy lines of the design are noticeable, as is the distinctive front-end surround for the radiator, a hallmark of the majority of the locomotives in the range.

of the main frame, cross stretchers and buffer beams was based on steam locomotive practice using rivets and fitted bolts. The frames plates and stretchers were 1½in thick mild steel and the buffer beams 2½in thick. In the case of the first locomotive the track gauge was the New Zealand standard of 3ft 6in, despite which the frames were inside the wheels, and central drawgear was fitted; wheel diameter was 3ft 3¾in and the wheelbase ten feet. The engine was a National M4AA6 six

cylinder in-line four-stroke unit developing 240bhp @ 1500rpm, driving via a Vulcan-Sinclair type 23 fluid coupling to a Self Changing Gears (SCG) Wilson CA5 air operated five-speed epicyclic gearbox. The drive thence was via a SCG RF11 sliding dog-clutch final drive located behind the trailing axle, a jackshaft and conventional side rods. This arrangement of power train with the exception of different engines, along with the size and capacity of the other components,

Photograph looking south in the New Erecting Shop in late 1955 with the New Zealand Railway diesel-mechanical locomotives in various stages of construction. To the bottom right is one of the two Brush Bagnall 0-6-0 diesel-electrics for the NCB at Cwm Colliery.

remained standard for all the diesel-mechanical locomotives the Company built, which eventually totalled 43. The locomotive had roller bearing axle boxes, under slung laminated leaf springs, manganese steel horn-block and axle-box liners and both a straight air brake, and provision to operate the automatic air train brakes, as standard on the NZGR; the air was provided by twin belt driven Westinghouse air compressors. The completed locomotive could traverse curves of three chains radius and the speed in the five gears on level track were respectively: 4.3; 7.6; 11.4; 17.6 and 32.9mph; in first gear it was capable of hauling 400 tons on a gradient of 1 in 100. Allocated manufacturer's number 3076, despatch from Stafford was on 14 September 1955 and the cost £15,445 free-on-board; it remained in use until 1985.

Hard on the heels of this order and also as a direct result of Smyth's trip to New Zealand was one placed on 21 May 1954 when the High Commissioner for New Zealand ordered 10 locomotives for the NZGR. To all intents and purposes these locomotives were identical to the Tasman one, with the same National M4AA6 engine rated at 240 horsepower. The manufacturer's numbers allocated were 3079 to 3088, and the locomotives were despatched between July and October 1956 with the NZGR numbers 240 to 249. Prior to despatch of the first locomotive a demonstration was arranged at the Castle Engine Works on Tuesday 17 July for representatives of the Crown Agents and the New Zealand Government, Messrs A Campbell and H Elder respectively, along with other invited guests including potential users of the type of locomotive. The party afterwards repaired to the Swan Hotel where they were entertained by WA Smyth and Harry Davies. Designated NZGR class DS (later DSa) they cost £14,350 each free-on-board Liverpool. Although the NZGR had been well pleased with the performance of the Gardner engine in its earlier Drewry and Hunslet locomotives it was felt that something more powerful was required, hence the choice of the National,

First member of 10 0-6-0 diesel-mechanical locomotives supplied to the New Zealand Government Railway in 1956, although the last numerically; manufacturer's numbers 3079 to 3088, NZGR Nos 240 to 249. The locomotive is being unloaded from the ship at Wellington, probably in early September 1956; it left Stafford on 23 July and is recorded as entering service in September.

An example of the four-wheel design of diesel-mechanical locomotive, of which in the event only seven were built, all in one batch for the New Zealand Government Railway. This one is manufacturer's number 3108 of January 1957, NZGR No 152, outside the New Erecting Shop finish painted and ready for delivery. The small plate on the rearmost engine compartment records the firm's New Zealand agent, Russell Searle Limited.

although it has to be added that in view of the ongoing relationships within the Brush and Heenan & Froude groups, the use of an engine from one of the group members was an issue. These locomotives were intended for shunting operations around Wellington and they had comparatively long lives, but in view of the rather poor performance of the National engine they were all re-engined in 1965 and 1966. In this exercise the opportunity was taken to increase the power of the locomotives by replacing the mechanical transmission consisting of the fluid flywheel and epicyclic gearbox, by a Twin Disc torque converter, and the engine chosen was the Caterpillar D343T rated at 304bhp @ 2,000rpm. Despite the higher power output the weight of the locomotives would have been reduced had not ballast weights been added to compensate. Incidentally in 1964 the Tasman locomotive had also been similarly re-engined with a Caterpillar unit and fitted with a hydraulic transmission.

The poor performance of the National engines was the subject of some quite acrimonious correspondence between the NZGR and Bagnall, and whilst to some extent Bagnall had been obliged to recommend the National engine in view of the ongoing connections with the Brush/ABOE group, it resulted in not inconsiderable embarrassment. This was particularly damaging as the Company was only just embarking on the field of diesel-mechanical locomotives, and even more so in establishing a New Zealand market. Despite the issue to a large extent being one between the NZGR and the National Company, as the main contractor Bagnall took the brunt of it. After the delivery of the first locomotive, which as it happened was the last numerically, number 3088 as NZGR No 249 - it left Stafford on 23 July 1956 and entered service on 28 September 1956 - it was not long before engine problems manifested themselves. The engines suffered fuel dilution of the lubricating oil and a loss of oil pressure due to surging of the oil in the sump when the locomotive was moving. This resulted in the remainder of the locomotives not being accepted by the inspecting engineer on behalf of the NZGR, causing acute space problems at Stafford. Several modifications were eventually agreed between the parties, but it was not until these had been implemented that deliveries recommenced, and the last two locomotives did not leave Stafford until 30 October.

It is worth mentioning that the Bagnall locomotives

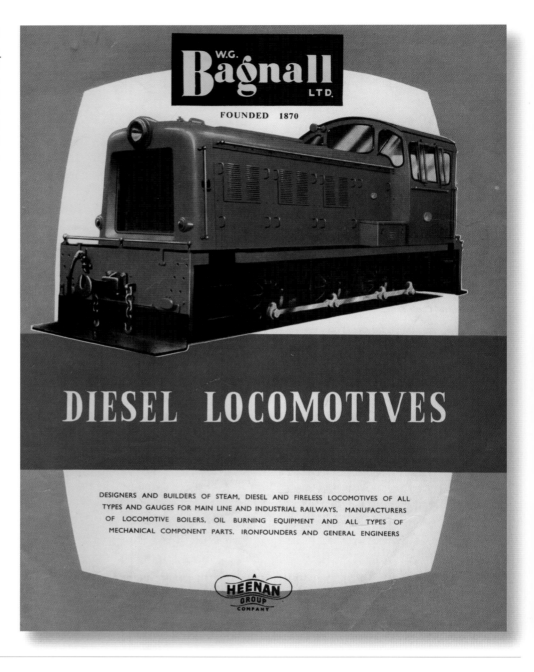

were not alone in experiencing problems with the National engines, as for the same reason regarding power output the locomotives supplied by both Hunslet and Drewry at about the same time were also powered by National engines with the same technical issues. The Bagnall locomotives remained in use shunting in and around Wellington and in some cases for their entire lives of upwards to 35 years. A few of them later migrated to other parts of the country and were engaged in slightly less arduous duties, and later still two of them were sold into industrial use, whilst another has been

preserved. Despite the shortcomings of the original engines these Bagnall locomotives were perhaps the most successful of a variety of 0-6-0 diesel shunting locomotives supplied to the NZGR over the years, and by a variety of builders. Several of them remained in service longer than the majority of their contempories, albeit after the new engines and transmissions were fitted, and some even outlasted other builders locomotives designed for similar duties delivered several years later.

Two more locomotives of basically the same type

The first members of the new range of diesel-mechanical locomotives for the home market were ordered by the National Coal Board in July 1955. Two six-wheelers, numbers 3092 and 3092, originally for a new colliery being sunk at Lea Hall near Rugeley in South-Staffordshire, but as this pit was not ready to start production when the locomotives were ready, they went to Norton Colliery in Stoke-on-Trent. This is the second one, NORTON 2D, with the engine compartment doors removed to show the National diesel engine and other equipment. Notice that the rear buffer beam is thinner than the front one, an issue discussed in the adjacent text.

were supplied to Wilsons (New Zealand) Portland Cement Company Limited, for use at its plant at Portland near Whangarei on the North Island; they too, were ordered via the agents Russell Searle. These two were manufacturer's numbers 3132 despatched on 6 February 1958, and number 3144 despatched on 6 May the same year; they cost £18,716 each free-on-board Liverpool. Despite the problems being experienced by NZGR with the National engines these two locomotives were fitted with the same engine, but they too, soon had to have replacement engines fitted. In this case however the lower powered Gardner 8L3 engine was chosen rated at 204 horsepower, but the transmission system remained the same. As fleet Nos 10 and 11 the two locomotives remained in use at Portland until 1990, and although both are still in existence and on the face of it preserved, they have had their engines removed for use elsewhere which illustrates both the adaptability and longevity of the Gardner engine.

There was another order from New Zealand, again for the NZGR and on this occasion an 0-4-0, and as events unfolded the only four-wheel version of the

diesel-mechanical designs the Company built. Seven locomotives were ordered on 1 September 1955, once again via the agents Russell Searle Limited. It was the practice of the NZGR to station small locomotives which it called tractors, and not locomotives, at wayside stations around the country to undertake occasional shunting operations when main-line goods trains called, and it was for this type of service the Bagnall locomotives were required. The basic design and construction was the same as the six-wheel locomotives, but in this case the wheelbase was seven foot, although the wheel diameter was the same at 3ft 3¾in. However, in view of the problems being encountered with the National engines the NZGR elected not to have any more! The tried, tested and well known Gardner engine was preferred, especially as the power required of these smaller locomotives could easily be accommodated in the Gardner range. Unfortunately at the time Gardners were extremely busy, with the result that delivery could not be guaranteed to meet the required timescales. Gardners had long standing arrangements with a several builders of heavy goods road vehicles and buses, which for obvious reasons they did not want to upset; for example the two well known and long established Cheshire based builders with works at Sandbach - Fodens Limited and ERF. Nevertheless a compromise was suggested; two of the seven locomotives to be fitted with Gardner engines, but at an extended delivery timescale, and the other five with McLaren engines. McLaren remember, was another member of the Brush/ABOE Group, and this offer was accepted. As it turned out the delivery of the locomotives with the Gardner engines was only a few weeks behind the last of those with the McLarens. The locomotives were given the NZGR classification TR, and the five with McLaren engines were despatched between 1 January and 22 February 1957, manufacturer's numbers 3106 to 3110 and running numbers were 150 to 154. The two with the Gardner engines were despatched on 11 and 22 March the same year, numbers 3104 and 3105, running numbers 155 and 156.

In the case of the McLaren engine the one selected was the M6, a six-cylinder in-line four-stroke rated at 155bhp @ 1200 rpm. The Gardner engine was the 6L3, also a six-cylinder in-line four-stroke, rated at 153bhp @ 1200rpm. In both cases the transmission was via a Vulcan-Sinclair fluid coupling like the six-wheelers, but in this case a smaller four-speed SCG epicyclic gearbox of type SE4, and an RF11 final drive with jackshaft and side rods. The weight in working order was 20½ tons and the speed in the four gears respectively: 3.25; 5.5; 8.25 and 13.2 mph. Unlike the larger locomotives there was no provision for operating train brakes and the locomotives cost £11,138 for those with Gardner engines, and £11,399 for those with the McLaren engines, in each case free-on-board Liverpool. Perhaps surprisingly the locomotives with Gardner engines cost less than the ones with the McLaren. Unfortunately like the National engines the McLarens were not a complete success and they too were eventually replaced with the Gardner 6L3 in 1974 and 1975. The locomotives gave excellent service otherwise and it was only the gradual closure of goods facilities at the stations where they were used that saw their demise. Apart from two that have been preserved the others were scrapped between 1989 and 2002.

Before leaving New Zealand it is worth mentioning that early in 1957 the firm responded to a tender request from the NZGR for 18 400-500 horsepower Bo-Bo diesel-electric locomotives to be delivered in 1958 and 1959. Out of 12 firms tendering Bagnall was one of only five that were compliant, offering a locomotive without any direct financial input from Brush, although it was proposed to use Brush electrical equipment along with a choice of engines from the National, Paxman, McLaren and Rolls Royce ranges. The tender price of between £41,000 and £42,000 was however the highest - but only £1,000 higher than the English Electric tender - and the order went to the British Thompson-Houston Limited (BTH). The locomotives, delivered in 1959, became NZGR class DSc, and were assembled by Clayton Equipment Limited with a Rolls Royce engine and Associated Electrical Industries (AEI) electrical equipment, as BTH and AEI were associated companies at that time - the contract price was £30,816 per locomotive. Later locomotives of a similar type were built in New Zealand.

An interesting sideline regarding McLarens is worth a note here. The chief designer at the firm's Hunslet works in Leeds was Geoffrey Howard, who had served his time at the Castle Engine Works. When Harold Wood started his apprenticeship in August 1935 he met Geoff of his first day, and later worked with him on the marking-off tables. Although Geoff was still serving his apprenticeship he was older than Harold and the foreman put them to work together informing Harold that Geoff would tell him everything he needed to know and do; later they were both employed in the drawing office. Geoff's father, Thomas, since 1905 had been in charge of the LMS locomotive shed at Stafford, but he died in 1930 when quite young with Geoff was still at school; being well known to WS Edwards, his son was taken on as an apprentice. For all the criticism that might be levied at Edwards as a hard employer, he was ever generous in situations like this. The two lost touch with each other during the war when Geoff went to work for Henry Meadows in Wolverhampton, as he wanted to get involved with diesel engines, but they met up again years later. By this time, 1960, Geoff had moved to the McLaren works in Leeds - remember that at one period both companies came under the ABOE umbrella - and Harold was visiting as Brush were considering using a new range of McLaren engines in locomotives.

There is one other issue concerning the locomotives

supplied to New Zealand. When the inspecting engineer came to accept the smaller 0-4-0 locomotives on behalf of the NZGR, it was discovered that they were slightly heavier than the weight agreed in the specification - about 10 cwt - for which there was a penalty clause. However when the time came for the final payment to be authorised, the chief mechanical engineer of the NZGR considered that in view of the excellent relationships his staff had been able to establish with the people at Stafford, especially concerning the problems with the earlier 0-6-0 locomotives, the penalty clause should not be implemented. And indeed it was not.

The design staff at Stafford was very proud of the neat and smart lines of the range of diesel-mechanical locomotives, and a lot of trouble was taken in this respect. When they were compared with the much more box-like lines of the diesel-electric locomotives the contrast was very noticeable, particularly the arrangement of the front grill and radiator cover with its pleasing and curvaceous lines embodying the headlamp. This was the brainchild of Jim Webberley the chief draughtsman and consisted of a one piece iron casting; it was designed as a casting to help the overall weight distribution of the locomotives with the heavy final drive located behind the trailing axle. Even so, with the first two locomotives built for use in this country, manufacturer's numbers 3092 and 3093 for the NCB at Norton Colliery in Stoke-on-Trent, it was necessary to remove the rear buffer beams and reduce their

Another of the six-wheel diesel-mechanical locomotives delivered to local collieries is the one illustrated here, manufacturer's number 3119 of September 1957, new to Hem Heath Colliery in Stoke-on-Trent, but by the time this photograph was taken on 23 April 1970, at Silverdale Colliery in nearby Newcastle-under-Lyme. This locomotive later migrated to Holditch Colliery and has survived into preservation.

This photograph illustrates one of the larger 308 horsepower six-wheel diesel-mechanical locomotives, number 3123 of December 1957. They can be identified from the 208 horsepower version by a longer engine compartment with one extra door. New to Littleton Colliery near Penkridge in South Staffordshire, the locomotive is seen here on 7 March 1970, busy shunting with a covering of late winter snow on the ground at West Cannock Colliery near Hednesford.

thickness after the completed locomotives had been weighed, to get a better weight balance. The whole issue of the weight of these locomotives caused a number of shop floor problems in experimenting to get as good a compromise as possible.

A lot of publicity surrounded the design with articles appearing in the trade press and local newspapers, and a special colour brochure was produced. Numerous photographs were taken both of the completed locomotives and while under construction. A special effort was made to congregate as many of them as possible in the new erecting shop, the pictures making the works look extremely busy; taken from the vantage point of one of the overhead cranes they were given wide circulation. This exercise was in no small measure helped by so many of the New Zealand locomotives being held back due to the engine problems.

The six-wheel diesel-mechanical locomotive adapted for standard-gauge became quite popular with the West Midlands Division of the NCB, and locomotives of basically the same design as those supplied to New Zealand were delivered to Norton (mentioned above), Stafford, Wolstanton and Hem Heath Collieries in Stoke-on-Trent, along with Lea Hall Colliery at Rugeley. Most of these locomotive had the National M4AA5 engine, a five-cylinder version rated at 208bhp @ 1500rpm, but the later ones supplied to Wolstanton

had the Gardner 8L3 engine. This was the result of exactly the same problems being encountered with the National engine as occurred in New Zealand. Although the National engines lasted longer in the NCB locomotives than they did in New Zealand, most of them were replaced in the mid 1960s, but in their case the new engine was a Ruston 4RPH four-cylinder four-stroke V form turbo-charged unit rated at 200 horsepower. The Company also introduced a more powerful six-wheeler, in this case fitted with the larger National M4AA7 engine, a seven-cylinder unit rated at 308bhp @1500 rpm. Two locomotives of this type were built, numbers 3122 and 3123, despatched in November and December 1957 respectively, one each to Hilton Main and Littleton Collieries in South Staffordshire. These two locomotives had a slightly longer overall length, with a 10, as opposed to a nine-foot wheelbase and a weight in working order of 38 tons rather than 30 tons. They can easily be recognised in photographs by one extra engine compartment door, in view of a longer engine room to accommodate the higher powered engine. Whilst on all the locomotives supplied to New Zealand the brake blocks were applied to the front of the wheels with the brake cylinder located at the rear of the locomotive, on those supplied for use in this country the brake blocks were at the rear of the wheels with the brake cylinder at the front of the

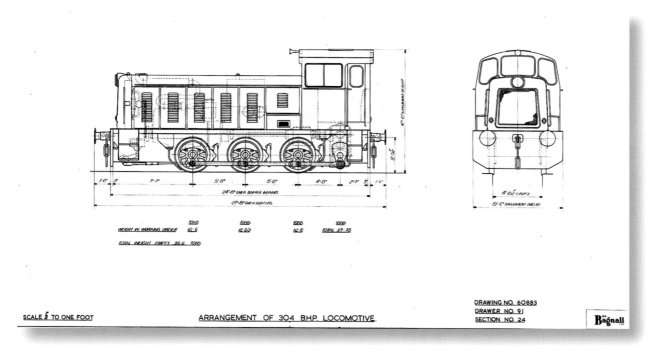

Outline drawing No 60883 illustrating the larger, 304 horsepower 0-6-0 diesel-mechanical locomotives.

A rather nice period picture of one of the 208 horsepower diesel-mechanical locomotives, manufacturer's number 3117 of May 1957, NCB No 1. This locomotive was originally ordered for use at Hem Heath Colliery at Trentham, south of Stoke-on-Trent, where a large development scheme was underway. However, as the pit was not ready for rail traffic when the locomotive was completed, it was diverted to the West Cannock Collieries at Hednesford. This picture however, taken in April 1960, is after its transfer to Hollybank Colliery at Essington. The line connecting the pit with the main-line railway exchange sidings crossed the A462 Cannock to Birmingham road at this rather delightful level crossing with its interesting signal-box. This locomotive was later transferred to Lea Hall Colliery.

Loaded on main-line railway wagons for movement to the docks are the two 0-8-0 diesel-mechanical locomotives for Iraq, manufacturer's numbers 3114 and 3115, United Cement Nos. 2401 and 2402. Shipment was to Basra and as they are recorded as despatched on 14 October 1957, this photograph was doubtless taken on or about that date. New Erecting Shop to right, Tank & Frame Shops to left.

locomotive. The reason for this was the space available at the rear of the locomotives alongside the final drive, bearing in mind the closer frame spacing due to the narrower track gauge of the New Zealand locomotives. Most of the Bagnall built diesel-mechanical locomotives built for use in this country had comparatively long lives, and three of them survive in preservation.

For service in Iraq an eight-wheel version of the diesel-mechanical locomotive was designed, three being supplied via agents Railway Mine & Plantation Equipment Limited, for use at a cement factory belonging to the United Cement Company Limited in Baghdad. The track gauge was metre and the locomotives had outside frames, fly cranks and a driving wheel diameter of three-foot; the wheelbase was 11ft 3in and the weight in working order equalled 32 tons. The order for the first two was placed on 5 September 1955 and the engine selected was, perhaps surprisingly, a National again - the M4AA6 - but in this installation

slightly de-rated to deliver 234bhp @ 1500rpm. The transmission was via a size 23 Vulcan-Sinclair fluid coupling, a SCG CA4 four-speed epicyclic gearbox and an Alfred Wiseman type 15RLGB jackshaft final drive. These locomotives had less pleasing lines than their predecessors with a much squarer engine compartment and radiator grill. The manufacturer's numbers were 3114 and 3115 and they were despatched on 15 October 1956 as U.C.C. Nos. 2401 and 2402; the cost was £17,500 each free-on-board Liverpool. A repeat order was received on 6 September 1960 and number 3205 was allocated; this locomotive differed from the earlier ones in being fitted with a Dorman 6QAT engine rated at 240bhp @ 1500 rpm, as by this time WG Bagnall Limited had become a part of the Dorman group. The Dorman engine was a six-cylinder in-line four-stroke with a turbo-charger, and at the same time two kits of parts were supplied to enable the earlier locomotives to be converted to the same Dorman power

First of the two two-foot gauge diesel-mechanical locomotives for the Rustenburg Platinum Mines in South Africa, number 3124 of December 1957, posed in the works yard for its official photographs. In this picture however, standing by the locomotive are from left to right: Jim Webberley Chief Draughtsman; Sydney Ridgway Works Manager; Stuart Keay Fitter; JM (Mac) Durber Erecting Shop Foreman.

units. This third locomotive was despatched in 1961 as U.C.C. 2403, and cost £18,000 free on board Liverpool. In March 1964, the English Electric Company, as successors to WG Bagnall Limited, supplied three sets of equipment to modify these locomotives so that they could operate vacuum braked trains. As a point of interest the original order was for three locomotives, the third one, allocated number 3116 was cancelled before work started.

Despite having taken delivery of two steam locomotives in December 1953 the Bagnall South African agents Baldwins (South Africa) Limited ordered two two-foot gauge diesel-mechanical locomotives for the Rustenburg Platinum Mines. For this customer Bagnall designed a quite neat locomotive generally following the lines and constructional features of the bigger ones, but with rather unfortunately from an aesthetic point of view, a much squarer radiator cowl with a headlamp more or less perched on top, rather than being embodied in the casing. The wheel diameter was three-foot, the wheelbase was nine-foot and the weight in working order 25 tons; the frames were of course outside and the rotating balance by fly cranks. In the case of these locomotives the engine was the trusty Gardner 8L3 rated at 204bhp @ 1,200 rpm, and the transmission was via the usual fluid coupling, a SCG CA4 four-speed epicyclic gearbox and a Wiseman 15RLGB final drive unit, thence by jackshaft and side

rods. These locomotives were capable of hauling a trailing load of 820 tons on level track and 125 tons up a 1 in 30. As manufacturer's numbers 3124 and 3125 they left Stafford on 6 and 12 December 1957 respectively, as R.P.M. Ltd Nos. 9 and 10, and the cost was £14,484 each free-on-board Liverpool. A repeat order was received in 1961, number 3204 being allocated. With the designation R.P.M. Ltd No 11, it cost £17,900 and was despatched on 31 March 1961, carriage insurance and freight paid to Durban. All three of these locomotives survive, they finished work at Rustenburg in about 1988 and have migrated to the Alfred County Railway at Port Shepstone.

In August 1955 it was announced that the Company had entered into an agreement with an Australian firm, Morrison & Bearby Limited of Newcastle in New South Wales, to act as its agents in that country. However, the agreement went beyond a pure agency as Morrison & Bearby were engineers with manufacturing facilities and it was anticipated that Bagnall design diesel-mechanical locomotives would be built at Newcastle under a form of licence agreement. Subsequent to the agreement a lot of design and manufacturing drawings were sent to Australia, including a significant amount of design work specifically with the Australian market in view. As events unfolded however, Morrison & Bearby neither sold any Stafford built locomotives in Australia, or built any under the licence agreement. Nevertheless, it

Last of the Brush Bagnall six-wheel diesel-electric locomotives that were fully erected and delivered from Stafford were two for the NCB at Cwm Colliery in South Wales. This is the second one, number 3073, in the works yard with the engine compartment doors removed to expose the National engine and other power equipment. Notice how the design of engine compartment has been modified from the earlier locomotives in an attempt to give the crew better forward vision.

remained the Bagnall agent in Australia until the Company became part of the WH Dorman group.

We must now retrace our steps somewhat to continue the story of the diesel-electric locomotives, but in doing so it is well to remember that initially at least, the arrangements with the Brush Company continued despite Alan Good's death. In May 1953 Brush Bagnall Traction Limited placed an order on Bagnall to fulfil one it had received from the NCB for two locomotives of the 0-6-0 design for use at Cwm Colliery near Llantwit Fardre in South Wales. These two, manufacturer's numbers 3073 and 3074, were completely erected, tested and despatched from Stafford. The cost for the mechanical portion and without the power equipment, but including erection testing and delivery was £8,700 each. The engine was a National R4AA6 unit, a six-cylinder in-line four-stroke rated at 400bhp @ 750 rpm, directly coupled to a Brush compound wound main generator delivering 213kW @ 425volts and 500amps, and there were two Brush series wound axle-hung and nose-suspended traction motors, one each on the leading and trailing axles. Wheel diameter was four-foot, the wheelbase was 12ft and weight in working order 50 tons. These locomotives differed from the earlier Steel Company of Wales (SCOW) examples in having the power equipment housing over the generator lowered to give a better forward vision for the crew - crew vision had been a

point of particular concern with the earlier locomotives of this general design. As No 1 and No 2 they were delivered from Stafford on 5 September and 15 November 1955 respectively, having relatively long lives at Cwm and surviving as the sole standard-gauge motive power until the pit closed in 1987; both were then scrapped. There were two more similar locomotives, numbers 3094 and 3095, but in this case only the mechanical parts were built at Stafford, the final erection taking place at Loughborough. In this case the engine was a Mirrlees TLT6 unit, a six-cylinder in-line four-stroke rated at 366bhp @ 650rpm. The mechanical parts were delivered to Brush on 31 January 1956, but as this was a Brush stock order there was no immediate end customer; in fact number 3094, after being completed was used as a demonstration locomotive. It was on loan to Moor Green Colliery in Nottinghamshire in July 1956, and was later at Coppice Colliery in Derbyshire. In the event both the locomotives were sold to Stewarts & Lloyds Limited and initially went to the ironstone mines at Rockingham near Corby; in later years they migrated to the adjacent Corby iron and steelworks where as numbers 6 and 7 in the steelworks fleet, they survived until about 1976.

There were further orders from the SCOW in 1955, eight of 0-4-0 design and three of the larger double bogie locomotives, all erected at Loughborough with

Two pictures of one of the larger horsepower Bo-Bo diesel-electric locomotives for the Steel Company of Wales, and taken 50 years apart. Manufacturer's number 3113, running number 953. The first view shows the locomotive when new and immediately after delivery, while the second was taken outside the locomotive shed at Margam on 14 August 2007. Locomotives from this batch differed from the earlier ones in the design of bogie, a heavier construction with equalising beams, although there have been some changes of bogies following two of these locomotives being scrapped. Compare the bogies under this locomotive with the photograph of an individual bogie in the last Chapter.

mechanical parts from Stafford. The four-wheelers differed from the earlier ones in having an increased fuel capacity, a second fuel tank located between the frames in front of the leading axle in an attempt to improve the weight balance; they also had roller bearing side rods as opposed to the plain bearings on the earlier locomotives. The three Bo-Bos also differed from the earlier ones in being fitted with more powerful engines and electrical equipment. In this case the engine was the Mirrlees JS6, rated at 600bhp @ 850rpm, a turbo-charged version of the J6 fitted to the earlier locomotives, with a one hour rating of 660bhp @ 875rpm, and it was these latter figures that were used in the publicity material! The continuous generator output was 322kW. The manufacturer's numbers allocated were 3111 to 3113, the running numbers 951 to 953, and in view of the higher engine output the underframes were of heavier and stronger construction, as were the bogies which embodied weight equalising beams between the axles, in total increasing the weight in working order to 90 tons. The locomotives were capable of hauling 600 tons up a 1 in 70 gradient, with a starting tractive effort of 50,000lb at 25% adhesion and a maximum speed of 28mph. In 1961, in view of the increasing train weights at the steelworks the engines were uprated to 750 horsepower, but as was the case with the other Bo-Bo locomotives they were subsequently re-engined with Rolls Royce units.

To complete the story of the SCOW fleet as far as Bagnall was concerned there was one more order, in this case for seven more Bo-Bo locomotives, but in this case with complete erection, testing and final despatch from Stafford. The numbers allocated were 3137 to 3143 and the order was placed by Brush on 22 May 1957. With this order there was a reversion to the smaller Mirrlees J6 engine rated at 515 horsepower, but with some re-design of the mechanical parts; the fuel capacity was increased from 350 to 550 gallons (as was the case with numbers 3111 to 3113) and the buffer beams were both thicker and deeper, the latter to reduce damage when the locomotives derailed, and the weight in working order increased by five tons. As SCOW Nos. 904 to 910 these locomotives cost £14,119 each complete, and were despatched to Margam in 1958. Most of the Bo-Bo locomotives supplied to the SCOW at Margam are still in use there, although most of the survivors have been fitted with replacement Rolls

Royce DV8TCE eight-cylinder V form turbo-charged engines rated at 515bhp @ 1,800rpm. Three of them have however, been completely rebuilt with Perkins CV12 3000 series V form 12 cylinder turbo-charged engines, also rated at 515bhp @ 1,800rpm, a Brush alternator and inverters replacing the generator, along with new superstructure and cabs. As mentioned in the last Chapter several of the four-wheelers survive too, fitted with replacement Rolls Royce DV8N eight-cylinder V form engines rated at 335bhp @ 1,250rpm, whilst others were converted into slave units with cabs and driving control equipment removed. In this form they were semi-permanently coupled to conventional locomotives, forming in effect 670 horsepower units. While as mentioned in the last Chapter these slave units have since been phased out of service, some have been converted into un-powered brake tenders with heavy ballast weights added to operate in tandem with other locomotives to improve brake power.

As built the later Brush Bagnall Bo-Bo locomotives for the SCOW had equipment to operate a straight air

The last batch of Brush Bagnall Bo-Bo diesel-electrics for the Steel Company of Wales, numbers 3137 to 3143, were the only bogie ones fully erected at Stafford. At the time the Brush works at Loughborough was busy with the large order for A1A-A1A Type 2 locomotives for British Railways (later Class 31), hence the decision to complete this order at Stafford. These two, numbers 3138 and 3139, are awaiting despatch standing outside the Old Erecting Shop, although they were built in the new one. In view of the axle-load of 22½ tons, they were fitted with special 'accommodation' bogies for the rail journey south, with their own bogies accompanying them on flat wagons to be re-fitted on arrival at Margam. Notice the pleasing shade of maroon as the SCOW livery at the time.

Well advanced construction in the New Erecting Shop is one of the Steel Company of Wales Bo-Bo diesel-electrics, numbers 3137 to 3143, built in their entirety at Stafford.

brake on twin match wagons, which were positioned each end of the locomotive to give increased brake force when hauling the hot metal ingot wagons. They also had equipment to enable the hot metal wagons to be uncoupled automatically by pneumatic means. This equipment served the dual purpose of keeping the hot metal ingots away from the locomotive, and saving the shunting staff having to manually uncouple them, important in view of the heat. The earlier locomotives, including some of the four-wheelers, were subsequently fitted with this equipment by the SCOW on-site at Margam. When the ingot method of steel making was replaced by continuous casting, the new hot-metal torpedo wagons were originally fitted with air brakes and the locomotives were modified to operate this equipment, but in the light of in-service problems this method has since fallen out of use and the equipment has been removed from the locomotives.

Before leaving the subject of the SCOW locomotives in is worth exploring the situation with those still in use. A visit to Margam iron and steelworks in August 2007 found seven of the double-bogie locomotives still in use and apart from the replacement engines little altered from when built; they retain all the original mechanical parts and electrical equipment although, inevitably,

there has been much swapping of parts. These locomotives are still regularly handing their design trailing loads and more, moving the enormous 450 ton hot metal torpedo wagons from the blast furnaces to the steel making plant, up gradients of 1 in 70 and round curves of seven chains radius. There are also four of the 0-4-0 locomotives, similarly little altered except for the engines, and now coupled to un-powered brake tenders as described above. Worth a mention is that the three Bo-Bo locomotives that have been rebuilt with Caterpillar engines, alternators and new superstructures, are not as popular with either the crews or maintenance staff as the un-modified locomotives. The SCOW locomotives are the oldest industrial shunting locomotives still in commercial use in this country performing the task for which they were designed, and by a wide margin. The designers and builders at both Stafford and Loughborough can be justly proud; they are also just about the only remaining Bagnall locomotives in true commercial use anywhere in the world.

In late 1955 Brush Bagnall Traction Limited received an order from the British Transport Commission for 20 diesel-electric locomotives; a pilot order under the 1955 Modernisation Plan for British Railways (BR). The

Photograph taken in 1968 at the Steel Company of Wales Abbey Iron & Steel Works with No 906, Bagnall 3139, at work shunting the large hot-metal torpedo wagons. These wagons are used to transport the molten iron from the blast furnaces to the steel making plant and are continually rotated to keep the metal molten on its journey between the two plants

locomotives were of a power capacity in the BR Type B range - the later familiar Class 31 - with an A1A-A1A wheel arrangement, like the Ceylon locomotives, and powered by a Mirrlees JVS12T engine. This was a 12-cylinder vertical V form four-stroke turbo-charged engine rated at 1250bhp @ 850rpm. The engine was direct coupled to a Brush 823kW DC generator and there were four traction motors one on the outermost axle of each bogie; they were axle-hung and nose-suspended machines. It was decided to build these locomotives at Loughborough, but for the mechanical parts to be sub-contracted and of the first 20, 15 sets of mechanical parts came from the Gorton, Manchester builder Beyer Peacock and five from Stafford. The 20 locomotives took the BR numbers D5500 to D5519,

and the five sets of mechanical parts built at Stafford, which included the bogies, were allocated manufacturer's number 3127 to 3131, and became BR Nos. D5515 to D5519. By the time delivery of the completed locomotives commenced in October 1957, the Brush Bagnall partnership had fallen away and the Company had changed its name to Brush Traction Limited. By this time Brush Traction Limited had received significant further orders for similar locomotives which under a revised classification scheme by BR fell into the Type 2 category, and it soon became apparent at Brush that despite increased production facilities at Loughborough to meet the agreed delivery programme, assistance would still be needed with the manufacture of mechanical parts. So

Bagnall and Beyer Peacock continued to receive orders until by late 1961, when the last set was despatched a total of 52 had been supplied from Stafford. Unfortunately apart from the first five with one exception we do not know which under-frames and sets of mechanical parts became which BR locomotives. The one exception was number 3218, which was the last of the sets built at Stafford as the under-frame built to this order was specially strengthened. The locomotive concerned - BR D5845 - was fitted with an experimental up-rated version of the Mirrlees engine, in this case rated at 1950 horsepower and as a result the locomotive concerned was classified by BR as a Type 3.

It is worth a mention that the BR locomotives were to some extent based on the earlier A1A-A1A locomotives supplied to Ceylon, and that the mechanical parts were designed under the direction of Harold Wood, who as we have seen was Bagnall trained and went on to have a very distinguished career with Brush. As briefly alluded to earlier to assist with the supply of mechanical parts Brush Traction had also entered into an agreement with Beyer Peacock & Company Limited. With the severance of the Brush Bagnall connection, use of the Bagnall sequence of manufacturer's order numbers for the locomotives ceased, and starting with the BR locomotives an independent Brush Traction series was introduced. The initial Brush Traction number was 71, allocated to the first of the BR locomotives, number D5500, and this number was arrived at by adding the total number of locomotives built under the Brush Bagnall Traction partnership to the sets of electrical equipment supplied earlier and outlined in the last Chapter; that is the five sets for Ireland and one each for the London & North Eastern Railway and BR Western Region.

There was much other activity in the period covered here, but before going into some detail of specific orders it is worth discussing a business trip WA Smyth made to South Africa. The Company had done a lot of business in that part of the world and over many years, and it was felt appropriate not only to visit old customers, but to try and generate new business. Smyth left this country for Johannesburg on Monday 15th February 1954, returning on Tuesday 9 March. During the course of the trip he visited four gold mines, one platinum mine, two engineering works, eleven sugar estates, the HQ of the South African Railways, the Electricity Supply Commission offices in Johannesburg and Durban and of course the offices of the Company's agents - these were Baldwins (South Africa) Limited in Johannesburg and A&H MacNay (Pty) Limited in Durban; he also visited the offices of Brush/ABOE (South Africa) Limited in Johannesburg. As can be imagined he had a busy couple of weeks, especially as Durban is some 480 miles by train from Johannesburg.

Following the visit Smyth compiled a detailed report and, in his introduction to the country painted a most enlightening and vivid picture of life in South Africa, in particular the issues connected with apartheid; he made the point that whilst the Union was ruled by about 2,750,000 Europeans, its economy was supported by over 10,000,000 coloured natives who had absolutely no say whatever in how the country was governed, or in anyway their own destiny. Gold mining was the dominant factor in the economy and over half the world's gold came South Africa. At the time Smyth reckoned that there were 178 steam locomotives employed in industrial service in South Africa (we would question this number), of which 38 were Bagnall, making them the second largest with a percentage share of 21%; Hunslet had the most with a share equal to 25%, whilst the North British Locomotive Company came third with a share of 13%. However, in the diesel field Hunslet dominated the market and it was particularly galling, he felt, that the enquiries for diesel locomotives that had come the way of Bagnall during the chairmanship of Alan Good had been passed on to Hunslet. Smyth felt that many of these enquiries could have been turned into positive orders, but the position Hunslet had achieved made it very difficult to make any inroads into this market. However, as we have already seen Bagnall did manage to sell some diesels to the Rustenburg mines.

Smyth then gave a summery of the business the Company had done in South Africa in the period 1950 to 1953, broken down into spares and complete locomotives, and via the different agents. In this period spares to the value of £12,564 had been ordered via A&H MacNay, plus two articulated locomotives for the Hulett sugar estates in 1953. In the same period Baldwins (South Africa) Limited had ordered spares to the value of £5,130, plus two steam locomotives for the Rustenburg mines. As at 1 March 1954 spares orders to the total value of £5,006 were outstanding, but Smyth was very critical of MacNay's, considering that they had not done anything like enough to promote the Bagnall product, and in fact had been marking up spares to the tune of 10%, against the 2½ to 5% agreed. As a result of this and some other issues he cancelled the agency so far as the two Rhodesian counties were concerned and transferred this to Baldwins, as it was felt they were much more proactive in that area. Baldwins executive in charge of the Bagnall account, EW Gurney, impressed Smyth by accompanying him on all his visits in the Johannesburg area.

The report outlines in some detail each visit made and crystallises the views of those concerned in operating and maintaining the Bagnall locomotives on each site where they were employed. It is worth mentioning that several years ago one of the authors was able to discuss the report with Smyth and as might be expected a lot of flavour was added to the written word. One of the most significant issues raised was the unsuitability of the articulated locomotives for use on the sugar estates, despite the design ostensibly having been tailor-made for this type of environment, and repeat orders having been received - indeed the latest deliveries were the year before the visit! It was considered that this design was too delicate for the conditions appertaining, and that rugged simplicity should be the dominant feature of any locomotives offered in the future. At the Illovo sugar estate the locomotive - number 2544 of 1936 - was already out of use and semi-derelict. The engineer there stated it had only worked for 12 years, was under-powered for its work (hardly the fault of the locomotive one would think), difficult to maintain, primed badly and he had no intention of putting it back into working order. A sorry state indeed.

At Hulett's Darnall estate where there were three of these locomotives in use, numbers 2830, 2831 and 3015; while they were powerful enough they were considered difficult to maintain. The steam and exhaust pipes were almost impossible to keep steam tight, the tubes were difficult to keep tight, the sand boxes were not big enough and the brake cross-beam kept striking the exhaust pipes. Smyth reckoned that the circular firebox boiler should not be offered again on locomotives destined for the South African sugar estates. At Felixton where number 3014 was located the story was the same, and according to the

chargehand fitter everything was wrong with the Bagnall. After only five months work the side rod bushes were worn out and the crankpins were seven thousands of an inch oval, and to cap it all it was reckoned to take 16 hours to raise steam! Lastly at Crookes Brothers Renishaw estate the picture was a bit better, and although problems were experienced with the steam and exhaust pipes the chief engineer was generally satisfied with the engine, and it is worth remembering this was one of the original articulated locomotive built, number 2545 dating from 1936 - a new set of tyres were ordered for it in 1958.

The various mines operating the large 3ft 6in gauge 0-8-0 and 4-8-2 tank engines were generally satisfied with them, but there was a clear preference for the North British Locomotive Company product, which was much more prolific in the numbers supplied. Smyth considered the Company had 'shot its self in the foot' by its practice of supplying complete sets of drawings of the locomotives it had supplied, either on delivery or subsequently on request, and as a result the mines were able to either make spare parts themselves or source them locally. Apparently North British did not do this, and he considered that Bagnall should not do so either on any future orders.

The Tongaat Sugar Company which operated the largest number of Bagnall locomotives - an exclusive fleet of 11 - customers since 1906, were generally satisfied with the engines. This was the largest sugar company in Africa and the Tongaat estates had an annual output of some 750,000 tons of cane, 40% of which was conveyed over two unconnected tramways operated exclusively by the Bagnall locomotives. However, the circular firebox boiler was giving problems here too and Smyth recommended that if any further locomotives were ordered consideration should be given to fitting a conventional firebox boiler. Although the possibility of ordering further locomotives was intimidated during the visit, which the chief engineer said would be ordered from Bagnall, in the event none were.

One positive result of Smyth's trip along with the Rustenburg diesel order already mentioned followed a visit to the Natal Estates Limited. This was another sugar estate and mill, in this case at Mount Edgecombe, where Bagnall number 2543 of 1936 operated alongside products of Fowler, Hunslet and Avonside. Despite problems with the bogie centre casting on the locomotive, which it was stated was not peculiar to the Bagnall, and which they had modified along with some minor alteration to the smokebox, the Bagnall engine was well liked here. As a result of the visit Bagnall got the order for a new locomotive - works number 3090 CAMPBELL which has already been described. It is interesting to speculate why in the case of this locomotive a completely new design was evolved, as the specification could easily have been addressed by existing designs, or by relatively minor modifications to them. The obvious conclusion is that the time and cost were considered justified, in the hope that more orders might be forthcoming, but in the event the era of the steam locomotive on the sugar estate railways, and indeed in many cases the railways themselves, was rapidly coming to its conclusion.

In summery Smyth felt his visit was well worthwhile and as we have seen some orders did result. He was also able to generate several orders for spare parts and establish better contacts with the Company's agents. Interesting to note that the visit cost £470 of which £340 was spent on travel, the majority on the air fares. The most memorable aspect of the discussion with Smyth on his report was the prolific use he saw being made by the local people of welding, and he felt that in many places if a locomotive could not be repaired by welding, it would not be repaired! At Renishaw it was stated that the tyres of Hunslet locomotives were more weldable than the Bagnall ones. In general he felt the standards of maintenance were extremely poor hence the comment about only offering the most robust locomotives for any future orders. Tongaat was an exception to the rule where Smyth felt maintenance standards were excellent; indeed he found the whole presentation of the estate and mill at Tongaat was much in advance of the other sugar estates he visited.

A significant number of locomotives were sent into the works for repairs and overhaul during the period covered by this Chapter. In fact between 1953 and 1958 no less that 20 were dealt with plus two others that were unusually allocated numbers in the main locomotive numerical list. The locomotives sent in for overhaul and repairs came from a range of customers and locations, including the NCB, the Ministry of Supply, West Midlands Gas Board, ICI, and Worthington & Company Limited the Burton-on-Trent

brewers to name but a few. In some cases these were Bagnall built locomotives but in many cases they were not. Perhaps the most significant overhaul jobs, involving the largest locomotives ever handled at the Castle Engine Works, were three that came from the War Department camp at Longmoor in Hampshire. In late 1953 the Company was successful with its tender to overhaul one of the wartime built 2-10-0 Austerity locomotives, along with one of the United States Army Transportation Corps (USATC) S160 class 2-8-0 locomotives, and these two arrived at Stafford in January. One of them was the now comparatively well known GORDON, WD No 600 currently preserved on the Severn Valley Railway at Bridgenorth in Shropshire, whilst the other with MAJOR GENERAL CARL R GREY Jnr, WD No 700. GORDON was built by the North British Locomotive Company in 1944 - number 25437 - whilst the S160 was a product of the American Locomotive Company (ALCO) - number 71512 of 1944. Due to their size both these locomotives were dealt with in the new erecting shop, and in the case of the ALCO as few drawings were available a comprehensive set of photographs were taken before, during and after dismantling so as it make the process of reassembly easier. In both cases a comprehensive overhaul took place which included removal of the boilers from the main-frames. The locomotives were despatched back to Longmoor on 23 March 1955, but not before GORDON had partially demolished one of the large sliding doors of the new erecting shop. It was discovered with some pain that a large 2-10-0 does not stop as quickly as the much smaller engines the staff were more accustomed to. These locomotives arrived dead hauled by a BR locomotive, and in the case of GORDON with the trailing wheel set removed and stowed in the tender, and they returned under the same arrangements but with all their wheels in place.

These two were followed by one of the British 2-8-0 Austerity locomotives; in this case WD No 401 MAJOR GENERAL McMULLEN, which had been built by the Vulcan Foundry - number 5193 of 1945 - and the order was placed by Longmoor in November 1954. The level of overhaul was similar to the other two, and the engine was despatched back to Longmoor on 24 May 1956. As with the other two this locomotive was handled in the new erecting shop although it did have to go almost into the old erecting shop for some

Before and after views of the War Department 2-10-0 Austerity locomotive GORDON, which came to the works for overhaul in 1954. Notice that the engine arrived with its trailing set of coupled wheels removed, and although it came by rail one wonders if British Railways were aware of this in view of the consequent increased axle-load on the remaining wheel sets! The second view has the locomotive ready for despatch back to Longmoor, with the American 2-8-0 S160 class engine behind - they went back together.

tests. There was a need to test parts of the valve gear following some of the repairs, and it was concluded the best way to do this was on the set of track mounted rollers located on the multi-gauge test track situated just on the approach to the old shop. With the driving wheels on the rollers it was possible to run the engine without it moving, but the operation had to be

undertaken very carefully as the rollers were not designed to accommodate such a large and powerful locomotive.

Another significant and no less interesting rebuild involved what can only be described as the remains of a metre-gauge GS class 4-8-0 tender engine which came back from India in 1958. It was an unusual event to bring previously exported locomotives back to this country for attention, and by any of the builders in the trade. The West of India Portuguese Railway (WIPR) which dates from 1887, and was situated in that enclave of the Indian sub-continent on the south-west coast south of Bombay called Goa, had been operated under an agreement by the Madras & Southern Mahratta Railway, and later the nationalised Indian Southern Railway, since 1902. As a result there had been some interchange of locomotives belonging to the two companies, and we saw in Chapter Seven that Bagnall supplied engines of the GS class concurrently to both systems back in 1925. In 1955 there was a disagreement between the Indian and Portuguese governments and the working agreement was terminated, and indeed the connection between the two systems was severed. As a result the WIPR found itself short of motive power and in November 1957, via consulting engineers Sir Bruce White, Wolfe Barry & Partners, four new GS class boilers were ordered to enable four otherwise withdrawn locomotives of this type to be put back into service. At the same time the dismembered remains of an almost complete locomotive, identified as Bagnall manufacturer's number 2246 of 1925, came back to Stafford. This locomotive had clearly been used as a source of spare parts for other members of its class, and was without a whole host of parts including a tender. The requirement was to undertake the minimum amount of work to put the engine into working order, and as the boiler was found to be beyond repair one of the four spare ones ordered was used, and a fifth one was ordered to replace it. As the engine arrived with no cab - presumably it was left behind in Goa - and as one was not fitted at Stafford, the engine presented an interesting sight when it was tested in steam prior to re-delivery as well as providing a somewhat precarious situation for the testing crew - remember there was no tender either! The contract also covered the supply of a number of other spare parts for the engines that remained in Goa, including several pairs of coupled wheel-sets. The issues between the governments of India and Portugal were eventually settled; Goa was ceded to India in December 1961, and so far as the WIPR was concerned normal working was resumed.

The two overhauled locomotives given numbers in the locomotive numerical list were both diesels that the Company acquired second-hand, gave attention to and

then sold. This was not a line of business that had been a particular speciality in the past, and it is interesting to speculate what prompted the purchase of these two locomotives. The first one was a small 2ft 6in gauge four-wheel machine built by Hunslet in 1940 - number 2664 - and fitted with a Perkins 46 horsepower diesel engine. It had worked for John Heaver Limited at some gravel pits near Chichester and Bagnall obtained it from Chichester via GE Slinn (Machinery) Limited of Sheffield, in February 1953. It cost £750 plus £50 for the move to Stafford. After attention which included rebuilding to suit standard-gauge and the addition of a cab, it was sold to Metropolitan Vickers Company Limited following an order dated 23 November 1954, and despatched to its Wythernshawe factory on 19 May 1955. Sold for £1,549, so presumably a reasonable profit was made on the transaction - the number allocated was 3062. The second locomotive came via H Dunn, a plant & machinery dealer from Bishops Auckland and it arrived at Stafford in March 1958. This locomotive had been built by EE Baguley Limited at Burton-on-Trent, but to a Drewry Car Company order and it carried the Drewry number 2262; it had been delivered new in September 1949 to the Harrogate Gas Works. The locomotive was an 0-6-0 with mechanical transmission built to suit two-foot gauge and fitted with a Gardner 6LW engine rated at 102bhp @ 1700rpm. Made redundant when the narrow-gauge system at the gas works closed in July 1956, Dunn purchased it in early 1958, but appears to have almost immediately sold it to Bagnall, as it came to Stafford direct from Harrogate. Allocated manufacturer's number 3152, it was overhauled - it had originally been designed to clear a quite restrictive loading gauge - and sold to agents Jacks Fencing & Engineering Works (Pty) Limited of Johannesburg in South Africa. This company was acting as agents for Rhodesia Chrome Company Limited, and the engine went to work at its mines at Selukwe. It was despatched on 18 January 1960, and whilst Bagnall paid £1,000, it was sold for £2,197 against an order dated 24 November 1959; once again delivering a nice profit.

A steady supply of orders for spare parts for locomotives was always part of the works production including boilers and fireboxes. No less than 38 new boilers were supplied between 1953 and 1958, many of them for India, along with a similar number of separate

Pages from a brochure produced in November 1958, when the firm was quite successful in diversifying into general engineering, but also anxious to extend these activities with locomotive and other railway related orders becoming harder to come-by. The information includes details of machining capability.

new fireboxes. Often in the case of British customers boilers were sent in for repair, new fireboxes and tubes being the usual requirement. In many cases the spares orders were for significant quantities, and frequently for locomotives that were not of Bagnall manufacture; the Crown Agents in particular were almost continually ordering large quantities; motion parts for example.

Considerable efforts were made to diversify into general engineering when it was realised that locomotive orders were getting harder and harder to obtain and a new brochure was produced in November 1958 illustrating the wide range of general engineering that could be undertaken, with details of the capacity and type of machine tools the Company had available. Vic Betteley the contracts engineer at this time spent a lot of his time touring round the country on the lookout

for general engineering work, and with a significant measure of success.

A working relationship was established with George Fletcher & Company Limited (later Fletcher & Stewart), a company with good business in the supply of machinery used in the processing of sugar. Although it had an extensive works in Derby, additional manufacturing capacity was sometimes required and Bagnall were on occasions able to help fill the gap. Among the work undertaken was construction of 10ft and 13ft diameter calandrias, large cylindrical vessels with a number of tubes passing through them and used as heat exchangers, and in this case in connection with the vacuum pans in the sugar refining process. These were quite large items of equipment and cost around £1,000 each, so it was good business. Four were supplied in June 1958 for example, two of each size. Similarly the General Electric Company (GEC) through its subsidiary Frazer & Chalmers Engineering Works at Erith in Kent (who operated a couple of Bagnall locomotives by the way), placed a number of orders including a large Pennsylvania hammer mill shipped to a company at Durgapur in India. In 1958 the Company built a large coal scrubbing plant for Frazer & Chalmers powered by GEC motors; this was for use in Africa and the contract was worth a little over £5,000 to the Castle Engine Works.

Other non-locomotive work included excavator buckets for JCB Limited, vehicle tow-bars for the British Army, concrete mixer drums and other pressings for Benfords Limited, in several cases as many as 100 drums at a time, and there was a lot of general machining of all sorts of components for numerous customers. On occasions cast gearbox housings were machined for Alfred Wiseman & Company Limited of Birmingham, often gearboxes for use in locomotives, large and complicated castings providing a significant work-load for the machine shop.

A particular job worth special mention and once again for Frazer & Chalmers, in this case on behalf of the United Kingdom Atomic Energy Authority, was two sets of equipment for moving charge-discharge machines, each to carry a 350-ton load. This equipment was for use at Hunsterston nuclear power station on the south bank of the River Clyde near East Kilbride, which was under construction at the time.

The order was placed in late 1958, although it was 1960 and into the next era of our story before the work was complete. Each machine consisted of one large transfer-car which ran on rails with a rail-head centre-to-centre gauge of 17ft 3in, powered by a Dorman 3LB diesel engine generator set and electric motors, along with two smaller transfer-cars. These ran on two side-by-side tracks, each with a centre-to-centre rail-head gauge of 2ft 4in, situated at right-angles to the main track. The function of the equipment was to move the nuclear fuel charge-machines containing the fuel from the charge-machine building to the reactors, while the purpose of the smaller transfer-cars was to move the main car on and off the wider gauge track, on to what was referred to as a parking-track, so that the larger cars could pass each other. The all-up weight of the two small cars, one large car and the charge machine itself, was 500 tons, and the equipment included a hydraulic pump to operate locking gear to retain the charge machines in position. There were a number of other ancillary equipment items too. This is another example of a job of some magnitude which along with some on-site equipment was a contract to the tune of over £30,000, keeping Stuart Johnson, a senior designer, and one of the draughtsman, Owen Ellis, occupied for a long time. The work included erection and commisioning on site at Hunsterston; the adjoining photographs give some idea of the size and complexity of the job. Incidentally, at around the same time this work was undertaken the Company received several other quite

This photograph illustrates part of two sets of equipment each consisting of two each of these narrow-gauge vehicles described as transfer-cars, along with one of the larger vehicles also called a transfer-car and seen in the next photograph. They were designed to carry a 350 ton load for use at the nuclear power station then building at Hunsterston on the south bank of the River Clyde near East Kilbride. The order numbers were 7687 and 7688 of December 1958, and the job included erecting the vehicles on site and commissioning them.

substantial orders for machinery for nuclear power stations via Frazer & Chalmers.

The boiler shop made some large pressure vessels for petroleum vapour for the Esso Petroleum Company, and for the old-established customer of locomotives, Bowaters Lloyd Limited at Sittingbourne in Kent, spare parts for paper-making machinery were manufactured. A lot of machining was undertaken for the parent Heenan & Froude, as well as Walker Brothers (Wigan) Limited, well known as makers of lightweight diesel railcars. There were a host of other customers too, sometime with just the one order and worth but a few pounds, to others worth several thousand. By these and other means the Company was able to keep its work force fully employed during the ups and downs of locomotive orders. There was even an order as late as January 1959 for Owen poppet valve regulators, in this case via Henry Owen Limited for Nigerian Railways.

One more venture in diversification remains to be described in this Chapter, and the Company's one and only venture in to powered vehicles not for use on rail - The Bagnall-Burns tractor. In 1955 John Stephen Burns was able to interest the Company in an idea of his involving hydraulic transmission systems for vehicles; according to the late WA Smyth he just 'knocked on the door one day'! As a result of this the Company, in partnership with Burns, applied for a British patent on 9 August 1955, filing the complete specification on 23 July the following year. A patent was eventually granted, number 807550, published on 14 January

View taken from one of the overhead cranes in the New Erecting Shop showing the two almost complete larger transfer-cars, one for each set of equipment; these cars were designed to carry the nuclear fuel charge-machines from the charge machine building to the reactors. The smaller narrow-gauge cars were to transfer the larger car from the main track to a parking track, so that the larger cars could pass each other. The larger cars were self propelled while the narrow-gauge ones were moved by sets of hauling equipment mounted on overhead cranes. The upturned locomotive underframe on the left is for one of the Brush Traction British Railways Type 2 A1A-A1A diesel-electric locomotives, while the locomotive in advanced stages of construction is the prototype standard-gauge 0-6-0 diesel-hydraulic number 3191 - a development described in the next Chapter. Behind the locomotive is its axle mounted final drive and wheelset.

1959; the title was *Improvements in Wheeled or Tracked Vehicles*. John Burns ACGI joined the staff at Stafford as an unpaid special consultant, as he was termed, on 25 January 1955, once a decision had been taken to develop the idea and build a prototype track-laying tractor. The principle involved the use of two separate hydraulic drive systems, one for the drive on each side of the tractor, driven through a gearbox by a common engine. Each drive line consisted of a variable delivery pump of the swash-plate type capable of varying the fluid flow and pressure, each line having an independent closed-circuit fluid system with its respective hydraulic motor driving the track wheels. A series of relief valves were incorporated in the circuits arranged to accommodate the direction of flow, along with the pressure, through by-pass circuits for forward and reverse motion of the hydraulic drive motors. The speed and direction of the hydraulic motors were thereby controlled completely independently of each other by the variably delivery swash-plate pumps. It was

claimed of the idea that a maximum number of nine components were necessary in each drive train, against anything up to 15 in other less developed designs. Control was extremely easy the driver having but two tillers, one for each drive line, and these were all that was necessary to control movement in both directions, speed and turning, and when both levers were in a neutral position the vehicle was fully braked.

Two tractors were designed and built on these lines, and they embodied a number of other innovative features including two independent articulated bogies. The leading one carried an unsprung supporting idler above the bogie wheels and adjacent to the drive sprocket, providing compensating adjustment in the upper run of the track for variation of the lower run as the tractor covered uneven ground. The engine was a Meadows 4DC 420, a four-cylinder in-line four-stroke diesel rated at 90bhp @ 2,000rpm, the maximum speed of the tractor being 7mph. The speed control was completely step-less and the drawbar pull 15,000lb.

One of the large pressure vessels made for Esso Petroleum; although made in the Boiler Shop it is seen here in the old Erecting Shop where it had been moved to allow ultrasonic testing of the welding to be undertaken.

Publicity brochure dated November 1958 for the Bagnall-Burns tractor. The hydraulic motors are at the top (front), mounted vertically, and the pumps horizontally at the bottom (rear).

SPECIFICATION

of the **BAGNALL-BURNS BB90** TRACKED TRACTOR with **HYDROSTATIC TRANSMISSION**

TRAVEL SPEED AND DRAWBAR PULL

Stepless from 0-7 m.p.h. in both forward and reverse.

Rated Drawbar pull 15,000 lbs.

HYDROSTATIC TRANSMISSION

B.B. Motors, 2 & Lucas Pumps, 2 Motors, Radial Piston.
Number of Cylinders: 7.
Bore and Stroke: $4\frac{1}{2}'' \times 2\frac{3}{4}''$.
Maximum Pressure: 3000 p.s.i.
Maximum Torque: 10,500 lbs./ft.

PUMPS
Lucas I.P. 3000.
Flow reversible by Control Lever.
Fluid Displacement: 100 g.p.m. at 2000 r.p.m.
Working Pressure: 3000 p.s.i.
Inlet Boost Pressure: 100 p.s.i.

STEERING
CLUTCHLESS AND WITH-OUT BRAKE BANDS.

CAPACITY, FUEL
40 gallons.

WEIGHT
8 tons.

SUSPENSION
Resilient Idlers.

ENGINE
Meadows 4 DC 420.
Number of Cylinders, 4.
Bore and Stroke: 130 mm × 130 mm ($5\frac{1}{8}'' \times 5\frac{1}{8}''$).
Piston Displacement: 6.9 litres (422 cu. ins.).
R.P.M. Governed at full load: 2000.
Lubrication: Full Pressure with Full Flow Oil Filters.
B.H.P. at 2000 r.p.m. : 90.
Starting method: Electric, 24 volts.

TRACK
Number of Links (each side): 48.
Width of Standard Link: 15".
Height of Grouser: 2".
Length of Track on Ground: 7' 1".
Track Gauge: 58".

TRACK SUSPENSION
Articulating Bogies with compensation.

GENERAL DIMENSIONS
Length (overall): 12' 10".
Width (overall): 6' 1".
Height exclusive of Exhaust Pipe: 6' 1½".
Drawbar Height: 1' 2".
Ground Clearance: 1' 1".

The Track Suspension of the Bagnall-Burns Tracked Tractor can be easily converted from an articulated suspension to a rigid suspension by the addition of a locking bar. Provision has also been made for the fitment of any mounted ancillary.

HEENAN GROUP COMPANY

W. G. BAGNALL LTD.

CASTLE ENGINE WORKS STAFFORD
Tel. Stafford 321/322. Grams: Bagnall Stafford.

dm BL32 2M 11/58 JV

The completed tractors were 12ft 10in long, 6ft 1in wide and 6ft 1½in high to the top of the engine's exhaust pipe, presenting a very modern and pleasing appearance. One of them was exhibited at the Public Works Exhibition at Olympia in London during November 1958, where it received very favourable comment in the technical press. It has to be remembered that vehicles with comparatively simple, but nevertheless sophisticated hydrostatic drive systems, while extremely common place today, were still very much under development in the late 1950s, and it

will be noted that it took several years of development work to take Burns's idea into a potential marketable product. There was more work to be done to refine the prototypes into a tractor suitable for a production run, and following the success so far and the acclaim achieved at the exhibition, plans were being formulated when yet another change in ownership of the Company put a stop to any further work on the project. This was a great shame as the tractor showed much potential, and while both machines were moved to the Heenan & Froude works at Worcester at the change of ownership,

Bagnall-Burns BB-90 tractor under test in the works yard. The driver is Alf Armstrong, a chargehand in the Fitting & Erecting Shop who was one of the few members of staff dedicated to this project. With him is Bob Gibbens, an apprentice at the time. The building behind was built specially for spray painting excavator buckets made for JCB Limited.

nothing seems to have been done with them and they were subsequently scrapped. John Burns left the Company immediately on the change of ownership; as we have seen he was never on the pay-roll at Stafford, the arrangement did not pay him a salary and his reward, if any, was tied into the agreement on any commercial development of the tractor. On the 11 February 1959 the patent application was amended to delete reference to WG Bagnall Limited and establish John Burns as the sole patentee; the amendment gave his address as 46 Princes Court Brompton Road London SW3. A lot of money had been sunk into the development of the tractor and the results were looking very promising for a good return, as it turned out to no avail. Moreover, the principles involved in the design to no small extent paved the way for others to follow.

WA Smyth was extremely keen on the training of engineers and craftsman for the locomotive industry, and he achieved at lot whilst at Stafford in developing, and improving training schemes. For example he wrote a number of articles in the trade and local press and he made it his business to get to know the head masters of the local schools and technical collages; in this he was of course, following in the footsteps of his predecessor WS Edwards. Early in his tenure as managing director

in May 1953 he invited the head masters of the local schools and technical colleges to a presentation and lunch at the Swan Hotel in Stafford where, along with his senior members of staff, they were entertained. A nicely produced brochure was issued and in December 1958 an apprentice training school was opened at the works; Harry Owen, brother of Geoff, was the Instructor. Much encouragement was given to all levels of staff to encourage and help trainees in whatever they were engaged, and many of the recruitment interviews were conducted by Smyth himself. In no small way did these efforts help to keep the works busy in the difficult times to come.

Another initiative during Smyth's tenure of office concerned the drawings. A decision was taken, both in view of the deteriorating condition of many of them, along with the storage space needed, to copy the vast majority onto half-plate negatives ($6\frac{1}{2}$in x $4\frac{1}{2}$ in). A print room was established in the new office accommodation and equipment purchased to undertake this work, which took several years and was largely done by a Polish member of staff by the name of Zigmund Kordas. When the work was complete most of the original drawings were destroyed as excellent prints could be obtained from the negatives. However, a few

WA Smyth, Managing Director, making a long service presentation to Bob Kemsley at the firm's 1952 Annual Smoking Concert. Later, in the 1954 Queen's birthday honours, Bob was awarded the British Empire Medal.

of the very early drawings were retained, especially the original hand-drawn and coloured ones mounted on cloth, two of which adorn the end-papers of this book, and are an excellent example of both the draughtsman's and colouring artist's work. Following the establishment of what was in effect a photographic department, the Company managed the bulk of its own photographic work with the result that a much better record of production and other events around the works exists, than in earlier days when the work was contracted out.

Smyth was enthusiastic about all his people, and this is well illustrated by his on-going support for the annual smoking concerts originally initiated in Marriott's time. At the event held in the Borough Hall at Stafford on March 4 1952, over 500 members of staff, relations and friends gathered together. During the course of the evening Smyth made presentations to 15 long serving employees of the Company, each having at least 40 years service. Bob Kemsley was the most senior with 54 years, followed by William Lakin 53 years, George Banks 51 years, and W Rupert Machin 47 years,

accompanied by Walter G Anthony, William T Biddulph, Arthur Woollams, Harry R Chambers, Horace Banner, Andrew J Birtles, Tommy Dawkes, George H Norwood, Albert E Hubball and Walter H Skelton. They were all presented with an illuminated address and a cash sum. At a similar event held on 1 April 1955, further presentations were made to men having been with the firm for over 40 years; among them was Arthur Owen the works accountant. At that time there were still 14 men employed over 65 years of age, and five of them had given more that 50 years faithful service. It is worth saying a little more about Robert - Bob - Kemsley, as he was awarded the British Empire Medal in the 1954 Queen's birthday honours. Bob was 71 years old at the time and had been employed by the Company for 57 years, starting in 1897 as an apprentice blacksmith; some years earlier he had declined the foreman's job! The first locomotives he worked on were the 2ft 5½in gauge 4-4-0s for the Egyptian Delta Light Railways. The medal was presented to him at a ceremony at the County Buildings on 10 December 1954, by Mr Wallace Copeland, Her

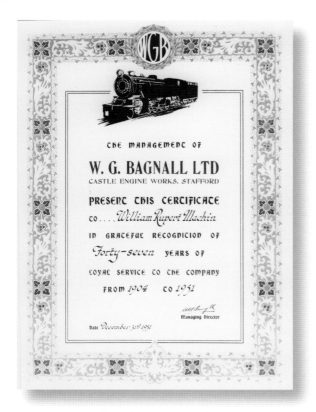

This is an example of the Company's long service certificates, presented along with a gift, and in this case awarded to William Rupert Machin for 47 years service. At the time Rupert Machin was the chargehand in the wheel-bay.

Majesties Lord Lieutenant of the county, and he was accompanied by his wife and daughter-in law.

By this time in the history of the Company the smithy was largely disused, the type of work undertaken there very much on decline with the demise of steam locomotive production. The large 10 ton Massey steam hammer was silent and the ex main-line locomotive boilers purchased many years earlier second-hand from the dealer TW Ward were cold and rusting. In fact these boilers were only used during the summer months when the main works boilers, which were also used for heating, were not in steam. Much of the smithy was used as a finished parts store while the boiler shop as has already been mentioned took on much of the fabrication work

Before closing this Chapter with details of the change of ownership of the Company briefly mentioned above, a number of senior staff changes need a mention. Harold Shaw the buyer retired on 1 September 1956 and his erstwhile assistant Stanley T Ponting took his

place. In February 1958 Sydney Ridgway left the Castle Engine Works to take up an appointment as production engineer in the chief mechanical engineer's department of British Railways Western Region at Swindon. This was quite a loss to the Company, as much had been achieved during his time as works manager and WA Smyth recalled to the authors how sorry he was to see him go, but nevertheless strongly advised him to accept the position in view of his own career prospects. Ridgway went on to have a very successful career with BR and in 1960 took up the position of works manager at Swindon Works, moving on in 1962 to become carriage & wagon engineer for the Western Region, but still based in Swindon. Two years later on further promotion he became chief mechanical & electrical engineer Western Region with offices in Paddington. Shortly after British Rail Engineering Limited was formed in 1972, Ridgway became its engineering director and took over as managing director the following year; this was his last appointment and he retired in 1976. Sydney Ridgway was the chairman of the Railway Division of the Institution of Mechanical Engineers in the session 1974-5, and he passed away on 1 September 1999. Ridgway's position at Stafford was partly filled by Arthur Woollams, but with the different title of chief works engineer, and about the same time Vic Betteley became production manager; in effect Ridgway's old job was split into two. At the same time John Cartlidge who had been one of the senior draughtsman and the assistant contracts engineer from April 1955, became contracts engineer, and JM (Mac) Durber took up a new position of service manager, to look after work the Company was undertaking off-site.

In the period 1954 to 1958 the average trading profit was £44,462, the average net profit £25,309 and the profit after tax £12,263.

The Heenan & Froude interest in WG Bagnall Limited was never great, and we have already seen how Alan Good used Heenan & Froude as a convenient way to acquire a locomotive builder to further his interests in the Brush/ABOE group. With Good gone the Brush link became more tenuous, and as the export market for locomotives declined the trading environment for WG Bagnall Limited became a more difficult one. This was the principal reason for the diversification of products outlined in this Chapter. In addition to this situation at Stafford, the other railway related Heenan Group subsidiary Associated Locomotive Equipment Limited, which although not a manufacturer itself, was finding less and less business for its products which were primarily concerned with steam locomotives. The directors of Heenan & Froude were therefore, and had been for some time, on the look out for a suitable customer for WG Bagnall Limited, and one eventually came along in the shape of another long established Stafford engineering company, WH Dorman & Company Limited. In late January 1959 it was announced that WH Dorman & Company Limited was in the final stages of negotiation with Heenan & Froude to acquire the entire share capital of WG Bagnall Limited, and that is what happened.

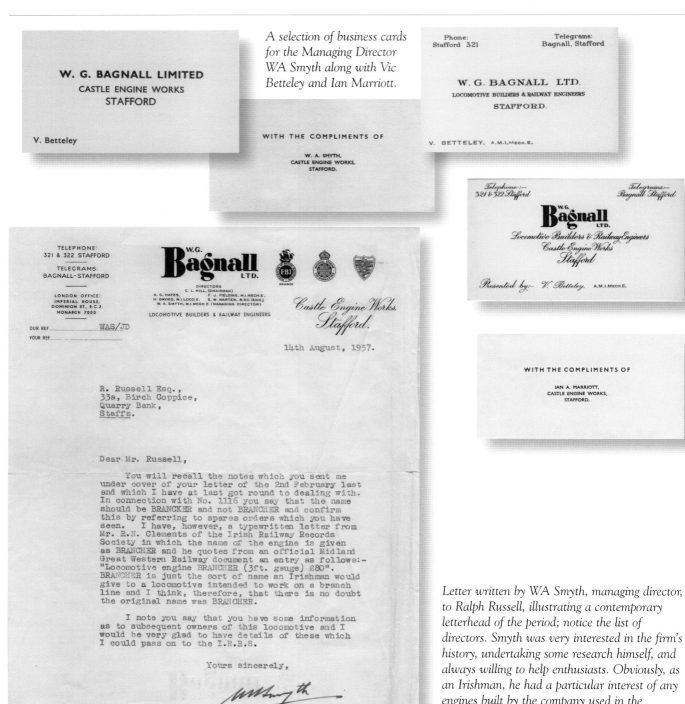

A selection of business cards for the Managing Director WA Smyth along with Vic Betteley and Ian Marriott.

Letter written by WA Smyth, managing director, to Ralph Russell, illustrating a contemporary letterhead of the period; notice the list of directors. Smyth was very interested in the firm's history, undertaking some research himself, and always willing to help enthusiasts. Obviously, as an Irishman, he had a particular interest of any engines built by the company used in the Emerald Isle, as is the case here.

Chapter Fourteen

THE DORMAN PERIOD

On 27 January 1959 WH Dorman & Company Limited issued a press announcement that it had entered into an agreement, subject to Stock Exchange approval (this was because Dorman was listed a public company) to acquire a controlling interest in WG Bagnall Limited from Heenan Group Limited. We met the Dorman company in earlier Chapters, another old established Stafford business in this case specialising in the design and manufacture of small and medium size internal combustion engines. The company also had a range of other products, although nowhere near its output of internal combustion engines. Established in 1870 by William Henry Dorman with workshops in Foregate Street, the company originally specialised in the design and manufacture of machinery for the burgeoning local shoe and boot making industry. The first internal combustion engines dated from 1903 and from that date onwards paraffin, petrol and later diesel engines were predominant in the firm's activities. There was a big demand for the company's products during the First World War and additional premises were acquired; an existing foundry in Newport Road was purchased. However, due to the magnitude of the war-time workload the foundry at Foregate Street remained in production too. A particular product in great demand

was the patent Constantinesco machine gun synchronising gear, as Dormans had the manufacturing rights by an agreement with its designer, an expatriate Rumanian by the name of George Constantinesco. When fitted to the single engine aircraft of the day, the gear enabled machine guns mounted at the front and operated by the pilot, to fire at a rate of up to 2,000 rounds a minute, the fire being interrupted at the split second the propeller blocked the line of fire. On planes fitted with the gear pilots were able to fly directly at any adversary, firing the gun straight ahead, and initially at least, this provided them with a distinct advantage over the enemy; until that is, the German's developed a similar system!

Shortly after the end of the First World War a large plot of land adjacent to Tixall Road to the east of the town was acquired and a completely new factory built there. A lot of thought went into the design of this factory, laid out as it was for the mass production of internal combustion engines and over the next few years there was a gradual migration from both Foregate Street and Newport Road, such that the latter premises were vacated in 1929. However, it was not until 1939 that the Foregate Street Works was finally closed, only to be requisitioned on the outbreak of the Second World War by the government, and some time later

Aerial photograph of the Castle Engine Works at its largest extent. Although this view was taken a few years before the period covered by this Chapter, it makes a good companion for the plan of the works that appears next. Notice the New Erecting Shop to top right and the British Railways Stafford Motive Power Depot to bottom left - the bridge over the railway lines was, and is, known as Bagnalls Bridge. Just outside the Old Erecting Shop and partly under the steaming shed - that is the building with the curved roof - can just be discerned one of the war-time Austerity 0-6-0 saddle tanks at the works for overhaul, whilst at the other end of the shed is the British Austerity 2-8-0 also for overhaul - this would date the photographs as early in 1956. The three railway lines to the middle right are from top to bottom: to Wellington and Shrewsbury; Crewe and the north; Stafford Common and Uttoxeter.

occupied by the English Electric Company to expand its activities due to increased wartime demand. After the war part of the Foregate Street workshops were used by a company called Doorframes Limited, although English Electric again used a section for its publicity department; later still Dormans - by then part of the English Electric Group - returned to occupy a section during a particularly busy period in the late 1960s.

Unlike his contemporary Gordon Bagnall, William Dorman did not participate in any local government or political activities, and while there is no evidence that the two came into contact with each other, they must have done at some stage in their respective careers, although perhaps infrequently. Dorman was born in

1831 and by 1891 was living at 27 Newport Road; at the same time Bagnall was living at No 11, so it would be extremely unlikely if they did not at the very least occasionally pass the time of day. The WH Dorman Company was registered as a public limited company on 16 December 1897, converted into a private one in 1908, only to become a public company again in August 1917. In 1911 Walter Haddon, a well established London city figure with a wide range of financial and business connections, became chairman and managing director, and members of the Haddon family continued to be involved in the company for the remainder of its independent existence. John Haddon, Walter's son, was the chairman and managing director until his death

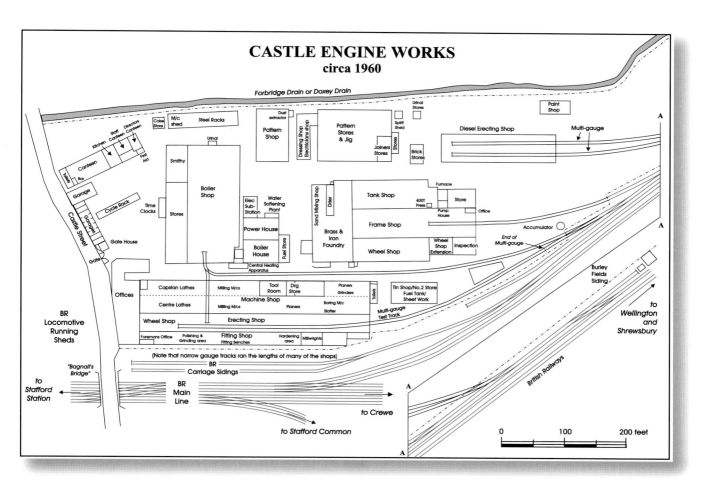

CASTLE ENGINE WORKS
circa 1960

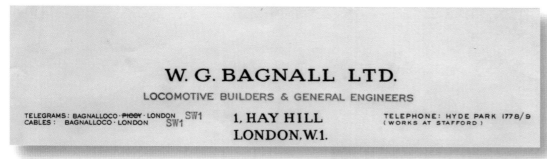

in 1938. By 1947 Darby Haddon, John's son, was a director, and at the time of the acquisition of WG Bagnall Limited chairman of WH Dorman & Company Limited; 53 years old he lived at Slaughter Farm, Bourton-on-the-Water in Gloucestershire. Darby Haddon was also a director of Darby Haddon Investments Limited, but listed himself in company documents as a farmer. The managing director at the time was Jack Walter Whimpenny of Grove Cottage, Cannock Road in Penkridge; 49 years old at the time he

took on the additional role of managing director of WG Bagnall Limited, although his office remained at the Tixall Road Works. William Dorman by the way, departed this life in 1926.

The acquisition was funded in two separate ways against an agreed purchase price of £458,304. Part payment was in shares in WH Dorman & Company Limited, with the remainder in cash, although part of the cash payment was by transfer of a monetary loan to WG Bagnall Limited from the balance sheet of the

Heenen Group, to WH Dorman. For the transfer of shares Dorman converted each of 100,000 of its preference shares of £1 each, which at the time had not been issued, into 10 shares of 2/- (10p) each; 850,000 of these new shares were then issued to the Heenen Group at par, equivalent to £85,000. Of the cash payment of £373,304, £137,804 was by discharge of the loan, leaving £236,500; the loan was then between WH Dorman & Company Limited and WG Bagnall Limited, at the same figure of £137,804. The financial arrangements between Heenen and Bagnall were part of the purchase agreement when Alan Good brought WG Bagnall Limited into his group; remember it was cash from the Heenan Group balance sheet that was used. As at 31 August 1958, the balance sheet of WG Bagnall Limited stood at £488,166; the freehold property was valued at £8,519; the leasehold land, sidings and buildings at £124,784; plant, machinery and office equipment at £70,550; stock-in-trade and work in progress £203,143. The share capital remained at £250,000, and it was anticipated by WH Dorman that the annual profit to accrue from the acquisition would be no less than £28,000.

WA Smyth first heard of the potential sale of the Company while attending the Public Works & Municipal Services Exhibition at Olympia in November 1958, where it will be recalled from the last Chapter the Bagnall-Burns tractor was on display. He told the authors that the news came like the proverbial bolt out of the blue. Jim Fielding, the managing director of the Heenan Group, who was also by the way the son of the founder of Fielding & Platt Limited, casually mentioned the sale to Smyth in a very matter-of-fact sort of way. It was in the form of a casual comment in passing, and in a tone and demeanour that inferred he was surprised Smyth did not already know about it, and that it was an issue of little consequence to Heenan & Froude anyway! Smyth and Fielding had never completely seen eye to eye; it had been made obvious by Jim Fielding on several occasions since Alan Good died that he had little interest in the medium-or-long term activities at Stafford, although this did not stop him interfering on occasions. In Smyth's own words 'he (Fielding) made no secret of his pleasure at the sale of the company to Dorman'. In fact Heenan & Froude had been on the look out for a potential customer for some time. At the time the Heenan Group was not doing particularly well

with a steady downward trend in its business; in 1959 its order book stood at £3,600,000, against £4,000,000 the previous year, and the profit after tax was down from £169,314 to £158,880.

The sale agreement was concluded following a shareholder EGM of WH Dorman & Company Limited, and Stock Exchange approval on Monday, 2 March 1959. The previous Thursday Smyth had been asked to clear his desk, and given but one day to do so, despite having three years of his contract to run. There was a nasty taste left in the mouths of most of the senior staff, as relationships between the two companies, WG Bagnall and WH Dorman, had over the years, and at best, only been cordial, as the respective managements considered themselves far superior to the other in the hierarchy of local engineering companies. There were 360 employees on the Bagnall books at the time against 1,100 with WH Dorman.

Before proceeding with the history of the Company it is perhaps worth relating the ongoing career of WA Smyth. Fortunately he never moved the family home to Stafford; when appointed to the position at Henry Meadows in 1949, he established home in Wombourne, a small village south of Wolverhampton, in somewhat of a hurry on leaving British Railways (BR) at Doncaster. Following his appointment to Henry Meadows, and as he came to know Alan Good better, he drew the conclusion that Good might move him around any one of the numerous companies he controlled, and at short notice; hence he elected to stay put and travel daily to and from Stafford. On leaving WG Bagnall Smyth went to see an old friend from Guest, Keen & Nettlefolds (GKN) days, KS Peacock, at the time managing director of the group. Despite being none too pleased at his having left GKN in the first place, Peacock offered Smyth a new position as industrial engineering advisor at the group's head office in Birmingham, and he remained with GKN until his retirement in 1967. His last appointment was director of GKN Engineering Limited based in Wolverhampton.

In retirement Smyth and his wife Meriol went to live in Worthing where he passed away in a nursing home on 23 December 1990, but a few days after his 54th wedding anniversary for which he had briefly been able to return home. His wife passed away on 16 September the following year. They had one child, a son named Anthony who is currently Vicar of St Ethelburga's at St

Leonards-on-Sea. WA Smyth was a wonderful character, a true railwayman and a very sound engineer who made an enormous impression on the people at the Castle Engine Works. He accomplished much for the welfare of the management and staff, and in particular in the recruitment and training of young men and boys. He also made a significant name for himself in the industry, as well as upholding the good name of WG Bagnall Limited in the locomotive manufacturing industry generally. In his time with Bagnall the firm achieved a lot and he was in no small measure responsible for the success the Company enjoyed in the decade of the 1950s; an excellent judge of men Smyth gathered around him an extremely sound and loyal team. He always felt that his years at the Castle Engine Works were among the happiest of his long and distinguished professional life.

The Heenan Group directors of WG Bagnall Limited, with one exception, resigned en-block on 2 March 1959 and were replaced by Darby Haddon and Jack Whimpenny. The exception was Norman Stokes, as he had been partly instrumental in negotiating the 'deal' with Dormans; this behind-the-scenes activity on his part had been without the knowledge of either Smyth or Harry Davies, and quite obviously had a demoralising effect among the senior staff. Harry Davies was in fact demoted to a position of commercial manager; he did not stay long and left the company on 8 January 1960 - he had to all intents and purposes been given the sack. Vic Betteley did not remain long either, also becoming very disillusioned and left for pastures new in October 1959. Other senior staff changes concerned Jim Webberley who became chief engineer in early 1960 - a new position - and Bill Brookes who took over from Jim as chief draughtsman.

Harry Davies went to work for a company of steel merchants in Liverpool, moving house to live on the Wirral, in the first instance at Hoylake and later at Heswall. Davies was a great loss to the locomotive manufacturing industry as he had been involved in it for most of his working life. An accomplished sportsman he played cricket for Milford, which was a village near the Stafford suburb of Weeping Cross where along with his family he lived. Davies was also a good footballer, as well as very experienced snooker player and as if this was not enough to occupy his leisure hours he was an accomplished painter in water colours. Harry Davies

had, or so the story goes, honed his snooker playing skills whilst still a young man and living with his parents. Remember his father was a senior policeman, and Harry was able to use the excellent snooker facilities in the police recreation clubs at the various police stations his father was stationed at! Harry Davies passed away on 13 December 1981; his wife Minnie died shortly after Christmas in 1989. They had a son named Trevor.

Vic Betteley went to work for the Atomic Energy Authority in London moving home to Orpington. He was involved in the design and construction of nuclear power stations, in particular at Trawsfynydd in North Wales; later he became a senior lecturer in production engineering at Woolwich Polytechnic. Vic Betteley was elected a member of The Institution of Mechanical Engineers on 18 November 1955; proposed by WA Smyth, among his supporters were Sydney Ridgway and Bill Brookes. Vic passed away after a long illness in December 2003, and is survived by his wife Doris and three of their four children. Vic was a great railway enthusiast and like Harry a sad loss to the industry; WA Smyth always referred to him as the Company's unofficial archivist, and he would often pass on to Vic letters from enthusiasts. He would also generally conduct any groups of enthusiasts or like-minded individuals round the works. It is in no small measure due to Vic's effects in this direction that so much of the company's records have survived in one form or another.

Whilst on the subject of people, a few other points are worth a mention before moving on to the activities of the Company under the Dorman umbrella. After the takeover the shareholding in the Company consisted of 248,500 shares held by WH Dorman & Company Limited, and 500 each by Haddon, Whimpenney and Stokes. On 2 January 1961 Robert Anthony Wenham was elected to the board; he was the London & export sales manager of GM Wenham & Company Limited of Horley House, Upper Regent Street London W1, and a company that acted for Dormans. Later, on 5 April 1961, George David Robinson joined the board; 39 years old at the time Robinson had been appointed general manager of WG Bagnall Limited about the time Harry Davies left. At the time of the acquisition the London office of the Company was moved to 1 Hay Hill, London SW1, the Dorman office in the capital.

There is an interesting story regarding Norman Stokes which is well worth telling. Leaving the Company in late 1961 - he resigned from the board on 8 December - he returned to work for his former employer, Bright Westland, accountants in Stafford. However, he did not stay there long and soon moved to the Manchester area to work for another accountancy firm. In about 1965 he applied for a job with GKN and attended an interview at its Birmingham HQ. On this occasion he was, ironically, interviewed by a panel which included WA Smyth: it will come as no surprise to readers that he was unsuccessful in his application.

Locomotives were by no means new to WH Dorman as the company had been supplying its petrol and later diesel engines for use in locomotives since the First World War. Mention was made in Chapter Five that some of the early Bagnall petrol-locomotives had Dorman engines. During the First World War, once it had become clear that light and simple narrow-gauge railways would be of enormous advantage in supporting the form of trench warfare adopted in France and Belgium, there was a demand for locomotives, both steam and internal combustion. The Motor Rail & Tram Car Company Limited of Bedford had developed a small lightweight narrow-gauge locomotive powered by a petrol engine, a Dorman engine being selected to provide the power. No less than 590 Dorman 2JO two-cylinder vertical four-stroke petrol engines were supplied for the smaller 20 horsepower Motor Rail locomotives, and another 200 of the larger 4JO engines for the 40 horsepower locomotives; the locomotives were marketed under the product name Simplex. The bigger engine was also used in a significant number of the petrol-electric locomotives built by British Westinghouse and Dick Kerr, and we saw in Chapter Six how WG Bagnall Limited had been involved in manufacturing the mechanical parts for some of this type of locomotive.

It goes without saying perhaps, that in its acquisition of WG Bagnall Limited Dorman saw a significant market for its diesel engines in Bagnall locomotives. Mention was made briefly in the last Chapter that Dorman engines were substituted for other makes in a few of the diesel-mechanical locomotives that were either on hand, or under construction at the date of takeover. However, even before the Dorman involvement it was becoming apparent to the design

staff at the Castle Engine Works that the mechanical transmission for diesel shunting locomotives was becoming more and more outmoded. The Company had gained some valuable experience of hydraulic transmissions with the Bagnall-Burns tractors, a transmission mode with the potential to provide a much smoother take-up of torque. With no requirement for manual, or indeed automatic mechanical gear changes, hydraulic transmissions have an uninterrupted power to speed curve. Employment of true hydraulic transmissions for locomotives in anything other than the odd prototype, along with a few miniature locomotives built in the early 1930s by Hudswell Clarke & Company Limited of Leeds for use in pleasure parks and the like, had been pioneered in this country by the North British Locomotive Company of Glasgow. North British had entered into an agreement with the well established German manufacturer of hydraulic transmissions, JM Voith Machinenfrabik GmbH of Heidenheim, to build locomotives using Voith technology as early as 1950. Later, under a licence agreement, North British built the transmission units itself establishing a manufacturing facility at its Queens Park Works in Glasgow. Several British locomotive builders designed and built various types of locomotive transmissions in an attempt to combine what were considered the best points of both the mechanical and hydraulic systems - it has to be added that varying degrees of success followed most of these ventures. The Hunslet Engine Company and Hudswell Clarke & Company fell into this category, as did Ruston & Hornsby of Lincoln. In the case of Bagnall however, a decision was made to use the well-proven technology embodied in the designs of British Twin Disc Limited and J Brockhouse & Company Limited of Wolverhampton.

British Twin Disc with works at Rochester in Kent, manufactured torque converters under licence from Twin Disc Clutch AG, a Swiss company based in Zurich. The Twin Disc converters worked on the hydrokinetic principle and could be supplied with single, two or three stages depending on the power and speed ranges required, and in a variety of sizes to suit engine output. For locomotive use the converters incorporated an over-centre clutch allowing the engine to be disengaged from the transmission. The Brockhouse converter was a much smaller unit employing a single fluid circuit and worked on the hydrodynamic principle; for locomotive use it was coupled to epicyclic gear trains to give forward and reverse movement. The first use of Twin Disc converters in locomotives in this country was in 1957, when they were fitted into shunting locomotives built by Andrew Barclay Sons & Company Limited of Kilmarnock.

There was a lot of competition in the market for industrial diesel shunting locomotives at the time Bagnall decided to introduce hydraulic transmissions. All the established builders were moving in the same direction, and there was a new competitor in the industry. In November 1956 Rolls-Royce Limited acquired Sentinel (Shrewsbury) Limited, with its extensive workshops at Shrewsbury, from its parent Metal Industries Limited. At the time Rolls-Royce was expanding its diesel engine manufacturing capability and had been on the look out for additional facilities. When the acquisition took place Sentinel were still building the geared chain-drive steam locomotives for which it was so well known and briefly described in Chapter Nine. Rolls-Royce engineers soon realised that the design of these steam locomotives was such that the underframe, wheels and chain-driven final drive arrangements could equally well be used with a diesel engine and hydraulic transmission instead of a high-speed enclosed steam engine. Like British Twin Disc Limited Rolls-Royce too, negotiated a licence agreement with the Swiss parent company to manufacture the torque converters in this country, and a production line was introduced at its Derby works. It was this design of converter that was used in the new design of Sentinel diesel locomotive, and some time later Rolls-Royce acquired control of the British Twin Disc Company. In conjunction with the well established Sentinel agents Thomas Hill (Rotherham) Limited, arrangements were made to convert existing Sentinel steam locomotives to diesel hydraulic power, at a cost much below that of a new locomotive. Sometimes this was achieved by converting customers existing locomotives, and in other cases by purchasing otherwise redundant Sentinel steam locomotives and converting them for resale. The converted locomotives were marketed under the trade-name Vanguard.

Concurrently with this activity by Thomas Hill, Rolls-Royce designed a range of diesel-hydraulic shunting locomotives using many of the mechanical design principles for the underframes and running gear of the steam locomotives. The first new diesel-hydraulic locomotive appeared from the Shrewsbury works in 1959; the range embraced locomotives from around 200 to 700 horsepower, and from small four-wheel locomotives with chain-drive to eight-coupled locomotives with side-rod drive. The company was extremely successful with this range of locomotives and as well as supplying numerous customers in this country there was an expanding export market too. The locomotives, originally marketed under the Sentinel name, were striking in appearance and at one point responsible for an industrial design award. The excellent power to size ratio of the Rolls-Royce engines, along with the design of the locomotive frame, facilitated the engine being mounted comparatively low, such that the whole engine compartment could also be low and a large commodious cab almost centrally placed gave excellent vision for the crews. Special attention was given to access for shunting staff along with the general all-round comfort of the crews. A total of almost 300 locomotives were built before production ceased in 1971, from which readers will understand that notwithstanding the activities of the traditional builders, Bagnall was facing a lot of competition for its new range of locomotives.

Before moving on to describe the range of diesel-hydraulic locomotives designed at Stafford, one more issue needs mentioning. The Dorman agent in South Africa was a company called EC Lenning & Company, a firm that not only marketed Dorman diesel engines, but had entered into an agreement in 1950 to sell small narrow-gauge Simplex diesel locomotives built in this country by Motor Rail Limited of Bedford. At the time these small locomotives were very popular in the South African mining industry. The Lenning agreement was with the South African Motor Rail agents Railway Mine & Plantation Equipment Limited, and the success of the venture was the willingness of Lenning to invest in, and import, a range of locomotives holding them as stock so as to be able to affect immediate delivery against orders. This was in general terms alien to the locomotive manufacturing business, where the practice was for locomotives to be built against specific orders, with the consequent time lag for the build and delivery. Following the success of this arrangement Lenning established a further agreement with Margolis & Ralph

Two official views of the small four-wheel diesel-hydraulic locomotive number 3188 as built to suit 2ft 6in gauge track, and based on the M&R Engineering design as described in the adjoining text. Prior to delivery this locomotive was converted to two-foot gauge.

of Germiston, a suburb of Johannesburg in the Transvaal, and this company, via a subsidiary trading as M&R Engineering (Pty) Limited with workshops at Germiston, started to build narrow-gauge locomotives. These locomotives were to all intents and purposes identical to the Motor Rail designs, and like the homemade version they all had Dorman engines. It appears that somehow or other through this connection, WH Dorman came-by the design drawings for a small four-wheel chain-drive diesel-hydraulic locomotive, and on acquiring control of WG Bagnall Limited passed the information on to the design staff at the Castle Engine Works.

In 1966 EC Lenning acquired control of its sub-contractor M&R Engineering, and the range of locomotives constructed expanded considerably. Around 800 locomotives are thought to have been built by the company, many of them still in use in South Africa today. Subsequently Lenning acquired CKK Engineering (Pty) Limited of Benoni, also in the Transvaal, a company which had the manufacturing licence via Hubert Davies to build in South Africa the well-established American design of Goodman narrow-gauge electric and battery-electric locomotives. These locomotives were also very popular with the South African mining industry, in particular for use underground, and are still being manufactured in South Africa today under licence from the Goodman Equipment Corporation of Chicago. They are sold under the Goodman-Lenning name.

The range of diesel-hydraulic locomotives developed at Stafford consisted of four basic types and six prototypes were built. They were:

1. A small narrow-gauge four-wheel chain-driven locomotive based on the M&R Engineering drawings. This design was offered in power ranges from 30 to 60 horsepower and in track gauges up to metre. The engine was from the Dorman LB series, both a two or three-cylinder version and the transmission a Brockhouse torque converter and then separate roller chains to each axle. Frames were outside, wheel diameter 1ft 6in and the wheelbase 3ft 6in. Maximum speed was eight mph, weight in working order in the range 4½ to 8½ tons and the loads that could be hauled on level track from 180 to 345 tons.

2. A larger narrow-gauge design suitable for track gauges up to about 3ft 6in and power ranges from 70 to 100 horsepower. This was another outside-frame four-wheel design with an engine from the Dorman LB range, but in this case the four and five-cylinder units. Transmission was via a single-stage British Twin Disc torque converter and a frame-mounted Wiseman dog-clutch final drive unit, and thence roller chains to the trailing axle, and a further chain to couple the two axles together. Wheel diameter was two-foot, wheelbase 3ft 9in, weight in working order in the range eight to 10 tons, maximum speed 16½ mph and the loads hauled on level track in the range 325 to 405 tons.

3. This was a small lightweight four-wheel chain-driven standard-gauge locomotive that could be

These two illustrations are of the second size of diesel-hydraulic design, in this case completely designed at Stafford; number 3190, two-foot gauge and new to the Ashanti Goldfields for use in Ghana. The first view is an official one, whilst the second was taken on location at Ashanti in about 1975. By this time the locomotive had some modifications, including the wheel-sets and a Gardner engine; as can be seen it has also suffered not a small amount of wear and tear! Note however, it retains its Bagnall manufacturer's plate on the cab side. (Right hand picture - Collection Frank Jux)

supplied in power ranges 70 to 100 horsepower. The engine was again from the Dorman LB range in four and five-cylinder configurations and the transmission a single-stage British Twin Disc torque converter. Final drive was via a frame-mounted Wiseman unit and then roller chains to the trailing axle, and from that axle to the leading one. The wheel diameter was 2ft 6in and the wheelbase five-foot, weight in working order in the range eight to 10 tons, maximum speed 16½ mph and the loads hauled on level track between 325 and 405 tons. It would have been possible to make locomotives of this design to suit track gauges from metre upwards, although the two built were for standard-gauge.

4. Largest of the range was a six-coupled standard-gauge locomotive for the power range 230 to 460 horsepower with a Dorman engine from the Q range, with either six or eight-cylinders. Transmission was via a three-stage British Twin Disc torque converter and a Wiseman final drive unit mounted on the trailing axle, and thence conventional side-rods. Although the prototype was an 0-6-0 the design could easily be adapted for four or eight-wheel configurations. Wheel diameter was 3ft 4in, the wheelbase was ten-foot and the maximum speed between 15½ and 23½mph. Weight in working order in the range 29 to 54 tons and the loads that could be hauled on level track between 1,180 and 2,200 tons.

The prototypes built consisted of six locomotives, two of types 1 and 3, and one each of the other two. Manufacturer's numbers 3188 and 3189 were built to the M&R Engineering design as outlined in 1 above, 3188 to suit 2ft 6in gauge and 3189 two-foot gauge. The first one had a Dorman 3LB111 engine rated at 49 horsepower and the second a 2LB11 engine rated at 30 horsepower. Number 3190 was of the type described under 2 above, with a Dorman 5LB engine rated at 93 horsepower and built to suit two-foot gauge. Two locomotives of the lightweight standard-gauge design in 3 above were built, works numbers 3207 and 3208, and despite having been laid down to stock orders in September 1960, when positive orders were received the diesel engines had not been installed, or indeed ordered. Hence, at the customers request Gardner engines were specified in both cases and the unit selected the well-established 5LW rated at 89 horsepower. Last of all number 3191 was of the largest design described in 4 above, fitted with a Dorman 6QAT six-cylinder turbo-charged engine rated at 342 horsepower.

Before describing what happened to these six locomotives it is necessary to mention that in July 1961 WH Dorman & Company Limited, and hence WG Bagnall Limited, were acquired by the English Electric Company Limited, and very soon after a decision was

The third size of diesel-hydraulic locomotive, again designed at Stafford, is this standard-gauge four-wheel model with a Gardner 5LW 89 horsepower engine. Two were built and these two photographs show number 3207, new in October 1961 to Leys Malleable Castings Limited, for use at its works in Derby. The first view is of the locomotive when new standing outside the New Erecting Shop, while the second one taken on 27 September 1963 shows it at work. This locomotive and its sister number 3208, survive in preservation. (Right-hand view late Brian Webb Collection - Industrial Railway Society)

taken to cease locomotive production at Stafford. The two small locomotives manufacturer's numbers 3188 and 3189, despite being to all intents and purposes complete - 3189 was in fact largely a collection of finished parts - were unsold and taken to the Robert Stephenson & Hawthorn (RSH) works at Darlington. It will be recalled from an earlier Chapter that this company was also part of the English Electric group, and at the time industrial locomotive production was being concentrated at Darlington. Number 3188 was eventually sold to the Assam Railways & Trading Company for use at coal mines in Upper Assam, but before delivery it was converted to suit two-foot gauge and had its engine up-rated to 64 horsepower - despatch was in January 1963. Its sister went via Calcutta-based Indian agents George Miller & Company (Private) Limited, to the Indian Sri Amritnagar Selected Collieries - despatch was also in 1963.

Manufacturer's number 3190, also sent to Darlington as it was unsold at the time of the English Electric takeover, was eventually sold to an old Bagnall customer, the Ashanti Goldfields Corporation Limited. Despatched in November 1963 via Middlesbrough docks to Ghana, the sale price was £3,700 free-on-board. The two lightweight standard-gauge locomotives were both despatched from Stafford.

Number 3207 was sold in October 1961 to Leys Malleable Casting Limited for use at its works in Derby, while sister number 3208 was sold to another Leys company, Harrison & Company Limited, for use at its works at North Hykeham in Lincolnshire - it was despatched in November 1961.

Worth a brief mention at this point is that when in 1968 Baguley-Drewry Limited of Burton-on-Trent, were building three 80 horsepower four-wheel diesel-hydraulic locomotives with Perkins engines for Westminster Plant, the under-frames were based on the Bagnall design of numbers 3207 and 3208. The Bagnall drawings were supplied to Baguley by GEC Traction Limited, as successors to English Electric, and the locomotives, Baguley numbers 3655 to 3657, were for the civil engineering contractor Costain, for use in Dubai.

The last of the four designs was manufacturer's number 3191, completed in late 1960 and initially used for trials and demonstration purposes. First of all it went to the Shelton Iron & Steel Company Limited to work at its Etruria works in Stoke-on-Trent, followed by John Lysaght's Scunthorpe Works Limited for trials at the Normanby Park Steel Works at Frodingham. On return to Stafford following this in-service experience a number of modifications were undertaken, in particular to the electrical wiring and the engine and transmission cooling systems. The locomotive was then sold in July 1961 to the National Coal Board (NCB) for use in South Wales. However it was December before it was ready for despatch, leaving Stafford on 29 December 1961 for the Aberaman colliery and coal preparation plant complex near Aberdare.

The complete range of these diesel-hydraulic locomotives departed from the conventional riveted plate frame construction of the earlier diesel locomotives with mechanical transmission, which were not unlike the steam locomotives in this respect. Extensive use of welding was employed such that in the case of the larger locomotives, the entire frame assembly, complete with the buffer beams and mounting bearers for the power equipment, was an integral welded steel structure. This method of construction not only significantly reduced manufacturing costs, but it also gave a much stronger assembly, far better able to absorb the riggers of every-day operation, while at the same time providing a simple method of adjusting the final weight of a locomotive to suit particular customers requirements. By varying the thickness of the various steel sections the frame weight could be varied, and with far less risk of weakening the overall frame structure than with a conventional riveted

arrangement. Equally it made adding weight easy too, when a high axle-load was a requirement. This form of construction required new skills among the workforce along with the requirement for investment in both additional, and in many cases more sophisticated, welding equipment.

A lot of thought went into these new locomotive designs, and they all had neat and handsome lines; the large standard-gauge locomotive was particularly pleasing in external design characteristics with a distinct family likeness to the earlier diesel-mechanical locomotives. Like the Rolls-Royce engines fitted in the Sentinel locomotives, the Dorman 6QAT engine also had a good power to size ratio allowing it to sit low-down in the locomotives frames. Therefore, in the case of the Bagnall design a low engine compartment allowed for an almost centrally mounted large cab with excellent all-round crew vision. There were also good facilities for shunting staff with ample provision of steps and hand rails in all four corners. The Company had a lot of success with orders for locomotives of this general design. In February 1961 three standard-gauge locomotives with an 0-4-0 wheel arrangement had been ordered for use at the Royal Ordnance Factory at Pembrey in South Wales. Work had commenced in

Manufacturer's number 3191 was the last and largest of the diesel-hydraulic designs, a standard-gauge 0-6-0, the prototype for several built later to the same generic design. This one was eventually sold to the NCB for use in South Wales. The external lines of this locomotive were partly responsible for the later English Electric design of 'Stephenson' diesel-hydraulic shunting locomotives.

Like most locomotives used in the coal-mining industry in this country, especially in later years, Bagnall 3191 had a rough time, evidence this view taken one evening in July 1973, with its days work done, outside the locomotive shed at Mountain Ash Colliery. This colliery was near Aberdare in South Wales, where the locomotive was scrapped in June 1985, after the pits and associated plant closed.

building these three when the decision was taken to cease locomotive production at Stafford. As a consequence the parts already made along with the material on-hand were transferred to Darlington, where the locomotives were erected. In April 1961 the Central Electricity Generating Board ordered two similar locomotives for a new power station being built at Richborough in Kent. July 1961 saw a further order, in this case from the Nyasaland Railways for two 3ft 6in gauge six-wheel locomotives, followed in December 1961 by the Sudan Railways ordering six four-wheelers, also for 3ft 6in gauge. Lastly the BP Trading Company Limited ordered an 0-4-0 for its Baglan Bay works near Swansea. All these locomotives were built at Darlington but to Bagnall design principles, although where the locomotives differed slightly from the earlier ones, the actual design work was undertaken in the Darlington drawing office.

During the period of Dorman ownership there were two repeat orders for diesel-mechanical locomotives and although details were given in the last Chapter, a brief mention is worth while at this point. One was another metre-gauge 0-8-0 for Iraq; in fact three had originally been ordered but one was later cancelled - this was its replacement. The new one replacing the cancelled order was manufacturer's number 3205, despatched in March 1961, and unlike the earlier two it had a Dorman 6QAT engine rated at 240 horsepower. The cost was £18,000 free-on-board and at the same time two new Dorman engines and conversion kits,

which included the engine bed-plates, were supplied to re-engine the earlier locomotives. Like most operators the people in Iraq were having problems with the National engines originally fitted. The Rustenburg Platinum Mines ordered another two-foot gauge 0-6-0, identical to the earlier two; this one was number 3204 and the price, £17,900 carriage, insurance and freight paid to Port Elizabeth.

Three of the standard-gauge 0-6-0 diesel-mechanical designs that had been laid down to stock were still on hand when Dorman assumed control. One was of the smaller 200 horsepower design and the other two of the larger 300 horsepower configuration. Manufacturer's number 3151 of the smaller size had been laid down to stock in March 1958, completed with a Gardner 8L3 engine rated at 204 horsepower, it was then stored in the old erecting shop. In July 1961 a decision had been made to modify this locomotive installing a Dorman 6QAT engine rated at 204 horsepower along with complete flame-proofing equipment, and in February the following year it went on loan to the British Petroleum oil refinery on the Isle-of-Grain. Returning from loan in October 1962, the locomotive went to the RSH works at Darlington where, following removal of the flame-proofing equipment, it was sold to British Waterways for use at Sharpness Docks in Gloucestershire. It was despatched in May 1963 and has survived in preservation. The first of the larger locomotives, number 3160, was laid down in September 1958 and fitted with a Dorman 6QAT engine rated at

Picture taken in the New Erecting Shop in 1961 with a Dorman 6QAT diesel engine complete with torque-converter, ready to be fitted to a locomotive, in this case for number 3205, a metre-gauge 0-8-0 for the United Cement Company in Iraq. Notice on the right an upturned under-frame for the Brush Traction British Railways A1A-A1A Type 2 diesel locomotives, and to the left a new locomotive firebox. This view helps to illustrate that boiler related work was still a prominent element of production even at this late date. The particular firebox, consisting of both the inner firebox and the outer wrapper, order number 9500 of March 1960, was ordered by Crown Agents for Nigerian Railways. It would have been in this shop while being prepared for shipment - notice the timber packing around part of it.

Photograph taken outside the New Erecting Shop some time in late 1961, showing a selection of new locomotives; from left to right they are: numbers 3190; 3161; 3188 (in front); 3191. Notice that both the diesel-mechanical locomotive number 3161, and the diesel-hydraulic locomotive number 3191, had already been sold to the NCB for use in South Wales as they both have the initials NCB painted on the cab-sides. At this time these two locomotives would have been awaiting delivery and the opportunity was taken to photograph the four together.

Front page of one of a series of four publicity leaflets encompassing the new range of diesel-hydraulic locomotives. This one covers the 70 to 100 horsepower four-wheel narrow-gauge design with a single-stage Twin Disc torque converter; it is dated July 1960.

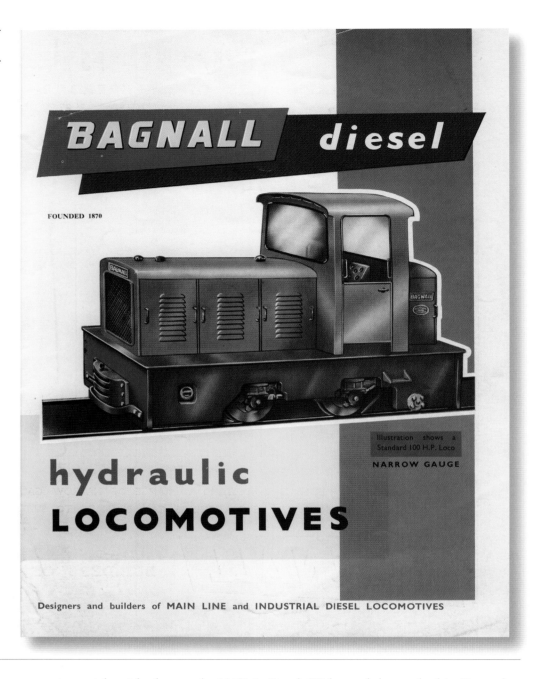

FOUNDED 1870

Illustration shows a Standard 100 H.P. Loco

NARROW GAUGE

hydraulic
LOCOMOTIVES

Designers and builders of MAIN LINE and INDUSTRIAL DIESEL LOCOMOTIVES

304 horsepower. After demonstration trials with the NCB on the Bowes Railway in Durham in mid-1959, and later with Dorman Long (Steel) Limited at Lackenby near Middlesbrough, it was sold to the Mobil Oil Company Limited for use at its refinery at Coryton in Essex. The selling price was £14,700 and despatch on 28 October 1959. Last of the trio, number 3161 with the same engine as 3160, and laid down to stock at the same time, was also loaned for demonstration purposes for a period in the late summer of 1959, again to Dorman Long at Lackenby. It was eventually sold to

the NCB in South Wales and despatched in December 1961; it went to Aberaman Colliery at Aberdare where it worked alongside number 3191 mentioned above - in fact the locomotives were despatched together. When 3160 and 3161 were ordered for stock, the plan was to fit the National M4AA7 engine rated at 308 horsepower; however, there is some doubt if in fact the National engines were ever fitted, or even ordered, and in any event both locomotives were sold with Dorman engines.

Brush Traction Limited continued to order sets of

An example of the diesel-hydraulic locomotives ordered from Bagnall, but in the event built at Darlington, although largely to the Bagnall design principles. In July 1961 the Nyasaland Railways ordered two of these 3ft 6in gauge six-wheelers, allocated Bagnall numbers 3220 and 3221, and RSH numbers 8369 and 8370. They had Rolls Royce C8TFL eight-cylinder 342 horsepower engines and cost £17,500 each free-on-board at Liverpool, where they were sent in November 1962. Fitted with vacuum brakes they turned the scales at 40 tons 10 cwt in working order and had a maximum speed of almost 24 mph.

mechanical parts and bogies for the BR Type Two A1A-A1A diesel-electric locomotives it was building. Fifteen sets were ordered on 22 May 1959, 10 on 30 September, 12 on 15 February 1960, with the final order for five sets on 19 May 1961. The last set of parts from this final order which was allocated works number 3218, as mentioned in the last Chapter, had a specially strengthened underframe to take an uprated 1,950 horsepower Mirrlees engine; it was used for the locomotive allocated BR number D5845. As delivery of some of these underframes and mechanical parts was after the English Electric take-over, one can imagine the new owners were not too happy, as English Electric and Brush were in direct competition in tendering for BR orders! However, work was too far advanced to do very much about it.

There were a number of other orders either on hand at the time of acquisition by English Electric, or obtained before WG Bagnall Limited ceased to exist as a separate entity. Indeed at the close of 1961, the Bagnall order book for locomotives had a value of £285,000. However, apart from two cases, one of which was for a steam locomotive, all the other orders were fulfilled by locomotives to existing English

Electric/Robert Stephenson & Hawthorns designs. The exception in the case of a diesel locomotive was another of the small four-wheel locomotives based on the M&R Engineering design, Bagnall number 3237 (RSH 8389), once again for the Sri Amritnagar Selected Collieries in India. For a short time after the English Electric acquisition industrial diesel shunting locomotives were marketed under the joint Robert Stephenson & Hawthorns and WG Bagnall name, and they had manufacturers plates with both names on them. However, a decision was taken by English Electric in 1964 to not only close the Darlington works of RSH, but henceforth to market all locomotives under the English Electric name. Thus the individual names of Robert Stephenson & Hawthorns, Vulcan Foundry and of course WG Bagnall Limited, disappeared.

Although there is no common agreement, the present authors are of the view that the prototype Bagnall standard-gauge 0-6-0 diesel-hydraulic shunting locomotive design, as embodied in manufacturer's number 3191, influenced the design of the English Electric range of diesel-hydraulic shunting locomotives. The first of these locomotives, which took the type name 'Stephenson', appeared from the RSH works at

Another example of the locomotives ordered from Bagnall but built by RSH is this one; a four-wheeler allocated Bagnall number 3228 and RSH 8377. Ordered by the BP Trading Company Limited for its Baglen Bay plant near Swansea in South Wales, it was fitted with a Rolls Royce C6TFL engine rated at 262 horsepower. Despatch from Darlington was in early 1962, and the selling price £14,580. Bagnall had quoted for this locomotive on 17 June 1961, and the order was received on 19 October. Notice the family likeness to number 3191 illustrated earlier. The first illustration shows part of the interior of the cab and drivers desk; notice the excellent crew vision.

Darlington in 1963, the production line in effect following on from the Bagnall orders transferred to Darlington from Stafford as outlined above. The new locomotives, initially at least, used engines from the Dorman range with British Twin Disc torque converters and either a Wiseman or Self Changing Gears final drive. As with the Bagnall prototype most of the locomotives had the final drive mounted on the rear axle and there was thus, no jackshaft, which in turn helped to simplify the design. The general external lines of the locomotives were similar to the Stafford product, but rather more austere and without such smooth and rounded lines. Be that as it may, the English Electric range of diesel-hydraulic shunting locomotives became a successful one, and no fewer than 140 where built between 1963 and 1979 when production ceased, the first 14 from Darlington and the remainder, except for 12 built under licence in Spain, from the Vulcan Foundry in Newton-le-Willows.

Before leaving the diesel-hydraulic locomotives it is worth mentioning that in the period from 1958 to 1961 no fewer than 250 design proposals were drawn up by the drawing office - some for locomotives with mechanical transmission. In every case there was a

This is an example of the manufacturer's plates fitted to the locomotives that were ordered from Stafford but built at Darlington; it was a style also used on a few other locomotives built at Darlington for which Bagnall had no input. In all cases where a Bagnall number had been allocated, only the RSH one was quoted on the plates. This particular plate is from one of the two locomotives, Bagnall numbers 3212 and 3213, RSH 8367 and 8368, for the Central Electricity Generating Board at Richborough Power Station in Kent. Ordered in April 1961, in this case some material was ordered and delivered to Stafford, and work was commenced before the various parts and material was moved to Darlington.

customer in mind; sometimes the proposals were part of a formal tendering process and on other occasions more speculative; but each and every one of them employed a lot of effort. The proposed designs covered all number of combinations of wheel arrangement, power equipment, track-gauge, train coupling arrangements and overall size. Some progressed to actual orders being placed, only to be cancelled subsequently. For example on 22 December 1957 the Altos Hornes de Vizcaya Iron & Steel Company ordered two metre-gauge 105 horsepower 0-4-0 diesel-mechanical locomotives for use at its works at Bilbao in Northern Spain. A price of £10,929 each was agreed free-on-board Liverpool and a Dorman 6LB engine was selected, but the order was cancelled before any physical work was undertaken. In this case the design was based on the New Zealand shunting tractors supplied earlier.

The steam locomotive on hand at the time of the English Electric takeover had been ordered early in 1961 by the London based agents Railway Mine & Plantation Equipment Limited, on behalf of a Dutch customer NV Voorheen Ruhaak & Company. For use on a 700m/m gauge railway at an oil palm plantation in Sumatra, the order was for an 0-6-2 tender engine with 10x12in cylinders and two-foot diameter driving wheels, to an earlier design dating from 1940. This was manufacturer's number 2628 - also for use on an oil palm estate but in that case in Malaya. For the new

order Bagnall allocated number 3233 and the agreed price was £20,125 free-on-board Liverpool. Some material had been ordered, but no physical work had started, when the decision was taken to cease locomotive work at Stafford, and the order was sub-contracted by English Electric - actually RSH - to Andrew Barclay Sons & Company Limited of Kilmarnock, as that company was still in the market for building steam locomotives. The material ordered was despatched to Kilmarnock along with the drawings and patterns, and as Barclay manufacturer's number 2377, the locomotive was despatched on 25 September 1962 to Glasgow Docks for shipment. The only significant difference from the earlier locomotive was the extensive use of welding rather than rivets. It is interesting to speculate why Bagnall offered this rather unusual design for what was a new customer; perhaps the fact that the earlier engine had worked successfully at another oil palm plantation was a factor.

A number of steam locomotives came into the works for overhaul and other attention during the period of Dorman ownership, and the work usually involved extensive attention to the boilers including replacement fireboxes. The NCB was a good customer, locomotives arriving from a number of its areas, and a particularly interesting job involved one from Baddersley Colliery in Warwickshire. In this case the engine was a member of the war-time Austerity design of 0-6-0 saddle tank,

Front page of the specification for a steam locomotive dated October 1960, a locomotive that in the event was sub-contracted by RSH to Andrew Barclay Sons & Company Limited and built at Kilmarnock. Allocated Bagnall number 3233, the order was placed by NV Voorheen Ruhaak & Company, a Dutch organisation operating oil-palm plantations in Indonesia, via the agents Railway Mine & Plantation Equipment Limited. The Barclay number was 2377 and the locomotive, based on an earlier Bagnall, number 2628 which had been sent to Malay in 1940 - see Chapter 10 - was despatched in September 1962.

TELEPHONE:
321 & 322 STAFFORD

TELEGRAMS:
BAGNALL-STAFFORD

LONDON OFFICE:
XXXXXXXXX
LONDON S.W.1.
XXXXXXXX XXXXXX XXXXXXX

OUR REF. AJW/WBB/PJM/2213.

YOUR REF. RTW.4683.

W.G. Bagnall LTD.

LOCOMOTIVE BUILDERS & RAILWAY ENGINEERS

Castle Engine Works. Stafford.

SPECIFICATION 4th October, 1960.

of

AN 0-6-2 TYPE TENDER LOCOMOTIVE.

For Messrs. **Railway, Mine and Plantation Equipments Ltd.,**
P.O.Box No. 41,
Imperial House,
Dominion Street,
London. E.C.2.

The whole of the material used in the construction of this Locomotive to be of the highest quality procurable, and to conform to the latest Specifications of the British Engineering Standards Institution for Railway Rolling Stock Material. The workmanship to be of the best description.

SUMMARY OF LEADING PARTICULARS

Gauge of Railway	700	mm.		Heating Surface of Tubes	238	sq. ft.	
Wheeling Arrangement	0-6-2			,, ,, ,, Firebox	49	sq. ft.	
Diam. of Cylinders	10	ins.		,, ,, ,, Superheater	--	sq. ft.	
Stroke of Pistons	12	ins.		Total Heating Surface	287	sq. ft.	
Diam. of Driving Wheels	2 ft. 0	ins.		Grate Area	10	sq. ft.	
,, Leading ,,	2 ft. 0	ins.		Working Pressure	160	lbs. per sq. in.	
,, Trailing ,,	1 ft. 7	ins.		Bunker Capacity	120	cb. ft.	
Rigid Wheelbase(**engine**)	5 ft. 0	ins.		Tank	500	galls.	
Total	10 ft. 8½	ins.					
Maximum Height	9 ft. 5	ins.		Weight when empty (approx.)	13.6	tons.	
,, Width	6 ft. 9	ins.		,, in working order ,,	15	tons.	
,, Length ⎫				Tractive effort at 85% B.P.	6,800	lbs.	
Over Buffer Beams ⎭	17 ft. 7½	ins.		Ratio Adhesion/Tractive Effort	3.95 to 1.		

Description	The Engine to be carried on **eight** wheels, and to be of the 0-6-2 type, with outside cylinders and **tender** Tank, the general design to be similar to that shown by the accompanying **Drawing No. 25928 and photograph type E2628.**
Boiler and Firebox Casing	The Boiler casing to be of best Siemens Martin open Hearth Acid Basic Steel Plates. The barrel to be 7 ft. 3 ins. long, in **one** ring xxxbx xxxkxbxxing 2 ft. 7 ins. diameter inside, 3/8 ins. thick ; the longitudinal seams to be double rivetted **butt** joints ; circumferential seams **single** rivetted. Smokebox Tube-plate 5/8 ins. thick. The firebox to be of the **round top** type, the shell to be 3 ft. 10 ins. long by 3 ft. 6 ins. wide outside at foundation ring. The top and side plates to be 3/8 ins. thick, the throat plate 3/8 ins. thick and the back plate 3/8 ins. thick. The whole of the rivets in the Boiler Casing to be 13/16 ins. diam. 1⅞ ins. pitch, hydraulically rivetted wherever possible. A Steam Dome to be securely rivetted to the Boiler Barrel with a heavy strengthening ring inside the barrel directly underneath. A liberal supply of Mud Plugs and wash out facilities to be provided, the Boiler Plates to be suitably stiffened where mud plugs are screwed in. The Foundation and Firehole Rings to be forged from welding quality mild steel.

actually one built by RSH - number 7752 of 1953. As well as the repairs to the locomotive itself, it was fitted with an underfeed mechanical stoker, the actual stoker feed screw being driven by a small diesel engine located on the right-hand side foot framing alongside the smokebox.

There were several locomotives at the works for attention on which little or no work had begun when the decision was taken to stop locomotive work at Stafford, and, like the new steam locomotive order, they were transferred to Andrew Barclay Sons & Company Limited for completion. Three former BR Western Region 0-6-0 outside-cylinder 1500 class pannier tanks had been bought by the NCB for use at Coventry Colliery, and had already been moved to Stafford for overhaul. Before these particular locomotives could be moved to Kilmarnock by rail, the cylinders had to be

removed as the locomotives would not otherwise clear the Scottish Region loading gauge. After removal the cylinders were placed in railway wagons which accompanied the engines on their journey; obviously on completion of the repairs in Scotland they had to be transported to Coventry Colliery by road.

The very last locomotive to be overhauled at Stafford only just made it. The nearby English Electric factory (the former Siemens works) had a small four-wheel battery-electric locomotive used for shunting its sidings, and it needed its tyres re-profiling. As the wheel lathe was still in place and operable at the Castle Engine Works arrangements were made with BR for the locomotive to be hauled across in the early months of 1962, and the work was completed.

As well as boilers from complete locomotives the boiler shop was also busy with orders for spare boilers

Andrew Barclay number 2377 under steam test in the Erecting Shop at Kilmarnock. Had this locomotive been built at Stafford, it is likely to have been the last steam locomotive built there; in the event it was the last steam locomotive built by Andrew Barclay.

Bagnall 3161, sold in December 1961 along with 3191 to the NCB in South Wales, was one of the last diesel-mechanical locomotives sold. Laid down to a stock order as far back as September 1958, but not completed until after the Dorman acquisition, it was fitted with a Dorman engine; in this case a six-cylinder 6QAT rated at 304 horsepower. It is seen awaiting despatch.

Another of the diesel-mechanical locomotive that were in effect, left-over when English Electric assumed control, is this 208 horsepower example. Number 3151, photographed on 17 April 1990 at the British Waterways Sharpness Docks, where it went in May 1963, having earlier been on-loan to the BP oil refinery at Grain in Kent. This locomotive has survived into preservation and is currently with the Appleby Frodingham Railway Preservation Society at Scunthorpe.

and fireboxes, no less than six fireboxes being supplied in 1961, along with two new boilers for the two-foot gauge Bagnall 2-6-2 tank engines belonging to the Burma Mines. The very last boiler made was completed in 1961, a replacement for number 2537, which was one of the two Kerr, Stuart Moss Bay design locomotives the Company had built before the war for use in Pakistan. WS Edwards would have had a wryly smile about that!

In the late 1950s Peckett & Sons Limited, the Bristol based locomotive builder, came to the conclusion that the amount of boiler related work was insufficient to keep its boiler shop fully employed, closing it as a result. This was not however before entering into a 10 year agreement with Bagnall to sub-contract any boiler work to the Castle Engine Works. As events transpired in November 1961 the Peckett Company, which was a private one, was acquired by another Bristol based company, Reed Crane & Hoist Company Limited, itself a subsidiary of Harper Engineering & Electronics Limited, and it was not long before locomotive production ceased and the Peckett Atlas Works was closed. After the English Electric acquisition of WG Bagnall Limited, arrangements were made to transfer all boiler work, including any resulting from the Peckett agreement, to Andrew Barclay at Kilmarnock.

Shortly after WH Dorman acquired control a complete valuation of the works, plant and machinery was undertaken; it was dated 22 July 1960. The leasehold property together with the freehold land was valued at £175,000, and the plant, machinery, motor transport etc., at £181,181, giving a total valuation of £356,181. The leasehold land consisted of a little over seven acres and the lease ran for a period of 99 years from 25 March 1948 - the rent was £350 per annum - the freehold land comprised something over 12 acres.

Apart from the new erecting shop which has already been described, the principal buildings were:

Erecting shop. Flanked to the east by the fitting shop and to the west by the machine shop, this building after its several extensions, and minus the two flanking buildings, measured 340ft by 26ft 3in. One of the two bays had an 80ft long inspection pit and there were two Heywood 20 ton capacity electric overhead travelling

Mention has been made several times in these pages regarding the manufacture of turntables, and of one configuration or another, they remained a feature for almost the entire period of the firm's existence. This is a nine-foot diameter example to carry a load of six tons, and dating from the very last period of production. The last turn-table was built in February 1961, a 35ft diameter example for the Gaiety Theatre in Portsmouth.

cranes; one of the bays, the one to the east, had a multi-gauge track throughout its length, but there were no rails in the other bay. The construction of this shop betrayed its various extensions over the years in the design of the uprights to support the crane runners. The first 121ft from the south had timber uprights, the next 151ft brick uprights and the final 68ft steel stanchions. The working floor area amounted to 8,925 sq ft.

Fitting shop. To the east side of the erecting shop, 307ft long and 18ft 6in wide with a 33ft long and 12ft wide extension. The working floor area was 6,075 sq ft and there was a three ton hand-operated overhead travelling crane running the full length of the shop.

Machine shop. This building, to the west of the erecting shop, consisted of four sections respectively 341ft 6in; 259ft 6in; 11ft 9in and 66ft 9in long, and between 24ft and 25ft 6in wide. There were two overhead crane gantries, one 260ft long, a second 66ft long, and a total of five overhead travelling cranes of two tons capacity each, along with a variety of smaller hand and electrically operated cranes. The total working floor area equalled 16,360 sq ft.

Frame shop. This building was 181ft 6in long and 42ft wide, traversed by an overhead crane gantry for its entire length; this had a capacity of 20 tons although the Heywood overhead electric travelling crane only had a capacity of 15 tons. The working floor area amounted to 7,623 sq ft.

Wheel shop. Along side the frame shop and to its east, this building was 111ft long and 33ft 6in wide; there was an extension northwards 71ft long and 28ft 6in wide. The main part of this shop was traversed by a Heywood five-ton electric overhead travelling crane and the working floor area was 5,446 sq ft. This crane by the way, although motorised and modified by Heywood, had actually been built by the Company in 1909.

Tank shop. This shop was on the opposite, west side of the frame shop and was 112ft long and 44ft wide; a five-ton capacity Heywood overhead electric travelling crane traversed the entire shop. The working floor area was 4,956 sq ft.

Brass & iron foundries. These two buildings to the south of the frame shop were respectively 125ft 9in and 71ft long, and between 27ft 6in and 28ft 6in wide. Total working floor area was 5,536 sq ft.

Boiler shop. Large shop with three bays, each 179ft

Jimmy Budd with 'his' large planning machine busy machining a gear-case to an order from Walker Brothers Limited of Wigan; it was part of some machinery in connection with making paper - order numbers 9978 to 9983. The Company undertook quite a lot of heavy machining work for this customer, and this is yet another example of the diversification of work undertaken as locomotive and other railway related orders got more difficult to come by.

9in long and respectively 15ft 9in; 29ft 9in and 32ft wide; the total working area was 13,932 sq ft. Two of the bays had overhead crane gantries one of five-ton capacity and the other 10, and as with several of the other shops the electric overhead travelling cranes were of Heywood manufacture.

The total working floor area of the workshops was 112,105 sq ft and this included 7,436 sq ft of the new erecting shop. The complete working floor area including the offices, canteen, garages etc., equalled 125,074 sq ft. By this time although the electric power supply came from the National Grid the power house remained in use to house the electrical distribution arrangements and two electrically driven Bellis & Morcom two-stage vertical air compressors; from here compressed air was piped around most of the shops. For use around the works there was a Lansing Bagnall (no connection between this company and WG Bagnall) 12 horsepower petrol-driven industrial tractor and two Lister seven horsepower trucks, one petrol driven and

one diesel. There was also a Bray hydraulic loading shovel with a capacity of one ton and the Coles six-ton diesel-electric mobile crane described earlier. The Company owned seven Ford Consul saloon cars, one a 1958 model and the others 1959, as well as an Austin 10 cwt van and a two ton short wheelbase Bedford lorry. This vehicle by the way, complete with a temporary canvas cover, was utilised to take the works football team to away fixtures! The Consuls, a far cry from the Jaguars and Daimlers of the WS Edwards era. The inventory also lists the preserved locomotive ISABEL, although no value was attached to it.

The machinery was a combination of old and new, some dating back many years but all in good condition and adequate for the tasks they had to perform. Particular investments over the proceeding few years had been welding equipment, as this form of construction gradually overtook riveting for many operations. Some interchange of machinery took place with the Dorman works, although the Company already owned a number of Dorman designed and built grinding machines, which were another speciality of WH Dorman. For example there was a specially designed Dorman machine for grinding the curved expansion links of the valve motion, dating from 1905 it was in use until locomotive work came to an end.

An early decision of Dormans was closure of the iron foundry, and transfer of this work to the foundry at Tixall Road. At the Castle Engine Works it was replaced by equipment for casting aluminium as extra capacity was required for this type of work. The Dorman design of self-contained power units had a number of aluminium components and the extra manufacturing facilities available at Stafford, after closure of the iron foundry, were dedicated to this work.

The period of Dorman ownership continued to find the Company anxious to take on almost any work that it was capable of, and this included jobs on sub-contract from the Tixall Road works. One particular production line transferred en-block to the Castle Engine Works consisted of the manufacture of the patent Flextel piping and joints. This invention, which dates from 1921, consisted of a means whereby piping for gas or liquids could be easily adjusted to suit pipe movements, and at the same time was extremely light. Developments over the years made the Flextel coupling ideal for the steam and exhaust pipes of for example, articulated steam locomotives, as it worked on the ball and socket principle. Indeed we have already seen how this type of joint was used on the Bagnall articulated steam locomotives supplied to the South African sugar industry. This production line, moved to the Castle Engine Works shortly after Dorman took over, released space at Tixall Road for increased diesel engine production, and a small shop was set aside specifically for the work. It was however, not an entirely a new job for the staff, as Bagnall had on occasions in the past undertaken some Flextel work on sub-contract between the two companies.

Dorman had a longstanding arrangement with the very old established Cornwall firm of engineers, Holman Brothers Limited, and Dorman engines were frequently used in Holman machinery. In particular Holman built air compressors as well as portable rock drills mounted on track laying vehicles, and Dorman engines were often employed. Sometimes the erection work on the vehicles was sub-contracted to Dorman,

and some of this work came the way of the Castle Engine Works too.

During the three years of Dorman ownership the Company made a profit in two, and a loss in the other one. In 1959 on a trading profit of £57,989 the profit after tax amounted to £10,839, while in 1960 there was a trading loss of £14,889. In the last year, 1961, the trading profit was £30,361 and the profit after tax £12,126. While these figures are not too bad in themselves, they did not live up to the projections when the Company was bought by WH Dorman.

Brief reference was made earlier in this Chapter of the final demise of WG Bagnall Limited as a seperate entity. Whatever might or might not be said of the period of Dorman control, the Company had continued to trade on its own right. The English Electric Company Limited had long been on a trail of acquiring the manufacturers of locomotives and other railway rolling stock, as well as diesel engines. Mention has already been made of its acquisition in 1955 of the Vulcan Foundry and Robert Stephenson & Hawthorns. English Electric had in its range of manufacturing activities the capability to manufacture medium and slow-speed diesel engines, but not the smaller high-speed engines necessary if it was to expand locomotive building into a smaller range of locomotives for industrial shunting. For the previous few years main-line diesel-electric locomotives had been the principal product of the Vulcan Foundry, and to a lesser extent the RSH works at Darlington, although Vulcan did have a long standing arrangement with the Drewry Car Company Limited to build diesel-mechanical locomotives to Drewry designs, as this Company had no manufacturing facilities of its own. At the time of the English Electric interest in WH Dorman, it was considered that the Drewry designs were becoming outmoded by modern standards, and it appears too, that the licence arrangement with Drewry was not as profitable as English Electric would have liked. English Electric saw in WH Dorman & Company Limited an ideal opportunity to acquire a designer and builder of the range of diesel engines it wanted access to, and at the same time an opportunity to eliminate a competitor in the industrial locomotive market.

WH Dorman & Company Limited was a public company listed on the London stock exchange when English Electric started to buy shares on the open

One of the very last advertisements of the Company's independent existence is this one, which appeared in the Journal of the Institution of Locomotive Engineers in October 1961. The locomotive is number 3191, described earlier in this Chapter.

market. Eventually it arrived at a position, in accordance with the stock exchange rules, where it had to make a offer to the shareholders to acquire overall control. The offer was successful and an announcement was made on 3 June 1961, that an agreement had been reached, subject to Stock Exchange approval, to acquire the entire share capital of WH Dorman & Company Limited. The sale arrangements were completed on 22 July the same year, and as an wholly-owned subsidiary of WH Dorman & Company Limited, WG Bagnall Limited became a wholly-owned company within the English Electric Group. On 2 August Sir George H Nelson, chairman of the English Electric Company, along with Edward John Banks, were appointed directors of WG Bagnall Limited, and on 15 September 1961 Haddon, Whimpenny, Wenham and Robinson resigned, although the latter remained as general manager. At this same time Gerald Collingwood was appointed a director; Collingwood was the managing director of the Vulcan Foundry Limited. Nelson by the way was president at the time of the Locomotive & Allied Manufacturers Association. On 22 May 1962 the registered office of the Company was moved to the Vulcan Foundry at Newton-le-Willows, and on 11 June 1964 it was moved again, this time to the English Electric head office in London, located in The Strand.

And so it came about after 86 years in the trade and approaching 2,000 locomotives built, the manufacture of locomotives for the world's railways at Stafford, came to an untimely end.

In the late 1950s the Company built a wooden replica of a small locomotive for use as a float at local events, Stafford town carnival and the like. Mounted on the works Lansing Bagnall road tractor, it caused considerable amusement. Here it is on its way to one such event, unmistakably a product of the Castle Engine Works. Named THUNDERBOLT it was made by the pattern makers - notice the registration number of the tractor, which as it happens, was the same number as ISABEL, the locomotive preserved at the works. (Peter Dyer)

Chapter Fifteen

ENGLISH ELECTRIC & AFTER

The rest of the story need not keep the reader long. After the cessation of locomotive work described in the last Chapter the business was transferred to the Robert Stephenson & Hawthorn works at Darlington, as already noted a company also under the English Electric (EE) umbrella. The WG Bagnall Limited name continued to be used for a couple of years. The later diesel-hydraulic locomotives mentioned in the last Chapter which were completed or built at Darlington, basically to Bagnall designs, had builders plates reading: 'ROBERT STEPHENSON & HAWTHORNS Ltd AND W.G. BAGNALL Ltd LOCOMOTIVE WORKS DARLINGTON', with RSH manufacturer's numbers and the year of completion. Some other locomotives for which orders had been received at Stafford, but were not built to Bagnall designs, also had plates of this style. Many of the locomotives had manufacturer's numbers allocated in both the Bagnall and RSH lists. RSH used headed notepaper with the words in brackets: 'In Association with WG Bagnall Limited', and this continued until late 1962. The Darlington works closed in 1964 and all English Electric locomotive work was concentrated at the Vulcan Foundry in Newton-le-Willows. The registered office of WG Bagnall Limited was moved to Vulcan on 22 May 1962, and on 11 June 1964, to the English Electric head office in London on The Strand.

On 1 June 1962 English Electric formed a new company, a wholly owned subsidiary under the name English Electric Traction Limited, to bring together under a single management all the traction activities of the English Electric group, and this included the Vulcan Foundry, RSH and WG Bagnall. The headquarters was at Vulcan and the directors were:

EJ Banks - chairman
HJH Nethercote - managing director
Lord Bridgeman
Gerald Collingwood
HM Matthews
W Shorrock
CCH Wade

Most of the Bagnall records and drawings, or those that it was considered worth saving, were initially moved to Darlington and later to the Vulcan Foundry; there was, unfortunately for the future historian, a general thinning out on the occasion of each of these moves. Some material was at the London office and this later migrated to the headquarters of the Traction Division of the General Electric Company Limited (GEC), after the two companies GEC and EE

Robert Stephenson & Hawthorns Limited letter heading from the period when it was trading in 'Association with WG Bagnall Limited', at the time when both companies were part of the English Electric Group. The London office address was shared with the Locomotive & Allied Manufacturers Association of Great Britain, as the LMA had by this time become. A number of locomotive builders had, over the years, used the LMA offices as their London address, by maintaining a presence there.

combined, situated at the former Metropolitan Vickers works at Trafford Park in Manchester. The London office of EE Traction Limited was at Locomotive House Buckingham Gate SW1. None of the Bagnall employees, salaried or otherwise, transferred with the locomotive business and they either stayed as the Castle Works as it became, or transferred to the existing EE works in Stafford - which became known as the main works - or the WH Dorman works. WH Dorman, by the way, continued to trade under its existing name, albeit under the umbrella of the EE Diesel Engine Division.

The EE main works was principally concerned with the design and manufacture of electricity generators, transformers and switch-gear, but was also the home of the company's experimental and development laboratories. At the time of the acquisition of the Bagnall and Dorman companies the English Electric works in Stafford was experiencing a shortage of machine tool capacity; it was part of the plan that the cessation of locomotive work at the Castle Engine Works would release machining capacity. This was another reason why English Electric had been anxious to acquire the company, apart from eliminating a competitor in the locomotive industry. Briefly mentioned in Chapter Five the main works dates from the beginning of the last century and was originally established by an English subsidiary of the German company Siemens Brothers. During the First World War, in January 1916, as a result of its German ownership it was sequestrated by the government and

along with most other engineering works in this country participated in the manufacture of munitions, or other work to assist the war effort, under the control of the Ministry of Munitions. It was not handed back to Siemens at the end of the war, but in December 1918 became one of the original constituents of the English Electric Company Limited, having been purchased from the Board of Trade under whose auspices it had latterly been managed on behalf of the government. The

Combined manufacturer's plate for Robert Stephenson & Hawthorns and WG Bagnall, in this case for a standard RSH design of a small 0-4-0 diesel-mechanical locomotive of the makers Husky design, that was in stock at Darlington at the time of the English Electric acquisition of Bagnall. This is the reason for the early RSH number but late date of 1963; although in this case the order had nothing whatsoever to do with Bagnall, nevertheless it illustrates the policy at the time of marketing locomotives under the combined names. The locomotive in question was sold to the Metal Box Company Limited for use at its factory at Neath in South Wales. (Kevin Lane)

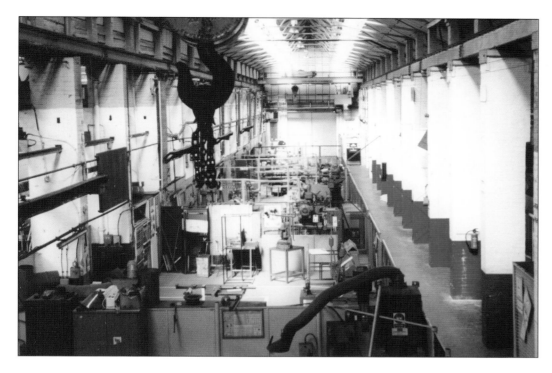

This photograph and the next four were taken on 7 April 2003 and depict scenes at the Castle Engine Works as it still exists. They deserve a study and comparison with the earlier photographs in the proceeding Chapters taken from similar vantage points. Almost the entire works buildings survive and so far as the authors are aware, present the most complete example of a British private locomotive builder's works still extant. This view from an elevated position looks north along the former Erecting Shop with the overhead cranes still in position; by this time the roof had been lagged, along with most of the other buildings - something not felt necessary in the days of WG Bagnall Ltd.

To the west of the Erecting Shop was the Machine Shop and this photograph was taken from the south-end with the Erecting Shop on the right; to the left was the former Tool Room, by this time bricked-off and used as a store. Once again the overhead cranes are still in situ. Both Erecting and Machines Shops are currently used for various light engineering activities.

View looking south towards the office building which can be seen at the extreme end, with the former Wheel Shop, Iron Foundry, Boiler Shop and Smithy buildings to the right, Machine Shop to the left - the high building was the war-time extension. One of the authors recalls the 8400 class pannier tanks for British Railways running up and down between these building while on test, something perhaps, difficult to visualise from this photograph.

The New Erecting Shop - or New Bay as it was referred to - looking south with the former Pattern Shop Stores behind - the Pattern Shop itself was behind the stores building. The Erecting Shop originally had twin sets of entrance doors and half-way down the west-side, which is the one seen here, the Foreman's office protruded outside, as it was half inside the shop and half out. On one occasion it almost got demolished when a British Railways A1A-A1A diesel-electric locomotive underframe was being turned round by the overhead cranes - the Foreman at the time was not amused! The structural steel work for this building had been a turbine hall at Whitebirk powerstation at Blackburn - all 87.5 tons of it.

View looking across the north-end of the works yard showing from right to left, the former Frame, Inspection Shop and Wheel Bay, followed by the Tin Shop with the main-line railway just in sight beyond. The vertical cylinder to the extreme right was the works oxygen supply.

Castle Works became a subsidiary operation of the main works, and MA Palmer was appointed as works manager to supervise the re-organisation of the workload. Later some of the machine tools and other equipment were moved to either the Main Works or the Dorman works at Tixall Road, with the new workload being largely in connection with electrical switchgear and ancillary components.

Since the time when locomotive and railway work ceased, the works has gone through a number of changes, becoming a part of the GEC combine when the two companies joined forces in November 1968; however, it remained a subsidiary of the main works. Since that date whilst the buildings still exist just about in their entirety, the works has been split into a number of leased factory units used for a variety of purposes. Not only are all the larger buildings still extant but many of the overhead cranes survive too, including all those in the two erecting shops. Some of the other equipment also survives, for example the 450 ton Fielding & Platt flanging press is still in situ. Most of the railway lines have been removed from outside the buildings, but the odd bit of track can still be located

and this includes parts of the multi-gauge test track, although it is partly buried by years of non railway operations. The site is today probably the last remaining complete set of workshops of a British private locomotive builder; long may it remain so, although there have been rumours of demolition and replacement by a housing estate. The current site is still largely part of Lord Stafford's Castlechurch estate, leased and managed by St Modwen Properties PLC.

Castle Hill House, long time home of the Bagnall family, survives too, albeit with slightly less grounds and hidden from view from the Newport Road by newer properties. WG Bagnall leased the property from William Bowen, although part of the land was already leased to Bowen from Lord Stafford's Castlechurch estate. The lease was dated 12 November 1889 for 14 years, initially at an annual rent of just £34, and the rights and privileges of the lease included the extension to the property that can be seen on the photograph at the end of this chapter. The cost of the works was £500, paid by Bagnall as part of the agreement and a contract was signed with a local builder, John Brookes, to undertake this work. The lease included a stable block

In 1975 the Visvesvaraya Iron & Steel Works (formerly known as the Mysore Iron & Steel Works), at Bhadravati in Karnataka, about 140 miles north-west of Bangalore, built the locomotive seen in this photograph taken on 6 February 1978. It is an exact copy of the earlier locomotives supplied for the two-foot gauge railways radiating from the works to various quarries, manufacturer's numbers 2903 to 2906 of 1950, along with the very last steam locomotive the Company built, number 3126 of 1957. Taking the next number in the works fleet, No 16, the construction was an exercise of some magnitude as although Bagnall had some years earlier supplied a spare boiler, along with other spare parts, including wheel-sets, cylinders and some motion parts, the bulk of the locomotive was built on site in the workshops at Bhadravati. Notice that the locomotive has a Bagnall plate on the smokebox, as the works indiscriminately swapped the boilers around between the locomotives. So the legacy lived on 15 years or so after production ceased at Stafford!

In 1977 the small locomotive ISABEL, number 1491 of 1897, was returned to the Castle Engine Works, courtesy of GEC, who at the time still operated in part of the site, for cosmetic restoration after years of being out in all weathers on its plinth in the Victoria Gardens. The work was quite extensive including a lot of new plate work. Here is the engine on 20 August 1977, a photograph taken inside the former Inspection Shop and Wheel Bay on 20 August 1977, immediately prior to being returned to its plinth. As related in this Chapter the engine has since been returned to working order and is kept on the railway at the Amerton Working Farm. This locomotive by the way, at the time of writing is having a completely new boiler constructed, so it should see many more years of use.

Not only could an Indian iron and steel works built a locomotive to a Bagnall design, but so could one of the authors. PEARL 2 was quite amazingly designed and built by Allen Civil, largely in his garage and back-garden, and completed in 1997. Two-foot gauge with 5½x7½in cylinders, 1ft 4in diameter driving wheels, the wheel arrangement is 0-4-2 and the locomotive sports a circular firebox boiler pressed to 160 psi, Bagnall-Price valve gear, an inverted saddle-tank and roller bearing axle-boxes throughout. These features, apart from the roller bearings, while so typical of the maker, in fact never came together in a single locomotive built by the firm, but were felt by the builder to be well worth combining, if for no other reason than as a tribute to the hundreds of men who over 85 years designed and built Bagnall locomotives. Photograph taken on 15 June 2007 at Newlands Inn on the Golden Valley Railway at Butterley in Derbyshire, where it is kept and can occasionally be seen in operation. It shares its name with Allen's wife - who is of course Pearl 1!

with living accommodation for a groom and family, a coach-house, various other out-buildings and a small pool. By the time of Gordon Bagnall's death in 1907, the lessors were two unmarried Bowen ladies, presumably daughters of William, their father having also passed away. The property was re-leased to Mrs Mary Hubball Sylvester, described as a widow, from 31 December 1907; the Bagnall family had, by that time, moved to smaller premises in Brocton. The current owners are Barrie and Marion Liss, who have been of great help to the authors in this part of their research, as well as entertaining us in rooms where the Bagnall family lived, as well as allowing a comparison of the property as it is now, with photographs and plans from over one hundred years ago.

Returning to the products of the Company, and in particular the locomotives, many of which continued to give years of service with a continuing supply of spare parts available, first from RSH at Darlington and later the Vulcan Foundry, although often the work was sub-contracted to a whole range of suppliers. In this country the main-line steam locomotives built by the Company for the London Midland & Scottish, Great Western, Somerset & Dorset Joint and British Railways, as well as those built for the War Department that were later acquired by the London & North Eastern Railway, had all disappeared by 1967; none surviving into preservation. In industrial use by the mid to late 1970s most of the steam locomotives the Company had supplied for use in this country had been scrapped, although a significant number have survived in preservation, all listed in Appendix V. The industrial diesels lasted a bit longer, as would be expected, but apart from a few of the Brush Bagnall diesel-electrics at the Corus Iron & Steel Works at Margam in South Wales, formerly the Steel Company of Wales, there are

Bagnall number 1888 of 1910, a 2ft 6in gauge 5in cylinder 0-4-0 circular firebox saddle tank with Bagnall-Price valve gear, an example of what in some cases 'preserved' means - see Appendix V. The photograph was taken on 30 January 1987 in Chile, at the junction of the Iquique Road with the Pan-American Highway. Supplied to the Chilean agents Mitrovich Brothers Limited, latterly it was in use with the Anglo-Chilean Nitrate Company, at the Humberstone nitrate mines. When new it was named CHILHEAITA, which means young Chilean girl! (Late Wilf Simms)

Towards the end of the last war, a certain JHE Rodgers, built a 5in gauge live-steam working model largely based on Bagnall number 2515 KENFIG - he called it ANNE OF HOLLAND - having obtained an outline drawing and photograph from the Company. Later a number of similar models appear to have been made by model engineers and in December 1948, one of them was acquired by the Company at a cost of £200. The works then set-about making some passenger trucks for it to haul and a portable track to run on, and the whole lot was often taken to local fetes and the like, where rides were given to children, along with anybody else who was interested. This practice continued long after locomotive building ceased, first under the auspices of English Electric and later GEC. The engine and other equipment was kept at the works, originally on display in the entrance hall to the offices, but later looked after, maintained and operated, successively by Dennis Edwards and Alan Jones, both employees. This picture was taken at the works shortly after the engine was acquired and shows a group of apprentices enjoying the engine in steam, although with little track on which to show its paces. Named EDWARD when acquired by the firm it later rejoined in the more appropriate WG BAGNALL Ltd, and is now in the custody of the Stafford & District Model Engineering Society (although the property of Alstom - as successors to WG Bagnall Ltd) and can occasionally be seen running and giving rides on its track at the Country Show Ground.

This is the little engine that had a lot to do with one of the authors great interest in the firm. WG BAGNALL is the 2½in gauge live-steam working model of a 7in cylinder 0-4-2 with circular firebox boiler and Bagnall-Price valve gear mentioned in the authors Preface. The late Horace Lorton, a member of the cost office staff, started to build it in the early 1930s, with castings made in the works at quite times and behind WS Edwards's back! It was completed by the late Stephen Baker - father of one of the authors - in 1965. The actual prototype is number 1902 of 1911 - see page 223.

none in commercial use today although, once again, a few have survived into preservation and they too, are listed in Appendix V.

As the country with the largest number of Bagnall steam locomotives India remained a stronghold until relatively recent times and there were still several hundred in use in the early 1970s, the last ones being in service until steam traction had been all but phased out in that country in the early 1990s. Once again however, several have survived in preservation and there may still be the odd one in industrial use. The Indian Railways workshops were extremely well equipped to maintain steam locomotives, and were largely self-sufficient in terms of spare parts. Of the other locomotives scattered around the world, then again several have survived in preservation of one sort or another, and some of them still see occasional use; at the Burma Mines for example, although these days it could hardly be said for any significant commercial purpose. There may of course be others the records of which have escaped us. A small number of diesels that were exported are also known to have survived, in particular in New Zealand, and one of the Brush

Bagnall A1A-A1A diesel-electrics is preserved in Sri Lanka (Ceylon) seeing occasional use on high days and holidays. Where details are known all the locomotives preserved around the world are listed in Appendix V.

The small narrow-gauge locomotive ISABEL which had been preserved in the works, was donated by EE via the good offices of the Stafford Railway Circle, to Staffordshire Borough Council. In 1962 arrangements were made for it to be mounted on a plinth alongside the Victoria Gardens outside Stafford railway station, where it remained for many years. With the occasional repaint by members of the Circle it was kept looking quite respectable. However, being exposed to the weather its condition inevitably deteriorated and in August 1977 it was arranged between the Borough Council and the local management of GEC - which at that time still occupied the Castle Engine Works - for the engine to be returned for a cosmetic refurbishment. A nice job was made including replacement of plate work which had suffered from rust, some of the work being undertaken by members of staff who had earlier worked for Bagnalls. On conclusion of the work the engine was returned to its plinth where it remained

Castle Hill House in Newport Road Stafford, one time home of WG Bagnall and his family, as it appears today, a photograph taken on 29 January 2008. The original building is to the left with the 1889-90 extension, undertaken before the Bagnall family moved in and part of the lease agreement, on the right. The former stable block, coach-house and living accommodation for the groom, gardener and their families, are to the extreme left, currently in part used as a garage. This photograph is reproduced through the courtesy of Barrie and Marion Liss, the present owners. Compare with the illustrations of the house in Chapter One.

until late 1984 when, due once again to its deteriorating condition, not helped by the attention of vandals, it was moved to the local council depot. Following this and to cut a long story short, the engine has been restored to working order, in no small measure due to the efforts of one of the authors, and is a regular performer at weekends on the Staffordshire Narrow Gauge Railway Society's railway at the Amerton working farm, Stowe-by-Chartley, which is on the A518 road from Stafford to Uttoxeter about one mile east of Weston.

In concluding this story it only remains to mention that the Company remains officially in existence on the register of companies under the various Companies Acts legislation, albeit no longer trading. The registered office was moved on 1 April 1969 to the GEC Traction Limited headquarters at Trafford Park in Manchester, prior to which on 11 November 1968, the capital was reduced to £10, divided into 10 shares of £1 each. It became in effect what is known as a shelf company - one that is not trading, but on the shelf so to speak, and available at short notice by its parent for any new business developments. This quite common practice avoids the necessity of otherwise registering a new company with the associated time delay and expense. The name of the Company was changed on 5 November 1971 to English Electric - AEI Projects Limited, and again on 29 November 1982 to GEC Traction International Limited, and it is under this name that it is still registered, or was, until at least a couple of years ago.

The works football team, a photograph taken in 1960; they played in a local league. The players are, from left to right:

Back Row: Willy Cassidy; Brain Mould; Dave Cleary; John Middleton; Pete Rose; Jim Giles. The gentleman in the suit is the Manager of the Team, Tom Barrett, who was not a Bagnall employee.

Front Row: Alan Jones; Bill Williams; Owen Ellis; Tom Beech; David Holson.

ACKNOWLEDGEMENTS, BIBLIOGRAPHY
& LIST OF SOURCES

ACKNOWLEDGEMENTS

Mention is made in the preface of a difficult decision the authors were faced with; whether to list in detail all their sources, be it by footnotes, chapter end-notes or a separate chapter by chapter list at the end of the main text. In the final analysis and largely in view of the fact that much of the primary source material is in private hands and not accessible to the general readership, a decision has been taken to restrict references to the form as presented here. It has to be added that this decision was made easier by the shear size of the book and how much bigger it would have been, or alternatively how much other material would have to have been omitted. The authors are of the view that the vast majority of readers prefer the maximum amount of historical material rather than long lists of source notes. Despite the forgoing we have tried to make these acknowledgements as comprehensive as possible, adding additional details as appropriate regarding specific documents and where they can be located. In addition the accompanying bibliography has also been expanded to include for example, details of a number of articles that appear in specialist society magazines and journals relating to Bagnall locomotives.

Over the 45 years or so the authors have been engaged in their research culminating in this work, an enormous number of people have been of assistance in one way or another. A few of them have been singled out and mentioned in the preface, but this does not diminish our indebtedness to the others, all of whom we sincerely hope are mentioned below. It was a salutary fact in compiling this list to appreciate that so many of them are no longer with us. Inevitable perhaps in view of the long time this book has been in gestation, it is nevertheless regrettable that so many old friends are unable to see the culmination of our efforts and justification of the faith they put in us however small their individual contributions. Needless to say, if by any oversight we have omitted to mention any individual or other source, we offer sincere apologies as it has not been intentional, but after so many years we hope perhaps understandable.

Particular mention is nevertheless appropriate for Louise Glennie of LG Design. Louise has been responsible for the design of this book, alone undertaking its entire layout, putting up with far too much interference and mind swings from one of the authors in the process! All in the friendliest atmosphere however, it has been a great pleasure to work with Louise, nothing being too much trouble, during the almost 12 months it has taken. There were occasions when the three of us, had doubts that we might ever achieve our common objective! We would also like to particularly thank Angela Baker, wife of one of the authors, for her work with the family trees that appear in Appendix XII. Richard Cook of Amadeus Press has also gone out of his way to ensure the quality of this book.

Fellow trustees of the Phyllis Rampton Narrow Gauge Railway Trust, along with Peter Rampton, have also been of enormous support. This has not only been in agreeing to publish this book, the Trust's first significant entry into the book publishing business, but also in the enormous amount of freedom we have had in its form, style and not least size. We can only hope that their confidence is rewarded by its popularity with readers.

Rather than list individuals and organisations in a single alphabetical list, we have decided on separate lists for each category. Where WG Bagnall Ltd appears in brackets after a name, the individuals concerned formerly worked for the Company.

A. INDIVIDUALS.

The late George Alliez; The late Jessica Alsop (daughter of WG Bagnall); Alycidon; Malcolm Armstrong; The late G Arnott (English Electric Co Ltd); Philip Ashforth; Philip Atkins (National Railway Museum); Ann Bagnall; Nicholas Bagnall; Philippa Bagnall; Shelia Bagnall; Peter Bagshawe; Rita Bailey; Jack Baker (WG Bagnall Ltd); The late Stephen Baker; Ron Balding (WG Bagnall Ltd); Jim Ballantyne; Frank Beech (WG Bagnall Ltd); John Benson; Uwe Bergemann; Colin Betteley; Doris Betteley; The late Vic Betteley (WG Bagnall Ltd); The late Maurice Billington; Max Birchenough; Lloyd Boardman; The late Harold Bowtell; David Bradbury; Vic Bradley; The late Bill Brooks (WG Bagnall Ltd); Terry Brooks (GEC Traction Ltd); Wilf Burley (WG Bagnall Ltd); John Cartlidge (WG Bagnall Ltd); Vanessa Chapman; The late Doug Clayton; Keith Clingan; Derek Cobby (WG Bagnall Ltd); Hugh E Colvin (McLeod Russell & Co Ltd); Michael Cook; Doris Cooper (WG Bagnall Ltd); Harry Cooper (WG Bagnall Ltd); TL Coxen (British Gypsum Ltd); The late Percy Critchley (WG Bagnall Ltd); The late Harry Davies (WG Bagnall Ltd); Bob Darvil; Peter Dewhurst; Bill Dickins; Dave Donkin; The late AE (Dusty) Durrant; Peter Dyer (WG Bagnall Ltd); Bert Edwards (WG Bagnall Ltd); PS Eilersen; Owen Ellis (WG Bagnall Ltd); Ray Ellis; Roy Etherington; David Fakes; The late Ivor Farr (WG Bagnall Ltd); The late Kathleen Farr; Mike Fell; Ian Ferguson; John Fletcher; Jeff Foley (Corus - Margam Iron & Steel Works); Andy Forret (GEC Traction Ltd); Horace Gamble; Rob Gambrill; Brian Gibbens (WG Bagnall Ltd); Bob Gibbens (WG Bagnall Ltd); Doreen Giles (WG Bagnall Ltd); Jim Giles (WG Bagnall Ltd); Louise Glennie; Henry Gunston; The late Clive Guthrie; Alan Hartley; Roger Hateley; Brian Hazeldene (WG Bagnall Ltd); Hans De Herder; The late Selwyn Pearce Higgins; Geoff Hill; John Hill; Late Alf Hodson (WG Bagnall Ltd); Peter Holmes; Dave Holyrode; John Homer; Richard Horne; Roger Hornsby; The late Hugh Hughes; John Hutchins; The late David Hutchinson Smith; Jill Hutchinson Smith; David

·607·

Ibbotson; Mike Jackson; Jim Jarvis; Stuart Johnson (WG Bagnall Ltd); Alan Jones (WG Bagnall Ltd); The late Frank Jones; Frank Jux; The late S Kaneda (Japan); John Kirchner; Robin Lake; Late Alice Lamb (WG Bagnall Ltd); Kevin Lane; Jeff Lanham; Graham Lee; Sydney Leleux; Barrie & Marion Liss; The late Horace Lorton (WG Bagnall Ltd); Merlin Maddock (WG Bagnall Ltd); Fred Marris; Lawrie Marshall; Paul Martin; Michael Messenger; Roger & Paula Masters; Robert J Meyer (New Zealand Railway & Locomotive Society); Brian Morrison; Colin Mountford; Andrew Neale; Late GN Nowell-Gossling; Michael J O'Conner; Leith Paxton; Late Jim Peden; Stuart Pitchford Pearson; Ken Plant; Stan Ponting (WG Bagnall Ltd); Martin Potts; Gordon Price (WG Bagnall Ltd); The late RC Prosser (WG Bagnall Ltd); Peter Rampton; Jim Redfern (WG Bagnall Ltd); George Reeve; The late Sydney Ridgway (WG Bagnall Ltd); The late Bernard Roberts; The late Peter Rowbottom; Peter Rowledge; Derek Rowley (WG Bagnall Ltd); The late Ralph Russell; The late Mike Satow; Mike Scott (GEC Traction Ltd); John Selway; Ray Shill; John Shoebridge; Tim Shuttleworth; The late Wilf Sims; The late Hugh Smedley (former chief draughtsman Vulcan Foundry); John Smith (Churchwarden St Paul's Golds Hill); The late WA Smyth (WG Bagnall Ltd); Paul Spencer; The late Ray Stephens (WG Bagnall Ltd); The late Derek Stoyel; Mike Swift; Edorado Tonerelli; The late Eric Tonks; Don Townsley; The late JA Twentyman (Henry Rogers Sons & Co); The late Ted Wade; Andrew Waldron; Russell Wear; The late Rodney Weaver; The late Brian Webb; Roger West; The late Bob Wheeler; The late Bill Williams; John Williams; The late F Harold Wood (WG Bagnall Ltd); Ken Wood (WG Bagnall Ltd); The late George Woodcock.

Our thanks are also due to the numerous firms and railways all over he world for allowing visits to installations as well as photography. Also on occasion facilities to study records and other literature, along with answering endless correspondence. Most of the firms are no longer in existence, although this does not diminish our indebtedness to them and their people, many of the individuals are of course still around. A special word of appreciation is appropriate for the erstwhile National Coal Board, and similarly the Indian Railways, in the latter case for allowing almost unrestricted access to study and photograph Bagnall locomotives in that wonderful country.

B. LIBRARIES/DEPOSITORIES/STATUTORY BODIES

THE ROYAL AGRICULTURAL SOCIETY OF ENGLAND LIBRARY, STONELEIGH PARK NEAR COVENTRY.
This Library has original copies of the annual show catalogues which of course, include all the shows where WG Bagnall, as well as other light railway manufacturers, had exhibits. Philip Sheppy, the most enthusiastic Librarian, was of great assistance in helping to find the way round the vast and wonderful collection of material he is custodian of.

BOURNEMOUTH RAILWAY CLUB.
The Club holds the photograph collection of the late WC Kelland, a professional railwayman and keen photographer, who spent a substantial part of his career in India.

THE BRITISH LIBRARY - NEWSPAPER LIBRARY COLINDALE.
This library contains copies, either originals or on micro-film, of the vast majority of national and provincial newspapers published in this country. It also holds copies of a large range of journals and magazines.

THE BRITISH LIBRARY ST PANCRES LONDON.
Patents abridgements for all British registered patents are available on the open shelves. The former India Office records are located within the library embracing a vast archive of material on the railways of India.
Coopers Hill Engineering College. India Office References L/PWD/8 and L/PWD/10, contain documents relating to the college.

INSTITUTION OF CIVIL ENGINEERS LIBRARY LONDON
(available to non-members on application to the Librarian).
The Civil Engineers library contains a wealth of information; for example details of members along with their original application forms and the Institution's printed Proceedings. Included within the Proceedings are papers presented by members, obituaries, and much else of interest. The library has an enormous collection of technical journals along with archive material on railways all over the world.

COMPANIES HOUSE CARDIFF & LONDON.
The company files for WG Bagnall Limited (company number 24807); John Bagnall & Sons Limited (company number 7101); Brush Bagnall Traction Limited (company number 401466) and Porn & Dunwoody Limited (company number 213879) are held in Cardiff. These files along with several others relating to companies mentioned in the text have been consulted.

DEVON RECORD OFFICE.
The Ordination Register for the Exeter Diocese and associated papers are held here, containing information on the career of Thomas Walter.

FAMILY RECORDS CENTRE (National Register Office) Myddelton Street London EC1. (This collection is scheduled to be moved to The National Archives at Kew some time in 2008)
The registers referencing births, marriages and deaths registered in England and Wales, as well as the census records, are held here. The registers are also available on-line via Ancestry UK.

GWYNEDD COUNTY RECORD OFFICE DOLGELLAU.
Details of WS Edwards relating to his bungalow in Fairbourne.

THE INDUSTRIAL LOCOMOTIVE SOCIETY LIBRARY (ILS). (normally only available to members)
The Library of this Society holds a few items relating to WG Bagnall Limited, but more significantly it has a large photographic collection of industrial locomotives throughout the world, many of which depict Bagnall locomotives. The Frank Jones Collection, which was of enormous value to the authors during Frank's lifetime, is now in the custody of the ILS.

THE INDUSTRIAL RAILWAY SOCIETY LIBRARY (IRS). (normally only available to members)
The IRS Library has a number of files relating to the Company, some of which were deposited by the late WA Smyth. For example there

is a copy of a report following his visit to South Africa and there are files relating to the last few diesel locomotives built, along with those built by Robert Stephenson & Hawthorns at Darlington to fulfil orders placed with Bagnall. Some items in the IRS collection are deposited at the Stafford County Record Office, including a number of early original drawings of locomotives; these are printed on linen and in many cases hand coloured. The Society also holds a large collection of photographs depicting Bagnall locomotives, largely from the collections of various individuals.

INSTITUTION OF MECHANICAL ENGINEERS LIBRARY LONDON. (available to non-members on application to the Librarian)
The I Mech E Library, as with the Civil's, contains the original membership applications of its members along with any later paperwork, if for example the status of membership was changed - associate member to full member perhaps. These documents along with papers presented by members in the printed Proceedings, notices of career moves and obituary notices etc., are an extremely valuable source of information. Many of the individuals mentioned in this book presented papers to the Institution, and/or contributed to the discussions following papers read at its meetings by others, and these too, are extremely useful sources of information. The library holds a vast range of technical journals and other material relating the railways and locomotives. The library also contains the published papers and records of the Institution of Locomotive Engineers, formed in 1911 and combined with the I Mech E in 1969. The Journal and published papers of the I Loco E., like the Mechanical's and Civil's, contain much of relevance to WG Bagnall Limited and its people. Keith Moore, a one time Librarian, was particularly helpful in locating a vast amount of information from the archives of this Institution.

THE NATIONAL ARCHIVES AT KEW.
Public & Private Companies. Reference BT31 refers the Companies House files of a large number of defunct limited liability companies that have been deposited here. A significant number of files of individual companies have been consulted. Other references are:
The Locomotive Manufacturers Association. References RAIL 424/5; T2014/11/38 and IR82/10, contain papers relating to the activities of this trade body.
Labour Relations. Files LAB 2/37 IC3480/1916 and LAB 2/46 IC8327/1918 relate to issues during, and just after the First World War, in connection with the Company.
Richard Gordon Bagnall. File W 339/31636 contains the personal papers regarding this officer's Army service.
The Army List. A complete set of this work is on the open shelves.

THE NATIONAL RAILWAY MUSEUM YORK.
The Locomotive Manufacturers Association. A considerable amount of documentation has been deposited here by the successor body to the LMA - The Railway Industry Association.
WG Bagnall Limited. The library has one of the original sets of single-line registers recording locomotives built during the whole period of the Company's existence. They include details of the locomotives built.

PATENT OFFICE CARDIFF.
The complete specifications of all patents registered in this country are held at Cardiff. However, copies of the abridgements are available on the open shelves at The British Library in London. All patents referred to in this book have their numbers and dates of sealing mentioned in the main text; the complete specifications and abridgements can be traced by these numbers.

PRINCIPAL PROBATE REGISTRY HIGH HOLBORN LONDON.
Original copies of the wills of people who died in England and Wales since 1858 (earlier ones are at the Family Records Centre), as well as details of those individuals who died intestate, are held here.

STAFFORD COUNTY RECORD OFFICE.
WG Bagnall Limited. Reference D 4338/A/7 is a private ledger of the Company covering the period 1887, when the limited liability company was formed, until 1924.
D 709/2 is a Machinery and Plant Ledger covering the period 1916 to 1927.
D 709/1 is a Sales Day Book covering the period 1915 to 1921.
A number of early original drawings of locomotives, the property of the Industrial Railway Society, are deposited here and there are a number of other items relating to the Company.
John Bagnall & Sons Limited. Reference D 611/4 is a volume of press cuttings dated 1877.
The Record Office also has a sizable collection of large scale Ordnance Survey maps which cover the Castle Engine Works at different periods.

STAFFORD PUBLIC LIBRARY.
A number of local newspapers are available at the library on micro-file.

STEPHENSON LOCOMOTIVE SOCIETY (SLS) LIBRARY. (normally only available to members)
The SLS library contains a wealth of information on private locomotive builders as well as an extensive collection of magazines, books and other literature.

THE WILLIAM SALT LIBRARY AT STAFFORD
The Library contains a large selection of books on Staffordshire as well as copies of local newspapers.

The staff at all the various depositories mentioned above have during many visits, gone out of their way to assist in locating the most elusive documents. In particular the former Librarian of the I Mech E, Keith Moore, went to enormous lengths as did Phillip Sheppy at the Royal Agricultural Society of England. Philip Atkins the recently retired Librarian at the National Railway Museum has also been a great help.

C. OTHER ORGANISATIONS & COMPANIES.

CHARTERHOUSE SCHOOL RECORDER'S OFFICE.
Details of Harold Gordon Bagnall & Richard Gordon Bagnall during the time they were at this school.

CROWN AGENTS FOR OVERSEAS GOVERNMENTS. (Formerly Crown Agents for the Colonies)
Records of equipment, and in particular locomotives, supplied by the Crown Agents on behalf of the Crown Colonies are held here. However, they are by no means complete and for the years prior to the First World War, only photograph albums have survived.

EATON COLLEGE LIBRARY.
Details of Thomas Walter and Gilbert Claughton's time at this school.

GEC TRACTION LIMITED (ALSTOM LIMITED).
The original successor to WG Bagnall Limited was the English Electric Company Limited, and later GEC Traction Limited after the two companies combined. GEC joined forces with the French company Alsthom in 1990, thereafter trading as GEC Alsthom Limited, the traction element of this Company becoming Alstom Limited in more recent times. However, it was largely in the period of English Electric & GEC Traction Limited ownership, that the authors had access to the surviving Bagnall records. Originally we were helped by Hugh Smedley, the chief draughtsman at the Vulcan Foundry, and later by Andy Forret who had charge of the industrial locomotive section. Andy in particular, over a period of almost 15 years, was of enormous assistance in helping us dig out all sorts of documents, giving us in effect, unrestricted access and the ability to search around at will.

Among our most pleasant memories are the days we spent under the water tower at the Vulcan Foundry, in a room where the archive material was stored - despite the occasional leakage from the tank! Mike Scott and Terry Brooks from the traction headquarters of GEC at Trafford Park was also able to assist us in a number of ways.

BIBLIOGRAPHY

A. JOURNALS & MAGAZINES

THE ARMY LIST - a complete set is available on the open shelves at the National Archives.

THE COLLIERY GUARDIAN - has many references to Bagnall locomotives and other products, especially in the early years. In particular advertisements for locomotives both new and second-hand.

THE CONTRACT JOURNAL - this journal has the odd reference to early Bagnall locomotives, and numerous advertisements for second-hand sales.

CONTINENTAL RAILWAY JOURNAL - despite its title this quarterly magazine, dating from 1969, covers railway activities throughout the world and contains numerous references to Bagnall locomotives.

DIESEL RAILWAY TRACTION - this publication which started life in 1933 as a supplement to *The Railway Gazette*, later became a stand-alone journal and contains numerous references regarding technical and other information on the diesel traction activities of WG Bagnall Limited.

THE ENGINEER - along with its contemporary *Engineering*, contains an enormous amount of information regarding the company and its products, especially in its early years reporting on for example, the Royal Agricultural Society Shows when Bagnall was an exhibitor. Many specific references are given in the main text of the book.

ENGINEERING - see comments for *The Engineer* above, as they apply to both journals.

ENGINEERING IN MINATURE - this magazine contains the following articles:
The Bagnall Locomotive Valve-Gears - a series of articles by the late Ray Stephens, a former employee of the Company. Issues between August and December 1988 inclusive.

IMPLEMENT & MACHINERY REVIEW - as with *The Engineer* and *Engineering*, this journal has many articles and smaller items concerning the firm, especially covering the early years, many of which are referenced in the main text.

THE INDUSTRIAL LOCOMOTIVE - journal of the Industrial Locomotive Society. This journal has numerous references to the company; listed below are articles contributed by the present authors which provide significant detail of particular locomotives:
Some Turkish Industrials - Vol. 1 Summer 1977
Bagnalls for Tongaat - Vol. 2 Spring 1979
Bagnall Austerity Biography (with Derek Stoyel) - Vol. 2 Spring, Summer & Autumn 1979; Summer & Autumn 1980
Pauling & Cos 'Kenya' Locomotives (with Derek Stoyel) - Vol. 2 Summer 1980
The ROF Bagnalls - Vol. 5 Winter 1989
Blackbrook Colliery - Vol. 6 No 62 1991
A Gasworks Mystery - Vol. 6 No 65 1992
A Bagnall Quartet - Vol. 7 No 71 1992
The Bagnall Front Tanks - Vol. 7 No 73 1994
Last Days at Bagnall - Vol. 8 No 82 1996
Second-hand Locomotive Dealings of WG Bagnall Ltd - Vol. 10 No101 2001
Tunis - An Early Bagnall - Vol. 11 No110 2003

THE INDUSTRIAL RAILWAY RECORD - journal of the Industrial Railway Society. Like *The Industrial Locomotive*, this journal too, has numerous references to the company and its locomotives. Below are specific articles by the authors.
Bagnall Locomotive Valve Gears - Vol. 1 No 11 1966
Bagnall Articulated locomotives - Vol. 2 No 16 1967
The End of an Era at Shelton Bar - (15in locos) Vol. 5 No 50 1974
Topham (17in locos) - Vol. 5 No 58 1975
Bagnall 16in Locomotives - Vol. 7 No 77 1978
Bagnall Industrials Par Excellence - Vol. 8 No 83 1979
The First Hundred Bagnalls - Vol. 9 No 100 1985
Bagnall Post-War Diesel Mechanical Locomotives - Vol. 10 No 115 1988
Bagnall & The WDLR 2ft 0in Gauge Locomotives - Vol. 12 No 130 1992
Bagnall Diesel-Hydraulic Locomotives - Vol. 13 No 146 1996
Some Early Bagnall Standard Gauge Locomotives - Vol. 13 No 153 1998

LOCOMOTIVES INTERNATIONAL - this relatively recent journal (introduced in 1989) has many references to WG Bagnall Ltd and a number of articles by one of the authors. These are listed below:
Gaekwar's Baroda State Railways - Part 1 Metre Gauge Lines - No 6 October 1990
WA Smyth - An Obituary - No 12 December 1991
Coffee, Cacao or Palm Oil? - Two Little Bagnalls - No 14 May 1992
Gaekwar's Baroda State Railways - Part 2 Narrow Gauge Lines - No 17 December 1992 & No 19 May 1993
World Beaters on the Metre Gauge - No 41 December 1997/January

1998 & No 42 March/April 1998
The Burma Mines Railway Bagnalls - No 58 May/June 2001

THE LOCOMOTIVE MAGAZINE (later *The Locomotive Magazine Carriage & Wagon Review*) - this journal which ran from 1896 to 1959 has numerous references to the company, its locomotives and individuals; a number of specific items are mentioned in the text.

MACHINERY MARKET - a particularly important article appears in this journal, issue dated 1 October 1895, containing extended details of a visit to the works by a member of its staff and an interview with WG Bagnall. There are a number of other references too, particularly in the early years, as well as advertisements for new locomotives and light railway material along with second-hand locomotives sales.

THE MODEL ENGINEER - there are many references in this old established magazine, in particular relating to the miniature Stirling Single locomotive, manufacturer's number 1425, along with its twin, described in some detail in the main text. There are also a series of extremely comprehensive articles on these engines by the late Ray Stephens, a former employee. These articles are referenced below:
A Tale of Two Singles - Vol. 180 - Nos 4060/2/4/6/8 - January to June 1998

THE NARROW GAUGE - journal of the Narrow Gauge Railway Society. As with *The Industrial Locomotive* and *The Industrial Railway Record*, this journal has numerous references to the locomotives and firm. Listed below are articles by one of the authors:
Turkish Delight - No 75 Spring 1977
The Stirling Singles - No 76 Summer 1977
Stafford's 'Haigs' - No 77 Winter 1977-8
Bagnall Petrol Locomotives - No 80 Summer 1978
Jessies, Concords & Polar Bear - No 84 Summer 1979
Margarets & Mercedes - No 89 Autumn 1980
The 7in Bagnalls - No 99 Spring 1983
Anglo-Scottish Twins - No 107 Summer 1985
The McLeod Light Railways & Their Bagnall Locomotives - No 119 Summer 1988
Brave Little Bagnalls in County Clare - Nos 125-6 Winter 1989-90: Spring 1990
Peter - No 128 Autumn 1990
Rheidol- Putting the Record Straight - No 132 Autumn 1991
Thompstone's Bosley Tramway - No 150 Winter-Spring 1996
Bagnall: A Narrow Gauge Legacy - No 156 Spring 1997
The Scropton Tramway - No 164 Spring 1999
Nizhhe Tagil - A Bagnall Mystery No 170 Summer 2000
Little Bagnalls - No 180 Spring 2003
Danish Bagnalls - No 189 Summer 2005
Two Trips To Hong Kong - No 198 Summer 2007

NEW ZEALAND RAILFAN - this bi-monthly magazine published in New Zealand, often contains articles and paragraphs on Bagnall locomotives that worked in that Country.

THE OIL ENGINE (later *The Oil Engine & Gas Turbine*) - from the time the company built its first diesel locomotive, there are many references to diesel locomotives in this journal.

THE RAILWAY ENGINEER - this journal contains the occasional technical description of Bagnall locomotives.

THE RAILWAY GAZETTE - there are numerous references and short articles in this journal covering almost the whole period of locomotive production; includes many references to people, appointments, obituaries etc (see also *Diesel Railway Traction* above). For many years in the 1930s and post-war, *The Railway Gazette* published an Overseas Railway number, in effect a special edition of the journal, and these have been of particular help. In the years between the wars there was also the occasional special issues on specific countries, or geographically adjacent countries; for example India (covering Burma and Ceylon too), South America and Africa.

THE RAILWAY MAGAZINE - this journal has the odd reference to the company and its locomotives.

RAILWAY WORLD - this journal contains a number of references to Bagnall locomotives.

STEPHENSON LOCOMOTIVE SOCIETY JOURNAL - this journal contains numerous references to the locomotives built by WG Bagnall Limited, especially issues in the period from about 1950 to 1980.

B. NEWSPAPERS

THE DAILY TELEGRAPH

THE TIMES

EVENING SENTINEL (Stoke-on-Trent, North Staffordshire and South Cheshire local daily) - there is also a *Weekly Sentinel*, a weekly edition that often contains additional details of local people and events.

STAFFORD NEWSLETTER

STAFFORDSHIRE ADVERTISER

STAFFORDSHIRE CHRONICLE

C. BOOKS

ATKINS, PHILIP - The Golden Age of Steam Locomotive Building - Atlantic Transport Publishers 1999

BAGNALL, NICHOLAS - A Little Overmatter - Southover Press 2002

BAKER, AC & CIVIL TDA:
Bagnalls of Stafford - Oakwood Press 1973
Bagnall Locomotives - A Pictorial Album of Bagnall Narrow Gauge Locomotives - Trent Valley Publications 1990
Bagnalls of Stafford - Locomotive Works List - Industrial Locomotive Society 1984
Bagnall Locomotives - A Pictorial Album of Bagnall Standard Gauge Locomotives - Plateway Press 2001
Fireless Locomotives - Oakwood Press 1976

BILLINGTON, MAURICE - The Cliffe Hill Mineral Railway (2nd edition revised by David H Smith) - Plateway Press 1997

BOWTELL, HAROLD D - Reservoir Railways of the Yorkshire Pennines - Oakwood Press 1979

BURKE'S PEERAGE, BARONETAGE & KNIGHTAGE - Harrison & Sons; various editions

CHAPMAN, SIMON - Grosmont & its Mines - Industrial Archaeology of Cleveland (Peter Tuffs) 2002

COLE, DAVID - Swedish Private Railways - Union Publications 1971

COLE, DAVID - Swedish Industrial Steam Locomotives - Union Publications 1983

DILWORTH, D - The Tame Mills of Staffordshire - Phillimore 1976

DURRANT, AE; LEWIS, CP; JORGENSON, AA - Steam in Africa - Hamlyn 1981

GODDARD, NICHOLAS - Harvests of Change The Royal Agricultural Society of England 1838-1988 - Quiller Press 1988

HERDER H DE - Nederlandse industrielocomotieven - Utigeverji Uquiloair BV 2001

HEYWOOD, SIR ARTHUR PERCIVAL - Minimum Gauge Railways (reprint of 3rd edition of 1898) - Turntable Publications 1974

HILL, RICHARD - SUDAN TRANSPORT - Oxford University Press 1965

HUGHES, HC - Indian Locomotives Parts 1 to 4 - Continental Railway Circle 1990-6
Steam Locomotives in India Parts 1, 2 & 3 - Continental Railway Circle 1977-80
Middle East Railways - Continental Railway Circle 1981

INDIA, GOVERNMENT OF (RAILWAY BOARD) - History of Indian Railways Constructed and in Progress Corrected up to 31 March 1939 - Government of India Press 1940

INDUSTRIAL RAILWAY SOCIETY (formerly The Birmingham Locomotive Club Industrial Locomotive Information Section) - over many years this Society has published a series of pocket books, later termed handbooks, with extensive details of locomotives employed on industrial and private railways in both this country and several others. The list is far too extensive to individually itemise here. While many of the books are long out of print, the Society has a policy of continually updating and issuing revised editions, many of which are available; a current list can be obtained from the Society

JONES, ROBERT & MARRIOTT - Anatomy of a Merger - Jonathan Cape 1970

JUX, FRANK - KERR STUART & CO. LTD. Locomotive Works List - Industrial Locomotive Society 1992

KELLY'S HANDBOOK TO THE TITLED, LANDED & OFFICIAL CLASSES - Kelly's Directories Ltd; various editions

KIDNER, ROGER - The Light Railway Handbook - Oakwood Press 6th collected edition 1971

LEWIS, ROY - Stafford Past - Phillimore 1997

LEWIS ROY - Images of England - Around Stafford - Tempus 2004

LONDON UNIVERSITY - The Victoria History of the County of Stafford Vol. V1 1995
(this Volume covers the town of Stafford)

McCLARE, EJ - Steam Locomotives of New Zealand Parts 2 & 3 - New Zealand Railway & Locomotive Society 1988 & 1991

MOIR, SYDNEY M - Twenty Four Inches Apart - Oakwood Press 1963

PEARCE, JOHN - The History of Saint Pauls Church Golds Hill 1882-2002 - St Pauls Church 2002

PEASE, JOHN - The History of J&H McLaren of Leeds - Landmark Publishing 2003

PETRIE, GERALD - New Zealand Steam Locomotives by Official Number - Locomotive Press 1993

POLITICAL & ECONOMIC PLANNING - Locomotives - PEP Engineering Reports 111 1951

RADFORD, JB - Derby Works & Midland Locomotives - Ian Allan 1971

RAILWAY PUBLISHING CO LTD - The Railway Year Book (Late The Universal Directory of Railway Officials & The Railway Year Book); various years

RONALD, DW & CARTER, RJ - The Longmoor Military Railway - David & Charles 1974

SLEIGH, JOHN - History of the Parish of Leek - Bemrose Derby, 2nd edition 1883 (this book contains much biographical detail of the Bagnall family)

STAMFORD, FE; Stuckley, EG; Maynard, GL - Powelltown A History of its Timber Mills & Tramways - Light Railway Research Society of Australia 1984

TALBOT, E - Steam from Keyna to the Cape - Continental Railway Circle & Halycon Books 1975

TAYLOR, PATRICK (edited by Allan C Baker) The West Clare Railway - Plateway Press 1994

TOMS, GEORGE - Brush Diesel Locomotives 1940-78 - Turntable Publications 1978

TONKS, ERIC - The Ironstone Railways & Tramways of the Midlands - Locomotive Publishing Company 1959

UNDERHILL, BRIG. WE OBE - The History of the Royal Leicestershire Regiment 1928-1956 - Naval and Military Press 2006

WARD, JOHN - The Borough of Stoke-upon-Trent - W Lewis & Son London 1843

WEAVER, RODNEY - Baguley Locomotives 1914-1931 - Industrial Railway Society 1974

WHITEHOUSE, CJ & GP - A Town for Four Winters - CJ&GP Whitehouse 1978

WOLFF, CE - Modern Locomotive Practice - Scientific Publishing Company (undated but c/1900). This book contains the only known description of how to design Baguley valve gear

YATE, BOB - The Shropshire Union Railway - Oakwood Press 2003

Three typical pages from one of the engine order registers. Notice how in some cases entries have been altered to reflect later owners of the locomotives.

APPENDIX I

LIST OF LOCOMOTIVES BUILT

This list contains details of all locomotives known to have been built by the Company, whether steam or by other forms of power. It includes at the end, and not therefore in date sequence, petrol, petrol-electric and electric locomotives that were not numbered in the main numerical list used for new locomotives. Some of these locomotives were built in conjunction with other manufacturers, when Bagnall was not the main-contractor. Also included are those locomotives ordered from Bagnall but not completed until its demise as a builder, and constructed by Robert Stephenson & Hawthorns at Darlington in the case of the diesels, and Andrew Barclay Sons & Company Limited at Kilmarnock in the case of a solitary steam locomotive. In the case of some of the diesels work had started at Stafford and the material, or some of it, had been ordered and assembled, subsequently the completed parts and the material were moved to Darlington where the locomotives were completed - this was the case with Bagnall numbers 3209 to 3213 and to a lesser extent 3189. In all cases the number allocated by Darlington and Kilmarnock is also quoted. Only four locomotives that were not built new are included here as they were allocated numbers in the same list as those built new - 612; 2908; 3062; 3152. Lastly, the locomotives built under the Brush Bagnall Traction Limited marketing banner, although Brush Electrical Engineering Company Limited was the main-contractor, are included as they were all allocated a number in this numerical sequence and were completely, or in part, built at Stafford. The list makes clear the identity of those locomotives that were completely erected and despatched to the end-customer from Stafford, and those that were completed at Loughborough.

In its early days the Company used one numerical list of orders for all the work it undertook, and this is why there are numerous gaps in the sequence until number 1410 of 1893. It was the arrival of Ernest Baguley into the management team that instigated the change, with this numerical sequence confined to locomotive orders, a separate system being introduced for other work as described in the main text of the book. Where orders were cancelled after a number had been allocated, and the number was not subsequently used, a relevant entry has been made. The abbreviations used are those it is felt the vast majority of readers interested in this level of detail will be familiar with; hence a decision that the space otherwise necessary is better put to other use.

Space has of course, been an obvious consideration in compiling this list and much as it would have been desirable to include details of the later owners of many of the locomotives, such detail would have occupied an inordinate amount of room. However, where it has been possible within the constraints of the page-layout, additional detail has been included. In cases where the information is not from the maker's surviving records, this is indicated by the relevant entry being in brackets. All dimensions are in imperial measures, the cylinder dimensions are in inches and in the case of petrol and diesel locomotives the horsepower figures quoted are the makers quoted continuous brake horsepower (bhp) ratings of the engines. This list should be used in conjunction with Appendix Two which contains the principal dimensions of the locomotives. Where a column is blank the relevant information is unknown.

As anybody who has ever attempted to compile a list of this magnitude will know, it is extremely difficult and time consuming to be sure that each and every detail is 100% correct. While not offering this as an excuse for any entry that a diligent reader might detect as being wrong in some way or other, every effort has been made to ensure accuracy. This is not the first list of Bagnall locomotives the present authors have published, but it will almost certainly be the last; where there are differences from earlier published lists then the information here should be taken as the correct version.

The column headings are from left to right: Manufacturer's Number; Date despatched; Track Gauge; Type of Locomotive; Cylinder Size - Bore and Stroke in inches; Driving Wheel Diameter in feet and inches; Name and/or Number; Purchaser and Destination. Information in brackets is not from the manufacturer's surviving records, although a lot of effort has been expended in ensuring its accuracy.

Abbreviations, used in this and Appendices 11,111 and 1V are:			Type/Drive cont.:	ic	-	inside cylinders
Gauge - Std - Standard gauge (4ft 8½in)				IST	-	Inverted Saddle Tank
				Mech	-	Mechanical
Type/Drive:	bg	- Bogie Tender Wheel Arrangement		oc	-	outside cylinders
	bhp	- Brake Horsepower		OHW	-	Overhead Wire Current Collection
	DE	- Diesel-Electric Transmission		PE	-	Petrol Electric Transmission
	DH	- Diesel Hydraulic Transmission		PM	-	Petrol Mechanical Transmission
	DM	- Diesel Mechanical Transmission		PT	-	Pannier Tanks
	E	- Electric		T	-	Side Tanks
	F	- Fireless		Ten	-	Tender Locomotive
	FT	- Front Side Tanks		wl	-	Wheel
	Hyd	- Hydraulic		WT	-	Well Tank

Manu No	Date Desp	Gauge	Type	Cyls	Dwl Dia	Name/No	Purchaser/Destination
16	12/1876	Std	0-4-0ST	7⅝x11		BUCKINGHAM	Chaplin & Horne (loaned Wotton Tramway first)
94	9/1877	1'10"	0-4-0ST ic	4x6	1'6"	ADA	W Rees (Maesarddafen Colly Carmarthenshire)
120	12/1877	Std	0-4-0IST ic	8x12	2'6"	WOTTON	Wotton Tramway Co (Buckinghamshire)
128	12/1877	1'10½	0-4-0IST ic	5x7½	1'6"	SISSY	Henry Lodge (Hill Main Colly Royston Yorks)
138	3/1878	3'0"	0-4-0IST ic	5x7½	1'6"	ERNEST	River Dee Co (Cheshire)
210	3/1879	1'8"	0-4-0IST ic	4x6	1'3"	BRICK	Beckenham & Penge Brickworks (Kent)
265	10/1879	3'0"	0-4-0IST ic	6x9	1'6"	KENT	HB James (Hythe Kent)
272	12/1879	2'7"	0-4-0IST ic	3½x5¼	1'0"	SAMSON	Stubbs Brothers (Winsford Cheshire)
284	1/1880	2'2"	0-4-0IST ic	4½x7½	1'3"	MERCEDITA	Manlove Alliott & Co agents for Porto Rica
285	2/1880	2'6¼	0-4-0IST ic	4½x7½		CLARA	Pascual Bros Cuba
300	1/1880	2'0"	0-4-0IST ic	5x7½		TERRIER	Beauchamp (Windsor Hill Quarries Somerset)
304	4/1880	3'4⅛"	0-4-0	5½x9		MERAPI	Bow McLachlan & Co agents for Java
305	5/1880	3'4⅛"	0-4-0	5½x9		SINIROE	Bow McLachlan & Co agents for Java
308	6/1880	Metre	0-4-0	8x12		LA LOZERE	Plissonier et Fils agents for France (or a French Colony)
312	8/1880	3'8"	0-4-0	5½x9		PAULINA	EH Doriga, (Mina Paulina, Nueva Montana, Spain)
315	11/1880	2'6"	0-4-0	5x7½			Clarke & Co for Ceylon
316	5/1881	2'3½"	0-4-0	4½x7½		TRANSVAAL	H Figee (agent) for Holland
320	1/1882	2'0"	0-4-0	5½x9		HELENA	GFC Rose for Java
334	12/1880	2'0"	0-4-0	4x6		SULTANEE	Harris McLean & Co for Ryan Yuban Zanzibar
340	3/1882	2'4¼"	0-4-0	5½x9		GELDROP	HB Geldrop for Java
358	2/1882	2/4"	0-4-0IST oc	4½x7½	1'3"	TUNIS	Figee Bros (for C Langeveld contr' Holland)
364	6/1881	1'6"	0-4-0IST ic	4x6		HAMPSON	Ibbotson Bros & Co (may have gone to DeBeers Mines Kimberley South Africa)
377	7/1881	2'0"	0-4-0	4½x7½		ACTIVE	Henry Hughes & Co (as agents for Sydney Island)
410	4/1882	1'8"	0-4-0	4½x7½		DARWIN	Bowman Heirs for South America
412	2/1882	2'2"	0-4-0	4½x7½		JULITA	Manlove Alliott & Co agents
414	2/1882	1' 11⁵⁄₁₆"	0-4-0	4x6		CAUCASE	Manlove Alliott & Co agents
416	4/1882	3'6"	0-4-0IST ic	5x7½		MENTONI	Laughland McKay & Co (for Komata Reefs Goldmining Waiki New Zealand)
418	3/1884	2'6"	0-4-0	4½x7½			Bates Stokes & Co (1908 spares with No 1748 via Straits)
428	6/1882	2'4"	0-4-0	6½x8		SYDNEY	J Glasbrook for a Colly nr Swansea (Garnock & Gorsenion Colly)
434	9/1882	2'0"	0-4-0	5x7½		BATTERS	CJ Batters (Point of Ayr Colly' Flint) Originally ordered by JH Riddell
436	10/1882	2'6"	0-4-0	5½x9		PIETERMARITZBERG	Bolling & Lowe agents (may have gone to South Africa)
440	8/1882	2'6"	0-6-0	8x12		EL CONGRESO	Denniston Cross & Co
450	9/1882	3'0"	2-4-0T oc	5x7½		RIATO	G Bailey Toms & Co agents
451	9/1882	3'0"	2-4-0T oc	5x7½		CUBA	G Bailey Toms & Co agents
493	4/1884	1'8"	0-4-0	4x6		PRINCEZA	Henry Rogers Sons & Co (agents for Pernambuco Brazil)
511	10/1883	2'0"	2-4-0T oc	5x7½	1'3"	SIRDAR	Walsh Lovett & Co (for India)
512	2/1886	2'0"	2-4-0T oc	5x7½	1'3"	SOUDAN	Stothert & Pitt (agents)
520	5/1883	2'7¾"	0-4-0	6x9		MAURITIUS	Ruston Proctor & Co for Mauritius
523	6/1883	3'6"	0-6-0 (T)	11x16½			Schulte & Schumann for Lautaro Nitrate Co Chile
524	6/1883	3'6"	0-6-0 (T)	11x16½			Schulte & Schumann for Lautaro Nitrate Co Chile
556	12/1883	2'6"	0-4-0	7x10		FERRETT	R Bealey & Co (Radcliffe Lancs')
566	12/1883	3'0"	0-6-0T oc	7½x10		MARLAND	Marland Brick Co (Peters Marland Devon)
590	4/1884	2'0"	0-6-0	5x12		EXPERIMENT	Hartley & Marshall (Colly' at Banksville Pittsburg USA)
592	4/1884	3' 1⅛"	0-6-0T oc	12x18	2'9"	FOSSANO	Lavista, (Mondovi Fossano Cava Railway Italy)
593	4/1884	3' 1⅛"	0-6-0T oc	12x18	2'9"	MONDOVI	Lavista, (Mondovi Fossano Cava Railway Italy)
612	/1884	Std	0-4-0ST oc	13x18		BRIGGS	Lenox Clithero (rebuild for Briggs of Clithero Lancs')
614	8/1885	Std	0-6-0T oc	12x18	3'0"	IDDESLEIGH	Dorman Brown & Co (contr' Malmo-Kontienten Rly Sweden)
632	6/1884	1'8"	0-4-0	5x7½		S JOSE	Henry Rogers Sons & Co (agents for Pernambuco Brazil)
646	11/1884	3'0"	2-4-0T oc	6x9		LERMA	Ybarrondo, (FC Merida a Campeche Railway Mexico)
660	11/1887	Std	0-4-0ST oc	10x15		BIGNALL HILL	Bignall Hill Colly Co, (Jamage Colly Newcastle Staffs')
663	1/1885	3'1⅛"	0-4-0	9x13½		MALINO (MILANO)	G J Schlegel (Italian contractors)
667	11/1884	3'6"	0-4-0	6x9		HANNAH	A Verse & Co - gauge changed to 80c/m and name to MAGRA
680	3/1885	3'0"	2-4-2T oc	10x17		CAMPECHANA	Ybarrondo, (FC Merida a Campeche Railway Mexico)
682	2/1885	3'0"	2-4-0T oc	5½x9		KARTOUM	J Terry & Co, (agents Beconsfield Tramway, Tasmania)
691	3/1885	2'6"	0-4-0IST oc	6x9		CECIL	Aire & Calder Navigation (Goole Docks)
699	5/1887	3'0"	0-4-0IST oc	6½x10		MINNIE	Enoch Tempest contr' (later at Clough Bottom Reservoir Lanc's)
700	5/1889	2'5½"	2-4-0T oc	6½x10		FORTUNA	Bale & Edwards sold as No 1046 - spares 6/06 Achilles Jesi
702	4/1885	2'5½"	0-4-0	5x7½		ROLLO	Selig & Sonnenthal (London acting as agents)
710	6/1885	1'6"	0-4-2FT oc	7½x12	2'0¾"	SERIPIS	HM Government Royal Arsenal Woolwich
711	6/1885	1'6"	0-4-2FT oc	7½x12	2'0¾"	OSIRIS	HM Government Royal Arsenal Woolwich
712	8/1885	1'6"	0-4-2FT oc	7½x12	2'0¾"	ANUBIS	HM Government Royal Arsenal Woolwich
713	8/1885	1'6"	0-4-2FT oc	7½x12	2'0¾"	ISIS	HM Government Royal Arsenal Woolwich
714	8/1885	1'6"	0-4-2FT oc	7½x12	2'0¾"	APIS	HM Government Royal Arsenal Woolwich
730	1/1886	3'0"	0-6-0T oc	13x20	3'6"	No 1	West Clare Railway Ireland
738	6/1886	3'0"	0-6-0T oc	13x20	3'6"	No 2	West Clare Railway Ireland
745	12/1885	1'8"	0-4-0	5½x8¼			Henry Rogers Sons & Co (agents for Pernambuco Brazil)
760	4/1886	2'7½"	0-4-0IST oc	10x15	2'3"	(DINA)	Centi (contr, Cappuccini Botteghe Spezia Italy)
761	4/1886	2'7½"	0-4-0IST oc	10x15	2'3"		Centi (contr, Cappuccini Botteghe Spezia Italy)
770	4/1886	2'6"	0-4-0	4½x7½			Diekmann (Brothers & Co London for Burmah)
778	6/1886	1'11⅝"	0-4-0IST oc	6½x10		SPEZIA	Fedozzi (contr' Cave di Reboco Spezia Railway, Italy)
792	1/1887	3'0"	0-6-0T oc	14x20	3'6"	No 3 (CLIFDEN)	West Clare Railway Ireland
793	1/1887	3'0"	0-6-0T oc	14x20	3'6"	No 4 (BESBOROUGH)	West Clare Railway Ireland
812	10/1886	2'7½"	0-4-0	8x12		SELLA	Piatti (contr' Casa Corvi to Guinada Railway Spezia Italy)
835	12/1886	metre	2-4-0T oc	6x9			AL Dunphy; returned and sold JK Hodgson & Son (may have worked in Cumberland)
840	3/1887	3'0"	0-4-0IST oc	8x12		JUBILEE	H Fotherby & Son (contr' Burnley Corp' Cant Clough Reservoir Const')
842	2/1887	2'6"	2-4-0T oc	7x10½	1'9"	BARONEZA	Henry Rogers Sons & Co (for Pernambuco Brazil)
870	5/1887	2'4½"	0-4-0IST oc	10x15	2'3"		Peggazano (contr' Spezia Biassa Railway Italy)
872	5/1887	2'7½"	0-4-0IST oc	10x15	2'3"	AUDACE	Centi contr, (Cappuccini Botteghe Spezia Italy)
874	3/1887	2'6"	0-4-0	4½x7½			Diekmann (Brothers & Co London for Burmah)
891	5/1887	3'2½"	0-4-0IST oc	9x13½	2'3"	DENSHAW	Oldham Corp' (Castleshaw Reservoir const' Delph Lancs)
892	6/1887	3'2½"	0-4-0IST oc	9x13½	2'3"	PIETHORN	Oldham Corp' (Castleshaw Reservoir const' Delph Lancs)

Manu No	Date Desp	Gauge	Type	Cyls	Dwl Dia	Name/No:	Purchaser/Destination
902	5/1887	3'0"	0-4-0IST oc	9x13½	2'3"	VICTORIA	H Fotherby & Son (contr' Burnley Corp' Cant Clough Reservoir Const')
905	6/1887	2'7½"	0-4-0IST oc	9x13½	2'3"	GARIBALDI	Piatti (contr' Casa Corvi to Guinada Railway Spezia Italy)
912	9/1887	3'0"	0-4-0IST oc	9x13½	2'3"	HAROLD	Enoch Tempest (contr') later with Crawshay Bros' [Cyfarthfa] Ltd South Wales
918	9/1887	3'0"	0-4-0IST oc	10x15	2'3"	DAISY	Job Hartley (May be JW Hartley of Stoke-on-Trent)
922	9/1887	2'6"	0-4-0IST oc	5x7½		MAGNET	FR Thompstone & Sons (Dane Corn Mills Bosley Cheshire)
930	10/1887	1'11⅝"	0-4-0IST oc	7x10½		QUEENIE	Coalbrookdale Co (agents Gilgwyn Slate Quarry Nantlle Caern')
934	11/1887	1'11"	0-4-0IST oc	7x10½		MIDGE	Hawley & Bridgewood (Mossfield Colly, Longton Stoke-on-Trent)
950	11/1887	2'7½"	0-4-0IST oc	9x13½		JESSIE	F Cretzberg (agent for NC Monberg contr' Copenhagen, Denmark)
954	2/1889	Std	0-4-0FT oc	10x15			M&W Grazebrook (Netherton Staffs) later part exchange for 1432
968	3/1888	2'6"	0-4-0	4½x7½			Diekmann (Brothers & Co London for Burmah)
970	4/1888	1'11½"	0-4-0IST oc	5x7½	(1'3¼")	EXCELSIOR	CJ Naylor (Kerry Tramway Montgomery - rebuilt as 0-4-2)
983	6/1888	metre	0-4-0	6½x10		DIANA	A Zavala (may have gone to Zavala Nitrate Mines in Chile)
984	6/1888	metre	0-4-0	6½x10		AMARA	A Zavala (may have gone to Zavala Nitrate Mines in Chile)
1000	9/1888	2'6"	0-4-0ST oc	8x10		ROBINSON	Manchester Corporation (Carrington Sewage Estate Cheshire)
1002	7/1888	2'6"	0-4-0IST oc	8½x12		EBENEZER	G Hodsman Lunedale Whinstone & Co (Middleton-in-Teesdale Yorks')
1024	10/1888	3'0"	0-4-0IST oc	8x14	2'0"	GERTRUDE	Islip Iron Co (Islip Quarries Northants)
1046	5/1889	2'5½"	2-4-0T oc	6½x10		FORTUNA	No 700 sold under this number
1050	1/1889	3'0"	0-4-0IST oc	6x9		JC STATON	JC Staton & Co (Scropton Tramway Tutbury Staffs')
1052	2/1889	1'11"	0-4-0IST oc	4x6		MARGARET	Hall & Boardman (Swadlincote Derbys')
1058	1/1889	1'11⅝"	2-4-0T oc	4½x7½		CASTRO	Henry Rogers Sons & Co (agents for Pernambuco Brazil)
1076	3/1889	3'0"	0-4-0IST oc	7x10½		ANNIE	Enoch Tempest (contr', Matlock Derbys')
1084	3/1889	3'9"	0-4-0IST oc	6x9	1'9"	MARIA	William Bickley (Pool Hayes Colly Willenhall Staffs')
1092	11/1889	3'0"	0-4-0IST oc	8x12		WINDSOR	Kerr Stuart & Co (India - later in Malay)
1116	5/1889	3'0"	0-4-0IST oc	9x13½	2'3"	BRANCKER	C Braddock (contr' Chedworth Section MSWJ Rly const')
1120	5/1891	3'6"	0-4-0IST oc	9x13½	2'6"	WHITAKER	B Whitaker & Son (Pool Quarry Horsforth Yorks')
1122	10/1889	2'0"	0-4-0IST oc	5½x8¼	2'0"	GORDON	Great Wyrley Colly' (Cheslyn Hay Staffs')
1134	12/1889	3'0½"	0-4-0IST oc	7x10½		NELSON	R Boulton & Co (agents Henckill du Buisson & Co Santa Lucia Antigua)
1183	10/1889	2'0"	0-4-0	4½x7½		MOSQUITO	Clark & Co (may have gone to Ceylon)
1184	10/1889	2'0"	0-4-0	4½x7½		HORMICA	Clark & Co (may have gone to Ceylon)
1188	11/1889	2'6"	2-4-0T oc	6x9		MEZOHEGYES	WA Stone (agent sent to Mezohegyes Hungary)
1189	11/1889	2'6"	2-4-0T oc	6x9		PEREG	WA Stone (agent sent to Mezohegyes Hungary)
1198	11/1889	2'3⅝"	2-4-0T oc	6x9			WA Stone (agent sent to Mezohegyes Hungary)
1206	12/1889	Std	0-4-0IST oc	10x15		PIETRO MICCA	Piatti (contr' Casa Corvi to Guinada Railway Spezia Italy)
1212	1/1890	1'11⅝"	2-4-0T oc	6x9		C de FIGUEIREDO	Henry Rogers Sons & Co (agents for Pernambuco Brazil)
1230	1/1890	2'6"	0-4-0	5x7½		VIRGINIA	Colonial Co - 5/96 & 8/00 spares New Colonial Co Ltd London
1232	9/1891	3'0"	0-4-0IST oc	8x12		J C STATON	J C Staton & Co (Scropton Tramway Tutbury Staffs')
1258	3/1890	2'5½"	2-4-0T oc	6x9			Dieckmann (Brothers & Co London for Burmah)
1260	2/1891	2'6"	0-4-2T oc	10x15	2'9"	CHESHIRE	HM Government (many have gone to Chatterden Kent - was there later)
1272	6/1890	3'0"	0-6-0T oc	9x13½	2'2"	BOTTESFORD	Stanton Ironworks Co (Wartnaby Quarries Leics')
1278	8/1890	1'11½"	0-4-0IST oc	6x9		EDITH	JW Greaves & Son (Llechwedd Slate Quarries Merioneth)
1296	9/1890	2'7 9/16"	0-4-0	6½x10		PAULINO & ST CASTALDO	Bale & Edwards (agents - this might be two locomotives)
1308	11/1890	3'6"	0-6-0T oc	14x20		ST PHILIP	Barbados Railway Co (later Demerara Railway Co)
1310	4/1891	3'6"	0-6-0T oc	14x20		ST ANDREW	Barbados Railway Co (later Demerera Railway Co)
1334	4/1891	2'7½"	0-4-0	6½x10		MINGARDO	Bale & Edwards agents
1340	6/1891	metre	0-4-0	7x10½		SOCORRO	Sim & Coventry Ltd (agents Orconera Iron Ore Co Santander Spain)
1344	7/1891	3'9½"	0-4-0IST oc	9x14	2'9½"	CEMENT	IC Johnson & Co (Greenhithe Kent)
1350	9/1891	3'2¼"	0-4-0IST oc	11x18		No 7	New British Iron Co (Cradley Heath Staffs')
1354	9/1891	3'0"	0-4-0IST ic	5x7½	1'3"	COKE	South Metropolitan Gas Co (Vauxhall Works London)
1365	9/1891	1'8"	0-4-0IST ic	4x6½	1'3"		W Reid & Co
1381	11/1891	3'0"	0-4-0IST ic	5½x10	1'8"	CHARGER	Palmers Shipbuilding Co (Jarrow Durham - later with Sir John Jacksopn contr')
1392	1/1892	Std	0-4-0FT oc	12x18	3'1"	BIGNALL HILL	Bignall Hill Colly Co (Jamage Colly' Newcastle Staffs')
1399	2/1892	2'5½"	2-4-0T oc	8x12	2'0"	FRATERINDADE	Henry Rogers Sons & Co (agents for Pernambuco Brazil)
1402	3/1892	Std	0-4-0FT oc	12x18	3'0"	ALEXANDER	John Needham & Sons (agent for Birchenwood Colly Co Kidsgrove Staffs')
1408	5/1892	1'11"	0-4-0IST oc	6x9	1'8"	JACK	Hall & Boardman (Swadlincote Derbys')
1410	11/1893	2'6"	0-4-0ST oc	6x9	1'6"	HAULIER	LNWR Engineers Dept' - later name PLATELAYER
1411	11/1893	Std	0-4-0ST oc	12x18	3'0"	BAGNALL	Roberts & Co (Tipton Staffs')
1412	6/1892	2'5½"	2-4-0T oc	9x14	2'7"	UNIAO	Henry Rogers Sons & Co (agents for Pernambuco Brazil)
1413	4/1894	3'0"	0-4-0ST oc	9x14	2'7"	REDE	Snowball & Co (agents Newcastle & Gateshead Water Co Cateleugh)
1414	7/1892	2'10"	0-4-0ST oc	6x10	1'9"	No 4	Bowling Iron Co (Bradford)
1415	10/1892	3'0"	0-4-0IST ic	5x7½	1'3"	JASON	South Metro Gas Co (Vauxhall Gas Works London)
1416	7/1893	2'0"	0-4-0ST oc	6x9	1'6"	F R S No 2	W Barrington (may have been for Fergus Reclamation Syndicate Ireland)
1417	1/1893	3'9½"	0-4-0FT oc	9x14	2'7"	SAMSON	IC Johnson & Co (Greenhithe Kent)
1418	6/1893	3'6"	2-4-0T oc	13x20	3'6"	3 CORBIERE	Jersey Railway Co, (Channel Islands)
1419	4/1893	3'0"	2-4-0T oc	8x12	2'2½"	MAURITIUS	Mauritius Estates & Assets Co Mauritius
1420	5/1893	3'0"	0-4-0IST oc	8x12	2'0"	ADA	Enoch Tempest (contr' Clough Bottom Reservoir const' Lancs')
1421	10/1893	3'0"	2-4-0T oc	5½x9	1'6"	CONCORD	South Metropolitan Gas Co (Old Kent Road Works London)
1422	7/1893	2'5½"	2-4-0T oc	9x14	2'7"	TRIUMPHO	Henry Rogers Sons & Co (agents for Pernambuco Brazil)
1423	7/1893	3'0"	0-4-0IST oc	8x12	2'0"	FLYING ROCKET	J&M Hawley (contr' Grimwith Reservior const' Pateley Bridge Yorks')
1424	12/1893	3'6"	0-4-0IST oc	7x12	2'0"	No 2	London County Council (Beckton Sewage Works)
1425	9/1893	1'6"	4-2-2+6wl ten oc	4x6½	2'6"	778	Faulkner Bedford & Co (agents for Lord Downshire Easthampstead Berks')
1426	2/1894	3'0"	0-4-0IST oc	8x12	2'0"	MINNIE	Snowball & Co (agents Newcastle & Gateshead Water Co Cateleugh)
1427	2/1894	metre	2-4-2T oc	12x20	3'0"	ASTILLERO	Sim & Coventry Ltd (agents Orconera Iron Ore Co Santander Spain)
1428	12/1893	Std	0-4-0ST oc	7x12	2'0"		Kannreuther & Co
1429	10/1894	1'8"	0-4-0ST oc	6x9	1'6"	MARGARET	Essington Fram Colliery Co (Bloxwich Staffs')
1430	2/1895	2'0¼"	0-4-0ST oc	6x9	1'6"	SLAVE	Peacock Colliery Co (Ilkestone Derbys')
1431	4/1894	2'6"	0-6-0T oc	8x12	2'6"	SUCCESS	John Birch & Co (agents Japan - Ohme Rly No2)
1432	2/1895	Std	0-4-0ST oc	12x18	3'0"	GRAZEBROOK	M&W Grazebrook (Netherton Staffs') Part exchange for 1884
1433	9/1894	3'0"	0-4-0IST oc	8x12	2'0"	GORDON	Enoch Tempest (contr' Rawtenstall Lancs')
1434	11/1894	3'0"	0-4-0IST oc	8x12	2'0"	ALSTON	Preston Corporation (Alston No 2 Reservoir const' Lancs')
1435	11/1894	3'9"	0-4-0IST oc	8x12	2'0"	FITZ	Butterley Co (Hilts Limestone Quarry Crich Derbys')
1436	9/1894	2'0"	0-4-2ST oc	5½x9	1'6"	NAMDANG	Assam Railways & Trading Co (Margherita Assam India)
1437	9/1894	2'0"	0-4-2ST oc	5½x9	1'6"	TIRAP	Assam Railways & Trading Co (Margherita Assam India)

Manu No	Date: Desp	Gauge	Type	Cyls	Dwl Dia	Name/No:	Purchaser/Destination
1438	9/1894	2'0"	0-4-2ST oc	5½x9	1'6"	PEKOE-TIP	Jokai (Assam) Tea Co Ltd Assam India
1439	11/1894	2'0"	0-4-0IST oc	5x8	1'2"	IRIS	Gas Light & Coke Co Nine Elms Works London
1440	9/1894	2'3½"	0-6-0T oc	7½x12	1'9½"	D d S No 1	Rahr & Raundrup (Hojbyguard Suger Factory Denmark)
1441	11/1894	metre	4-4-0T oc	8½x14	2'6"	HERCULES	Pollock & McNab (agents Pernambuco Brazil later at Usina Paranague)
1442	1/1895	1'6"	0-4-0IST oc	7x12	2'1"	AJAX	HM Government Royal Arsenal Woolwich
1443	12/1895	2'3½"	0-4-0ST oc	4½x7½	1'1¾"	PEPITO	Appleby Bros Leicester agents shipped from Liverpool
1444	7/1897	1'8"	0-4-0ST oc	4½x7½	1'1¾"	EXPLORER	Carthago Exploration Syndicate Ltd Tunis (returned, re-gauged 2'9" to Gas Light & Coke Co London as MABEL)
1445	10/1895	1'11⅝"	0-4-0ST oc	6x9	1'6"	MARGARET	JW Greaves & Son (Llechwedd Slate Quarries Merioneth)
1446	2/1896	2'1"	0-4-0ST oc	6x9	1'6"	MOUNTAINEER	Hurst Nelson & Co Motherwell (for The South Tyne Granite Quarries Northumb')
1447-51	4-5/1895	metre	0-4-0IST oc	8x12	2'0½"	No 1 - No 5	Admiralty Gibralter Naval Yard
1452	2/1896	1'6"	0-4-0IST oc	8x12	2'0½"	RAMESES	E Legget - War Office for Egyptian Government
1453	10/1895	Std	0-4-0ST oc	13½x20	3'6"	PHILLIS	Sir Alfred Hickman (Springvale Furnaces Bilston Staffs')
1454	7/1895	1'11⅝"	2-4-0T oc	7x11	1'9½"	TEIMOSA	AB Ghewey - Heirdeiros Bowman Ltd (Davino S Portugal Pernambuco Brazil)
1455	7/1895	2'0"	0-4-0ST oc	8x12	2'0½"	COLLIER	Finlay Muir & Co for India via Calcutta
1456	6/1895	4'0"	0-4-0ST oc	6x9	1'6"	ANNIE	George Talbot (contr' Glasgow Underground Railway)
1457	1/1896	4'0"	0-4-0ST oc	6x9	1'6"	No 2	George Talbot (contr' Glasgow Underground Railway)
1458	6/1897	metre	0-6-0ST oc	8x12	1'9½"	BENGUELLA	W Roughton
1459	7/1897	Std	0-4-0ST oc	12x18	3'0"	STAFFORD	Roberts & Co (Tipton Green Blast Furnaces Staffs')
1460	11/1895	2'0"	0-4-0IST oc	5x8	1'2"	AJAX	Gas Light & Coke Co Nine Elms Works London
1461	7/1895	3'0"	2-4-0T oc	5½x9	1'8"	CAMBER	EPS Jones Rye, Rye & Camber Tramway (Rye Sussex)
1462-5	10/1895	1'8"	0-4-0ST oc	6x9	1'6"	LEWIS JONES & CO No 1 - No 4	William Jones London (for constr' work Assam-Bengal Railway India)
1466	1/1896	3'6"	2-4-0T oc	13x20	3'6"	4 ST BRELADES	Jersey Railway Co, (Channel Islands)
1467-74	12/95-2/96	metre	0-4-0IST oc	8x12	2'0½"	No 6 - No 13	Admiralty Gibralter Naval Yard
1475	12/1896	2'5½"	0-4-0ST oc	7x12	1'9½"	MAMELUCO	Dale & Oliver (agents Usina Mameluco Pernambuco Brazil)
1476	3/1896	1'11⅝"	0-4-0ST oc	6x9	1'6"	SANTO ANTONIO	F Mills Companhia Lupton (Usina Santo Antonio of Sao Luis Quilunde Alagoas Brazil)
1477-9	5-6/1896	3'0"	0-4-0ST oc	6x9	1'6"	No 15 - 17	Glasgow Iron & Steel Co Ltd (Wishaw Lanarks')
1480	9/1897	3'0"	0-4-0IST oc	8x12	2'0½"	CROSSHAVEN	John Best (contr' for regauging work Cork Blackrock & Passage Rly Ireland)
1481	9/1897	2'11½"	0-4-0IST oc	8x12	2'0½"	CAROLINE	Wynmalen & Hausman shipped from Hull to Holland
1482	4/1896	Std	0-4-0ST oc	10x15	2'6"	A S J No 2	HC Petersen & Co for Anderson Sorenson & Jessen contrs' Copenhagen
1483	8/1896	2'5½"	0-4-2ST oc	7½x12	1'9½"	LIMOEIRINHO	James Milne & Co (agents Usina Mameluco) Pernambuco Brazil
1484	5/1896	2'0"	2-4-0T oc	4½x7½	1'2"	SEA LION	RM Broadbent Howstrake Estate Co (Groudle Glen Rly Isle of Man)
1485	11/1897	3'0"	0-4-0ST oc	5x7½	1'3"	DORIS	Enoch Tempest (contr' Molyneux Brow Clifton Radcliffe Lancs')
1486	9/1896	2'0"	0-4-0ST oc	5½x9	1'6"	DASSIE	African Saltpetre Co (Namaqualand Cape Province)
1487	11/1896	2'0"	0-4-0ST oc	6x9	1'6"	CLIFFE	Cliffe Hill Granite Co (Markfield Leics')
1488	4/1897	2'0¾"	0-4-0ST oc	6x9	1'6"	JUBILEE 1897	Darwen & Mostyn Iron Co (Darwen Furnaces Lancs)
1489	4/1897	2'0"	0-4-0ST oc	6x9	1'6"	THELMA	Queenborough Cement Co (Queenborough Kent)
1490	10/1896	metre	0-4-0IST oc	8x12	2'0½"	VICTORIA	Assam Railways & Trading Co for Assam Oil Co
1491	2/1897	2'0"	0-4-0ST oc	7x12	1'9½"	ISABEL	Cliffe Hill Granite Co (Markfield Leics')
1492	6/1897	metre	0-4-0ST oc	5x7½	1'3¼"	LOUISE	M Samuel & Co (Louise Concession Borneo)
1493-6	12/96-2/97	Std	0-4-0ST oc	10x15	2'9"	No 1 - No 4	Admiralty Portland Dockyard Extensions Dorset
1497	8/1897	2'3"	2-4-0T oc	8x12	2'3"	TALYBONT	Plynlimon & Hafan Tramway (Talybont Cardigan')
1498	9/1896	2'3½"	0-4-0ST oc	5x10	1'4"	COLONIA	Jones Burton & Co (agents Usina Colonia Bahia Brazil)
1499-1500	12/1896	2'6"	0-4-0IST oc	7x12	2'0"	AUGUSTA & BEATRICE	J Morrison & Co (Northern Kyushu Japan)
1501	3/1897	3'0"	6 wheel geared	5x9	1'3¼&1'¼"	JENNIE	Walker Hill & Co (fairground loco - circular track)
1502	4/1897	3'2½"	0-4-0ST oc	10x15	2'6"	WASSELL	Shelagh Garrett & Co (Cradley Heath Worcs')
1503	3/1897	2'5½"	0-4-0ST oc	7x12	1'9½"	PICON	Carlos Yenson (sent to Spain)
1504	5/1897	3'0"	0-4-0IST oc	10x15	2'7½"	BLAKELEY	Huddersfield Corporation (Deerhill Reservoir const' Yorks')
1505-6	6/1897	2'0"	0-4-2ST oc	5½x9	1'6"	SAIDROW & HASANG	Assam Railways & Trading Co (Margherita Assam India)
1507	7/1897	1'11⅝"	0-4-0ST oc	6x9	1'6⅝"	TIMBO REAL No 1	Hurst Nelson & Co (agents Usina Timbo Real Santa Valley Peru)
1508-9	11/1897	2'0"	0-4-0ST oc	6x9	1'6⅝"	BEATRICE & LOUISE	Oppenheimer Freres & Co (Japanese Military Railways)
1510	9/1897	2'3"	0-4-0ST oc	6x9	1'6⅝"	HAFAN	Plynlimon & Hafan Tramway (Talybont Cardigan')
1511	6/1897	3'0"	2-4-0T oc	6x10	2'0½"	VICTORIA	EPS Jones Rye, Rye & Camber Tramway (Rye Sussex)
1512	8/1897	2'5½"	0-4-2ST oc	6x9	1'6⅝"	KNORRING	Axel Von Knorring (contr' Finnish State Railways const')
1513	1/1898	2'6"	0-6-0T oc	10x15	2'6½"	STAFFORD	HM Government (Chattenden & Upnor Railway Kent)
1514	1/1898	2'6"	0-6-0ST oc	11x16½	2'6½"	BAGNALL	HM Government (Chattenden & Upnor Railway Kent)
1515	5/1898	1'11⅝"	0-4-0ST oc	6x9	2'0"	OCEJA No 1	Carlos Yenson (sent to Spain)
1516	8/1898	3'0"	0-4-0ST oc	6x9	1'8"		Morrison & Mason (contr' Elan Valley-Birmingham Pipeline Contract)
1517	11/1898	2'0"	0-4-0ST oc	6x9	1'8"	MARY	JW Davis (Pouk Hill Quarry Bentley Moor Walsall Staffs')
1518	9/1898	2'3"	0-4-0ST oc	6x9	2'0"	THE SCOTCHMAN	John Shaw Ltd for export (Reunion Sugar Estate Natal South Africa)
1519-28	1-5/1898	2'5½"	4-4-0T oc	9½x14"	2'6"	C F A No 1 - 10	Egyptian Delta Light Railways
1529	4/1898	2'0"	0-4-0PT oc	4½x6½	1'3¼"	FEODORE	H Ahrens & Co Japan (at one period used on Sagami Rly)
1530	5/1898	3'6"	0-4-0ST oc	8x12	2'3"	ENDEAVOUR	John Birch & Co (agents Hokkaido Govt' Harbour const' Otaru) Japan
1531	8/1898	2'0"	0-4-0ST oc	7x12	1'9½"	THE ROCKET	Cliffe Hill Granite Co (Markfield Leics')
1532	5/1898	2'6"	0-4-0ST oc	6x10	1'8"		Jessop & Appleby Ltd agents (for export)
1533	5/1898	1'10"	0-4-0ST oc	4x7½	1'1"	(Arabic script)	G Bailey Toms & Co agents, Alexandria Egypt
1534	8/1898	3'0"	2-4-0T oc	7x11	1'10"	UNITY	South Metropolitan Gas Co Old Kent Road Works London
1535	8/1898	2'5½"	0-4-0ST oc	5½x9	1'4"	No 8	South Metropolitan Gas Co East Greenwich Works London
1536	12/1898	3'0"	0-4-0IST ic	5½x7½	1'4"	ORION	South Metropolitan Gas Co Vauxhall Works London
1537	10/1898	Std	0-4-0ST oc	12x18	3'0½"	No 11 (Roman two)	Sheffield United Gas Co (Grimesthorpe Works Sheffield)
1538-9	7/1898	2'5½"	0-4-2ST oc	6x9	1'6⅝"		Axel Von Knorring (contr' Finnish State Railways const')
1540-9	12/98-4/99	2'5½"	4-4-0T oc	9½x14	2'6"	C F A No 11 - 20	Egyptian Delta Light Railways
1550	9/1898	3'6"	0-4-0ST oc	12x18	3'0"	TAMAR No 77	S Pearson & Son (contr' Gunnislake Quarry Cornwall)
1551	9/1898	3'0"	0-4-0ST oc	7x12	1'9½"	MOURNE	Fisher & Le Fanu (contr' Goulds Cross & Cashel Railway const' Ireland)
1552	2/1899	2'6"	0-4-0ST oc	6x9	1'7"	S L G R No 3	Crown Agents Sierra Leone Govt' Railway
1553	11/1898	2'9"	0-4-0ST oc	6x9	1'7"	IRIS	Gas Light & Coke Co Bromley-by-Bow Works London
1554	12/1898	2'7"	0-4-0ST oc	6x9	1'7"	LLANDOUGH	D Thomas & Son Llandough (Glam')
1555	2/1899	2'0"	0-4-0ST oc	6x9	1'7"	SUSAN	Queenborough Cement Co (Queenborough Kent)
1556-7	4/1899	2'0"	0-4-2SToc	6x9	1'7"	TARAKUSI & KOLAPINI	Assam Railways & Trading Co (Margherita Assam India)
1558	1/1899	2'6"	0-4-0ST oc	6x9	1'7"	ROBERT	RW Fitzmaurice & Co Rowley Regis (Hailstone Granite Quarry Staffs')

Manu: No	Date Desp	Gauge	Type	Cyls	Dwl Dia	Name/No	Purchaser/Destination
1559	12/1898	1'11⅝"	0-4-0ST oc	5½x9	1'6"		John Aird & Co for export - quantity of wagons sent with loco
1560	3/1899	1'6"	0-4-0ST oc	4½x7½	1'2"	BREDE	Hastings Corporation (Brede Water Works Sussex)
1561	4/1899	2'6"	0-4-0ST oc	6x9	1'9"	CONSTRUCTOR	Aire & Calder Navigation Co (River Aire Diversion Works Hunslet Leeds)
1562	6/1899	3'0"	0-4-0ST oc	7x12	1'9½"	CHARGER	Parkgate Iron & Steel Co (Rotherham Yorks')
1563	5/1899	3'0"	0-4-0ST oc	9x14	2'6½"	SLIPTON No 4	Islip Furnace Co (Islip Quarries Northants')
1564	6/1899	3'2¼"	0-4-0ST oc	12x18	3'0½"	MABEL	Congreaves Furnace Co (Cradley Heath Staffs')
1565	7/1899	2'9"	2-4-0T oc	8x12	2'2½"	RIO DO OURA	JM Sumner & Co Lisbon (agents Conde De Valle Flor, San Thome Africa)
1566	12/1899	3'0"	0-4-0ST oc	6x9	1'7"	MARPLE	Enoch Tempest (contr' Oakdene drainage cont' Marple Cheshire)
1567	12/1899	3'0"	0-4-0ST oc	8x12	2'0½"	WALSHAW DEAN	Enoch Tempest (contr' Walshaw Dean Reservoir const, Halifax Corp' Yorks)
1568	9/1899	1'11⅝"	0-4-0ST oc	6x9	1'7"	DOROTHY	JW Greaves & Sons (Llechwedd Slate Quarries Merioneth)
1569	12/1899	1'11⅝"	0-4-0ST oc	6x9	1'7"	SNOWDON	Oakeley Slate Quarries (Blaenau Festiniog Merioneth)
1570	12/1899	1'11⅝"	0-4-0ST oc	6x9	1'7"	JEANNE	JW Van der Elst for Dutch use (sent to Holland) to suit Dutch Govt' regulations
1571	07/1900	1'11⅝"	0-4-0ST oc	6x9	1'7"	SANFORD	Owen Issac & Owen ((agent for Maen Offeren Slate Quarry Blaenau Festiniog)
1572-3	8-10/1899	2'6"	0-4-2SToc	6x9	1'7"	No 1 - No 2	Crown Agents (thought to be for Perak Public Works Dept' Malay)
1574	8/1899	2'6"	0-4-0ST oc	8½x15	2'8"	No 4 TREVOR	Manchester Corp' (Cleansing Dept. Chat Moss Estate Lancs')
1575	9/1899	Std	0-4-0ST oc	14x20	3'6"	MOUNTFIELD	Subwealdon Gypsum Co (Mountfield Sussex)
1576-80	10-12/1899	2'5½"	4-4-0T oc	9½x14	2'6"	C F A No 21 - 25	Egyptian Delta Light Railways
1581	8/1899	2'6⅞"	0-4-0ST oc	5x7½	1'3¼"	S F J	H C Peterson & Co (contr' const' of South of Funen Railway Denmark)
1582	7/1899	3'9½"	0-4-0ST oc	10x15	2'9¼"	MAMMOTH	IC Johnson & Co (Greenhithe Kent)
1583	12/1899	Std	0-4-0ST oc	10x15	2'6"	DUVALS	Grays Chalk Quarries Co Ltd (Grays Essex)
1584	11/1899	Std	0-4-0ST oc	14x20	3'6"	SUCCESS	Wolverhampton Gas Co (Wolverhampton Staffs)
1585-6	10-11/1899	1'11⅝"	0-4-0ST oc	7x11	2'0"	No 138 - No 139	John Aird & Co (contr') later spares sent to Egypt, order of Egyptian Govt
1587	02/1900	1'11⅝"	0-4-0ST oc	9x14	2'3½"	STANTON No 14	Stanton Ironworks Co Ltd (Harston Quarries Leics')
1588	03/1900	4'3½"	0-4-0ST oc	12x18	3'0½"	GOLIATH	Trechmann Weekes & Co (Halling Kent)
1589	05/1900	2'0"	0-4-0ST oc	6x9	1'7"	EDITH	Cliffe Hill Granite Co (Markfield Leics')
1590-1	04/1900	2'5½"	0-4-0ST oc	6x9	1'7"	MALAESPERA & ALEN	TF Cowbrick shipped to Bilbao (5/1906 spares El Material Industrial)
1592	12/1900	2'0"	0-4-0ST oc	6x9	1'7"	BOBS	Enderby & Stoney Stanton Granite Co Ltd (Enderby Quarries Leics')
1593	11/1900	2'6"	0-4-2ST oc	6x9	1'7"	No 3	Crown Agents for Perak Public Works Dept' (Malay)
1594	11/1900	2'0¾"	0-4-0ST oc	6x9	1'7"	BOBS	Darwen & Mostyn Iron Co (Darwen Furnaces Lancs)
1595	02/1900	3'6"	0-6-0ST oc	9x14	2'3½"	2	Crown Agents Gold Coast Govt' Railway
1596	07/1900	3'9"	0-4-0IST oc	8x12	2'0½"	SALISBURY	Butterley Co Ltd (Hilts Limestone Quarry Crich Derbys')
1597	04/1900	1'11"	0-4-0ST oc	8x12	2'0½"	NORA	Llanelly Steel Co (Llanelly Carmarthenshire)
1598-1607	4-11/1900	2'5½"	4-4-0T oc	9½x14	2'6"	CFA No 26 - 35	Egyptian Delta Light Railways
1608	05/1900	2'4"	0-4-0ST oc	8x12	2'0½"	THRELKELD	Threlkeld Granite Co Ltd (Keswick Quarry Cumberland)
1609	08/1900	3'9½"	0-4-0ST oc	10x15	2'9¼"	LEVIATHAN	IC Johnson & Co (Greenhithe Kent)
1610	03/1900	2'0"	0-4-0ST oc	5x7½	1'3¼"	SIR RALPH	Crown Agents (retd from Southern Nigeria for reps 7/04 and sent back)
1611	05/1900	Std	0-4-0ST oc	8x12	2'0"	ROIKEN	W Fischer & Son Christiania (Andenes breakwater Norway)
1612-3	09/1900	Std	0-4-0ST oc	10x15	2'10"	No 9 - No 10	South Metropolitan Gas Co (East Greenwich Works London)
1614	10/1900	1'11⅝"	0-4-0ST oc	7x12	1'9½"	ISABEL	George Farren Welsh Granite Co (Trevor Quarry Caerns')
1615-6	12/1900	1'11⅝"	2-4-0T oc	8x12	2'3"	No 1 ARCENIEGA & No 3 SODUPE	Rosing Bros & Co Materials De Construction Zaragoza (Spain)
1617	10/1900	metre	0-4-2ST oc	8x12	2'3"	VIRGINIA	A&PW McOnie Glasgow (agents for Usina Sao Bento Bahia Brazil)
1618	11/1900	2'0"	0-4-0ST oc	7x12	1'9½"	LESTER	Carnarvonshire Granite Co (Tyddyn Hywel Quarries Clynnog Caerns')
1619	09/1900	2'6"	0-4-0ST oc	6x9	1'9"	CONSTRUCTOR No 2	Aire & Calder Navigation Co (River Aire Diversion Works Hunslet Leeds)
1620-9	6-10/1901	2'6"	2-4-2ST oc	8x12	2'3"	No 51 - No 60	Indian States Railways Kushalgar Kohat Thal Railway India
1630	11/1900	3'6"	0-4-0ST oc	6x9	1'7"	No 1	JC Mounsey & Co (Callenders Cables Construction Co Belevedere Kent)
1631	12/1900	2'6"	0-4-0ST oc	6x9	1'7"	MIKASA	James Fisher & Sons (Glenravel Bauxite Mines Cargan Antrim Ireland)
1632-3	08/1901	3'0"	0-4-0ST oc	6x9	1'7"	ROBINSON & WALTON	Enoch Tempest (contr' Walshaw Dean Reservoir const, Halifax Corp' Yorks)
1634	02/1901	3'6"	0-4-0ST oc	7x12	2'3"	BOBS	North Staffordshire Railway (Caldon Low Quarries Staffs')
1635	01/1901	metre	0-4-0ST oc	7x12	1'9½"	HILIKA A.F.T.Co	James Reid & Co (Assam Frontier Tea Co India)
1636	01/1901	2'5½"	0-4-2ST oc	7½x12	1'9½"	H B PERRY & CO BAHIA	HB Perry & Co Bahia El Salvador (Brazil)
1637	06/1901	Std	0-4-0ST oc	10x15	2'6"	AMOS	Grays Chalk Quarries Co Ltd (Grays Essex)
1638-9	6-7/1901	3'0"	0-4-0ST oc	8x12	2'0½"	WADE & LIPSCOMB	Enoch Tempest (contr' Walshaw Dean Reservoir const, Halifax Corp' Yorks)
1640-1	5-6/1901	3'0"	0-4-0ST oc	6x9	1'7"	BOBS & FRENCH	Parkgate Iron & Steel Co (Rotherham Yorks')
1642	09/1901	1'7⅝"	0-4-0ST oc	6x9	1'7"	CARRASCAL	Sim & Coventry (agents Spain - for Jose Machennan de Minas - spares via Bilbao)
1643	09/1901	2'0"	0-4-0ST oc	6x9	1'7"	C B No 1	C Barlow (Finedon Ironstone Quarry Northants')
1644-5	03/1901	1'11⅝"	0-4-0ST oc	7x12	1'9½"		Mitrovich Bros London & Iquique (agents for Chile)
1646-8	5-6/1901	2'0"	0-4-2ST oc	7x12	1'9½"	No 1 - No 3	Thomas Wilson & Co Manchester (agents for export)
1649	07/1901	Std	0-4-0ST oc	12x18	3'0½"	CAPPONFIELD	Thomas & Issac Bradley (Capponfield Furnaces Tipton Staffs')
1650	07/1901	2'0"	0-4-0ST oc	7x12	1'9½"	JACK	Cliffe Hill Granite Co (Markfield Leics')
1651	10/1902	2'0"	0-4-0ST oc	5x7½	1'3¼"	ANT	Blackbrook Colliery Co Ltd (Glamorgan)
1652-3	11/!901	Std	0-4-0ST oc	10x15	2'10"	No 12 - No 13	South Metropolitan Gas Co (East Greenwich Works London)
1654	11/!901	Std	0-4-0ST oc	14x20	3'6"	WEDGWOOD	Bignall Hill Colliery Co (Jamage Colly' Newcastle Staffs')
1655	09/1901	2'6"	0-4-0ST oc	7x12	1'9½"	STRACHAN No 9	J Strachan (contr' Welsbhpool & Llanfair Railway const')
1656	12/1901	2'6"	0-6-0T oc	8x12	1'9½"	No 4	Takata & Co (contr' Ohme Railway Construction Japan)
1657	05/1902	3'0"	0-4-0ST oc	8x12	2'0½"	PARKER	Enoch Tempest (contr' Walshaw Dean Reservoir const, Halifax Corp' Yorks)
1658	07/1902	3'0"	0-4-0ST oc	8x12	2'0½"	NIDD	Holme & King Ltd (contr' Pateley Bridge Yorks')
1659-60	12/01-2/02	2'0"	0-4-0ST oc	6x9	1'7"	BULLER & KITCHENER	Enderby & Stoney Stanton Granite Co (Enderby Quarries Leics')
1661	01/1902	1'11⅝"	0-4-2ST oc	6x9	1'7"	DREFUS-RAU	Henry Rogers Sons & Co (agents for Pernambuco Brazil)
1662	09/1902	2'0"	0-4-0ST oc	6x9	1'6⅞"	C B No 2	C Barlow (Finedon Ironstone Quarry Northants')
1663	11/1902	1'11"	0-4-0ST oc	6x9	1'8"	SIR J T FIRBANK	Old Delabole Slate Co (Camelford Cornwall)
1664	04/1903	2'7½"	0-4-2ST oc	6½x10	1'9"	No 1	L Mitchell agents Les Forges & Founderies de Maurice Mauritius Name: ANDRE L D'ARIFAT LA BARAQUE
1665	04/1903	2'7½"	0-4-2ST oc	6½x10	1'9"	No 2	L Mitchell agents Les Forges & Founderies de Maurice Mauritius Name: THOMY L D'ARIFAT LA BARAQUE
1666	04/1903	2'7½"	0-4-2ST oc	6½x10	1'9"	No 4	L Mitchell agents Les Forges & Founderies de Maurice Mauritius
1667	04/1903	2'7½"	0-4-2ST oc	6½x10	1'9"	No 5	L Mitchell agents Les Forges & Founderies de Maurice Mauritius
1668	04/1903	2'0"	0-4-0ST oc	6x9	1'6⅞"	MINERALS	R White & Sons agents of Widnes to Liverpool for shipment to Scotland (later Arening Granite Co Merioneth)
1669	12/1901	3'0"	0-6-0ST oc	9x14	2'3½"	TENACITY	Enoch Tempest (contr' Walshaw Dean Reservoir const', Halifax Corp' Yorks)
1670	11/1901	2'11¾"	0-4-0ST oc	7x12	1'9½"	SIR BOSDIN	Manchester Corp' (Rivers Dept' Davyhulme Lancs's)
1671	01/1902	Std	0-4-0ST oc	10x15	2'6"	JAMES NELSON & SONS LTD	James Nelson & Sons Ltd (Bramley Moor Liverpool)

Manu No	Date Desp	Gauge	Type	Cyls	Dwl Dia	Name/No	Purchaser/Destination
1672	02/1902	Std	0-4-0ST oc	12x18	3'0½"	BROADOAK	Samuel Thomas (Broadoak Collieries Gorseinon Glam')
1673	03/1903	Std	0-4-0ST oc	14x20	3'6"	CARBON	Wolverhampton Gas Co (Staffs)
1674	12/1901	3'0"	0-4-0ST oc	7x12	1'9½"	CRAY	Swansea Corp' (Cray Reservoir const, Glam')
1675	03/1902	2'6"	0-4-0ST oc	7x12	1'9½"		Mitrovich Bros Iquique (agents Santiago Nitrate Co Chile)
1676	06/1902	2'11¾"	0-4-0ST oc	7x12	1'9½"	DREYFUS	Manchester Corp' (Rivers Dept' Davyhulme Lancs's)
1677	10/1902	2'6"	0-4-0ST oc	7x12	1'9½"		Mitrovich Bros London & Iquique (agents for Santiago Nitrate Co Chile)
1678	12/1901	3'0"	0-4-0ST oc	9x14	2'3½"	GILWEN	Gilwen Colliery Co (Ystalyfera Glam')
1679	01/1902	1'11⅝"	2-4-0T oc	9x14	2'2"	JACOB WALTER	Jacob Walter & Co agents for Companhia Mineira Oeste de Minas Brazil
1680	02/1904	Std	0-4-0ST oc	10x15	2'6"	WATERLOO	C Sebastion Smith Shipley Colliery Co (Derbys')
1681	05/1903	Std	0-4-0ST oc	12x18	3'0½"	FORWARD No 3	Birmingham Corp' Gas Dept' Swan Village Works Birmingham
1682-3	5-9/1902	3'0"	0-4-0ST oc	9x14	2'3½"	GEORGE & ANNIE	Enoch Tempest (contr' Walshaw Dean Reservoir const' Halifax Corp' Yorks)
1684	05/1903	2'7½"	2-4-0T oc	8x12	2'0½"	No 3	L Mitchell agents Les Forges & Founderies de Maurice Mauritius
1685	04/1902	2'4"	0-4-0ST oc	8x12	2'0½"	EDWARD V11	Threlkeld Granite Co Ltd (Keswick Quarry Cumberland)
1686	04/1902	2'3½"	0-6-0T oc	7½x12	1'9½"	D de S No 2	Rahr & Raundrup (Hojbyguard Sugar Factory Denmark)
1687	06/1902	2'3½"	0-4-0ST oc	5x7½	1'3¼"	HOWARTH ERSKINE Ld BANGKOK	James Pollock Sons & Co agents Howarth Erskine Ltd Bangkok
1688-1690	8/1902	2'6"	2-4-2ST+4wl ten oc	8x12	2'3"	No 71 - No 73	Indian States Railways Kushalgar Kohat Thal Railway India
1691-1700	9-11/1902	2'6"	2-4-2ST oc	8x12	2'3"		Indian States Railways (Military Reserve Rawalpindi India)
1701	04/1903	2'6"	0-4-0ST oc	7½x12	1'10½"	MENDIP	Oakhill Brewery Co (Somerset)
1702-3	12/1902.	Std	0-4-0ST oc	12x18	3'0½"	LORD KITCHENER & THE COLONEL	HM Government War Office Woolwich Arsenal (London)
1704	12/1902	3'0"	0-4-0ST oc	7x12	2'0"	PENWYLLT	Swansea Corp' (Water Works Cray Reservoir const')
1705	10/1903	3'6"	0-4-0ST oc	12x18	3'0½"	THISTLE No 1	Sir Douglas Fox for The British Central Africa Co
							Shire Highlands Rly (Nyasaland)
1706-15	3-6/1903	2'6"	2-4-2SToc	8x12	2'3"		Indian States Railways (Military Reserve Rawalpindi India)
1716	02/1903	2'5½	0-4-0ST oc	7x12	1'9½"	OCHANDIANO	Ricardo de Damborino (El Material Industrial Spain)
1717	02/1903	3'0"	0-4-0ST oc	7x12	1'9½"	MARY	W&J Foster (Grane Reservoir Reservoir const' Haslingden Lancs')
1718	08/1903	3'6"	0-4-0ST oc	7x12	1'9½"		New Plymouth Timber Co Tariki New Zealand
1719	10/1903	3'6"	0-4-0ST oc	12x18	3'0½"	SHAMROCK No 2	Sir Douglas Fox for The British Central Africa Co
							Shire Highlands Rly (Nyasaland)
1720-1	05/1903	2'7½"	0-4-2ST oc	7x12	1'9½"	No 6 - No 7	L Mitchell agents Les Forges & Founderies de Maurice Mauritius
1722-3	05/1903	1'11⅝"	0-4-0ST oc	5x7½	1'3¼"		L Mitchell agents Les Forges & Founderies de Maurice Mauritius
							Names: EILEEN No 8 & CENT GAULETTES No 9
1724	10/1903	2'0"	0-4-0ST oc	6x9	1'6⅞"	GLADYS	Wrexham & East Denbighshire Water Co (Tymawr Reservoir const' Wrexham)
1725	06/1903	2'0"	0-4-0ST oc	6x9	1'6⅞"	CONCRETE	John Linton & Co Ltd (New Westbury Iron Co)
1726	10/1903	2'0"	0-4-0ST oc	6x9	1'6⅞"	RICHARD BELL	North Wales Quarries Ltd (Bethesda Caern')
1727	09/1903	2'0"	0-4-0ST oc	6x9	1'6⅞"	WINNIE	W Cunliffe (contr') Water Orton (Warks')
1728	11/1903	1'9"	0-4-0ST oc	6x9	1'6⅞"	HAMPSTEAD	Price & Reeves (contr' Charing Cross-Euston-Waterloo Elec' Rly const')
1729	01/1904	2'6"	0-4-0ST oc	6x9	1'6⅞"		Mussabini & Co Melbourne
							(agents Long Tunnel Extended Co Ltd Walhalla Australia)
1730	07/1903	3'0"	0-4-0ST oc	6x9	1'6⅞"	MERCEDES	Greaves Bull & Lakin Ltd (Harbury Cement Works Warks')
1731	07/1903	1'11½"	0-4-0ST oc	6x9	1'6⅞"	PROGRESS	A Krauss & Son (contr' PB&SSRly const. Dinas Caern') nearest Station Dinas
1732-3	05/1904	2'0"	0-4-0ST oc	7x12	1'9½"	LHASI IAN & RAM RING	Assam Railways & Trading Co (Margherita Assam India)
1734	10/1903	2'9"	0-4-0ST oc	7x12	1'9½"	LYDIA	Gas Light & Coke Co Bromley-by-Bow Works (London)
1735	12/1904	2'5½	0-4-0ST oc	7½x12	1'9½"	BS MATAPIRUMA No 3	James Milne & Co Edinburgh (agents Usina Mameluco) Pernambuco Brazil
1736	05/1904	3'0"	0-4-0ST oc	8x12	2'0½"	ESAU	Enoch Tempest (contr' Walshaw Dean Reservoir const, Halifax Corp' Yorks)
1737	09/1903	metre	0-4-0ST oc	8x12	2'0½"	JOAO FELIPPE	Henry Rogers Sons & Co (agents for Pernambuco Brazil)
1738	05/1906	Std	0-4-0ST oc	12x18	3'0½"	No 1	Coventry Corp' Gas Dept' (Foleshill Gas Works Coventry)
1739	04/1907	Std	0-4-0ST oc	14x20	3'6½"	ENTERPRISE	Exhall Colliery & Brickworks Ltd (Exhall Colly' Bedworth Warks')
1740	10/1903	2'0"	0-4-0ST oc	6½x10½	1'9½"	GLADYS	Wrexham & East Denbighshire Water Co (Tymawr Reservoir const' Wrexham)
1741-46	5-8/1904	2'0"	4-6-0+ bogie ten oc	11¾x16	2'9"	No 1 - No 6	Sir Douglas Fox for Cape Govt' Rlys'
							(Cape Province South Africa)
1747	10/1904	3'6"	0-4-0T oc	8x12	2'6"	(No 1)	Mitsui & Co IGR Contract Imperial Japanese Railway Japan
1748	06/1904	2'6"	0-4-0ST oc	4½x7½	1'1¾"		Hainsworth Watson & Co ship via Straits for plantation work
1749	07/1904	3'6"	0-4-0ST oc	9x14	2'3½"	LEICESTER	Jessop & Appleby Bros' (Mossel Bay Harbour Board South Africa)
1750-2	10/1904	metre	0-4-0T oc	9x14	2'3½"	No 1 - No 3	Admiralty Civil Eng' in Chief Works' Loan, Gibralter Dockyard
1753-4	10-11/1904	1'10"	0-4-0ST oc	6x9	1'6⅞"	No 1 - No 2	Presta Block A Ltd per WR Tuck (Fura-Broomassie Tramway Gold Coast)
1755	11/1904	2'0"	0-4-0ST oc	6x9	6x9	COMPANHIA PROGRESSO	Merchant Banking Co Ltd sent to Rio de Janerio Brazil
1756	02/1905	3'0"	0-4-0ST oc	6x9	1'6⅞"	IDIOT	Bowes Scott & Western Ltd Sarawak Govt' Borneo
1757	04/1905	2'0"	0-4-0ST oc	7x12"	1'9½"	No 3	Queenborough Cement Co Ltd (Queenborough Kent)
1758	04/1905	2'6"	0-4-0ST oc	7x12"	1'9½"		Mitrovich Bros Liverpool & Iquique (agents for Santiago Nitrate Co Chile)
1759	03/1906	2'6"	0-4-0ST oc	7x12"	1'9½"		Mitrovich Bros Liverpool & Iquique (agents for Santiago Nitrate Co Chile)
1760	05/1906	1'10¾"	0-4-0ST oc	7x12"	1'9½"	SYBIL	Ernest Neale Port Dinorwic (Dinorwic Slate Quarry Llanberis Caerns')
1761	08/1905	3'0"	0-4-0T oc	9x14	2'3½"	OGDEN	P Drake & Son (contr' Grane Reservoir const') Haslingden Lancs'
1762	10/1904	1'11⅝"	2-4-0T oc	9x14	2'3"	DOUTER HEILBORN	Jacob Walter & Co Ltd agents Companhia Mineira Oeste de MInas Brazil
1763	08/1905	metre	0-4-0ST oc	6x9	1'6 7.8"	ANORGA	John Miller & Co Liverpool (agents for Cuba)
1764	09/1905	1'10"	0-4-0ST oc	6x9	1'7"	No 3	Presta Block A Ltd per P Tarbutt London
							(Fura-Broomassie Tramway Gold Coast)
1765	07/1906	2'0"	0-4-0ST oc	6x9	1'7"	MERCEDES	Joseph Buggins & Co Birmingham Drainage Board Minworth Warks'
1766	01/1907	1'11½"	0-4-0ST oc	6x9	1'7"	SKINNER	Maenofferen Slate Quarry Co Ltd Duffws (Merioneth)
1767	11/1904	1'7 11/16"	0-4-0ST oc	4½x7¼	1'1¾"	NEVES	Jacob Walter & Co Ltd agents Companhia Mineira Oeste de Minas Brazil
1768-70	12/1904	3'6"	0-4-0ST oc	4½x7½	1'6"	No 14 - No 16	Okura & Co London (agents for Yahata Ironworks Kyushu Japan)
1771-3	03/1905	2'6"	2-4-2ST+4wl ten oc	8x12	2'3"	74 - 76	Indian States Railways Kushalgar Kohat Thal Railway India
1774	02/1905	2'9"	2-4-0T oc	8x12	2'2½"	SANTA CLARA	Whitehead, Sumner Harker & Co
							(agents for Conde De Valle Flor, San Thome Africa)
1775-6	06/1905	Std	0-6-0ST oc	15x20	3'7"	SNR No 4 - No 5	Matheson & Co agents Shanghi Nanking Rly China
1777	06/1906	2'5½"	0-4-0ST oc	7x12	1'9½"	OCHANDIANO No 2	El Material Industrial sent to Bilbao Spain
1778	07/1906	2'6"	0-4-0ST oc	7x12	1'9½"		Mitrovich Bros' Liverpool & Iquique (agents for Chile)
1779	07/1907	2'6"	0-4-0ST oc	7x12	1'9½"	KOKOMAIKO	Crown Agents Lagos (Steam Tramway) Nigeria
1780	06/1907	2'0"	0-4-0ST oc	7x12	1'9½"		Takata & Co London sent to Kobe Japan
1781	06/1905	2'0"	2-4-0T oc	5x7½	1'3½"	POLAR BEAR	Howstrake Estate Ltd (Groudle Glen Rly' Isle of Man)
1782	09/1905	3'0"	0-4-0ST oc	5x7½	1'3¼"	MAUDIE	Greaves Bull & Lakin Ltd Harbury Cement Works Warks'
1783	5/!905	1'11⅝"	2-4-0T oc	9¼x14	2'3½"	Dor ARDUINI	Jacob Walter & Co Ltd agents Companhia Mineira Oeste de Minas Brazil
1784	07/1905	2'3½"	0-6-0T oc	7½x12	1'9½"	D de S No 3	Rahr & Raundrup Manchester (for Hojbyguard Suger Factory Denmark)

W. G. BAGNALL, Ld. Castle Engine Works STAFFORD

Manu No	Date Desp	Gauge	Type	Cyls	Dwl Dia	Name/No:	Purchaser/Destination
1785	10/1905	2'6"	0-6-0T oc	10x15	2'6"	TOGO	EP Davis Storefield Ironstone Pits (Kettering Northants')
1786	10/1905	Std	0-4-0ST oc	8x12	2'1"	SIEMENS BROs & Co Ltd	Siemens Bros' & Co Ltd (Stafford)
1787	10/1905	2'4½"	0-4-0ST oc	8x12	2'0"	THE DOLL	The Briton Ferry Works Ltd (Briton Ferry Glamorgan)
1788-9	12/1905	metre	0-4-0ST oc	6x9	1'7"	ASHLYNS & SHENSTONE	Wm Cooper & Nephews -12/1918 spares Cia Tunica & Importadones SA Buenos Aires
1790	03/1906	metre	0-4-2ST oc	6½x9	1'7"	ALVARO MACHADO	Henry Rogers Sons & Co (agents for Pernambuco Brazil)
1791	06/1906	1'10"	0-4-0ST oc	6x9	1'7"	No 4	Presta Block A Ltd (Fura-Broomassie Tramway Gold Coast)
1792	11/1905	1'11⅝"	0-4-2T oc	7½x12	1'9½"	S.A.W.K. No 4 1905	Mansfield & Sons Ltd (agents for Societe Anonyme de Wadi Kon Ombo Egypt)
1793-4	06/1906	1'7 11/16"	0-4-0ST oc	6x9	1'7"	RUBIA No 1 & RUBIA No 2	Adolpho T Simpson Bilbao (agents for Rubia Mine Spain)
1795	08/1906	1'10"	0-4-0ST oc	6x9	1'7"	No 5	Presta Block A Ltd (Fura-Broomassie Tramway Gold Coast)
1796	10/1906	2'5½"	0-4-0ST oc	6x9	1'7"		Rosing Bros' shipped to Rio de Janerio Argentina
1797	02/1906	2'4"	0-6-0T oc	12x18	2'9¼"	DENNIS	Dennis & Son Snailbeach District Rly' Pontersbury Salop'
1798	04/1906	2'6"	0-4-0T oc	10x15	2'6"		Crown Agents for Irrigation Dept' of Ceylon
1799	06/1906	2'6"	0-4-0ST oc	5x7½	1'3½"	HILSEA	Portsea Island Gas Light Co (Portsmouth Hants')
1800	05/1906	2'0"	2-4-0T oc	9x14	2'3½"	TONGAAT	Tongaat Sugar Co Ltd (Tongaat Estate Natal South Africa)
1801	09/1906	2'6"	0-4-0ST oc	6x9	1'7"		Mussabini & Co (agents Long Tunnel Extended Co Ltd Walhalla) Melbourne Australia
1802	02/1907	2'0"	0-4-0ST oc	6x9	1'7"	C.B. No 3	C Barlow Burton Latimer (Finedon Ironstone Quarry Northants')
1803	02/1907	3'0"	0-4-0ST oc	6x9	1'7"		JJ Niven & Co agents (for AL Siefert & Co Shannon) New Zealand
1804	03/1907	1'10"	0-4-0ST oc	6x9	1'7"	No 6	Presta Block A Ltd (Fura-Broomassie Tramway Gold Coast)
1805	04/1906	1'7 11/16"	0-4-0ST oc	6x9	1'7"	URSULA	Sim & Coventry Ltd Liverpool (agents for Rubia Mine Spain)
1806	08/1907	1'10"	0-4-0ST oc	6x9	1'7"	No 7	Presta Block A Ltd (Fura-Broomassie Tramway Gold Coast)
1807-10	06/1906	2'6"	0-6-0T oc	9x14	2'3½"	No 7 - No 10	Mitrovich Bros' Liverpool & Iquique shipped to Antofagasta (Chile)
1811	10/1906	5'6"	0-4-0ST oc	14x20	3'7"	No 7	Madras Port Trust Madras India
1812-3	5-6/1907	Std	2-4-2T ic	15½x24	4'6"	12 - 13	Egyptian Delta Light Rlys' Ltd Helwan Link Line Egypt
1814-17	11-12/1906	1'6"	0-4-2WT oc	12x15	2'2"		De Beers Consolidated Mines Ltd Kimberley South Africa
1818-9	08/1906	1'11⅝"	0-4-0ST oc	7x11	2'0"	203 & 230	John Aird & Co (contr' Nile Delta Contract) Alexandria Egypt
1820	07/1907	3'0"	0-4-0ST oc	7x12	1'9½"	RHIW	HB Smith Liverpool (agent for North Wales Iron & Manganese Mines Rhiw Aberdaron)
1821	10/1907	2'0"	0-4-0ST oc	7x12	1'9½"	BANGU	London & Hanseatic Bank Ltd (agents) for export
1822	09/1906	3'0"	0-4-0ST oc	8x12	2'0½"	THE PRESTON	Preston Corp' Water Works (Spade Mill No 1 Reservoir const') Longridge Lancs'
1823-4	02/1907	2'6"	0-6-0T oc	11x15	2'6"	ESMERALDA & NINULA	Mitrovich Bros' Liverpool & Iquique (agents) shipped to Caleta Coloso Chile
1825	10/1906	2'0"	0-6-0T oc	9¼x14	2'3½"		Hurst Nelson & Co Ltd (agents Columbia Sugar Refining Co Tamanua Mill Fiji)
1826-8	12/1906	2'6"	0-6-0T oc	9x14	2'3½"		Mitrovich Bros' Liverpool & Iquique (agents) shipped to Caleta Coloso Chile
1829	12/1906	3'6"	0-4-0ST oc	10x15	2'9¼"		Crown Agents Accra Harbour Works Gold Coast
1830-1	08/1907	metre	0-4-0ST oc	12¼x18	3'0"	65 - 66	Bengal & North Western Rly India
1832	12/1906	1'11⅝"	0-4-2T oc	7½x12	1'9½"	W.K.O. No 5 1906	Mansfield & Sons Ltd (agents Societe Anonyme de Wadi Kon Ombo Egypt)
1833	02/1907	2'6"	0-4-0ST oc	5x7½	1'3¼"	SOUTHSEA	Portsea Island Gas Light Co (Portsmouth Hants')
1834-5	1-2/1907	1'11⅝"	0-4-0ST oc	8x12	2'0½"	15 & 75	John Aird & Co (contr' Nile Delta Contract) Alexandria Egypt
1836-8	2-9/1907	2'6"	0-6-0T oc	9¾x14	2'3½"		Mitrovich Bros' Liverpool & Iquique (agents) shipped to Caleta Coloso Chile
1839	04/1907	Std	0-4-0ST oc	8x12	2'0½"	OXFORD GAS Co	Oxford Gas Light & Coke Co (Oxford Gas Works Oxford)
1840	04/1907	1'11⅝"	0-4-2T oc	7½x12	1'9½"	W.K.O. No 6 1907	Mansfield & Sons Ltd (agents Societe Anonyme de Wadi Kon Ombo Egypt)
1841	06/1907	3'6"	0-6-0T oc	11x16½	2'9¼"	No 9	Baburizza & Co Lautaro Nitrate Co Ltd Liverpool shipped to Chile
1842	05/1907	1'6"	0-4-0ST oc	4x7½	1'3¼"	ALFRED HERBERT Ltd	Alfred Herbert Ltd (Edgwick Works) Coventry
1843	10/1907	1'11⅝"	0-4-2ST oc	4½x7½	1'3¼"		Henry Rogers Sons & Co (agents for Pernambuco Brazil)
1844	09/1907	3'0"	0-4-0ST oc	5x7½	1'3¼"	MILDRED	Greaves Bull & Lakin Ltd Harbury Cement Works Warks'
1845	07/1907	1'11⅝"	0-4-0ST oc	4½x7½	1'3¼"		Gustav Halberstadt (Valby Gas Works) Copenhagen Denmark
1846	10/1907	2'9½"	0-4-0ST oc	6x9	1'7"	MERCEDES	Adolpho T Simpson Bilbao (agents shipped to Bilbao Spain)
1847	10/1907	1'5 11/16"	0-4-0ST oc	6x9	1'7"	DEMASIA Sn BENITO No 1	Adolpho T Simpson Bilbao (agents shipped to Bilbao Spain)
1848	11/1907	1'8"	0-4-0ST oc	6x9	1'7"	HORSESHOE	Mussabini & Co (agents for Golden Horseshoe Estates Kalgoorlie Australia)
1849	12/1907	1'7 11/16"	0-4-0ST oc	6x9	1'7"	RUBIA No 4	Adolpho T Simpson Bilbao (agents for Rubia Mine Spain) shipped to Bilbao
1850-1	12/1907	1'6"	0-4-0ST oc	6x9	1'7"		James Pollock Sons & Co Ltd agents Howarth Erskine Ltd Singapore
1852	10/1907	2'6"	0-4-0ST oc	7x12	1'9½"		Mitrovich Bros' Liverpool & Iquique (agents) shipped to Iquique Chile
1853	04/1908	2'6"	0-4-0ST oc	7x12	1'9½"	FERRET 11 (Roman 2)	AC Bealey & Son Radcliffe Lancs'
1854	01/1909	2'6"	0-4-2T oc	7x12	1'9½"		John Birch & Co Ltd London (agents) shipped to Manila
1855	01/1909	2'9"	0-4-0ST oc	7x12	1'9½"	BEATRICE	Gas Light & Coke Co Bromley-by-Bow Works London
1856	07/1909	3'0"	0-4-0ST oc	7x12	1'9½"	POLEFIELD	James Byrom Ltd (contr' Heaton Park Reservoir const' Lancs')
1857	07/1909	3'6"	0-4-0ST oc	7x12	1'9½"		John Terry & Co London (agents for Christchurch Gas Works New Zealand)
1858	06/1907	2'0"	0-4-0ST oc	6½x10	1'8"	DEMPSTER	Dempster Moore & Co Ltd Glasgow shipped to Yokohama Japan
1859	08/1907	2'6"	0-4-0T oc	10x15	2'6"		Crown Agents Irrigation Dept' of Ceylon
1860	07/1907	2'0"	0-6-0T oc	9½x14	2'3½"		FG Colenbrander (New Guelderland Natal South Africa) shipped to Durban
1861	09/1907	2'6"	0-6-0T oc	10x15	2'6"	STAFFORD	EP Davis Storefield Ironstone Pits Kettering (Northants')
1862	09/1907	2'6"	0-4-2ST oc	8x12	2'0½"	LASTENIA	Mitrovich Bros' Liverpool & Iquique (agents) shipped to Caleta Coloso Chile
1863	11/1907	2'0"	0-4-0ST oc	6½x10	1'7"	J C GRAY	North Wales Quarries Ltd Bethesda (Caerns')
1864-5	10/1907	2'6"	0-4-0ST oc	8x16	2'3½"		Jones Burton & Co Liverpool (agents 1940 spares 1864 Beau Vallin Estate Mauritius)
1866-7	5-6/1908	2'0"	4-6-2T oc	11¾x16	2'9"		Agent General Cape of Good Hope Cape Govt' Rlys', South Africa
1868	01/1908	1'11"	0-4-0ST oc	4½x7½	1'3¼"	SIPAT	Chittenden & Co London for shipment
1869	12/1907	3'6"	0-4-0ST oc	10x15	2'9¼"	(OPAPA - later No 1)	Crown Agents Lagos Harbour Nigeria
1870	12/1907	2'0"	0-4-0ST oc	8x12	2'3¼"	ELLA	James Morrison & Co Ltd (agents for British Phosphate Commission) Ocean Island
1871-2	8-11/1908	2'6"	0-6-0T oc	9¾x14	2'3½"		Mitrovich Bros' Liverpool & Iquique (agents) shipped to Caleta Coloso Chile
1873	12/1907	2'0"	4-4-0T oc	9x14	2'3½"	SUCCESS	Tongaat Sugar Co Ltd (Tongaat Estate Natal South Africa)
1874	03/1908	3'6"	0-4-0ST oc	10x15	1'3¼"		Crown Agents Accra Harbour Works Gold Coast
1875-6	6/08 & 9/11	2'0"	0-4-0ST oc	6x9	1'7"	CHITI-DAND & WADALA	Punjab Coal Co Abbottabad India
1877	05/1909	2'6"	0-4-0ST oc	6x9	1'7"	MAGNET 11(Roman 2)	FR Thompstone & Sons (Bosley Mill Cheshire)
1878	04/1910	1'8"	0-4-0ST oc	6x9	1'7"	HORSESHOE 11(Roman 2)	AG Kidston & Co (Horseshoe Estates Kalgoorlie Australia)
1879	10/1910	2'6"	0-4-0ST oc	6x9	1'7"	NIVENCO	JJ Niven & Co Ltd (agents for Gisborne Council Gentle Annie Quarry New Zealand)
1880	11/1911	metre	0-4-0ST oc	6x9	1'7"	CEARA	R Singlehurst & Co Ltd Liverpool (agents) for HS Tregonning (shipped to Ceara Brazil)

Manu No	Date Desp	Gauge	Type	Cyls	Dwl Dia	Name/No	Purchaser/Destination
1881	05/1908	3'0"	4-6-0T oc	15x20	3'6"	KILKEE 11	West Clare Rly Co Ltd Dublin, deliver to Ennis Ireland
1882	06/1908	5'6"	0-4-0ST oc	14x20	3'7"	No 8	Madras Port Trust Madras India
1883	05/1908	metre	0-4-0ST oc	10x15	2'9¼"		Mitrovich Bros' Liverpool & Iquique (agents) shippped to Iquique Chile
1884	07/1908	Std	0-4-0ST oc	12x18	3'0½"	GRAZEBROOK	M&W Grazebrook (Netherton Staffs') allowance for old engine £100 (1432)
1885	09/1909	3'0"	0-4-0ST oc	5x7½	1'3¼"		Jones Burton & Co (agents FC Talima Col0mbia) shipped to Cartagena
1886	10/1909	1'11⅝"	0-4-0ST oc	5x7½	1'3¼"	EUGENIA	Oliviearas & Diogo Liverpool shipped to Lisbon Portugal (thought to be for Angola)
1887	03/1910	3' 5⅜"	0-4-0ST oc	5x7½	1'3¼"	LION (in Abaric)	Bolling & Lowe agents for export
1888	04/1910	2'6"	0-4-0ST oc	5x7½	1'3¼"	CHILENITA	Mitrovich Bros' Liverpool & Iquique (agents) shipped to Chile
1889	05/1911	3'0"	0-4-0ST oc	6x9	1'7"	No 1	Judkins Ltd (Tuttle Hill Granite Quarry) Nuneaton Warks'
1890	09/1911	2'6"	0-4-0ST oc	6x9	1'7"	PAMPINO	A Trugeda & Co for export
1891	07/1912	2'0"	0-4-0ST oc	6x9	1'7"	FORWARD	J Buggins agent Birmingham Tame & Rea Dist' Drainage Board' Minworth Warks'
1892-3	11/09-1/10	2'7½"	0-4-0ST oc	7x12	1'9½"	PACA No 2 & PACA No 3	Adolpho T Simpson Bilbao (agents) shipped to Bilbao Spain
1894	07/1912	2'6"	0-4-0ST oc	7x12	1'9½"	RANGER	JVM Money-Kent Cape Copper Co (Port Nolloth Namaqualand) sent to South Wales
1895	02/1909	2'6"	0-4-0ST oc	7x12	2'0½"	NIPPER	HM Govt' Admiralty Chatham Dockyard (for Hoo Ness Island)
1896-8	4-6/1909	1'7¹¹⁄₁₆"	0-4-0ST oc	5x7½	1'7"		Central Uruguay Eastern Extension Railway Co Ltd
1899	10/1909	5'6"	0-4-0ST oc	14x20	3'7"	No 9	Madras Port Trust Madras (India)
1900	07/1912	2'6"	0-6-0ST oc	7x12	1'9½"	MURIEL	Arakan Flotilla Co Ltd per Edward Calthrop & Partners (Burma)
1901	10/1911	2'10½"	0-4-0ST oc	7x12	1'9½"	POWERFULL	Kneeshaw Lupton & Co Llandulas (Denbighshire)
1902	02/1911	3'6"	0-4-0ST oc	7x12	1'9½"		John Birch & Co (agents for Powell Process Ltd Westland New Zealand)
1903-4	11/1909	metre	4-4-0T oc	11x18	3'6½"	203-204	Madras & Southern Mahratta Rly' India
1905	07/1909	metre	2-4-2T oc	13x18	3'0½"	SINHASINHA	Jones Burton & Co agents Passo Cardozo & Marques Usina Passagem Brazil
1906	01/1913	2'5½"	2-4-0T oc	9x14	2'3½"	SANTA THEREZA	Herdeiros Bowman Ltd (Usina Santa Thereza) ship to Pernambuco Brazil
1907	10/1909	1'6"	0-4-0ST oc	4x7½	1'3¼"	SCOUT	George Thomas & Co (Bolton Model Poultry Farm Lancs') delivery to Manchester
1908	10/1909	metre	0-4-0ST oc	8x12	2'0½"	COBARON	Sim & Coventry (agents for Cobaron Mine) shipped to Bilbao Spain)
1909	11/1909	2'9¼"	4-4-0ST oc	8x12	1'9½"	B. S. CACHOEIRINHA No 4	James Milne & Sons Ltd (agents for Usina Mameluco Pernambuco Brazil)
1910	11/1910	3'0"	0-4-0ST oc	8x12	2'0½"	DUDDO	Stephen Eastern Ltd (contr' St Mary's Hospital cont') Stannington nr Morpeth
1911	03/1918	2'6"	0-6-0T oc	10x15	2'6"		Ministry of Munitions (Ridham Salvage Depot) Sittingbourne Kent
1912	12/1909	1'11⅝"	2-4-0T oc	7x11	1'9½"	TEIMOSA 2A	Herdeiros Bowman Ltd shipped to Pernambuco Brazil
1913	12/1909	1'7¹¹⁄₁₆"	0-4-0T oc	5x7½	1'7"		Central Uruguay Eastern Extension Railway Co Ltd
1914	06/1910	2'6"	0-4-0ST oc	5x7½	1'3¼"	DIECIOCHO	Mitrovich Bros' Liverpool & Iquique (agents for Chile)
1915	05/1910	1'11⅝"	0-4-0ST oc	5x7½	1'3¼"	HURON	United Alkali Co Ltd (Spain)
1916	10/1910	1'11⅝"	0-4-0ST oc	5x7½	1'3¼"		Glyn Quarries Ltd (Cambrian Quarry Glyn Denbigh')
1917	06/1910	2'6"	0-4-0T oc	8½x12	2'6"	ZURIEL	GB Hodsman Lunedale Whinstone Co Middleton-in-Teesdale
1918	06/1910	3'0"	0-4-0ST oc	9x14	2'3½"	GILWEN No 3	Gilwen Colliery Co Ltd (Ystalyfera Glamorgan)
1919	07/1910	2'9¼"	0-4-2T oc	8x12	2'0½"	BATATA	Dussault Chovil & Co Birmingham (agents Usina Santa Thereza Pernambuco Brazil)
1920	09/1910	3'6"	0-4-2T oc	10x15	2'9¼"	No 2	Crown Agents Lagos Harbour Nigeria
1921	09/1911	2'0"	0-4-2ST oc	5x7½	1'3¼"		M Samuel & Co engineers and contractors shipped to Shanghai China
1922	12/1911	2'6"	0-4-2T oc	5x7½	1'3¼"	ANNIE	Gisborne Corporation (Gentle Annie Tramway) Gisborne New Zealand
1923	06/1912	1'11⅝"	0-4-0ST oc	5x7½	1'3¼"	URSULA	Diogo & Co shipped to Lisbon Portugal
1924	07/1913	1'7¹¹⁄₁₆"	0-4-0ST oc	5x7½	1'3¼"	TENTATIVA 1913	Companhia Agricola do Dande (Tentativa Sugar Factory Angola) ship via Lisbon
1925	09/1910	2'9¼"	0-4-2T oc	8x12	2'0½"	BEATRIZ	Henry Rogers Sons & Co Ltd (for Pernambuco Brazil - Usina Sta' Tereza de Goiana)
1926-8	7-8/1910	2'0"	0-6-0 + 6wl ten oc	6½x9	1'7"		S Pearson & Sons Ltd (FC Cobos A Furbero Mexico) Names: POTRERO: SAN MARCOS: EL MESON
1929	12/1910	2'0"	4-4-0T oc	9x14	2'3½"	REPEAT	Tongaat Sugar Co Ltd (Tongaat Estate Natal South Africa)
1930-2	12/10-2/11	2'6"	0-6-0T oc	9x14	2'3½"		Dodwell & Co Ltd agents LJ Healing & Co Ltd contr' Japan shipped to Takao
1933	03/1911	3'6"	0-6-0T oc	11x16½"	2'9¼"	No 14	Baburizza & Co Lautaro Nitrate Co Ltd Chile
1934	01/1913	3'0"	0-4-0ST oc	6x9	1'7"	No 2	Judkins Ltd (Tuttle Hill Granite Quarries) Nuneaton Warks'
1935-6	06/1913	2'6"	0-4-0T oc	6x9	1'7"	(No 1 - No 2)	EH Hunter & Co (Chuen Railway) Japan)
1937	08/1912	2'0"	0-4-0ST oc	6x9	1'7"	YENI No 3	Bolling & Lowe (agents) for export - wood burner
1938-9	8-9/1912	2'5½"	0-4-0ST oc	7x12	1'9½"	LULES & PABLO	Mc Carter & Kerr Bock Cia Hydro Electric de Tucuman shipped to Buenos Aires
1940	06/1911	3'6"	0-4-0ST oc	10x15	2'9¼"	No 3	Crown Agents Lagos Harbour Nigeria
1941	06/1911	2'6"	0-4-0ST ic	7½x12	2'0½"	TEJON	United Alkali Co Ltd Heulva (Sotiel Coronada) Spain
1942	05/1918	3'3"	0-4-0ST oc	8x12	2'0½"	No 10	Wellingborough Iron & Steel Co (Finedon Quarries Northants')
1943	07/1911	2'0"	0-4-2T oc	8x12	2'0½"	MARY	Cliffe Hill Granite Co Bardon Hill (Markfield Leics')
1944	09/1911	2'6"	0-4-0ST oc	7x12	1'9½"		Crown Agents Lagos (Steam Tramway Nigeria)
1945	10/1911	2'0"	0-6-0T oc	9x14	2'3½"	KING GEORGE	Irish Industrial Minerals Ltd Westport (for Achill Island Co. Mayo Ireland)
1946	11/1911	3'0"	0-4-0T oc	9x14	2'7"	SLIPTON No 5	Islip Iron Co Ltd (Islip Quarries Northants')
1947	01/1912	2'6"	0-4-0ST oc	7x12	2'0½"	NESS	HM Govt' Admiralty Chatham Dockyard (for Hoo Ness Island)
1948	02/1912	metre	0-4-0ST oc	10x15	2'9¼"	MAISIE	Assam Oil Co Ltd (Assam India)
1949	01/1912	1'11⅝"	0-4-0ST oc	5x7½	1'3¼"		Jones Burton & Co Liverpool (agents) for export
1950	05/1912	3'6"	0-4-0ST oc	10x15	2'9¼"		Crown Agents (Accra Harbour Works) Gold Coast
1951	04/1912	2'6"	0-6-0ST oc	9¾x15	2'3½"	GEORGINA	Mitrovich Bros' Liverpool & Iquique (agents) shipped to Antofagasta Chile
1952	07/1912	Std	0-4-0ST oc	14x20	3'6½"	EXHALL No 4	Exhall Colliery & Brickworks Ltd (Exhall Colly') Bedworth (Warks')
1953	08/1912	2'0"	0-6-0T oc	8x12	2'0½"	No 1	T&W Morgans Hyderabad [Deccan] Co Ltd (Singareni Colly' India)
1954	08/1912	metre	2-4-2T oc	13x18	3'0½"	GUILHERMINA	Jones Burton & Co agents Passo Cardozo & Marques Usina Passagem Brazil
1955	09/1912	3'8"	0-6-0ST oc	13x18	2'9¼"	HARDINGSTONE	Exectors of late P Phipps (Hunsbury Iron Co Hunsbury Hill Quarries) Northampton
1956	11/1912	3'8"	0-6-0ST oc	13x18	2'9¼"	WOOTTON	Exectors of late P Phipps (Hunsbury Iron Co Hunsbury Hill Quarries) Northampton
1957	12/1912	3'8"	0-6-0ST oc	13x18	2'9¼"	NORTHAMPTON	Exectors of late P Phipps (Hunsbury Iron Co Hunsbury Hill Quarries) Northampton
1958	10/1912	2'6"	0-6-0T oc	13x18	2'9¼"	SLANO	Mitrovich Bros' Liverpool & Iquique (agents) shipped to Antofagasta Chile
1959	12/1912	Std	0-4-0ST oc	12x18	3'0½"	No 2	Coventry Corp' Gas Dept' (Foleshill Gas Works) Coventry
1960	11/1912	2'6"	0-6-0T oc	9¾x14	2'3½"	PROGRESO	Mitrovich Bros' Liverpool & Iquique (agents) shipped to Chile

Manu No	Date Desp	Gauge	Type	Cyls	Dwl Dia	Name/No	Purchaser/Destination
1961	01/1913	3'0"	0-4-0ST oc	7x12	1'9½"	TOM	Park Gate Iron & Steel Co Ltd Rotherham (Yorks')
1962	06/1913	2'0"	0-4-0ST oc	7x12	1'9½"	NAMCHIK	Assam Raiways & Trading Co Ltd (Margherita Assam India)
1963	04/1914	2'6"	0-4-0ST oc	7x12	1'9½"	RAMBLER	JVM Money-Kent Cape Copper Co (Jersey Marine Glamorgan) sent to South Wales
1964	04/1914	2'9"	0-4-0ST oc	7x12	1'9½"	RUTH	Gas Light & Coke Co Ltd (Bromley-by-Bow Works London)
1965	01/1913	3'0"	0-6-0 + 6wl ten oc	11x16½	2'6"	POWELLITE	Powell Process Co Ltd (Victoria Hardwood & Sawmilling Co) Melbourne Australia
1966	12/1912	2'5½"	0-4-2T oc	8x12	2'0½"		Thos' W Cunningham & Co Ltd (agents) Barneto & Co Pernambuco Brazil
1967	01/1913	2'0"	4-6-0+bogie ten oc	11¾x16	2'9"	NG No 36	High Commissioner for Union of South Africa (Cape Govt' Rly Natal)
1968-71	6-7/1913	2'6"	0-6-2 + 6 wl ten oc	11x15	3'0"	(16 - 19)	Rendel & Robertson for Bombay Baroda & Central India Rly' India
1972-6	7-9/1913	2'6"	0-6-2 + 6 wl ten oc	11x15	3'0"	(20 - 24)	Rendel & Robertson for Baroda State Rlys' India
1977	07/1912	3'6"	2-6-2T oc	13½x18	3'0½"		De Beers Consolidated Mines Ltd Kimberley (South Africa)
1978	06/1913	2'6"	0-4-0T oc	9x14	2'3½"	RATTLER	JVM Money-Kent Cape Copper Co (Jersey Marine Glamorgan) sent to South Wales
1979	11/1913	5'6"	0-4-0ST oc	14x20	3'7"	No 10	Rendel & Robertson for Madras Port Trust Madras (India)
1980	11/1913	3'0"	0-6-0ST oc	13x18	2'9¼"	PIONEER	Eastwell Iron Ore Co Ltd Eaton Siding (Eastwell Quarries Northants')
1981	07/1913	2'5½"	0-4-2T oc	8x12	2'0½"	CATU	Dussault Chovil & Co Birmingham (agents Usina Santa Thereza Pernambuco Brazil)
1982-3	09/1913	2'6"	0-4-0T oc	6x9	1'7"	(No 3 - No 4)	EH Hunter & Co (for Chuen Railway Japan)
1984	12/1913	2'6"	4-6-0 + 6 wl ten oc	12x20	3'3	C.S.R No 5	Indian States & Eastern Agency Cutch State Railway India
1985	01/1914	5'6"	0-4-0ST oc	14x20	3'7"	No 11	Rendel & Robertson for Madras Port Trust Madras India
1986-7	11/1913	2'5½"	0-4-0ST oc	6x9	1'7"	SAN-LUIS No 1 & JOSEFA No 1	Gortazar y Goyarrola shipped to Bilbao Spain
1988	02/1914	2'0"	0-4-2T oc	9x14	2'3½"	No 2	T&W Morgans for Hyderabad [Deccan] Co Ltd (Singareni Colly' India)
1989	04/1914	2'6"	4-6-0 + 6 wl ten oc	12x20	3'3	C.S.R. No 6	Indian States & Eastern Agency Cutch State Railway India
1990-2	5-6/1914	2'6"	0-6-2 + 6 wl ten oc	11x15	3'0"	(25 - 27)	Rendel Palmer & Tritton for Baroda State Rly' India
1993	01/1914	2'6"	4-4-0 + 6 wl ten oc	11x15	3'3"	No 4	Bolling & Lowe London (agents for Tezpur Balipara Tramway Assam India)
1994-5	04/1914	2'6"	0-6-2 + 6 wl ten oc	11x15	3'0"	(1 - 2)	Forbes, Forbes Campbell Co Ltd for Jacobabad Kushmore Rly' India
1996	06/1914	3'6"	0-6-0T oc	11x16½	2'9¼"	No 16	Lautaro Nitrate Co Ltd Chile
1997	05/1914	2'6"	0-4-0ST oc	7x12	1'9½"		Crown Agents for Ceylon
1998	05/1914	2'6"	0-4-0ST oc	6x9	1'7"	PORTSEA	Portsea Island Gas Co (Portsmouth Hants')
1999	04/1915	2'6"	0-4-0ST oc	6x9	1'7"	KITCHENER	LNWR Permanant Way Dept' (Marsden Reservoir Works Lancs') free on rail Stafford
2000-1	11/1914	metre	0-6-0 + 6wl ten oc	14x20	3'7"	(55 -56)	Rohilkund & Kumaon Railway Co Ltd London shipped to India
2002-3	12/1914	metre	0-6-0 + 6wl ten oc	14x20	3'7"	(6 & 9)	Bengal Dooars Railway Co Ltd shipped to India
2004	06/1914	2'6"	0-4-0ST oc	7x12	1'9½"	RAVEN	JVM Money-Kent Cape Copper Co (New Rakha Mines Jamshedpur India)
2005	07/1914	2'0"	0-4-2T + 4wl ten oc	7½x12	1'9½"	PIONEER	The Borneo Co Ltd for shipment - 7/23 spares sent to Penang Malay - wood burner
2006	12/1914	2'6"	0-6-4T oc	12x18	3'0½"	(No 1) SIR TREVREDYN WYNNE	Mc Leod Russell & Co Ltd Burdwan Katwa Rly' Co Ltd India
2007	04/1915	2'6"	0-6-4T oc	12x18	3'0½"	(No 2) CHARLES NORMAN McLEOD	Mc Leod Russell & Co Ltd Burdwan Katwa Rly' Co Ltd India
2008	/1915	2'6"	0-6-4T oc	12x18	3'0½"	(No 3) C.C. McLEOD	Mc Leod Russell & Co Ltd Burdwan Katwa Rly' Co Ltd India
2009	/1915	2'6"	0-6-4T oc	12x18	3'0½"	(No 4) S.C. GHOSE	Mc Leod Russell & Co Ltd Burdwan Katwa Rly' Co Ltd India
2010	08/1914	2'6"	0-4-0ST oc	7x12	1'9½"	RACOON	JVM Money-Kent Cape Copper Co (New Rakha Mines Jamshedpur India)
2011-3	05/1915	metre	0-6-0 + 6wl ten oc	14x20	3'7"	(11: 13: 15)	Bengal Dooars Railway Co Ltd shipped to India
2014-5	06/1915	2'6"	0-6-0 + 6wl ten oc	11x15	3'0"	(28 - 29)	Rendel Palmer & Tritton for Baroda State Rly' India
2016	07/1916	2'6"	0-6-4T oc	12x18	2'10"	(No 5) SIR R.W. GILLAN	Mc Leod Russell & Co Ltd Bankura Damoodar River Rly' India
2017	07/1916	2'6"	0-6-4T oc	12x18	2'10"	(No 6) PATRICK YOUNG	Mc Leod Russell & Co Ltd Bankura Damoodar River Rly' India
2018-9	12/1916	2'6"	0-6-4T oc	12x18	2'10"	(No 1 - No 2)	Mc Leod Russell & Co Ltd (Kalighat Falta Railway India)
2020-1	02/1917	2'6"	0-6-4T oc	12x18	2'10"	(No 5 - No 6)	Mc Leod Russell & Co Ltd (Ahmadpur Katwa Rly' India)
2022-5	4-7/1916	2'5½"	2-6-2T oc	12x16	3'0½"	No 1 - No 4	Egyptian Delta Light Railways
2026	07/1917	2'6"	2-6-2T oc	12x16	3'0½"	No 4	Secretary of State for India Eastern Bengal Rly (Jacobabad Kushmore Rly India)
2027	11/1917	2'5½"	2-6-2T oc	12x16	3'0½"	No 5	Egyptian Delta Light Railways
2028-30	11/1916	2'6"	2-6-2T oc	12x16	3'0½"	(No 3 - No 5)	Mc Leod Russell & Co Ltd Kalighat Falta Railway India
2031	11/1917	2'6"	2-6-2T oc	12x16	3'0½"	No 5	Secretary of State for India Eastern Bengal Rly (Jacobabad Kushmore Rly India)
2032	11/1917	2'5½"	2-6-2T oc	12x16	3'0½"	No 6	Egyptian Delta Light Railways
2033	04/1918	2'6"	2-6-2T oc	12x16	3'0½"		Secretary of State for India Bengal Provincial Rly' (India - lost at sea)
2034	/1915	2'0"	0-4-2T oc	8x12	2'0½"	JACK	Cliffe Hill Granite Co Ltd Bardon Hill (Markfield Leics')
2035	/1915	2'0"	0-4-0ST oc	6x9	1'7"	No 2	Mark Wilson Ltd Koedoeshoek Forest Rly' South Africa
2036	/1916	2'6"	0-4-0ST oc	6x9	1'7"	NORTHSEA	Portsea Island Gas Light Co Hilsea Siding (Portsmouth Hants')
2037	/1916	2'0"	0-4-0ST oc	6x9	1'7"	No 3	Liverpool Gas Co Linacre Gas Wks' Liverpool
2038	/1915	2'6"	0-4-0ST oc	7x12	1'9½"	ROVER	JVM Money-Kent Cape Copper Co (Port Nolloth Namaqualand) ship from Swansea
2039	/1916	2'6"	0-4-0ST oc	7x12	1'9½"	RACER	JVM Money-Kent Cape Copper Co (for Rakha Mine Jamshedpur India?)
2040	02/1916	2'6"	0-4-0ST oc	7x12	1'9½"		United Alkali Co Ltd (sent to Spain) supplied in parts for machining etc in Spain
2041	/1916	2'6"	0-6-2 + 6wl ten oc	11x15	3'0"	(No 3)	Forbes, Forbes Campbell & Co Ltd for Jacobabad Kushmore Rly India
2042	12/1917	2'0"	0-4-0ST oc	6x9	1'7"	HENLOW	MofM Aeronautical Dept' Uxbridge Middlesex
2043	12/1917	2'0"	0-4-0ST oc	6x9	1'7"	KIDBROOKE	MofM Aeronautical Dept' Marske-by-Sea York's
2044	12/1917	2'0"	0-4-0ST oc	6x9	1'7"	FILTON	MofM Aeronautical Dept' Filton Bristol
2045	03/1918	2'0"	0-4-0ST oc	6x9	1'7"		MofM Air Board Director of Inland Waterways & Docks Chepstow
2046	03/1918	2'0"	0-4-0ST oc	6x9	1'7"		MofM Air Board FD Cowieson & Co contr' West Fenton Aerodrome Cullane
2047	03/1918	2'0"	0-4-0ST oc	6x9	1'7"		MofM Air Board Director of Inland Waterways & Docks Chepstow
2048	03/1918	2'0"	0-4-0ST oc	6x9	1'7"		MofM Air Board Dymchurch Aerodrome const' Hythe Kent
2049	04/1918	2'0"	0-4-0ST oc	6x9	1'7"		MofM Air Board Beaulieu Aerodrome const' Brockenhurst Hants'
2050	04/1918	2'0"	0-4-0ST oc	6x9	1'7"		MofM Air Board Kidbrooke Aerodrome Kent
2051	/1916	2'0"	0-4-0ST oc	6x9	1'7"	KUTHALA	Punjab Coal Co Ltd (Karachi India)
2052	6-8/1916	2'6"	0-4-0ST oc	7x12	1'9½"		United Alkali Co Ltd (Sotiel Coronada Spain) sent in parts in two shipments
2053	01/1917	3'6	0-4-0ST oc	6x9	1'7"	THE MIGHTY ATOM	Callenders Cables Construction Co Ltd Belverdere Kent
2054	12/1918	2'7½"	0-4-0ST oc	7x12	1'9½"	GASTONORGE	Gaston, Williams & Wigmore Ltd for export
2055	08/1917	Std	0-4-0ST oc	14x20	3'6½"	No 10	Cammell Laird & Co Yorkshire Iron & Steel Works Penistone Yorks'
2056	03/1918	2'6"	0-4-0ST oc	7x12	1'9½"	RAINBOW	JVM Money-Kent Cape Copper Co (Rakha Mine Jamshedpur India) ship from Swansea
2057	01/1918	Std	0-6-0ST oc	14x20	3'6½"		Schneider & Co for French Ministry of Munitions (Usine du Creusot France)

Manu No	Date Desp	Gauge	Type	Cyls	Dwl Dia	Name/No	Purchaser/Destination
2058	12/1917	3'0"	0-4-0ST oc	7x12	1'9½"	C.T.S. 1	War Office Timber Supply Depot 4 Mech' Section Corbridge Northum'
2059	01/1918	3'0"	0-4-0ST oc	7x12	1'9½"	C.T.S. 2	War Office Timber Supply Depot 4 Mech' Section Corbridge Northum'
2060	03/1918	3'0"	0-4-0ST oc	7x12	1'9½"	C.T.S. 3	War Office Timber Supply FD Cowison & Co contr' Aircraft Repair Dpt' Renfrew
2061	02/1918	3'0"	0-4-0ST oc	9x14	2'3½"	PROGRESS	Park Gate Iron & Steel Co Ltd Rotherham Yorks'
2062	04/1918	2'4½"	0-4-0ST oc	9x14	2'3½"	B.F.W. No 5	The Briton Ferry Works Ltd Briton Ferry (Glamorgan)
2063	07/1918	2'6⁵⁄₁₆"	0-4-0ST oc	7x12	1'9½"		Schneider & Co for French Ministry of Munitions (Usine du Creusot France)
2064-5	04/1919	Std	0-4-0ST oc	14x20	3'6½"		Schneider & Co for French Ministry of Munitions (Usine du Creusot France)
2066	01/1918	1'8"	0-4-0ST oc	5x7½	1'3¼"	BOBS	William Firth Ltd Sherburn-in-Elmet Yorks'
2067	12/1918	3'0"	0-4-0ST oc	7x12	1'9½"		MofM OC 111 Coy' Canadian Forestry Corps Longtown Cumb'
2068	08/1918	2'6"	0-4-0ST oc	8x12	2'0½"	(CLINKER)	CJ Wills & Son Ltd Tees Navel Base Bolckow Vaughan Sidings Middlesbro'
2069	06/1918	2'0"	0-4-0ST oc	6x9	1'7"		MofM Detling Aerodrome Maidstone Kent
2070	06/1918	2'0"	0-4-0ST oc	6x9	1'7"		MofM Aldeburgh Aerodrome Snape Suffolk
2071	06/1918	2'0"	0-4-0ST oc	6x9	1'7"		MofM Aldeburgh Aerodrome Snape Suffolk
2072	07/1918	2'0"	0-4-0ST oc	6x9	1'7"		MofM OCC ACC Hanworth Rd Sdgs' Sunbury Middlesex
2073	06/1918	2'0"	0-4-0ST oc	6x9	1'7"		MofM OCC ACC Hanworth Rd Sdgs' Sunbury Middlesex
2074	07/1918	2'0"	0-4-0ST oc	6x9	1'7"		MofM E Thornton & Co sent to Swansea
2075	09/1918	2'0"	0-4-0ST oc	6x9	1'7"		Liverpool Gas Co Linacre Gas Wks' Liverpool
2076	10/1918	2'0"	0-4-0ST oc	6x9	1'7"		MofM E Thornton & Co sent to Swansea
2077	10/1918	2'0"	0-4-0ST oc	6x9	1'7"		MofM War Office Stamford Aerodrome Lincs'
2078	11/1918	2'0"	0-4-0ST oc	6x9	1'7"		MofM E Thornton & Co sent to Swansea
2079	11/1918	2'0"	0-4-0ST oc	6x9	1'7"		MofM E Thornton & Co sent to Swansea
2080	11/1918	2'0"	0-4-0ST oc	6x9	1'7"		MofM E Thornton & Co sent to Swansea
2081	02/1919	3'0"	0-4-0ST oc	7x12	1'9½"		MofM OC 126 Coy' Canadian Forestry Corps Downham Hall Brandon Suffolk
2082	02/1919	3'0"	0-4-0ST oc	7x12	1'9½"		MofM OC 105 Coy' Canadian Forestry Corps Wool Dorset
2083	02/1919	3'0"	0-4-0ST oc	7x12	1'9½"		MofM OC 110 Coy' Canadian Forestry Corps Netley Bridge
2084	03/1919	3'0"	0-4-0ST oc	7x12	1'9½"		MofM Technical Warehouse Canadian Forestry Corps Bellingham London
2085	03/1919	3'0"	0-4-0ST oc	7x12	1'9½"		MofM Technical Warehouse Canadian Forestry Corps Bellingham London
2086	03/1919	3'0"	0-4-0ST oc	7x12	1'9½"		MofM Technical Warehouse Canadian Forestry Corps Bellingham London
2087-8	04/1919	2'0"	0-4-0ST oc	6x9	1'7"	VICTORY & ARMISTICE	Birmingham Tame & Rea District Drainage Board Water Orton (Minworth Warks')
2089	04/1919	2'6"	0-4-0ST oc	6x9	1'7"		Partington Iron & Steel Co Wakerley Ironstone Mine Lincs'
2090	04/1919	2'0"	0-4-0ST oc	6x9	1'7"	PIXIE	Staveley Coal & Iron Co Pilton Ironstone Co Luffenham (Rutland)
2091	08/1919	2'0"	0-4-0ST oc	6x9	1'7"	WENDY	Votty & Bowydd Slate Quarries Duffws Blaenau Festiniog
2092-5	9-12/1919	1'11½"	0-4-0ST oc	6x9	1'7"	LEON: JOB: CHARLES: JACQUES	Elias Wild & Son Ltd sent to Leon Waenseggens Bodega Menin Belgium
2096	06/1920	metre	0-4-0ST oc	6x9	1'7"		Felber Jucker & Co Ltd Manchester (agents) for export
2097	07/1920	1'11⅝"	0-4-0ST oc	6x9	1'7"	ANGELITA	Adolpho T Simpson agent for Jose Goenaga Bilbao Spain
2098	11/1920	2'6"	0-4-0ST oc	6x9	1'7"		Blair Campbell & McLean Ltd Glasgow agents for Chawndi Sugar Factory Rangoon
2099	05/1919	2'5½"	0-4-0ST oc	6x9	1'7"	MARIA LA CHICA No 2	Adolpho T Simpson (agents) shipped to Bilbao Spain
2100	07/1919	2'0"	0-4-0ST oc	7x12	1'9½"		Assam Rlys' & Trading Co (Margherita Assam India) shipped to Calcutta
2101	08/1919	1'11⅝"	0-4-0ST oc	7x12	1'9½"	D'HUBERT	Bolling & Lowe Ltd London (agents) for R Hamilton & Co Liverpool for shipmemt
2102	08/1919	2'6"	0-4-0ST oc	7x12	1'9½"		India Office Cossipore Ordnance Factory India
2103	07/1919	2'6"	0-4-0ST oc	7x12	1'9½"	RYDER GIBSON	Towcester Mineral & Brick Co Ltd (Easton Neston Mines Northants') per EC Cornforth
2104	9/1919	2'5½"	0-4-0ST oc	7x12	1'9½"	MARIA LA CHICA No 1	Adolpho T Simpson (agents) shipped to Bilbao Spain
2105-6	11/1919	Std	0-4-0ST oc	14x20	3'6½"		Barrow Hematite Steel Co Barrow-in-Furness (Lancs')
2107	09/1922	Std	0-4-0ST oc	14x20	3'6½"	ALEXANDER	Birchenwood Colliery Co (Kidsgrove Staffs') pt exchange for 1402
2108	10/1923	Std	0-4-0ST oc	14x20	3'6½"	No 5	Worthington & Co Ltd, Burton-on-Trent
2109	07/1919	2'5½"	0-4-2T oc	8x12	2'0½"		William Lancaster Moore & Co for export (for Pernambuco) same as 1919
2110-16	3-7/1920	metre	0-6-0 + 6wl ten oc	14x20	3'7"	(57-58: 68-70: 84:169)	Rohilkund & Kumaon Rly' shipped to Calcutta India
2117-29	7/20-5/21	metre	0-6-0 + 6wl ten oc	14x20	3'7"	(347 - 359)	Bengal & North Western Rly' shipped to Calcutta India
2130	06/1920	2'5½"	0-4-0ST oc	7x12	1'9½"	MARIA LA CHICA No 3	Adolpho T Simpson (agents) shipped to Bilbao Spain
2131-2	06/1924	2'0"	0-4-0ST oc	7x12	1'9½"	JOAN & TONY	Assam Rlys' & Trading Co Ltd (Margherita Assam India) shipped to Calcutta
2133	07/1924	3'6"	0-4-0ST oc	7x12	1'9½"	WOTO	Callenders Cables Construction Co Ltd Belverdere Kent
2134	10/1924	2'0"	0-4-0ST oc	7x12	1'9½"	DAVID	Assam Rlys' & Trading Co Ltd (Margherita Assam India) shipped to Calcutta
2135	04/1926	3'6"	0-4-0ST oc	7x12	1'9½"	SIR TOM	Callenders Cables Construction Co Ltd Belverdere Kent
2136	10/1920	2'6"	4-4-0 + 6wl ten oc	11x15	3'3"	No 5	Bolling & Lowe London (agents for Tezpur Balipara Tramway Assam India)
2137	09/1920	3'0"	0-4-2T oc	8½x12	2'0½"		Crown Agents Zanzibar (Railway)
2138-42	7-8/1921	2'6"	0-6-0 + 6wl ten oc	11x15	3'0"	(30 - 34)	Bombay Baroda & Central India Rly' Co Ltd London shipped to Bombay India
2143	04/1921	5'6"	0-4-0ST oc	14x20	3'7"	(No 12)	Rendel Palmer & Tritton for Madras Port Trust Madras India
2144	03/1921	2'6"	0-4-0ST oc	6x9	1'7"		Blair Campbell & McLean Ltd (agents for Chawndi Sugar Factory) ship to Rangoon
2145	07/1921	2'0"	0-4-0ST oc	6x9	1'7"		MacKinlay & Co London agents Sundays River Irrigation Board South Africa
2146	09/1922	1'11⅝"	0-4-0ST oc	6x9	1'7"	GARGALHEIRAS	CH Walker & Co agents Gayalheira Dam const' Natal (Pernambuco) Brazil
2147	08/1924	2'0"	0-4-0ST oc	6x9	1'7"		Miller & Allan Ltd agents Sungi Besi Mines Ltd ship to Port Swettenham Malay
2148	11/1924	2'0"	0-4-0ST oc	6x9	1'7"		Kaye & Co Ltd sent to Southam & Long Itchington Stn (Cement Works Warks')
2149	04/1925	2'0"	0-4-0ST oc	6x9	1'7"	CAPSTAN	British Standard Cement Co Rainham Works Kent
2150-2	10-11/1921	2'6"	2-6-2 + 6wl ten oc	13x16	3'0"	No 1 - No 3	Forbes, Forbes Campbell & Co for Larkana Jacobabad Rly' India
2153	10/1921	3'6"	0-4-0ST oc	10x15	2'9¼"		LNWR Carriage Dept' Wolverton (Wolverton & Stony Stratford Tramway Bucks')
2154-9	6-8/1921	2'0"	0-6-0T oc	7¼x12	1'9½"		India Office United Provinces Public Works Dept' Irrigation Works shipped to Bombay
2160-2	5-6/1921	2'0"	0-6-0 + 4wl ten oc	7x12	1'9½"	No 3 - No 5	Anglo Mexican Petroleum Co Ltd Tuxpan Tampico Mexico
2163	12/1921	5'6"	0-4-0ST oc	14x20	3'7"	(No 13)	Rendel Palmer & Tritton for Madras Port Trust Madras India
2164-5	3-4/1922	2'0"	2-6-2 + 6wl ten oc	13x16	2'6"	26 - 27	Burma Corporation Ltd Burma Mines Rly' ship to Nam Yaw via Rangoon Burma
2166	11/1931	Std	0-4-0ST oc	8x12	2'1"	SALVAGE	Don Engineering Co Ltd Sheffield (for Sheffield Corp' Cleansing Dept')
2167-9	12/21-2/22	Std	0-6-0ST oc	13x18	2'9¼"	MOMBASA: KILINDINI: NAIROBI	Pauling & Co Ltd London (contr' Kilindini Harbour Works Kenya) ship to Kilindini
2170	12/1921	Std	0-4-0ST oc	9x14	2'3½"	KENYA	Pauling & Co Ltd London (contr' Kilindini Harbour Works Kenya) ship to Kilindini

Manu No	Date Desp	Gauge	Type	Cyls	Dwl Dia	Name/No	Purchaser/Destination
2171-8	12/21-9/22	Std	0-4-0ST oc	12x18	3'0½"	STR 1 - STR 8	India Office for Salsette Trombay Railway Bombay India
2179	08/1922	2'0"	2-6-2 + bg ten oc	13x16	2'6"	28	Burma Corporation Ltd Burma Mines Rly' ship to Nam Yaw via Rangoon Burma
2180	09/1922	metre	0-4-0ST oc	10x16	2'9¼"		East Indian Rly Co Colliery Dept' shipped to Calcutta
2181-90	3-6/1922	2'0"	0-4-0T oc	6½x10	1'7½"	M1 - M10	East Indian Rly Co (Colliery Dept') shipped to Calcutta
2191	08/1922	2'6"	0-6-0T oc	7¼x12	1'9½"		Crown Agents (Public Works Dept') Mauritius
2192	09/1922	2'6"	0-6-2T oc	13X18	2'9¼"	CONQUEROR	Edward Lloyd Ltd Sittingbourne (Kent)
2193	11/1922	Std	0-6-0ST oc	17x24	3'9"	TOPHAM	West Cannock Colliery Co Ltd to Hednesford (Staffs') under own steam
2194	10/1922	metre	0-4-0ST oc	10x16	2'9¼"		East Indian Rly Co Colliery Dept' shipped to Calcutta
2195-6	11/1922	2'6"	0-6-2 + 6wl ten oc	11x15	3'0"	35 - 36	Rendel Palmer & Tritton for Baroda State Railway India
2197	12/1922	Std	0-6-0ST oc	13x18	2'9¼"	THIKA	Pauling & Co Ltd London (contr' Kilindini Harbour Works Kenya) ship to Kilindini
2198	12/1922	Std	0-4-0ST oc	9x14	2'3½"	NYERI	Pauling & Co Ltd London (contr' Kilindini Harbour Works Kenya) ship to Kilindini
2199-2201	04/1923	metre	0-6-0 + 6wl ten oc	14x20	3'6½"	(F35; F36; F38)	South Indian Railway Co shipped to Madras (India)
2202	06/1923	3'6"	0-6-0T oc	15x23	3'6¾"	18	Crown Agents Nigerian Railways for Nigeria Eastern Rly' (construction of line)
2203	06/1923	3'0"	0-6-0ST oc	13x18	2'9¼"	MOUNTAINEER	Eastwell Iron Ore Co Eaton Branch Waltham (Eastwell Quarries Leics')
2204-6	03/1923	2'0"	0-4-0T oc	7¼x12	1'9½"		India Office United Provinces Irrigation Branch for Banbasa Bombay
2207-9	04/1923	2'0"	0-6-0T oc	7¼x12	1'9½"		India Office United Provinces Irrigation Branch for Shahgarh Bombay
2210	07/1923	2'6"	2-6-2 + 6 wl ten oc	13x16	3'0"	(No 4)	Forbes, Forbes Campbell & Co for Larkana Jacobabad Rly' India
2211-13	09/1923	metre	2-6-2T oc	12x18	2'9¼"	RIO LOA: RIO SABRADOR: RIO SALADO	Baburizza & Co Ltd (for Lautaro Nitrate Co) shipped to Antofagasta Chile
2214	05/1923	3'0"	0-4-0ST oc	7x12	1'9½"	DOT	Charles Abell Ltd Hartshill Granite Quarries Nuneaton Warks'
2215	07/1923	metre	0-4-0ST oc	9x14	2'3¼"	No 1	Norton Griffiths & Co Ltd (contr' Uganda Rly' const' Nakura-Turbo) ship to Loanda
2216	02/1924	2'6"	0-4-2F oc	18½x18	2'9¼"	UNIQUE	Edward Lloyd Ltd Sittingbourne (Kent)
2217	11/1923	metre	0-4-0ST oc	9x14	2'3¼"	No 2	Norton Griffiths & Co Ltd (contr' Uganda Rly' const' Nakura-Turbo) ship to Loanda
2218-9	11/1923	3'0"	0-4-0ST oc	10x16	2'9¼"	RHONDDA; RHYMNEY	Taff Fechan Water Supply Board Taff Fechan Reservoir const' Merthyr
2220	04/1924	2'0"	0-4-0PM	20 bhp	1'3¼"		Eastern Assam Co Ltd Dibrugarh Assam India shipped to Calcutta
2221	06/1927	Std	0-6-0ST oc	13x18	2'9¼"	LEWISHAM	Shropshire Beet Sugar Co Lrd Allscot (Salop')
2222	07/1929	5'6"	0-6-0ST oc	13x18	2'9¼"	No 1	Burn Craddock & Co Ltd Howrah Ironworks Calcutta India
2223	10/1924	Std	0-6-0ST oc	15x20	3'7"	ELSIE	Stewarts & Lloyds Ltd Kilnhurst Colliery Rotherham (Yorks')
2224	03/1931	Std	0-6-0ST oc	15x20	3'7"		Redpath Brown & Co Ltd Trafford Park Manchester
2225-6	04/1924	3'6"	0-6-0T oc	11½x16	2'9¼"	KADE; HUNI	Crown Agents Gold Coast Rly (const' Huni Valley to Kade) shipped to Secondee
2227-8	06/1924	2'0"	0-4-4T oc	10x15	2'9"		Crown Agents Kowloon Canton Rly British Sect' (Sha Tau Kok Tramway) Hong Kong
2229	03/1924	Std	0-4-0ST oc	12x18	3'0½"	CENTENARY	York Gas Co (Layerthorpe Gas Wks') York
2230-2	07/1924	3'6"	0-6-0T oc	12x16½	2'9¼"	No 1 - No 3 (in Chinese characters)	Light Railways Ltd (for Chang Chang [Great Wall] Rly') ship to Chin Wang Tao China
2233	07/1924	3'0"	0-4-0ST oc	10x16	2'9¼"	MERTHYR	Taff Fechan Water Supply Board Taff Fechan Reservoir const' Merthyr
2234	10/1924	metre	4-6-0 + 8wl ten oc	16½x22	4'9"	P 450	Madras & Southern Mahratta Railway Co Ltd shipped to Marmagao India
2235	01/1925	metre	4-8-0 + 8wl ten oc	17x22	3'7"	G 470	Madras & Southern Mahratta Railway shipped to Madras India
2236-7	09/1924	2'6"	0-6-0T oc	11x16½	2'6"	No 5 - No 6	African Manganese Co Ltd shipped to Sekondi (Gold Coast)
2238-42	10-11/1924	2'6"	2-6-2T oc	12x18	2'9¼"	7/1 - 7/5	Baburizza & Co (for Lautaro Nitrate Co Chile). Can be altered to suit metre-gauge
2243-4	11/1924	2'6"	0-6-0T oc	13x18"	2'9¼"	EUGENIA: MORENA	Mitrovich Bros' Ltd London & Iquique for Aguas Blanca Nitrate Co ship to Antofagasta
2245	12/1924	2'6"	0-6-0T oc	7¼x12	1'9½"		Crown Agents Public Works Dept' Mauritius
2246-9	3-5/1925	metre	4-8-0 + 8wl ten oc	17x22	3'7"	G 503-4; G 351; G 376	Madras & Southern Mahratta Railway Co Ltd shipped to Marmagao India
2250	05/1925	3'6"	0-8-0T oc	18x24	3'3"	NEW STATE AREAS	Light Railways Ltd for New State Areas (Springs Transvaal South Africa) ship Durban
2251-3	07/1925	2'0"	2-6-2 + 6wl ten oc	13x16	2'6"	35 - 37	Burma Corporation Ltd Burma Mines Rly' ship to Nam Yaw via Rangoon Burma
2254	10/1925	Std	0-4-0ST oc	10x16	2'9¼"	B.R.C.	British Reinforced Concrete Engineering Co Ltd Stafford under own steam
2255	06/1925	2'6"	4-6-0 + 6wl ten oc	11x15	2'9¼"	No 6	McLeod Russell & Co Ltd for Tezpur Balipara Tramway Assam India
2256	09/1925	2'6"	0-6-4T oc	12x18	3'0"	(KF 6)	McLeod Russell & Co Ltd (for Kalighat Falta Railway Calcutta India)
2257	07/1925	2'6"	0-6-2T oc	11x15	2'6"	No 3	Strain & Robertson Glasgow for Salar del Carmen Nitrate Syndicate Ltd Chile
2258	05/1925	3'9"	0-4-0ST oc	10x15	2'9¼"	NEW ELEPHANT	APCM Ltd Johnsons Branch Cement Wks', Greenhithe Kent - 9/27 convt' Std Gauge
2259	09/1925	2'6"	0-6-4T oc	12x18	3'0"	(KF 7)	McLeod Russell & Co Ltd for Kalighat Falta Railway Calcutta India
2260	07/1925	2'0"	0-4-0ST oc	6x9	1'7"		Millar & Allen Ltd for Sungei Besi Mines, Malaya shipment to Port Swettenham
2261	03/1927	1'11⅝"	0-4-0ST oc	6x9	1'7"		Baerlein & Sons Ltd Agents for Ilha do Principe, via Bremen (later spares via Lisbon)
2262	03/1927	2'0"	0-4-0ST oc	6x9	1'7"	CAPSTAN 11 (Roman two)	British Standard Cement Co Ltd Rainham Works Kent
2263-71	12/25-3/26	metre	4-8-0 + 8wl ten oc	17x22	3'7"	G 407 - 413; WIP 505-6	Madras & Southern Mahratta Railway India shipped to Marmagao
2272	09/1925	std	0-4-0ST oc	14x20	3'6½"	BESSIE	Exhall Colliery & Brickworks Ltd, Exhall Colliery Bedworth (Warks')
2273	08/1925	2'6"	0-4-0PM	20 bhp	1'3¼"	BUCHIVACOA	Norton Griffiths & Co Ltd for Britrish Controlled Oilfields Ltd Maracaibo (Venezuela)
2274	10/1925	2'6"	0-4-0PM	40 bhp	1'7"	PRESIDENTE BOLIVAR	Norton Griffiths & Co Ltd for Britrish Controlled Oilfields Ltd Venezuela
2275	10/1925	2'6"	0-4-0PM	40 bhp	1'7"	PRESIDENTE GOMEZ	Norton Griffiths & Co Ltd for Britrish Controlled Oilfields Ltd Venezuela
2276-7	6-12/1926	2'6"	0-6-2T oc	11x15	2'6"	No 4 - 5	Strain & Robertson for Salar del Carmen Nitrate Syndicate Ltd Ship to Iquique (Chile)
2278-83	12/25-½6	2'6"	0-6-4T oc	11x15	3'0"		Rendel Palmer & Tritton for Gaekwar's Baroda State Railway India shipped to Bombay
2284-5	05/1926	2'6"	0-6-0T oc	11x16 ½	2'6"	No 7 - 8	African Manganese Co Ltd shipped to Sekondi (Gold Coast)
2286	02/1926	Std	0-4-0ST oc	12x18	3'0½"	No 3	Coventry Corp' Gas Dept' Foleshill Gas Wks' Coventry
2287	03/1926	2'0"	4-4-0T oc	10x15	2'6"	SINEMBE	Tongaat Sugar Co Ltd (Tongaat Estate Natal South Africa)
2288-2302	8/26-6/27	Std	0-6-0T oc	18x26	4'7"	16535 - 16549	London Midland & Scottish Railway free on rail Stafford
2303	06/1926	metre	0-6-0T + 4wl ten oc	9x14	2'3½"	HILIKA	RG Shaw & Co for Assam Frontier Tea Co (Assam India) shipped to Calcutta
2304	09/1926	2'6"	0-4-0PM	40 bhp	1'7"	EL MENE	Norton Griffiths & Co Ltd for Britrish Controlled Oilfields Ltd Maracaibo (Venezuela)
2305	06/1927	metre	0-8-0T oc	14½x20	3'3"	17	Bengal Dooars Railway Co Ltd shipped to Calcutta (India)

Manu No	Date Desp	Gauge	Type	Cyls	Dwl Dia	Name/No	Purchaser/Destination
2306	03/1927	2'6"	2-4-0T oc	8½x12	2'0½"		High Commissioner for India Eastern Bengal Railway India
2307-12	7-9/1927	3'6"	0-6-0T oc	15x23"	3'6¾"	25 - 30	Crown Agents Nigerian Railways for Nigeria (Eastern Rly' const') shipped to Apapa
2313-16	11/1927	metre	2-6-2T oc	15x22	3'7"	343 - 346	Bengal & North Western Railway Co Lrd (India) shipped to Calcutta
2317-20	12/1927	metre	2-6-2T oc	15x22	3'7"	154 - 157	Burma Railways Co Ltd shipped to Rangoon
2321	05/1927	2'6"	2-6-2T oc	12x18	2'9¼"	RIVERVIEW	Umfolozi Sugar Planters Ltd (Natal South Africa) shipped to Durban
2322	09/1927	2'0"	2-6-2 + 6wl ten oc	13x16	3'0"	No 41	Burma Corporation Ltd (Burma Mines Rly') ship to Nam Yaw via Rangoon Burma
2323-7	01/1928	metre	0-6-2T oc	13x20	3'3"	26 - 28: 70 - 71	Crown Agents for Federated Malay States Railway shipped to Port Swettenham
2328-9	03/1928	metre	4-6-0 + 6wl ten oc	15½x22	4'9"	51 - 52	Assam Railways & Trading Co Ltd (Dibru Sadiya Railway Assam India)
2330	03/1928	2'6"	4-8-0 + 6wl ten oc	12x16	2'4"	(3)	Robert White & Ptnr's for Bhavnagar State Railway India shipped to Bombay
2331	08/1928	2'6"	0-6-4T oc	12x18	2'10"	(BK 9)	McLeod Russell & Co Ltd Burdwan Katwa Railway India shipped to Calcutta
2332-7	4-5/1928	3'6"	0-6-0T oc	15x23	3'6¾"	2 - 7	Crown Agents Nigerian Railways for Nigeria (Eastern Rly' const') shipped to Apapa
2338	03/1928	2'0"	2-6-2 + 6wl ten oc	13x16	3'0"	No 42	Burma Corporation Ltd (Burma Mines Rly') ship to Nam Yaw via Rangoon Burma
2339-40	10/1928	2'6"	2-6-2 + 6wl ten oc	12x18	2'10"	201 - 202	High Commissioner for India Indian State Railways North Western Railway India
2341	04/1928	2'0"	0-4-0ST oc	6x9	1'7"		Kirkwood Coates & Co shipped to Korot Areas, Bukuru via Apapa (Nigeria)
2342	06/1928	2'0"	4-4-0T oc	10x15	2'6"	MONA	F Stanley Morris Liverpool for Tongaat Sugar Co Ltd (Tongaat Estate Natal) South Africa
2343-52	8-11/1928	Std	0-6-0T oc	18x26	4'7"	16675 - 16684	London Midland & Scottish Railway free on rail Stafford
2353	06/1928	metre	0-6-0T oc	12½x16½	2'9½"	PRH-EP	Perak River Hydro Electric Co Malim Nawar Power Station Malay
2354	09/1928	2'6"	0-6-0T oc	7½x12	1'9½"		Crown Agents Public Works Dept' Mauritius
2355-7	04/1929	Std	0-6-0ST oc	18½x24	4'0"	No 32 - 34	Peruvian Corporation Ltd Central Railway of Peru shipped to Callao
2358-64	12/28-2/29	Std	0-6-0T oc	18x26	4'7"	19 - 25	Somerset & Dorset Joint Railway delivered to Bath
2365	02/1929	metre	2-6-2T oc	15x22	3'7"	103	Rohilkund & Kumaon Railway Co Ltd India shipped to Calcutta
2366	01/1929	2'6"	0-4-0F oc	9x14	2'3½"	VICTOR	Edward Lloyd Ltd Sittingbourne (Kent)
2367-8	05/1929	metre	4-6-0 + 6wl ten oc	15x22	4'9"	21 - 22	Robert White & Partners for Morvi Railway India, shipped to Bombay
2369	06/1929	Std	0-4-0ST oc	14x20	3'6½"	SIRAPITE	Gypsum Mines Ltd Mountfield Siding Battle Station (Sussex)
2370	05/1929	Std	0-6-0F oc	20x18	2'9¼"		The Distillers Co Ltd Salt End Chemical Works Hull
2371-2	07/1929	metre	2-6-2 + 6wl ten oc	12x18	2'10"	20 - 21	Bombay Baroda & Central India Railway shipped to Bombay
2373	04/1929	3'6"	0-4-0ST oc	10x15	2'9¼"		Crown Agents - Port Elizabeth Harbour Dept' New Carter Bridge cont' Apapa (Nigeria)
2374	04/1929	2'0"	4-4-0T oc	10x15	2'6"	ISIBUTU	Tongaat Sugar Co Ltd (Tongaat Estate) Natal South Africa
2375-6	12/1929	2'6"	4-6-0 + 6wl ten oc	12x20	3'3"	No 7 - No 8	Cutch State Railway India shipped to Bombay
2377	10/1929	metre	2-6-2T oc	15x22	3'7"		Crown Agents for Tanganyika Railway shipped to Dar-es-Salaam
2378-80	12/1929	2'0"	2-6-2T oc	13x16	2'6"	45 - 47	Burma Corporation Ltd (Burma Mines Rly') ship to Nam Yaw via Rangoon Burma
2381-2405	2-10/1930	Std	0-6-0PT oc	17½x24	4'7½"	6700 - 6724	Great Western Railway delivered to Swindon
2406-7	12/1929	2'6"	2-6-2T oc	11x16	3'0½"	No 1 - No 2	Kilburn Brown & Co for Singri-Panchnoi River Tramway Co Ltd shipped to Calcutta
2408	03/1930	2'0"	0-4-0ST oc	6x9	1'7"		Millar & Allan Ltd (for Sungei Besi Mines Ltd) shipped Port Swettenham Malay
2409	03/1930	3'0"	0-4-0ST oc	6x9	1'7"		Brown Douglas & Co (for Briandale Coal Co Ten Mile Runanga) New Zealand
2410	02/1930	2'6"	0-6-0T oc	7¼x12	1'9½"		Crown Agents Public Works Dept' Mauritius
2411-2	05/1930	2'6"	2-6-2T oc	12x16	1'9½"	(KF 10 - KF 9)	McLeod Russell & Co agents for Kalighat Falta Railway shipped to Calcutta (India)
2413	06/1930	2'6"	0-6-0T oc	11x16½	2'6"	AMC No 9	The African Manganese Co Ltd shipped to Takoradi (Gold Coast)
2414	03/1930	2'0"	0-4-0ST oc	6x9	1'7"		Sir John Norton Griffiths & Co (contr' Aswan Dam Contract Egypt)
2415	08/1933	metre	0-4-0ST oc	6½x9	1'7"		McLeod & Co (for Shree Hanuman Sugar Mills Ltd) Molihari India
2416-21	10/30-5/31	metre	4-6-0 + 6wl ten oc	15½x22	4'0"	53 - 58	Assam Railways & Trading Co (Dibru Sadiya Railway Assam India) via Chittagong
2422-46	11/30-7/31	Std	0-6-0PT oc	17½x24	4'7½"	8725 - 8749	Great Western Railway delivered to Swindon via Bushbury
2447-8	11/30-7/31	2'0"	0-4-0ST oc	7x12	1'9½"	SALLY: BETTY	Assam Railways & Trading Co Ltd (Margherita Assam India)
2449	01/1931	2'6½"	0-6-0T oc	9x14	2'3½"	LONDESBOROUGH	Jees Hartshill Granite & Brick Co Ltd Hartshill Quarries (Nuneaton Warks')
2450	04/1931	Std	0-4-0ST oc	12x18	1'9½"	J T DALY	Horseley Bridge & Engineering Co Ltd Great Bridge (Birmingham)
2451	08/1931	Std	0-4-0ST oc	12x18	1'9½"		Taylor Tunnicliff & Co Ltd Stone Staffs'
2452			0-4-0DM	25 bhp			Stock order not proceeded with
2453-60	1-3/1932	2'0"	4-6-2 + bg ten oc	11x18	2'9"	34 - 41	McLeod & Co agents for Gwalior State Railway India shipped to Bombay
2461-3	11/1931	metre	0-4-0T oc	12¼x18	3'0"	67 - 69	Bengal & North Western Railway Co Ltd (India) shipped to Calcutta
2464-5	03/1932	metre	2-6-2T oc	11½x18	3'7"	91 - 92	HH Maharajah of Mysore, Mysore Railway India per Rendel Palmer & Tritton
2466	03/1932	4'0"	0-4-0ST oc	7x12	1'9½"	WHITEHAVEN No 1	The Steetley Lime & Basic Co Ltd (Whitehaven Quarry) Porthywaen Oswestry
2467-8	04/1932	metre	0-6-0T oc	11½x16	2'9¼"	1 - 2	Chinese Govt' Pur' Com' (Huainan Coal Mining Admin') Hwai Nan Coal Mines
2469	03/1932	Std	0-4-0ST oc	12x18	3'0½"	V 75	Frazer & Chalmers Engineering Works Erith Kent
2470	05/1932	metre	0-4-0ST oc	10x16	2'9¼"		Burn Craddock & Co Ltd for Okha Cement Co Ltd India ship to Dwarka via Port Okha
2471	05/1932	2'0"	4-4-0T oc	10x15	2'6"	WEWE	Tongaat Sugar Co Ltd (Tongaat Estate) Natal South Africa
2472	08/1932	2'6"	0-6-2T oc	10x15	2'3"	ALPHA	Edward Lloyd Ltd Sittingbourne (Kent)
2473-4	10-11/1932	Std	0-4-0F oc	18½x18	3'0½"	No 1 - No 2	Huntley & Palmers Ltd Reading Berks'
2475	10/1932	3'6"	0-6-0T oc	11x16½	2'9¼"		Union Cold Storage Co Ltd (Tomoana Freezing Wks' Hastings) ship to New Zealand
2476-7	06/1933	2'6"	2-6-2 + 6wl ten oc	12x18	2'10"	210 - 211	Greaves Cotton & Co for North Western Railway India shipped to Karachi
2478	07/1933	2'6"	2-6-2 + 6wl ten oc	12x18	2'10"	No 22	Bombay Baroda & Central India Railway shipped to Bombay
2479	01/1933	2'0"	4-4-0T oc	10x15	2'6"	TONGAAT	A&H MacNay for Tongaat Sugar Co (Tongaat Estate) Natal South Africa
2480	02/1933	2'6"	2-4-2T oc	9½x14	2'6"	1J	TA Martin Calcutta for Bukhtiapur-Bihar Light Railway India
2481-4	03/1933	metre	2-6-2T oc	11½x18	3'7"	(93 - 96)	Mysore Govt' per Rendel Plamer & Tritton - Mysore Railway India shipped to Madras
2485-7	09/1933	2'6"	2-4-2T oc	8x12	3'0"	(2 - 4)	Mysore Govt' per Rendel Plamer & Tritton - Mysore Railway India shipped to Madras
2488-93	4-5/1933	metre	4-6-0 + 6wl ten oc	15½x22	4'0"	(85 - 90)	Gaekwar's Baroda State Railway India per Rendel Palmer & Tritton ship Port Okha
2494	06/1933	2'0"	0-4-0+0-4-0DM	62½ bhp	2'0"	No 1	Ashanti Goldfields Corporation Ltd Ashanti Gold Coast shipped to Takoradi

Manu No	Date Desp	Gauge	Type	Cyls	Dwl Dia	Name/No	Purchaser/Destination
2495-6	07/1933	2'6"	0-4-0T oc	7¼x12	1'9½"		McLeod & Co Calcutta agents for for Vizagapatam Harbour construction
2497	07/1933	4'0"	0-4-0ST oc	7x12	1'9½"	WHITEHAVEN No 2	The Steetley Lime & Basic Co Ltd Whitehaven Quarry Porthywaen Oswestry
2498	03/1934	1'10½"	0-4-0+0-4-0DM	24 bhp	1'4"		Halkyn District United Mines Ltd Penbryn Mine Halkyn Holywell (Flint)
2499	03/1934	1'11⅝"	4wl DM	8 bhp	1'2"		Oakley Slate Quarries Co Ltd Duffws Blaenau Festiniog (Merioneth)
2500-2	02/1934	metre	2-8-0 + 6wl ten oc	16¾x22	3'7"	1 - 3	Greaves Cotton & Co Bombay agents for Udaipur Chitorgarh Railway India
2503-4	03/1933	Std	0-4-0ST oc	12½x18	3'0½"	No 1 - No 2	Crown Agents for Shing Mun Valley Waterworks const' Hong Kong PWD
2505	03/1924	2'6"	2-4-2T oc	9½x14	2'6"	J2	TA Martin & Co Ltd for Baraset-Basirhat Light Railway India
2506	05/1934	2'6"	0-4-0DM	24 bhp	1'4"		RG Shaw & Co for Budla Beta Tea Co Ltd Assam for Pengaree-Digboi Trolley Line
2507	05/1934	metre	0-4-0DM	50 bhp	2'3½"		Assam Railways & Trading Co Ltd (Assam India)
2508	04/1934	Std	0-6-0ST oc	15x22	3'4½"	AMINGTON No 3	Glascote Colliery Co Ltd (Amington Colliery) Tamworth Staffs'
2509-10	06/1934	metre	0-8-0T oc	14½x20	3'3"	51 G - 52 G	Robert White & Partners for Bhavnagar State Railway India shipped to Bhavnagar
2511	04/1934	2'6"	0-6-2T oc	10x15	2'3"	TRIUMPH	Edward Lloyd Ltd Sittingbourne (Kent)
2512	03/1934	1'10"	0-4-0ST oc	6x9	1'7"	FRANCIS ALLEN	Ariston Gold Mines Ltd (Gold Coast) shipped to Takoradi
2513	06/1934	2'9"	2-4-2PT oc	10x16	2'6"	EMPIRE	The Waihi Gold Mining Co Ltd Waihi New Zealand shipped to Auckland
2514	10/1934	2'0"	0-4-0+0-4-0DM	62½ bhp	2'0"	No 2	Ashanti Goldfields Corporation Ltd Ashanti Gold Coast shipped to Takoradi
2515	08/1934	Std	0-4-0ST oc	17x24	3'9"	KENFIG	The British (GKB) Iron & Steel Co Ltd Margam I&S Works (Port Talbot) Glamorgan
2516	01/1935	2'0"	0-4-0DM	45 bhp	1'8"		Coltness Iron Co Ltd Kingshill Colliery Morningside (Midlothian)
2517	10/1934	Std	0-4-0ST oc	14x20	3'6½"	NEW CRANSLEY NO 4 DAVID	The New Cransley I&S Co Ltd, Cransley Quarries (Northants)
2518-20	1-2/1935	metre	4-6-0 + 6wl ten oc	14½x22	4'0"	19 - 21	Robert White & Partners for Junagadh State Railway India shipped to Vereval
2521		Std	4wl+4wl TG	6x6 (8)	3'1"		Sentinel Waggon Works, for LNER - not proceeded with
2522	02/1935	2'0"	4-4-0T oc	10x15	2'6"	SIMPOLA	A&H MacNay for Tongaat Sugar Co Ltd (Tongaat Estate) Natal South Africa
2523	02/1935	2'6"	2-4-2T oc	9½x14	2'6"	3J	TA Martin & Co Calcutta for Bukhtiapur-Bihar Light Railway India
2524	01/1935	2'0"	4wl DM	8 bhp	1'2"		New Consoladated Goldfields Ltd - Lagares Tin Mines [1933] Ltd
2525	03/1935	Std	0-4-0ST oc	13x18	3'0½"	GASKELL	ICI (General Chemicals) Ltd Gaskell Deacon Works Widnes (Lancs')
2526-7	05/1935	metre	2-6-2T oc	11½x18	3'7"	(97 - 98)	Rendel Palmer & Tritton for Mysore Railway India shipped to Madras
2528-9	10-11/1935	metre	2-8-2 + bg ten oc	19x24	4'0"	20 - 21	Parana Plantations Ltd, Sao Paulo-Parana Railway Brazil shipped to Santos
2530	4/1935	metre	0-4-0 DM	77 bhp	2'3½"		Assam Railways & Trading Co Ltd (Assam India)
2531-3	09/1935	metre	4-6-0 + 6wl ten oc	15½x22	4'0"	91 - 93	Gaekwar's Baroda State Railways India shipped to Port Okha
2534	10/1935	3'6"	0-8-0T oc	16x24	3'3"	No 3	Baldwins [South Africa] Ltd for Springs Mines Ltd (Transvaal South Africa)
2535	10/1935	3'6"	0-8-0T oc	16x24	3'3"	No 1	Baldwins [South Africa] Ltd for South African Land & Exploration Ltd (Transvaal SA)
2536	01/1936	5'6"	0-6-0F oc	20x18	2'9¼"	PETER	Killick Nixon & Co Ltd for Punjab Portland Cement Ltd Wah (India) ship via Karachi
2537	12/1935	5'6"	0-4-0ST oc	15x20	3'6"	RICHARD	Killick Nixon & Co Ltd for Punjab Portland Cement Ltd Wah (India) ship via Karachi
2538	11/1935	2'6"	4-8-0 + 6wl ten oc	12x16	2'4"	T No 5	Robert White & Partners for Bhavnagar State Railway India shipped to Bhavnagar
2539-40	12/1935	2'6"	2-4-0T oc	8½x12	2'0½"	(15 - 16)	McLeod & Co Calcutta for Eastern Bengal Railway
2541	12/1935	2'6"	0-4-0T oc	7¼x12	1'9½"		McLeod & Co for Vizagapatam Harbour construction
2542	02/1936	Std	0-4-0ST oc	12x18	3'0½"	JUBILEE	Edward Lloyd Ltd Sittingbourne Kent for Kemsley Extns' consign to Queenborough
2543	04/1936	2'0½"	4-4-0T oc	11½x15	2'6"	BURNSIDE	A&H MacNay Ltd for Natal Estates Ltd (Natal South Africa) ship to Durban
2544	09/1936	2'0"	0-4-0+0-4-0	7¼x12 (4)	2'0"	2	A&H MacNay Ltd for Illovo Sugar Estates Ltd (Natal South Africa) ship to Durban
2545	05/1936	2'0"	0-4-0+0-4-0	9x12 (4)	2'0"	RENISHAW No 5	A&H MacNay Ltd for Crookes Brothers Ltd Renishaw Estate (Natal S Africa)
2546	08/1936	2'0"	0-4-0+0-4-0DM	62½ bhp	2'0"	No 3	Ashanti Goldfields Corporation Ltd (Ashanti Gold Coast) shipped to Takoradi
2547	06/1936	Std	0-6-0ST oc	16x22	3'4½"		War Office Director of Army Contract consign to RE Stores Changi Singapore
2548-9	12/1936	metre	2-8-0 + 6wl ten oc	16¾x22	3'7"		Greaves Cotton & Co Bombay for Udaipur Chitorgarh Rly India shipped to Bombay
2550-64	7-10/1936	Std	2-4-2T oc	13½x20	3'8"	1131 - 1145	Egyptian Govt' for Egyptian State Railways shipped to Port Said
2565	11/1936	Std	0-4-0ST oc	13x18	3'0½"	N.E.L.& P. Co Ltd	Northampton Electric Light & Power Co Ltd Hardingston Power Station
2566	02/1937	2'6"	2-6-2T oc	13x16	2'6"	A.M.C. No 13	The African Manganese Co Ltd shipped to Takoradi (Gold Coast)
2567	02/1937	2'6"	0-6-0DM	120 bhp	2'9¼"	A.M.C. No 14	The African Manganese Co Ltd shipped to Takoradi (Gold Coast)
2568	01/1937	2'0"	0-4-0+0-4-0DM	62½ bhp	2'0"	No 4	Ashanti Goldfields Corporation Ltd (Ashanti Gold Coast) shipped to Takoradi
2569-70	06/1937	metre	2-6-2T oc	16½x22	3'7"	104 - 105	Rohilkund & Kumaon Railway Co Ltd (India) shipped to Calcutta
2571	07/1937	3'6"	0-6-0F oc	20x18	2'9¼"	ESCOM	A&H MacNay, Elec' Supply Com' South Africa Colenso (Power Stn' Natal South Africa)
2572	09/1937	Std	0-4-0ST oc	10x16	2'9¼"	JUDY	Port of Par Ltd Par (Harbour) Cornwall
2573	09/1937	2'0"	0-6-0DM	120 bhp	2'6"	DARNALL No 2	A&H MacNay for Sir John Hulett & Sons Ltd (Darnall Sugar Estate Natal South Africa)
2574	04/1937	Std	0-4-0ST oc	12x18	3'0½"	SLAGDALE	Apedale Slag & Tarmacadam Co Ltd Apedale Sidings (Staffs')
2575	08/1937	3'6"	4-8-2T oc	16x24	3'3"	No 4	Baldwins [South Africa] Ltd for Springs Mines Ltd (Transvaal South Africa)
2576	08/1937	3'6"	4-8-2T oc	16x24	3'3"	No 3	Baldwins [South Africa] Ltd for Daggafontein Mines Ltd (Transvaal South Africa)
2577	10/1937	Std	0-4-0 DM	77 bhp	2'9¼"	V.L. 3	FH Lloyd Ltd (James Bridge Steel Works) Darlaston Staffs'
2578-9	9-10/1937	Std	0-8-0T oc	18x24	3'9"	No 1 - No 2	Braithwaite & Co (Engineers) Ltd for Karabuk I&S Works Turkey
2580-1	12/1937	2'6"	0-6-2 + 6wl ten oc	11½x15	3'0"	(14 - 15)	Bombay Baroda & Central India Railway shipped to Bombay
2582	02/1938	3'6"	4-8-2T oc	16x24	3'3"		Baldwins [South Africa] Ltd for West Springs Mines Ltd (Transvaal) South Africa
2583	02/1938	3'6"	4-8-2T oc	16x24	3'3"	No 1	Baldwins [South Africa] Ltd for East Daggafontein Mines Ltd (Transvaal) South Africa
2584-5	04/1938	2'6"	0-4-0ST oc	6x9	1'7"	No 1 - No 2	Greaves Cotton & Co for North Western Rly India (Dhilwan Creosoting Plant Punjab)
2586	03/1938	Std	0-4-0ST oc	14x22	3'6½"	PHORPRES	London Brick Co Ltd Calvert Brickworks (Bucks')
2587	04/1938	Std	0-6-2T oc	18x24	4'3"	KITCHENER	War Office, Railway Training Centre Longmoor (Hants')
2588	05/1938	3'6"	0-4-0ST oc	12x18	3'0½"		Baldwins [SA] Ltd for Stewarts & Lloyds [SA] Ltd (Vereeninging Transvaal South Africa)
2589	10/1938	metre	4-6-0 + 6wl ten oc	16x22	4'9"	No 13	Robert White & Partners for Gondal Railway (India) shipped to Porbander
2590	06/1938	Std	0-4-0ST oc	15x22	3'6½"		South Wales Coalite Co Ltd Wern Tawr Colliery South Rhondda (Glamorgan)
2591	04/1938	Std	0-4-0ST oc	14x22	3'6½"	(TRAFFORD)	Metropolitan Vickers Elec' Co Ltd Trafford Park (Manchester)

Manu No	Date Desp	Gauge	Type	Cyls	Dwl Dia	Name/No	Purchaser/Destination
2592	06/1938	Std	0-4-0ST oc	13x18	3'0½"	POCKET NOOK	Forsters Glass Co Ltd Pocket Nook Works St Helens (Lancs')
2593-4	12/1938	2'6"	2-6-4T oc	11½x18	3'0"	5 - 6	Rendel Palmer & Tritton for Mysore Railway (Bangalore-Bangarapet section India)
2595	06/1938	2'0"	0-4-0 DM	12 bhp	1'4"		RG Shaw & Co for Budla Beta Tea Co Ltd (Assam India)
2596	08/1938	Std	0-4-0ST oc	14x22	3'6½"	Yard No 1596	Admiralty Royal Naval Cordite Factory Holton Heath Dorset
2597	10/1938	5'6"	0-4-0ST oc	15x20	3'6½"		Greaves Cotton & Co for Indian Army GHQ Simla, for Jupbulpore Factory GC (India)
2598	01/1939	3'6"	4-8-2T oc	16x24	3'6"	BON ACCORD	Baldwins [SA] Ltd for New Kleinfontein Co Ltd (Kleinfontein Mines Transvaal SA)
2599	10/1939	2'0"	4-4-0T oc	10x15	2'6"	W.J.MIRRLEES	A&H MacNay for Tongaat Sugar Co Ltd (Tongaat Estate) Natal South Africa
2600-1	5-6/1939	2'6"	4-6-4 + bg ten oc	15x18	3'6"	(9 & 39)	Barsi Light Railway Co Ltd London shipped to Bombay India
2602	02/1939	Std	0-4-0ST oc	12x18	3'0½"	(No 18)	Admiralty HM Dockyard Portsmouth (Hants')
2603	03/1939	2'5½"	0-6-0T oc	8¼x12	1'11⅝"	BRETON	L Mitchell & Co (for Alma Sugar Estate) Mauritius
2604-5	7-8/1939	Std	0-6-0ST oc	16x22	3'6½"	BUTTERLEY No 30: BUTTERLEY NO 31	Butterley Co Ltd (Summit Colly Kirkby 2604; Ollerton Colly Notts' 2605)
2606	09/1939	Std	0-4-0ST oc	15x22	3'6½"	HAIG	War Office Royal Arsenal Woolwich (London)
2607	10/1939	Std	0-4-0ST oc	15x22	3'6½"	BUTTERLEY No 50	Butterley Co Ltd (Bailey Brook Colliery Ripley Derbys')
2608-10	6-7/1940	5'6"	4-8-0 + bg ten oc	17x22	4'0"	334 - 336	Crown Agents for Ceylon Government Railways shipped to Colombo
2611	11/1939	3'6"	0-6-2T oc	15x22	3'3"	No 1	Mufulira Copper Mines Ltd (Northern Rhodesia) ship via Biera to In Bond n' dola
2612	11/1939	Std	0-4-0ST oc	12x18	3'0½"	ATLANTIC WORKS	George Richards & Co Ltd Broadheath Altringham Manchester
2613	09/1940	Std	0-6-0PT oc	13x18	2'11½"		Admiralty Machinery Depot California Works Stoke-on-Trent Staffs'
2614-6	9-11/1940	Std	0-6-0PT oc	13x18	2'11½"		Admiralty HM Dockyard Rosyth Scotland Names: No 4 FIFE: No 7 FORTH: No 8 CALEDONIA
2617	10/1940	metre	0-6-0PT oc	13x18	2'11½"	No 21	ETI Bank for Eregli Kozmurlerli Isletmesi shipped to Zonguldak Turkey
2618	06/1940	2'0"	0-4-0WT oc	6½x9	1'8"	G.C.G.D No 5	Glasgow Corporation Gas Dept' Dalmarnock Gas Works Glasgow
2619	04/1940	Std	0-4-0ST oc	15x22	3'6½"	BUTTERLEY No 51	Butterley Co Ltd (Ollerton Colliery Notts')
2620	04/1940	Std	0-4-0ST oc	15x22	3'6½"	No 1	ICI Ltd Middleton Works Heysham Harbour (Lancs')
2621	09/1940	Std	0-6-0ST oc	16x22	3'6½"	BUTTERLEY No 32	Butterley Co Ltd (Ripley Colliery Derbys')
2622	10/1940	Std	0-4-0ST oc	15x22	3'6½"	BUTTERLEY No 52	Butterley Co Ltd (Bailey Brook Colliery Derbys')
2623	11/1940	Std	0-4-0ST oc	15x22	3'6½"	HAWARDEN	Shelton Iron Steel & Coal Co Ltd Etruria Stoke-on-Trent (Staffs')
2624	08/1940	2'6"	0-6-2T oc	10x15	2'3"	SUPERB	Edward Lloyd Ltd Sittingbourne (Kent)
2625-6	5-9/1943	metre	2-8-2 + bg ten oc	19x24	4'0"	(1 - 2)	MofS War Dept' India Stores Dept', loan Bombay Baroda & Central India Rly
2527	02/1941	2'0"	4-4-0T oc	10x15	2'6"	A. BOULLE	Tongaat Sugar Co Ltd (Tongaat Estate) Natal South Africa
2628	02/1941	2'3½"	0-6-2T + 6wl ten oc	10x12	2'0"	S.L. No 4	Guthrie & Co Ltd Dorking agents Uli Remis (Rubber) Estate Malay ship to Singapore
2629	02/1941	Std	0-6-0ST oc	15x22	3'4½"	STAVELEY	Staveley Coal & Iron Co Ltd (Pilton Ironstone Mines) Luffenham Northants'
2630-2	12/40-3/41	Std		17x24	3'9"	No 11 - No 13	Guest Keen & Baldwins I&S Co Ltd Margam I&S Wks' Port Talbot Glamorgan
2633-5	12/1943	metre	4-4-0 + 6wl ten oc	14x20	4'5½"	012 - 014	Robert White & Partners for Jaipur State Railway India shipped to Bombay
2636		1'6"	0-4-0ST oc	7x12	1'9½"		War Office Royal Arsenal Woolwich - not proceeded with parts used on 2841
2637-8	11/41-1/42	1'11⅝"	2-8-2T oc	13x16	2'6"	No 40 AMBOIM: No 41 CUANZA-SUL	Engineering Co of Portugal for Cia do Caminho de Ferro du Amboim Portuguese West Africa
2639-42	5-6/1941	metre	0-6-0PT oc	13x18	2'11½"	No 22 - No 25	ETI Bank for Eregli Kozmurlerli Isletmesi Zonguldak Turkey
2643	9/1941	Std	0-6-0PT oc	13x18	2'11½"	73	MofS War Office for Meole Brace Shropshire
2644		metre	4-6-0 + 6wl ten oc	16½x22	4'9"		Jamnagar & Dwarka Railway India - not proceeded with
2645-6	11/1941	metre	0-6-0PT oc	13x18	2'11½"	10T -11T	Robert White & Partners for Jaipur State Railway India shipped to Bombay
2647	04/1942	2'0"	4-4-0T oc	10x15	2'6"	EDWARD SAUNDERS	Tongaat Sugar Co Ltd (Tongaat Estate) Natal South Africa
2648	12/1941	Std	0-4-0ST oc	14½x22	3'6½"	R.O.F. 18 No 2	MofS Royal Ordnance Factory Burghfield Reading Barks'
2649	12/1941	Std	0-4-0ST oc	14½x22	3'6½"	R.O.F. 16 No 3	MofS Royal Ordnance Factory Elstow Bedford
2650	12/1941	Std	0-4-0ST oc	14½x22	3'6½"	R.O.F. 14 No 1	MofS Royal Ordnance Factory Ruddington Notts'
2651	12/1941	Std	0-4-0ST oc	14½x22	3'6½"	R.O.F. 10 No 2	MofS Royal Ordnance Factory Rearsby Leics'
2652	01/1942	Std	0-4-0ST oc	14½x22	3'6½"	R.O.F. 10 No 1	MofS Royal Ordnance Factory Rearsby Leics'
2653	09/1942	Std	0-4-0ST oc	14½x22	3'6½"	R.O.F. 15 No 2	MofS Royal Ordnance Factory Bescot Staffs'
2654	02/1942	Std	0-6-0ST oc	15x22	2'3½"	CHERWELL	Parkgate Iron & Steel Co Ltd Charwelton Ironstone Mines Northants'
2655	02/1942	Std	0-6-0ST oc	15x22	2'3½"	BYFIELD No 2	Parkgate Iron & Steel Co Ltd Byfield Quarries Northants'
2656	02/1942	Std	0-4-0ST oc	8x12	2'0½"	OW 6	Oxford & District Gas Co Oxford Gas Works
2657-8	03/1942	Std	0-4-0ST oc	12x18	2'9"	No 7 - No 8	Gas Light & Coke Co Ltd Beckton Gas Works London
2659	04/1942	Std	0-4-0ST oc	12x18	2'9"	PARKGATE No 5	Parkgate Iron & Steel Co Ltd Parkgate Works Rotherham
2660	04/1942	Std	0-4-0ST oc	14x22	3'6½"	MOS SPROTBOROUGH No 1	HA Brassert Co Ltd contr' ROF Sprotborough New Factory Doncaster Yorks'
2661	04/1942	Std	0-4-0ST oc	14x22	3'6½"	VICTORY	Wolverhampton Gas Co (Wolverhampton) Staffs'
2662	06/1942	2'0"	0-4-0WT oc	6½x9	1'8"	G.C.G.D. No 9	Glasgow Corporation Gas Dept' Tradeston Gas Works Glasgow
2663	06/1942	Std	0-4-0ST oc	12x18	3'0½"	BRAFOS No 1	Bradley & Foster Ltd Darlaston (Green Blast Furnaces Staffs')
2664	06/1942	Std	0-4-0ST oc	12x18	3'0½"	S.D.F. No 1	Smethwick Drop Forgings [Kidderminster] Ltd Kidderminster (Worcs')
2665	05/1942	Std	0-4-0ST oc	14x22	3'6½"	GENERAL WADE HAYES	Edmundson Electricity Corp' Ltd (Little Barford Power Stn, Beds')
2666	05/1942	Std	0-4-0ST oc	14x22	3'6½"	No 4	ICI Ltd Middleton Works (Heysham Harbour) Lancs'
2667	05/1942	Std	0-4-0ST oc	14x22	3'6½"	JENNIFER	ICI Ltd Prudhoe Works Northumberland (destinations 2666-7 may have been reversed)
2668	5/1942	Std	0-6-0ST oc	15x22	3'4½"	CRANFORD No 2	Cranford Ironstone Co Lrd Cranford (Quarries Northants')
2669-70	07/1942	Std	0-6-0ST oc	15x22	3'4½"	LAMPORT No 2: LAMPORT No 3	Staveley Coal & Iron Co Ltd Lamport Ironstone Mines Brixworth (Northants')
2671	09/1942	Std	0-4-0ST oc	14x22	3'6½"	No 3	Vickers Armstrong Ltd Elswick Works Newcastle-on-Tyne
2672	09/1942	Std	0-4-0ST oc	14½x22	3'6½"	Y.E.P. Co No 3	Yorkshire Electric Power Co Thornhill Power Station (Yorks')
2673	10/1942	Std	0-4-0ST oc	12x18	3'0½"	YARD No 1	Admiralty Director of Naval Contracts Royal Naval Stores Dept' Dunfermline (Fife)
2674	09/1942	Std	0-4-0ST oc	14x22	3'6½"	No 4	Coventry Corporation Gas Dept' (Foleshill Gas Works) Coventry
2675	11/1942	2'7½"	0-6-0T oc	8¼x12	1'11⅝"		Frank Ross & Co (agents) shipped to Mauritius
2676	10/1942	Std	0-4-0ST oc	14½x22	3'6½"	R.O.F. 10 No 3	MInistry of Works & Buildings ROF Machine Store Queeniborough Rearsby (Leics')
2677	10/1942	Std	0-4-0ST oc	14½x22	3'6½"	R.O.F. 16 No 6	MInistry of Works & Buildings ROF Machine Store Elstow Bedford
2678	10/1942	Std	0-4-0ST oc	14½x22	3'6½"	R.O.F. 18 No 3	MInistry of Works & Buildings ROF Burghfied Reading (Barks')
2679	08/1943	Std	0-4-0ST oc	14½x22	3'6½"	Y.E.P Co No 4	Yorkshire Electric Power Co Thornhill Power Station (Yorks')
2680	12/1942	Std	0-6-0ST oc	16x24	3'6½"	No 4	Birchenwood Coal & Coke Co Lrd Harecastle Sdgs (Kidsgrove Staffs')
2681	12/1942	Std	0-6-0ST oc	16x24	3'6½"	WILLIAM	Sneyd Collieries Ltd Cobridge Sdgs (Burslem Stoke-on-Trent Staffs')

Manu No	Date Desp	Gauge	Type	Cyls	Dwl Dia	Name/No	Purchaser/Destination
2682	02/1942	Std	0-6-0ST oc	16x24	3'6½"	PRINCESS	Ribble Navigation Preston Docks (Lancs')
2683-7	5-7/1943	1'11⅝"	2-8-2 + bg ten oc	15¾x17¾	3'1 13/32		MofS Vicicongo Railway Belgian Congo (Africa)
2698-2700		1'11⅝"	2-8-2 + bg ten oc	15¾x17¾	3'1 13/32		MofS Vicicongo Railway Belgian Congo (Africa) - not proceeded with
2701	08/1943	Std	0-4-0ST oc	14x22	3'6½"	SIR HOLBROOK	ICI (General Chemicals) Ltd Gaskell Deacon Works Widnes
2702	06/1942	Std	0-4-0ST oc	10x16	2'9¼"		Thomas Firth & John Brown Ltd MofS Factory Monk Bretton (Barnsley Yorks')
2703-4	12/1948	1'11⅝"	0-6-2T oc	10x14	2'2"		Sucreries et de la Raffinieree d' Egypt Egyptian Sugar Refineries
2705-6							Numbers blank in order books
2707-36		1'11⅝"	2-8-2 + bg ten oc	15¾x17¾	3'1 13/32		MofS Vicicongo Railway Belgian Congo (Africa) - not proceeded with
2737	11/1943	Std	0-4-0ST oc	12x18	3'0½"	V.L. 4	FH Lloyd & Co Ltd (James Bridge Steel Works) Darlaston Staffs'
2738	05/1944	Std	0-6-0ST ic	18x26	4'3"	5150	MofS War Dept' Steventon Berks'
2739-40	05/1944	Std	0-6-0ST ic	18x26	4'3"	5151-2	MofS War Dept' Long Marston Warks'
2741	06/1944	Std	0-6-0ST ic	18x26	4'3"	5153	MofS War Dept' Melbourne Military Rly Derby's
2742	06/1944	Std	0-6-0ST ic	18x26	4'3"	5154	MofS War Dept' loan to Shell Chemicals Ltd Thornton-le-Moors Cheshire
2743	06/1944	Std	0-6-0ST ic	18x26	4'3"	5155	MofS War Dept' Barby, near Rugby Warks'
2744-5	06/1944	Std	0-6-0ST ic	18x26	4'3"	5156-7	MofS War Dept' sent to France
2746	07/1944	Std	0-6-0ST ic	18x26	4'3"	5158	MofS War Dept' Hilsea Hants'
2747-8	7-8/1944	Std	0-6-0ST ic	18x26	4'3"	5159-60	MofS War Dept' sent to France
2749	08/1944	Std	0-6-0ST ic	18x26	4'3"	5161	MofS War Dept' loan to Ministry of Fuel & Power West Hallam Notts'
2750	09/1944	Std	0-6-0ST ic	18x26	4'3"	5162	MofS War Dept' Bramley Hants'
2751-2	09/1944	Std	0-6-0ST ic	18x26	4'3"	5163: 75164	MofS War Dept' Longmoor Military Railway Hants'
2753	09/1944	Std	0-6-0ST ic	18x26	4'3"	75165	MofS War Dept' Long Marston Warks'
2754	10/1944	Std	0-6-0ST ic	18x26	4'3"	75166	MofS War Dept' Barby, near Rugby Warks'
2755	10/1944	Std	0-6-0ST ic	18x26	4'3"	75167	MofS War Dept' loan to Ministry of Fuel & Power Hartley Main Colly' Northum'
2756	10/1944	Std	0-6-0ST ic	18x26	4'3"	75168	MofS War Dept' loan to Port of London Authority London Docks
2757	10/1944	Std	0-6-0ST ic	18x26	4'3"	75169	MofS War Dept' Kineton Warks'
2758	11/1944	Std	0-6-0ST ic	18x26	4'3"	75170	MofS War Dept' loan to Ministry of Fuel & Power Blaenavon Opencast Glam'
2759	11/1944	Std	0-6-0ST ic	18x26	4'3"	75171	MofS War Dept' Kineton Warks'
2760	11/1944	Std	0-6-0ST ic	18x26	4'3"	75172	MofS War Dept' Longmoor Military Railway Hants'
2761	11/1944	Std	0-6-0ST ic	18x26	4'3"	75173	MofS War Dept' loan to Ministry of Fuel & Power Manvers Main Colly' Yorks'
2762	01/1945	Std	0-6-0ST ic	18x26	4'3"	75174	MofS War Dept' Melbourne Military Rly Derby's
2763	01/1945	Std	0-6-0ST ic	18x26	4'3"	75175	MofS War Dept' Longmoor Military Railway Hants'
2764	01/1945	Std	0-6-0ST ic	18x26	4'3"	75176	MofS War Dept' Moreton-on-Lugg Hereford
2765-6	1-2/1945	Std	0-6-0ST ic	18x26	4'3"	75177-8	MofS War Dept' Longmoor Military Railway Hants' - later to France
2767	02/1945	Std	0-6-0ST ic	18x26	4'3"	75179	MofS War Dept' Queensferry Flintshire
2768	04/1944	Std	0-4-0ST oc	17x24	3'9"	No 6	Guest Keen & Baldwins I&S Co Ltd (Margam I&S Wks' Port Talbot Glamorgan)
2769-70	02/1945	metre	0-4-0ST oc	9x14	2'3½"	YARD No 1728: YARD No 1729	Admiralty Directory of Naval Contracts (Gibralter Dockyard)
2771	5/1944	Std	0-4-0ST oc	12x18	3'0½"	(YARD No 1)	Admiralty Director of Naval Contracts (Dumbarton Scotland)
2772	06/1944	Std	0-4-0ST oc	12x18	3'0½"		Admiralty Director of Naval Contracts (Llangennech Camarthershire)
2773-4	03/1945	Std	0-6-0ST ic	18x26	4'3"	75250-1	MofS War Dept' Longmoor Military Railway Hants'
2775	05/1945	Std	0-6-0ST ic	18x26	4'3"	75252	MofS War Dept' Barby, near Rugby Warks'
2776-7	05/1945	Std	0-6-0ST ic	18x26	4'3"	75253-4	MofS War Dept' Kineton Warks'
2778	5-6/1945	Std	0-6-0ST ic	18x26	4'3"	75255	MofS War Dept' Longmoor Military Railway Hants'
2779-81	6-7/1945	Std	0-6-0ST ic	18x26	4'3"	75256-8	MofS War Dept' Longmoor Military Railway Hants' (store WGB until 12/1945)
2782-94	7/45-2/46	Std	0-6-0ST ic	18x26	4'3"	75259-71	MofS War Dept' Longmoor Military Railway Hants'
2795-2804		Std	0-6-0ST ic	18x26	4'3"	71527-36	MofS War Dept' - order transferred to Andrew Barclay Sons & Co Lrd Kilmarnock
2805-14	12/43-4/44	2'6"	4-8-0 + bg ten oc	12x16	2'4"	91 - 100	Ministry of Supply for Sierra Leone Government Railway shipped to Freetown
2815	03/1945	Std	0-4-0ST oc	14x22	3'6½"	No 1	Wothington & Co Ltd Burton-on-Trent (Staffs')
2816-7	5-6/1945	Std	0-6-0ST oc	16x22	3'6½"		Butterley Co Ltd (Bailey Brook Colliery Derbys') Names: BUTTERLEY No 35: BUTTERLEY No 34
2818	08/1945	Std	0-6-0ST oc	16x24	3'6½"	No 17	Norton & Biddulph Collieries Ltd Ford Green Works Stoke-on-Trent Staffs'
2819-20	03/1946	2'0"	4-4-0T oc	10x15	2'6"	CHARLES WHYTOCK: EGOLOMI	A&H MacKay (Pty) Ltd for Tongaat Sugar Co Ltd (Tongaat Estate) Natal South Africa
2821-2	06/1945	Std	0-4-0ST oc	14x22	3'6½"	BAGNALL No 11: BAGNALL No 12	Staveley Coal & Iron Co Ltd Devonshire Works Staveley (Derbys')
2823	11/1945	5'6"	0-4-0ST oc	12x18	3'0½"		Admiralty Director of Naval Contracts Veyangoda Dockyard Colombo Ceylon
2824-5	02/1946	2'6"	0-6-2T oc	10x15	2'6½"		Anglo Iranian Oil Co Ltd shipped to Ahwaz Iran
2826	04/1946	Std	0-4-0ST oc	12x18	3'0½"	V 103	Frazer & Chalmers Engineering Works Erith (Kent)
2827	03/1946	2' 5½"	0-6-0T oc	8¼x12	1'11⅝"	ST. ANTOINE	A Gloster for Ireland Frazer & Co (St Antoine Sugar Estate) ship Pt Louis Mauritius
2828-9	11/45-4/46	Std	0-4-0ST oc	14x22	3'6½"	No 1 ANNE: No 2 MURIEL	North West MIdlands Joint Electricity Authority Meaford Power Station (Staffs')
2830-1	07/1945	2'0"	0-4-0+0-4-0T oc	9x12	2'0"	TUGELA: NONOTI	A&H MacNay (Pty) Ltd for Sir J L Hulett & Sons Ltd (Felixton Natal South Africa)
2832-7	12/46-5/47	metre	2-8-2 + 8 wl ten oc	17x23	3'7"	700 - 705	Crown Agents for Tanganyika Railways shipped to Dar es Salaam
2838-40	6-7/1946	Std	0-6-0ST oc	16x24	3'6½"		Ribble Navigation Preston Docks (Lancs') Names: ENERGY: PERSEVERANCE: ENTERPRISE
2841	10/1945	1'11⅝"	0-4-0ST oc	7x12	1'9½"		MofS United Nations Relief & Rehabilitation Association (UNRRA) ship to Yugoslavia
2842	07/1946	Std	0-4-0ST oc	14x22	3'6½"	2	City of London Electricity Supply Department Kent Electricity Power Co Littlebrook Power Station Dartford Kent
2843-4	09/1947	metre	4-6-0 + 6 wl ten oc	16½x22	4'9"	19 - 20	Wolf Barry Robert White & Partners for Jamnagar & Dwarka Railway (India)
2845-8	9-10/1946	metre	0-6-0PT oc	13x18	2'11½"	No 26 - No 29	ETI Bank-British Geco Engineering Co Ltd (for Eregli Kozmurlerli Isletmesi, Zonguldak Turkey
2849-50	04/1948	3'6"	2-6-2T oc	15x22	3'7"	No 41 - No 42	Crown Agents Nigerian Railways shipped to Apapa (original order for Bolivar)
2851	09/1947	Std	0-4-0F oc	1½x18	3'0½"		Prince Regent Tar Diltillers Ltd Silvertown London
2852-5	1-2/1948	metre	4-6-0 + 6 wl ten oc	15½x22	4'0"	94 - 97	Rendel Palmer & Tritton for Gaekwar's Baroda State RLy (India) shipped to Port Okha
2856-9	11/1948	2'6"	0-6-2 + 6wl ten oc	11½x15	3'0"	15 - 18	Rendel Palmer & Tritton for Gaekwar's Baroda State Railway (India)
2860-9	04/1948	1'11⅝"	0-4-0ST oc	4½x7½	1'3¼"	No 1 - No 10	British Geco Engineering Co Ltd (for Eregli Kozmurlerli Isletmesi Zonguldak Turkey)

Manu No	Date Desp	Gauge	Type	Cyls	Dwl Dia	Name/No	Purchaser/Destination
2870	07/1948	2'0"	0-4-2T oc	9x14	2'3½"	(No 1)	Baldwins (SA) Ltd for Rustenburg Platinum Mines Ltd (Transvaal South Africa)
2871	12/1947	Std	0-4-0F oc	18½x18	3'0½"	BADGEWORTH HALL	Gloucester Carriage & Wagon Co Ltd Gloucester
2872-5	2-3/1949	metre	4-6-2 + 6wl ten oc	15x22	4'0"	28 - 31	Sir Bruce White Wolf Barry & Partners for Morvi Railway India
2876-8	4-5/1949	metre	4-6-0 + 6 wl ten oc	16¾x22	4'0"	25 - 27	Greaves Cotton & Co Ltd for Mewar State Railway (India)
2879	10/1948	Std	0-4-0ST oc	14½x22	3'6½"	COMET	Thurrock Chalk & Whiting Co Ltd West Thurrock (Essex)
2880-7	4-6/1948	Std	2-4-2T oc	13½x20	3'8"	1121 - 1126: 1146 - 7	Egyptian Govt' for Egyptian State Railways
2888-9	08/1950	2'5½"	2-8-2 + bg ten oc	15x20	3'0"	2003 - 2004	Egyptian State Railways for Western Oases Railway
2890	06/1949	2'5½"	0-4-0ST oc	7x12	1'9½"	HCB	United Africa Co Ltd (Huileries du Congo Belge Belgian Congo Alberta New Mill)
2891-3	11-12/1948	Std	0-6-0ST oc	16x24	3'6½"		Ribble Navigation Preston Docks (Lancs') Names: PROGRESS: COURAGEOUS: CONQUEROR
2894	07/1948	2'5½"	0-6-0T oc	8¼x12	1'11⅝"	BELLE VIEW	A Gloster & Co (for Belle View Sugar Estate) shipped to Mautitius
2895	07/1948	2'0"	0-4-2T oc	9x14	2'3½"	(No 2)	Baldwins (SA) Ltd for Rustenburg Platinum Mines Ltd (Transvaal South Africa)
2896	07/1948	2'0"	0-4-2T oc	9x14	2'3½"		McLeod & Co Ltd for Golapara Forest Tramway (Assam) India
2897	07/1948	2'0"	0-4-2T oc	9x14	2'3½"		McLeod & Co Ltd for Divisional Forest Officer Kachugaon Division (Assam) India
2898	09/1948	Std	0-4-0F oc	18½x18	3'0½"		Sir Alexander Gibb & Partners for Paton & Baldwins Ltd Darlington (Durham)
2899-00	10/1949	2'6"	4-6-0 + 6wl ten oc	12x20	3'3"	(No 9 - No 10)	Greaves Cotton & Co Ltd for Cutch State Railway India
2901-2	10-11/1950	metre	2-6-2T oc	16x22	3'7"	(150 -151)	Crown Agents for Tanganyika Railway
2903-6	4-5/1950	2'0"	2-8-2 + bg ten oc	13½x18	2'9"	11: 13-15	Capt' ST Binstead Mysore Iron & Steel Works (Bhadravati) Mysore India
2907	10/1949	Std	0-4-0ST oc	16x24	3'6½"	D.N.T.	Staveley Coal & Iron Co Ltd Foundry A (Devonshire Works) Staveley (Derbys')
2908	12/1947	Std	0-4-0ST oc	14x20	3'6"	BERRY HILL No 3	NCB Berry Hill Colliery Stoke-on-Trent (Staffs') Rebuild of 1584 to order No 4723
2909	11/1949	3'6"	0-6-2T oc	15x22	3'3"		Mufulira Copper Mines Ltd (Northern Rhodesia)
2910-59	7/49-7/54	Std	0-6-0PT oc	17½x24	4'7½"	8400 - 8449	The Railway Executive BR Western Region delivered to Swindon (Wilts')
2960		2'6"	2-6-4T oc	11x16	2'9¼"		Jaynagar Janakpur Railway Nepal - not proceeded with
2961	06/1950	Std	0-4-0ST oc	14½x22	3'6½"	CHISLET No 2	National Coal Board Chislet Colliery Sturry near Canterbury (Kent)
2962	07/1950	Std	0-4-0ST oc	14½x22	3'6½"	No 19	Admiralty HM Dockyard Devonport (Plymouth)
2963	10/1950	Std	0-4-0ST oc	14½x22	3'6½"	(No 5)	Courtaulds Ltd Greenfield Works Holywell (Flint)
2964-70	10/51-3/52	metre	4-6-0 + 6 wl ten oc	15½x22	4'0"	(98 - 104)	Rendel Palmer & Tritton for Gaekwar's Baroda State Rly (India)
2971	10/1951	Std	0-6-0DE	355 bhp	4'0"	(MONTGOMERY OF ALEMEIN)	Lever Brothers Ltd (Port Sunlight Cheshire)
2972-4	8/52-7/53	Std	0-6-0DE	355 bhp	4'0"	713: 711: 712	Steel Company of Wales Abbey Works (Port Talbot Glamorgan)
2975-6		Std	0-6-0DE	355 bhp	4'0"		Stock Order not procceeded with
2977-86	6-12/52	2'6"	2-6-2 + 6wl ten oc	12x18	2'10"	78 - 97	Rendel Palmer & Tritton for Gaekwar's Baroda State Rly (India)
2987-8	11/1950	metre	0-8-0T oc	14½x18	3'3"	BARREIROS: RIO FORMOSO	Henry Rogers & Co Ltd (Cia Acucareira Santo Andre do Rio Una) Pernambuco (Brazil)
2989	04/1951	Std	0-4-0F oc	18½x18	3'0½"	HUNCOAT No 1	British Electricity Authority Huncoat Generating Station Accrington (Lancs')
2990	04/1951	Std	0-4-0F oc	18½x18	3'0½"	WESTWOOD No 1	British Electricity Authority Westwood Generating Station (Wigan Lancs')
2991	09/1950	Std	0-6-0ST oc	16x24	3'6½"	No 1	NCB Florence Colliery (Longton Stoke-on-Trent)consign to Trentham Staffs'
2992	08/1950	Std	0-6-0ST oc	16x24	3'6½"	No 3	NCB Deep Pit Unit consign to Cobridge (Stoke-on-Trent) Staffs'
2993	11/1950	Std	0-4-0ST oc	16x24	3'6½"	No 4	Glasgow Corp' Gas Dept' Dawsholme Gas Works Glasgow
2994-6	2-3/1951	Std	0-6-0ST oc	18x26	4'3"	401 - 403	Steel Company of Wales Margam Works Port Talbot (Glamorgan)
2997-9		metre	2-6-2 + 6wl ten oc	13x16	3'6½"		Crown Agents North Borneo Railway - not proceeded with
3000-3	2-6/1951	Std	0-6-0DE	480 bhp	4'0"	701 - 703: TROSTRE No 1	Steel Company of Wales Abbey Works: 3003 Trostre Works
3004-9	6-8/1951	5'6"	4-8-0 + bg ten oc	17x22	4'0"	357 - 362	Crown Agents for Ceylon Government Railways
3010-12		3'6"	4-8-2T oc	15x22	3'3"		Nyasaland Railways - not proceeded with
3013	02/1952	metre	0-4-0ST oc	12x18	2'9½"	HUGH F MARRIOTT	ICI Ltd Magadi Soda Co Ltd (Lake Magadi Kenya)
3014-5	06/1953	2'0"	0-4-0+0-4-0T oc	9x12	2'0"	MBOZAMA: SINKWAZI	A&H MacNay (Pty) Ltd for Sir J L Hulett & Sons Ltd (Felixton Estate) Natal South Africa
3016-8	04/1952	2'0"	4-4-0T oc	10x15	2'6"	No 1 - No 3	Greaves Cotton & Co Ltd for Phalton Sugar Works Ltd Phalton (near Poona) India
3019	05/1952	Std	0-6-0F oc	20x18	3'0½"	No 5	Shell Refining & Marketing Co Ltd (Middleton Works Heysham Lancs')
3020-1	02/1952	Std	0-6-0DE	355 bhp	4'0"	5 - 6	Consett Iron Co Ltd Consett Durham
3022	08/1953	Std	0-4-0F oc	18½x18	3'0½"	HUNCOAT No 2	British Electricity Authority Huncoat Generating Station (Accrington Lancs')
3023	03/1953	2'0"	0-4-2T oc	9x14	3'0½"		Baldwins (SA) Ltd for Rustenburg Platinum Mines Ltd (Transvaal South Africa)
3024	07/1953	2'6"	0-4-0+0-4-0T oc	9x12	2'0"	MONARCH	Bowaters Lloyd Pulp & Paper Mills Ltd Sittingbourne (Kent)
3025-49	11/52-10/55	5'6"	AIA-AIADE	1000 bhp	3'7"	539 - 563	Crown Agents Ceylon Government Railways mech pts only supplied to Brush
3050	03/1953	2'0"	0-4-2T oc	9x14	2'3½"		Baldwins (SA) Ltd for Rustenburg Platinum Mines Ltd (Transvaal South Africa)
3051	11/1953	2'5½"	0-4-2ST oc	7x12	1'9½"	HCB	United Africa Co Ltd (Huileries du Congo Belge Belgian Congo Alberta New Mill)
3052	12/1953	2'6"	0-4-0T oc	7¼x12	1'9½"		Vizagapatam Port (India)
3053	10/1953	2'6"	2-6-2T oc	12x16	3'0½"	(BK 13)	McLeod & Co Ltd (for Burdwan Katwa Railway India)
3054-5	10-11/1953	2'6"	2-6-2T oc	12x16	3'0½"	(BDR 13: BDR 10)	McLeod & Co Ltd (for Bankura Damoodar River Railway India)
3056	04/1954	3'6"	0-4-0ST oc	14½x22	3'6½"	SALT RIVER	Merz McLellan Ltd for Salt River Power Station (Cape Province) South Africa
3057		3'6"	AIA-AIADE				Queensland Government Railway Australia - not proceeded with
3058	01/1954	Std	0-4-0ST oc	10x16	2'9¼"	ALFRED	Sellick Nicholls & Co Ltd Port of Par Cornwall
3059	01/1954	Std	0-6-0ST oc	16x24	3'6½"	FLORENCE No 2	NCB Florence Colliery Longton (Stoke-on-Trent) Staffs'
3060	02/1954	Std	0-6-0ST oc	16x24	3'6½"	SNEYD No 4	NCB Sneyd Colliery (Burslem Stoke-on-Trent) Staffs'
3061	10/1954	Std	0-6-0ST oc	16x24	3'6½"	NCB No 6	NCB Rawdon Colliery Leics'
3062	05/1955	Std	4wlDM	46 bhp	2'0"		Met-Vic Elec' Co Ltd Dukinfield Cheshire (rebuild of 2'6" gauge HE 2664/40)
3063-5	3-6/1955	Std	Bo-BoDE	460 bhp	3'6"	901 - 903	Steel Company of Wales (Abbey Works Port Talbot Glamorgan) mech pts to Brush
3066-72	12/54-6/55	Std	0-4-0DE	275 bhp	3'6"	501 - 507	Steel Company of Wales (Abbey Works Port Talbot) Glamorgan
3073-4	9-11/1955	Std	0-6-0DE	366 bhp	4'0"	CWM No1: CWM No 2	NCB Cwm Colliery (Glamorgan) South Wales
3075	11/1954	Std	0-6-0ST oc	16x24	3'6½"	BERRY HILL NO 4	NCB Berry Hill Colliery Stoke-on-Trent Staffs'
3076	09/1955	3'6"	0-6-0DM	240 bhp	3'3¾"		Russell Searle Ltd for Tasman Pulp & Paper Co Ltd Auckland New Zealand
3077-8	6-7/1955	Std	0-6-0ST oc	16x24	3'6½"	HEM HEATH No 1 HEM HEATH No 2	NCB Florence Colly - 3077: Hem Heath Colliery - 3078 (Stoke-on-Trent Staffs')
3079-88	7-10/1956	3'6"	0-6-0DM	240 bhp	3'3¾"	DS240 - DS249	High Commissioner for New Zealand for New Zealand Government Railways
3089		Std	0-6-0ST oc	16x24	3'6½"		Stock Order - not proceeded with (parts sold to NCB North Staffs Area inc boiler)
3090	01/1956	2'0½"	2-6-2T oc	12x16	2'7"	CAMPBELL	A&H MacNay (Pty) Ltd for Natal Sugar Estates Ltd (Natal South Africa)

Manu No	Date Desp	Gauge	Type	Cyls	Dwl Dia	Name/No	Purchaser/Destination
3091		Std	0-4-0DM	153 bhp	3'3¾"		Stock Order - not proceeded with
3092-3	12/56-2/57	Std	0-4-0DM	208 bhp	3'4"	NORTON 1D: NORTON 2D	NCB Norton Colliery (Ford Green Stoke-on-Trent) ordered for Lea Hall Colly
3094-5	01/1956	Std	0-6-0DE	370 bhp	3'6"	No 6 - No 7	Stewarts & Lloyds Ltd Corby Steelworks Northants mech pts to Brush
3096	03/1956	Std	0-4-0DE	275 bhp	3'6"	1	Steel Co of Wales Ltd Trostre Works (Glamorgan) mech pts to Brush
3097	03/1956	Std	0-4-0DE	275 bhp	3'6"	L.D. 1	Steel Co of Wales Ltd Velindre Wks (Camarthenshire) mech pts to Brush
3098-103	5-10/1956	Std	0-4-0DE	300 bhp	3'6"	508 - 513	Steel Company of Wales (Abbey Works Port Talbot Glam') mech pts to Brush
3104-5	03/1957	3'6"	0-4-0DM	153 bhp	3'3¾"	TR155 - TR156	Russell Searle Ltd for New Zealand Government Railways
3106-10	1-2/1957	3'6"	0-4-0DM	155 bhp	3'3¾"	TR150 - TR154	Russell Searle Ltd for New Zealand Government Railways
3111-13	2-3/1957	Std	Bo-BoDE	600 bhp	3'6"	951 - 953	Steel Company of Wales (Abbey Works Port Talbot Glam') mech parts to Brush
3114-5	10/1956	metre	0-8-0DM	234 bhp	3'0"	U.C.C 2401: U.C.C 2402	Railway Mine & Plantation Equip' Ltd (for cement factory in Bagdad) Iraq
3116		metre	0-8-0DM	234 bhp	3'0"		As 3114-5 Order Cancelled - not proceeded with
3117-8	05/1957	Std	0-6-0DM	208 bhp	3'4"	No 1 - No 2	NCB West Cannock Collieries - ordered for Hem Heath Colliery
3119	09/1957	Std	0-6-0DM	208 bhp	3'4"	HEM HEATH 3D	NCB Hem Heath Colliery (Trentham Stoke-on-Trent Staffs') ordered for Norton Colly
3120	11/1956	Std	0-4-0DE	275 bhp	3'6"	514	Steel Company of Wales (Abbey Works Port Talbot Glam') mech pts to Brush
3121	04/1957	Std	0-4-0F oc	18½x18	3'0½"		English Clays Lovering Pochin Co Ltd Plympton near Plymouth (Devon)
3122	04/1957	Std	0-6-0DM	308 bhp	3'4"	No 4	NCB Hilton Main Colliery (Staffs')
3123	11/1957	Std	0-6-0DM	308 bhp	3'4"	No 5	NCB Littleton Colliery (Staffs')
3124-5	12/1957	2'0"	0-6-0DM	204 bhp	3'0"	No 9 - No 10	Baldwins (SA) Ltd for Rustenburg Platinum Mines Ltd (Transvaal South Africa)
3126	07/1957	2'0"	2-8-2 + bg ten oc	13½x18	2'9"	No 15	Trade Agent Govt' of Mysore Mysore Iron & Steel Works (Bhadravati Mysore) India
3127-31	9/57-12/58	Std	AIA-AIADE	1250 bhp	3'7"	D5515-5519	BR Eastern Region mech pts' to Brush
3132	02/1958	3'6"	0-6-0DM	240 bhp	3'3¾"	No 10	Russell Searle Ltd for Wilsons (NZ) Portland Cement Co Ltd (Whangarei) New Zealand
3133		3'6"	0-4-0DM	155 bhp	3'3¾"	Stock Order - not proceeded with	
3134-6	3-5/1958	Std	0-6-0DM	208 bhp	3'4"	HEM HEATH 4D - HEM HEATH 6D	NCB Hem Heath Colly (Trentham Stoke-on-Trent) 3134 ordered for Norton Colly
3137-43	6-12/1958	Std	Bo-BoDE	460 bhp	3'6"	904 - 910	Steel Company of Wales Abbey Works (Port Talbot Glamorgan)
3144	05/1958	3'6"	0-6-0DM	240 bhp	3'3¾"	No 11	Russell Searle Ltd for Wilsons (NZ) Portland Cement Co Ltd (Whangarei) New Zealand
3145-6		metre	0-4-0DM	105 bhp	3'3¾"		Altos Hornes de Vizcaya Bilbao Spain - Order Cancelled - not proceeded with
3147	04/1959	Std	0-6-0DM	204 bhp	3'4"	WOLSTANTON No 1	NCB Wolstanton Colliery (Newcastle-under-Lyme Staffs')
3148	12/1959	Std	0-6-0DM	204bhp	3'4"	D1	Briton Ferry Steel Co Ltd (Albion Works Glamorgan) originally ordered for NCB Wolstanton
3149-50	02/1960	Std	0-6-0DM	204 bhp	3'4"	WOLSTANTON No 2: WOLSTANTON No 3	NCB Hem Heath Colliery (Trentham Stoke-on-Trent) ordered for Wolstanton
3151	02/1962	Std	0-6-0DM	204 bhp	3'4"		BP Grain Refinary Kent on hire; 5/63 British Waterways Sharpness Docks Glos'
3152	01/1960	2'0"	0-6-0DM	102 bhp	2'0"		Jacks Fencing Rhodesia Chrome Ltd Selukwe Rhodesia (rebuild of DC 2262/49)
3153		3'6"	0-6-0DM	240 bhp	3'6"		Wilsons (NZ) Portland Cement Co Ltd (Whangarei) New Zealand - Order Cancelled
3154			0-6-0DM	240 bhp	3'6"		Stock Order - not proceeded with
3155-9	2-4/1959	Std	AIA-AIADE	1250 bhp	3'7"		BR Eastern Region mech pts' to Brush
3160	10/1959	Std	0-6-0DM	304 bhp	3'4"		Mobil Oil Co Ltd Coryton Refinery Essex
3161	12/1961	Std	0-6-0DM	304 bhp	3'4"		NCB Aberaman Colliery (Glamorgan)
3162		Std	0-4-0DH	194 bhp			Stock Order - not proceeded with
3163-87	11/59-11/60	Std	AIA-AIADE	1250 bhp	3'7"		BR Eastern Region mech pts' to Brush
3188	01/1963	2'0"	4wIDH	64 bhp	1'6"	sold as Bagnall 3234/RSH 8430	Assam Railways & Trading Co Ltd Assam India
3189	/1963	2'0"	4wIDH	50 bhp	1'6"	sold as Bagnall 3237/RSH 8379	George Miller & Co (Private) Ltd for Sri Amritnargar Selected Collieries India
3190	11/1963	2'0"	4wIDH	93 bhp	2'0"		Ashanti Goldfields Corporation Ltd Gold Coast (Ghana)
3191	12/1961	Std	0-6-0DH	342 bhp	3'4"		NCB Aberaman Colliery (Glamorgan)
3192-203	12/60-8/61	Std	AIA-AIADE	1250 bhp	3'7"		BR Eastern Region mech pts' to Brush
3204	03/1961	2'0"	0-6-0DM	204 bhp	3'0"	No 11	Baldwins (SA) Ltd for Rustenburg Platinum Mines Ltd (Transvaal) South Africa
3205	/1961	metre	0-8-0DM	240 bhp	3'0"	U.C.C. 2403	Railway Mine & Plantation Equipment Ltd (agents for a cement factory in Iraq)
3206		Std	0-4-0DH	303 bhp			Stock Order - not proceeded with
3207	10/1961	Std	4wIDH	89 bhp	2'6"	LEYS	Leys Malleable Castings Co Ltd Derby
3208	11/1961	Std	4wIDH	89 bhp	2'6"	BAGNALL	Harrison & Co Ltd Lincoln
3209-11	/1962	Std	0-4-0DH	179 bhp	3'4"	No 8 - 10	War Dept' Royal Ordnance Factory Pembrey Carmarthenshire (RSH 8364-6)
3212-3	/1962	Std	0-4-0DH	262 bhp	3'4"	HENGIST: HORSA	CEGB Richborough Power Station Kent (RSH 8367-8)
3214-7	8-10/1961	Std	AIA-AIADE	1250 bhp	3'7"		BR Eastern Region mech pts' to Brush
3218	10/1961	Std	AIA-AIADE	1950 bhp	3'7"	D5845	BR Eastern Region mech pts' to Brush
3219	/1962	5'6"	0-4-0DH	107 bhp	2'9"		Lummus & Co Ltd India (built RSH 7903 'Husky' design)
3220-1	11/1962	3'6"	0-6-0DH	342 bhp	3'4"	101 - 102	Nyasaland Railways (Malawi - built RSH 8369-70)
3222-7	10/62-2/63	3'6"	0-6-0DH	342 bhp	3'4"	100 - 105	Sudan Railways Sudan (built RSH 8371-6)
3228	05/1962	Std	0-4-0DH	262 bhp	3'4"		British Petroleum Co Ltd Baglan Bay Glamorgan (built RSH 8377)
3229-32	/1962	5'6"	0-4-0DH	107 bhp	2'9"	No 1 - No 4	Commenwealth Traders Ltd Gammon Pegson Pakistan (built RSH 'Husky' design)
3233	/1962	700m/m	0-6-2 + 6wl ten oc	10x12	2'0"		N.V. Voorheen Ruhaak & Co for Indonesia (built AB 2377)
3234	/1962	2'0"	4wIDH	64 bhp	1'6"		Built by Bagnall as 3188 and sold by RSH as 8430 - see above
3235	/1963	Std	0-4-0DM	107 bhp	2'9"	(RSH 'Husky' design)	Societe General Egyptian de Material de Chem der Fer (built RSH 8379)
3236	24/03/1963	Std	0-6-0DH	195 bhp	3'6"	(Drewry design)	CEGB Aberthaw Power Station Glamorgan (built RSH 8199)
3237	/1963	2'0"	4wIDH	50 bhp	1'6"	(sold as RSH 8379 - erected at RSH)	George Miller & Co (Private) Ltd for Sri Amritnargar Selected Collieries India
3238	/1963	2'0"	4wIDH	30 bhp	1'6"	(built RSH 8378)	George Miller & Co (Private) Ltd for Sri Amritnargar Selected Collieries India

0 365	/1897	Std	4wIE		2'7"	No 19	Elec' Const' Co Ltd Wolverhampton (for City of South London Rly) mech parts
0 371	/1897	Std	4wIE		2'7"	No 18	Crompton & Co Ltd (for City & South London Railway) mech parts
0 967	/1904	3'0"	4wIE OHW			No 2 HARWOOD	Ellis & Ward Hadfield mech parts (for Woodhead Valley Res' const' Tintwistle)
0 605	/1906	Std	4wIE OHW		2'9"		British Westinghouse mech parts (for Neptune Bank Power Stn Wallsend)
0 54 (2)	/1907	Std	4wIE OHW		3'0½"		British Westinghouse for Great Cobar (Mines Ltd New South Wales Australia)
0 245 (3)	/1908	metre	Bo-BoE OHW		2'9"	No 1 - No 3	British Westinghouse for Thamshavenbann (Trondheim Norway) mech parts
0 256	/1907	2'6"	0-4-0E OHW		2'4½"	No 3	British Westinghouse for Oakbank (Oil Co Lothian Scotland) mech parts
0 504	/1908	Std	4wIE OHW		2'3"		British Westinghouse mech parts (Dunstan Power Station Newcastle)
0 550	/1908	Std	4wIE OHW		3'0½"		British Westinghouse for Great Cobar (Mines Ltd New South Wales Australia)
0 47(2)	/1910	metre	4wIE OHW		2'4½"		Siemens Bros Ltd for Mysore Gold Mining Co (Mysore India)

Manu No	Date Desp	Gauge	Type	Cyls	Dwl Dia	Name/No	Purchaser/Destination
P 50	06/1912	2'0"	0-4-0PM	20 bhp	1'3¼"		Eastern Assam Oil Co Ltd Babjan Tea Plantation Assam India
P 51	06/1913	1'11⅝"	0-4-0PM	40 bhp	1'7"	MARIA	Gloag & Sommers Glasgow agents shipped to Philippines
P 52	08/1912	1'11⅝"	0-4-0PM	20 bhp	1'3¼"	ESTELLA	George Wilson Glasgow agents shipped to Philippines
O 4397-9	1-7/1917	2'0"	0-4-0PE	40 bhp	2'8"		Nasymth Wilson & Co Ltd 25 sets mech parts (Ministry of Munitions)

APPENDIX II

LIST OF PRINCIPAL LOCOMOTIVE DIMENSIONS

This list is divided into three parts, the first and largest covering steam locomotives, and the second tenders and the third those powered by other power, principally diesel. In the case of steam locomotives with tenders, the tender details are listed separately. The early locomotives are omitted because so few dimensions are known from the surviving records, and most of those that are known, appear in Appendix I. All the dimensions are given in imperial measures, liquid in gallons, heating surfaces and grate areas in square feet, boiler pressure in pounds per square inch, tractive effort in pounds, fuel capacity (except in the case of oil fuel) in cubic feet on the basis that one ton equals 45 cubic feet, and weights in tons and hundredweights. In the case of petrol and diesel engine locomotives power outputs are given as the engine brake horsepower (bhp), usually the manufacturer's quoted continuous rating. Engine manufacturers often quote in their specifications two horsepower figures; e.g. 50/57 - where 55 is the continuous rating and 57 a one-hour rating. The symbol / in a column means the dimension is not relevant to the locomotive concerned, while a blank means the dimension is unknown.

In view of the firm's extensive use of Baguley and Bagnall-Price valve gears, the opportunity has been taken to note for all the locomotives the type of valve-gear fitted. The abbreviations are: B - Baguley; BP - Bagnall-Price; MB - Modified Baguley; S - Stephenson; W - Walschaerts. With Bagnall-Price gear the addition of the word inside, means the gear was completely between the frames on an inside-cylinder locomotive (in fact only one locomotive - number 1941 - was so fitted), and where the word outside appears the entire gear was outside the frames using a return-arm for the primary motion, rather than an eccentric. In the case of Caprotti and Lentz poppet-valve valve-gears the full name is quoted.

A word or two about tractive effort may not go amiss, especially for the non-engineers among readers. While most builders and the main-line railway companies frequently quoted tractive effort as a measure of locomotive power, often rather naughtily for comparison purposes, as it can be a very misleading statistic. The figures quoted in the accompanying table are the maximum calculated tractive effort; that is the force a locomotive is capable of exerting at the treads of its coupled wheels from a standstill - it neglects any friction internal to the locomotive and it quickly reduces as speed increases.

Even so the figures quoted would only be possible in practice if the design of locomotive has the correct factor of adhesive weight to tractive effort - the factor of adhesion - which should approximate to a ratio of 4-3. If the adhesive weight is too light a locomotive will not be able to exert its calculated tractive effort, no more if rail conditions are such that the coefficient of friction is reduced. The figures quoted here are calculated using a mean effective steam pressure at 85% of boiler maximum working pressure. This was, latterly at least, the norm in the industry, although in its early days Bagnall often quoted figures at 75% of maximum boiler pressure. The difference between the two figures, maximum and mean, allows for thermal losses between the boiler and the cylinders, condensation, wiredrawing and a number of other factors. When the industry established the figure of 85%, it assumed that the maximum cut-off for steam entry into the cylinders would be 75% of the piston stroke, although it is doubtful if the quoted figures could be attained at much less than 90%. The continuous power of a locomotive is dependent on a host of other factors, that need not detain us here, but boiler capacity and steam raising efficiency along with the mechanical efficiency of the moving parts, frictional resistance etc., all have a part to play. Having said all this, at the end of the day, as a universally adopted measure by builders all over the world, the calculated tractive effort using the unit of measure in imperial pounds at 85% of boiler maximum working pressure was a universally adopted standard and is used here in good faith.

To save space in the first column, in the case of the locomotives listed below - the first one in each case - the additional locomotive numbers were to the same basic specification:

1411 - 1649/72/81/1702-3/5/19/1884/1959/2286

1420 - 1480-1/90/1596

1429 - 1486-9/1507-10/15-18/32/52-5/66/8-71/89-92/4/1630-3/ 1640-3/59-60/2-3/8

1436 - 1539/56-7/72-3/93/1661/4-7

1443 - 1610/51/87

1475 - 1635/44-5/55/70/4-7/1704/16-18

1482 - 1612-13/37/52-3/71/80

1567 - 1822/1908/10/42

1722 - 1844/68/86-8/1907/14-16/23/2066

1724 - 1791/3-6/1801-6/46-51/63/75-80/9-91/1934-6/82-3/6-7/
1998-9/2035-7/51/2512

1732 - 1821/52-3/5-7/92-4/1901/37-9/61-4/97/2004/10/38-40/52

1739 - 2055/64-5/2105-8/2143/63/2272/2369/2517

1807 - 1951/60

1829 - 2153/80/94/2218-9/33/54/8/2373/2470/2702

1862 - 2109/37

1873 - 2522/99/2627/47/2819-20/3016-8

1968 - 2138-42/95-6/2580-1/2856-9 (note: 2856-9 had
Walschaerts valve gear)

2042 - 2260-2/2341/2408-9/2414-5/2584-5

2054 - 2130-5/2214/2447-8/66/97/2890

2450 - 2588/92/2602/12/57-9/63-4/73/2737/71-2/2823/6/3013

2473 - 3022/3121

2586 - 2671-2/4/6-9/2701/2815/21-2/8-9/42/79/2961-3/3056

2680 - 3059-61/75/77-8

A lot of time and effort has been expended in compiling this list to ensure as far as possible its accuracy; it will not however be 100% accurate in some cases. Despite locomotives being of the same basic design and built to a similar specification, there will be minor differences in for example, weights, both empty and in working order, depending on any specific equipment fitted to meet a customers requirements, or because of items like cabs, chimneys and domes reduced in height to clear special loading gauges. The groupings of locomotives in these lists however, are against the locomotives concerned having been built to the vast majority of the same manufacturing drawings. Despite this, in some cases other external features might be quite different too. Nevertheless with the exception of weights and the odd half inch in cylinder and wheel diameters (with consequent different tractive effort figures), the dimensions quoted can be taken as accurate.

(i) Steam Locomotives

Manu No	Cyls	Dwl Dia	FWB	TWB	Ld Wl Dia	Tr Wl Dia	Valve Gear	Water Capy	Fuel Capy	HS Tubes	HS FB	HS Sup	HS Total	Grate Area	WP	TE	W in Wo
1392/1402	12X18	3'0"	5'6"	5'6"	/	/	S			326.6	46.40	/	373.00		140	8208	17-10
1354/1415/1536	5x7½	1'3"	3'0"	3'0"	/	/	S	130	2.00	55.4	12.60	/	68.00	2.00	140	1800	5-00
1408	6x9	1'8"	2'9"	2'9"	/	/	S	160	10.00	62	11.50	/	73.50	2.90	140	1758	5-15
1410/4	6x9	1'6"	3'6"	3'6"	/	/	S	140	7.50	63	13.00	/	76.00	2.90	140	2040	5-10
1411/32/59/1537/50/64/88	12x18	3'0½"	5'6"	5'6"	/	/	S	425	20.00	358	38.00	/	396.00	6.60	140	8568	17-15
1412/22/1679	9x14	2'7"	5'3"	9'3"	1'9"	/	S	290	48.00	206	28.00	/	234.00	5.70	140	4353	12-00
1416	6x9	1'6"	3'0"	3'0"	/	/	W	104	4.80	64	9.77	/	73.77	3.28	140	2142	5-10
1418/66	13x20	3'6"	7'0"	13'0"	2'6"	/	S	550	56.00	518	54.00	/	572.00	9.00	135	10449	23-00
1419	8x12	2'2½"	5'0"	9'6"	1'6"	/	S	250	32.00	162.8	28.08	/	190.88	5.30	140	3448	10-15
1420/3/6/33-5/47-52/67-74	8x12	2'0"	3'6"	3'6"	/	/	S	230	10.00	135.28	23.70	/	158.98	3.50	140	3808	10-00
1421/61/1511	5½x9	1'6"	3'3"	6'3"	1'0"	/	S	150	16.00	62.72	16.14	/	78.86	3.06	150	1928	6-00
1424	7x12	2'0"	4'6"	4'6"	/	/	B	190	15.00	110	20.00	/	130.00	3.75	120	2499	8-00
1425	4x6½	2'6"	/	7'8¼"	1'0"	1'0"	S	/	/	45.65	7.35	/	53.00	1.35	150	633	2-10
1427	12x20	3'0"	5'0"	18'0"	2'1"	2'1"	S	525	47.00	450	47.00	/	597.00	8.25	140	9520	22-00
1428/1611/1786/2166	7x12	2'0"	5'0"	5'0"	/	/	S	200	10.00	147	22.00	/	169.00	4.00	120	2499	10-0
1429-30/45-6/56-7/76-9	6x9	1'6"	3'0"	3'0"	/	/	B	104	5.00	80	9.00	/	89.00	3.28	140	2142	5-10
1431	8x12	2'6"	4'0"	7'0"	/	/	S	240	10.50	126.25	38.00	/	164.25	6.60	140	3264	10-16
1436-9/62-5/1505-6/12/38-9	5½x9	1'6"	3'0"	6'0"	/	9"	B 1556-7 S	104	7.00	80	9.77	/	89.77	3.28	140	1800	6-00
1439/60	5½x9	1'2"	2'9"	2'9"	/	/	MB	60	5.50	49.5	11.50	/	62.00	1.88	140	1700	4-5
1440/1686/1784	7½x12	1'9½"	5'8"	5'8"	/	/	S	205	18.00	128.25	21.00	/	140.25	4.00	150	4003	10-16
1441	8½x14	2'6"	4'9"	12'6"	1'8"	/	S	262	31.00	177.5	24.25	/	201.75	4.90	140	4012	11-10
1442	7x12	2'1"	2'9"	2'9"	/	/	S	180	8.00	113.7	18.00	/	121.70	3.20	140	2999	8-00
1443-4/85/92//1533/60/81	4½x7½	1'1¾"	2'6"	2'6"	/	/	MB	71	3.00	52	7.00	/	59.00	2.45	140	1623	3-0
1453/1575/84/1654/73	13½x20	3'6½"	5'6"	5'6"	/	/	S	550	24.00	500	50.00	/	550.00	9.00	140	10328	25-00
1454/1912	7x11	1'9½"	4'6"	8'0"	1'3"	/	B	215	18.50	110	21.65	/	131.65	3.85	140	2983	8-10
1455/1597/1608/85	8x12	2'0½"	4'0"	4'0"	/	/	B	240	14.00	147	16.00	/	163.00	4.25	140	3730	8-10
1458	8x12	1'9½"	7'6"	7'6"	/	/	B	240	23.00	147	16.00	/	163.00	4.25	140	4251	9-10
1475/91/1503/51/62/1614/8	7x12	1'9½"	3'6"	3'6"	/	/	B	190	7.00	118	12.50	/	130.50	4.00	140	3256	7-10
1482/93-6/1502/82-3/1609	10x15	2'6"	5'3"	5'3"	/	/	S	330	15.00	281	28.00	/	309.00	5.40	140	5950	14-10
1483/1636/46-8/1720-1	7½x12	1'9½"	3'6"	7'3"	/	1'1"	B	190	10.00	118	12.50	/	130.50	4.00	140	3730	8-10
1484	4½x7½	1'2"	2'6"	5'0"	9"	/	MB	60	4.75	52	7.00	/	59.00	2.40	140	1716	3-15
1497/1615-6/84	8x12	2'2½"	5'0"	9'6"	1'3"	/	B	260	25.00	160	26.00	/	186.00	5.35	140	3245	13-10
1499-1500	7x12	2'0"	3'0"	3'0"	/	/	S	160	6.00	106	18.00	/	124.00	3.25	140	2916	7-80
1504	10x15	2'7½"	4'9"	4'9"	/	/	B	285	17.00	300	31.00	/	331.00	5.10	140	5007	15-00

Manu No	Cyls	Dwl Dia	FWB	TWB	Ld Wl Dia	Tr Wl Dia	Valve Gear	Water Capy	Fuel Capy	HS Tubes	HS FB	HS Sup	HS Total	Grate Area	WP	TE	W in Wo
1513	10x15	2'6½"	7'6"	7'6"	/	/	B	500	30.00	300	24.00	/	324.00	6.00	140	6689	16-00
1514	11x16½	2'6½"	8'6"	8'6"	/	/	S	500	15.60	370	36.50	/	406.50	7.50	160	8902	19-00
1519-28/40-9/76-80/98-1607	9½x14	2'6"	8'6"	13'6"	1'9"	/	B 1519-28 S	300	20.00	224	30.00	/	254.00	5.00	140	5013	14-00
1530	8x12	2'3"	5'0"	5'0"	/	/	B	264	9.50	145.5	22.50	/	168.00	3.75	140	3385	10-0
1531/1650	7x12	1'9½"	3'6"	3'6"	/	/	B	200	3.95	147	25.67	/	172.67	4.81	150	3487	8-1
1534	7x11	1'10"	3'0"	6'3"	1'4"	/	S	200	16.00	110	21.00	/	131.00	4.00	150	3124	10-10
1535/59	5½x9	1'4"	3'0"	3'0"	/	/	B	80	5.00	63.6	16.14	/	79.74	2.85	140	2025	3-15
1558	6x9	1'7"	3'0"	3'0"	/	/	B	100	5.00	85.25	12.25	/	97.50	3.90	140	2030	
1561/1619	6x9	1'9½"	3'6"	3'6"	/	/	S	120	7.00	281	28.00	/	309.00	5.40	140	1836	7-4
1563	9x14	2'6½"	5'0"	5'0"	/	/	S	300		243	26.00	/	269.00	5.00	150	4740	12-10
1565/1774	8x12	2'2½"	4'0"	7'0"	1'4"	/	B	230		159	22.50	/	182.75	4.37	140	3445	10-10
1567/1638-9/57-8/1736-7	8x12	2'0½"	3'6	3'6"	/	/	S	200	10.00	135.28	19.80	/	155.08	3.67	140	3730	10-00
1574	8½x15	2'8"	4'6"	4'6"	/	/	B	230		196	31.00	/	227.00	5.00	150	4318	11-12
1585-6/1818-9	7x11	2'0"	3'9"	3'9"	/	/	B	150		126.5	17.00	/	143.50	3.25	150	2863	7-12
1587/1678/82-3/1749/1918	9x14	2'3½"	4'3"	4'3"	/	/	S	300	13.00	206	24.00	/	230.00	4.90	140	4907	11-10
1595	9x14	2'3½"	9'10"	9'10"	/	/	B	500		243	27.00	/	270.00	5.00	140	4907	14-5
1617	8x12	2'0½"	4'0"	7'6"	/	/	B	240	14.00	147	16.00	/	163.00	4.25	140	3385	9-10
1620-9/88-1700/6-15/71-3	8x12	2'3"	4'0"	13'0"	1'7"	1'7"	B	300	20.00	196.9	26.00	/	222.90	5.40	150	3627	12-6
1634	7x12	2'3"	3'10"	3'10"	/	/	S	150	8.00	128	18.00	/	146.00	3.40	140	2592	6-6
1669	9x14	2'3½"	9'0"	9'0"	/	/	S	300	13.00	206.26	24.24	/	230.50	4.90	140	4907	14-00
1701	7½x12	1'10½"	3'9"	3'9"	/	/	S	150	14.00	128	18.00	/	146.00	3.75	150	3825	
1722-3/48/67/82/99/1833/42	5x7½	1'3¼"	2'6"	2'6"	/	/	BP	70	4.00	60	8.00	/	68.00	2.70	140	1483	3-15
1724-31/40/54-6/63-6/88-9	6x9	1'6⅞"	3'0"	3'0"	/	/	BP	100	5.00	80	9.80	/	89.80	3.28	140	2043	5-5
1732-5/57-60/77-8/80/1820	7x12	1'9½"	3'6"	3'6"	/	/	BP	150	7.00	118	13.00	/	131.00	4.20	140	3256	7-15
1739/1811/82/99/1952/79/85	14x20	3'6½"	5'6"	5'6"	/	/	S	660	35.00	510	50.00	/	560.00	9.00	160	12683	24-14
1741-6/1967	11¾x16	2'9"	6'3"	13'1"	1'10"	/	S	/	/	378	40.40	/	418.40	7.60	180	10240	20-5
1747	8x12	2'6"	3'9"	3'9"	/	/	S	190	6.00	135	19.50	/	154.70	4.00	150	3264	9-14
1750-2/61/1978	9x14	2'3½"	4'6"	4'6"	/	/	BP	300	11.00	224.7	21.30	/	246.00	5.50	150	5258	12-14
1762/83/1906	9x14	2'3½"	4'0"	8'6"	1'4"	/	BP	300	18.00	216	23.25	/	239.25	6.00	150	5605	10-13
1768-70	4x7½	1'6"	3'6"	3'6"	/	/	BP	50	4.00	45	6.00	/	51.00	2.40	140	793	4-4
1775-6/2223-4	15x20	3'7"	11'0"	11'0"	/	/	S	720	60.00	653.25	65.25	/	711.50	14.00	160	14233	32-10
1779/1944	7x12	1'9½"	3'6"	3'6"	/	/	BP	150	7.00	128.5	17.00	/	145.50	3.50	140	3256	7-15
1781	5x7½	1'3¼"	2'6"	5'0"	0'9"	/	BP	60	4.75	60	8.00	/	68.00	2.70	140	1463	3-15
1785/1861	10x15	2'6"	8'0"	8'0"	/	/	BP	300	32.00	281	32.00	/	313.00	5.40	140	5950	16-10
1787	8x12	2'0½"	4'0"	4'0"	/	/	BP	200	7.00	147	16.00	/	163.00	4.25	140	3730	8-10
1790	6½x9	1'7"	3'0"	3'0"	/	/	BP	100	5.00	80	9.77	/	89.77	3.28	150	2552	6-10
1792/1832/40	7½x12	1'9½"	3'6"	7'3"	1'1"	/	BP	140	5.00	118	14.00	/	132.00	4.50	150	4003	8-8
1797	12x18	2'9¼"	8'6"	8'6"	/	/	BP	300	20.00	380	49.00	/	429.00	6.50	150	9939	20-0
1798/1859	10x15	2'6"	4'9"	4'9"	/	/	BP outside	300	15.00	262.5	36.00	/	298.50	6.30	150	6375	14-11
1800	9x14	2'3½"	4'0"	8'6"	1'7"	/	BP	300	18.00	216	21.30	/	237.30	5.50	150	5285	10-10
1807-10/25-8/36-8/60/71-2	9x14	2'3½"	6'6"	6'6"	/	/	BP	210	21.00	222.5	20.00	/	242.50	5.00	150	5258	11-17
1812-3	15½x24	4'6"	8'0"	20'0"	3'7"	3'7"	S	900	85.00	851.5	89.50	/	941.00	17.10	160	14522	45-13
1814-17	12x16	2'2"	5'0"	8'10"	/	1'8"	BP outside	120	25.00	470	30.00	/	500.00	7.00	140	9886	16-5
1823-4	11x15	2'7"	8'0"	8'0"	/	/	BP	300	28.00	338	25.30	/	363.00	6.50	150	7465	17-0
1829/69/74/83/1920/40/8/50	10x15	2'9¼"	5'0"	5'0"	/	/	BP	300	18.00	280.8	31.20	/	312.00	6.00	150	5752	14-13
1830-1/2461-3	12¼x18	3'0"	6'3"	6'3"	/	/	S	300	15.00	355	41.00	/	396.00	6.30	160	8929	17-0
1834-5/70	8x12	2'0½"	3'9"	3'9"	/	/	S	190	7.00	135.2	19.50	/	154.70	4.25	150	3734	9-5
1839/2656	8x12	2'0½"	5'0"	5'0"	/	/	S	240	14.00	147	16.00	/	163.00	4.25	140	3734	10-5
1841/1933/6/2230-2/53	11x16½	2'9¼"	10'0"	10'0"	/	/	S	550	35.00	326.9	42.50	/	369.40	7.13	150	7599	19-10
1843/1921-2	4½x7½	1'3¼"	2'6"	5'6"	/	1'1"	BP	70	4.00	52	7.00	/	59.00	2.40	140	1185	4-0
1845/85/1949	4½x7½	1'3¼"	2'6"	2'6"	/	/	BP	70	5.00	56.9	11.50	/	68.40	2.10	140	1463	5-15
1854/1902	7x12	1'9¼"	3'6"	7'3"	/	1'1"	BP	150	7.00	118	13.00	/	131.00	4.20	160	3763	8-10
1858	4½x10	1'8"	3'6"	3'6"	/	/	BP	50	4.00	43.92	11.28	/	55.20	1.90	120	1033	4-0
1862/1919/25/43/66/81/2034	8x12	2'0½"	4'0"	8'10"	/	1'7"	BP	240	40.00	165	25.00	/	190.00	4.40	140	3730	9-10
1864-5	8x16	2'3½"	4'6"	4'6"	/	/	BP	300	11.00	178	21.20	/	199.20	4.86	140	4431	11-7
1866-7	11¾x16	2'9"	6'3"	19'1"	1'10"	1'10"	W	550	20.00	374.5	38.90	/	413.40	7.60	180	10242	28-14
1873/1929/2287/342/74/471	9x14	2'3½"	4'0"	12'6"	1'7"	/	BP	300	28.00	216	21.30	/	237.30	5.50	150	5258	13-10
1881	15x20	3'6"	8'4"	19'2"	2'3"	/	BP	860	40.00	622	73.00	/	695.00	12.00	160	13660	36-0
1895/1947	7x12	2'0½"	3'6"	3'6"	/	/	BP	150	7.00	124	17.70	/	141.70	3.34	150	3060	7-15
1896-8/1913	5x7½	1'7"	2'6"	2'6"	/	/	BP	70	4.00	59.6	11.50	/	68.40	2.10	140	1174	4-0
1900	7x12	1'9½"	6'0"	6'0"	/	/	BP	150	11.00	115	13.00	/	128.00	4.20	150	3487	
1903-4	11x18	3'6½"	5'6"	14'0"	2'1¼"	/	W	600	80.00	390	50.00	/	440.00	7.50	180	7841	25-15
1909	8x12	1'9½"	4'0"	11'4"	1'3¼"	/	BP	220	28.00	178	21.00	/	199.00	5.50	150	4554	11-0
1911	10x15	2'6"	8'0"	8'0"	/	/	BP	215	18.50	110	21.65	/	131.65	3.85	140	5950	8-10
1917	8½x12	2'0½"	4'0"	4'0"	/	/	BP	196	5.25	160	21.00	/	181.00	3.40	150	4512	8-17
1926-8	6½x9	1'7"	5'9"	5'9"	/	/	BP	/	/	115	13.00	/	128.00	4.20	160	2722	6-10
1930-2/45	9x14	2'3½"	6'6"	6'6"	/	/	BP	210	23.00	211.5	29.50	/	241.00	5.00	150	5258	12-0
1941	7½x12	2'0¼"	3'8"	3'8"	/	/	BP	100	4.00	145	21.00	/	166.00	3.16	160	3785	7-12
1946	9x14	2'7"	5'0"	5'0"	/	/	BP	300	12.00	244	27.00	/	271.00	4.90	150	4664	14-0
1953	8x12	2'0½"	7'8"	7'8"	/	/	BP	200	21.00	165	30.00	/	195.00	5.90	140	3730	11-10
1955-7/80/2203	13x18	2'9¼"	8'6"	8'6"	/	/	BP	500	20.00	300	50.60	/	430.20	7.50	160	12442	22-2
1958/2243-4	13x18	2'9¼"	8'6"	8'6"	/	/	BP	500	20.00	380.2	50.00	/	350.60	10.00	150	11685	22-2
1965	11x16½	2'6"	9'0"	9'0"	/	/	S	/	/	326.95	57.70	/	384.62	8.75	160	9035	17-0
1968-76/90-5/2014-5/41	11x15	3'0"	7'0"	13'6"	/	2'0"	BP	/	/	442	47.27	/	489.27	11.50	160	6875	18-5
1977	13½x18	3'0½"	8'9"	20'9"	2'0"	2'0"	W	800	40.00	544.5	78.50	/	623.00	14.00	160	12223	31-0
1984/9/2375-6/2899-2900	12x20	3'3"	7'6"	16'6"	2'0"	/	W	/	/	433	75.37	/	508.37	8.00	150	9415	25-0
1988/2870/95-7/3023/50	9x14	2'3½"	5'0"	11'0"	/	1'7"	BP	480	30.00	281	36.50	/	317.50	7.65	160	5608	16-0
1993/2136	11x15	3'3"	6'6"	15'7"	2'0"	/	W	/	/	346	52.87	/	398.87	7.45	176	8166	18-10
2000-3/11-13/110-2201	14x20	3'7"	11'0"	11'0"	/	/	S	/	/	575	62.60	/	637.60	12.50	160	12393	23-10
2005	7½x12	1'9¼"	3'3"	7'0"	/	1'7"	BP	130	6.00	175	21.00	/	196.00	5.50	140	4259	9-5
2006-9/16-21/2256/9/2331	12x18	3'0"	7'0"	17'0"	/	2'0"	BP	800	60.00	496	47.27	/	543.27	11.50	160	9792	28-0
2022-33/2411-2/3053-5	12x16	3'0½"	6'11"	18'8"	2'0½"	2'0½"	W	500	40.00	500	50.00	/	550.00	11.90	160	8585	28-10

Manu No	Cyls	Dwl Dia	FWB	TWB	Ld Wl Dia	Tr Wl Dia	Valve Gear	Water Capy	Fuel Capy	HS Tubes	HS FB	HS Sup	HS Total	Grate Area	WP	TE	W in Wo
2042-50/3/69-80/7-98/2144-9	6x9	1'7"	3'6"	3'6"	/	/	W	100	5.00	80	9.00	/	89.00	3.25	150	2174	5-5
2054/6/8-60/3/7/81-6/99-104	7x12	1'9½"	3'6"	3'6"	/	/	W	150	7.00	115	13.00	/	128.00	4.20	150	3487	7-15
2057	14x20	3'6½"	10'10"	10'10"	/	/	S	670	80.00	510	50.00	/	560.00	9.00	160	12544	28-10
2062	9x14	2'3½"	4'6"	4'6"	/	/	W	300	11.00	224.3	21.30	/	246.00	5.50	150	5258	12-10
2068	8x12	2'0½"	4'0"	4'0"	/	/	BP	200	7.00	164.9	17.00	/	181.90	4.50	150	3997	9-5
2150-2/2210	13x16	3'0"	7'0"	20'0"	2'0"	2'0"	W	/	/	508	124.00	62	692.00	14.00	160	10200	27-10
2154-9/91/2207-9/45/354/410	7¼x12	1'9½"	6'0"	6'0"	/	/	W	150	20.00	115	14.00	/	129.00	4.60	160	3990	8-0
2160-2	7x12	1'9½"	6'0"	6'0"	/	/	W	/	/	115	14.00	/	129.00	4.60	160	3719	7-10
2164-5/79/251-3/322/38	13x16	2'6"	6'0"	17'9"	1'7"	1'7"	W	/	/	635	52.00	/	687.00	16.00	180	13790	30-0
2167-9/97/2221-2	13x18	2'9¼"	9'7"	9'7"	/	/	BP	500	30.00	420.2	52.75	/	472.95	9.60	150	11654	25-0
2170/98	9x14	2'3½"	5'0"	5'0"	/	/	BP	300	19.00	206	29.00	/	235.00	6.00	150	5258	14-10
2171-8/2229	12x18	3'0½"	5'3"	5'3"	/	/	S	550	16.00	448	46.00	/	494.00	7.50	160	9658	21-0
2181-90	6½x10	1'7½"	3'6"	3'6"	/	/	W	100	8.00	131	19.00	/	150.00	4.30	150	2725	5-18
2192	13x18	2'9¼"	7'0"	13'3"	/	1'10"	BP	500	25.00	498	47.00	/	543.00	11.50	160	12442	27-0
2193	17x24	3'9"	12'0"	12'0"	/	/	W	1000	60.00	855	81.00	/	946.00	15.00	160	20962	45-0
2202/2307-12/2332-7	15x23	3'6¾"	12'0"	12'0"	/	/	W	700	45.00	698	76.00	/	774.00	12.75	160	16463	35-0
2204-6	7¼x12	1'9½"	4'9"	4'9"	/	/	W	150	20.00	115	14.30	/	129.30	4.60	160	3990	8-0
2211-13/38-42/2321	13x18	2'9¼"	6'8"	17'11"	1'10"	1'10"	W	750	140 galls	520	50.00	/	570.00	11.50	160	10602	28-0
2215/7	9x14	2'3½"	4'6"	4'6"	/	/	W	300	14.00	206	24.00	/	230.00	4.90	150	5258	13-10
2216	18½x18	2'9¼"	5'6"	10'6"	1'10"	/	W	/	/	/	/	/	/	/	220/80	12599	26-0
2225-6	11½x16	2'9¼"	7'9"	7'9"	/	/	W	300	20.00	331	44.00	/	375.00	7.57	170	9187	21-5
2227-8	10x15	2'9"	5'0"	14'0"	/	1'8"	W	530	20.00	448	41.00	/	489.00	8.00	140	5409	21-2
2234	16½x22	4'9"	12'0"	21'1½"	2'4½"	/	W	/	/	695	107.00	180	982.00	15.40	160	14291	35-5
2235/46-9/63-71	17x22	3'7"	12'0"	20'6"	2'4½"	/	W	/	/	785	124.00	150	1059.00	16.80	160	20109	42-0
2236-7/84-5/2413	11x16½	2'6"	8'0"	8'0"	/	/	BP	420	45.00	312	42.00	/	354.00	6.30	150	8485	19-5
2250	18x24	3'3"	13'6"	13'6"	/	/	W	1200	60.00	900	123.00	/	10123.00	17.00	175	29658	55-0
2255	11x15	2'9¼"	6'0"	15'0"	2'0"	/	W	/	/	345	52.87	/	397.87	7.45	176	8186	18-10
2257/76-7	11x15	2'6"	5'10"	11'9"	/	1'9½"	W	500	70 galls	354	36.00	/	390.00	7.80	150	7510	20-15
2278-85	11x15	3'0"	7'0"	18'0"	/	2'0"	BP	750	80.00	448	65.00	/	520.70	14.80	160	6856	27-15
2288-302/43-52/8-64	18x26	4'7"	16'5"	16'5"	/	/	S	1200	45.00	970	110.00	/	1080.00	16.00	160	20830	50-0
2303	9x14	2'3½"	6'6"	6'6"	/	/	BP	236	21.00	223.5	20.50	/	244.00	4.50	150	5257	19-0
2305	14½x20	3'3"	13'3"	13'3"	/	/	W	880	50.00	584	87.00	105	776.00	13.00	180	16500	38-12
2306/2539-40	8½x12	2'0½"	4'0"	8'0"	1'4"	/	BP	260	10.00	138.5	28.00	22.5	189.00	4.40	150	4512	11-13
2313-20/65-70/849-50	15x22	3'7"	10'0"	24'0"	2'4½"	2'4½"	W	800	65.00	926	100.00	/	1026.00	12.75	180	17613	44-3
2323-7	13x20	3'3"	9'9"	15'7½"	/	1'11"	W	750	70.00	368	54.00	/	422.00	9.60	170	12523	30-0
2328-9/67-8/589/843-4	15½x22	4'9"	12'0"	21'1½"	2'4½"	/	W	/	/	960	103.00	/	1063.00	15.50	180	14300	34-0
2330/2538	12x16	2'4"	9'0"	16'0"	1'6"	/	W	/	/	635	54.00	/	689.00	12.00	160	11191	24-0
2339-40/71-2/2977-86	12x18	2'10"	6'7½"	19'7"	2'0"	2'0"	W	/	/	521	66.00	125	612.00	14.00	160	10368	28-15
2355-7	18½x24	4'0"	9'0"	9'0"	/	/	W	1000	I Ton Oil	1110	91.00	/	1201.00	18.50	180	26182	51-8
2366	9x14	2'3½"	4'6"	4'6"	/	/	W	/	/	/	/	/	/	/	220/80	2867	17-5
2370/2536	20x18	2'9¼"	10'0"	10'0"	/	/	W	/	/	/	/	/	/	/	250/80	14724	32-0
2377/2901-2	15x22	3'7"	11'6"	26'6"	2'4½"	2'4½"	W	1200	50.00	926	100.00	/	1026.00	12.75	160	17613	50-14
2378-80	13x16	2'6"	6'0"	17'10"	1'7"	1'7"	W	700	30.00	474	52.00	94	620.00	16.00	180	15700	37-4
2381-405/2422-46	17½x24	4'7½"	15'6"	15'6"	/	/	S	1200	40.00	1075.7	102.30	/	1178.00	15.30	200	22514	49-10
2406-7	11x16	3'0½"	7'0"	17'3"	1'10"	1'10"	W	436	45.00	281	42.00	/	323.00	6.00	160	7214	19-10
2416-21	15½x22	4'0"	12'0"	21'1"	2'4½"	/	W	/	/	1190	102.50	/	1292.50	25.50	180	16848	38-14
2449	9x14	2'3½"	6'6"	6'6"	/	/	BP	210	23.50	211.5	29.50	/	241.00	5.00	160	5600	12-10
2450-1/69/503-4/25/42/65/74	12x18	3'0½"	5'6"	5'6"	/	/	S	550	18.50	337	38.00	/	435.00	6.50	160	9675	22-0
2453-60	11x18	2'9"	6'6"	20'2"	1'8"	1'8"	W	/	/	530	62.00	130	722.00	12.30	180	10190	27-2
2464-5/81-4/2526-7	11½x18	3'7"	8'1"	19'9"	2'4½"	2'4½"	W	850	70.00	334	75.40	51	459.50	8.75	180	8460	34-5
2467-8/2475	11½x16	2'9¼"	7'6"	7'6"	/	/	W	500	45.00	375	39.00	/	414.00	7.13	180	9750	21-0
2472/2511/2624	10x15	2'3"	5'6"	11'6"	/	1'6"	S	420	40.00	280.8	46.00	/	326.80	7.65	160	7555	16-15
2473-4/2851/71/98/2989-90	18½x18	3'0½"	5'6"	5'6"	/	/	W	/	/	/	/	/	/	/	200/80	11400	27-0
2476-8	12x18	2'10"	6'7½"	19'7"	2'0"	2'0"	Caprotti	/	/	521	66.00	125	612.00	14.00	160	10368	28-5
2480/2505/23	9½x14	2'6"	4'9"	16'1"	1'9"	1'9"	BP	375	54.00	236	42.00	/	278.00	8.35	160	5728	18-15
2485-7	8x12	3'0"	5'6"	16'11"	2'0"	2'0"	Lentz	400	35.00	264.5	30.00	/	294.50	6.75	160	2900	18-10
2488-93/531-3/2852-5/964-70	15½x22	4'0"	11'0"	20'1"	2'4½"	/	W	/	/	655.28	75.85	123.12	854.25	18.25	160	14976	34-0
2495-6/2541/3052	7¼x12	1'9½"	4'9"	4'9"	/	/	W	150	20.00	113	15.00	/	128.00	4.20	150	4485	7-6
2500-2/48-9	15¾x22	3'7"	12'6"	19'6"	2'6"	/	W	/	/	888	100.00	176	1164.00	25.50	180	21980	44-10
2508/629/54-5/68-70	15x22	3'4½"	10'6"	10'6"	/	/	S	800	60.00	601	65.50		666.50	13.75	180	18700	39-0
2509-10/2987-8	14½x22	3'3"	12'0"	12'0"	/	/	W	750	40.00	207.75	72.50	/	280.25	15.50	180	16497	34-0
2513	10x16	2'6"	4'9"	16'6"	1'10"	1'10"	BP	500	27.00	375	38.00	/	413.00	7.72	180	8165	20-0
2515/2630-2/2768	17x24	3'9"	6'6"	6'6"	/	/	S 2515-W	1000	40.00	855	81.00	/	936.00	15.00	160	20962	43-0
2518-20	14½x22	4'0"	11'0"	20'0½"	2'4½"	/	W	/	/	935	87.00	9 arc tub	1031.00	20.70	180	14744	36-0
2528-9/2625-6	19x24	4'0"	13'5"	27'9"	2'4½"	2'4½"	W	/	/	1290	154.00	322	2066.00	32.33	180	27616	60-10
2534-5	16x24	3'3	12'0"	12'0"	/	/	W	800	60.00	795	105.00	/	900.00	13.00	180	24103	41-0
2537/97	15x20	3'6"	5'6"	5'6"	/	/	S	685	38.00	559	57.50	/	416.50	9.85	160	14571	25-15
2543	11½x15	2'6"	4'0"	13'6"	1'7"	/	BP	500	28.00	500	33.00	60	593.00	9.00	180	10117	21-5
2544	7¼x12(4)	2'0"	3'3"	16'3"	/	/	W	500	50.00	230	33.00	60	393.00	9.00	185	8606	24-0
2545/830-1/3014-5/24	9x12 (4)	2'0"	3'3"	18'3"	/	/	W	500	40.00	395.5	36.00	70	501.50	11.50	185	12400	28-13
2547	16x22	3'4½"	10'6"	10'6"	/	/	S	660	60.00	621.5	65.50	/	697.00	13.75	160	18912	35-6
2550-64/2880-87	13½x20	3'8"	7'3"	22'0"	2'7"	2'7"	W	1000	90.00	635.5	71.50	/	707.00	13.00	160	11266	42-10
2566	13x16	2'6"	6'0"	17'0"	1'7"	1'7"	W	675	30.00	474	58.00	94	620.00	16.00	180	13790	37-10
2571	20x18	2'9½"	10'0"	10'0"	/	/	W	/	/	/	/	/	/	/	280/80	15000	30-0
2572/3058	10x16	2'9½"	5'0"	5'0"	/	/	BP	300	18.00	280.8	31.20	/	412.00	6.00	160	6544	16-14
2575-6/82-3/98	16x24	3'3"	12'0"	29'0"	2'4½"	2'4½"	W	1200	70.00	1069	112.00	/	1181.00	17.00	180	24200	58-0
2586/91/6/648-53/60-1/5-7	14x22	3'6½"	5'6"	5'6"	/	/	S	660	36.00	498	52.00	/	550.00	9.00	160	13798	27-0
2587	18x24	4'3"	10'6"	17'0"	/	2'9"	W	1500	100.00	975	99.00	/	1074.00	18.00	180	23325	55-5
2590/606-7/19-20/22-3	15x22	3'6½"	5'6"	5'6"	/	/	S	920	36.00	550	54.00	/	604.00	10.00	180	17820	33-10
2593-4	11½x18	3'0"	7'3"	23'9"	2'0"	2'0"	W	1200	90.00	436.6	65.00	119.3	620.90	14.80	160	8993	36-0
2600-1	15x18	3'6"	8'0"	25'11"	1'11"	1'11"	W	/	/	813	75.00	177	1065.00	20.50	160	13114	35-15
2603/75/2827/94	8¼x12	1'11⅝"	4'7½"	4'7½"	/	/	BP	250	22.50	174	26.00	/	200.00	5.50	176	5172	8-5

Manu No	Cyls	Dwl Dia	FWB	TWB	Ld Wl Dia	Tr Wl Dia	Valve Gear	Water Capy	Fuel Capy	HS Tubes	HS FB	HS Sup	HS Total	Grate Area	WP	TE	W in Wo
2604-5/21/2816-7	16x22	3'6½"	10'6"	10'6"	/	/	S	1000	67.50	618.5	76.00	/	694.50	15.00	180	20275	42-1
2608-10/3004-9	17x22	4'0"	14'0"	23'8½"	2'6"	/	W	/	/	857	114.50	201	1272.50	23.50	180	20286	48-19
2611/2909	15x22	3'3"	8'0"	15'0"	/	2'4½"	W	800	60.00	795	105.00	/	900.00	13.50	160	17262	41-5
2613-7/39-43/5-6/2845-8	13x18	2'11½"	7'10½"	7'10½"	/	/	W	600	60.00	418	52.00	/	470.00	10.25	180	13114	28-5
2618/2662	61/2x9	1'8"	2'10"	2'10"	/	/	S	22	3.60	88	16.00	/	104.00	2.50	140	2262	4-0
2628/3233	10x12	2'0"	5'0"	10'8½"	/	1'7"	W	/	/	238	49.00	/	287.00	10.00	160	6800	15-0
2633-5	14x20	4'5½"	6'0"	15'5"	2'5"	/	W	/	/	398	58.00	66.5	522.50	12.50	150	9342	26-5
2637-8	13x16	2'6"	9'0"	20'10"	1'7"	1'7"	W	700	175.00	613	63.00	131	807.00	16.00	180	13790	42-0
2680-2/818/38-40/91-3/991-2	16x24	3'6½"	10'6"	10'6"	/	/	S	1000	67.50	713	79.50	/	792.50	15.00	180	22118	42-5
2683-7	15¾x17¾	3'1⅜"	11'9¾"	26'10⅞"	1/11⅝"	1'11⅝"	W	1122	/	869.73	97.95	/	968.00	24.22	170	17009	42-7
2703-4	10x14	2'2"	5'4"	11'0½"	/	1'7"	W	375	50 galls	281	49.50	/	330.50	9.70	170	7781	17-5
2738-67/2773-92	18x26	4'3"	11'0"	11'0"	/	/	S	1200	101.00	872.5	87.50	/	960.00	16.82	170	23868	48-4
2769-70	9x14	2'3½"	4'6"	4'6"	/	/	W	330		205	26.50	/	231.52	4.80	160	5608	13-15
2805-14	12x16	2'4"	9'0"	16'0"	1'6"	/	W	/	/	669	54.00	/	723.00	12.00	160	11191	24-10
2824-5	10x15	2'6½"	6'0"	12'4"	/	1'8"	W	520	200 galls	350	55.00	/	405.00	10.30	180	7524	24-15
2832-7	17x23	3'7"	12'0"	26'9"	2'4½"	2'4½"	W	/	/	1271	139.00	320.5	1730.50	27.00	180	23651	56-15
2841/2890	7x12	1'9½"	3'6"	3'6"	/	/	W	190	7.00	109.5	14.00	/	123.50	4.20	160	3720	7-15
2860-9	4½x7½	1'3¼"	2'6"	2'6"	/	/	W	70	4.00	57	11.50	/	68.50	2.60	170	1439	4-6
2872-5	15x22	4'0"	9'6"	25'8"	2'4½"	2'4½"	W	/	/	1078	127.00	286	1491.00	25.00	180	15778	45-0
2876-8	16¾x22	4'0"	11'0"	20'2"	2'40½"	/	W	/	/	888	100.00	176	1164.00	25.50	180	19674	41-6
2888-9	15x20	3'0"	10'3"	23'0"	2'0½"	2'0½"	W	/	/	876	67.00	/	943.00	15.00	160	17000	34-2
2903-6/3126	13½x18	2'9"	9'9"	20'7"	1'8"	1'8"	W	/	/	730	68.50	163	971.50	17.10	180	15210	34-5
2907	16x24	3'6½"	6'0"	6'0"	/	/	S	1000	45.00	713	79.50	/	792.50	15.00	180	22118	40-0
2910-59	17½x24	4'7½"	15'6"	15'6"	/	/	S	1300	40.00	1245.7	101.70	/	1347.40	17.40	200	22515	55-0
2993	16x24	3'6½"	6'0"	6'0"	/	/	S	1000	45.00	751	72.00	/	823.00	12.40	180	22118	40-0
2994-6	18x26	4'3"	11'0"	11'0"	/	/	W	1500	90.00	855	100.00	/	955.00	18.50	180	25272	55-10
3019	20x18	3'0½"	10'0"	10'0"	/	/	W	/	/	/	/	/	/	/	300/80	16053	34-0
3051	7x12	1'9½"	3'6"	8'3½"	/	1'4½"	W	190	7.00	136.6	25.60	/	162.20	4.28	160	3719	9-12
3090	12x16	2'7"	5'10"	17'7"	1'9"	1'9"	W	1000	54.00	495	51.00	/	546.00	10.00	180	11372	30-0

(ii) Steam Locomotive Tenders

Manu No	Wl Dia	FWB	TWB	Water	Fuel	WinWo	TWB E&T
1425	1'0"	3'0"	3'0"	66	3	2-0	13'0½"
1688-90/1771-3	1'7"	4'6"	4'6"	400	97	7-14	24'4½"
1741-5/1967	1'10"	4'1"	13'7"	1500	205	19-0	36'10½"
1792/1832/1840	1'8"	3'6"	3'6"	400	67.5	5-8	15'5"
1926-8	1'7"	3'0"	3'0"	300	150 galls	5-0	20'10"
1965	1'9½	7'6"	7'6"	800	150	11-10	24'5½"
1968-76/90-5/2014-5/41	2'0"	7'6"	7'6"	1000	95	10-19	27'1¼"
2138-42/95-6	2'0"	7'6"	7'6"	1000	95	10-19	27'1¼"
1984/9/2375-6/2899-2900	2'0"	7'3"	7'3"	1600	145	16-15	34'1"
1993/2136	2'0"	6'0"	6'0"	800	95	10-15	28'6"
2000-3/11-13/2110-29/99-2201	2'4½"	10'6"	10'6"	2000	180	23-0	31'2½"
2005	1'7"	3'3"	3'3"	400	87.4	5-0 approx	16'0"
2150-2/2210	2'0"	7'0"	7'0"	1300	90	14-0	36'6½"
2160-2	1'7"	3'0"	3'0"	454	261 galls	6-0	15'6"
2164-5/79/2251-3/2332/8	1'9"	3'6"	11'0"	1240	100	14-10	33'10½"
2234	2'4½"	12'0"	12'0"	2500	240	29-1	43'2¼"
2235/2246-9/63-71	3'7"	12'0"	12'0"	2650	202.5	29-5	42'2¼"
2255	2'0"	6'0"	6'0"	800	95	11-10	28'6"
2303	2'0½"	3'9"	3'9"	620	85	10-15	18'4½"
2328-9/67-8/2589/2843-4	2'4½"	11'0"	11'0"	2500	202	34-10	24'5"
2330/2538	1'6"	7'0"	7'0"	1100	135	11-10	31'4"
2339-40/71-2/2476-8	2'3"	7'0"	7'0"	1300	102	16-4	34'3½"
2416-21	2'4½"	11'0"	11'0"	2500	202	26-15	42'1¼"
2453-60	1'8"	3'9"	12'1"	1500	180	20-9	40'3½"
2488-93/531-3/2852-5/2964-70	2'4½"	11'0"	11'0"	2000	180	24-2	40'3¼"
2500-2/48-9	2'4½"	11'0"	11'0"	2500	202.5	27-0	42'1½"
2518-20	2'4½"	11'0"	11'0"	2200	180	24-10	44'1"
2528-9	2'4½"	5'0"	14'0"	3200	400	34-18	51'6½"
2580-1	2'0"	7'6"	7'6"	1200	115	13-5	27'4¼"
2600-1	1'11"	4'3"	13'0"	1700	215	23-0	44'8"
2608-10	3'0"	5'3"	15'3"	2700	180	35-19	48'3½"
2625-6	2'4½"	5'0"	14'0"	3350	400	40-10	51'6½"
2628/3233	1'7"	5'10"	5'10"	500	120	7-10	21'0"
2633-5	2'5"	11'0"	11'0"	3000	112.5	17'5	36'4¼"
2683-7	1'5¼"	3'9½"	11'7¼"	1100	247	13-4	47'7½"
2805-14	1'10"	3'9"	15'0"	1667	180	25-10	39'11¼"
2832-7	2'9½"	13'0"	13'0"	4200	250+530	32-10	49'4"
2856-9	2'3"	7'0"	7'0"	1400	135	17-0	28'5¼"
2872-5	2'4½"	11'0"	11'0"	2200	180	25-5	45'1"
2876-8	2'4½"	11'0"	11'0"	3000	225	29-4	41'9½"
2888-9	2'0½"	4'0"	12'0"	2000	750 galls	24-18	41'4"
2903-6/3126	1'8"	3'9"	15'6"	2800	122	24-0	44'3"
2977-86	2'3"	7'0"	7'0"	1500	135	17-15	34'0¼"
3004-9	3'0"	5'3"	15'0"	2700	180	36-11	48'2"

Abbreviations
(see also abbreviations on page 614)

Dwl	-	*Driving Wheel Diameter*
FWB	-	*Fixed Wheelbase*
TWB	-	*Total Wheelbase*
Ld Wl Dia	-	*Leading Wheel Diameter*
Tr Wl Dia	-	*Trailing Wheel Diameter*
HS	-	*Heating Surface - in square feet*
FB	-	*Firebox*
Sup	-	*Superheater*
WP	-	*Working Pressure - in psi*
TE	-	*Tractive Effort - in lb*
WinWO	-	*Weight in Working Order - tons and cwt*
TWB E&T	-	*Total Wheelbase Engine & Tender*
Trans	-	*Transmission*

(iii) Diesel, Petrol & Electric Locomotives

Manu No	Dwl Dia	FWB	TWB	Type	Eng Type	Power	Drive	Fuel Capy	WinWO	Trans
0-365	2'7"	5'6"	5'6"	Electric Const' Co	/	TE 2300lb	Electric	/	10-7	City & South London Rly No 19
0-371	2'7"	5'6"	5'6"	Crompton & Co	/	TE 2300lb	Electric	/	10-7	City & South London Rly No 18
0-897	3'0"			Ellis & Ward	/	35	Electric	/		Manchester Corp Hadfield
0-605	2'9"	7'0"	7'0"	British Westinghouse	/		Electric	/	15-0	Carville Power Station
0-54	3'0½"	6'0"	6'0"	British Westinghouse	/	TE 12000lb	Electric	/	25-0	2 Locos - Great Cobar Mines
0-245	2'9"	6'6"	18'6"	British Westinghouse	/	160	Electric	/	20-0	3 locos Thameshaven Bann
0-256	2'4½"	3'6"	3'6"	British Westinghouse	/	TE 6500lb	Electric/side rods	/	11-0	Oakbank Oil Co
0-504	2'3"	7'6"	7'6"	British Westinghouse	/		Electric	/		Dunston Power Stn?
0-550	3'0½"	6'0"	6'0"	British Westinghouse	/	TE 12000lb	Electric	/	25-0	Great Cobar Mines
0-47	2'9"	6'0"	6'0"	Siemens Brothers	/		Electric	/	16-0	2 locos Mysore Gold Mines
P50	1'3¼"	3'0"	3'0"	Bagnall	Coventry Simplex	20	Mech chain/rods	24	4-5	Petrol/paraffin
P51	1'7"	4'10"	4'10"	Bagnall	Dorman	40	Mech shaft/rods	24	6-0	Petrol/paraffin
P52	1'3¼"	3'0"	3'0"	Bagnall	Coventry Simplex	20	Mech chain/rods	24	4-5	Petrol/paraffin
0-4397-9	2'8"	5'6"	5'6"	Nasmyth Wilson	Dorman	40	Electric			Petrol - 25 sets mechanical parts
2220	1'3¼"	3'0"	3'0"	Bagnall	Ford	20	Mech chain/rods	24	3-15	Petrol/paraffin
2273	1'3¼"	3'0"	3'0"	Bagnall	Ford	20	Mech chain/rods	24	4-0	Petrol/paraffin
2274-5	1'7"	3'6"	3'6"	Bagnall	Dorman 4JO	45	Mech Jackshaft/rods	24	6-5	Petrol/paraffin
2304	1'7"	3'6"	3'6"	Bagnall	Dorman 4JO	45	Mech Jackshaft/rods	24	6-5	Petrol/paraffin
2494/514/46/68	2'0"	3'0"	15'0"	Bagnall	Gardner 6L2	62.5	Mech shaft/rods	60	11-18	Diesel - last 3 weight 11-6
2498	1'4"	2'0"	14'3"	Bagnall	Deutz OMZ 117	22-24	Mech shaft/rods		6-10	Diesel
2499/2524	1'2"	1'11"	1'11"	Bagnall-Deutz	Deutz MAH 514	8.5	Mech chain		3-14	Diesel - 2524 weight 2-16
2506	1'4"	3'0¾"	3'0¾"	Bagnall-Deutz	Deutz OMZ 117	22-24	Mech shaft/rods		4-10	Diesel
2507	2'3½"	4'7⅛"	4'7⅛"	Bagnall-Deutz	Deutz OME 125	50-55	Mech Jackshaft/rods	15	11-10	Diesel
2516	1'8"	3'3⅜"	3'3⅜"	Bagnall-Deutz	Deutz A4M 317	45-50	Mech Jackshaft/rods		8-10	Diesel - 4 stroke
2530	2'3½"	4'7⅛"	4'7⅛"	Bagnall-Deutz	Deutz OMZ 130	70-77	Mech Jackshaft/rods		15-10	Diesel
2567	2'9¼"	7'3"	7'3"	Bagnall-Deutz	Deutz OMD 130	110-120	Mech Jackshaft/rods		18-0	Diesel
2573	2'6"	7'3"	7'3"	Bagnall-Deutz	Deutz OMD 130	110-120	Mech Jackshaft/rods		16-10	Diesel
2577	2'9¼"	5'3"	5'3"	Bagnall-Deutz	Deutz OMZ 130	70-77	Mech Jackshaft/rods		22-0	Diesel
2595	1'4"	3'0¾"	3'0¾"	Bagnall-Deutz	Deutz OME 117	11-12	Mech shaft/rods		4-0	Diesel
2971-4	4'0"	11'6"	11'6"	Brush Bagnall	Mirrlees TLT6	355	Electric/side rods	800	51-0	Diesel-Electric
3000-3	4'0"	11'6"	11'6"	Brush Bagnall	Mirrlees TLST6	480	Electric/side rods	800	55-0	Diesel-Electric
3020-1	4'0"	11'6"	11'6"	Brush Bagnall	Mirrlees TLT6	355	Electric/side rods	800	55-0	Diesel-Electric
3025-49	3'7"	10'6"	37'6"	Brush Bagnall	Mirrlees JS12VT	1000	Electric	775	75-0	Diesel-Electric Erection-Loughborough
3062	2'0"	4'0"	4'0"	Bagnall	Perkins Leopard	46	Chain		9-0	Overhaul of Hunslet 2664/1940
3063-5	3'6"	8'0"	26'6"	Brush Bagnall	Mirrlees J6	460	Electric	550	70-0	Diesel-Electric Eection-Loughborough
3066-72	3'6"	8'0"	8'0"	Brush Bagnall	National M4AAU6	275	Electric/side rods	275	43-5	Diesel-Electric
3073-4	4'0"	12'0"	12'0"	Brush Bagnall	National R4AA6	366	Electric/side rods	400	51-0	Diesel-Electric
3076/3132/44	3'3¾"	10'0"	10'0"	Bagnall	National M4AA6	240	Mech Jackshaft/rods	240	30-0	Diesel-Mechanical
3079-88	3'3¾"	10'0"	10'0"	Bagnall	National M4AA6	240	Mech Jackshaft/rods	240	30-0	Diesel-Mechanical
3092-3/3117-9/34-6	3'4"	9'0"	9'0"	Bagnall	National M4AA5	208	Mech Jackshaft/rods	200	29-15	Diesel-Mechanical
3094-5	4'0"	12'0"	12'0"	Brush Bagnall	Mirrlees TLST6	400	Electric/side rods	275	50-0	Diesel-Electric Eection-Loughborough
3096-3103/20	3'6"	8'0"	8'0"	Brush Bagnall	National M4AAU6	275	Electric/side rods	415	43-5	Diesel-Electric Eection-Loughborough
3104-5	3'3¾"	7'0"	7'0"	Bagnall	Gardner 6L3	153	Mech Jackshaft/rods	75	20-10	Diesel-Mechanical
3106-10	3'3¾"	7'0"	7'0"	Bagnall	McLaren M6	155	Mech Jackshaft/rods	75	20-10	Diesel-Mechanical
3111-13	3'6"	8'0"	26'6"	Brush Bagnall	Mirrlees JS6	600	Electric	550	90-0	Diesel-Electric Eection-Loughborough
3114-5	3'0"	11'3"	11'3"	Bagnall	National M4AA6	234	Mech Jackshaft/rods	250	32-0	Diesel-Mechanical
3122-3	3'4"	10'0"	10'0"	Bagnall	National M4AA7	308	Mech Jackshaft/rods	250	38-0	Diesel-Mechanical
3124-5/3204	3'0"	9'0"	9'0"	Bagnall	Gardner 8L3	204	Mech Jackshaft/rods	150	25-0	Diesel-Mechanical
3127-31/55-9/63-87	3'7"	14'2"	42'10"	Brush Bagnall	Mirrlees JVS12T	1250	Electric	550	104-0	Diesel-Electric Eection-Loughborough
3137-43	3'6"	8'0"	26'6"	Brush Bagnall	Mirrlees J6	460	Electric	550	75-0	Diesel-Electric
3147-50	3'4"	9'0"	9'0"	Bagnall	Gardner 8L3	204	Mech Jackshaft/rods	200	33-10	Diesel-Mechanical
3151	3'4"	9'0"	9'0"	Bagnall	Dorman 6QAT	204	Mech Jackshaft/rods	200	33-10	Diesel-Mechanical
3152	2'0"	6'0"	6'0"	Bagnall	Gardner 6LW	102	Mech Jackshaft/rods	55	12-4	Diesel-Mech Overhaul Drewry 2262/49
3155-9/63-87/92-3203	3'7"	14'2"	42'10"	Brush Bagnall	Mirrlees JVS12T	1250	Electric	550	104-0	Diesel-Electric Eection-Loughborough
3160-1	3'4"	10'0"	10'0"	Bagnall	Dorman 6QAT	304	Mech Jackshaft/rods	250	38-0	Diesel-Mechanical
3188	1'6"	3'4"	3'4"	Bagnall	Dorman 3LB	52	Chain	10	5-0	Diesel-Hydraulic
3189	1'6"	3'6"	3'6"	Bagnall	Dorman 3LB	52	Chain	10	7-0	Diesel-Hydraulic
3190	2'0"	3'9"	3'9"	Bagnall	Dorman 5LB	93	Chain	30	10-0	Diesel-Hydraulic
3191	3'4"	10'0"	10'0"	Bagnall	Dorman 6QAT	342	Hyd/rods	260	48-0	Diesel-Hydraulic
3205	3'0"	11'3"	11'3"	Bagnall	Dorman 6QT	240	Mech/Jackshaft/rods	250	32-0	Diesel-Mechanical
3207-8	2'6"	5'0"	5'0"	Bagnall	Gardner 5LW	89	Hyd/chain	50	14-0	Diesel-Hydraulic
3209-11	3'4"	6'0"	6'0"	Bagnall	Rolls Royce C6NFL	179	Hyd/jackshaft/rods	150	24-0	Diesel-Hydraulic Finished at RSH
3212-3	3'4"	7'0"	7'0"	Bagnall	Dorman 6QA	262	Hyd/rods	250	40-0	Diesel-Hydraulic Erected at RSH
3214-7	3'7"	14'2"	42'10"	Brush Bagnall	Mirrlees JVS12T	1250	Electric	550	104-0	Diesel-Electric Eection-Loughborough
3218	3'7"	14'2"	42'10"	Brush Bagnall	Mirrlees JVS12T	1950	Electric	550	104-0	Diesel-Electric Eection-Loughborough
3220-1	3'4"	10'0"	10'0"	Bagnall/RSH	Rolls Royce C8TFL	342	Hyd/rods	300	40-5	Diesel-Hydrauilic built RSH
3222-7	3'4"	7'0"	7'0"	Bagnall/RSH	Rolls Royce C8TFL	342	Hyd/rods	300	32-0	Diesel-Hydrauilic built RSH
3228	3'4"	7'0"	7'0"	Bagnall/RSH	Rolls Royce C6TFL	262	Hyd/rods	250	34-0	Diesel-Hydrauilic built RSH

APPENDIX III

LIST OF LOCOMOTIVES OVERHAULED & REPAIRED

This list includes all those locomotives known to have come into the works for attention of one sort or another, irrespective of whether they were originally of Bagnall manufacture or not. The first column is the date of the order which it should be noted, is not necessarily the date the locomotive arrived, although where known, the date of despatch is quoted in the last column. The second column gives the order number allocated followed by a brief description of the type of repair. Opinions vary among historians, and indeed locomotive engineers, on what constitutes an overhaul as opposed to a repair, and in this list we have used whatever description the Company used in its surviving records, or our best judgement in cases where no specific mention is made, in the light of such knowledge as we have. In general terms an overhaul would consist of a greater scope of work than a repair, with the boiler removed from the frames, while a repair might be quite a small job, for example fitting new tyres to wheels. The third column has the identity of the locomotive using the generally accepted abbreviations for the builder, followed by its number and date of building; the fourth column gives the locomotives name, number or other designation where known; the fifth the type; sixth the track-gauge and the last the customer along with any other relevant details. Where a column is blank the information is unknown.

It is extremely unlikely that this list is complete; that each and every locomotive that ever came into the works has an entry, in fact the reverse is likely to be the case. This is especially so in the years prior to about 1894, although from then onwards it is doubtful if many, if any, locomotives are missing. Nevertheless it is felt that the inclusion of this information will be of considerable interest to enthusiasts of industrial steam locomotives, as well as adding to the knowledge of the more general reader in forming a view of the total works output over the years. In any event it illustrates that along with the supply of spares parts covered in some detail in the main text of this book, as well as in Appendix IV, providing a service for the overhaul and repair of locomotives at Stafford was a sizable workload. In addition to locomotives brought to Stafford for attention the Company frequently sent men to locations all over the country to effect repairs on-site. Where this attention was extensive, entailing the despatch of significant quantities of new material, for example in changing the track-gauge of a locomotive, then such cases, where known, are included in this list with a suitable note to the effect. It is also worth mentioning that there are many cases where although the complete locomotive was not sent to the works, significant parts were, including boilers - see Appendix IV - wheel-sets, water tanks, cylinders and in the odd case frames.

Because the surviving general order books of the Company are by no means complete, for some periods the information has been collated from a variety of sources. For example the drawing registers, which are complete post 1892, are helpful as in many cases new drawings had to be prepared, and there are the personal recollections of the staff concerned at the time, and in other cases the records of the locomotive owners. These sources along with a number of other avenues of research have all contributed, and the authors are especially grateful to the late Ralph Russell for the research he undertook with the firm's records before a lot of material went on the proverbial bonfire. It has been a fascinating experience over a good number of years assembling this information and it is hoped it will prove as worth while to readers as the enjoyment the authors have had in its compilation.

Date	Order No	Type of Repair	Loco Identification	Name	Type	Gauge	Customer
/1878		repairs	WGB 16/1876	BEE	0-4-0STic	Std	? - South Wales
c/1885		repairs		TARGET	0-4-0SToc	Std	? - Photographic evidence
12/1884	668	hire		WITLEY			Witley Colliery Co Ltd Halesowen - unknown loco subject to Hire Purchase agreement commencing 1/1/1885 to 30/9/1886.
/1884	612	rebuilt		BRIGGS	0-4-0SToc	Std	Richard Briggs &Sons Bankfield Lime Works Clitheroe Lancs'.
3/1894	294	rebuilt	WGB 934/1887	MIDGE	0-4-0ISToc	1'11"	William Rigby & Co Mossfield Colliery Longton Staffs
4/1894	311	repairs	BH 174/1871	SWALLOW	0-4-0SToc	Std	Griff Colliery Co Warwick's
7/1894	396	overhaul	WGB 710/1885	OSIRIS	0-4-2Toc	1'6"	HM Govt' Woolwich Arsenal
8/1894	423	overhaul	WGB 892/1897	PIETHORN	0-4-0ISToc	3'3"	Oldham Corporation Water Works return to New Hay Stn Lancashire & Yorkshire Railway
2/1895	585	rebuilt	WGB 954/1889		0-4-0FT oc	Std	Pt Exchange for WGB 1432 sold to Murgatroyds Syndicate Ltd Sandbach Cheshire.
7/1895	702	overhaul	MW 704/1878	LYNN JARVIS	0-4-0ST oc	Std	S Pearson & Son contr'
10/1895	772	overhaul	HH		0-4-0ST oc	Std	Pt Exchange for WGB 1453 sold as 898 10/1898 to Aldershot Gas Company Hants.
12/1895	850	hire					Hire of loco to J Moreton Co (possibly the Henry Hughes loco ex Hickman in 772 above)
3/1896	915	repairs		STAFFORD	0-4-0ST oc	Std	Possibly s/h from R Vernon & Son; sold to Roberts & Co Tipton
4/1896	953	alterations					J Buggins
5/1896	963	repairs	WGB 699/1887	MINNIE	0-4-0IST oc	3'0"	Enoch Tempest contr'
6/1896	1002	repairs	WGB 912/1887	HAROLD	0-4-0IST oc	3'0"	Enoch Tempest contr'
8/1897	434/6	repairs			0-4-0ST oc	Std	Roberts & Co Tipton (12" cylinder loco)
10/1897	490	overhaul	WGB 912/1887	HAROLD	0-4-0IST oc	3'0"	s/h ex Enoch Tempest sold to Crawshay Bros Cyfarthfa Limited Merthyr

Date	Order No	Type of Repair	Loco Identification	Name	Type	Gauge	Customer
10/1897	490	overhaul	WGB 1076/1888	ANNIE	0-4-0IST oc	3'0"	s/h ex Enoch Tempest sold to Crawshay Bros Cyfarthfa Limited Merthyr
5/1898	709	overhaul	WGB 1122/1889	GORDON	0-4-0IST oc	2'0"	Great Wyrley Colliery Co Staffs.
11/1898	959	repairs	WGB 1350/1891	No 7 DOLLY	0-4-0IST oc	3'2½"	Corngreaves Furnace Co Cradley Staffs.
12/1898	973	repairs	MW 1064/1888	No 7	0-6-0ST ic	Std	J Strachen contr'
12/1898	998	repairs				3'0"	Enoch Tempest contr' 7" cylinder loco
1/1899	11	overhaul	WGB 1408/1892	JACK	0-4-0IST oc	1'11"	Hall & Boardman Cadley Hill Collieries Swadlingcote Derby's
4/1899	113	repairs	WGB 1420/1893	ADA	0-4-0IST oc	3'0"	Enoch Tempest contr'; return to Molyneux Brow Lancs'
7/1899	235	overhaul	John Smith/1865	PORTOBELLO	0-4-0T ic	3'2¼"	s/h from Ward & Sons (2'6" gauge) re-gauged and sold to W Bassano & Co Corngreaves Furnaces Cradley Staffs'.
7/1899	236	repair	WGB 1350/1891	No 7	0-4-0IST oc	3'2½"	W Bassano & Co Corngreaves Furnaces Cradley Staffs.
8/1899	272	overhaul					W Pattison & Sons contrs' Ruskington & London (cab fitted)
9/1899	295	repairs	WGB 1564/1899	MABEL	0-4-0ST oc	3'2½"	W Bassano & Co Corngreaves Furnaces Cradley Staffs.
3/1900	533	repairs	WGB 699/1885	MINNIE	0-4-0IST oc	3'0"	Enoch Tempest contr
3/1900	534	repairs	HE 92/1872	BALDERSDALE	0-4-0ST oc	3'0"	Enoch Tempest contr
5/1900	611	repairs	WGB 1485/1897	DORIS	0-4-0ST oc	3'0"	Enoch Tempest contr
6/1900	660	repairs	WGB 1434/1894	ALSTON	0-4-0IST oc	3'0"	Barnsley Corp' Water Works
7/1900	704	repairs	HE 165/1876	CLIFTONVILLE	0-6-0ST ic	Std	JT Firbank contr'
7/1900	701	repairs	HE 92/1872	BALDERSDALE	0-4-0ST oc	3'0"	Enoch Tempest contr' Walshaw Dean Reservoir const' Halifax Corp' York's'
8/1900	740	repairs	HE 170/1877	NEWPORT	0-4-0ST oc	Std	JT Firbank contr'
9/1900	786	repairs	HE 188/1877	WALSALL	0-6-0ST ic	Std	JT Firbank contr'
10/1900	791	repairs	HE 4/1865	PORTSMOUTH	0-6-0ST ic	Std	JT Firbank contr' - work done on site at Cliftonville
11/1900	841	repairs	WGB 1434/1894	ALSTON	0-4-0IST oc	3'0"	Barnsley Corporation Water Works (Midhope Reservoir const)
1/1901	914	repairs	WGB 1414/1892	CLENT	0-4-0ST oc	2'10"	Abraham Kellett & Sons
2/1901	959	hire	WGB 1651/1901		0-4-0ST oc	1'6"	Willans & Robinson Queensferry new loco on hire
4/1901	27	repairs	WGB 660/1887	BIGNALL HILL	0-4-0ST oc	Std	RN Wood Bignall Hill Colliery Newcastle Staffs.
7/1901	191/202	alterations	WGB 1497/1897	TALYBONT	2-4-0T oc	2'3"	Pethick Bros' contrs Vale of Rheidol Rly bought by WGB from Plynlimon & Hafan Tramway re-gauged to 1'11½"
7/1901	192	alterations	WGB 1510/1897	HAFAN	0-4-0ST oc	2'3"	Bought from Plynlimon & Hafan Tramway re-gauged to 3'0" for stock; sold to Enoch Tempest contr'
9/1901	28	repairs	WGB 660/1887	SAMSON	0-4-0ST oc	Std	Pt Exchange for WGB 1654/1901 sold to Blackbrook Colliery Co St Helens Lancs'
9/1901	297	repairs	WGB 1344/1891	CEMENT	0-4-0IST oc	3'9½"	IC Johnson & Co Ltd Greenhithe Kent
11/1901	370	repairs	WGB 1510/1897	HALIFAX	0-4-0ST oc	3'0"	Enoch Tempest contr on site at (Walshaw Dean reservoir const Hebden Bridge)
12/1901	375	repairs	WGB 1639/1901	LIPSCOMB	0-4-0ST oc	3'0"	Enoch Tempest contr on site at (Walshaw Dean reservoir const Hebden Bridge)
12/1901	375	repairs	HE 92/1872	BALDERSDALE	0-4-0ST oc	3'0"	Enoch Tempest contr on site at (Walshaw Dean reservoir const Hebden Bridge)
1/1902	428	repairs	WGB 1392/1892	BIGNALL HILL No2	0-4-0FT oc	Std	Bignall Hill Colly Co (Newcastle under Lyme)
2/1902	460	repairs					Graham, Morton & Co Ltd (loco sent in for repair is only reference)
9/1902	831	repairs	WGB 1429/1894	MARGARET	0-4-0ST oc	1'8"	Essington Farm Colly Co Staffs
12/1902	997	repairs	WGB 660/1887	SAMSON	0-4-0ST oc	Std	Blackbrook Colliery Co St Helens Lancs'
3/1903	104	repairs		DARYL	0-4-0ST	Std	Pt Exchange for WGB 1673/1903 sold to John Freakley slag dealers Pelsall became ENTERPRISE
1/1904	605	repairs	MW 373/1871	No 5	0-6-0ST ic	Std	J Strachan contrs'
5/1904	736	repairs	WGB 1669/1901	TENACITY	0-6-0ST oc	3'0"	Enoch Tempest contr on site at (Walshaw Dean reservoir const Hebden Bridge)
5/1904	737	repairs	WGB 1510/1897	HALIFAX	0-4-0ST oc	3'0"	Enoch Tempest contr on site at (Walshaw Dean reservoir const Hebden Bridge)
3/1904	762	overhaul	WGB 1408/1892	JACK	0-4-0IST oc	1'11"	Halls' Collieries Ltd Swadlingcote Derby's
5/1905	797	repairs	WGB 1567/1899	WALSHAW DEAN	0-4-0ST oc	3'0"	Enoch Tempest contr' - renamed SMITH (Walshaw Dean reservoir const Hebden Bridge)
5/1905	799	repairs	WGB 1420/1893	ADA	0-4-0IST oc	3'0"	Enoch Tempest contr' (Walshaw Dean reservoir const Hebden Bridge)
6/1904	830	repairs	WGB 1537/1898	No 1	0-4-0ST oc	Std	Sheffield United Gas Co
6/1904	843	repairs	WGB 1350/1891	PRINCESS	0-4-0IST oc	3' 2¼"	Robert Fellows Corngreaves Furnaces Cradley Heath Staffs
7/1904	856	rebuilt	WGB 1610/1900	SIR RALPH	0-4-0ST oc	2'9"	Crown Agents returned from Nigeria and despatched back
1/1905	64	overhaul	WGB 1724/1903	GLADYS	0-4-0ST oc	2'0"	Blackbrook Colliery Co Ltd
9/1905	342	overhaul	WGB 1671/1902		0-4-0ST oc	Std	James Nelson & Sons Ltd Bramley Moor Liverpool
3/1905	118	Rep/new blr	WGB 1502/1897	WASSELL	0-4-0ST oc	3'2¼"	Shelagh Garratt & Sons New British Collieries Cradley Heath Staffs'
1/1906	500	repairs	WGB 1781/1905	POLAR BEAR	2-4-0T oc	2'0"	Howstrake Estate Ltd Groudle Glen Railway Isle of Man
1/1906	509	repairs	WGB 1671/1902		0-4-0ST oc	Std	James Nelson & Sons Ltd Bramley Moor Liverpool
6/1906	705/973	rebuilt	WGB 1551/1898	MOURNE	0-4-0ST oc	3'0"	Fisher & Le Fann contrs'; left on WGB hands sold 2/1907 James Byrom Ltd contr' sent to Ewood Bridge Lancs'
5/1907	44	repairs	WGB 1653/1901	No 12	0-4-0ST oc	Std	South Metropolitan Gas Co East Greenwich London
6/1907	135	repairs	WGB reb 104/1903	ENTERPRISE	0-4-0ST	Std	John Freakley & Co Ltd Pelsall - new boiler fitted- see above
9/1907	275	repairs	WGB 300/1880?		0-4-0IST oc	2'0"	Somerset Mineral Syndicate Brendon Hill Somerset
6/1908	517	repairs	WGB 1671/1902		0-4-0ST oc	Std	James Nelson & Sons Ltd Bramley Moor Liverpool
9/1908	588	repairs	WGB 1432/1894	GRAZEBROOK	0-4-0ST oc	Std	Pt Exchange for WGB 1884/1908 sold 4/1910 Barmoor Coal Co Morpeth
10/1909	929	repairs		HORWICH			A Koppel (register states Repairs to loco under Tariff Reform; loco made in Germany)
4/1909	777	repairs	HE 222/1879	BRITANNIA	0-6-0ST ic	STD	Griff Colliery Co Ltd Nuneaton Warks
7/1910	255	repairs	WGB 1678/1902	GILWEN No 1	0-4-0ST oc	3'0"	Gilwen Colly Co Ltd
2/1911	904	repairs	WGB 1730/1904	MERCEDES	0-4-0ST oc	3'0"	Greaves Bull & Lakin Ltd Harbury Cement Works Warks'
5/1911	89	repairs	St Helens/c1853	No 2 HECATE	0-4-2ST ic	Std	HF Stephens Shropshire & Montgomeryshire Railway
11/1911	985						Cutting up old loco for scrap (thought to be WGB 1426/1893 came in Pt Exc for WGB 1901/1911)
7/1912	877	rebuilt	WGB 1662/1902	CB No 2	0-4-0ST oc		Charles Barlow Finedon Quarries Wellingborough Northants'

Date	Order No	Type of Repair	Loco Identification	Name	Type	Gauge	Customer
10/1912	1197	rebuilt	WGB 1671/1902		0-4-0ST oc	Std	James Nelson & Sons Ltd Bramley Moor Liverpool
2/1913	257	rebuilt	HE 937/1907	ANGEL	0-4-0ST oc	2'6½"	Jees Hartshill Granite & Brick Co Ltd Nuneaton Warks'
8/1913	963	repairs	WGB 1564/1899	MABEL	0-4-0ST oc	3'2½"	Garretts Ltd New British Collieries Cadley Heath
1/1914	124	repairs	WGB 1671/1902		0-4-0ST oc	Std	James Nelson & Sons Ltd Bramley Moor Liverpool
7/1914	746	overhaul	WGB 1574/1899	TREVOR No 4	0-4-0ST oc	2'6"	Manchester Corp' Cleansing Dept' Manchester (returned 3/1915)
2/1915	150	repair	MW 1227/1895	No 13	0-6-0ST ic	Std	Baldry Yerburgh & Hutchinson contr - on site Cannock Chase Military Railway
7/1915	750	alter gauge	WGB 1728/1903	HAMPSTEAD	0-4-0ST oc	1'9"	W Alban Richards & Co (altered to 2'0" and returned 9/1915)
8/1915	830	repairs					JB Ball (may be road steam traction engine/roller)
11/1915	1260	overhaul	WGB 1786/1905		0-4-0ST oc	Std	Siemens Brothers Dynamo Works Ltd Stafford
4/1916	362	repairs?	WGB 1643/1901	CB No 1	0-4-0ST oc	2'0"	Charles Barlow Finedon Quarries Wellingborough Northants'
9/1916	3960	rebuilt	WGB 1493/1896	No 1	0-4-0ST oc	Std	Ministry of Munitions came from quarry at Brixham sent 2/1917 HM Factory Watford Herts.
11/1916	3767	repairs					to locomotive - only reference
3/1917	4539	overhaul	WGB 1649/1901	CAPPONFIELD	0-4-0ST oc	Std	T&I Bradley Ltd Capponfield Furnaces Bilston Staffs'
10/1917	5345	repairs	AB 837/1898	CHRISTIE	0-4-0ST oc	Std	Alfred Hickman Ltd Springvale Furnaces Bilston Staffs' (returned 12/1918)
3/1918	5914	repairs	AB 226/1881	No 2	0-4-0ST oc	Std	T&I Bradley Ltd Capponfield Furnaces Bilston Staffs'
6/1918	6165	repairs	WGB 1725/1903	CONCRETE	0-4-0ST oc	2'0"	Air Ministry Luchars Aerodrome Scotland
6/1918	6123	repairs	ALCO 57131/1917	1240/1287	2-6-2T oc	1'11⅝"	Ministry of Munitions (complete 9/1918)
6/1918	6174	repairs	ALCO 57159/1917	1268	2-6-2T oc	1'11⅝"	Ministry of Munitions (complete 11/1918)
7/1918	6215	repairs	ALCO 57178/1917	1287	2-6-2T oc	1'11⅝"	Ministry of Munitions (complete 3/1918)
7/1918	6226	repairs	BWN 44758/1917	853	4-6-0T oc	1'11⅝"	Ministry of Munitions (complete 10/1918)
7/1918	6254	repairs	BWN 45138/1917	556	4-6-0T oc	1'11⅝"	Ministry of Munitions (complete 9/1918)
7/1918	6273	repairs	BWN 44703/1917	798	4-6-0T oc	1'11⅝"	Ministry of Munitions (complete 10/1918)
9/1918	6514	repairs	BWN 45215/1917	633	4-6-0T oc	1'11⅝"	Ministry of Munitions (complete 12/1918)
10/1918	6539	repairs	BWN 44717/1917	812	4-6-0T oc	1'11⅝"	Ministry of Munitions (complete 10/1918)
10/1918	6540	repairs	BWN 44522/1917	722	4-6-0T oc	1'11⅝"	Ministry of Munitions (complete 11/1918)
10/1918	6545	repairs	BWN 44657/1916	779	4-6-0T oc	1'11⅝"	Ministry of Munitions (complete 12/1918)
10/1918	6518	repairs	BWN 45143/1917	561	4-6-0T oc	1'11⅝"	Ministry of Munitions (complete 10/1918)
10/1918	6596	repairs	BWN 44549/1916	749	4-6-0T oc	1'11⅝"	Ministry of Munitions (complete 1/1919)
10/1918	6616	repairs	BWN 44360/1916	515	4-6-0T oc	1'11⅝"	Ministry of Munitions (complete 1/1919)
10/1918	6634	repairs	BWN 44783/1917	878	4-6-0T oc	1'11⅝"	Ministry of Munitions (complete 12/1918)
10/1918	6635	repairs	BWN 45142/1917	560	4-6-0T oc	1'11⅝"	Ministry of Munitions (complete 11/1918)
11/1918	6781	repairs	BWN 52000/1917	1068	4-6-0T oc	1'11⅝"	Ministry of Munitions (complete 12/1918)
11/1918	6819	repairs	BWN 44552/1917	752	4-6-0T oc	1'11⅝"	Ministry of Munitions (complete 5/1919)
11/1918	6823	repairs	BWN 44696/1917	791	4-6-0T oc	1'11⅝"	Ministry of Munitions (complete 2/1919)
12/1918	6875	repairs	BWN 44705/1917	800	4-6-0T oc	1'11⅝"	Ministry of Munitions (complete 2/1919)
12/1918	6876	repairs	BWN 44362/1916	517	4-6-0T oc	1'11⅝"	Ministry of Munitions (complete 2/1919)
12/1918	6883	repairs	BWN 44383/1916	538	4-6-0T oc	1'11⅝"	Ministry of Munitions (complete 4/1919)
1/1919	7010	repairs	BWN 45172/1917	590	4-6-0T oc	1'11⅝"	Ministry of Munitions (complete 4/1919)
3/1919	7125	repairs	BWN 44737/1917	832	4-6-0T oc	1'11⅝"	Ministry of Munitions (complete 9/1919)
3/1919	7144	repairs	BWN 44695/1917	790	4-6-0T oc	1'11⅝"	Ministry of Munitions (complete 9/1919)
3/1919	7152	repairs	AB 1075/1906	LUCY	0-4-0ST oc	Std	Alfred Hickman Ltd Springvale Furnaces Bilston Staffs' (prepared for transit to Kilmarnock)
3/1919	7172	repairs	AB 1035/1904	CHARLIE	0-4-0ST oc	Std	Alfred Hickman Ltd Springvale Furnaces Bilston Staffs'
3/1919	7173	repairs	AB 1182/1909	BLUEBELL	0-4-0ST oc	Std	Alfred Hickman Ltd Springvale Furnaces Bilston Staffs'
12/1919	8172	overhaul	WGB 1889/1911	No 1	0-4-0ST oc	3'0"	Judkins Ltd Nuneaton Warks'
3/1920	8466	overhaul	WGB 2044/1917	FILTON	0-4-0ST oc	2'0"	Pur' from MofM Disposal Board, regauged to 1'11 ⅝"; sold Schill Bros Ltd for export - sent 6/1920
7/1920	8945	repairs	WGB 2071/1918		0-4-0ST oc	2'0"	RH Neal & Co dealers to Charnwood Granite Co Leics' 12/1920
7/1920	8945	repairs	WGB 2070/1918		0-4-0ST oc	2'0"	RH Neal & Co dealers to A Bradley & Co for shipment to South Africa 1/1921
7/1920	8944	repairs	WGB 2073/1918		0-4-0ST oc	2'0"	RH Neal & Co dealers to W Muirhead McDonald Wilson & Co sent to Barkingside Essex 7/1921
7/1920	8944	repairs	WGB 2048/1918		0-4-0ST oc	2'0"	RH Neal & Co dealers to W Muirhead McDonald Wilson & Co sent to Barkingside Essex 7/1921
5/1920	9148	overhaul	AB 226/1881		0-4-0ST oc	Std	Bradley & Foster Ltd Darlaston Green Furnaces Staffs
10/1920	9262	overhaul	WGB 1726/1903	RICHARD BELL	0-4-0ST oc	2'0"	Henry Boot & Sons contrs'
12/1920	9484	repairs	WGB 2046/1918		0-4-0ST oc	2'0"	Alfred Hickman Ltd Springvale Furnaces Bilston Staffs' (loco arrived from Glasgow)
6/1921	3127	repairs	WGB 1839/1907		0-4-0ST oc	Std	Oxford Gas Light & Coke Co (returned 9/1921)
10/1921	3453	overhaul	WGB 1608/1900	THRELKELD	0-4-0ST oc	2'4"	Threlkeld Granite Co Ltd Keswick (included new boiler loco returned 5/1922)
10/1921	3546	overhaul	WGB 1669/1901	DUKINFIELD	0-6-0ST oc	3'0"	Abertillary District Water Board, returned to Llanvihangel via Shrewsbury
1/1922	3755	rebuild	WGB 2067/1918	PETER	0-4-0ST oc	3'0"	Pur'; from A Hammond dealer rebuilt and regauged to 2'0" sold Cliffe Hill Granite Co Markfield Leics' sent 8/1922
2/1922	3900	overhaul	WGB 1672/1902	BROADOAK	0-4-0ST oc	Std	Broadoak Collieries Ltd Glamorgan (included new boiler)
4/1922	4130	repairs	WGB 1911/1918	STAFFORD	0-6-0T oc	2'6"	Jee's Hartshill Granite & Brick Co Ltd Nuneaton Warks' (ex M of M Ridham Dock Kent)
6/1922	4401/4582	overhaul	WGB 1402/1892	ALEXANDER	0-4-0 FT oc	Std	Birchenwood Colliery Co Lrd Kidsgrove Staffs' (in very bad condition, scrapped and replaced by WGB 2108/1922)
3/1923	5291-5299		WGB 2214/1923	DOT	0-4-0ST oc	3'0"	Make up from parts left over from 2067 - Charles Abell Ltd Hartshill Granite Quarries Nuneaton
2/1923	5324	repairs	Eastleigh /1910		0-4-0T oc	Std	Barnstone Cement Co Ltd Notts' (ex M of M formerly LSWR 101 S14 class) delivered 6/1923
4/1923	5582	repairs	WGB 2085/1923	KITTY	0-4-0ST oc	3'0"	Charles Abell Ltd Hartshill Granite Quarries Nuneaton Warks'
10/1927	5291-5299	regauging	WGB 2258/1925	NEW ELEPHANT	0-4-0ST oc	3'9"	British Portland Cement Manufacturers Greenhithe Kent (rebuilt to Std gauge - work done at Greenhithe)
11/1923	6415	overhaul	P 822/1899		0-4-0ST oc	Std	Butterley Co Ltd Bull Bridge Iron Works Derbys' - returned 4/1924
4/1929	7632	overhaul	WGB 2216/1924	UNIQUE	2-4-0F oc	2'6"	Edward Lloyd Ltd Sittingbourne Kent - returned 8/1929

Date	Order No	Type of Repair	Loco Identification	Name	Type	Gauge	Customer
7/1929	7699	overhaul	WGB 2177/1922	WADE DEACON	0-4-0ST oc	Std	Liverpool Gas Co Garston Gas Works - despatched 7/1929 (ex Bombay India)
2/1930	8424	overhaul	WGB 2048/1918		0-4-0ST oc	2'0"	Sir John Norton Griffiths contr' Aswan Dam Contract Egypt
7/1930	9020-9022	repairs	WGB 2254/1925	B.R.C.	0-4-0ST oc	Std	British Reinforced Concrete Engineering Co Ltd Stafford - returned 9/1930
10/1930	9341	overhaul	WGB 2216/1924	UNIQUE	2-4-0F oc	2'6"	Edward Lloyd Ltd Sittingbourne Kent - returned 1/1931
2/1932	4205	repairs	AB 1576/1918	No 1	0-6-0ST oc	Std	Alders Paper Mills Ltd Tamworth Staffs'
8/1932	4847	repairs	HL 3524/1923	No 3	0-4-0ST oc	Std	Fenton Collieries Limited, Fenton Stoke-on-Trent
12/1932	5182	repairs	HL 3531/1922	SELBOURNE	0-6-0ST oc	Std	HM Govt' Longmoor Camp Hants'
2/1933	5370	repairs	Deutz 92972/		4wDM	1'11⅝"	Votty & Bowydd Slate Quarries Ltd Bleanau Festiniog
9/1933	6124	overhaul	WGB 2108/1923	No 5	0-4-0ST oc	Std	Worthington & Co Ltd Burton-on-Trent
11/1933	6419	repairs	P 1068/1905	HESKETH	0-6-0ST ic	Std	Madeley Collieries Ltd, Madeley Staffs'
1/1934	6686	overhaul	HL 3642/1925	AMINGTON No 2	0-6-0ST oc	Std	Glascote Colliery Co Ltd Tamworth Warks'
3/1934	6807	overhaul	YE 1011/1908		0-4-0ST oc	Std	Midland Tar Distillers Ltd Milton Staffs'
3/1934	6970	overhaul	HL 3081/1914	FORWARD No 26	0-4-0ST oc	Std	Birmingham Corporation Gas Dept' Saltley Gas Works Birmingham
6/1934	7155	repairs	WGB 2366/1925	VICTOR	0-4-0F oc	2'6"	Edward Lloyd Ltd Sittingbourne Kent - returned 9/1934
8/1934	7752	repairs	HL 3669/1937	ROSABEL	0-4-0ST oc	Std	Courtaulds Ltd Wolverhampton - returned 9/1934
9/1934	7865	overhaul	WGB 2498/1934		0-4-0+0-4-0DM	1'1 ½"	Halkyn District United Mines Ltd Penbryn Mine Holywell Jun - returned 10/1934
4/1935	8452-8458	gauge change	WGB 1588/1900	THAMES	0-4-0ST oc	4'3 ½"	BPCM Johnson's Branch Greenhithe Kent - rebuilt on site to Std gauge
7/1935	8958	rebuild	WGB 2216/1924	UNIQUE	2-4-0F oc	2'6"	Edward Lloyd Ltd Sittingbourne Kent
7/1935	9048	repairs	KS 4272/1922	WITCH	0-4-0ST oc	Std	Middlewich Salt Co Ltd Middlewich Cheshire
1/1936	9634	repairs	AB 1480/1916	BONIFACE	0-4-0ST oc	Std	Mitchells & Butlers Ltd Smethwick Staffs'
3/1936	9966	repairs	EB 24/1888	NEWTON	0-4-0WT oc	Std	ICI (Alkali) Ltd Winnington Cheshire - returned 7/1936
3/1937	4487-8	repairs	WGB 2223/1924	ELSIE	0-6-0ST oc	Std	Stewarts & Lloyds Ltd Tinsley Park Colliery Kilnhurst Yorks' - returned 7/1937
4/1937	4595	repairs	WGB 2499/1934		4wDM	1'11⅝"	Votty & Bowydd Slate Quarries Ltd Bleanau Festiniog - returned 5/1937
2/1938	6121	repairs	WGB 2450/1931	JT DALY	0-4-0ST oc	Std	Horseley Bridge & Thomas Piggott Ltd Dudley Port Staffs'
10/1938	7037	repairs	AB 1703/1920	No 3	0-4-0ST oc	Std	Dunlop Rubber Co Ltd Castle Bromwich Staffs'
5/1939	8004	overhaul	HL 3460/1921	TONY	0-6-0ST oc	Std	TA Hawkins & Sons Ltd Old Coppice Colliery Cheslyn Hay Staffs' - returned 8/1939
6/1939	8247	repairs	Butt /1892	B3C	0-6-0ST ic	Std	Butterley Co Ltd Bailey Brook Colly Derbys' - returned 11/1939
8/1939	8488	s/h for resale	Butt /1889	B2C	0-4-0ST oc	Std	s/h from Butterley Co Ltd Codnor Park; sold to Brereton Collys, Brereton Staffs' - no work carried out at WGB
11/1939	8802	overhaul	P 1114/1907	No 4	0-4-0ST oc	Std	Dunlop Rubber Co Ltd Castle Bromwich Staffs'
8/1941	4613	repairs	WGB 2177/1901	STR No 7	0-4-0ST oc	Std	Liverpool Gas Co Garston Gas Works
10/1941	4863	repairs	BH 864/1886	No 18	0-4-0T oc	Std	Gas Light & Coke Co Ltd Beckton Gas Works Essex (damaged by enemy action)
10/1941	4864	repairs	AB 636/1889	No 33	0-4-0ST oc	Std	Gas Light & Coke Co Ltd Beckton Gas Works Essex (damaged by enemy action)
10/1941	4904	overhaul	AE 1804/1918	37	0-4-0ST oc	Std	Metropolitan-Cammell Carriage & Wagon Co Ltd Saltley Warks' - returned 12/1942
4/1942	5442	overhaul	WGB 2229/1924	CENTENARY	0-4-0ST oc	Std	York Gas Co York Gas Works - returned 12/1942
7/1942	5804	repairs	VF 1236/1888	PARTINGTON	0-6-0ST ic	Std	Ministry of Supply ROF No 6 Risley near Warrington (Sir Lindsay Parkinson & Co Ltd contr')
7/1942	5805	overhaul	P 889/1886	ROCKET	0-6-0ST ic	Std	Ministry of Supply sent to ROF Fetherstone Factory Coven near Wolverhampton
7/1942	5807	repairs	MW 1742/1908	LLANGENNECH	0-6-0ST ic	Std	Ministry of Supply probably ROF No 6 Risley near Warrington (Sir Lindsay Parkinson & Co Ltd contr')
7/1942	5808	repairs	MW 1568/1902	WARBURTON-LEE	0-6-0ST ic	Std	Ministry of Supply probably sent for use by the Port of London Authority
9/1942	8794	boiler repairs	WGB 1943/1911	MARY	0-4-2T oc	2'0"	Cliffe Hill Granite Co Ltd Markfield Leics' - returned 9/1942
9/1942	6015	repairs	KS 4030/1919	No 4	0-4-0ST oc	Std	John Bowes & Partners Ltd Springwell Durham - returned 7/1943
10/1942	6087	repairs	WGB 2653/1942	ROF No 15 No 2	0-4-0ST oc	Std	Ministry of Supply
9/1942	6111	repairs	WGB 1673/1903	CARBON	0-4-0ST oc	Std	Wolverhampton Gas Co Wolverhamptron Gas Works - returned 10/1943
10/1942	6169	repairs	WGB 2077/1919	MABEL	0-4-0ST oc	2'0"	Cliffe Hill Granite Co Ltd Markfield Leics' - work stopped and loco returned /1946 in dismantled state
12/1942		repairs	KS 3090/1917	KINLOCHLEVEN	0-4-0ST oc	2'0"	Balfour Beatty & Co Ltd returned 1/1943
12/1942		repairs	WGB 1610/1900	No 9	0-4-0ST oc	Std	South Metropolitan Gas Co East Greenwich Gas Works London - returned 1/1943
8/1943	6427	rebuilt	AE 1382/1897	No 2	0-6-0ST ic	Std	Birchenwood Coal & Coke Co Lrd Kidsgrove Staffs' - returned 4/1944 - including new boiler
6/1943	6826	repairs	HE 1849/1937	17	0-6-0ST ic	Std	Guest Keen & Baldwins East Moors Cardiff - work done at Cowlishaw Walker Biddulph with parts from Stafford
6/1943	6901	repairs	HE 1873/1937	18	o-6-0ST ic	Std	Guest Keen & Baldwins East Moors Cardiff - work done at Cowlishaw Walker Biddulph with parts from Stafford
5/1943	6799	repairs	AB 1613/1918		0-4-0ST oc	Std	ICI (Dyestuffs) Ltd Huddersfield Yorks' - returned 5/1944
7/1943	7011	repairs	WGB 2676/1942	ROF No 10 No 3	0-4-0ST oc	Std	Ministry of Supply Eastriggs (converted from oil to coal fuel) - returned 8/1943
9/1943	7297	repairs	P 820/1900	WD 4584 DOUGLAS	0-4-0ST oc	Std	Ministry of Supply WD Queensferry Factory - returned 10/1943
9/1943	7094	repairs	MW 863/1883	WD 223	0-4-0ST oc	Std	Ministry of Supply WD Melbourne Military Railway Repton Derbys' - returned 2/1944
10/1944	7180	repairs	WGB 2613/1940		0-6-0PT oc	Std	Admiralty Machinery Depot Stoke-on-Trent returned 12/1944
1/1944	7741	repairs	AE 1572/1910	WOOLMER	0-6-0ST oc	Std	Ministry of Supply (Royal Engineers) WD Longmoor Camp Hants' - returned 6/1944
1/1944	7742	repairs	P1326/1915	PORTSMOUTH WD1326	0-4-0ST oc	Std	Ministry of Supply (Royal Engineers) WD Hilsea Camp Hants' - returned 6/1944
2/1944	7829	repairs	WGB 2621/1940	BUTTERLEY No32	0-6-0ST oc	Std	Butterley Co Ltd Derbys' - returned 8/1944

Date	Order No	Type of Repair	Loco Identification	Name	Type	Gauge	Customer
3/1944	7884	overhaul	SS 3670/1890	No 1	0-4-0CT oc	Std	Guest Keen & Baldwins Iron & Steel Co Ltd East Moors Cardiff - returned 12/1944
3/1944	7911	repairs	WGB 2652/1942	WD 237	0-4-0ST oc	Std	Ministry of Supply ROF Rearsby Factory Leics' (convert oil to coal fuel)
6/1944	7990	overhaul	Crewe /1865	KYNOCK No 4	0-4-0ST ic	Std	ICI (Metals) Ltd Kynock Factory Lancs' (ex LNWR 3042)
7/1944	8230	repairs	WGB 2650/1942	ROF No 14 No 1	0-4-0ST oc	Std	Ministry of Supply ROF Ruddington Notts - returned 12/1944 (convert coal to oil fuel)
8/1944	8314	repairs	WGB 2772/1944		0-4-0ST oc	Std	Admiralty Llangennech Camarthenshire - returned 9/1944
11/1944	8644	repairs	WGB 2664/1942	SDF 1	0-4-0ST oc	Std	Smethwick Drop Forgings (Kidderminster) Ltd Worcs' ret 12/2/1945
3/1945	9066	repairs	HE 1335/1919	No 40	0-4-0ST oc	Std	Gas Light & Coke Co Ltd Beckton Gas Works Essex (sub-con to Cowlishaw Walker Biddulph)
3/1945	9067	repairs	Beckton 1/1902	No 30	0-4-0ST oc	Std	Gas Light & Coke Co Ltd Beckton Gas Works Essex - returned 11/1946 (sub-con to Cowlishaw Walker Biddulph)
3/1945	9068	repairs	BH 864/1886	No 19	0-4-0ST oc	Std	Gas Light & Coke Co Ltd Beckton Gas Works Essex - returned 3/1947 (sub-con to Cowlishaw Walker Biddulph)
4/1947	4723	rebuilt	WGB 1584/1899		0-4-0ST oc	Std	NCB Berry Hill Colliery Stoke-on-Trent - sold as manufacturer's No 2908 (has been p/exc for WGB 2661/1942)
8/1948	6298	repairs	WGB 1537/1900	No 1	0-4-0ST oc	Std	East Midlands Gas Board Sheffield Gas Works - returned 11/1953
9/1948	6351	repairs	WGB 2750/1944	75162	0-6-0ST ic	Std	Ministry of Supply - returned to Bramley Hants' 6/1949
10/1948	6440	overhaul	WGB 2623/1940	HAWARDEN	0-4-0ST oc	Std	Shelton Iron Steel & Coal Co Lrd Etruria Stoke-on-Trent - returned 8/1949
7/1949	7295	repairs	WGB 2759/1944	75171	0-6-0ST ic	Std	Ministry of Supply - returned to Bramley Hants' 10/1950
6/1950	8208	overhaul	WGB 2370/1929		0-6-0F oc	Std	British Industrial Solvents Ltd Salt End Hull - returned 5/1952
10/1950	8631	repairs	RSH 7162/1944	71508	0-6-0ST ic	Std	Ministry of Supply - returned to Skiers Springs opencast coal site Yorks' 5/1952
12/1951	4035	repairs	WGB 2908/1947	BERRY HILL NO 3	0-4-0ST oc	Std	NCB Berry Hill Colliery Stoke-on-Trent Staffs' - returned 12/1953
7/1952	4711	overhaul	HC 1754/1942	ARTHUR LEIGHTON	0-6-0ST ic	Std	NCB Foxfield Colliery Cheadle Staffs' - returned 3/1956
4/1953	4833	repairs	HC 1418/1923	WINWICK	0-6-0Toc	Std	NCB Holditch Colliery Newcastle-under-Lyme Staffs'
8/1953	6283	repairs	JF 22877/1938	No 168	0-4-0DM	Std	Air Ministry Director General of Works - returned 12/1953
10/1953	6468	overhaul	WGB 1673/1902	CARBON	0-4-0ST oc	Std	West MIdlands Gas Board Wolverhampton Gas Works - returned 3/1954
10/1953	6519	overhaul	HL 2782/1909	No 9	0-4-0ST oc	Std	Patent Shaft & Axletree Co Ltd Wednesbury Staffs' - returned 7/1954
12/1953	8355	repairs	WGB 2787/1945	DILHORNE No 3	0-6-0ST ic	Std	NCB Foxfield Colliery Cheadle Staffs'
1/1954	6747	overhaul	ALCO 71512/1944	CARL R GRAY Jnr	2-8-0 oc + ten	Std	Ministry of Supply Longmoor Camp Hants' - returned 3/1955
1/1954	6748	overhaul	NBL 25437/1944	600 GORDON	2-10-0 oc + ten	Std	Ministry of Supply Longmoor Camp Hants' - returned 3/1955
1/1954	6759	repairs	WGB 2067/1918	PETER	0-4-0ST oc	2'0"	Narrow Gauge Railway Society (ex Cliffe Hill Granite Markfield Leics') Cancelled stripped but no work undertaken
3/1954	7077	overhaul	RSH 7111/1943	WD 111	0-6-0ST ic	Std	Ministry of Supply - returned 4/1955
3/1954	7078	overhaul	RSH 7268/1945	WD 164	0-6-0ST ic	Std	Ministry of Supply - returned to Bicester Oxen' 2/1955
3/1954	7079	overhaul	WGB 2740/1944	WD 143	0-6-0ST ic	Std	Ministry of Supply - returned 10/1955
5/1954	7300	overhaul	HL 3642/1935	AMINGTON No 2	0-6-0ST oc	Std	NCB Kingsbury Colliery Warks' - returned 4/1956
6/1954	7350	repairs	AE 1843/1919	RS 4 1919	0-4-0ST oc	Std	ICI Lime Division Long Siding Works Tunstead Drbys' - returned 1/1955
7/1954	5614	repairs	WGB 2216/1924	UNIQUE	2-4-0F oc	2'6"	Bowaters Lloyd Pulp & Paper Mills Sittingbourne - work done on site at Sittingbourne
8/1954	7656	repairs	WGB 2108/1923	No 5	0-4-0ST oc	Std	Worthington & Co Lrd Burton-on-Trent Staffs' - returned 7/1955
11/1954	7962	overhaul	VF 5193/1945	Mjr Gen Mc MULLEN	2-8-0 oc + ten	Std	Ministry of Supply Longmoor Camp Hants' - returned 5/1956
12/1954	7999	overhaul	AE 1794/1918	No 3	0-4-0ST oc	Std	Patent Shaft & Axletree Co Ltd Wednesbury Staffs' - returned 2/1956
8/1955	9202	repairs	WGB 3077/1955	HEM HEATH No 1	0-6-0ST oc	Std	NCB Florence Colliery Stoke-on-Trent Staffs' (loco damaged in run-away incident)
3/1956	8056	repairs	WGB 3024/1953	MONARCH	0-4-0+0-4-0T oc	2'6"	Bowaters Lloyd Pulp & Paper Mills Sittingbourne - work done on site at Sittingbourne
5/1956	4250	repairs	RSH 7285/1945	MICHAEL	0-4-0ST oc	Std	NCB Cinderhill Colliery Notts' - returned 11/1956
10/1958	6567	overhaul	WGB 2246/1925		4-8-0 oc	metre	West India Portuguese Railway - returned to Goa
11/1958	7613	overhaul	VF 5305/1945	HORDON No 5	0-6-0ST ic	Std	NCB Easington Colly Durham
11/1959	8655	repairs	KS 4421/1929		6wDM	Std	NCB Wingate Grange Colly Durham (work included fitting new Dorman engine)
11/1960	5169	overhaul	P 2061/1945	No 6	0-6-0ST oc	Std	NCB Mountain Ash Colliery Aberdare
10/1960	5309	overhaul	HL 2769/1909	JEAN	0-6-0ST ic	Std	NCB Wearmouth Colliery Durham - returned 1/1962
10/1960	5335	repairs	RSH 7752/1953	WARWICKSHIRE	0-6-0ST ic	Std	NCB Baddersley Colly Warks' (included fitting mechanical stoker)
/1960	6292	overhaul	HL 3440/1920	HORDON No 2	0-6-0ST oc	Std	NCB Hordon Colliery Durham - returned 11/1962
/1960	6399	repairs	HC 1255/1917	30 19	0-6-0ST ic	Std	NCB Springwell Bank Foot Durham (stripped for repairs and transferred to Andrew Barclay for completion)
/1961	6633	repairs	HL 3766/1930	HENRY C EMBLETON	0-6-0ST oc	Std	NCB Derwenthaugh Durham (cylinders removed and loco transferred to Andrew Barclay)
4/1961	6535	repairs	AB 1321/1913	No 24	0-6-0ST oc	Std	NCB Eastington Colly Durham - returned 10/1962
11/1961	7088	repairs	SWN /1949	1501-2/9	0-6-0ST oc	Std	NCB Coventry Colly Warks' (cylinders removed and locos transferred to Andrew Barclay - 3 locos)
12/1961		repairs	EE 788/1930		4wBE	Std	English Electric Co Ltd Main Works Stafford (tyres reprofiled/axle-box /brake-gear attn)

APPENDIX IV

LIST OF SPARE & SEPARATE BOILERS & FIREBOXES SUPPLIED

In this list an attempt has been made to list all the separate boilers and fireboxes supplied over the years; that is when not part of a new locomotives. In some cases they were spares or replacements for existing Bagnall locomotives, and in others for locomotives built by other manufacturers. In the latter case this was frequently for the Indian and other overseas markets, often boilers of standard designs for BESA and IRS design locomotives, with the orders placed by consulting engineers, or perhaps, the Crown Agents. In other cases the locomotives themselves were at Stafford for attention - see Appendix III - when new boilers were supplied, or replacement fireboxes were fitted to existing boilers. In other cases only the boilers were sent to Stafford for new fireboxes to be fitted and there are instances when on these occasions it was discovered on detailed examination that repairs would not be an economical proposition, and after negotiation with the customer a new boiler was supplied instead. By cross referencing between this Appendix and Appendix III, readers will be able to establish those locomotives that came to the works for attention, including supply of a new boiler or firebox, and those that did not.

As with the Appendix III it is unlikely that this list is exhaustive; however, it is likely to be so for new boilers from about 1894 onwards. Mention is made in Appendix III that all the general order books have not survived, but the drawing registers covering the entire period from 1894 have, along with the vast majority of the drawings covering the same period. Actually, as noted in the text of the book, in most cases the drawing were copied on to negatives in the 1950s and it is these negatives that survive. When new boilers were supplied they were either to a new design, new that is to Bagnall, in which case either drawings would have to be made, sometimes using the old boiler as a pattern, or they would be supplied by the customer, which was usually the case when consulting engineers were involved. Alternatively, if to an established Castle Engine Works design, or similar to one supplied

earlier, existing drawing would be used with a relevant entry made on them. With the same objectives as Appendix III, in compiling this list the authors hope readers will not only gain a better insight into the totality of the firm's workload over the years, but the information will also be of interest to those readers with a particular interest in industrial locomotives used in this country. In terms of workload it is worth bearing in mind that the boiler is the largest single component of most locomotives, construction of which in the days before the more universal adoption of welding, was a labour intensive job requiring a high level of skilled input. Mention has been made in the text, particularly in the period between the wars, that many of the orders for the Indian metre-gauge railways were part of a policy of converting locomotives to use superheated steam. Consequently, in a significant number of cases the orders included the supply of a whole range of associated fittings, including new piston valve cylinders and motion parts; additionally, in some cases the opportunity was also taken to fit the locomotives concerned with train braking equipment, involving yet another set of parts to be supplied. There are also cases of other smaller modifications. The type of work we are concerned with here could, and sometimes did, cause an imbalance of workload across the works and was one of the reasons why the Company was able to employ a number of skilled boilermakers from the Kerr, Stuart works at nearby Stoke-on-Trent, when it closed in 1930.

In this list the columns are: date of order; order number and whether boiler or firebox (in the cases of boilers it can be taken that a firebox would also be supplied); quantity; customer and where known, the locomotive, or class of locomotives concerned. In the case of fireboxes in some instances both the inner and outer members were supplied completely assembled, such that all that was needed by the customer was for the barrel to be fitted and the tubes inserted. A blank indicates the information is unknown.

Date	Order No	Type	Qty	Locos For	Customer/Other details
/1893	217	firebox	1		?
3/1895	603	boiler	1	Coalbrookdale /1865	Coalbrookdale Co Ltd Shropshire (Loco No 5)
11/1894	764	boiler	1	WGB 668/85 (repair)	Witley Colliery Co Halesowen Staffs'
1/1896	852	boiler	1	WGB 1455/1895	Finley Muir & Co for India
1/1897	120	boiler	1	18" gauge GNR No 1	Regent Street Polytechnic School of Engineering London (for 18" gauge miniature GNR 4-2-2)
5/1897	169	boiler	1	WGB 730/8/1886	West Clare Railway Ireland (old boiler sent for repair and scrapped and new one supplied)
2/1897	200	firebox	1		?
8/1897	318	boiler	1	Lewin /1868	B Fayle & Co Norden Clay Mines Corfe Castle Dorset (loco TINY, formerly CORFE)
8/1897	419	boiler	1		?
1/1898	623	boiler	1	WGB 1491/1897	Cliffe Hill Granite Co Ltd Markfield Leics' (loco ISABEL)
5/1898	709	boiler	1	WGB 1122/1889	Great Wyrley Colliery Cheslyn Hay Staffs' (loco GORDON)
9/1898	820	firebox	1	WGB 1414/1892	Bowling Iron Co Bradford (Loco No 4)
4/1899	113	boiler	1	WGB 1420/1893	Enoch Tempest contr' Molyneux Brow Clifton Junction Lancs' (Loco ADA)
5/1899	118	boiler	1	WGB 1050/1889	Joseph Boam Ltd East Winch Kings Lynn
5/1899	124	firebox	1	WGB 1120/1891	B Whitaker & Son Horsforth Leeds (Loco WHITAKER)
8/1899	200	boiler	1	WGB 954/1889	Brunner Mond & Co Ltd (Loco ARGON)
9/1899	246	boiler	1	WGB 1134/1889	Minvalle & Chasteret agents for Henckill du Buisson & Co Santa Lucia Antigua
1/1900	399	boiler	1	WGB 1000/1888	Manchester Corporation Rivers Dept' (Loco ROBINSON later GRANTHAM)
1/1900	416	boiler	1		WH Dickson
11/1900	839	boiler	1		?

Date	Order No	Type	Qty	Locos For	Customer/Other details
12/1900	852	boiler	1	WGB 1467-74/1895-6	Admiralty Gibraltar Dockyard (for conversion of one of these locos to a circular firebox boiler)
3/1901	979	boilers	10	Stock	Boilers 'MARGARET' type (6" cylinder) bought from Abbott & Co Newark, for stock
3/1901	991	boilers	7	Stock	Boilers 'MARGARET' type (7" cylinder) bought from Abbott & Co Newark, for stock
9/1901	283	boiler	1	WGB 1455/1895	Finley Muir & Co Calcutta (Loco COLLIER)
9/1902	842	boiler	1	WGB 1467-74/1895-6	Admiralty Gibraltar Dockyard (this was a circular firebox type boiler - as new engines had conventional fireboxes)
11/1902	920	boiler	1	WGB 1411/1893	Roberts & Co Ltd Tipton Staffs'
6/1903	294	firebox	1	WGB 1350/1891	Robert Fellows Ltd Congreaves Furnaces Cradley Heath Staffs' (Loco No 7)
8/1903	350	firebox	1	WGB 1564/1899	H&J Danks for "Robert Fellows Ltd Congreaves Furnaces Cradley Heath Staffs' (loco MABEL)
4/1904	365/612	boiler	1	WGB 792-3/1887	West Clare Railway Ireland
2/1904	629/232	boiler	1	Dubs 2890/1892	West Clare Railway Ireland (Loco SLIEVE CALLAN)
7/1904	781	boiler	1	WGB 436/1882	Bolling & Lowe
2/1905	82	boiler plates	1	WGB 1431/1894	Orme Railway Japan
3/1905	118	boiler	1	WGB 1502/1897	Shelagh Garrett & Sons New British Collieries Cradley Heath Staffs' Loco WASSELL)
5/1905	193	boiler	1	WGB 1563/1899	Islip Iron Co Ltd Northants' (Loco SLIPTON No 4)
5/1905	714	firebox	1	WGB 1134/1889	Heckill du Buisson & Co Santa Lucia Antigua
12/1905	237	boiler	1	Lewin 684-5/1877	Great Laxey Mining Co Ltd Isle of Man
7/1905	246	firebox	1	WGB 714/1885	Royal Arsenal Woolwich London (Loco APIS)
12/1905	461	boiler	1	Lewin 684-5/1877	Great Laxey Mining Co Ltd Isle of Man
10/1905	362	boiler	1	WGB 1704/1902	Swansea Corp' Cray Reservoir const' Glamorgan (Loco PENWYLLT)
10/1905	361	firebox	1		?
4/1906	602	boilers	2		Egyptian Delta Light Railways
6/1907	135	boiler	1	WGB Rebuild 104/1903	John Freakley Pelsall Staffs' (Loco ENTERPRISE)
10/1907	293	boiler	1	WGB 1418/1893	Jersey Railways & Tramways Jersey (loco CORBIERE)
10/1907	303	boiler	1	Stock	Spare 6" 'MARGARET' type for stock
6/1908	428	firebox	1	WGB 1354/1891	South Metropolitan Gas Co Vauxhall Works London (Loco COKE)
10/1908	602	boiler	1	WGB 1491/1897	Cliffe Hill Granite Co Ltd Markfield Leics' (Loco ISABEL)
10/1908	620	boiler	1	WGB 1024/1888	Islip Iron Co Northants' (Loco GERTRUDE)
10/1908	627	boiler	1	MW 917/1884	Jersey Railways & Tramways Jersey (Loco St AUBYN'S)
2/1909	717	boiler	1	WGB 1402/1892	Birchenwood Colliery Co Ltd Kidsgrove Staffs' (Loco ALEXANDER)
2/1909	718	boiler	1	WGB 1683/1902	James Byrom contr' Heaton Park Manchester (Loco ANNIE)
4/1909	777	firebox	1	HE 222/1879	Griff Colliery Co Ltd Nuneaton Warks' (Loco BRITANNIA)
9/1909	882	boilers	2	WGB 1903-4	Indian State Railways (Madras & Southern Mahratta Rly)
10/1909	900	boiler	1	WGB o/900	for 6 hp 'Colonial' stationary engine and boiler unit
10/1909	936	firebox	1	T Green /1900	West Clare Railway Ireland (Loco No 2 ENNIS)
10/1909	929	firebox	1	A Koppel	Repairs to loco under Tariff Reform (Loco named HORWICH)
4/1910	102	boiler	1	MW 916/1884	Jersey Railways & Tramways Jersey (Loco St HELIER)
4/1910	119	firebox	1	NW 304/1886	Chatterley Whitfield Collieries Ltd Staffs' (Loco ROGER)
7/1910	260	boiler	1	WGB 1454/1895	Davino dos Santos Pernambuco Brazil (Loco TEIMOSA)
10/1910	282	firebox	1		Cannock & Rugeley Collieries Cannock Staffs'
7/1910	299	boiler	1	WGB 1134/1889	Minvalle & Chasteret agents for Henckill du Buisson & Co Santa Lucia Antigua (Loco NELSON)
11/1910	351	firebox	1	WGB 1650/1901	Cliffe Hill Granite Co Markfield Leics' (Loco JACK)
10/1910	367	boiler	1	WGB 1678/1902	Gilwen Colliery Co Ltd Glamorgan (Loco GILWEN)
11/1910	521	boiler	1	Shelton 2/1910	Shelton Iron, Steel & Coal Co Ltd Etruria Staffs' (new loco built at Shelton - WALMER)
10/1910	531	firebox	1	WGB 1680/1904	Shipley Collieries (Loco WATERLOO)
3/1911	979	firebox	1		?
4/1911	33	boiler	1		Duncan Fox & Co Ltd (Barclay Style)
5/1911	122	boiler	1	Shelton 3/1911	Shelton Iron, Steel & Coal Co Ltd Etruria Staffs' (new loco built at Shelton - SHELLINGFORD)
5/1911	223	boiler	1	AB 215/226/1880-1	T&I Bradley Ltd Capponfield Furnaces Bilston Staffs'
7/1911	411	boilers	2	WGB 1505-6/1897	Assam Railways & Trading Co Ltd Assam India
8/1911	588	boiler	1	WGB 1869/1908	Crown Agents for Lagos Harbour Nigeria
9/1911	710	firebox	1	WGB 1675/1902	Mitrovich Brothers Ltd for Santiago Nitrate Co Chile
9/1911	742	firebox	1	WGB 1563/1899	Islip Furnace Co Northants (Loco SLIPTON No 4)
10/1911	808	firebox	1	P 809/1900	TA Hawkins & Sons Ltd Old Coppice Colliery Staffs'
10/1911	858	boiler	1	WGB 1000/1888	Manchester Corporation Sewage Dept' Manchester (Loco GRANTHAM)
11/1911	991	boiler	1	WGB 1829/1906	Crown Agents for Accra Harbour Gold Coast
12/1911	1086	firebox	1	WGB 1653/1901	South Metropolitan Gas Co East Greenwich London (Loco No 12)
1/1912	54	boiler	1	WGB 1869/1908	Crown Agents Lagos Harbour Nigeria
3/1912	220	boiler	1	WGB 1466/1895	Jersey Railways & Tramways Jersey (loco St. BRELADES)
2/1912	262	boiler	1	Shelton 4/1912	Shelton Iron, Steel & Coal Co Ltd Etruria Staffs' (new loco built at Shelton - GLENALMOND)
2/1912	263	firebox	1	WGB 1488/1897	Darwen & Mostyn Iron Co Darwin Lancashire (Loco JUBILEE 1897)
3/1912	342	firebox	1	WGB 1829/1906	Crown Agents for Accra Harbour Gold Coast
6/1912	359	firebox	1	WGB 1738/1906	Coventry Corp' Gas Dept' Foleshill Gas Works Coventry (Loco No 1)
4/1912	413	firebox	1	WGB 1652/1901	South Metropolitan Gas Co East Greenwich London (Loco No 11)
6/1912	727	boilers	2		Duncan Fox & Co Ltd (Barclay Style - new saddle tank supplied also to Barclay style)
7/1912	838	firebox	1	WGB 1652-3/1901	South Metropolitan Gas Co East Greenwich London
8/1912	989	boiler	1	WGB 1134/1889	Minvalle & Chasteret agents for Henckill du Buisson & Co Santa Lucia Antigua (Loco NELSON)
10/1912	1134	firebox	1		'German Loco under Tariff Reform'
10/1912	1184	boiler	1	WGB o/1184	for 6 hp 'Colonial' stationary engine and boiler unit
2/1913	257	firebox	1	HE 937/1907	Jee's Hartshill Granite & Brick Co Ltd Nuneaton Warks' (Loco ANGEL)
9/1913	1007	firebox	1	WGB 1583/1899	Grays Chalk Quarries Grays Kent (Loco DUVALS)
5/1913	556	boiler	1	WGB 1738/1906	Coventry Corp' Gas Dept' Foleshill Gas Works Coventry
6/1913	574	boiler	1	WGB 1487/1896	Cliffe Hill Granite Co Markfield Leicestershire (Loco CLIFFE)
3/1914	124	firebox	1	WGB 1671/1902	J Nelson & Sons Ltd Bramley Moor Liverpool
3/1914	259	boiler	1	WGB 1427/1894	Orconera Iron Co Spain (Loco ASTILLERO)
5/1914	384	boilers	2		Sir Duncan Fox & Co Ltd (Barclay Style - as 727 above)
7/1914	746	firebox	1	WGB 1574/1899	Manchester Corporation Sewage Dept' Manchester (Loco TREVOR)
6/1915	560	boiler	1	WGB 1841/1907	Lautaro Nitrate Co Chile
8/1915	786	firebox	1	WGB 1134/1889	Minvalle & Chasteret agents for Henckill du Buisson & Co Santa Lucia Antigua (Loco NELSON)
8/1915	863	firebox	1	WGB 1612/1900	South Metropolitan Gas Co East Greenwich London (Loco No 9)
3/1916	55	firebox	1	WGB	Charles Barlow Finedon Quarries Northants' (probably for WGB 1643/1901)
/1916	260	repair boiler	1		Cliffe Hill Granite Co Ltd Markfield Leics'
1/1917	4318	firebox	1	WGB 1613/1900	South Metropolitan Gas Co East Greenwich London (probably for WGB 1613/1900)
5/1917	4341	boiler	1	WGB 1869/1908	Crown Agents for Lagos Harbour Nigeria

Date	Order No	Type	Qty	Locos For	Customer/Other details
8/1917	4890	boiler	1	WGB 1459/1897	Roberts & Co Tipton Green Furnaces Staffs' (Loco STAFFORD)
5/1918	5845	boilers	4	AB	Ministry of Supply WD for Barclay 0-6-0WToc locos War Dept' Light Railways
8/1918	6188	firebox	1		Associated Portland Cement Manufacturers Ltd (Loco No 3)
9/1918	6495	boiler	1	WGB 1842/1907	Alfred Herbert Ltd Coventry
5/1918	8856	firebox	1	WGB 1738/1906	Coventry Corp' Gas Dept' Foleshill Gas Works Coventry
10/1918	4539	boiler	1	AB	T&I Bradley Limited Capponfield Furnaces Bilston Staffs' (for Andrew Barclay loco)
12/1918	6860	boilers	2	SS 3369/73/1887	Clogher Valley Railway Ireland
1/1919	6992	boiler	1	Gilker Wilson 128/61	Weardale Steel Co (loco No 3 - possibly Gilkes Wilson 128/1861 CRAWLEYSIDE)
2/1919	7087	firebox	1	AB	T&I Bradley Ltd Capponfield Furnaces Bilston Staffs' (Loco CHRISSIE)
/1919	7179-80	boilers	2		Bolivar Railway Co Venezuela
6/1919	7186	boiler	1	WGB 1441/1894	Pollock & Mc Nab agents sent to Pernambuco Brazil (Loco HERCULES)
7/1919	7234	boilers	3		Bengal & North Western Railway India
5/1919	7406	firebox	1	WGB	Rahr & Ramdrup Hojbyguard Sugar Factory Denmark (suitable for WGB 1440/1894:1686/1902:1784/1905)
6/1919	7545	boiler	1	WGB 1618/1900	Enderby & Stoney Stanton Granite Co Ltd Enderby Leics' (Loco LESTER)
2/1920	7919	boiler	1		Lautaro Nitrate Co Chile
1/1920	8259	boiler	1	WGB 1731/1904	Croft Granite Brick & Concrete Co Ronez Quarry Jersey (Loco PROGRESS)
1/1920	8281	boiler	1	WGB 1636/1901	HB Perry & Co Bihia El Salvador
3/1920	8503	boiler	1	WGB 1418/1893	Jersey Railways & Tramways Jersey (Loco CORBIERE)
4/1920	8581-2	firebox plates	4 sets		E Thornton & Co (for locos 11,13,15,16)
10/1920	9254	firebox	1	WGB 1453/1895	Alfred Hickman & Co Ltd Bilston Staffs' (Loco PHILLIS)
10/1920	9314	boiler	1	WGB 1996/1914	Lautaro Nitrate Co Chile (Loco No 16)
1/1921	2513	boiler	1	WGB 1461/1895	EPS Jones for Rye & Camber Tramway Kent (Loco CAMBER)
1/1921	2531	boiler	1	WGB 1820/1907	North Wales Iron & Manganese Mines Rhiw Aberdaron (Loco RHIW)
1/1921	2534	boiler	1	WGB 1660/1902	Enderby & Stoney Stanton Granite Co Ltd Enderby Leics' (Loco KITCHNER)
5/1921	3014	boiler	1	WGB 1453/1895	Alfred Hickman & Co Ltd Bilston Staffs' (Loco PHILLIS)
7/1921	3220	boiler	1	WGB 1723/1903	Robert Hudson for Les Forges & Foundries du Maurice Mauritius
8/1921	3258	boiler	1	WGB 1929/1911	Tongaat Sugar Co Natal South Africa (Loco REPEAT)
10/1921	3294	boiler	1	HL 2085/1889	South Metropolitan Gas Co East Greenwich London (Loco No 3 - firebox supplied by customer)
10/1921	3294A	boiler	1	HL 2095/1887	South Metropolitan Gas Co East Greenwich London (Loco No 2)
8/1921	3295	boiler	1	WGB 1614/1900	Penmaenmawr & Welsh Granite Co Penmaenmawr (Loco ISABEL)
10/1921	3453	boiler	1	WGB 1608/1900	Threlkeld Granite Co Ltd Keswick Cumberland (Loco THRELKELD)
12/1921	3693	boiler	1		Jodhpur Railway India (for metre gauge M and P class 4-6-0 engines)
12/1921	3694	boiler	1		Jodhpur Railway India (for metre gauge J and O class 4-4-0 engines)
12/1921	3695-6	boilers	2		Jodhpur Railway India (for metre gauge EE class 2-4-0 engines)
2/1922	3697-3705	boiler plates	9 sets		Rendel Palmer & Tritton Ltd for Indian Sates Railways
4/1922	3752	boiler	1	HC	Rendel Palmer & Tritton for Indian State Railways (for 2'6" gauge 2-8-2)
2/1922	3900	boiler	1	WGB 1672/1902	Broadoak Collieries Gorsenion Glamorgan (Loco BROADOAK)
3/1922	3905	firebox	1	HE 976/1908	Jee's Hartshill Granite & Brick Co Ltd Nuneaton Warks' (Loco NORWOOD)
6/1922	4331	boiler	1	WGB 1635/1901	Assam Frontier Tea Co Assam India
7/1922	4424	boiler	1		North Western Railway India (for 2'6" gauge 0-6-2 J class)
7/1922	4541	boiler	1	WGB 1000/1888	Manchester Corporation Sewage Dept' Manchester (Loco GRANTHAM)
8/1922	4568	boiler	1	WGB	Baroda State Railway India (for 2'6" gauge 0-6-2 W class)
9/1922	4679	boiler	1	WGB 1874/1908	Crown Agents for Accra Harbour Gold Coast
2/1923	4887	boiler	1	WGB 1560/1899	Hastings Corp' Brede Water Works Sussex (Loco BREDE)
12/1922	5114	boiler	1		Yorkshire Engine Co Ltd Sheffield
3/1923	5304	firebox	1	WGB 2072/1918	BEA Fibre & Industrial Co Ltd Mosongateni Estate Mombasa Nigeria
1/1923	5542	boiler	1	WGB 1766/1907	Meanofferen Slate Quarry Bleanau Festiniog (Loco SKINNER)
4/1923	5543	boiler	1	WGB 1617/1900	Blair Campbell & Mclean Ltd agents for Usina Sao Bento Bahia Brazil (Loco VIRGINIA)
7/1923	5946	Boiler	1	Lill /1872	Cannock & Rugeley Collieries Ltd Staffs' (Loco No 4 RAWNSLEY)
11/1923	6297	boiler	1	AB	Warrington Gas Works (for either AB 806/1897 or AB 876/1900)
12/1923	6549	boiler	1	WGB 1869/1901	Crown Agents for Lagos Harbour Nigeria
1/1924	6589	boiler	1	WGB 1738/1906	Coventry Corp' Gas Dept' Foleshill Gas Works Coventry
1/1924	6600	boiler	1		South India Railway (for metre gauge 0-6-0 F class)
1/1924	6607	boiler	1		South India Railway (for metre gauge 4-4-0 O class)
2/1924	6828	boiler	1	WGB 2051/1916	Punjab Coal Co Karachi India (Loco KUTHALA)
3/1924	6898	boiler	1	WGB 1659/1901	Enderby & Stoney Stanton Granite Co Ltd Enderby Leics' (Loco BULLER)
8/1924	7531	boiler	1	WGB 1952/1912	Exhall Colliery & Brickworks Exhall Warks' (Loco EXHALL No 4)
10/1924	7632	boiler	1	BH 877/1886	Manchester Corporation Sewage Dept' Manchester (Loco HUGO SHAW)
9/1924	7637	boiler	1	WGB 1660/1902	Enderby & Stoney Stanton Granite Co Ltd Enderby Leics' (Loco KITCHNER)
12/1924	7966	boiler	1	WGB 1823-4/1908	Mitrovich Brothers Ltd for export to Chile
12/1924	7967	boiler	1	WGB 1871-2/1908	Mitrovich Brothers Ltd for export to Chile
3/1925	8324	firebox	1	WGB 1534/1898	South Metropolitan Gas Co Old Kent Road Works London (Loco UNITY)
4/1925	8578	boiler	1		Madras & Southern Mahratta Railway India (for metre gauge 4-8-0 GS class)
5/1925	8563	boiler	1	WGB 1977/1913	Dobson & Dawson for De Beers Consolidated Mines Ltd South Africa
7/1925	8884	boilers	1	WGB 2238-42/1924	Baburizza & Co for Lautaro Nitrate Co Chile
8/1925	8990	boiler	1	Gilber 1659/1901	Enderby & Stoney Stanton Granite Co Enderby Leicestershire (Loco BULLER)
9/1925	9090	firebox	1	WGB 1993/1914	Mc Leod Russell & Co Ltd for Tezpur Balipara Railway Assam India (Loco No 4)
11/1925	9194	boiler	1	WGB 1438/1894	Jokai (Assam) Tea Co Ltd Assam India (Loco PEKOE TIP)
11/1925	9259	boiler	1	WGB 1424/1893	London County Council Beckton Sewage Works London (Loco No 2)
11/1925	9267	boiler	1	WGB	Rendel Palmer & Tritton for Bombay Baroda & Central India Railway (2' 6" gauge W class)
1/1926	3054	boiler	1	WGB 1962/1913	Assam Railways & Trading Co Ltd Assam India (Loco NAMCHICK)
1/1926	3130	boiler	1	WGB 1437/1894	Assam Railways & Trading Co Ltd Assam India (Loco NAMDANG)
1/1926	3131	boiler	1	WGB 1556/1899	Assam Railways & Trading Co Ltd Assam India (Loco TARAKUSI)
4/1926	3420	boiler	1		McLeod Russell & Co Ltd for India
12/1926	4105	boiler	1	WGB 2014-5/1915	Baroda State Railway (for 2'6" gauge 0-6-2 W class)
1/1927	4247	boiler	1	WGB 2110-29/1920	Indian State Railways (for metre gauge 0-6-0 F class)
2/1927	4345	boiler	1	WGB 1596/1900	Butterley Co Ltd Hilts Limestone Quarry Derbys' (Loco SALISBURY)
1/1927	4411	firebox	1	WGB 2233/1924	Lehane McKenzie & Shand Ltd contrs' Holmbridge Reservoir const, Batley Yorks' (Loco BATLEY)
2/1927	4484	boiler	1	WGB 1739/1907	Exhall Colliery & Brickworks Exhall Warks' (Loco ENTERPRISE) order included Owens poppet valve regulator
2/1927	4544	boiler	1	WGB 1779/1906	Crown Agents for Nigerian Railways
3/1927	4624	boiler	1	WGB 1941/1911	United Alkali Co Ltd Soliel Coronada Spain (Loco TEJON)
5/1927	4759	boilers	3	WGB 2278-83/1925-6	Gaekwar's Baroda State Railway India
5/1927	4785	firebox	1	WGB 1535/1898	South Metropolitan Gas Co East Greenwich Works London (Loco No 8)

Date	Order No	Type	Qty	Locos For	Customer/Other details
6/1927	4913	boilers	2	MW/VF	Bengal Provincial Railway India (for 2'6" gauge 2-4-0T locos built by MW and VF 1893-1909)
6/1927	4941	boilers	5		Bengal Dooars Railway India (for metre gauge 0-6-0 F class engines)
7/1927	4998	firebox	1	WGB 1980/1913	Eastwell Iron Ore Co Eastwell Quarries Leics' (sent Markham & Co Chesterfield where loco PIONEER under repair)
11/1927	5449	boiler	1		North Western Railway India (for 2' 6" gauge 2-8-2 G/S class)
12/1927	5575	boiler	1	WGB 1484/1896	John & James Knox for Groudle Glen Railway Isle of Man (Loco SEA LION)
3/1928	5974	firebox	1	WGB 2218/1923	Lehane Mc Kenzie & Shand Ltd contr' Gorple Reservoir const' Yorks (Loco HALIFAX)
7/1928	6420	boiler	1	WGB 1940/1911	Crown Agents for Lagos Harbour Nigeria
4/1929	7333	firebox	1	WGB 1392/1892	Staffordshire Chemicals (1917) Co Ltd Longport Staffs'
4/1929	7456	boiler	1	WGB 1563/1899	Islip Iron Co Ltd Islip Quarries Northants' (Loco SLIPTON No 4)
5/1929	7462	firebox	1	HE	North Western Railway of Uruguay
4/1929	7496	boiler	1	Brighton /1877	Cannock & Rugeley Collieries Ltd Staffs' (Loco No 9 CANNOCK WOOD)
5/1929	7524	boiler	1	WGB 1993/1914	McLeod Russell & Co for Tezpur Balipara Tramway Assam India (Loco No 4)
5/1929	7581-2	fireboxes	2		Great Southern of Spain Railway
6/1929	7686	boiler	1	WGB 1000/1888	Manchester Corporation Sewage Dept' Manchester (Loco GRANTHAM)
7/1929	7777	boilers	4	WGB 2328-9/1928	Assam Railway & Trading Co Ltd Assam India (for metre gauge 4-6-0 H class engines)
8/1929	7832	boiler	1	WGB 1618/1900.	Enderby & Stoney Stanton Granite Co Ltd Enderby Leics' (Loco LESTER)
12/1929	8307	boiler	1	WGB 1781/1905	John & James Knox for Groudle Glen Railway Isle of Man (Loco POLAR BEAR)
5/1930	8819	boiler	1	WGB 1574/1899	Manchester Corporation Sewage Dept' Manchester (Loco No 4 TREVOR)
6/1930	8905	boiler	1	WGB 1944/1911	Crown Agents for Nigeria
9/1930	9207-9	firebox plates	3 sets	KS	Gwalior State Railway India
9/1930	9210	boiler	1	KS 1207/1911	Gwalior State Railway India (2'0" gauge 2-8-2)
12/1930	9497	boilers	2		South India Railway (for metre gauge 0-6-0 N class engines)
4/1931	9534	firebox	1	WGB 2272/1925	Exhall Colliery & Brickworks Ltd Exhall Colliery Warks' (Loco BESSIE)
4/1931	9583	boiler	1	WGB 1952/1912	Exhall Colliery & Brickworks Exhall Warks' (Loco EXHALL No 4)
3/1931	9650	boiler	1	WGB 1491/1897	Cliffe Hill Granite Co Ltd Markfield Leics' (Loco ISABEL)
3/1931	9701	boiler	1	BP	Peruvian Corporation Ltd Central Railway of Peru (for Std gauge Class 20 engines)
6/1931	3509	boilers	4		Bengal & North Western Railway India (for P and New B class 4-6-0 metre gauge engines)
6/1931	3510	boiler	1		Bengal & North Western Railway India (for Old B class 4-6-0 metre gauge engines)
11/1931	3927	boilers	6		HRH Nizam's State Railway India (for metre gauge 0-6-0 F class engines)
11/1931	3949	boiler	1	WGB 1741/1904	Eastern Province Cement Co Natal South Africa
2/1932	3954	boilers	5		Assam-Bengal Railway Assam India (for metre gauge 0-6-0 F class engines - superheated)
2/1932	4213	boiler	1		Madras & Southern Mahratta Railway India (for metre gauge 4-8-0 GS class engines - superheated)
4/1932	4312	boilers	11		South India Railway (for converting metre gauge 4-6-0 B class engines to superheat)
4/1932	4343	boiler	1	WGB 1787/1905	The Briton Ferry Works Ltd Briton Ferry Glamorgan (Loco THE DOLL)
4/1932	4411	firebox	1	WGB 2233/1924	Lahane McKenzie & Shand Ltd contrs' Gorple Reservoir Wks Hebden Bridge Yorks' (Loco BATLEY)
6/1932	4490	firebox	1	WGB 2193/1922	West Cannock Colliery Co Ltd Hednesford Staffs' (Loco TOPHAM)
7/1932	4636	firebox	1	KS 4034/1920	Edward Lloyd Ltd Sittingbourne Kent (Loco SUPERIOR)
7/1932	4670	boilers	5		McLeod Russell & Co Ltd for Eastern Bengal Railway India (for converting P class metre gauge to superheat)
7/1932	4677	boilers	5		McLeod Russell & Co Ltd for Eastern Bengal Railway India (for converting R class metre gauge to superheat)
7/1932	4698	firebox	1	WGB 1681/1903	Birmingham Corp' Gas Dept' Swan Village Works Birmingham (Loco FORWARD No 3)
8/1932	4795	boilers	2		North Western Railway India (for Q class 2' 6" gauge 4-6-2)
8/1932	4797	boilers	4		North Western Railway India (for G class 2' 6" gauge 2-8-2)
8/1932	4829	boilers	3		North Western Railway India (for K class 2' 6" gauge 2-6-2T)
9/1932	4863	boiler repairs	1	WGB 2233/1924	Lahane McKenzie & Shand Ltd contrs' Gorple Reservoir Wks Hebden Bridge Yorks' (Loco BATLEY)
11/1932	4868	firebox plates	1		Dorking Greystone Lime Co Ltd Betchworth Surrey
11/1932	5159	boiler	1	WGB 1753/1904	Ariston Gold Mines (1929) Ltd Gold Coast
3/1934	4934	boiler	1	KS 4055/1920	L Mitchell & Co Ltd for Mauritius
11/1932	4937	firebox	1	KS 3096/1918	Baldwins Ltd Port Talbot Steel Works (Loco ITALY)
1/1933	5243	boiler rebuilt	1	HE 544/1891	Pooley Hall Colliery Co Ltd Polesworth Warks' (loco COWBURN new firebox fitted)
3/1933	5535	boiler	1	KS 4064/1924	L Mitchell & Co Ltd for Mauritius
/1933	5704	boiler	1		S Yates (vertical cross tube boiler)
7/1933	5974	firebox	1	WGB 2218/1923	Lahane McKenzie & Shand Ltd contrs' Gorple Reservoir Wks Hebden Bridge Yorks' (Loco HALIFAX)
7/1933	5979	boiler	1	WGB 2378-80/1929	Burma Corporation Ltd Burma Mines
8/1933	6065	boiler	1	MW/VF	Bengal Provincial Railway India (for 2'6" gauge 2-4-0T locos built by MW and VF 1893-1909)
9/1933	6124	boiler	1	WGB 2108/1923	Worthington & Co Ltd Burton-on-Trent Staffs' (Loco No 5)
9/1933	6125	boiler parts	1		Uruguay Northern Railway
10/1933	6220	firebox	1	WGB 2219/1923	Lahane McKenzie & Shand Ltd contrs' Gorple Reservoir Wks Hebden Bridge Yorks' (Loco TAFF FAWR)
1/1934	6419	firebox	1	P 1068/1905	Madeley Collieries Ltd Leycett Staffs' (Loco HESKETH - firebox fitted to boiler at Stafford)
12/1934	6468	firebox	1		?
12/1933	6591	boiler	1	KS 830/1903	L Mitchell & Co Ltd for Mauritius
5/1935	6631	boiler	1	KS 4045/1920	L Mitchell & Co Ltd for Mauritius
1/1934	6656	boiler	1	KS 840/1907	L Mitchell & Co Ltd for Mauritius
1/1934	6678	boiler	1	KS 4060/1921	L Mitchell & Co Ltd for Mauritius
5/1934	6686	firebox	1	HL 3642/1925	Glascote Colliery Co Ltd Amington Colly' Tamworth Warks' (loco AMINGTON No 2 at Stafford for overhaul)
1/1934	6767	firebox	1	KS 1358/1914	L Mitchell & Co Ltd for Mauritius
2/1934	6797	boilers	5		Assam-Bengal Railway (for metre gauge 0-6-0 F class engines - saturated)
2/1934	6844	firebox	1	DK	New Consolidated Goldfields Ltd Takoradi Gold Coast
2/1934	6845	firebox	1	DK	New Consolidated Goldfields Ltd Takoradi Gold Coast
2/1934	6846	firebox	1	DK	New Consolidated Goldfields Ltd Takoradi Gold Coast
2/1934	6847	firebox	1	DK	New Consolidated Goldfields Ltd Takoradi Gold Coast
3/1934	6934	firebox	1	KS 4064/1924	L Mitchell & Co Ltd for Mauritius
3/1934	6970	firebox	1	HL 3081/1914	Birmingham Corp' Gas Dept' Saltley Gas Works Birmingham (Loco FORWARD No 26)
5/1934	7024	boiler	1		West Cannock Colliery Co Ltd Hednesford Staffs'
5/1934	7200	boiler	1	HE 1356/1919	Jee's Hartshill Granite & Brick Co Ltd Hartshill Nuneaton Warks' (Loco 3240)
5/1934	7234	boilers	2		Jodhpur Bikaner Railway India (for metre gauge 4-6-0 MS class engines)
6/1934	7237	boilers	2		Jodhpur Bikaner Railway India (for metre gauge 4-6-0 P & M 4-6-0 engines)
6/1934	7264	firebox	1	P 1205/1909	Madeley Collieries Ltd Leycett Staffs' (loco LENA, boiler at Stafford for firebox to be fitted)
7/1934	7345	boilers	17		Eastern Bengal Railway India (for metre gauge 4-6-0 P class engines converted to superheat)
8/1934	7450	boilers	2	WGB 2136/1920	McLeod Russell & Co Ltd for Tezpur Balipara Tramway Assam India (Loco No 5)
8/1934	7590	boiler	1		Peruvian Corporation Ltd Central Railway of Peru (2-8-0 tender loco)
8/1934	7641	boiler	1		Guest Keen & Nettlefolds Ltd
9/1934	7669	firebox	1	WGB 1421/1893	South Metropolitan Gas Co Old Kent Road Works London (Loco CONCORD)
11/1934	8008	boilers	6		Iraq Government (for metre gauge 4-6-0 HGS class engines)

Date	Order No	Type	Qty	Locos For	Customer/Other details
12/1934	8138	boiler	1	WGB	Stock Boiler 6" cylinder circular firebox type
1/1935	8250	boiler repairs	1		The Horsehay Co Ltd Salop (either CF 1192/00 or AB 1094/06)
3/1935	8449-50	firebox plates	2	MW 1657/05 - P633/96	Associated Portland Cement Manufacturers Ltd Kent Works Stone Kent (locos APEX & HILTON)
3/1935	8425	boilers	2		Greaves Cotton Ltd for Great Indian Peninsular Railway (for 2'6" gauge 2-8-4T engines)
6/1935		firebox	1	HL	South Metropolitan Gas Co East Greenwich Works London
9/1935	8471	firebox	1	KS 4210/1920	L Mitchell & Co Ltd for Mauritius
3/1935	8475	boilers	2		Great Indian Peninsular Railway (for 2' 6" gauge 2-8-4T engines)
3/1935	8549	boilers	2	WGB 2278-83/1925-6	Gaekwar's Baroda State Railway India.
5/1935	8631	boiler	1	KS 4045/1920	L Mitchell & Co Ltd for Mauritius
6/1935	8702	firebox	1	HL	South Metropolitan Gas Co East Greenwich Works London
6/1935	8703	firebox	1	WGB 1653/1901	South Metropolitan Gas Co East Greenwich Works London (Loco No 12)
7/1935	8926	firebox	1		Messrs Blairs Ltd Mysore India (for a 2-4-2T loco unidentified)
8/1935	9021	boiler	1	Crewe /1865	ICI Ltd Witton Works Birmingham (ex LNWR 1439/3042)
10/1935	9168	boiler	1	AE 1695/1915	Powell Duffryn Ltd Aberaman Colly Glamorgan (Loco No 2)
9/1935	9177	boilers	2	WGB 1984-9/1914	Cutch State Railway India
2/1937	9276	boiler	1	KS 1170/1910	L Mitchell & Co Ltd for Mauritius
12/1935	9534	boiler	1	KS 2487/1916	ICI Ltd Winnington Works Northwich Cheshire (Loco CAVENDISH)
1/1936	9590	boiler	1	WGB1830-1/1907	Bengal & North Western Railway India
1/1936	9634	firebox	1	AB 1480/1916	Mitchells &Butlers Ltd Smethwick Staffs' (Loco BONIFACE)
3/1936	9688	firebox/blr reps	1	N 3451/1885	Gas Light & Coke Co London (loco No 16 boiler at Stafford for repairs)
1/1936	9751	boilers	2	KS 2394/1915	L Mitchell & Co Ltd for Mauritius
2/1936	9773	firebox	1	KS 1316/1915	L Mitchell & Co Ltd for Mauritius
2/1936	9807	fireboxes	3		Central Uruguay Railway
3/1936	9835	boiler	1	KS	L Mitchell & Co Ltd for Mauritius
3/1936	9888	boiler	1		?
8/1936	9897	boilers	5		Midland Uruguay Railway
3/1936	9918	firebox	1	WGB 2517/1934	New Cransley Iron Co Northants' (Loco No4 DAVID)
5/1936	9966	boiler	1	Borrows /1888	ICI Ltd Winnington Works Northwich Cheshire (loco NEWTON)
5/1936	9980	boilers	2		Jodhpur Railway India (for metre gauge P & M class 4-6-0 engines)
5/1936	3034	boilers	2		Great Indian Peninsular Railway (for 2' 6" gauge 2-8-4T engines)
5/1936	3054	boiler	1	KS 4410/11	Burma Corporation Ltd Burma Mines (KS 'HUXLEY' class engines)
5/1936	3055	boiler	1	KS 4139-42/1924-26	Burma Corporation Ltd Burma Mines (KS 'HUXLEY' class engines)
6/1936	3162	boilers	6		Gaekwar's Baroda State Railway (for metre gauge F class 0-6-0 engines)
9/1936	3465	boiler	1	HC 959/1911	Dholpur State Railway India (2'0" gauge 2-8-4T No 4)
9/1936	3468	boilers	2	KS	Dholpur State Railway India (2'0" gauge 2-6-2T KS 946/1906 or 974/1907 Nos 2-3)
8/1936	3481	firebox	1		Central Uruguay Railway
11/1936	3580	boiler	1	WGB 1870/1908	British Phosphate Commission Ocean Island (Loco ELLA)
12/1936	3805	boiler	1	WGB 2472/1932	Edward Lloyd Ltd Sittingbourne Kent (may have been for KS 4034/1920 SUPERIOR)
12/1936	3838	boilers	2		Assam Railways & Trading Co Ltd Assam India (for metre gauge 4-6-0 H class engines)
1/1937	3855	boilers	2	WGB	Cutch State Railway India (for 2'6" gauge 4-6-0)
12/1936	3886	firebox	1	KS 1297-8/1914	Gwalior Light Railway India (for 2'0" gauge 2-8-2 engines)
12/1936	3891	firebox	1	KS 2369-70/1915	Gwalior Light Railway India (for 2'0" gauge 2-6-2 engines)
12/1936	4058	boiler	1	D 2064/1884	Brymbo Steel Co Ltd Wrexham (Loco BASIC crane tank)
12/1936	4059	boiler	1	DS /1870	Berry Hill Collieries Ltd Stoke-on-Trent (loco BERRY HILL NO 2)
1/1937	4083	fireboxes	3		Egyptian Delta Light Railways Egypt
2/1937	4100	boiler	1	KS 4400-3/1938	Gwalior State Railway India
3/1937	3800	boiler	1		Gas Light & Coke Co London
3/1937	4112	boiler	1	KS 4048/1921	L Mitchell & Co Ltd for Mauritius
2/1937	4135	boiler shell	1	KS 1214/1914	L Mitchell & Co Ltd for Mauritius
3/1937	4137	boiler	1	NW 304/1886	Chatterley Whitfield Collieries Ltd Stoke-on-Trent (Loco ROGER)
3/1937	4194	boilers	2	HC	Great Indian Peninsular Railway (for 2' 6" gauge 2-8-4T engines)
4/1937	4299	firebox	1	WGB 2472/1932	Edward Lloyd Ltd Sittingbourne Kent (Loco ALPHA)
2/1937	4276	boiler	1	KS 1170/1910	L Mitchell & Co Ltd for Mauritius
2/1937	4332	boiler	1	KS 1214/1914	L Mitchell & Co Ltd for Mauritius
6/1937	4350	boilers	2		Great Indian Peninsular Railway
3/1937	4391	boiler	1	KS 814/1903	L Mitchell & Co Ltd for Mauritius
3/1937	4487-8	boiler	1	WGB 2223/1924	Stewarts & Lloyds Ltd Tinsley Park Colly' Kilnhurst York's (Loco ELSIE)
3/1937	4411	firebox	1	WGB 2233/1924	Lahane McKenzie & Shand Ltd contrs' Fernilee Reservoir Wks Derbys' (Loco BATLEY)
6/1937	4489	boilers	2		Madras & Southern Mahratta Railway India (for metre gauge 4-6-0 MHS class engines)
4/1937	4519	boilers	19		Buenos Ayres Western Railway (for F Class engines Nos 24-43)
3/1937	4527	boiler alterations	1	WGB 2108/1923	Worthington & Co Ltd Burton-on-Trent (Loco No 5)
4/1937	4535	firebox	1	Robert Heath No 7or 8	Cowlishaw Walker & Co Ltd Biddulph Stoke-on-Trent, for Norton & Biddulph Collieries Ltd
4/1937	4555	firebox	1	Robert Heath No 7or 8	Cowlishaw Walker & Co Ltd Biddulph Stoke-on-Trent, for Norton & Biddulph Collieries Ltd
6/1937	4601	boilers	2	KS/RS /1900-30	Fox & Mayo agents for Sao Paulo Railway (for steam brake locomotives)
6/1937	4732	boiler	1	HC	Manchester Ship Canal Co
6/1937	4921	boilers	2		Jodhpur Bikaner Railway India (for metre gauge P & M class 4-6-0 engines)
8/1937	5111	boiler	1	WGB 2202/2332-7/1928	Crown Agents Nigerian Railways
11/1937	5597	boiler	1		Madras & Southern Mahratta Railway India (for metre gauge VS Class)
11/1937	5598	boiler	1		Madras & Southern Mahratta Railway India (for metre gauge FS Class 0-6-0 engines - superheated)
11/1937	5599	boiler	1		Madras & Southern Mahratta Railway India (for metre gauge DS Class)
11/1937	5600	boiler	1		Madras & Southern Mahratta Railway India (for metre gauge AS class 2-4-0T engines)
11/1937	5601	boiler	1		Madras & Southern Mahratta Railway India (for metre gauge PWP Class)
3/1938	5705	boiler	1	CF 1172/1899	Chatterley Whitfield Collieries Ltd Stoke-on-Trent (Loco PHOENIX)
12/1937	5806	boilers	8		Bengal Nagpur Railway India (for 2' 6" gauge BS class 2-8-2 engines)
1/1938	6006	boiler	1		ICI Ltd Winnington Works Northwich Cheshire (KS PRIESTLEY Type)
1/1938	6018	boiler	1	YE 282/1876	Chatterley Whitfield Collieries Ltd Stoke-on-Trent (Loco KATIE)
6/1938	6215	repair boiler	1	N 5087/1896	Gas Light & Coke Co Ltd London (Loco No 25: new firebox fitted)
8/1938	6218	repair boiler	1	N 4250/1896	Gas Light & Coke Co Ltd London (Loco No 21: new firebox fitted)
6/1938	6298	firebox	1	K	Walsall Wood Colliery Co Ltd Brownhills Staffs'
4/1938	6349	boilers	8		Bengal Nagpur Railway India (for 2' 6" gauge 2-8-2 engines)
6/1938	6543	boilers	6		Bengal & North Western Railway (for metre gauge FS class 0-6-0 engines - superheated)
2/1939	6742	boiler	1	P 687/1898	Admiralty Portland Dockyard Dorset (Loco No 6)
9/1938	6886	firebox	1	Lewin /1868	B Fayle & Co Ltd Norden Clay Mines Corfe Castle Dorset (Loco TINY formerly CORFE)-new boiler found necessary

Date	Order No	Type	Qty	Locos For	Customer/Other details
9/1938	6913	firebox plates	1		South Metropolitan Gas Co London
11/1938	6992	firebox	1		East Hetton Collieries Ltd Durham
11/1938	7037	firebox	1	AB 1703/1920	Dunlop Rubber Co Ltd Fort Dunlop Birmingham (Loco No 3)
11/1938	7056	boiler	1		Bengal Dooars Railway India (for metre gauge FS 0-6-0 class engines)
11/1938	7076	firebox	1		Pinxton Collieries Ltd Notts'
12/1938	7114	boiler	1	Lewin /1868	B Fayle & Co Ltd Norden Clay Mines Corfe Castle Dorset (Loco TINY formerly CORFE) see 6886 above
11/1938	7203	firebox	1		Port of Calcutta Commissionaires India
12/1938	7207	firebox	1		Cyprus Railway
12/1938	7313	boilers	3	VF 3439-43/1921	Iraq Railways (metre gauge HGS class 4-6-0 engines)
4/1939	7520	boilers	2		Haines & Sons Ltd London for India or Burma
2/1939	7540	boiler	1	WGB 2488-93/1933	Gaekwar's Baroda State Railway India
4/1939	7663	boiler	1	MW 1913/1917	Cannock & Rugeley Collieries Ltd Staffs' (Loco 6 ADJUTANT)
4/1939	7612	boiler	1	HC 800/1908	Chatterley Whitfield Collieries Ltd Stoke-on-Trent (Loco ALEXANDRA)
3/1939	7674	firebox	1		Cowlishaw Walker & Co Ltd Biddulph Stoke-on-Trent
4/1939	7705	firebox	1		Carlton Main Colliery Co Ltd York's
3/1939	7737	boiler	1	KS 1297-8/1914	Gwalior Light Railway India (for 2'0" gauge 2-8-2 engines)
4/1939	7738	boiler	1	KS 2369-70/1915	Gwalior Light Railway India (for 2'0" gauge 2-6-2 engines)
4/1939	7816	boilers	2	HC	Great Indian Peninsular Railway (for 2' 6" gauge 2-8-4T engines)
4/1939	7817	boilers	2	NBL 21452-54/1917	Great Indian Peninsular Railway (for 2' 6" gauge B/1 class 2-8-2 engines)
4/1939	7833	boilers	4		Assam-Bengal Railway India (for metre gauge M class 4-6-0 engines)
4/1939	7836	firebox	1		Central Uruguay Railway
4/1939	7843	boiler	1	KS	Glasgow Corporation Gas Dept' Dalmarnock Works Glasgow (for 2'0" gauge 0-4-0WT locos)
5/1939	7853	boilers	5		Bengal & North Western Railway India (for metre gauge PS 4-6-0 class engines)
6/1939	7964	Boiler back end	1	WGB 2480-505/23/1933	T A Martin Light Railways India
6/1939	8004	firebox	1	HL 3460/1921	TA Hawkins & Sons Ltd Old Coppice Colly' Cheslyn Hay Staffs' (Loco TONY)
5/1939	8039	fireboxes	4		Barsi Light Railway India
6/1939	8066	firebox	1	DK /1901	Settle Speakman & Co Ltd Queenborough Wharf Kent (Loco MAYBURY)
5/1939	8114	firebox	1		Central Uruguay Railway
6/1939	8232	boilers	2	NBL	North Western Railway India (for 2' 6" gauge G class 2-8-2 engines)
7/1939	8247	firebox	1	Butt /1892	Butterley Co Ltd Bailey Brook Colly Derby's (loco B3C)
11/1939	8311	firebox	1	WGB 2321/1927	A&H MacNay Ltd Natal South Africa - for Umfolozi Sugar Plantations
8/1939	8425	boilers	2	WGB	India (for 2'6" gauge 2-6-2 ZB class engines)
9/1939	8437	boiler	1		Midland Uruguay Railway (convert loco to superheat)
10/1939	8656	boiler	1	KS 1108/1913	L Mitchell & Co Ltd for Mauritius
11/1939	8786	boilers	3		Assam-Bengal Railway Assam India (for metre gauge H class 4-6-0 engines)
11/1939	8799	boiler	1	WGB 2108/1923	Worthington & Co Ltd Burton-on-Trent (Loco No 5)
12/1939	8802	firebox	1	P 1114/1907	Dunlop Rubber Co Ltd Fort Dunlop Birmingham Warks' (Loco No 4)
12/1939	8820	firebox	1	WGB 2136/1920	Mc Leod Russell & Co Ltd for Tezpur Balipara Railway Assam India (Loco No 5)
1/1940	9045	firebox	1		Port of Calcutta Commissioners India
1/1940	9051	firebox	1		NV Nederlandish Spoonweg
2/1940	9056	boiler	1		WR Bland & Co Ltd
2/1940	9057	boiler	1		WR Bland & Co Ltd
5/1940	9075	firebox	1	YE 283/1876	Chatterley Whitfield Collieries Ltd Stoke-on-Trent (Loco ALICE)
4/1940	9084	boilers	3		Jodhpur Bikaner Railway (for metre gauge F class 0-6-0 engines)
3/1940	9103	boiler	1	HL 2593/1902	Chatterley Whitfield Collieries Ltd Stoke-on-Trent (Loco EDWARD V11)
2/1940	9141	boiler	1	WGB 2245/1924	L Mitchell & Co Ltd for Mauritius Savina Sugar Estate
6/1940	9142	boiler	1	MW 2018/1922	Littleton Collieries Ltd Huntington Staffs' (Loco LITTLETON No 5)
11/1940	9223	boilers	3	WGB 2306/1927	Eastern Bengal Railway India (spares for 'C' class 2'6" gauge 2-4-0T locos)
4/1940	9276	boiler	1	BH 242/1873	Shelton Iron Steel & Coal Co Ltd Stoke-on-Trent (Loco LORD FARINGDON)
5/1940	9361	firebox	1		Cowlishaw Walker & Co Ltd Biddulph Stoke-on-Trent
5/1940	9372	boilers	5		Rohilkund & Kumaon Railway India (for metre gauge P & B class 4-6-0 engines)
7/1940	9458	firebox	1	WGB 2107/1923	Birchenwood Coal & Coke Co Ltd Kidsgrove Staffs' (Loco ALEXANDER)
/1940	9463	boiler	1	KS	Glasgow Corporation Gas Dept' (for 2'0" gauge 0-4-0WT)
5/1940	9472	firebox	1	WGB 1421/1893	South Metropolitan Gas Co Old Kent Road Works London (Loco CONCORD)
6/1941	9655	firebox	1	WGB 1563/1899	Stewarts & Lloyds Ltd Islip Ironstone Quarries Northants' (Loco SLIPTON No 4)
6/1941	9675	boiler	1	P 1491/1917	Brereton Collieries Ltd Brereton Staffs' (loco VANGUARD)
5/1941	9747	boilers	4		Jaipur State Railway India (for metre gauge O class 4-4-0 engines)
8/1940	9762	firebox	1		Conduit Colliery Co Ltd Brownhills Staffs'
9/1940	9816	boiler	1	FE	African Reality Trust for Zbeediela Estates Transvaal South Africa (for Falcon 'Lawley' class 4-4-0 engine)
2/1941	9829	boiler	1	WGB 1884/1908	Somerset Collieries Ltd Norton Hill Colliery Somerset (Loco GRAZEBROOK)
11/1940	9849	firebox	1	AE 1343/1892	Berry Hill Collieries Ltd Stoke-on-Trent Staffs' (Loco BERRY HILL No 1)
1/1941	3681	firebox	1		Harton Coal Co Ltd Durham
2/1941	3698	firebox	1	OK 12430/1933	L Mitchell & Co Ltd for Mauritius (loco at Alma Sugar Estate 0-6-0T 2'5 ½" gauge)
2/1941	3793-4	firebox plates	2 sets		Linditives Stokvis (Dutch Co trading in Dutch East Indies) - sent to Celebes
1/1941	3819	boilers	5		Bengal & North Western Railway India (for metre gauge PS class 4-6-0 engines)
2/1941	3865	firebox	1	KS 814/1903	L Mitchell & Co Ltd for Mauritius
3/1941	3992	firebox plates	1		Linditives Stokvis (Dutch Co trading in Dutch East Indies) - sent to Celebes
8/1941	4014	boiler	1	WGB 1641/1901	Park Gate Iron & Steel Co Ltd Rotherham York's (Loco FRENCH)
10/1941	4033	boilers	2	AE 1724-5/1915	Port of Bristol Authority Avonmouth Docks (locos WILLIAM & HUDSON)
5/1941	4184	boiler	1	AB 1365/1914	Brereton Collieries Ltd Brereton Staffs' (No 3 loco)
7/1941	4511	boiler	1		Midland Uruguay Railway (conversion of engine to superheat) Replace 8437 lost at sea?
9/1941	4780-2	firebox plates	3 sets		Linditives Stokvis (Dutch Co trading in Dutch East Indies) - sent to Celebes
8/1941	4587	boiler	1	FE	African Reality Trust for Zbeediela Estates Transvaal South Africa (for Falcon 'Lawley' class 4-4-0 engine)
10/1941	4859	firebox	1		Linditives Stokvis (Dutch Co trading in Dutch East Indies) - sent to Celebes
10/1941	4904	firebox	1	AE 1804/1918	Metropolitan Cammell Carriage & Wagon Co Ltd Saltley Warks' (engine 37 at Stafford for repairs)
12/1941	5086	firebox	1		Linditives Stokvis (Dutch Co trading in Dutch East Indies) - sent to Celebes
1/1942	5089-5	firebox plates	7 sets		Linditives Stokvis (Dutch Co trading in Dutch East Indies) - sent to Celebes
1/1941	5161	firebox plates	1		Linditives Stokvis (Dutch Co trading in Dutch East Indies) - sent to Celebes
1/1942	5170	boilers	3		Rohilkund & Kumaon Railway India (for metre gauge P & B class 4-6-0 engines)
2/1942	5192	firebox	1	BH 826/1883	Harton Coal Co Ltd Durham (Loco No 4)
6/1942	5276	firebox	1	YE 326/1881	Chatterley Whitfield Collieries Ltd Stoke-on-Trent (Loco POLLIE)
4/1943	5410	firebox	1		Morvi Railway India (for metre gauge P class 4-6-0 engines)
4/1943	5411	firebox	1		Morvi Railway India (for metre gauge O class 4-4-0 engines)

Date	Order No	Type	Qty	Locos For	Customer/Other details
5/1943	5413	boiler	1		Morvi Railway India (for metre gauge E class 0-4-2 engines)
4/1943	5412	boiler	1	WGB 2367-8/1929	Morvi Railway India (for metre gauge P class 4-6-0 engines)
4/1942	5442	firebox	1	WGB 2229/1924	York Gas Co York Gas Works (Loco CENTENARY)
4/1943		boiler	1	WGB 2367-8/1929	Morvi Railway India
7/1942	5642	boiler	1	AE 1724/1915	Port of Bristol Authority Avonmouth Docks (loco HUDSON)
9/1942	5449	firebox plates	1		Stewarts & Lloyds Limited
9/1943	5511	boilers	5		Bengal & North Western Railway (for metre gauge 4-6-0 PS class engines)
10/1942	6028	firebox	1	Butt /1907	Butterley Co Ltd Ollerton Colliery Notts' (loco No 21)
6/1943	6035	firebox	1	HC 1452/1921	Stewarts & Lloyds Ltd Islip Ironstone Quarries Northants (DIKE - quoted as SLIPTON No 11)
7/1943	6090	boiler	1	AE 1382/1897	Birchenwood Coal & Coke Co Ltd Kidsgrove Staffs' (loco No 2 at Stafford for rebuilding)
5/1943	6111	boiler	1	WGB 1673/1902	Wolverhampton Gas Co Wolverhampton Gas Works (Loco CARBON)
6/1944	6169	boiler	1	WGB 2077/1918	Cliffe Hill Granite Co Ltd Markfield Leics' (loco MABEL at Stafford for repairs - work cancelled)
2/1943	6358	firebox	1		ICI Ltd Winnington Works Northwich Cheshire (for 'Burrows' well tank 0-4-0 loco)
4/1943	6547	boiler	1	KS 1049/1908	Edward Lloyd Ltd Sittingbourne Kent (loco EXCELSIOR)
5/1943	6629	firebox	1	WGB 1702/1943	Pauling & Co Ltd contrs'
4/1943	6590	firebox	1	AE 1770/1917	Brymbo Steel Co Ltd Wrexham (loco ARENIG)
9/1943	6768	firebox	1		Rendel Palmer & Tritton for Burma Railways
8/1944	6839	boiler plates	1		Rendel Palmer & Tritton for Mysore Railway (metre gauge 4-6-0)
8/1944	6840	boiler plates	1		Rendel Palmer & Tritton for Mysore Railway (metre gauge M class 4-6-0)
6/1943	6799	boiler	1	AB 1613/1918.	ICI (Dyestuffs) Ltd Huddersfield York's (loco 1613 at Stafford for repairs)
9/1943	6834	boilers	5		Bengal & North Western Railway India (for metre gauge PS class 4-6-0 engines)
6/1943	6846	boiler	1	WGB 2569-70/1936	Oudh & Tirhut Railway India
10/1943	7187	firebox	1	Lill	Lilleshall Co Ltd Okengates Salop'
/1943	7209	boiler	1	KS	Glasgow Corporation Gas Dept' (for 2'0" gauge 0-4-0WT)
11/1943	7399	firebox plates	1		Bradley & Foster Ltd
10/1943	7415	firebox	1	AB 1285/1914	Gloucester Railway Carriage & Wagon Co Ltd Gloucester (Loco PHOENIX)
2/1944	7493	firebox	1	KS	Workington Iron & Steel Co Ltd Workington (for 'Moss Bay' type 0-4-0ST locos Fleet Nos 15/55-7)
1/1944	7581	firebox	1	WGB 2475/1933	Union Cold Storage Co Ltd Westland New Zealand
2/1944	7717	boilers	2		Bengal & North Western Railway (for metre gauge PS class 4-6-0 engines)
11/1944	7718	firebox	1	WGB 1272/1890	Stanton Iron Works Co Ltd Holwell Works Fitting Shop Leics' (Loco BOTTESFORD)
3/1944	7890	boilers	5		Indian Stores Department (for metre gauge 4-6-0 P class engines)
3/1944	7903	firebox repairs	1	WGB 2622/1940	Butterley Co Ltd Bailey Brook Colliery Derby' (Loco BUTTERLEY No 52)
5/1944	7997	firebox	1	WGB 2203/1923	Eastwell Iron Ore Co Ltd Leics' (Loco MOUNTANEER)
10/1944	8039	firebox	1	Maffei	L Mitchell & Co Ltd for Mauritius
7/1944	8196	firebox	1		ICI Ltd Winnington Works Northwich Cheshire (for 'Burrows' well tank 0-4-0 loco)
2/1945	8319	boiler	1	WGB	Tongaat Sugar Co Tongaat Natal South Africa
1/1945	8445	firebox repairs	1	WGB 2605/1938	Butterley Co Ltd Ollerton Colliery Notts' (Loco BUTTERLEY No 31)
10/1944	8478	firebox plates	1		T A Martin & Co India
9/1945	8885	boiler	1	WGB 2545/1936	A&H MacNay Ltd for Crookes Bros' Renishaw Sugar Estates Natal South Africa (Loco RENISHAW No 5)
1/1946	9859	boiler	1	WGB 2406/1929	McLeod Russell & Co Ltd for Singri-Banchoi River Tea Co Ltd Assam India
6/1945	9048	firebox	1	WGB 1612/1900	South Metropolitan Gas Co East Greenwich Works London (Loco No 9)
11/1945	9067	firebox	1	Beckton 1/1902	Gas Light & Coke Co Beckton Gas Works London (Loco No 30)
11/1945	9068	firebox	1	N 3789/1888	Gas Light & Coke Co Beckton Gas Works London (Loco No 19)
4/1945	9172	firebox	1	KS	Workington Iron & Steel Co Ltd (spare for 'Moss Bay' type locos Nos 15;55;55;57)
12/1945	9188	boiler	1	WGB 2466/1932	Steetley Lime & Basic Co Ltd Porthywaen Lime Works Salop (Loco WHITEHAVEN No 1)
8/1945	9398	firebox	1	YE 282/1876	Chatterley Whitfield Collieries Ltd Stoke-on-Trent (Loco KATIE)
9/1945	9463	boiler	1	KS 1279/1912	Glasgow Corporation Gas Dept' Dawsholm Gas Wks Glasgow (for 2' 0" gauge 0-4-0WT)
9/1945	9515	firebox	1		Central Uruguay Railway
7/1946	9541	boiler	1	P 656/1897	British Soda Co Ltd Sandbach Cheshire
3/1946	9604	boiler	1	WGB 2843-4/1946	Jamnagar & Dawarka Railway India (spare to go with new locos)
9/1943	9747	boilers	4		Indian State Railways (for metre gauge 0 class 4-4-0 engines - ordered at same time as WGB 2633-5)
11/1945	9638	boiler	1	WGB 2611/1940	Mufulira Cooper Mines Northern Rhodesia
3/1946	9886	boiler	1	OK 12388/1932	A Gloster & Co Ltd for Mauritius (loco No 73)
3/1946	3554	boilers	2	WGB 2167-9/1921	Pauling & Co Ltd contrs'
4/1946	3594	boilers	12	WGB	Gaekwar's Baroda State Railway India (for 2' 6" gauge W class 0-6-2 engines)
4/1946	3631	boilers	2	WGB	McLeod Russell & Co Ltd for Tezpur Balipara Tramway India (spares for WGB 1993/2136/2255)
7/1946	3848	boiler	1	WGB 2515/1934	British (Guest Keen Baldwins) Iron & Steel Co Ltd Margam Glamorgan (Loco KENFIG)
7/1946	3911	boiler	1	WGB	McLeod Russell & Co Ltd for Tezpur Balipara Tramway India (spares for WGB 1993/2136/2255)
4/1947	3960	boilers	2		Barsi Light Railway India (for 2' 6" gauge F class 2-8-2 locomotives)
12/1946	4276	firebox plates	1		South Metropolitan Gas Co London
3/1947	4439-40	firebox plates	2 sets		British Geco Engineering Co Ltd London for export to Turkey
7/1947	4318	firebox	1	WGB 1534/1898	South Metropolitan Gas Co Old Kent Road Works London (Loco UNITY)
9/1947	4567	boiler	1	WGB	Tongaat Sugar Co Ltd Natal South Africa (spares for WGB 4-4-0T locos)
6/1948	4662	boilers	2	WGB 2447-8/1930-1	Assam Railway & Trading Co Assam India
8/1948	4669	boiler	1	Robert Heath No 15/1915	NCB Victory Colliery Biddulph Stoke-on-Trent (Loco No 15)
4/1947	4723	boiler repair	1	WGB 2908/1947	NCB Berry Hill Colliery Stoke-on-Trent (Loco BERRY HILL No 3 - rebuild of WGB 1584/1899)
/1947	4973	firebox	1	WGB	McLeod Russell & Co for India (spare for WGB 2022-31/2411-2) Mc Leods Light Railways
3/1949	4946	boiler	1		Glasgow Corporation Gas Dept'
9/1947	4952	fireboxes	4		TA Martin & Co Light Railways India
/1947	5170	boiler	1		Rohilkund & Kumaon Railway India
1/1948	5189	boiler	1	WGB 2413/1930	African Manganese Co Takoradi Gold Coast
1/1948	5238	boiler	1	WGB 2518-20/1935	Junagadh State Railway India
1/1948	5490	boiler	1		Jamnagar Dawarka Railway India (for metre gauge FM Class 0-6-0 engines)
5/1948	5380	boiler	1	WGB 2872-5	Morvi Railway India (spare boiler supplied with engines)
1/1948	5570	boiler	1	WGB 1952/1912	Leicestershire Colly & Pipe Co Ltd New Lount Colly Leics'
12/1947	5608	boiler	1	FE	African Reality Trust for Zbeediela Estates Transvaal South Africa (for Falcon 'Lawley' class 4-4-0 engine)
2/1949	5640	firebox	1	WGB 1459/1897	CA Parsons & Co Ltd Newcastle-on-Tyne
12/1949	5642	boiler	1	AE 1764/1917	Port of Bristol Authority Avonmouth Docks (loco PORTBURY) sub-let to Yorkshire Engine Co
3/1950	5643	boiler	1	P 1721/1926	Port of Bristol Authority Avonmouth Docks (loco FYFFE)
2/1949	5690	firebox	1	Butt 21C/1907	Butterley Co Ltd Ollerton Colliery Notts' (loco No 21)
3/1948	5756	boiler	1	WGB 2227-8	TH Davies & Co (New York) for North Negros Sugar Co Iloilo Philippines
5/1948		firebox	1		NCB Sneyd Colliery Burslem Stoke-on-Trent
10/1948	5918	boiler	1		Ceylon Government Railway (for 5' 6" gauge B1 class 4-8-0 engine)

Date	Order No	Type	Qty	Locos For	Customer/Other details
7/1948	5956	firebox	1	AB 1113/1907	NCB Florence Colliery Longton Stoke-on-Trent (Loco BOWOOD)
7/1948	6072	boiler	1	YE 326/1881	NCB Chatterley Whitfield Colliey Stoke-on-Trent (loco POLLIE)
7/1948		boiler	1		Anglo Iranian Oil Co
6/1948	6093	boilers	3	WGB	Tongaat Sugar Co Ltd Natal South Africa (spares for WGB 4-4-0T locos)
6/1948	6110	boilers	2	WGB 2447-8/1930-1	Assam Railways & Trading Co Assam India (boiler would be suitable for other WGB 7" locos owned by this Co)
7/1948	6184	boilers	3	WGB 2500-2/1934	Greaves Cotton & Co Ltd for Mewar State Railway India
7/1948	6185	boiler	1		Greaves Cotton & Co Ltd for Mewar State Railway India (for metre gauge G class 2-8-0 engines)
1/1949	6290	boilers	3	WGB 2480/2505/23/1933	TA Martin & Co Bukhtiarpur Bihar Light Railway India
11/1948	6420	boiler	1	WGB 2202/1923	Crown Agents Nigerian Railways
10/1948	6486	boiler	1	RHLM No 9/1926	NCB Victory Colliery Biddulph Stoke-on-Trent (Loco No 9)
4/1951	6542	boilers	2		Jodhpur State Railway (for metre gauge MS class 4-6-0 engines)
7/1951	6543	boiler	1		Jodhpur State Railway (for metre gauge T class 2-6-2T engines)
8/1950	6640	boiler	1	YE 947/1907	Goldendale Iron Co Ltd Chatterley Stoke-on-Trent (Loco CLIFFORD) sub-let to Yorkshire Engine Co
10/1948	6838	boiler	1	WGB 2526-7/1935	Mysore State Railway (for TS class 2-6-2T engines)
1/1947	6841	boiler	1		Rohilkund & Kumaon Railway India (for metre gauge TS class 2-6-2T engines)
1/1948	6842	boilers	2		Mysore State Railway (for metre gauge HPS class 4-6-0 engines)
5/1951	6883	firebox	1	YE 947/1907	Goldendale Iron Co Ltd Chatterley Stoke-on-Trent (Loco CLIFFORD) - presumably for another of their YE locos
9/1949	7140	firebox	1		Buchi Light Railway Nigeria
6/1949	7156	boiler	1	WGB 2227-8	TH Davies & Co (New York) for North Negros Sugar Co Iloilo Philippines
2/1949	7209	boiler	1	KS	Scottish Gas Board Glasgow
10/1949	7538	boiler	1		High Commissioner for Pakistan (for 2' 6" gauge ZB class engines)
11/1950	7605	firebox	1	P 879/1901	NCB West Cannock Colliery Hednesford Staffs' (loco No 3)
/1949	7717	boiler	1	WGB	Indian Stores Dept' (for 2'6" gauge 0-6-2 W class engines)
12/1949	7738	boiler	1	Robert Heath No16/1924	Norton & Biddulph Collieries Ltd Biddulph Stoke-on-Trent (Loco No 16)
7/1947	7890	boilers	5		Oudh & Tirhut Railway India (for metre gauge F class 0-6-0 engines)
9/1950	8075	firebox	1		Sierra Leone Government Railway (for 2' 6" gauge class 163 4-8-0 engines)
4/1950	8122	boiler	1		India Stores Dept' via Rendel Palmer & Tritton (for metre gauge ST class 2-6-4T engines)
8/1950	8343	firebox	1	WGB 2353/1928	Perak Hydro-Electric Co Malay (Loco PRH-EP)
4/1951	8378	boilers	3	NW	Bombay Port Trust India
4/1951	8468	firebox	1		Stewarts & Lloyds (South Africa) Ltd
1/1951	8727	firebox	1		Stewarts & Lloyds (South Africa) Ltd
3/1951	9034	firebox	1	YE 282/1876	NCB Chatterley Whitfield Colly Stoke-on-Trent Staffs' (Loco KATIE)
6/1951	9170	firebox	1	WGB 2578-9	Turkiye Demir Velelin Karabuk Iron & Steel Works Turkey
4/1951	9194	firebox	1		Guest Keen & Nettlefolds Ltd for Pakistan
8/1951	9259	firebox	1		Stewarts & Lloyds (South Africa) Ltd
9/1952	9302	firebox	1	WGB 2525/1935	ICI Metals Ltd Gaskell Works Widnes (Loco GASKELL)
9/1951	9452	fireboxs	2		Crown Agents
11/1952	9391	firebox	1	WGB 2221/1927	British Sugar Corporation Alscott Factory Salop' (Loco LEWISHAM)
/1951	9583	firebox	1	WGB 1952/1912	NCB New Lount Colliery Leics'
8/1951	9600	boiler	1	RHLM No 10/c1910	NCB Victory Colliery Biddulph Stoke-on-Trent (Loco No 10)
9/1951	9601	boiler	1	BH 949/1888	NCB Victory Colliery Biddulph Stoke-on-Trent (Loco No 11)
11/1951	9706	fireboxs	3		Crown Agents for Nigerian Railways
9/1951	9724	boilers	3	WGB 2016-21/1915	Mc Leod Russell & Co Ltd for McLeod owned railways in India
9/1951	9793	fireboxes	3		Martin Burn Ltd for export to India
1/1953	9892	firebox	1		Guest Keen & Nettlefolds Ltd for export to Pakistan
5/1952	9901	repair boiler	1	WGB 2107/1923	Birchenwood Coal & Coke Co Ltd Kidsgrove Staffs' (Loco ALEXANDER)
6/1952	9953	repair boiler	1		Bowaters Lloyd Ltd Sittingbourne Kent
8/1952	4060	firebox	1	WGB 2208/1923	Greaves Cotton & Co Ltd for export to India
9/1952	4153	firebox	1		Assam Railways & Trading Co Assam India
7/1952	4182	firebox	1	WGB 2816/1946	NCB Eastwood (Moor Green) Colliery Notts' (Loco BUTTERELEY No 35)
3/1953	4185	firebox	1	P 1491/1917	NCB Brereton Colliery Staffs' (loco VANGUARD)
2/1952	4228	firebox	1		New Cransley Iron & Steel Co Ltd Northants'
11/1952	4296	firebox	1	WGB 1673/1902	West Midlands Gas Board Wolverhampton Gas Works (Loco CARBON)
5/1952	4355	repair boiler	1	WGB 2451/1931	Taylor Tunnicliffe & Co Ltd Stone Staffs'
4/1952	4392	fireboxes	2	WGB 2630-2/1940	Steel Company of Wales Margam South Wales
8/1952	4409	boilers	5		Jodhpur Bikaner Railway India (for metre gauge SP 4-6-0 engines)
10/1952	4460	boiler	1	WGB 2108/1923	Worthington & Co Ltd Burton-on-Trent Staffs' (Loco No 5)
10/1952	4410	boilers	5		Jodhpur Bikaner Railway India (for metre gauge SP 4-6-0 engines)
9/1952	4628	repair boiler	1	P 1274/1912	NCB Silverdale Colliery Staffs' (Loco SILVERDALE No 11)
10/1952	4646	repair boiler	1	Borrows	ICI Ltd Winnington Works Northwich
7/1953	4711	firebox	1	HC 1754/1943	NCB Foxfield Colliery Cheadle Staffs' (Loco ARTHUR LEIGHTON)
4/1953	4806	firebox	1		NCB Eastwood (Moor Green) Colliery Notts'
10/1952	4833	firebox	1	HC 1418/1923	NCB Holditch Colliery Newcastle Staffs' (Loco WINWICK)
3/1953	4845	repair boiler	1	WGB 2469/1932	Frazer & Chalmers Engineering Co Ltd Erith Kent
1/1953	4919	firebox	1		Baldwins (South Africa) Ltd
1/1953	4985	firebox	1	WGB 2643/1941	NCB Moreton Colliery Derbys'
4/1953	5014	firebox	1	WGB 2623/1940	Shelton Iron & Steel Co Ltd Etruria Stoke-on-Trent Staffs'
7/1953	5107	firebox	1	MW 1913/1917	NCB Rawnsley Colliery Staffs' (for loco ADJUTANT)
9/1953	5251	boiler	1	G&SLE /1956	G&S Light Engineering Co Stourbridge (for new loco KATIE 15" gauge 2-4-2 for Dudley Zoo)
4/1954	5314	repair boiler	1	YE 326/1881	NCB Chatterley Whitfield Colly Stoke-on-Trent Staffs' (Loco POLLIE)
1/1953	5333	firebox	1		Sierra Leone Government Railway (for 2' 6" gauge SP class engines)
3/1954	5598	boiler back	1	WGB 2627/1940	Tozer Kemsley & Millbourn Ltd South Africa for Tongaat Sugar Co Natal.
8/1953	5492	firebox	1	WGB 2657-8/1952	North Thames Gas Board Beckton Gas Works London
3/1953	5609	firebox	1	WGB 2669/1942	Staveley Iron & Chemical Co Ltd Lamport Ironstone Mines Northants
2/1954	5627	fireboxes	2		Burma Corporation Ltd Burma Mines
7/1953	5693	firebox	1		NCB Eastwood (Moor Green) Colliery Notts'
6/1953	5770	boiler	1		Greaves Cotton & Co Ltd for India
5/1953	5802	repair firebox	1		Central Electricity Authority Meaford Generating Station Staffs'
5/1953	5803	repair firebox	1		Central Electricity Authority Meaford Generating Station Staffs'
4/1954	5806	fireboxes	2		Burma Corporation Ltd Burma Mines
10/1953	5937	firebox	1	P 1068/1905	NCB Madeley Colliery Staffs' (loco HESKETH)
5/1954	6056	boiler	1	Lill /1866	NCB Rawnsley Colliery Staffs' (for loco RAWNSLEY No 4)
7/1953	6149	firebox	1		Staveley Iron & Chemical Co Ltd Lamport Ironstone Mines Northants

Date	Order No	Type	Qty	Locos For	Customer/Other details
1/1954	6288	repair boiler	1		Pauling & Co Ltd contr'
3/1954	6351-2	fireboxes	2		NCB Ollerton Colliery Derbys'
10/1955	6369	boiler repairs	1	MW 1640/1904	NCB Stafford Colliery Fenton Stoke-on-Trent
10/1953	6376	firebox	1		Crown Agents for Nigerian Railways
12/1953	6422	firebox	1		Stewarts & Lloyds (South Africa) Ltd
1/1953	6486	boiler	1	RHLM No 9/1926	NCB Norton Colliery Stoke-on-Trent Staffs' (Loco No 9)
4/1954	6514	firebox	1	WGB 2991/1950	NCB Florence Colliery Stoke-on-Trent Staffs' (Loco No 1)
3/1952	6519	repair boiler	1	HL 2782/1909	Patent Shaft & Axletree Co Ltd Wednesbury Staffs (Loco No 9 at Stafford for repairs)
12/1953	6710	firebox	1		South Eastern Gas Board
6/1954	7157	boilers	2		Ministry of Supply War Department (spare boilers for 'Austerity' 0-6-0ST engines)
2/1955	6899	repair boiler	1		Shell Refining & Marketing Limited
5/1955	6253	repair boiler	1		WD Engineering Services
6/1955	7442	repair boiler	1		NCB Florence Colliery Stoke-on-Trent
7/1955	7208	boilers	2		Crown Agents for Nigerian Railways
8/1955	9081	repair boiler	1	WGN 2612/1939	George Richards & Company Limited Altringham
10/1955	7300	firebox	1		NCB Kingsbury Colliery Warks'
12/1955	5794	repair boiler	1		NCB Deep Pit Colliery Stoke-on-Trent
12/1955	8637	repair boiler	1		Parkgate Iron & Steel Company Limited
7/1954	7564	repair boiler	1	G&SLE /1949	G&S Light Engineering Co Stourbridge (for 15" gauge 4-6-0 loco 5751 under repair by G&LSE for Dudley Zoo)
8/1954	7609	fireboxes	2		India Stores Department (for 5'6" gauge locos)
12/1954	7652	boiler	1	WGB 2870/1948	Rustenburg Platinum Mines Ltd Rustenburg South Africa
4/1955	7684-5	boilers	2	WGB 2518-20/1935	Junagadh State Railway India
6/1954	8122	boiler	1		India Stores Department (superheated)
5/1955	8602	repair boiler	1	WGB 2450/1931	Horseley Bridge and Thomas Piggott Ltd Dudley Port - work done on-site
8/1955	8603	boiler	1		India Stores Department (for metre gauge N class 0-6-0 engines)
11/1955	8604	boiler	1		Bhavangar State Railway India (for 2'6" gauge 4-8-0 engines)
4/1954	9198	boiler	1		Crown Agents Mauritius Railways (spare for K 5440-3 std gauge 0-8-0T engines)
8/1954	9199	boiler	1		Crown Agents Mauritius Railways (VF 2-6-2T)
1/1957	9507/9557	boiler	1	G&LSE/1950	G&S Light Engineering Co Stourbridge (15" gauge 4-6-2 loco 57512 under repair by G&SLE for Dudley Zoo)
1/1956	6501	repair boiler	1		NCB Chatterley Whitfield Colliery Stoke-on-Trent
2/1956	9630	firebox	1		Stewarts & Lloyds Ltd export to South Africa
10/1956	9837	firebox	1		McLeod Russell & Co Ltd for India
9/1956	4251	repair boiler	1	RSH 7285/1945	NCB Cinderhill Colliery Notts
10/1956	4269	boiler	1	WGB 2588/1939	Stewarts & Lloyds (South Africa) Ltd Vereeniging Transvaal South Africa
7/1957	4279	boilers	2	WGB 2541/1935	Vizagapatnam Port Trust India (spares for 0-4-0T locos 2' 0" gauge supplied earlier)
6/1956	4354	boiler	1	WGB 2903-6/1950	Mysore Iron & Steel Works Bhadravati Mysore India
6/1956	4385	boiler	1	K 4737/1910	Dorman Long & Co Ltd Middlesbrough Yorks' (Loco No 26)
10/1956	4423	boiler	1	WGB 2369/1929	Gypsum Mines Ltd Mouthfield Sussex (Loco SIRAPITE)
7/1954	4567	boilers	4	WGB	Gaekwar's Baroda State Railway India (for 2'6" gauge W class 0-6-2 engines)
1/1954	4568	boiler	1	WGB 2453-60/1932	Gwalior Light Railway India
10/1957	5787	fireboxes	5		Crown Agents
7/1957	5463	boiler	1	KS	NCB Thornley Colliery Yorks' (for KS 0-6-0T oc)
1/1955	5820	boilers	2	WGB	Tozer Kemsley & Millbourn Ltd for Tongaat Sugar Co Natal South Africa (spares for 2' 0" gauge 4-4-0T engines)
8/1957	5838	firebox	1		FH Lloyd for 7¼" gauge Hilton Valley Railway Bridgenorth Salop (4-6-2 loco LORNA DOONE)
7/1955	5927	boiler	1	FE /1886	NCB Norton Colliery Stoke-on-Trent Staffs' (Loco No 6)
9/1957	5951	firebox	1		Stewarts & Lloyds Ltd
3/1958	5995	boilers	4	WGB	West India Portuguese Railway Goa, India (GS class 4-8-0 locos)
4/1958	6876	repair boiler	1	WGB 2167/1921	Pauling & Co Ltd contrs' (may have been for WGB 2167/1921 - work done on site at Coalville)
5/1958	6973	boiler	1	WGB	West India Portuguese Railway Goa, India
6/1958	7150	firebox	1		Guest Keen & Nettlefolds Ltd Pakistan (for North Western Railway 2' 6" gauge J class 0-6-2 engines)
9/1958	7442	repair boiler	1	BH 949/1888	NCB Victoria Colliery Biddulph Stoke-on-Trent Staffs' (Loco No 11new firebox fitted)
9/1958	7458	firebox	1	WGB 2545/1936	Tozer Kemsley & Millbourn Ltd for Crookes Brothers Ltd Renishaw Sugar Estate Natal South Africa
12/1958	7679	repair firebox	1	WGB 2672/1942	CEGB Thornhill Generating Station York's (Loco YEP No 3)
12/1958	7685	firebox/blr reps	1	KS 1049/1908	Bowaters Lloyd Ltd Sittingbourne Kent (loco EXCELSIOR)
12/1958	7735	fireboxes	2	KS 4385/93/1926-7	Burma Corporation Ltd Burma Mines
12/1958	7739	fireboxes	2	WGB 2378-80/1929	Burma Corporation Ltd Burma Mines
4/1959	7931-2	firebox plates	2		
7/1959	8752	firebox	1		Crown Agents
12/1955	8757	boiler	1	WGB	NCB West Midlands Div' North Staffs' Area (spare for WGB 16" 0-6-0ST locos built to manufacturer's No 3089 in Loco List)
10/1959	8805	firebox	1		NCB Littleton Colliery Huntington Staffs'
9/1959	9050	firebox	1		
11/1959	9094	boiler	1	RS 2730/1891	NCB Beamish Colliery Durham (loco TWIZELL)
6/1960	9353	firebox	1		NCB Littleton Colliery Huntington Staffs'
3/1960	9500	firebox	1		Crown Agents for Nigerian Railways
4/1960	4246	firebox	1		NCB Marley Hill Colliery Durham
10/1960	5309	firebox	1	HL 2769/1909	NCB Wearmouth Colliery Durham (Loco JEAN)
9/1960	5331	firebox	1	RSH 7132/1944	NCB Boldon Colliery Durham (Loco 7132)
8/1960	5463	firebox	1		Crown Agents
9/1960	5682	repair boiler	1	WGB 3059/1953	NCB Florence Colliery Stoke-on-Trent (Loco FLORENCE No 2)
12/1960	5707	firebox	1		NCB Ashington Unit Northumberland
9/1960	5787	firebox	1	KS	NCB Thornley Colliery Durham
/1960	6092	boilers	2	WGB 2378-80/1929	Burma Corporation Ltd Burma Mines (sub-contracted to Andrew Barclay Sons & Co Ltd Kilmarnock)
1/1961	6163	firebox	1		NCB Ashington Unit Northumberland
/1961	6244	boiler	1	WGB 2537/1935	Associated Portland Cement Co Ltd Wah Karachi Pakistan (Loco RICHARD)

APPENDIX V

PRESERVED BAGNALL LOCOMOTIVES

An attempt has been made here to list Bagnall locomotives known to have survived into some form of preservation. The words 'some form' are appropriate as in a number of cases the locomotives, while saved from scrap, have had little or in some instances no attention since. Several have been placed on plinths and while perhaps initially cosmetically attended to, have subsequently had no attention. However, while in some countries the climate is such that little deterioration takes place, in others this is by no means the case and some locomotives are in a pretty deplorable condition, with it would appear, little prospect of the situation changing. The columns have the manufacturer's number, the date the locomotive was built along with any name, number or other designation, followed by its last known location. Some locomotives on operating railways in this country are on occasions moved on a temporary basis between locations, either on-hire for periods or in connection with special events of one sort or another. In this list what is understood to be their 'permanent' home is the one shown. The last column has a letter or letters, a key in reference to the list below, of the last known condition of the locomotive concerned. In a number of cases where locomotives are used on preserved or other railways their condition at any particular point in time may vary allowing for overhauls, repairs and other attention. For example a locomotive shown in this list as in working order, in a year's time might have been taken out of service and dismantled, in whole or part, for overhaul. Readers should also note that in many cases the locomotives are on private property and not available for inspection without the permission of the owners. We cannot over emphasis that in such cases privacy should be respected. To the best of our knowledge this list is correct at March 2008.

a. In a dismantled condition; in some cases for overhaul/restoration to working order.

b. Cosmetically restored and on static-display; in most cases the locomotive concerned will be relatively easily available for inspection, although perhaps at restricted times - public open days for example.

c. Un-restored; may have parts missing or in fact be part or wholly dismantled.

d. Under restoration to working order.

e. Not available for inspection without permission of the owner.

f. In working order and occasionally in use on the railway where it is kept, or on loan or hire to other railways.

Readers wanting to be kept fully abreast of the on-going situation with the locomotives listed here can do no better than consult the Industrial Railway Society's Handbook - *Industrial Locomotives* - which lists all locomotives in the United Kingdom and Ireland not in the capital-stock of the main-line railways. The book is regularly reissued with updated information and between editions Society members receive regular updates based on observations. The Society also attempts to keep track through its other publications of locomotives in other countries, as does the *Continental Railway Journal*, published four times a year by the Continental Railway Circle.

Manu No	Year Built	Name/No	Location	Condition
1058	1889	38	Curitiba Railway Museum, Praca Eufrasio Correia, Brazil	b
1278	1890	THE COALITION	Llechwedd Slate Mine Blaenau Ffestiniog North Wales (converted to electric loco)	b
1425	1893		Michael List-Brain Preston Kent	c,e
1437	1894	HASSANG	Coal India Offices Margherita Assam India	b
1445	1895	THE ECLIPSE	Llechwedd Slate Mine Blaenau Ffestiniog North Wales (converted to electric loco)	b
1484	1896	SEA LION	Groudle Glen Railway Isle of Man	f
1491	1897	ISABEL	Amerton Working Farm Staffs'	f
1506	1897	HASANG	The Indian Railway Museum Delhi	b
1556	1899		Assam Oil Industry Museum Digboi Assam India	b
1568	1899	(DOROTHY)	Klondyke Mill Draycott-in-the-Clay Staffs'	c,d,e
1625	1901	N.W.R. 119 E	Mysore Railway Museum Karataka India	b
1705	1903	THISTLE No 1	Malawi Rly Limbe Station	b
1707	1903	PRIMROSE	Indian Railway Museum Delhi	b
1716	1903		Esplus, Huesca Province Spain	b
1719	1903	SHAMROCK No 2	Malawi Rly Malwi Museum Malawi	b
1760	1906	SYBIL	J Evans Callington Cornwall	d,e
1781	1905	POLAR BEAR	Amberley Industrial Museum Sussex	f
1801	1907	MARGARET	Cobdogla Irrigation & Steam Museum South Australia	f
1814	1906	OLIVE	De Beers Kimberley Mine Museum South Africa	b
1817	1906		Nazareth House Kimberley South Africa	b,e
1845	1907		Hedeland Veteran Railway Denmark	b
o/245	1908	No 2: No 3 (2 locos)	No 2 at Løkken Museum: No 3 at Trondheim University Norway	f,b
1857	1909		Ferrymead Museum New Zealand	c

Manu No	Year Built	Name/No	Location	Condition
1888	1910	CHILENITA	Humberstone, on Pan American Highway Iquique Chile	b
1889	1911	No 1	Amerton Working Farm Staffs'	a
1922	1911	ANNIE	Kauri Milling Museum Kerikeri New Zealand	f
1914	1910	DIECIOCHO	Oficina Pedro de Valdvia Chile	b
1981	1913	SANTA THEREZA	Santa Thereza Sugar Mill Goiana Pernambuco Brazil	b
1992	1914	577	Divisional Railway HQ Rajkot Western Railway India	b
1976	1913	574	Divisional Railway HQ Ajmer Western Railway India	b
2008	1915	BK 3	Sealdah Station Eastern Railway India	b
2009	1914	BK 4	Rambagh Palace Hotel Jaipur India	b
2029	1916	KF 4	Phyllis Rampton NG Railway Trust Godalming Surrey	c,e
2040	1916	1 ERICA	Verin, Galicia Spain	b
2043	1917	KIDBROOKE	Yaxham Light Railway Norfolk	f
2052	1916	2	Esplus, Aragon Spain	b
2064	1919		Transvap Connerre Sarthe France	f
2067	1918	PETER	Amberley Industrial Museum Sussex	a
2087	1919	LEONARD	Abbey Mills Pumping Stn Leicester	f
2088	1919	ARMISTICE	Bredger & Wormshill Rly Kent	f,e
2090	1919	PIXIE	Hollycombe Steam Collection Liphook West Sussex	f
2016	1916	No 5	Bankura Station South Central Railway India	b
2091	1919	WENDY	Amberley Industrial Museum Sussex	a
2021	1917	AK 6	Howrah Railway Station Calcutta	b
2094	1919		M Maginot Choloy-Menillot El-Moselle France	e,f
2133	1924	WOTO	Patrick Keef Ross-on-Wye Herefordshire	e
2135	1926	SIR TOM	Threlkeld Quarry Mining Museum Keswick Cumbria	a,d
2192	1922	CONQUEROR	Phyllis Rampton NG Railway Trust Godalming Surrey	e
2195	1922	585	Bilimora Junction Western Railway India	b
2193	1922	TOPHAM	Spa Valley Railway Tunbridge Wells Kent	f
2216	1924	UNIQUE	Sittingbourne & Kemsley Light Railway Kent	b
2221	1927	LEWISHAM	Foxfield Light Railway Blythe Bridge Staffs'	f
2227	1924		Tai Po Market Railway Museum Hong Kong	b
2228	1924		Vale of Rheidol Railway Aberstwyth	b
2250	1925		South African Steam & Rail Museum Chamdor Site Johannesburg	b
2278	1925	594	Indian Railway Museum Delhi	b
2287	1926	(SINEMBE)	Welsh Highland Light Railway Portmadoc North Wales	c
2323	1928	321-01	Kuala Lumper Railway Museum Malasia	b
2342	1928	TONGAAT	Paton County Railway Pietermaritzburg South Africa	d,e
2370	1929		Holt Farm Saddlery Broughton Astley Leics'	e
2450	1931	J T DALY	Pallot Heritage Steam Museum Trinity Jersey	f
2457	1932	762	Phyllis Rampton NG Railway Trust Godalming Surrey	e
2460	1932	765	Phyllis Rampton NG Railway Trust Godalming Surrey	e
2465	1932	37338	Mysore Railway Museum Karataka India	b
2469	1932	V75	Buckinghamshire Railway Centre Quainton Road Bucks'	b
2472	1932	ALPHA	Sittingbourne & Kemsley Light Railway Kent	f
2473	1931	No 1	Cholsey & Wallingford Railway Wallingford Oxon	e
2475	1932		Mainline Steam Excursions Auckland New Zealand	f
2480	1933	J. L. T. 1	Birla Industrial & Technical Museum Calcutta India	b
2511	1934	TRIUMPH	Sittingbourne & Kemsley Light Railway Kent	f
2538	1936	603	Divisional Railway HQ Ajmer Western Railway India	b
2522	1935	SIMPOLA	Longview Texas USA	e
2539	1935		Bangladash Railways Saidpur Workshops	b
2542	1935	JUBILEE	East Anglian Railway Museum Chappel & Wakes Colne Station Essex	f
2545	1936	(RENISHAW No 5)	Peter Rampton Godalming Surrey	e
2565	1936		Hunsbury Hill Industrial Museum Northants'	f
2572	1937	JUDY	Bodmin & Wenford Railway Bodmin Cornwall	f
2581	1937	587	Indian Railways on a plinth at Ahmadabad Station	b
2583	1938		South African Steam & Rail Museum Chamdor Site Johannesburg	b
2613	1940	BROOKFIELD	Mangapps Farm Railway Essex	f,e
2623	1940	HAWARDEN	Foxfield Light Railway Blythe Bridge Staffs'	f
2624	1940	SUPERB	Sittingbourne & Kemsley Light Railway Kent	f
2627	1941	A BOULLE	G Walton-Binns Cargo Fleet North Yorks'	d,e
2635	1943	641	Jaipur Station Indian Railways (Western Railway)	b
2646	1941	643	Indian Railway Museum Delhi	b
2648	1941	LINDA	Chasewater Railway Brownhills Staffs	f
2654	1942	CHERWELL	Rushton Historical Transport Society Rushton Northants'	b,e
2655	1942	BYFIELD	Plym Valley Railway Plympton Devon	f,e
2668	1942	CRANFORD No 2	Rutland Railway Museum Cottesmore Oakham Rutland	b,d
2670	1942	LAMPORT No 2	Battlefield Line Shackerstone Market Bosworth Leics's	f
2680	1942	No 4	SA Pye Bramford Ipswich Suffolk	d,e
2682	1942	PRINCESS	Lakeside & Haverthwaite Railway Cumbria	f
2702	1942		Middleton Railway Hunslet Leeds.	f
2746	1944	68012 THE DUKE	Peak Rail Darley Dale Derbys'	f
2749	1944		Caledonian Railway Brechin Montrose Scotland	f
2758	1944		Cefn Coed Colliery Museum Neath South Wales	b
2759	1944		Caledonian Railway Brechin Montrose Scotland	f
2766	1944		Bodmin & Wenford Railway Bodmin Cornwall	f
2777	1945	No 7	Bo'ness & Kinneil Railway Bo'ness West Lothian Scotland	f
2779	1945	No 20 TANFIELD	Tanfield Railway Marley Hill Durham	f
2819	1946	CHARLES WYTOCK	G Walton-Binns Cargo Fleet North Yorks'	d,e
2820	1946	ISIBUTU	Statfold Barn Railway, Nuneaton	e,f
2842	1946	(No 2)	Foxfield Light Railway Blythe Bridge Staffs'	d
2864	1948	No 1	Kozlu Colliery Zonguldak Turkey	b,e
2870	1948	No 1	Johannesburg Mining Museum Crown Mines South Africa	f
2895	1948	No 2	Peter Rampton Godalming Surrey	e

Manu No	Year Built	Name/No	Location	Condition
2898	1948	PATONS	Darlington Railway Preservation Society Hopetown Durham	
2962	1950	No 19	Bodmin & Wenford Railway Bodmin Cornwall	b,e
2994	1950	401 THOMAS BURT MP 1837-1922	Stephenson Railway Museum Chirton Northumberland	f
2996	1950	2996 VICTOR	Tyseley Locomotive Works Tyseley West Midlands	f
3013	1952	HUGH F MARRIOTT	Nairobi Railway Museum	e
3015	1953		Cripple Creak & Victor Narrow Gauge Railway Colorado USA	b
3019	1952		Shropshire Locomotive Collection Atcham Salop	b
3021	1951	6	McLarens Antiques Old Railway Workshops Oswestry	e
3023	1953	No 3 MOEL TRYFAN	Welsh Highland Railway Portmadoc North Wales	b
3024	1953	MONARCH	Welshpool & Llanfair Light Railway Mid Wales	c
3037	1953	551	Ceylon Govt' Railway Museum Ratmalana	d
3050	1953	GELERT	Welsh Highland Railway Portmadoc North Wales	b
3056	1956	SALT RIVER	Cape Western Railway Museum Epping Cape Town South Africa	f
3058	1953	ALFRED	Bodmin & Wenford Railway Bodmin Cornwall	f
3059	1953	FLORENCE No 2	Foxfield Light Railway Blythe Bridge Staffs'	f
3061	1954	EMPRESS	Mangapps Farm Railway Burnham-On-Crouch Essex	d
3085	1956	GVR No 10	Glenbrook Vintage Railway New Zealand	f
3096	1956	1	McLarens Antiques Old Railway Workshops Oswestry	f
3097	1956	34	Chasewater Railway Brownhills Staffs	b
3105	1957	TMR 592	Ferrymead Railway New Zealand	f
3107	1957	TMR 534 TONKA TOY	Main Line Steam Plimmerton New Zealand	b
3119	1957	HEM HEATH 3D	Chasewater Railway Brownhills Staffs	f
3121	1957		Bodmin & Wenford Railway Bodmin Cornwall	f
3124-3125	1957		Sandstone Heritage Trust Bloemfontein South Africa	c
3132	1958	No 10	Whangarei Museum Maunu New Zealand	c
3144	1958	No 11	Waitara Railway Museum New Zealand	d
3150	1960	WOLSTANTON No 3	Foxfield Light Railway Blythe Bridge Staffs'	d
3151	1962	DL2 01002	Appleby Frodingham Rly Preservation Society Scunthorpe	f
3204	1961		Sandstone Heritage Trust Bloemfontein South Africa	f,e
3207	1961	BAGNALL	Foxfield Light Railway Blythe Bridge Staffs'	d
3208	1961		John Watts Rye Farm Wishaw Warks'	f
3209	1962		Rutland Railway Museum Oakham Rutland	c,e
			(at Brush Traction Limited Loughborough)	
3211	1962	MYFANWY	Foxfield Light Railway Blythe Bridge Staffs'	f
3213	1962	2	Great Eastern Traction Hardingham Station Norfolk	f
				b

APPENDIX VI

DIRECTORS & PRINCIPAL OFFICERS

1. WG Bagnall Limited

i. Principal Officers

These details of the people holding the various senior posts, along with the Directors of the Company, are applicable from the incorporation of the Limited Company on 21 July 1887.

Managing Director
William Gordon Bagnall: 21 July 1887 - 19 July 1907
John Gifford Gifford: 20 July 1907 - 17 October 1932
William Sydney Edwards: 18 October1932 - 28 December 1946
James Cadman (Acting): 29 December1947 - 22 July 1947
Ian Arthur Marriott: December 1947 - 26 March 1950
William Addison Smyth: 27 March 1950 - 26 January 1959
Jack Walter Whimpenny: 27 January 1959 - 15 September 1961
Gerald Collingwood: 16 September 1961 - December 1962

General Manager
(This position was not always filled)
Arthur Hewitt Gilling: 1908 - 1912
William Sydney Edwards: 1912 - 17 October 1932

Harry Davies: 15 September 1947 - 8 January 1960 (Acting for a few months prior to formal appointment date)
George David Robinson: January 1960 - 15 September 1961

Chief Draughtsman/Designer
Ernest Edwin Baguley: 1892 - 1902
James Graeme Warren: April 1902 - March 1903
William Sydney Edwards: March 1903 - December 1915
Reginald John Gard: December 1915 - 1926
Arthur Burley: 1926 - 11 June 1931
Hugh R Taylor: 12 June 1931 - 1937
(Acting for first couple of months)
Francis Henry Barham Harris: 1937 - September 1947
(from early 1933 effectively senior to Hugh Taylor)
Fredrick Harold Wood: September 1947 - 31 October 1952
(on loan to Brush from 9 July 1952)
Arthur James Webberley: 1 November July 1952 - 1960
(Acting from 9 July)
William Alfred Brookes: 1960 - 12 December 1962
(Deputy from 1 November 1952)

Chief Works Engineer
Arthur James Woollams: January 1958 - 1960

Chief Engineer
Arthur James Webberley: 1960 - December 1962

Works Manager (Post abolished February 1958 and split into two
separate positions: Chief Works Engineer and Production Manager -
post re-established in 1960)
Samuel Thomas Price: 21 July 1887 - 1915
William R Parkinson: 1915 - 1930
Jack Dale: 1930 - 1943
Thomas Stockton: 1943 - October 1949
Arthur James Woollams (Acting): 1949 - April 1950 (Assistant from
1 May 1950)
Sydney Ridgway: 1 May - 1950 - January 1958 (took charge 17
August 1950 on return from his trip to USA)
James Glover: 1960 - 1961

Production Manager
Albert Henry Victor Betteley: January 1958 - October 1959

ii. Directors.
William Gordon Bagnall: 21 July 1887 - 19 July 1907 - Chairman
Thomas Walter: 21 July 1887 - prior to July 1901
Edward Salt: 21 July 1887 - prior to July 1901
Samuel Cookson: 21 July 1887 - prior to July 1901
John Gifford Gifford: by 27 July 1901 - 17 October 1932 - Chairman
from 20 July 1907
Richard Gordon Bagnall: August 1908 - 11 April 1911
James Caldwell Gifford: 31 October 1921 - 18 October 1925
William Sydney Edwards: 31 October 1921 - 28 December 1946
Charles Maitland: 1932 - 12 July 1938
Herbert Owen: 1933 - 13 December 1938
Colonel RG Lockhart-Jervis: 3 December 1938 - 13 December 1938
Leslie WR Robinson: 8 March 1938 - 13 December 1938
Norma Agnes Maxwell Maitland: 12 July 1938 - 13 December 1938
James Cadman: 13 December 1938 - 22 July 1947 - Chairman from
appointment
John Basil Cope Cadman: 19 December 1938 - 22 July 1947
James Simon Cadman: 7 March 1947 - 22 July 1947
George Charles Neilson: 7 March 1947 - 22 July 1947
Alan Paul Good: 22 July 1947 - 10 February 1953 - Chairman from
appointment to July 1952
Francis James Fielding: 22 July 1947 - 2 March 1959
Hon. Alexander Campbell Geddes: 22 July 1947 - 16 November
1953
Charles Loraine Hill: 22 July 1947 - 3 November 1949 and again as
Chairman 28 July 1952 to 2 March 1959 (from 20 November 1950
had been Alternate Director to Alan Good)
Ian Arthur Marriott: 22 July 1947 - 24 April 1950
John Fredrick Alcock: 11 March 1948 - 10 July 1953
Alexander Chetwyne Hayes: 3 February 1949 - ? and again - 22 June
1953 - 2 March 1959
William Addison Smyth: 12 September 1949 - 2 March 1959.
James Calderwood: 31 August 1949 - 16 January 1956
Hubert Harry Wheeler: 26 September 1949 - 18 December 1950
Edward Maurice Benjamin: 19 December 1949 - 18 December 1950
(Deputy Chairman - had managerial control during Marriott's
absence in USA)
Ernest William Marten: 24 April 1950 - 2 March 1959
Norman Alfred Stokes: 1 October 1952 - 8 December 1961

Harry Davies: 18 December 1953 - 2 March 1959
Darby Haddon: 2 March 1959 - 15 September 1961
Jack Walter Whimpenny: 2 March 1959 - 15 September 1961 -
Chairman
Robert Anthony Wenham: 2 January 1961 -
George David Robinson: 5 April 1961 - 15 September 1961
George Henry Nelson: 2 August 1961 -
Edward Bernard Banks: 2 August 1961 -
Gerald Collingwood: 15 September 1961 -

2. Brush Bagnall Traction Limited

Directors

This list includes all the Directors either already in place, or
appointed on 6 October 1950, when the Company was in effect
formed, although the name had been changed from what was in
effect a 'shelf company', Flather & Company Limited, on 11 July
1950. The events surrounding the Flather Company are covered
Chapter Eleven. The name of the reformed company was originally
Brush Bagnall Electric Traction Limited, but was changed to Brush
Bagnall Traction Limited on 20 November 1950. The October date
was when the formal relationship between WG Bagnall Limited and
the Brush Electrical Engineering Company Limited was established.
The list includes Directors appointed after 6 October 1950, and all
those continuing in office after the name changed to Brush Traction
Limited on 19 December 1955. This was when the formal
relationship between the two companies ceased; the list has the
eventual resignation dates of those Directors who continued in
office, but does not include any Directors appointed after the 19
December date.

Alan Paul Good: 6 October 1950 - 13 October 1952 (Chairman
until resignation)
Hon. Alexander Campbell Geddes: 6 October 1950 - 30 June 1953
John Whitfield Cumming Milligan: 6 October 1950 - 28 September
1954 (General Manager until Eckhard appointed)
William Addison Smyth: 6 October 1950 - 23 December 1955
Rex Bate: 6 October 1950 - 30 June 1954
James Calderwood: 6 October 1950 - 6 October 1958
Jesse Talbot Rymer: 6 October 1950 - 13 October 1952
Ernest William Martin: 6 October 1950 - 23 December 1955
Percival Clifford Sharp: 6 October 1950 - 17 April 1953 (was in
effect already in office as a Director and Secretary of Flather & Co
Ltd - Joint Secretary to resignation)
Richard Gilbert Watt: 6 October 1950 - 12 May 1958 (Joint
Secretary to 17 April 1953 and Secretary to 1 May 1958)
Miles Beever: 12 July 1951 - 31 December 1956 (Chairman from 13
October 1952)
Kenneth Newton Eckhard: 12 July 1951 - 3 February 1955 (General
Manager from date of appointment)
Henry (Harry) George Ivatt: 12 July 1951 - 8 August 1958 (Acting
General Manager from 3 February 1955)
Charles Fredrick Barnard: 13 October 1952 - 8 October 1958
John Humphrey Russell Nixon: 12 July 1951 - 6 August 1958
Ian Thomas Morrow: 23 February 1954 - 8 September 1958
Maurice Tattersfield: 5 October 1954 - 1 December 1958 (Managing
Director from 31 December 1956)

APPENDIX VII

ANNUAL LOCOMOTIVE PRODUCTION

Listed here by year, broken down by type of propulsion, are the numbers of locomotives ordered and despatched. Orders placed and subsequently cancelled are not included, and the numbers of locomotives shown as ordered in any particular year are those for which orders were placed by customers, and do not take account of any orders placed by the Company for stock. The year in this list under which stock locomotives are shown as ordered, is the year an order was received by a customer. This list is not intended to illustrate the totality of locomotive workload in terms of time, labour and materials, but rather to give readers an idea of the numbers of locomotives ordered and despatched each year, as the business and its markets expanded. There were many other steams of work, varying over the years, and in general terms the locomotives built got larger and more complicated as the years progressed. Therefore, comparisons should not be made on the basis of this list regarding the amount of work undertaken by the Company year by year.

(i) Steam

Year	Ordered	Despatched
1876	1	1
1877	4	3
1878	1	1
1879	3	3
1880	10	9
1881	8	3
1882	6	12
1883	9 (excluding 612)	6
1884	8	8
1885	12	12
1886	8	9
1887	14	20
1888	11	7
1889	16	17
1890	6	7
1891	9	11
1892	8	7
1893	10	13
1894	13	14
1895	31	21
1896	23	22
1897	33	27
1898	37	32
1899	31	40
1900	41	36
1901	20	38
1902	42	37
1903	30	35
1904	26	28
1905	21	22
1906	49	36
1907	36	47
1908	9	12
1909	20	21
1910	21	19
1911	18	18
1912	33	22
1913	31	27
1914	23	17
1915	9	23
1916	5	13
1917	20	15
1918	29	24
1919	38	19
1920	20	32

Year	Ordered	Despatched
1921	22	26
1922	25	30
1923	22	20
1924	32	30
1925	30	27
1926	25	24
1927	31	21
1928	32	32
1929	40	24
1930	36	39
1931	20	32
1932	24	19
1933	10	22
1934	16	18
1935	15	24
1936	28	28
1937	15	15
1938	11	10
1939	16	13
1940	35	22
1941	21	8
1942	25	35
1943	72	18
1944	10	29
1945	17	22
1946	54	24
1947	13	32
1948	78	31
1949	14 (including 2908)	15
1950	3	36
1951	10	19
1952	2	23
1953	0	19
1954	3	16
1955	1	2
1956	1	1
1957	1	2

(ii) Electric (mechanical parts)

Year	Ordered	Despatched
1897	2	2
1904	1	1
1906	1	1
1907	6	5
1908	2	3
1910	2	2

(iii) Petrol Mechanical

Year	Ordered	Despatched
1911	1	0
1912	1	2
1913	1	1
1917	25	25
1923	1	0
1924	0	1
1925	3	3
1926	1	1

(iv) Diesel Mechanical

Figures exclude two locomotives that while only rebuilt, were given numbers in the main list - 3062 and 3152.

Year	Ordered	Despatched
1933	3	1
1934	5	5
1935	1	3
1936	4	1
1937	1	4
1938	1	1
1953	1	0
1954	10	0
1955	18	1
1956	1	13
1957	4	15
1958	6	5
1959	0	3
1960	2	2
1961	1	4

(v) Diesel Electric (Brush Bagnall Traction)

This list is inclusive of whether the locomotives were completely erected at Stafford or by Brush at Loughborough. In the case of those locomotives erected at Loughborough the numbers shown in the despatched column are relative to the date the mechanical parts built at Stafford were sent to Loughborough, and not when the completed locomotives were despatched to the end customer from Loughborough. Details of which ones were completely built at Stafford and which ones were completed at Loughborough can be found in Appendix 1.

Year	Ordered	Despatched
1949	4	0
1950	28	0
1951	0	5
1952	3	12
1953	12	7
1954	0	7
1955	14	16
1956	5	11
1957	7	8
1958	5	7
1959	25	5
1960	12	23
1961	5	19

(vi) Diesel Hydraulic

Only the locomotives ordered prior to the English Electric take-over, and built to Bagnall designs are included here, although some of them were either partly, or completely, built at the Robert Stephenson & Hawthorns works at Darlington. Details of which ones were completed, or built whole at Darlington, can be found in Appendix 1.

Year	Ordered	Despatched
1960	2	0
1961	18	3
1962	0	14
1963	0	3

(vii) Totals

Steam	1610
Electric	14
Petrol Mechanical	33
Diesel Mechanical	58
Diesel Electric	120
Diesel Hydraulic	20
Grand Total	**1855**

APPENDIX VIII

SUMMERY OF FINANCIAL RESULTS

The figures below while by no means complete, have been compiled from what source material exists. It would have been possible to quote other, otherwise meaningful figures for various periods in the firm's history, but the intension has been to allow comparisons to be made on a like-for-like basis, despite the accountancy conventions changing over the years. In the main text of the book there are numerous other financial statistics for different periods, and the figures in this table should be used in conjunction with them. Attention is drawn to the losses incurred after the death of WG Bagnall in 1907 and leading up to the First World War, as well as in the mid 1930s. As is the case for all monetary sums mentioned in this book no account has been taken of inflation, but the figures should help readers for comparison purposes. Those wanting to equate them to current values should consult inflation multiplying tables that are readily available. There are no figures available for the years 1888 to 1889, apart from the combined work in progress figure for the years 1887-1889.

Year Ending	Turnover Net	Work in Progress	Sales	Profit (Loss)
31-03-1887	28,499	7,254 (1887-9)		
31-09-1890	39,040	5,080		1,490
30-09-1891	35,508	3,799		6
30-09-1892	34,012	6,493		601
30-09-1893	36,409	6,475		857

Year Ending	Turnover Net	Work in Progress	Sales	Profit (Loss)
30-09-1894	35,883	5,382		13
30-09-1895	38,128	7,122		1,342
30-09-1896	41,518	7,408		2,149
31-12-1897 (15 months)	45,968	3,131		1,927
31-12-1898	49,930	3,357	35,849	3,502
31-12-1899	55,592	2,866	54,853	8,951
31-12-1900	61,000	3,438	48,917	7,002
31-12-1901	61,034	3,124	41,913	3,295
31-12-1902	65,201	5,797	41,077	4,602
31-12-1903	71,269	10,133	43,870	5,451
31-12-1904 (+ 10 Months of 1905)	67,358	4,351	32341	1,804
31-12-1906 (+ 2 months of 1905)	77,135	9,633	38,245	2,060
31-12-1907	53,964	5,717	43,966	612
31-12-1908	45,448	3,617	28,794	(2,003)
31-12-1909	46,985	3,898	25,665	(2,183)
31-12-1910	51,478	4,854		(1,881)
31-12-1911	46,985	4,541		(2,799)
31-12-1912	50,346	6,198		(936)
31-12-1913	54,293	9,920		(382)
31-12-1914	57,798	8,274		1,196
31-12-1915	61,980	14,304		(2,149)
31-12-1916	59,820	12,869		1,591
31-12-1917	67,769	19,974		2,111
31-12-1918	73,865	21,817		5,861
31-12-1919	93,318	47,031		7,832
31-12-1920	122,557	57,964		19,138
31-12-1921	115,223	13,311		23,649
31-12-1922	109,390	15,585		10,728
31-12-1923	90,392	12,694		5,821

Year Ending	Turnover Net	Work in Progress	Sales	Profit (Loss)
31-12-1924	86,728	18,645		3,348
31-12-1925				3,232
31-12-1926	121,663	23,304	110,868	230
31-12-1927	137,046	20,794	114,250	878
31-12-1928	149,891	22,795	119,621	2,016
31-12-19291	53,041	30,268	120,953	2,684
31-12-19301	69,739	22,086	144,155	2,942
31-12-19311	24,592	25,583	109,872	1,352
31-12-1932	105,990	14,719	95,142	(4,618)
31-12-1933	96,758	10,847	85,221	(4,611)
31-12-1934	106,383	11,536	84,776	(655)
31-12-1935	126,968	21,605	117,227	2,806
31-12-1936	136,815	9,240	120,710	460
31-12-1937	146,989	16,140	116,489	5,852
31-12-1938	169,947	20,500	147,606	9,262
31-12-1939	166,979	22,341	138,605	6,935
31-12-1940	212,316	28,374	168,950	5,22
31-12-1941	214,077	43,365	192,855	6,398
31-12-1942	264,196	61,221	202,046	5,620

Year Ending	Turnover Net	Work in Progress	Sales	Profit (Loss)
31-12-1943	311,142	62,150	241,814	5,590
31-12-1944	375,643	69,328	383,975	5,492
31-12-1945	359,582	91,666	291,708	6,813
31-12-1946	354,449	67,874	280,235	2,988
31-12-1947	323,525	74,213	207,148	2,298
31-12-1948				11,172
31-12-1949				9,749
31-12-1950				8,677
31-12-1951				4,074
31-12-1952	460,767	290,214		16,833
31-12-1953				6,498
31-12-1954				9,982
31-12-1955				18,499
31-12-1956				13,961
31-12-1957				8,500
31-12-1958				8,094
31-12-1959				10,839
31-12-1960				
31-12-1961				12,126

APPENDIX IX

REPORT BY JOHN ALCOCK, DATED 21 AUGUST 1947, PRIOR TO BECOMING A DIRECTOR

Reproduced here is a copy of a report written by John Alcock of the Hunslet Engine Company Limited of Leeds, dated 21 August 1947. Retaining as much of the original layout and style as possible, it followed his first visit to the Castle Engine Works. This was at the time when his appointment as a director of WG Bagnall Limited was under consideration by Alan Good, and he was accompanied by Alexander Geddes, as Alan Good's representative, who at the time seems to have been charged with getting the relationship between Brush, Bagnall and potentially Hunslet, on to a sound footing. Along with some diagrams of the works layout (not included here) this report was later presented to a board meeting of the Company. There was a thought at the time, at least in Geddes mind, that Alcock might in fact take over the management of the Stafford works - presumably by some sort of remote control from Leeds. Alcock however, from the evidence of surviving correspondence, clearly had an alternative view, that of acquiring the goodwill of the Bagnall steam locomotive business to add to those of Kerr, Stuart & Avonside that Hunslet already had, leaving the Castle Engine Works to concentrate on the mechanical parts for diesel-electric locomotives under the Brush Bagnall umbrella. On being invited by Alan Good to join the Bagnall board, John Alcock must have felt that all his dreams had come true!

It has to be remembered in reading the report that there was an element of 'sour grapes' in John Alcock's demeanour at the time, of which Good and Geddes would have been largely oblivious. He had never forgiven WS Edwards over the Kerr, Stuart closure issues outlined in Chapter Eight, and was both annoyed and jealous of the amount of work the Company had been able to obtain as a result, which was perhaps, quite understandable bearing in mind Hunslet had legally and legitimately bought the Kerr, Stuart goodwill. In a letter dated 27 February 1948 to John W Vaughan, director of the Locomotive Manufacturers Association, referring to his appointment to the Bagnall board, he had, interalia, this to say: 'As you know, we have always in the past been unable to agree on anything (that is Hunslet and Bagnall) and I am quite confident that the close cooperation which might now be possible will not only do both of us a lot of good, but probably the industry as well'.

In reading Alcock's rather disparaging comments on what he found at Stafford, the situation should perhaps be looked at in a different light. This was a company that had never had any significant amount of capital at its disposal; until Edwards engendered the association with the Cadmans, to all intents and purposes it had been very much a one, or at the best, a two-man band. Almost all investment in plant and machinery had been from its own resources. The Maitlands, who as shareholders followed John Gifford, were there for what they could get, and not what they could give. Undoubtedly in the Cadmans Edwards saw an opportunity for investment in the plant and equipment, but no sooner were the new shareholders in place, when the country was plunged into a world war. With the war over, and before any schemes might have been brought to fruition, there were acute shortages of both man-power and raw materials, followed by the death of Edwards and consequent severance of the Cadman connection. But remember, that despite the condition of the plant and equipment as Alcock describes them, this was a firm that had designed and built what were at the time among the largest rigid framed metre-gauge steam locomotives in the world, and that locomotives it had built were still in everyday use in India 70 years after they left these shores. John Alcock was particularly unfair in his comments on the drawing office; Harris was still a very capable chief, with enormous experience, and the so called young men, were involved in much more than he claims - at the time of his visit for example, design work on the Morvi Railway pacifics, manufacturer's numbers 2872 to 2875, had only just been completed. It was a long standing objective of the Company, developed and fostered by Edwards, to develop young talent by getting promising youngsters on the ladder of advancement as early as possible. While there were undoubtedly ulterior motives in helping to keep the staff costs lower than might otherwise have been the case, it was a laudable, excellent, and no less proven practice as many of those who were involved over the years have been able to eloquently testify. See for example Derek Cobby's comments in Chapter Ten.

While Hunslet may have had better plant, machinery and other equipment, they certainly did not have better engineers and craftsman; whatever they did in Leeds, at Stafford it was the men who designed and made the locomotives that gave the firm its world wide reputation, more so than any plant, equipment or buildings!

Visit to Bagnalls Tuesday Morning 19 August 1947

Went round the shop with Colonel Marriott. Discussed points also with Mr Davies (General Manager), Mr Stockton (Works Manager) subsequently the Hon Alexander Geddes. Afterwards brought Geddes and Marriott back to Leeds and showed them round Hunslet.

The following are my views together with certain information picked up during my three hour visit.

The land is leasehold from Lord Stafford and has only 12 years to run. Marriott is trying to arrange purchase, but it appears that Lord Stafford is not anxious to sell and would prefer to extend the lease. The site is somewhat long and narrow and is only about half built up, so there is plenty of room for extension. The ground itself, however, is made up to a depth of approximately 10 ft and is unsatisfactory for foundations, but what is even more unsatisfactory is that beneath this there is nothing but sand which is inclined to be wet so that all foundations are most difficult. The adjoining land which is about 10 ft lower is quite boggy and is apt to be flooded. A stream runs down one side of the works, while the main line railway runs down the other. Railway access is really excellent and lends itself for future extension. Road access is almost hopeless, the only way into Stafford being over a hump-backed and difficult railway bridge, whereas in the other direction there is nothing but a country lane.

The buildings are very disappointing. There are very few of them with any reasonable structure and consequent on this cranage also is very poor.

The machine shop consists of two narrow bays with timber roof trusses of considerable antiquity. A considerable portion of the erecting shop is timber construction and heavy cranes can only run about half way down the shop. The fitting shop running down the railway side is more modern with steel trusses, but is only a lean-to while the boiler and smith's shops on the other side of the yard are thin corrugated sheeting which has long since perished. The only decent shops are the pattern shop and foundry and the only really new buildings are the brass foundry and the extension to the engine room, which now houses a recently installed electric power supply transformer and switch gear. The only other large shop, known as the wagon shop is a very poor sort of place with semi-circular shaped roofs supported on wooden trusses.

Frames are handled in the wagon shop. They are flame cut by a small machine running on plates and hand guided. Levelling is done where necessary in the bending rolls which are in this shop and are about 12 ft, these rolls are steam driven. They are slotted where necessary by a very old single head machine, the table of which is

only 6 ft long and the frames have to be reset for every horn. They are drilled on a set of three very old Asquith Radials and are then ready for the erecting shop.

The smithy is equipped with five steam hammers, the largest being 2 tons. There are only two furnaces, both fitted with waste heat locomotive boilers, but one has been out of action for 7 years and the other only has a door of about 18 inches by 2 ft. They apparently use flame cutting for rod ends, but have not used it in connection with brake shafts and reversing shafts. The flame cutting plant does not appear to be used very extensively. There is one Hancock machine and one very old small type BOC machine in the wagon shop, but only one man appears to be on the job and he is also using the flame profiler.

The boiler shop consists of two bays and a good deal of very old plant. The press is 300 tons and is similar in size to ours. There is a saw for the edges of flanged plates, a very old pair of light bending rolls about 9 ft, a riveting bed with hydraulic type of gib crane, but no boiler shell drill, barrels being opened out under a radial and fireboxes by air machines. Snap head rivets are used, but where necessary these are distorted to be ellipsoidal shape. When using ellipsoidal snaps there is considerable difficulty as the heads do not centralise satisfactorily.

There is a hydraulic accumulator outside with two sets of old fashioned 3 throw pumps just inside. Air is supplied from a 500 cub ft compressor housed in the power house. The power house also carries twin steam driven generators of 200 kVA each, DC. These have been superseded during the last 12 months only by the new power supply. The maximum power requirement of the works appears to be about 350 kVA in the winter time with lights on. During the middle of the morning, while I was present, requirements appeared to be about 200 kVA. The boiler house carries three boilers apart from two waste heat boilers in the smithy, but these are not all now in use and will only be necessary if for any reason they find it necessary to revert to generation of their own power again this winter.

In the iron foundry, they cast twice a week, approximately 4 tons each time and they supply all their own castings and also a few additional cylinders for the LMS. They cast approximately a pair of cylinders a week.

In the brass foundry they also cast all their own requirements, but have no spare capacity.

They are seriously thinking of extending the iron foundry and need new cupolas.

The joiners shop is housed in the wagon shop and is thus separate from the pattern shop.

They have recently acquired a 5 ton Coles Mobile Crane (diesel-electric) and this appears to be their only internal transport.

Shunting is done by the railway company and an electric capstan pulls engines out of the erecting shop.

I understand that most of their welded work has been sub-contracted out to Cowlishaw Walker & Co.

There are two very old small planers and one comparatively modern Louden, approximately 10 ft x 4 ft x 4 ft. They were, however, well equipped with vertical millers, in fact, too well equipped as most of them appeared to be standing. There were something like 7 or 8 Kendal & Gent or Reed Prentice machines of considerable size. There was also a very nice Butler slotter and they were quite well placed for boring machines, 3 small and 2 medium. Their grinding equipment was very poor indeed, the radius link grinder and the hole grinder were Dorman machines, separate, but otherwise very similar to our old BP machine. Their surface grinder is of a type which I have never seen and is I should think practically useless. There were two small cylindrical grinders, but even these were only used when absolutely essential for valve spindles etc., and one man worked all five machines.

The case hardening was pathetic, the box was packed on the floor in a small tin shed; firebricks were built around in honeycomb formation and a coke fire was lighted around and over the box which was kept in for two days. There was no temperature control, the parts were afterwards reheated in the fire and given a single quench, but again without temperature control, and the whole job entirely depended upon one man who has done this particular operation for 45 years. I must say he was doing it very satisfactorily.

The wheel lathe, wheel press and the quarter borer were all good old fashioned tools, but the quarter borer could not be used as such as it was not adaptable to boring taper holes. There was one first class Cincinnati vertical boring mill.

The erecting shop was extremely narrow and had one pit down one side. There was very little room when two locomotives were abreast and as there was not much head room, it must have been very difficult to lift one locomotive out which was half way down the shop. They have also two heavy cranes, weighing 20 tons each. Congestion was considerable due to a couple of tender engines stripped and packed and awaiting shipment. Two fireless locomotives were under construction, one set of frames were laid down, the boiler was ready together with another spare boiler, the shop was very full. Frame stays and attachments were all opened out by air drill.

In spite of considerable difficulties, the general standard of work appeared to me good. There seems little doubt that the class of labour is excellent. Nevertheless, to sum up, the whole place was very disappointing to me and it seemed difficult to believe that they could ever have been considered on our level or competitive.

The offices were even worse than the works and reminded me very much of Hudswell Clarkes old offices. In the drawing office old Mr Harris is still in charge: he is now 77 and there were about a dozen young lads with him, none of whom appeared to me to be more than about 22 or 23 and I was told they had long since given up any ideas of doing anything except mark up old drawings.

As far as output is concerned, it appears that they are getting out approximately 4 boilers per month, 2 of which are spares, the other 2 going into the 2 locomotives per month which they are building. On a value basis and averaging the boilers at £2,000 each and the

locomotives at £8,000 each with an approximate spares trade of, say, 10%, this means about £264,000 per annum. If they could get on a dead straight run, such as the Austerity, they are of the opinion that they could turn out an extra 1 to 1½ locomotives per month, which means about an extra £120,000 per annum, making a total of say, £384,000, and I should think this would be the limit. Their turnover last year was said to be £278,000 and the state of their order book at the moment is:

Locomotives & Boilers	£548,000
Spares	41,000
	£589,000

This includes 39 spare boilers at £81,000 and 58 locomotives at £467,000.

Their total covered area is 93,637 sq ft and this includes the foundry and the wagon shop. For comparison purposes, our covered area is 145,210 sq ft. As far as labour is concerned their works personnel including works staff is 301, against our 530, while office staff is 43 against our 145.

John Alcock

As event unfolded John Alcock was quite critical of the design of the diesel-electric shunting locomotives. The initial six-wheel locomotives based, as they were, on the English Electric design for the main-line railways, was in his view too complicated and therefore, too expensive to build for every day use at industrial locations. His view was that a range of locomotives should have been developed with the underframes, wheels, and brake gear, along with some other mechanical parts, based on steam locomotive practice. This was the case in the Hunslet designs, and could also have been adopted at Stafford based on Bagnall steam locomotive practice. It would have made the locomotives less expensive to design, build, operate and maintain. In the case of the SCOW locomotives, he even suggested that as many parts as possible should be common between the diesels and the three steam locomotives being built for the same customer, numbers 2994 to 2996; in fact they had absolutely nothing in common! Whilst this was an understandable point of view, in the light of the Hunslet experience, it went completely against the way Brush Bagnall philosophy was developed, and if longevity of service is a criteria, then while many of the locomotives supplied to the SCOW are still in everyday use, one would be hard pressed to find any Hunslet diesel-mechanical locomotives of similar vintage, still doing the job they were built for.

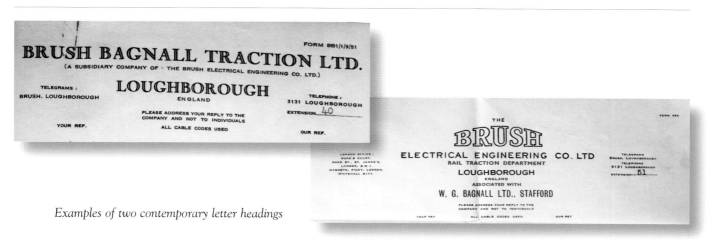

Examples of two contemporary letter headings

APPENDIX X

REPORT BY WA SMYTH MANAGING DIRECTOR ON PRODUCTION CAPACITY: 16 NOVEMBER 1951.

Reproduced below, retaining as much as possible of the original layout and style, is a paper produced by WA Smyth, the managing director at Stafford, in late 1951. By this time it was becoming apparent that the combined facilities at Stafford and Loughborough were struggling to maintain the delivery commitments for the diesel-electric locomotives Brush Bagnall Traction was contracted to build. When WG Bagnall Limited became part of the group of companies controlled by Alan Good, it was with the specific intention it became a supplier of mechanical parts for diesel-electric locomotives. However, at the end of 1951, it had a very large order book for steam locomotives, boilers and other spare parts, which along with some other miscellaneous items, added up to a selling price of £570,000, against £246,000 for diesel-electric locomotive mechanical parts. When the workload concerns were first raised as far back as March 1948, Alan Good had made it quite clear that so far as he was concerned, the sole reason for the Company joining his group was as a supplier of mechanical parts for the new range of diesel-electric locomotives being developed by Brush, and everything else should be subservient to that end.

One can see in Smyth's well constructed argument his concerns against the possibility of the group formed by Alan Good being broken up, as he was very conscious of Bagnall being a Heenan, and not a Brush owned company. While there had been discussions regarding this situation changing, nothing had transpired, and he once told the authors of his concerns about any long term commitment of the Heenan & Froude Group; this was the principal reason why he was anxious the Company maintained a measure of independence from Brush.

As things developed, events overtook any long term decisions following this report, with both the death of Alan Good, and the fact that steam locomotive orders all but dried up as the firm completed those it was already committed to at the time the report was written. In the years 1952 to the end of steam locomotive production, only eight more were ordered.

The reference in the report to sub-contracting the last 20 of the 8400 class pannier tank locomotives for British Railways was a real possibility. In late 1951 negotiations were entered into with the Yorkshire Engine Company of Sheffield, with this view in mind and costs were agreed, including the transfer of material already on hand from Stafford to Sheffield. Yorkshire were at the time building a batch of 30 of these locomotives in their own right, and a couple of years later, they built a further 20 on sub-contract from the Hunslet Engine Company - it was October 1956 before the last one was delivered. On 18 December 1951, Smyth wrote to KC Banks of Yorkshire, informing him that it had been decided to build the locomotives at Stafford, agreement having been reached with British Railways regarding revised delivery timescales, and in view of the otherwise unabsorbed costs of tools, patterns, jigs etc, that would devolve to the Company's overheads if the work was sub-contracted on the terms agreed. Reference to these locomotives also appears in Chapter Twelve.

WG Bagnall Limited   Stafford

Confidential

Potential Manufacturing Capacity for Mechanical Parts of Diesel electric Locomotives.

1. Introduction

At the Board Meeting held on 22 October 1951, the potential capacity of the Stafford Works was discussed in relation to the reported capacity of the Brush Bagnall Erecting Shop at Loughborough of 36 main line Diesel electric locomotives per annum. It was assumed that BBT could eventually obtain orders for such an output and that Brush and Mirrlees could supply the necessary electrical equipment and Diesel engines respectively. The writer was requested to submit a report to the Board on the steps which would have to be taken and the cost which would be involved in reorganising the Stafford Works to secure a corresponding output of mechanical parts. It was assumed that steam locomotive, boiler and locomotive spares production could be reduced or eliminated, if necessary, and also that final erection of all Diesel electric locomotives, both main line and shunters, would be concentrated at Loughborough in contrast to the present arrangement under which the shunters are fully erected at Stafford.

2. Limiting Factors

The principal limiting factors which must be considered in assessing the potential output of the works under the conditions set out above are:-

1. The covered floor space available for machining, fabrication, erection, storage etc.
2. The adequacy or otherwise, of the present labour force.
3. The adequacy and suitability of the machine tools and equipment available.

3. Conclusions

It is clear from the investigations that have been made that the output of Diesel electric mechanical parts could be brought up to a total of 36 main line units per annum by:-

a) Dropping the manufacture of steam locomotives, boilers, and locomotive spare altogether.
b) Providing about 4,000 sq ft of additional covered area - primarily for storage purposes.
c) Purchasing some additional machines and equipment.
d) Re-deploying the existing labour force.

It is considered that the reorganisation necessary for the complete change over would take between two and three years to complete and that the total cost would be between £25,000 and £30,000.

4. Present Order Book

The following is an analysis of the present order book:-

Product	Valve of Orders as at 1/9/1951	%	Months of Work at Present Level of Invoicing
Steam Locomotives	£486,233	56.0	24
Locomotive Boilers	£63,828	8.0	41
Locomotive Spares	£58,041	6.5	13
Diesel Electric Mechanical Parts	£249,808	29.0	47 *
Wagons & Misc.	£5,774	0.5	10
Total	£863,684	100	29

* Note: This figure is unrealistic as the rate of production of Diesel parts is increasing rapidly and a considerable increase will result from the completion of the New Erecting Shop in six months time.

At our present total invoicing level of £30,125 per period this order book represents over two years work. Even if we can arrange to sub-contract the remaining 20 British Railways shunting locomotives we will still have 34 steam locomotives on the order book. It must also be borne in mind that the increasing rate of output of Diesel electric mechanical parts inevitably means a slowing down of the steam engine production so that the time required to clear the order book will still be longer than calculated. These facts and figures have been taken into account in making the estimate of two to three years for the complete change over to Diesel electric mechanical parts.

5. Shop Space

Appendix No 1 to this report shows the present layout of the Works (not included here but similar to the one on page 575) with the area which could be allocated to fabrication and erection of Diesel electric frames and bogies suitably coloured (they are the old and New Erecting Shop, half the Boiler Shop along with the Tank & Frame Shops). Appendix No 2 (also not included here) shows six sets of main frames laid out in the New Erecting Shop and six sets of bogies in the existing Erecting Shop. Assuming an erection cycle time of eight weeks it will be seen that a total output of 36 sets of main line units could be obtained from these two shops per annum. Sufficient fabrication space could be found in the present Frame, Tank and Boiler Shops. The Machine Shop space is adequate. About 4,000 sq ft of additional space would be required, mostly for

storage, work in progress etc. If it were decided to abandon the production of iron and brass castings this spaces could be found in the present Foundry but extensive alterations would be required, including a new floor. If the Foundries are to be retained additional covered space could be built. Although this space would be required primarily for storage it would clearly be better to provide new production space and to utilise some of the older buildings for storage. The best solution would be an extension of about 100 ft on the centre bay of the existing Frame Shop. Part of the old Machine Shop could then be converted for use as a store.

6. Labour Force

The present direct labour force consists of 267 men averaging about 49 hours per week. Our present estimate of the man-hours involved in a set of Ceylon mechanical parts is 19,000 and on this basis the present labour force, if wholly employed on this work, could produce about 35 sets per annum. With improved methods and increased shop space the number of man-hours per loco will be reduced and not all the locomotives will be as large or as complicated as the Ceylon design. There is no doubt, therefore, as to the adequacy of the present labour force for the production of 36 sets of main line mechanical parts per annum but it will be appreciated that many of the present categories and trades would not be required for purely Diesel electrical production. A considerable amount of re-deployment and training of the direct labour force would, therefore, be necessary and this would inevitably take some time to achieve. Allowance has, of course, been made for the large amount of work sub-contracted on the Ceylon locomotives (e.g. wheels and axles, fuel tanks etc). In future large orders similar sub-contracting would be possible but where only one or two locomotives are ordered it would not be practicable to obtain wheels and axles on sub-contract and it would be necessary to retain the Wheel Shop in being. Increases in the number of indirect workers would be called for if the Works go over entirely to the manufacture of mechanical parts, particularly in the Stores and Planning and Inspection Sections.

7. Machinery & Plant

A review of our machinery and plant, in the light of the present proposals, reveals that a number of the lighter lathes and milling machines would become redundant and could be disposed of. They are mostly old machines and their recovery value is small. On the other hand some new machinery would have to be purchased, particularly additional gas burning and welding plant and a heavy straightening machine. Handling plant would have to be increased and an additional 12 ton overhead crane would be required in the proposed extension to the Frame Shop. Detailed estimates could be prepared for expenditure under this head after the Board has considered the matter in broad outline.

8. Implications

In considering the policy to be adopted in this matter the Board should be made aware of the implications of a complete change over from our present mixed production to the manufacture of Diesel electric mechanical parts only. These are:-

    a)   From Bagnalls point of view: the permanent loss of our steam business. Once we drop out of the market we can never hope to regain our position if a subsequent change of policy

transferred the manufacture of Diesel electric parts to Loughborough or some other Works. The possibility of selling the goodwill, patterns and drawings is not overlooked but the return for these would be a small reward for the loss of the business.

b) From BBTs point of view: the more or less permanent acceptance of the manufacture of mechanical parts in a works remote from that in which final erection takes place, an arrangement that can never be regarded as wholly satisfactory or economic.

It must also be appreciated that such a change in policy involves capital loss on recently purchased plant. The New Erecting Shop is to be equipped with 50 ton cranes and the structure and foundations have been designed to suit. If only frames and bogies are to be made in this shop instead of complete shunters, as planned, the cranes, structure and foundations are unnecessarily heavy and expensive. The recently purchased hydraulic press, pump and accumulator were only done on the assumption that we would be continuing to produce steam locomotive boilers. While the press can be used for forming diesel locomotive frame stays and other pressings it is unnecessarily heavy and expensive for such work and is not very well sited. The same remarks apply to the heavy boiler plate forming rolls now on order.

9. Alternative Proposals

The following alternative proposals are put forward for the earnest consideration of the Board.

a) Bagnalls to continue, as at present, with the manufacture of steam locomotives, boilers and spares but on a reduced scale. At the same time the complete building of diesel electric shunters be developed. Wagon, turntable and miscellaneous production to be dropped entirely. Production of main frames and bogies for the Ceylon and subsequent contracts to be continued until BBT can undertake this work at Loughborough.

b) BBT to develop at Loughborough facilities for the production of mechanical parts so as to be able, eventually, to build main line locomotives complete, except for the diesel engines from Mirrlees, leaving the production of shunters to Stafford.

In putting forward these alternatives proposals the writer is motivated by the following considerations:-

a) The development at Loughborough of an integrated diesel locomotive factory as the only real sound long term plan. Experience has proved that the physical separation of the works producing the frames and bogies from that erecting the locomotives can never be a satisfactory arrangement. Many of our competitors suffer from this disability and this is all the more reason why we should concentrate the manufacture of the main line units in one works.

b) The avoidance of a temporary arrangement which would eventually leave the Stafford Works without its steam locomotive business and no longer required for Diesel electric mechanical parts production. This would mean the end of the Company and, apart from sentiment altogether, there are sound business reasons why this would be most unfortunate. Bagnalls have a respected name in locomotive circles and the goodwill and prestige that the name brings to Brush Bagnall Traction depend, to a considerable extent, on our remaining in the locomotive business and maintaining our long established connections with Railway CMEs and industrial locomotive engineers throughout the World. If we stop accepting orders for locomotives, boilers and spare parts, particularly for our own locomotives, our name will soon become an embarrassment rather than an asset to the joint traction company.

10. Summery

a) It would be possible to achieve an output of 36 sets of main line, Diesel electric mechanical parts per annum from the Stafford Works if the present steam locomotive, boiler and spare part business were abandoned. The cost of the new buildings, machinery and plant required would be of the order of £25,000 to £30,000 and the changeover would take about three years to complete.

b) Alternatively, the steam programme at Stafford could be reduced, miscellaneous production abandoned and the building of Diesel electric shunters developed. Facilities could be developed at Loughborough for the manufacture of main line mechanical parts so that the units could be built there complete. While these facilities were being developed Stafford would continue to supply the mechanical parts for the existing Ceylon contract.

The writer has no hesitation in recommending the adoption of the alternative proposals.

16/11/1951   WA Smyth
                    Managing Director

Circulation

All Directors WG Bagnall Ltd
Mr. Miles Beever - Brush
Mr. Eckhard - Brush Bagnall Traction Ltd
Mt Milligan - Brush
cc Secretary
File

An interesting sideline regarding Smyth's remarks about the possibility of abandoning non locomotive work mentioned in 9 a, above, and the reference to turntables, which the firm had long made a speciality of, is worth recording. On 11 April 1951 John Alcock wrote to Smyth informing him that in a clear out at Hunslet, they had found a lot of patterns connected with the manufacture of turntables, that had come their way when Kerr, Stuart closed. As Hunslet had never entered this market Alcock offered them to Smyth as a gift. There were 130 patterns plus 53 core-boxes, along with some drawings; Smyth accepted the offer and the whole lot arrived at the Castle Engine Works shortly after! In actual fact, it would seem that the Company had long ago captured the Kerr, Stuart element of this market with its own designs.

APPENDIX XI

SOME BAGNALL FOLK IN THE FIRM'S LAST FEW YEARS

The Company was well known for the longevity of service by many members of staff; 50 years service not was not unknown and 40 odd years quite common. Working conditions in those days of course were much different than today, and each workshop had its own individual atmosphere, working conditions and not least characters. While it is impossible to name them all, these notes in moving from shop to shop, bring out those recalled for one reason or another. It has not been intentional to leave anybody out, but after so many years and so little space, it is nonetheless, hoped that this somewhat brief tour around the works will help readers gain a better understanding of the Company in its twilight years, and perhaps more importantly, the people who achieved so much.

Starting with the smithy as the shop was known to all, very much in decline and only half the size it had been, with the reduction in the type of work it performed following the introduction of the diesels. The space released by the way, became a stores for both finished parts and consumables. The days of Bob Kemsley with his 54 years service forging motion rods by the hundred and well earning his BEM were over; the large Massey steam hammer, once the scourge of local residents in Castle Street on night shifts, was silent. A 10 cwt pneumatic hammer sufficed for such forging work as remained. The locomotive type boilers purchased many years earlier to supply steam to the hammers in the summer months when the works heating boilers were shut down, were rusting away. Some of the characters recalled as working in this area are Charles Homer, George Dumbleton, Les Palmer, Harry Row, Jack Brownsword, Alf Follows, Archie Thompson, Dennis Hibbens and 'Dewi' Winston. A genuine black-hand gang if ever there was one.

The boiler shop next door was always busy with boilers along with a wide range of fabrication work. Boilers of all shapes and sizes, old and new, cluttered up the shop and the noise of the continual riveting was horrendous; most folk employed hereabouts were either deaf, or very nearly so, as ear defenders were unheard of in those days. Charlie Burghall, a long serving boilersmith and the foreman in later years, had passed away while still in the service in the late 1950s. A smallish guy, like most of his breed, years of practice had taught him to rely heavily on lip-reading! Well respected by one and all, his knack of sighting-up thick steel plates to put a set or joggle in them and getting it right first time, was remarkable. The loss of Charlie brought Arthur Roberts in as foreman and Bill Picking as the leading boilersmith. Some of the older hands still engaged included boiler mounting chargehand Sid Mathews, a very helpful and easy going man who would willingly show any aspiring apprentice the best way to do a job: in the 1930s Sid had been an active member of the works football team. Alec Stretton was Sid's main accomplice with Tommy Dawkes, another long serving member of staff, as the angle-smith. Other members of the team were Chris O'Grady, Fred Wright, Jack Hibbs, Harry Holding, Sid Jenkinson, Frank Lochlin, Jim Telfer, Joe Rutter, Fred Seaton, 'Yasser' Yeomans, George Banks, Fred Whiting, Eric Dawes and George Nablo. There is a story about George having been offered a

tripe sandwich, as he always seemed to be scrounging for food. Unbeknown to him it consisted of two discarded pieces of bread with parts of an industrial glove between them that had spent a few days in a boiler on steam test; trying to devour it, he said he thought it was very tough! Frank Asprey operated the overhead crane in the boiler shop, but he was often in demand to drive cranes in other shops. Colin Evans an apprentice boilersmith from Builth Wells left at the end of his training, but spent the rest of working life in the Stafford area, latterly with British Telecom. Finally Bill Spencer is worth a special word, a most particular leading-hand on boilers who was very fastidious with what he considered 'his' marking- off-table. Woo-betide any apprentice walking across it with his boots on!

The machine shop was the largest employer, although its varying accommodation can only be described as a hotchpotch from Gordon Bagnall's first low roofed wooden construction to the war-time steel framed bays complete with overhead cranes. Ben Lee was the foreman with little Dolly Austen as his clerk. The most southerly part of the low roofed section towards the offices, housed an array of centre, capstan and turret lathes, with Bert 'Edgo' Edgerton as the chargehand. One of the old-school originally from the shipyards at Birkenhead, or it might have been Barrow, a tobacco chewer by habit, and always muttering that somebody or other was after his job - he would however, at least offer you some tobacco to chew! The tool-setter was Bill Hughes, universally known as 'Billy Bags', who took the chargehand's job when Bert retired. Bill left in 1958 and was followed by Cyril Godfrey, another long serving employee, who was remembered when employed on the capstan lathes, along with Tom Buckingham, as making most of the boiler stays. Tom Buckingham is remembered as an older quiet man from the Wheaton Aston area unlike his colleague 'Dapper' Narroway, who was the noisy one on the section, but always with plenty to say on whatever was topical on the day. The quota of ever changing apprentices operated many of the other machines. Across the gangway where most of the centre lathes were situated, some quite modern, but others driven by flat belts from electric motors perched on the rafters - many of them would have originally been driven by line-shafting from the works steam engines. Each of these older lathes had a pile of gear change wheels on the floor and a back gear drive; good for the apprentices as if too large a cut was taken the belt slipped and nothing got broken. However, the wooden stick used to change the flat belt from one sized pulley to another when the motor was running, would not meet approval these days! Fred Skelton was the chargehand, a small man with not a lot to say but always helpful when needed. Apprentices remembered here are Pat Kilcoyne, Brian Mellor and Maurice Green, along with some of the craftsman Bill 'Tiger' Harvey, Charlie Skelton and the young Brian Bishop who was in charge of a large Broadbent lathe that was largely used on contracts for Walker Brothers, machining large castings for paper making machinery. Sid Shaw worked an old nondescript lathe mostly on work for the millwrights but how he achieved the accuracy and finish with all the backlash and wear present was amazing. After Dormans acquired the Company a tannoy system was installed in the shops; within a week or so the trumpets were well and truly stuffed with bungs of cotton waste - clean of course! As the apprentices became more experienced and proficient, they tended to be placed on piece-work, which meant a few more pence could be earned which along with a bit of overtime, resulted in the dizzy figure of £10 a week.

The marking-off tables were situated more or less centrally in the machine shop with the foreman's elevated office above one of them - adjacent tables had use of a travelling hand crane essential when marking-out, for example cylinder castings and large connecting rods. Reg. Moon had been in charge for some time but later moved on to inspection duties with Glyn Edmunds taking over responsibility, followed by Frank Bradshaw; a gang of apprentices encompassing the more mundane jobs. It has to be said that on occasions the white chalk based colourwash used to cover components prior to marking-out, found its way into all sorts of places and people!

Adjacent and to the north were situated the various drilling and milling machines, the millers under the control of Sid Vernon, a large man with a corresponding loud voice dominating any disputes that arose after marking-out. Bob Brown was the chargehand on the radial drilling machines and others recollected are Harry 'Ding Dong' Bell, Bert Baker, Joe Haywood and the three Cotterill brothers - two of them deaf and dumb, and the other bald. Moving further north were the larger machines, some adjacent to the tool room; for example the large planer operated by little Jimmy Budd, and beyond it the two large horizontal borers operated by Joe Johnson and the long serving Harold Till. Harold's displeasure was once incurred with a 'near miss' when a large wooden bung very rapidly escaped from a water tank being tested; the pressure was too high as it had been unknowingly fitted with a faulty pressure gauge! Jim Quinney worked on a surface grinder while Charlie Sneyd, Jack Roberts, 'Big' Maurice Adams and little George Watson were on the planers and slab millers. Charlie Sneyd, reputedly a 'Bevan Boy', working in the coal mines during the war, along with John Chattersingh - a native of Jamaica - worked another slotter as well as the long serving Harry Marshall - who in fact, spent most of his 54 years with the firm working on a slotter. Jack Baker from the millwrights related that one day in 1955 he was called by Harry as a problem had arisen with his machine. When the fault was repaired, Harry commented that the machine had never been the same since a German prisoner of war had used it - Jack thought about this for a day or so as nobody he had ever spoken to recalled any German prisoners of war working machines. As his inquisitive nature got the better of him, he questioned Harry again, and the reply he got was that it was 1918 or 1919!

The original erecting shop was referred to as the old erecting shop once the 1953 diesel erecting shop, or new bay as it was always referred to, was commissioned; one foreman however, covering both shops with his domain covering the fitting shop and the assembly side of the wheel bay too. The foreman was 'Mac' Durber in the mid 1950s, followed by Reg Moon and finally Harry Cooper: Harry had the nickname 'Minnie', from somewhere in the past, and long before the well known motor car appeared on the roads. The erection of locomotives had developed over the years into a gang build piecework system, a gang basically consisting of a chargehand, several fitter cum erectors and apprentices, allowed a given number of man hours to erect a locomotive. The less hours booked meant more bonus when the job was completed. Chargehands remembered are Don Metcalf, Stuart Keay, Harry Cooper, and Dennis Edwards,

although there were others. Some of the best remembered names were Bert Emery, 'Buller' Cartwright, Cliff Hart, Bill 'The Belgian' Imbrechts, Walter Skelton, Fred Hawkins on cylinders, 'Sapper' Simpson, George and Joe Flint, Dominic Kursul, Jim Sullivan, 'Danny' Kay, Tommy Kibble, Jim Davidson, Jim Lawler, Wilf Hodson and Stan Turner. Younger members and apprentices included Roy Newcombe, Vic Trumper, Richard Prosser, Peter Dyer, 'Paddy' O' Sullivan, Pat Kilcoyne, Frank Beech, John Prosser, Owen Ellis, Peter Firkin, Laurie Bagshaw, Mick Gallacher, Derek Luker, Alan Jones, Jim Giles, Jim Redfern, Harry Hume, Brian Hazeldene and Allen Civil. Later on came David Cleary and Willy Cassidy who had both come south having previously been with the Kilmarnock builder, Andrew Barclay Sons & Company.

There were other employees in the erecting shops, welders for example, Arthur 'Bronco' Andrews was one, always singing western songs hence his nick-name and eventually joining the professional club circuit. Harry 'Nobby' Clark was another who worked in a screened off bay in the old erecting shop; reputedly able to weld anything to anything - not quite true but he used to manage most metals. Entrance doors covering the rails to both shops were occasionally demolished in incidents with errant steam locomotives although no one was hurt - probably the less said the better - removable massive steel joists were later made to span the rails and protect the doors from the future testing of locomotives.

The fitting shop was adjacent to the old erecting shop and to a large extent engaged on ancillary functions; it was laid out as a series of work benches with the respective areas lined up underhand operated travelling cranes. The first bench for many years was the home of Horace Banner, who used to assemble locomotive motion parts of all sizes and shapes. Next came Les Arnold who concentrated on coupling and connecting rods followed by Alf Armstrong concentrating on cross-heads and valves. Alf later became heavily involved with the Bagnall-Burns hydrostatic tractors, in fact the tractors were erected only a few feet away in the erecting shop. It was here in the fitting shop the two Dorman built link grinding machines were situated, handy for the fitting benches. The next bench was the domain of the redoubtable Stan Baxter, a specialist on regulator valves along with handbrake columns and wheels. Stan used to bring a tear to the eye of many an apprentice when lapping in and testing regulator faces on his insistence - and rightly so - that the faces should be perfectly flat and not, as he would opine, like the Milford hills - these are well known locally and just south of Stafford! The last bench was under the control of Jess Harvey, who looked after reversing and brake gear. Depending on work-load some jobs would be moved around the various benches with other fellows such as Tommy Kibble and Stan Hill becoming involved. Many apprentices spent time on one or other of these benches, filing, grinding, lapping, drilling, tapping and generally learning their trade. Some of the individuals recalled are Brian Powell, John Prosser, Merlin Maddock, Peter Allen, Denys Penhale, Owen Ellis, Arun Chatterjee, Bob Gibbens, Frank Beech and Jim Maddock.

Next to the fitting benches came the rolls used for boiler cladding with Roy Newcombe and George Flint the two men remembered as working there, and there was a small hardening furnace just beyond with Frank Massey and Sam Birkin in charge. This was followed by the millwrights with Bert Lowe in charge of 'Big' Bob Astle, Jack Baker, Leo Costello, Cliff Hart, Reg Howard, Tommy Hawkins, Jack Foster and Les Goodall. Last of all was the area where the coppersmiths where located, Bill Newman, Freddy Hook and Tom

Worthington were employed here. The story goes that some unknown person had acquired dies for forming half crown pieces; the white metal version apparently looked great until dropped!

The three remaining production shops situated to the north of the works were actually in one building block. Nearest the main railway line was the wheel-bay, the hydraulic wheel press, fitter's bench and tyre shrinking equipment located at one end, while wheel lathe, axle lathe, vertical boring machines and crank quartering machine were at the other. Rupert Machin completed some 47 years service with the Company by 1952, most of it involved with wheel and axle assembly work and was greatly missed when he retired a few years later; a young Andy Smith his assistant taking over. In later years some other fitters helped out in this shop when it was busy, for example when the large orders for the under frames and mechanical parts were under way for the British Railways A1A-A1A Type Two locomotives. Some of the fellows employed were Fred Hawkins, Harry Hume, Ken Wood and Allen Civil. George Powell was the turner on the axle lathe and he used to double up on the quartering machine when required; an older methodical man who knew his job extremely well. The wheel lathe operator changed at times with Frank Lees and David Nicklin remembered at various times. The vertical borers were operated by Bill Pearce and the late Hugh McGlyn, who tragically lost his life while operating one of these machines. The overhead crane driver was normally Eric 'Charlie' Nicholson who tended to have a mind of his own, and did what he thought was right, rather than the instructions given, which was not always a good idea for a crane driver!

The frame shop was next door with its 15 ton overhead travelling crane traversing the whole length of the shop; here was located the permanent oxy-acetylene gear, a large frame slotting machine, radial drilling machines, a heavy steel cutting saw and a large set of rolls which up to the mid 1950s, were powered by a twin cylinder vertical steam engine. Steel bed joists were let into the floor to form a flat surface enabling heavy diesel locomotive under-frames to be fabricated and welded using inert gas electric welding methods. Ernie Getley was in charge of the metal cutting with Sid Bancroft on both the profile and freehand cutting; he seemed able to use a gas torch as accurately as a knife cutting butter. 'Ginger' Greenwood was in charge of the large plate rolls and although partly crippled with a bent back, he could swing a 28lb hammer with ease; his injury the result of a fall from a gas storage holder or pit accident, or so the story went. Neville Tunnicliffe, a fabricator, was the person most likely to be involved with assembling turntables, while to one and all he was known to be a bookies runner, taking the men's bets. Other names recollected in this shop are Harry Holding, Jim Duckers, Cyril Ryan, Ray Sommers, Harold Beard, and Ken Norris.

The final bay was known as the tank bay, with a five ton overhead crane serving the heating furnace, 450 ton flanging press, large plate shears, drilling machine and several large steel fabrication tables. Cabs, bunkers, and the engine compartments for the diesels were fabricated here, with Ted Beeston in charge of the furnace and press, assisted by 'Dasher' Machin, who lived up to his nick-name, as well as his other boasts that he was fond of making while busy forming throat and back-head boiler plates. George Norwood with some 50 years service controlled most of the fabrication plate-work, although others worked here too, including one called 'Geordie', for obvious reasons, whose full name has gone unrecorded. Alan Flowers an apprentice plater is remembered as working here, a avid enthusiast of Scott motorcycles with water cooled engines. One side of the shop contained a small hydraulic press used to form steel brackets and the like, always manned by an apprentice; Merlin Maddock is recalled as one, a job quite the opposite of his hobby of making Welsh harps.

The remaining shops employed few people and were largely in support of their larger brethren. The tool room was centrally placed adjacent to the machine shop, the foreman Bill Pittard, replaced when he retired in 1955 by Gordon Price - a grandson by the way, of Samuel Thomas Price, of valve gear fame. Craftsman employed included Sid Shaw, Fred Boult, Ron Brinson, Gilbert Wyman, George Watson, Tommy Durkin, Billy Franklin, with apprentice Bill Beaston and Dick Walker as the labourer.

The work inspectors were situated at the north end of the wheel-bay with Reg Moon in charge before he took on the job of erecting shop foreman. Albert Thompson, assisted by Harry Owen, then took over supervision of the inspectors. Among the inspectors were Albert Arnold and Jim Redfern. An interesting incident occurred with the inspectors involving one of the numerous spares orders from the Bowaters Lloyd paper mills at Sittingbourne. Some wheel-sets for one of the 2ft 6in gauge 0-6-2 locomotives had arrived for new tyres to be fitted; the procedure was for the old tyres to be removed, after which the inspectors would measure the wheel centres giving each a code letter or number. The dimensions of the new tyres would then be calculated allowing for the shrinkage fit, manufactured, machined and lettered to match. Any slight differences in wheel diameter could thus be allowed for, and in this case too, to ensure that any flangeless intermediate coupled wheels received the right tyres. All seemed to go well and after a lick of paint the wheel-sets were returned to Sittingbourne complete with new brasses in the axle-boxes. However they were back within a fortnight as someone had not checked the drawings properly and established that the driving axle on these locomotives was the third coupled axle and not the second, as the flangeless tyres had been measured and fitted to the trailing wheel-sets and not the intermediate ones! It would of course, be more normal practice for the intermediate wheel-set on a six coupled locomotive to be the driving axle.

The largest of the shops still to be described was the pattern shop, a separate building on the west side of the works, airy and relatively clean, it had a completely different environment the other shops - no metal just wood! Well equipped with woodworking machines that seemed to be able to produce any shape desired, with George White the foreman of many years, although Alf Homer was in charge latterly. Others names remembered are Arnold Follows, Bill Hill, Roy Broad, and Bob Gee, both father and son, Alf Goodall, Dennis Hibbens, Dereck Shoemark and apprentice Ken Lloyd.

By contrast the foundry was dark and full of smoke, environmentally friendly it certainly was not. George Carless was the foreman until he retired in 1959. During the period of Dorman ownership all the iron and brass casting work was transferred to the Dorman foundry in Tixall Road, replaced by the casting of components made of aluminium, as there was a shortage of this capacity at Tixall Road, while it had excess capacity for iron and brass. Fellows recalled here are Jack Bebbington, Albert Brumpton, Bill Simpson the core-maker and the one time crane driver Charlie Nickolson.

The electricians base was the power house, for obvious reasons, and as well as all works electrical plant and equipment, they were engaged on any electrical work on the locomotives, both steam and diesel, although there was never much electrical work on the steam locomotives - just the lighting perhaps. Eric Williams was the foreman with Edgar Bailey, Dennis Cope, Charlie Brown, Harold Clayton, Alec Edgerton, Ron Keeling, Alec Thompson and Jack Shorter reporting to him.

The painters led by Bill Monaghan consisted of Dennis Herriman and Ken Scarlet, while the joiners were Claud Adams and Harry Millward, who at some time had lost some of his fingers on one hand. 'Chick' Weather, senior and junior, are remembered as the 'brickies', while Jack Millgate and Stanley Fisher manned the plant boiler and power houses respectively. One of these two was also responsible for blowing the works hooter at the beginning and end of shifts. The main and finished parts stores came under the control of Albert Appleton, assisted by Kevin Edwards, J. Stokes and George Oxley, while Albert Cliff was resident in the works drawing stores. Not to be forgotten was the redoubtable long serving Harry Chambers in the gate house, in charge of all the time keeping arrangements - wow-betide any apprentice, or indeed anybody, caught not adhering to the correct clocking procedures! Other names remembered were Walter Lowe in first aid, Mrs Godwin and Mrs Davies in the canteen, Jack Petit the social club steward, and Allan Follows in the works garage. The yard gang appeared to locate themselves outside at the north end of the frame shop, Leo Fielding was in charge and he had an office in the main stores adjacent to the entrance yard. Jim Herriman was the Coles mobile crane driver while Jack Austen, Arthur Perry, Harry Rogers and Harry Owen, used the internal vehicles such as the Lister auto trucks, a Bray loading shovel and the Lansing Bagnall tractor which towed a trailer. In 1953 the tractor was cosmetically transformed by the pattern shop into an realistic looking 0-4-0 side tank locomotive to take part in that year's town pageant, appropriately named THUNDERBOLT (after the locomotive in the film of the period: The Titfield Thunderbolt), and bearing a not unrecognisable likeness to a Bagnall locomotive.

Moving on to the office block, the first office on entering from the oldest part of the machine shop was the progress office, housing amongst others Jack Allen, Harry Daniels, Wally Holdford, Ken Rouse and Bob Wood, although much of their time was spent in the shops chasing orders and components in the course of production. The drawing office on the upper floor, as would be expected, took up most of the space, although not all draughtsmen whose names appear below were active at the same time. Apprentices usually had three months in the drawing office as part of their training. Jim Webberley was the chief, with Bill Brooks his assistant, and among the draughtsman were Bill Browning, Frank Beech, Dennis Capey, Don Dutton, Peter Dyer, Alan Davies, Dennis Fisher, Mick Furber, Sen Gupta, Mick Gallacher, Laurie Bagshaw, Ron Glover, Dereck Rowley, Stuart Johnson, Colin Malpass, Richard Prosser, Laurie Middleton, Cecil 'Taffy' Maund, Tony Reynolds, Brian Hazeldene. They were assisted by the three tracers, Val Godwin, Dorothy Hucker and Winifred Watson. Sigmund Kordas, the photographer and printer, was also located close-by. Secretaries included Jean Dyson, Pauline Shorter, Pauline Shirley, Doris Cooper (nee Pegler) and Joan Duffy (nee Frost); Una Edwards is also recalled as a typist.

The accounts office included Arthur Owen, Beryl Coleing, Glenys Hook and Elsie Powell, while in the cost office were Les Brown, Ray Cunningham, Bert Edwards, Delia Follows, Ron Marklew, Doreen Machin, Mrs, Pyatt, Trevor Story and Pam Shaw. In the estimating office were George Brown along with John Cartlidge, Ken Davies, Bill Blood, Peter Firkin, Fred Fleming, Alf Hodson, Audrey Jones, Jim Pearson, John Sedgley and Don Talbot. Stan Ponting is also remembered with Pauline Shorter and Pat Westwood. The wages department consisted of George Colley, Tom Lloyd, Hilda Lymer, Jack Sales, Doreen Machin, Betty Shoemark, and Olive Husslebee. Other staff remembered are the office cleaners including Mrs Boult, Violet Follows and Elaine Gee. Bernard Lunt was the personnel manager while Des Ponting is recalled as a welding technologist. Hazel Sylvester and Olive Stannard manned the telephone switchboard while Cyril Thorpe was known as the shipping clerk. The short lived training school of 1958-9 had Harry Owen in charge and his first trainees were John Millichap from Rugeley along with local lads Dereck Jenkins and John Foster.

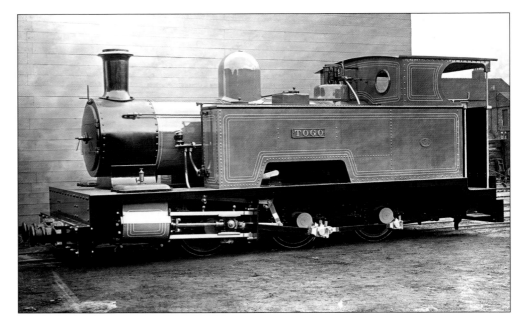

TOGO, manufacturer's number 1785 of October 1905, a 2ft 6in gauge six-coupled side tank new to E P Davis for use at the Storefield Ironstone Pits near Kettering. This locomotive was painted in a shade of light blue.

APPENDIX XII

FAMILY TREES: BAGNALL & ASSOCIATED FAMILIES

The family trees included in this Appendix should be studied in connection with references in the main text of the book to the families concerned. Largely, but not exclusively, the Bagnall family history is covered in Chapter One, while the Index will be found helpful in following the various strands. Although by no means complete, not least in view of space considerations, they should enable readers to see the various lineages leading to William Gordon Bagnall and his family, as well as his descendents.

(a) Descendants of ? Catterall

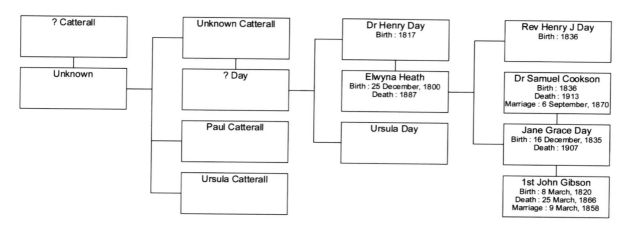

(b) Descendants of Josiah Child Heath

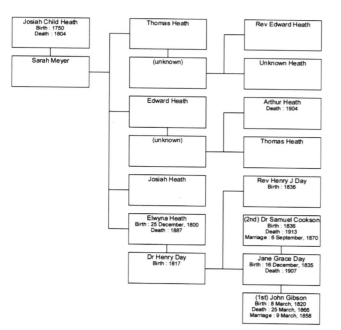

(d) Descendants of Dr Samuel Cookson

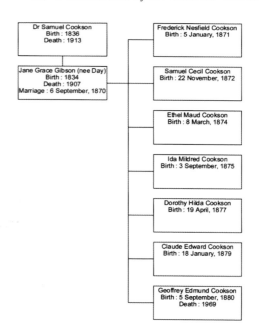

(b) Descendants of James Gibson

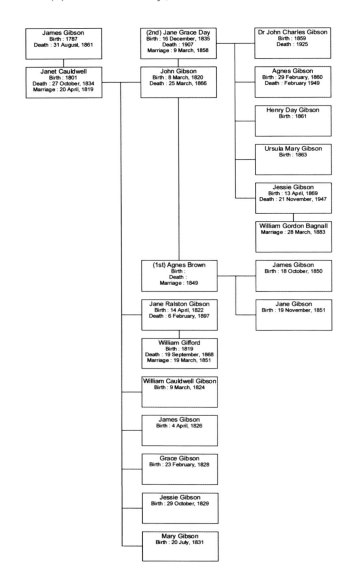

(e) Descendants of William Gifford

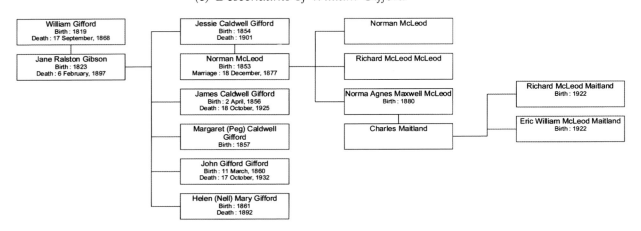

(f) Descendants of John Bagnall

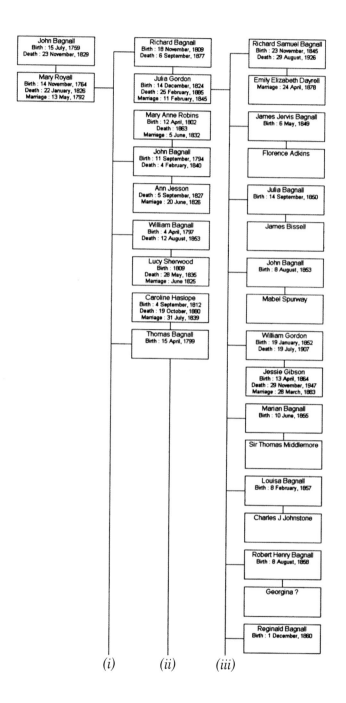

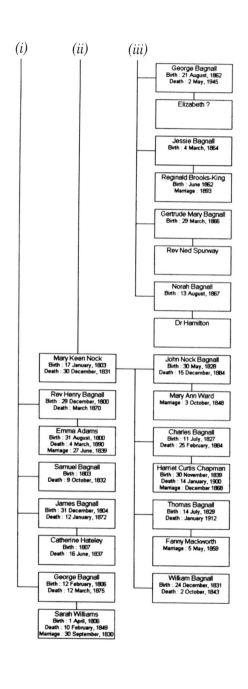

John Bagnall
Birth : 15 July, 1759
Death : 23 November, 1829

Mary Royall
Birth : 14 November, 1764
Death : 22 January, 1826
Marriage : 13 May, 1792

Richard Bagnall
Birth : 18 November, 1809
Death : 6 September, 1877

Julia Gordon
Birth : 14 December, 1824
Death : 25 February, 1885
Marriage : 11 February, 1845

Mary Anne Robins
Birth : 12 April, 1802
Death : 1863
Marriage : 5 June, 1832

John Bagnall
Birth : 11 September, 1794
Death : 4 February, 1840

Ann Jesson
Death : 5 September, 1827
Marriage : 20 June, 1826

William Bagnall
Birth : 4 April, 1797
Death : 12 August, 1853

Lucy Sherwood
Birth : 1809
Death : 28 May, 1835
Marriage : June 1825

Caroline Haslope
Birth : 4 September, 1812
Death : 19 October, 1880
Marriage : 31 July, 1839

Thomas Bagnall
Birth : 15 April, 1799

Richard Samuel Bagnall
Birth : 23 November, 1845
Death : 29 August, 1926

Emily Elizabeth Dayrell
Marriage : 24 April, 1878

James Jervis Bagnall
Birth : 6 May, 1849

Florence Adkins

Julia Bagnall
Birth : 14 September, 1850

James Bissell

John Bagnall
Birth : 8 August, 1853

Mabel Spurway

William Gordon
Birth : 19 January, 1852
Death : 19 July, 1907

Jessie Gibson
Birth : 13 April, 1864
Death : 29 November, 1947
Marriage : 28 March, 1883

Marian Bagnall
Birth : 10 June, 1855

Sir Thomas Middlemore

Louisa Bagnall
Birth : 8 February, 1857

Charles J Johnstone

Robert Henry Bagnall
Birth : 8 August, 1858

Georgina ?

Reginald Bagnall
Birth : 1 December, 1860

(i)   *(ii)*   *(iii)*

(i)   *(ii)*   *(iii)*

Mary Keen Nock
Birth : 17 January, 1803
Death : 30 December, 1831

Rev Henry Bagnall
Birth : 29 December, 1800
Death : March 1870

Emma Adams
Birth : 31 August, 1800
Death : 4 March, 1890
Marriage : 27 June, 1839

Samuel Bagnall
Birth : 1803
Death : 9 October, 1832

James Bagnall
Birth : 31 December, 1804
Death : 12 January, 1872

Catherine Hateley
Birth : 1807
Death : 16 June, 1837

George Bagnall
Birth : 12 February, 1806
Death : 12 March, 1875

Sarah Williams
Birth : 1 April, 1806
Death : 10 February, 1849
Marriage : 30 September, 1830

George Bagnall
Birth : 21 August, 1862
Death : 2 May, 1945

Elizabeth ?

Jessie Bagnall
Birth : 4 March, 1864

Reginald Brooks-King
Birth : June 1862
Marriage : 1893

Gertrude Mary Bagnall
Birth : 29 March, 1866

Rev Ned Spurway

Norah Bagnall
Birth : 13 August, 1867

Dr Hamilton

John Nock Bagnall
Birth : 30 May, 1829
Death : 15 December, 1884

Mary Ann Ward
Marriage : 3 October, 1848

Charles Bagnall
Birth : 11 July, 1827
Death : 25 February, 1884

Harriet Curtis Chapman
Birth : 30 November, 1839
Death : 14 January, 1900
Marriage : December 1868

Thomas Bagnall
Birth : 14 July, 1829
Death : January 1912

Fanny Mackworth
Marriage : 5 May, 1859

William Bagnall
Birth : 24 December, 1831
Death : 2 October, 1843

(g) Descendants of William Gordon Bagnall

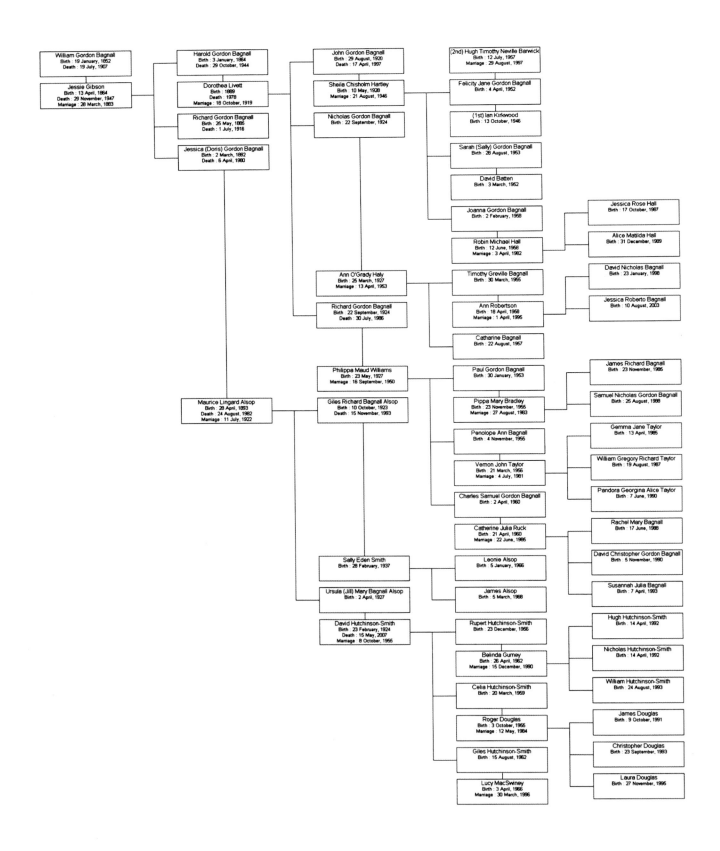

William Gordon Bagnall
Birth : 19 January, 1852
Death : 19 July, 1907

Jessie Gibson
Birth : 13 April, 1864
Death : 29 November, 1947
Marriage : 28 March, 1883

Harold Gordon Bagnall
Birth : 3 January, 1884
Death : 29 October, 1944

Dorothea Livett
Birth : 1899
Death : 1978
Marriage : 18 October, 1919

Richard Gordon Bagnall
Birth : 25 May, 1895
Death : 1 July, 1916

Jessica (Doris) Gordon Bagnall
Birth : 2 March, 1892
Death : 6 April, 1980

John Gordon Bagnall
Birth : 29 August, 1920
Death : 17 April, 1997

Sheila Chisholm Hartley
Birth : 10 May, 1928
Marriage : 21 August, 1946

Nicholas Gordon Bagnall
Birth : 22 September, 1924

Ann O'Grady Haly
Birth : 25 March, 1927
Marriage : 13 April, 1953

Richard Gordon Bagnall
Birth : 22 September, 1924
Death : 30 July, 1986

Philippa Maud Williams
Birth : 23 May, 1927
Marriage : 16 September, 1950

Giles Richard Bagnall Alsop
Birth : 10 October, 1923
Death : 15 November, 1993

Maurice Lingard Alsop
Birth : 28 April, 1893
Death : 24 August, 1982
Marriage : 11 July, 1922

Sally Eden Smith
Birth : 28 February, 1937

Ursula (Jill) Mary Bagnall Alsop
Birth : 2 April, 1927

David Hutchinson-Smith
Birth : 23 February, 1924
Death : 15 May, 2007
Marriage : 8 October, 1956

(2nd) Hugh Timothy Neville Barwick
Birth : 12 July, 1957
Marriage : 29 August, 1997

Felicity Jane Gordon Bagnall
Birth : 4 April, 1952

(1st) Ian Kirkwood
Birth : 13 October, 1946

Sarah (Sally) Gordon Bagnall
Birth : 28 August, 1953

David Batten
Birth : 3 March, 1952

Joanna Gordon Bagnall
Birth : 2 February, 1958

Robin Michael Hall
Birth : 12 June, 1958
Marriage : 3 April, 1982

Timothy Greville Bagnall
Birth : 30 March, 1955

Ann Robertson
Birth : 18 April, 1958
Marriage : 1 April, 1995

Catharine Bagnall
Birth : 22 August, 1957

Paul Gordon Bagnall
Birth : 30 January, 1953

Pippa Mary Bradley
Birth : 23 November, 1955
Marriage : 27 August, 1983

Penolope Ann Bagnall
Birth : 4 November, 1955

Vernon John Taylor
Birth : 21 March, 1956
Marriage : 4 July, 1981

Charles Samuel Gordon Bagnall
Birth : 2 April, 1960

Catherine Julia Ruck
Birth : 21 April, 1960
Marriage : 22 June, 1985

Leonie Alsop
Birth : 5 January, 1966

James Alsop
Birth : 5 March, 1968

Rupert Hutchinson-Smith
Birth : 23 December, 1956

Belinda Gurney
Birth : 26 April, 1962
Marriage : 15 December, 1990

Celia Hutchinson-Smith
Birth : 20 March, 1959

Roger Douglas
Birth : 3 October, 1955
Marriage : 12 May, 1984

Giles Hutchinson-Smith
Birth : 15 August, 1962

Lucy MacSwiney
Birth : 3 April, 1966
Marriage : 30 March, 1996

Jessica Rose Hall
Birth : 17 October, 1987

Alice Matilda Hall
Birth : 31 December, 1989

David Nicholas Bagnall
Birth : 23 January, 1998

Jessica Roberto Bagnall
Birth : 10 August, 2003

James Richard Bagnall
Birth : 23 November, 1985

Samuel Nicholas Gordon Bagnall
Birth : 25 August, 1988

Gemma Jane Taylor
Birth : 13 April, 1985

William Gregory Richard Taylor
Birth : 19 August, 1987

Pandora Georgina Alice Taylor
Birth : 7 June, 1990

Rachel Mary Bagnall
Birth : 17 June, 1988

David Christopher Gordon Bagnall
Birth : 5 November, 1990

Susannah Julia Bagnall
Birth : 7 April, 1993

Hugh Hutchinson-Smith
Birth : 14 April, 1992

Nicholas Hutchinson-Smith
Birth : 14 April, 1992

William Hutchinson-Smith
Birth : 24 August, 1993

James Douglas
Birth : 9 October, 1991

Christopher Douglas
Birth : 23 September, 1993

Laura Douglas
Birth : 27 November, 1995

APPENDIX XIII

THE PORTABLE CATALOGUE POEM

Quoted below is the poem composed by the youngest three of Gordon Bagnall's sisters, referred to in Chapter One. They are Jessie, Gertrude Mary and Norah, aged 21, 19 and 18 respectively, when it was composed on 23 June 1885. Gordon Bagnall was a pigeon fancier and at one stage in his life kept birds, the Horner being a particular species. It would appear from the poem that he named one of them LIVERPOOL, perhaps because its first trip 'home' was after being set free in that city; in any event it seems to have been one of his favourites and may have been his first. Mention of the names LIVADIA, PROGRESSION, VULCAN, LERMA and the nameless No6, are all references to engravings of locomotives that appear in the early catalogues, while the Soudan refers to the five 18in gauge locomotives, manufacturer's numbers 710 to 714 of 1885, designed and built for the abortive Saukin & Berber Railway scheme. They were in fact delivered to the Royal Arsenal at Woolwich.

As reproduced here, the poem has an interpretation of the pronunciation and use of upper and lower case which is as close as possible to the handwritten original. Adding much to our knowledge of the man and his family, he was quite obviously much loved by his sisters. The wording emphasises the importance attached to the firm's catalogues, which as mentioned several times in the main text of this book are beautifully produced, models of their kind, and largely the work of Gordon Bagnall personally. Clearly they were considered, at least by family members, and to a large measure, the reason for much of the firm's success. The original handwritten poem survives in the family collection, as do a number of the catalogues, and one can perhaps visualise the three sisters one summer's afternoon after lunch, or perhaps in the evening, sitting alongside a rivulet at Severn Bank, the family seat, and jokingly composing this work. The handwriting appears be that of Jessie, the eldest of the three sisters: she was a bridesmaid at his wedding and a photograph of her appears in the book with his wife, also Jessie, on that occasion. Reference to the catalogue being 'white and round' is presumably to assist the rhyme, because as outlined several times in this book, the majority of them were red and none of them were round!

One question that does raise is in verse seven, with the mention of 'my partner'; does this infer that relationships between Thomas Walter and Gordon Bagnall were not always on amiable terms, and that Walter was taking cash out of the business when Bagnall might have considered it best left to improve the capital position? In reference to his sons, at the time the poem was composed, Harold Gordon would have been 11 years old and Richard Gordon 10. Presumably, Bagnall's aspirations then were that both his sons would eventually follow him into the business, although in the event only the younger one did. Observe too, that the sisters refer to their brother by his first Christian name William, whilst family legend is that to relations and close friends he was known as Gordon. After his marriage however, his wife always called him Will.

The 'Portable' Catalogue.

T'was on a summer's evening
Old William's works was done
And he before his cottage door
Was sitting in the sun:
And by him, round him sat,
His 'Horners' longing for a chat.

He saw his favourite 'Liverpool'
Bring something white and round
That he beside the rivulet
In perching there had found,
He flew to show what he had found
That was so old and smooth and round.

Old William took it from the bird
That perched expectant by
Then the old man shook his head
And with a natural sigh;
T'is my old catalogue, quote he
The key to my great victory.

You'd find then in the Soudan
You'd find them in Heart!
And often in a temper,
I've hurled them at the cat!
But every one declared quoth he
T'was the key to my great victory.

Now tell us what t'was all about
The Horners seemed to cry
And the old Liverpool looks up!
With a twinkle in his eye
For he had heard the tale before
And knew those catalogues of yore.

T'was long ago old William cried
That first I brought them out,
But when at last I did succeed
To spread them well about,
All the world declared, said he,
T'was the key to my great victory.

My partner lived at Stafford then,
He was a clever chap
It took me pretty nigh all day
To see what he was at.
But filling his pockets you could see,
The key to my great victory.

First of all was 'Livadia',
'Progression' and 'Vulcan',
'Ordinary 6-wheel coupled engines'
With space for 'one hours run'.
That is how they stand, said he,
In the key to my great victory.

'No 6' you see is nameless,
'Four wheel coupled engine'
Then stands little 'Lerma'
The smallest on the line
These are the engines, as you will see
In the key to my great victory.

Great praise my Portable Railway won
In Queen Victoria's reign,
But t'was a very wicked thing
T'was not sent to Sudan - e
Nay! Nay! The pigeons turned to say
Still! t'was a famous victory.

And everybody praised me then,
Who this great fight did win
But what good came of it, at last,
Quoth his favoured pigeon?
It gave my sons a name, said he
That great and famous victory!!

J, GM & N Bagnall
Severn Bank
23 June 1895.

INDEX

In compiling this Index an attempt has been made to marry the twin objectives of making it as useful as possible commensurate with size, bearing in mind the majority of users will largely be interested in locomotive and railway related issues. Therefore, several people mentioned in the text have been excluded on the basis that readers will be unlikely to be looking for them in a book of this nature. For example while Field Marshall Sir Douglas Haig finds a place in the text, he has not been indexed.

Railways and Tramways are indexed under Railways, and Locomotive Builders under Locomotives. Where occupations are mentioned after individuals names, unless otherwise stated, it can be taken that they were in the employ of WG Bagnall Limited. On occasions to save space the Company name, and WG Bagnall himself, are abbreviated to WGB. There are a number of other abbreviations, once again in an attempt to save space, and will it is felt, be self explanatory to most readers.

Manufacturer's number 2850 of 1947

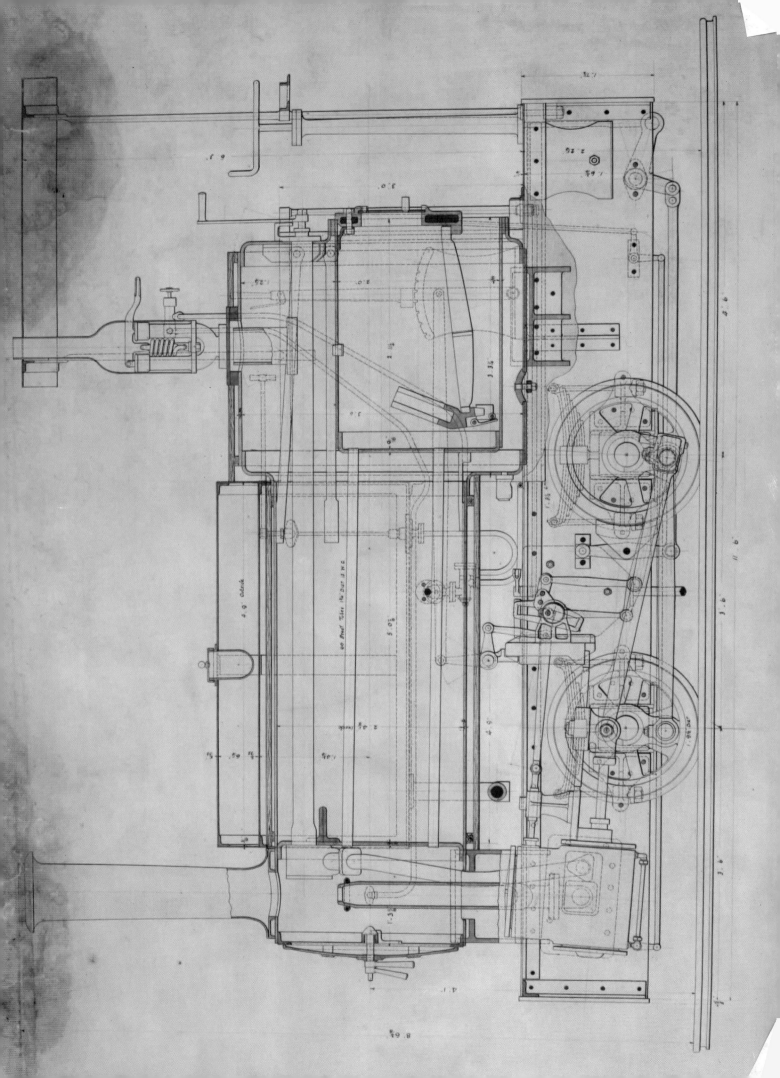